PREPARING AND WINNING MEDICAL NEGLIGENCE CASES

Third Edition

CYRIL H. WECHT, MD, JD,
FCAP, FASCP
Editor,
Adjunct Professor of Law,
Duquesne University
Distinguished Professor of Anatomy and Pathology,
Carlow University,
Pittsburgh, Pennsylvania,
Member of the Bars of Pennsylvania and
The Supreme Court of the United States

Juris Publishing, Inc.

Questions About This Publication

For assistance with shipments, billing or other customer service
matters, please call our Customer Services Department at:

1-631-350-2100

To obtain a copy of this book, call our Sales Department:

1-631-351-5430
Fax: 1-631-351-5712

Toll Free Order Line:

1-800-887-4064 (United States & Canada)

See our web page about this book:
http://www.jurispub.com

©2009

by Juris Publishing, Inc.

Printed in the United States of America
ISBN-13: 978-1-57823-238-3

Juris Publishing, Inc.
71 New Street
Huntington, New York, 11743
USA
www.jurispub.com

BIOGRAPHIES

EDITOR

CYRIL H. WECHT, MD, JD, FCAP, FASCP received his MD degree from the University of Pittsburgh, and his JD degree from the University of Maryland. Certified by the American Board of Pathology in anatomic, clinical, and forensic pathology, he is also a Fellow of the College of American Pathologists, the American Society of Clinical Pathologists, and the National Association of Medical Examiners. Formerly he was the Chairman of the Department of Pathology and President of the Medical Staff at St. Francis Central Hospital in Pittsburgh. He also served as the elected Coroner of Allegheny County for a total of 20 years. He is now actively involved as a medical-legal and forensic science consultant, as an author—with over 525 publications to his credit—and lecturer.

Dr. Wecht's achievements extend to academia where, in addition to lecturing at Yale Medical School, Harvard Law School, at the FBI Academy, and the Medical Division of the CIA, he is a Clinical Professor of Pathology at the University of Pittsburgh School of Medicine and Graduate School of Public Health; he is Adjunct Professor at Duquesne University Schools of Law, Pharmacy, and Health Sciences; Distinguished Professor of Anatomy and Pathology, Carlow University; Chairman of the Advisory Board of the Cyril H. Wecht Institute of Forensic Science and Law at Duquesne University School of Law; Past President of the American College of Legal Medicine and the American Academy of Forensic Sciences, and former Chairman of both the Board of Legal Medicine and the American College of Legal Medicine Foundation. He has served as Vice Chairman of the American Board of Disaster Medicine and is a Charter Diplomate of both the American Board of Legal Medicine and the American Board of Disaster Medicine.

Called to testify in more than 1,000 civil, criminal, and workers compensation cases throughout the United States and abroad, he has also appeared on numerous TV and radio shows to give his evaluation of the medico-legal and forensic scientific aspects of high profile cases ranging from the assassinations of Pres. John F. Kennedy and Sen. Robert F. Kennedy to the deaths of JonBenét Ramsey, Amadou Diallo, Laci Peterson, Anna Nicole Smith, Daniel Smith, Nicole Brown Simpson and Ronald Goldman, and Chandra Levy, among many others.

CONTRIBUTORS

LEONARD BERLIN, MD, FACR. Former Radiology Chairman at Rush North Shore Medical Center, Skokie IL; current Vice-Chairman at North Shore University Health System, Skokie, IL Hospital; Professor of Radiology at Rush University Medical College in Chicago; Past President of the Illinois Radiologic Society and the Chicago Radiological Society; Consultant to malpractice insurance companies; past Chairman of the American College of Radiology's Ethics Committee, and current Chairman of the Radiological Society of North America's Professionalism Committee; Awarded the Gold Medals for distinguished service to Radiology by both the American Roentgen Ray Society and the Chicago Radiological Society; Has presented more than 300 lectures nationally and internationally on risk management; Author of *Malpractice Issues in Radiology* and of more than 300 scientific articles.

MARY M. CARRASCO, MD, MPH. Director, International and Community Health, Pittsburgh Mercy Health System; Clinical Associate Professor of Pediatrics, University of Pittsburgh School of Medicine; Board Certified in Pediatrics; Fellow of the American Academy of Pediatrics; Licensed in Pennsylvania; Member of the American Academy of Pediatrics; Member of the Pennsylvania Attorney General's Medical Legal Advisory Board on Child Abuse and Neglect.

K. RYAN CONNOLLY, MS, MD. Chief Resident-Department of Psychiatry Hospital of the University of Pennsylvania and Philadelphia Veterans Affairs Medical Center.

L. JEAN DUNEGAN, MD, JD, FCLM. Diplomate, American Board of Surgery; Fellow, American College of Legal Medicine; Director, Ann Arbor Pain Consultants; Adjunct Faculty and Moot Court Judge, Ave Maria and University of Michigan Schools of Law; Medico-legal Consultant and Educator.

LOGAN A. GRIFFIN, AB, MD. Board-certified anesthesiologist (retired), Las Vegas, NV; He received his Bachelor of Arts (AB) degree from Harvard College, Cambridge, MA, and obtained his MD degree from the State University of New York Medical School at Buffalo, NY. He took his rotating internship at Mount St. Mary's Hospital, Niagara Falls, NY and residency in internal medicine at Knott Hospital, Schenectady, NY. He subsequently served for two (2) years in the US Air Force as a Medical Officer. He took his

Anesthesiology residency at the Albert Einstein Medical Center in Bronx, NY. He also took Fellowship in Anesthesiology at the Hospital for Sick Children in Toronto, Canada; Fellow of the American College of Anesthesiologists.

MATTHEW L. HOWARD, MD, FACS. Staff Head and Neck Surgeon Kaiser Permanente Medical Center Santa Rosa, CA (retired); Sole Practitioner Social Security Disability Law (retired); Admitted to practice in the State of California, the Northern District of California, the Court of Appeals for the Ninth Circuit and the U.S. Supreme Court; Graduate of UCLA School of Medicine and the Boalt Hall School of Law (UC Berkeley); Winner of the 2008 Distinguished Service Award from the National Organization of Social Security Claimants' Representatives.

JAMES C. JOHNSTON, MD, JD, FCLM, FACLM. Consultant Neurologist and Attorney at Law, Texas and Washington, USA; Barrister and Solicitor of the High Court of New Zealand, Auckland, New Zealand; Diplomate of the American Board of Psychiatry and Neurology; Additional Certification in Neurorehabilitation; Fellow of the American College of Legal Medicine, Fellow of the Australian College of Legal Medicine, Member of the New Zealand Law Society.

JULIUS LANDWIRTH, MD, JD. Associate Director, Yale University Interdisciplinary Center for Bioethics and Donaghue Initiative in Biomedical and Behavioral Research Ethics; Former Vice President for Medical Affairs, Newington Children's Hospital, Newington, Connecticut; Former Chief, Department of Pediatrics, Bridgeport and Hartford Hospitals; Clinical Associate Professor of Pediatrics, Yale University School of Medicine and Associate Chairman of Pediatrics at the University of Connecticut School of Medicine.

THOMAS D. MAHER, MD. Director of Quality and Surgical Outcomes in the Department of Thoracic and Cardiovascular Surgery for the West Penn Allegheny Health System, Pittsburgh, PA. He holds the rank of Assistant Professor of Surgery at the Drexel University College of Medicine in Philadelphia, PA. Dr. Maher earned his medical degree and completed his residency in General Surgery at Georgetown University, and went on to complete a residency in Thoracic Surgery, and began practice at Allegheny General in 1981. Dr. Maher is attending Cardiac Surgeon at the Gerald McGinnis Cardiovascular Institute specializing in complex coronary artery revascularization, repair of aortic aneurysms, valve repair/replacement and atrial fibrillation surgery.

WILLIAM J. MANGOLD, Jr., MD, JD. Contractor Medical Director for Medicare Part B for Arizona, Montana, Utah and Wyoming, prior Family Physician and for sixteen years conducted a solo practice of Plastic & Reconstructive Surgery in Tucson, AZ; Former Assistant Professor of Plastic Surgery at the University of Texas Health Science Center at San Antonio and President & CEO of Mutual Insurance Company of Arizona (MICA); Licensed in Medicine in Arizona and Texas; in Law in Texas; Fellow, American College of Legal Medicine and Diplomate American Board of Quality Assurance and Utilization Review Physicians.

DARREN P. MAREINISS, MD, JD, MBe. Received his MD from the NYU School of Medicine, where he was a member of the AOA Honor Medical Society. He did his internship in General Surgery at NYU Medical Center/Bellevue Hospital and continued residency training in General Surgery at UT Southwestern Medical Center. He obtained both his JD and a Masters in Bioethics from the University of Pennsylvania. Currently, Dr. Mareiniss is a Senior Consultant at the University of Maryland Center for Health and Homeland Security, and Adjunct Professor at the University of Texas School of Law. Dr. Mareiniss has published and lectured on bioethics, medicolegal issues and disaster issues. Licensed in Medicine in New York, New Jersey and Maryland; Licensed in Law in Texas; Member, American Academy of Disaster Medicine; Fellow, American College of Legal Medicine and Chair, Education Committee; Deputy Editor, *Legal Medicine Perspectives*; Member, University of Texas at Austin IRB.

ERNEST H. NEIGHBOR, MD, JD. Medical degree from the University of Kansas School of Medicine, Kansas City, Kansas in 1966; He obtained his JD from the University of Missouri—Kansas City Law School, Kansas City, Missouri in 1971. He took his rotating internship and subsequently residencies in general surgery and orthopedic surgery at the University of Kansas Medical Center from 1966–1974. He is Board Certified in Orthopedic Surgery and Legal Medicine. He is a member of the State Bar of Kansas and the Federal District Court of Kansas. He was a Captain in the US Air Force and a Vietnam Veteran. He is Clinical Assistant Professor at the University of Kansas Medical Center and has taught and published extensively in the areas of Orthopedics and Legal Medicine.

MATTHIAS I. OKOYE, MD, JD. Practicing Physician and Lawyer, Director of the Nebraska Institute of Forensic Sciences, Inc., and Nebraska Forensic Medical Services, PC; Clinical Associate Professor of Forensic

Pathology at Creighton University School of Medicine, Omaha, Nebraska; Adjunct Professor of Forensic Medicine and Pathology at several universities abroad; Formerly the Chief Medical Examiner for the District of Columbia, Washington,; He is a Consultant Forensic Pathologist with the State of Nebraska's Office of the Attorney General and serves as a coroner's physician and forensic pathologist for several Nebraska counties; Member of the Bars of Pennsylvania, US Supreme Court, and several federal courts; Member of the Board of Governors of the American College of Legal Medicine and the American Board of Legal Medicine; Member of the National Association of Medical Examiners and a Fellow of the College of American Pathologists. He has lectured and published extensively in the fields of forensic sciences, legal medicine, forensic medicine and pathology.

JEFFREY P. PHELAN, MD, JD. Chairman and Director of Quality Assurance, Department of Obstetrics and Gynecology, Citrus Valley Medical Center, West Covina, California. Member of San Gabriel Valley Perinatal Medical Group, Inc., West Covina, California; President and Director of Clinical Research, Childbirth Injury Prevention Foundation, City of Industry, California. Author of numerous medical/legal articles and Editor of Critical Care Obstetrics, currently in its fourth edition.

JULIUS S. PIVER, MD, JD, Obstetrician and Gynecologist in private practice, Chevy Chase, Maryland; Board-certified in Obstetrics and Gynecology; Clinical Chairman, Department of Obstetrics, Washington Hospital Center, Washington, DC; Fellow: American College of Obstetricians and Gynecologists, American College of Surgeons.

PARALUMAN Q. RAVANO, MD, FCAP, FASCP. Diplomate, American Board of Pathology in Anatomic and Clinical Pathology; Pathology Consultant, Cyril H. Wecht, MD, JD and Pathology Associates; Private Hospital Pathology Practice, Albert Einstein Medical Center, Philadelphia, PA and Altoona Regional Health Center, Altoona, PA.

ROBERT L. SADOFF, MD. Clinical Professor of Psychiatry, University of Pennsylvania; Director, Center for Studies in Social-Legal Psychiatry, University of Pennsylvania; Board certified in Psychiatry, Forensic Psychiatry, and Legal Medicine; Licensed in California, Massachusetts, Minnesota, New Jersey, New York, and Pennsylvania; Member of the American College of Psychiatrists (Fellow); American College of Legal Medicine (Fellow); American Academy of Psychiatry and the Law (Past President).

DAVID L. SAMANI, MD. Board-certified Orthopedic Surgeon. He obtained his MD degree from the University of Iowa College of Medicine, Iowa City, IA and then took his orthopedic surgery residency at the University of Kansas School of Medicine, Wichita, Kansas and subsequently a Fellowship in Trauma Surgery at the University of California—Davis, Sacramento, CA. Dr. Samani was on active duty and training and deployment with the US Air Force from 1980 through 1991. He has won several military medals and decorations including the Presidential Unit Citation and National Defense Medal. Fellow of the American Academy of Orthopedic Surgery and since 1997 has been an examiner for the American Board of Orthopedic Surgery.

S. SANDY SANBAR, MD, PhD, JD. Consultant and Lecturer in Legal Medicine; President, Royal Oaks Cardiovascular Clinic; Medical Consultant, Disability Determination Division, SSA, Oklahoma City, Oklahoma; Fellow, American College of Legal Medicine; Diplomate, American Board of Legal Medicine; Past President, American College of Legal Medicine; Chairman and CEO, American Board of Legal Medicine; President, American Board of Medical Malpractice; Editor, ACLM Textbook *Legal Medicine*, Elsevier Publisher; Editor, *ACLM Medical Malpractice Survival Handbook*, Elsevier Publisher; Editor, *The ABLM Board Review Exam & Study Guide*.

RICHARD S. WILBUR, MD, JD, FCLM, FACP, FACPE, FRSM, FICD(H). Chairman, American Medical Foundation for Peer Review and Education; Board Certified in Medicine and Gastroenterology; Past President of American College of Legal Medicine, American College of Physician Executives, National Resident Matching Board and American Board of Medical Management; Recipient Defense Dept. Distinguished Service Medal; Member, Institute of Medicine and County, State and National Law and Medical Associations; Licensed in Medicine and Law in Illinois.

BRUCE L. WILDER, MD, MPH, JD. Practicing Neurological Surgeon; certified by the American Board of Neurological Surgery; admitted to practice law in Pennsylvania and before the United States Supreme Court; graduate of the Johns Hopkins School of Hygiene and Public Health; Counsel to the law firm of Wilder & Mahood in Pittsburgh.

DEDICATIONS

This volume is dedicated to my wife, Sigrid Wecht, Esquire, and my four children—David, Daniel, Benjamin and Ingrid—as they continue to pursue their respective professional careers in law, medicine, and forensic science.

SPECIAL DEDICATION

It is also dedicated to Steve Bellman, an excellent editor and a true gentleman. Without his patience and professional expertise, this complex literary project would not have come to fruition.

CYRIL H. WECHT, MD, JD
FCAP, FASCP

PREFACE

It is difficult to think of a legal area involving civil litigation that has been the subject of as much contentious oral discussion and written commentary in the past forty years as medical malpractice. Unfortunately, many of these speeches, publications, and special programs have generated far more heat than light on this complex and emotionally charged, highly controversial topic. As a result, confusion and misunderstanding have resulted in much hostility among a great majority of physicians toward lawyers, particularly plaintiff trial attorneys.

This volume has been prepared by prominent, experienced medical specialists, all of whom have had much professional involvement and interest in legal medicine for many years. Therefore, while the chapters present a wealth of solid information for a variety of medical specialists, they are primarily designed to address important issues that will undoubtedly be of great value to all health care professionals, hospital administrative personnel, and both plaintiff and defense trial attorneys regarding medical malpractice cases.

Future supplements will deal with other medical specialties as they relate to medical malpractice matters. It is our objective to bring together the combined knowledge and experience of outstanding medical-legal scholars for the purpose of educating the concerned professional groups about this complex and difficult, multi-faceted area of civil litigation.

CYRIL H. WECHT, MD, JD
FCAP, FASCP

ACKNOWLEDGMENTS

I would like to acknowledge the special efforts and excellent work of all the contributing authors. Every one of them is an acknowledged expert in their respective areas of medical specialty. Their presentations, individually and collectively, will constitute a significant contribution to the medical-legal literature.

CYRIL H. WECHT, MD, JD,
FCAP, FASCP

SUMMARY TABLE OF CONTENTS

TABLE OF CONTENTS

Chapter 6 Psychiatry...327
Robert L. Sadoff, MD
K. Ryan Connolly, MS, MD

Chapter 7 General Surgery 367
L. Jean Dunegan, MD, JD, FCLM

Chapter 8 Anesthesiology 409
Matthias I. Okoye, MD, JD and Logan A. Griffin, AB, MD

Chapter 10 Plastic Surgery 535
William J. Mangold, Jr., MD, JD

Chapter 17 Orthopedic Surgery..1123

Ernest H. Neighbor, MD, JD, Mathias I. Okoye, MD, JD,
David L. Samani, MD

CHAPTER 1

HOSPITAL RISK MANAGEMENT
AND QUALITY CONTROL

Richard S. Wilbur, MD, JD, FCLM, FACP, FACPE, FRSM, FICD(H)

SYNOPSIS

§ 1.01 Introduction

This chapter will review the institutional liabilities of the hospital and its medical staff as contrasted with the individual professional responsibilities of the physician for patient care. Historically, most medical negligence jurisprudence and the literature written about it, has concentrated on the physician's interaction with the patient. The hospital's role has been secondary. The hospital was usually the site of the precipitating incident, but traditionally had not been an active participant in the litigation. However, the role of the hospital and of its medical staff in tort law have evolved more in the last few years than have even the concepts surrounding individual physician negligence. Therefore, the hospitals deserve this chapter of their own.

The American hospital is unique in the world in its community position, funding, relationship to its staff doctors and to the medical and legal systems of the country. Not surprisingly, the law applicable to risk management and quality control in American hospitals is also unique — and it is also evolving.

In recent years, the public's expectations from hospitals and, consequently, the legal duties and potential liability of hospitals, have increased radically. Many of these duties are similar to those in other areas of American society which have been responsive to the increasing institutional responsibilities under the laws of negligence, strict liability and warranty. However, the modern hospital has acquired a host of new and different duties to the general public and, especially, to the patients who come to it for care. The Institute of Medicine (IOM) Reports on Quality: "To Err is Human: Building a Safer Health System" and "Crossing the Chasm: Building a Safer Health System for the 21st Century" educated the public and the trial lawyer community about the high death and injury rates from hospital errors. This has further increased public awareness and the hospitals' risk for liability.

Some events have become almost automatic liability. Certain conditions are called "Never' events and are especially important to avoid since the Federal Government, through Medicare and Medicaid, will not pay for charges engendered by these Hospital Acquired Conditions (HACs). These are listed in CMS: August 22, 2007, effective October 1, 2008.[1]

1. Foreign Object retained after Surgery. 2. Air Embolism, 3. Blood Incompatibility, 4. Stage III and IV Pressure Ulcers, 5. Falls and Trauma leading to Fractures, Dislocations, Intracranial Injuries, Crushing Injuries, Burns, or Electric Shock, 6. Manifestations of Poor Glycemic Control such as Diabetic Ketoacidosis Nonketotic Hyperosmolar Coma, Hypoglycemic Coma, Secondary diabetes with Ketoacidosis, or Secondary Diabetes with Hyperosmolarity, 7. Catheter-Associated Urinary Tract Infection, 8. Vascular Catheter-Associated Infection, 9. Surgical Site Infection following: Coronary Artery Bypass Graft ("CABG") — Mediastinitis, Bariatric Surgery (Laparoscopic Gastric Bypass, Gastroenterostomy or Laparascopic Gastric Restrictive Surgery) and Orthopedic Procedures including Spine, Neck, Shoulder and Elbow and 10. Deep Vein Thrombosis ("DVT")/Pulmonary Embolism ("PE").

This list is subject to change and some health insurance companies have other listings. They are, obviously, very difficult to defend in any liability action. The Leapfrog Group of health purchasers recommends: After a "Never Event": 1. Apologize to patient and family, 2. Report to Joint Commission or other safety organization, 3. Perform a root cause analysis, 4. Waive all costs directly related to the error. Better yet, prevent it in the first place.

[1] Hospital Immunity

In the past, suing a hospital was often blocked by either governmental sovereign immunity or the charitable immunity doctrine.

---

[1] 73 Fed. Reg. 48473-48487.

[a] Governmental Immunity

The Eleventh Amendment to the U.S. Constitution forbids suits against States. The federal government itself enjoys a sovereign immunity which could be virtually complete. However, there are federal and state statutes permitting the right to sue governmental entities, including hospitals.

Successful suits against federal government hospitals, such as those operated by the military services and Veterans Administration, depend primarily on the finding of individual medical negligence by a health care practitioner. The Federal Tort Claims Act (FTCA)[2] allows for partial waiver of governmental immunity. Anyone with a potential claim against a federal hospital should study the FTCA before filing.

The immunity for city, county, and district hospitals is locally variable. The legal basis for the extent of immunity is the amount of state involvement. The variation among state laws makes any generalizations hazardous. One must learn the law of one's own state and this can change with each session of the legislature or the State Supreme Court. For instance, the Supreme Court of Nevada in *Martinez v. Maruszczak*,[3] found that the Nevada legislature had waived the state's sovereign immunity (NRS Chapter 41), but provided for an immunity for discretionary acts and a cap on damages for tort actions against state employees. Distinctions as to which types of acts by state employees are "discretionary " are discussed in *United States v. Gaubert*,[4] and *Berkovitz v. United States*[5] They are usually "policy," and not medical practice.

[b] Charitable Immunity

Hospitals were once charitable institutions in the ancient almshouse tradition. They were facilities for the poor supported by local government, charity and/or religious organizations. Few patients paid for their hospitalization and the physicians who cared for hospitalized patients ordinarily did not charge fees. These charitable purposes of the American hospital have been increasingly replaced by business objectives—a concern for the bottom line. The American hospital has responded more to the technological imperative and to budgetary concerns than it has to identified community health needs.

---

[2] 28 U.S.C. §§ 2671-2680.
[3] 168 P.3d 720 (Nevada 2007).
[4] 499 U.S. 315 (1991).
[5] 468 U.S. 531(1988).

The growth of private hospital insurance after World War II, and of Medicare and Medicaid payments since 1966, have resulted in most private hospitals being almost totally supported by patient charges. This change has fundamentally altered the hospitals' liability to their patients.

Charitable immunity had been based upon the theory that the donations that supported the charitable hospital were a trust fund which could not be diverted to non-patient care uses. The imposition of liability payments would do irreparable harm to the charitable hospital because awards for liability might discourage donations to charity.

However, the changing socioeconomic status of hospitals also changed the attitude of the courts who pointed out that hospitals were being supported by funds derived from the services they rendered, and, therefore, they should be treated as if they were businesses.[6] For all practical purposes, any nongovernmental hospital is now open to most of the claims for negligent operation that are filed against any other enterprise. Statutory benefits only set the non-profit tax-exempt hospital apart from a business for tax purposes. Most liability claims are covered under the hospital's liability insurance regardless of the "for-profit" status, and few patients in most private non-profit hospitals are true beneficiaries of charitable care. The vast majority pay, or have the charges paid for them by some form of insurance, and so the remaining charitable immunity is quite limited in actual effect. Liability suits against most hospitals can continue whether the defendants are for-profit, not-for-profit, or government hospitals.

§ 1.02 Liability Prevention by Risk Management

The first principle of hospital liability prevention is risk management. It includes all aspects of protection against liability. In this respect, risk management in a hospital is not too different from that in any other product or service organization in the American economy. As it applies to hospitals it is mandated by the Joint Commission (previously named the Joint Commission on the Accreditation of Healthcare Organizations (JCAHO) and most state hospital regulatory agencies

A major portion of the risk management activity is the provision of various forms of insurance against liability for corporate and employee negligence including errors and omissions protection for the members of their board of directors.

Risk managers are taught to manage risks by determining where things can go wrong within a hospital and estimating the likelihood of their

---

[6] President & Dirs. of Georgetown Coll. v. Hughes, 130 F.2d 810 (D.C. Cir. 1942).

occurrence. The elements of risk, loss, and prevention are common to many industries.

The hospital situation is different from other businesses, however, in the fact that the patients are less able physically, and often mentally, to protect themselves against further harm. Their reasonable reliance upon the hospital and its personnel is also greater than it is in other life situations. This means that judicial scrutiny of the reasonableness of a hospital failing to make the expenditures necessary for increased safety will be stricter than, for example, that of "innkeepers" (who already owe a higher level of care to their guests than that due a patron of a routine business). For example, to the hospital patient the risk of a building fire is significantly greater than it is for a hotel guest, and the hospital's responsibility for fire prevention is commensurately higher. Failure to budget sufficient funds for patient safety can be seen as negligence.

The oversight is through the hospital's Quality Control mechanism which is usually an administrative responsibility supported by appropriate review committees with membership from the medical staff. Liability comes from not having a well functioning system in place.

§ 1.03 Risk Management in Specific Areas

[1] Surgical Suite

Most surgical injuries result in suits against the surgeon or anesthesiologist. However, there are major areas which are largely the responsibility of the hospital. One is the lost surgical object, usually a sponge, but sometimes an instrument, which is left in the patient's body. These errors often result in serious injury with infection and require reoperation. There is almost no defense; the matter is *Res Ipsa Loquitur*. The settlements are usually large and most of it is paid by the hospital, since it is the responsibility of the charge nurse to assure the surgeon that all of the instruments, including the sponges, have been accounted for. The hospital is also responsible for the added costs of the extra hospitalization. As of 2008, Medicare refuses to pay these extra charges. With the availability of technology such as bar-coding to keep track of the sponges and operating instruments and of radio frequency detectors to check for them before closing an incision, this failure becomes even less defensible.

A similar, indefensible situation is the wrong operation. It is sometimes the wrong patient but, more often, the wrong side of the right patient. It can also be performing the wrong procedure on the right patient. The Joint Commission and the various state hospital agencies have made strenuous efforts to eradicate this through mandatory crosschecking of wrist bands, marking the skin over the correct site, etc. The main point is that the hospital must have an appropriate system in place to prevent these "never" events or be prepared to settle as rapidly and economically as possible. There is no escape from liability.

A related problem occurs in tertiary care centers when a patient receives the wrong transplant organ. Probably the most famous case is that from Duke University of Jessica Santillan, the Type 0-positive Mexican 17 year old, who on Feb. 7, 2003 was transplanted with type A heart and lungs flown in from Boston and who died two weeks later despite heroic salvage efforts. Duke made no effort to conceal the error and conceded that it was indefensible.

In addition, the Joint Commission's has six labeling requirements for all perioperative and procedural settings. All of these types of potential errors should be addressed by the medical staff in liaison with the Quality Control staff through protocols developed by doctors and administration in Committees and enforced cooperatively.

[2] Radiology

A report by the Center for the Advancement of Patient Safety[7] found that the most dangerous place for hospitalized patients is the radiology suite. The study found that patient-harming medication errors occurred seven times more often when a patient was undergoing a radiological procedure than they did in other hospital settings. Sources of these medication errors included the contrast used for radiological procedures, miscommunications related to other medications the patient was receiving and failure to learn of impaired kidney function. The number of errors was small compared with the total number of procedures, but when errors occurred they were much more likely to cause patient harm. The hospital Quality Control Committees must be sure that a system of checks is in place to prevent these interdepartmental dangers.

Risks to employees within the radiology department and the appropriate means of reducing them are dealt with in the chapter on radiology. While most departments are run under contract with a group of radiologists, some hospitals have employed radiologists on the staff.

[a] Radiation

Within every hospital there also is an increased general radiation hazard when compared with the nonhospital setting. Most hospitals built in the

---

[7] CapsLink USP 2006-01-01.

recent past have been provided with adequate protection against radiation of the public. However, occasionally smaller hospitals have been rebuilt by contractors who failed to understand the ability of radiation to penetrate ordinary building walls, resulting in undue radiation of other personnel, often clerical ones removed from radiology by job description, but not by desk location.

If a hospital utilizes radioactive materials within a nuclear medicine unit, it has special problems, particularly in the disposition of radioactive waste. Regulations for the disposal of radioactive waste are promulgated by both federal and state governments. In most instances, the technical personnel in the radiology and/or nuclear medicine departments are capable of handling the material appropriately, and breaches of standards are few and relatively non serious. However, when the disposal is in the hands of nontechnical personnel, particularly of the unskilled labor category, it is possible to have serious liability consequences. In large institutions there should be specially identified personnel responsible for this disposition, but in medium-sized institutions this task may be delegated to a relatively unsophisticated staff person lacking specific expertise in radiation hazards.

Also, contractors who remove infectious and radioactive waste from hospitals are sometimes irresponsible and fail to follow statutory guidelines. This has resulted in the disposal of radioactive and other hazardous waste in undesignated places, such as landfills, waterways, lakes and oceans. Such irresponsibility can be traced back to the hospital's failure to contract with responsible waste disposal companies and, therefore, has been a source of hospital liability.

[3] Emergency Department

The emergency department is an area of special peril to visitors. More attention is paid to stopping the flow of blood than to wiping it up from the floor. Much of the activity is at a frantic pace, and the safety of persons other than the patient being cared for is secondary in the minds of the emergency department personnel. There is a further hazard in the heavy flow of traffic in and out of the area—traffic which is unusually high in non hospital personnel. While most of these persons are acquainted with the hospital—police, ambulance drivers, paramedics, etc.—they present more than the usual employee risk. Here, as in other areas, overeager budget cutting can lead to a large liability settlement.

The difficulties in the emergency department are compounded by the high level of emotion, particularly among the visitors. The staff is usually aware of hazards and able to avoid them. Visitors, who tend to be far more concerned with the condition of their friend or relative than they are with their own safety, are inclined to be dangerous, not only to themselves, but often to others. This is particularly true when the various parties to an altercation have been brought to the same hospital for treatment. Failure to recognize this potential for risk can lead to more injury, liability and damages. Security measures in and around an emergency department require more than an ordinary level of watchfulness.

Especially the personnel must be trained to watch the waiting room for patients who are in need of immediate care and cannot wait their turn in a busy time. Triage of seriously ill patients is a necessity. There are specific rules for the care of special conditions such as chest pain and pneumonia which must be adhered to in order to avoid liability. There is also a requirement for assured follow-up of patients leaving the department who may not require immediate treatment or hospitalization, but who have a condition which could worsen without further care. They must be given careful warnings about the need for return to a physician.

[a]   EMTALA

A legislative mandate, the Emergency Medical Treatment and Active Labor Act, (EMALTA),[8] is an Act of Congress passed in 1986. It is also known as the patient anti-dumping law and "places obligations of screening and stabilization upon hospitals and emergency rooms that receive patients suffering from an 'emergency medical condition.'"[9]

In a medical emergency, a hospital must provide such medical examination and such treatment as may be required to stabilize the medical condition and then continue to treat the patient's condition at that hospital or transfer the patient to another medical facility where the appropriate care is available. This Act is particularly perilous because under EMTALA, a violation of the Act can occur without a demonstration of an improper motive on the hospital's part.[10]

The fact of the hospital's liability is spelled out. EMTALA's civil enforcement provisions specify that "any individual who suffers personal harm as a direct result of a participating hospital's violation of a requirement of [the Act] may, in a civil action against the participating hospital, obtain those damages available for personal injury under the law of the State in which the hospital is located."[11]

---

[8]   42 U.S.C. § 1395dd.

[9]   Roberts v. Galen of Virginia, 525 U.S. 249, 250 (1999).42 U.S.C. § 1395dd(b).

[10]   Roberts, 525 U.S. at 250.

[11]   42 U.S.C. § 1395dd(d)(2)(A).

[4] Obstetrical Suite

Injuries at birth are the basis of many high judgments and settlements. Most of these situations are covered in the relevant chapter on physician liability. However, with the increased presence of husbands and significant others in the obstetrical suite before and during delivery, the hospitals have acquired new responsibilities. The risk of physical harm to the husband is usually well covered in pre-delivery classes, carefully prepared consent forms, and the husband's own assumption of the risk. In July 2005, Jeanette Passalaqua, 32, filed suit against Kaiser Foundation Hospitals and Southern California Permanente Medical Group Inc. in San Bernardino County state court stating that her husband was asked by Kaiser staff to hold and steady his wife while an employee inserted an epidural needle into her back. The sight of the needle caused Steven Passalaqua, 33, to faint. He fell backward, striking his head on an aluminum cap molding at the base of the wall, suffered a brain hemorrhage and died two days later.

Courts are also increasingly open to suits for emotional injury, without requiring any accompanying physical injury, when a newborn child is subjected to significant injury within the father's sight and hearing. This can occur in the obstetrical area, in the postoperative recovery area, the intensive care unit, or even in the patient's room.

This expansion of the tort of emotional injury has required hospitals to take special precautions through sensitivity training of personnel likely to be dealing with visitors at a time of high emotional stress. Of course, a good many doctors would be helped by such training sessions as well.

§ 1.04 Risks to Employees

Most of the problems of employee safety in hospitals are the same as in the rest of society. There are, however, several unusual hazards in the hospital setting worthy of special mention.

[1] AIDS

No discussion about health care today can escape the topic of AIDS (Auto Immune Disease Syndrome). In the hospital, AIDS presents an unusual set of problems. Ordinarily, the disease is difficult to transmit by casual contact. It is most commonly spread through sexual contact or through the shared use of needles by intravenous drug abusers. However, hospitals tend to have an unusually high percentage of patients with AIDS, particularly those in the metropolitan areas of the country. This is complicated by the fact that infection with HIV (Human Immunodeficiency Virus), which causes AIDS, may be present for over a decade before clinical evidence of the disease becomes apparent to the patient or doctor.

Hospital employees and physicians must also use extreme caution to protect themselves while withdrawing blood. Serious problems arise when hospital personnel believe they were exposed to the AIDS or Hepatitis B or C viruses through a needle-stick. Physicians and health care employees have sued hospitals when they believe they may have been stuck by needles that have previously been contaminated with blood from an AIDS-infected person. These suits tend to be heavily laden with emotional overtones and damages.

The incidence of employees being stuck with needles in a hospital is low. "Epidemiological studies have indicated that the average risk for HIV transmission after percutaneous exposure to HIV-infected blood in health care settings is about 3 per 1,000 injuries."[12] This has given rise to concern over whether it is advisable, feasible, and legally possible to ascertain the Hepatitis and HIV positivity of every patient. Here, the patient's privacy protections, including HIPAA (Health Insurance Portability and Accountability Act of 1996),[13] must be weighed against the need of the potentially infected employee to know if there is a chance of infection. If a positive diagnosis is made on the patient, and the employee who has been stuck is notified, there are still the questions of prophylaxis and therapy — occupational HIV post-exposure prophylaxis (PEP). In some jurisdictions, it is considered below acceptable standards not to begin treatment with an anti-HIV regimen in the hopes of preventing the infection despite the low risk. Failure to diagnose, warn, and treat the employee are areas of potential liability for a hospital, whether the employee is a professional or not.

The risk manager is faced with the necessity to provide appropriate protection for all employees who might be exposed to a needle-stick. Such protection has included the use of double gloves and/or for operating room personnel and those engaged in venesection, gloves with a metal mesh. The careful disposal of needles, sharp instruments and all other blood-contaminated instruments is mandatory and has, itself, been the subject of suits when persons have stuck themselves while attempting to replace a needle cap or while picking up a plastic sack containing sharp instruments.

While there is some danger of transmission of AIDS by the splashing of blood on the mucus membranes or raw skin surfaces, this is an unusual means of transmission. The protection by mask and gown, therefore, is less likely to be required to reduce the hospital's liability. Special care of food

---

[12] HIV post-exposure prophylaxis: Guidance from the UK Chief Medical Officer's Expert Advisory Group on AIDS, 2nd edition, Department of Health, February 2004.

[13] Public Law 104-191.

implements and body wastes is always a good idea in a hospital, but this requirement is not increased by the AIDS virus.

The liability of the hospital for AIDS transmission from an infected health care professional to a patient is a volatile issue, because it requires the hospital to be responsible for knowing that the employee carried the HIV. In some jurisdictions this is regarded as an invasion of privacy. There is an excellent possibility that a significant percentage of employees and patients who enter a hospital will be carrying the virus, even if they are not obviously suffering from the disease. Because the laws covering consent for the drawing of blood for an HIV test are stringent in many states, and since they are subject to change with each meeting of the state legislature, it is essential that physicians know the local law. With increasing knowledge of the disease, there has been a trend toward a lessening of the earlier restrictions on drawing blood for the diagnosis of HIV.[14]

Transmission of the virus from an infected patient to a noninfected patient is a real hazard. The reuse of a needle previously used for an HIV patient on a second patient or the reuse of a bottle of medicine by drawing two or more doses from it for use on different patients, are among the means of transmission. Both are violations of accepted policy and are almost indefensible. New York state health officials in Nov 2007 notified 628 people that they should seek testing for HIV, hepatitis and other blood borne diseases because they were treated by a doctor who reused syringes when injecting patients with more than one drug, according to the *New York Times* Nov 20, 2007. Two patients of anesthesiologist Harvey Finkelstein of Plainview, N.Y. contracted hepatitis C. According to the *Times*, Finkelstein would use a new syringe for each patient. However, he used the same syringe to draw medicine from more than one vial when giving a patient more than one type of drug by injection, which caused the potential contamination of multi-dose vials. The blood of a patient with a virus could, by backing up through the needle and entering the vials, be transmitted to another person when that vial of medicine was reused. The hospital protocols must be strict to prohibit such dangerous practices which will lead to liability claims difficult to defend.

§ 1.05   Risks to Visitors

Hospital visitors present the usual risks of invitees or licensees on commercial premises. Hospitals are no different from office buildings in having persons slip on a wet floor, get caught in elevators, trip on stairs, etc.

---

[14] Calif. 2007,AB 329, Nakanishi, Chapter 386.

§ 1.06 Risks to Patients

Many of the risks faced by patients are not greatly different from those facing other persons in a place of business—the hazards of the wet floor, the breaking of a plumbing accessory, spilled hot coffee, the slips and falls in the hallway, and fires. In a hospital there are special problems, however, usually associated with the effort of the patient to accommodate himself or herself to confinement to bed during the waking hours.

[1] Falls

Falls from the bed often can be prevented by the use of bed rails, which are difficult for the patient to climb over. However, should the patient climb over the rail, the result is almost always a serious injury. It is, therefore, extremely important for risk managers and other hospital personnel to be certain that the use of bed rails or other restraints is actually going to protect that particular patient.

While most hospitals are able to deal with these problems satisfactorily, small hospitals, skilled nursing facilities and other institutions of the nursing home type have less supervision and thus a relatively high incidence of preventable injury due to the misapplication of restraints and bed rails. (Patients have been strangled by misapplied restraints.) There are standard instructions which can be given to nursing personnel which should diminish, if not do away with, these risks. Failure to give these instructions and failure to provide appropriate employee training are likely to lead to liability.

[2] Bathroom Hazards

Because many hospital patients tend to be weak and easily confused, the fact that the bathroom facilities are unfamiliar creates a special hazard. Many patients, because of their disease or condition, have an increased need to use urinals, bedpans or toilets, and in the absence of a speedy response to a request for help by nursing personnel, these patients are inclined to attempt to care for their own needs. Since many of them should not get out of bed unaided, there may be disastrous results. Here again, the liability can be disproportionately high compared to the cost of prevention. Appropriate instruction of the nursing personnel and the patients themselves is a requirement in all hospitals although the actual number of falls prevented may be low.[15]

---

[15] J Am Geriatr Soc. 2008;56(1):29-36.

[3] Effects of Medication

The medication of patients, particularly with mind-altering pharmaceuticals such as sedatives, tranquilizers, and painkillers puts a special responsibility on the nursing staff. Nurses must be aware of the increased risk of harm to a patient under sedation. The application of an overly warm hot water bottle or electric heating pad can lead to serious burns in a comatose or medicated patient, whereas the normal person would have been awakened by the first pains and removed the object. Also, patients who stand up rapidly after receiving medication are likely to faint and fall. They, too, need special warnings.

[4] Hospital Acquired Infection

With the advent of antibiotics, the threshold of concern about hospital infections, except for AIDS and hepatitis, has dropped, particularly among the general public. However, many of the infections found within the hospital (nosocomial infections) tend to be resistant to common, and sometimes even to uncommon, antibiotics. These infections are, therefore, more hazardous and more difficult to treat than the ordinary infection. Risk management includes the protection of patients, employees and visitors from infection. Careful staff training is an essential requirement. There is a particularly virulent strain of bacteria — Methicillin Resistant Staphylococcus Aureus (MRSA) or, if it is acquired in the hospital — HA-MRSA. MRSA pneumonia and blood poisoning have high death rates. According to the Center for Disease Control (CDC) the best means of prevention is hand washing by all employees, janitorial as well as professional, who have any contact with patients.[16]

The AIDS epidemic has led to a lively concern over the possibility of cross-infection. However, except for the hazards to hospital employees mentioned, *supra*, AIDS is a relatively low risk to persons in the hospital setting. The reverse, however, cannot be said. The AIDS (Acquired Immune Deficiency Syndrome) patient is at an unusual risk from infections because, as the name of the syndrome states, his immunity is impaired. For this reason, there are unusual problems in attempting to protect such patients from opportunistic infections from visitors, staff and other patients. In the case of the AIDS patient who is susceptible to otherwise relatively harmless infections brought by staff and visitors, there is a delicate balance between patients' rights and hospital responsibility. For instance, it could be considered to be negligence to allow an immune-compromised patient to be

---

[16] www.cdc.gov/ncidod/dhqp/ar_mrsa_healthcareFS.html.

exposed to tuberculosis in another patient or staff member.

Most of the problems in the treatment of infections are covered in the medical chapters of this volume. A general hospital problem, however, is the difficulty in the disposal of infectious waste. These problems are much like those for radioactive waste discussed supra.

[5] Mental Patients

There are particular requirements in mental health facilities for the prevention of injury to patients. These are discussed in Chapter 6 of this volume.

[6] Pharmaceutical Problems

It is the responsibility of the pharmacist and the hospital personnel, usually nurses, who transmit medications to make sure that each patient gets the right dose of the right medicine at the right time by the right route (orally, intramuscularly, or intravenously). With many medications, precise dosage and timing are not essential, although they are desirable. Usually, mistakes do not result in any measurable damage. However, for a patient who, for example, has severe diabetes, a delay in receiving medication or an incorrect dose can be fatal. Again, proper risk management will assure that the staff has been fully trained in techniques that reduce the possibility of mistakes in medication. The Joint Commission[17] and various hospital associations have established standards for the handling of medications, both on the floor and in the pharmacy. Confusion caused by similar sounding names for very different medications and packaging similarities for vastly different dosage levels have been causes for large liability suits.

There are also hazards due to the mishandling or misuse of dangerous drugs such as narcotics. Here again, careful regulation, training, and supervision can reduce this risk significantly. Precautions must be taken to protect hospital supplies of narcotics from professionals, RNs and MDs who are themselves users.

There is a special hazard from the use of a medication which, for some reason, is specifically contraindicated for a particular patient. This contraindication may be general to a class of patients, such as Afro-Americans with the sickle cell trait, or it may be specific to the individual, such as a person with an allergy to a particular pharmaceutical or food product such as wheat or nuts. In these cases, the responsibility is usually on

---

[17] 2008 National Patient Safety Goals—Medication Safety. http://www.jointcommission. org/AboutUs/ContactUs/.

the attending physician to be certain that the patient does not receive that medicine, even when that physician is not on call. There is also a nursing responsibility to check the chart before administering a newly ordered medication. This includes the responsibility to warn the on call doctor — who may be a resident house officer, or other physician unfamiliar with the patient — of the chart notations about drug sensitivity. Sometimes, a drug is contraindicated because the patient is receiving another medication, and the two are incompatible. While this is certainly the attending physician's responsibility, it can also be imputed to the hospital pharmacist and, therefore, directly to the hospital. This is particularly true of mixtures put together in the pharmacy for intravenous injection.

[7] Dietary Problems

There are obvious liabilities in serving salt to a hypertensive, sugar to a diabetic or peanuts to a hyperallergenic patient. Lawyers responsible for hospital liability must be sure that there are system checks similar to those for drugs in place to prevent such errors.

§ 1.07 Blood Bank Problems

Most of the problems involving transfusion of blood are considered in other chapters. However, the hospital blood bank itself poses several unique liability problems. The most common is the failure to get the right unit of blood cross-matched with the right patient and then delivered to that unique patient. This involves precise identification of the unit of blood, of the patient, and of the test done on the compatibility of the blood for that patient. Any failure in this chain is generally recognized as negligence. This is one of the "never" errors listed in § 1.01 which are pinpointed by HHS and the regulatory agencies, such as the Joint Commission, and for which the hospital has almost no defense in a malpractice action.

In addition, the blood must have been tested for the possibility of disease, particularly hepatitis A, B, and C and HIV. These tests must have been done appropriately and recorded properly. Furthermore, the blood must have been stored by proper methods, and must not be stored beyond the safe period of time for that blood product. This is usually measured in days.

§ 1.08 Incident Management Procedure

A hospital is expected to have a reporting system sufficiently comprehensive so as to warn the risk manager of potential hazards. An incident report should be required for any unusual or adverse occurrence. It should also be reviewed by not only the risk manager, but by an appropriate committee, including some physicians. In most jurisdictions, this incident report is obtainable by a plaintiff's attorney as a business record of the hospital. Occasionally, hospitals have the incident reports especially prepared for and sent to the hospital attorney with the intent that they become part of the attorney's work product and, therefore, be preserved from discovery by the plaintiff if a lawsuit develops. However, many believe this decreases the value of the incident report to those whose duty it is to change the hospital procedures to prevent recurrences of adverse incidents. Concerning this practice, one court has said: "A document which is not privileged does not become privileged by the mere act of sending it to an attorney."[18] Therefore, in most hospitals the report goes to a staff person and is then reviewed by the appropriate committee. It is not considered to be a part of the peer review mechanism which is protected under the Health Care Quality Improvement Act of 1986 or the many state versions of this protection. Failure of the hospital staff to respond appropriately to the warning given by an incident report makes the hospital vulnerable to a later liability action involving same hazard.

§ 1.09 Hospital Responsibility for Acts of Physicians

While hospital risk management shares a great deal in common with risk management in other organizations, the quality assurance aspects of physician performance are unique.

[1] Employed Physicians

A steady change in physician practice in hospitals has been the increased hiring of physicians in the auxiliary areas such as radiology, anesthesia, physiotherapy, emergency department, pathology and recently and rapidly, hospitalists or intensivists.

The concept of extending the hospital's responsibility for the professional conduct of employed physicians has accompanied the loss of charitable immunity. First came the establishment of vicarious hospital liability for the acts of the employed physician based on the *respondeat superior* theory. This is now well established as a simple extension of the ordinary law of agency.

At one time there was a distinction between the hospital's responsibility for an "administrative" act of an employed physician and its responsibility for a "professional" act; i.e., caring for a patient. However, that distinction

---

[18] St. Louis Little Rock Hosp., Inc. v. Gaertner, 682 S.W'.2d. 146, 151 (Mo. App.1984).

has been removed in recent years. The hospital is held responsible because it hires doctors and nurses and then it charges patients for the care these employed professionals give. The first case to make this clear was decided in New York in 1957,[19] and it has been widely followed since.[20]

A hospital also has been held liable for the acts of a part-time employed physician even when he was not serving in his employed capacity, but was seeing a private patient in the emergency room of the hospital at the request of another employee.[21]

A separate class is the employed physician who is in an administrative or executive position. While all of the usual liabilities of the nonprofessional in a management position are present, the healthcare professional has added responsibilities. Most of these have to do with assuring that the quality of professional care rendered in the hospitals is at or above the standard of care. This is done primarily through the Quality Control Committees of the hospital.

[2] Non-employed Physicians

In the United States, physicians traditionally used the hospital as a "doctors' workshop." Unlike other countries, where most hospital physicians are full-time employees, in the United States the physicians have been independent, often being on the staff of a number of hospitals. The relationship is to some extent analogous to that of the lawyer and the court-room. Once a lawyer has fulfilled the basic qualifications to practice in a specific court, he or she practices in an individual manner, subject to certain rules. The lawyer is responsible to the client and the doctor to the patient. They are not controlled by the management of their workplace as if they were the employees of a large corporation. The tradition in the United States has been that "hospitals do not practice medicine." [22]

Also, by tradition, negligence of nonemployee staff physicians was not imputed to the hospital because the physician was not an agent of the facility, but an independent contractor.[23] He was considered to have a contract with the patient which did not include the hospital[24] This all changed beginning in 1965

---

[19] Bing v. Thunig, 2 N.Y.2d 656, 143 N.E.2d 3, 163 N.Y.S.2d 3 (1957).

[20] Bernardi v. Colorado Comm. Hosp. Ass'n, 166 Colo. 280, 443 P.2d 708 (1968); Scott v. Brookdale Hosp. Ctr., 60 A.D.2d 647, 400 N.Y.S.2d 552 (1977); Wright v. United States. 507 F. Supp. 147 (E.D. La. 1980).

[21] Niles v. City of San Rafael, 42 Cal. App. 3d 260, 116 Cal. Rptr. 80l (1974).

[22] Curran, W.J., Hospital Liability for the Quality of Patient Care, 280 N. ENG. J. MED. 316-17 (1969).

[23] See Runyon v. Goodrum, 147 Ark. 481, 228 S.W. 397 (1921); Moon v. Mercy Hosp., 150 Colo. 430, 373 P.2d 974 (1962); Haven v. Randolph, 342 F. Supp. 538 (D.D.C. 1972).

[24] Rosane v. Senger, 112 Colo. 363,149 P.2d 372 (1944); Cooper v. Curry, 9~ N.M. 417. 589 P.2d 201, 203 (1978).

with the Illinois case of *Darling v. Charleston Community Memorial Hospital*.[25] Darling was a college football player who broke his leg and eventually suffered an amputation because of the negligence of an attending physician in a small Illinois hospital. The hospital was sued on the basis that it allowed the physician to practice a specialty—orthopaedics—in which he had not kept current. The hospital administrator testified that he had done nothing to find out whether the doctor had read any of the orthopaedics books in the hospital library or otherwise had kept himself up-to-date. The hospital had placed the doctor on its emergency room call list, but had not required the medical staff to supervise him as was called for by the hospital bylaws, under Illinois regulations, and by the standards of the then named Joint Commission on the Accreditation of Hospitals. The hospital failed to review the doctor's work and failed to require a consultation when he attempted to practice beyond his area of training and experience. The jury found this to be a failure to assure adherence to community standards, and, therefore, negligence on the part of the hospital, even though the doctor was an independent contractor. The Illinois Supreme Court held that a hospital undertakes to treat the patient, and to act through its nurses and doctors, even if the doctors are not its employees.[26]

§ 1.10 Board Responsibility

[1] Establishment of Board Responsibility

There have been attempts by hospitals to avoid *Darling-type* liability by expressly contracting with physicians or groups of physicians and stating in the documents that the doctors are "independent contractors." These attempts have not been particularly successful, especially in recent years. First, courts have found them only to be a transparent attempt to avoid the hospital's duty to the patient.[27] Second, courts have found that the hospitals were allowing patients to believe that doctors, especially those in the emergency department, were actually working for the hospital. The courts, therefore, applied the theories of apparent agency, ostensible agency and/or agency by estoppel to overcome the independent contractor theory, justifying their actions on the grounds that a community reasonably looks to hospitals to provide medical treatment, and hospitals represent to the patient that the doctors at the hospital will provide that treatment.[28] In this respect, hospitals are becoming victims of their own advertising, which often beckons the patient to come to a particular hospital to receive the exceptional medical care available at that institution.

---

[25] Darling v. Charleston Comm. Hosp., 33 Ill. 2d 326, 21 J N.E.2d 253 (1965).

[26] Ibid. at 329.

[27] Schor v. Medina, 421 So. 2d 271 (La. App. 1982).

[28] *See* Grewe v. Mt Clemens Gen. Hosp., 404 Mich. 240, 251, 273 N.W.2d 429, 433 (1978).

The courts also have found hospitals liable for negligence in granting staff privileges to unqualified doctors, and in failing to supervise the medical staff, even when the doctors were independent contractors and were perceived as such by the aggrieved patients. Since the *Darling* decision in 1965, there have been numerous cases indicating that hospitals have a responsibility to see that the physicians on the medical staff are appropriately selected and supervised. A hospital is clearly liable if it has granted staff privileges to an incompetent physician.[29]

Every hospital governing board is responsible for the conduct of its medical staff. As the Nevada Supreme Court said in *Moore v. Carson-Tahoe Hospital*, "All powers of the medical staff flow from the Board of Trustees, and the staff must be held accountable for its control of quality."[30] Some authors would like to go all the way and have the hospital totally responsible for the acts of all personnel, including independent physicians, on the basis of corporate negligence.[31]

[2] Implementation of Board Responsibility

As pointed out above, at one time most hospitals reacted to physician needs by simply furnishing the facilities and personnel requested to care for their patients. Most gave in to the doctors' demands, and the institutions were shaped to meet the medical staffs' methods of practice. Now, however, hospitals have assumed increasing organizational control, particularly since the introduction of the Diagnosis Related Groups (DRG) method of reimbursement under the federally funded Medicare and Medicaid programs. In this system, patient care given by the physician has a direct impact on the financial stability of the hospital. For a given diagnosis, the hospital is reimbursed a specific amount of money no matter how long the patient stays or how many resources are utilized to care for him. Obviously, the more efficient the doctor and the fewer complications the patient has, the shorter the stay and the more the hospital's margin of surplus. This has led to an increasing interest by hospitals in the activities of the staff doctors. While initially this concern was directed chiefly at reducing costs, it has also been directed toward the quality of care.

---

[29] Fiorentino v. Wenger, 19 N.Y.2d 407, 412, 227 N.E.2d 296. 299, 280 N.Y.S.2d 373, 378 (1967); Corleto v. Shore Mem. Hosp., 138 N.J. Super. 302,350 A.2d 534 (1975); Johnson v. Misericordia Comm. Hosp., 99 Wis. 2d 708, 301 N.W.2d 156 (1981); Andrews v. Northwestern Mem. Hosp., 540 N.E.2d 443 (Ill. App. 1989).

[30] Moore v. Board of Trustees of Carson-Tahoe Hosp., 88 Nev. 207, 495 P.2d 605, 608 (1972).

[31] Southwick, A. F., Hospital Liability, 4 J. Leg. Med. 1, 3 (Mar. 1983).

§ 1.11 Quality Assessment of Physicians

[1] Credentials

The hospital's responsibility for a medical staff member's performance involves several duties. The first involves obtaining and assessing the credentials of a physician when he or she first applies for privileges.

A hospital must be certain that the person is actually a licensed physician and has, in fact, earned the claimed credentials, i.e., graduation from medical school and specialty board certification. The Florida Supreme Court found a hospital liable to the estate of a patient for injuries caused by a staff member. The "physician" was a Canadian fugitive wanted on drug charges who had fraudulently obtained a Florida medical license. The imposter was practicing under an assumed name. The court found that the hospital was guilty of corporate negligence in selecting physicians to practice in the hospital.[32] It has been estimated that 5% of submitted physician credentials are fraudulent or at least deceptive.[33]

In addition to checking the authenticity of an applicant's credentials, it is essential that the hospital also check with any other hospital at which the applicant has or has had staff privileges, and with physicians in the area who should be knowledgeable of the applicant's history of training and performance. These requirements have been well established in case law, particularly since *Johnson v. Misericordia Community Hospital* [34] in 1981. They have since been implemented on a national basis by The Health Care Quality Improvement Act of 1986. Under this Act[35] a hospital is required to check each physician's credentials with the National Practitioner Data Bank (NPDB), established by the Department of Health and Human Services. This data bank became operational in 1990 and, as of 2008, had reports on some 200,000 doctors. Failure to check a physician's background through the NPDB at the time of granting privileges, and periodically thereafter, is cause to subject the hospital to sanctions and leave it vulnerable in any liability action against it for acts of that physician.

One of these new duties, for instance, is to assure the public that the staff physicians meet the community's standard of care applicable to hospital practices. Failure to evaluate a doctor's credentials prior to allowing staff practice privileges, or failure to monitor a doctor's performance while

---

[32] Insigna v. LaBella, 543 So. 2d 209 (Fla. 1989).

[33] N.E.J.M. Vol. 318:356-358, Feb 11, 1988 No.8.

[34] 99 Wis. 2d 708. 301 N.W.2d 156 (1981).

[35] 42 U.S.C. § 1101 et seq.

practicing in the hospital, is a breach of that duty by the hospital, and therefore a tort.

Neff v. Johnson Memorial Hosp[36] deals with reviewing a hospital's decision to credential a particular physician. In this case the Appellate Court of Connecticut found that to sustain a corporate negligence claim against a hospital, a hospital knew or should have known that the physician's actions would "obviously and naturally, even though not necessarily," expose the patient to "probable injury unless preventive measures were taken."

In *Johnson v. Misericordia, supra* the hospital failed to check a physician's background adequately so as to learn about malpractice problems which the physician had experienced in a hospital in a different state. The poor results suffered by the physician's patient in this hospital were similar to those suffered by other patients of his at the previous hospital. *Bell v. Sharp Cabrillo Hospital*[37] involved the failure of a hospital to discover that the privileges of a physician who had been on its staff for fourteen years without problems had not been renewed at another hospital, and that, at a third hospital, his privileges had been revoked. In addition, the defendant hospital had failed to discover that this staff member had stopped carrying medical malpractice insurance. When a patient was injured because of the physician's negligence, damages were assessed against the defendant hospital for its negligent examination of the physician's credentials.

In still another case, a court allowed a suit by a patient against a hospital,[38] because the hospital granted staff privileges to a physician who had allegedly misused alcohol in the past.

Granting staff privileges is chiefly a matter of careful attention to the details of credentials. In the case of a surgeon, however, it often becomes a matter of judgment, because the decision must be made as to which procedures the surgeon is capable of performing, based on his or her academic training in that field and clinical performance at other hospitals.

[2] Performance

A hospital has a duty to supervise the actual performance of a physician within the hospital. No matter how good a doctor's credentials may have been when privileges were granted; hospitals can be held liable if they do not make certain that the physician continues to perform within the parameters of appropriate practice in the community. In most cases, the courts have relied upon the fact that hospitals are expected to adhere to the Joint

---

[36] 889 A.2d 921 (Conn. 2006).

[37] 260 Cal. Rptr. 37 (Cal. App. 1989).

[38] Bay Med. Ctr. v. Sapp, 535 So. 2d 308 (Fla. App. 1988).

Commission standards, which define the applicable standard of care for the physician and the hospital's duty to supervise.[39]

In the often cited 1973 trial decision of *Gonzales v. Nork* [40] the hospital itself was held liable for the doctor's extensive malpractice on over 38 patients. There were both misdiagnoses and incompetently performed operations. Dr. Nork, by his own admission, was taking mind-altering drugs during this time. The hospital was held liable for its failure to supervise Dr. Nork's patient care through his long and increasingly obvious pattern of misbehavior. Because Dr. Nork had declared bankruptcy, the hospital became liable for payment of the entire $1.7 million in compensatory damages and $2 million in punitive damages. This doctrine of hospital corporate negligence for failure to supervise the medical staff is now generally accepted.[41]

The hospital's duty to supervise involves not only the actual care of patients but also the doctor's other behavior within the hospital. In a 1988 case, the Massachusetts Supreme Court, in considering a neurosurgeon's rape of a hospital employee, stated that, since the hospital knew of the doctor's previous questionable reputation, but took no action, it could have caused the employee's injuries, because the doctor's action was not "unforeseeable."[42]

[3] Standards of Care

The standards of care against which a physician's performance are measured are national in scope. Some are established by the Joint Commission and others by the specialty societies. Standards are also set by those certifying boards which are members of the American Board of Medical Specialties (ABMS).

There was a time when standards were set locally. This so-called "locality rule" allowed wide variations from one community to another. This rule, however, has been largely abandoned, since physicians now are trained by national standards, particularly those set by residency review committees, the Accreditation Council for Graduate Medical Education (ACGME) and the national certifying boards.

The Joint Commission standards, to which hospitals must adhere for their own accreditation, are also the same over the nation. The only variations allowed are related to the availability of specialized facilities and auxiliary personnel in each community. Thus, while the Joint Commission standards

---

[39] Andrews v. Northwestern Mem. Hosp., 540 N.E.2d 443 (Ill. App. 1989).

[40] Gonzales v. Nork, No. 228566 (Sup. Ct., Sacramento Ct., Cal., Nov. 19, 1973).

[41] *See* Pedrosa v. Bryant, 101 Wash. 2d 225, 677 P.2d 166) (1984).

[42] Copithorne v. Framingham Union Hosp., 401 Mass. 860, 520 N.E.2d 139 (1988).

are universal, adherence may be modified by the presence or absence of modern technology in the locality.

In recent years, a large number of organizations have been involved in setting standards for physician performance.

[a]   American Board of Medical Specialties

The American Board of Medical Specialties (ABMS) is composed of twenty-four medical certifying boards covering the major specialties and subspecialties. Each of these certifying boards has established standards for training physicians. These standards include the following requirements:

1. Graduation from an approved medical school and/or passage of a foreign medical graduate examination or the National Board of Medical Examiners examination;
2. The satisfactory performance of an accredited training residency lasting from three to nine years. This performance is supervised by and attested to by the program director;
3. The passage of an examination in the specialty.

Successful passage of the specialty examination allows the physician to be called a Diplomate of that particular board. This signifies that the physician satisfactorily completed training and passed the examination in that specialty. The certificate, however, does not indicate that the physician is competent to perform the *unsupervised* practice of that specialty. The standards set by the specialty certifying Board and by the residency accrediting body (Accreditation Council for Graduate Medical Education) are more appropriate for training than for practice. They are, therefore, the basic standards needed to *begin* practice.

Most of the certifying boards also have Certificates of Special Qualification or Certificates of Added Qualification in various subspecialties. Here, again, these are standards set for periods of training and for passage of an examination. These standards are meant to ensure appropriate training. They, also, are not standards against which a physician's actual clinical practice in the community can be measured.

ABMS boards also have a requirement for maintenance of certification (MOC). This requirement, implemented by all 24 Boards in 2006, requires a four point process for continuous learning in the six core competencies for quality patient care which have identified by ABMS. The methods of testing vary among the Boards. The crux is proof of both knowledge and performance. In general, recertification, like the original certification, is a test of a physician's knowledge, not of his or her competence to practice, and is far from a measurement of actual performance, even though some Boards do review patient records. Periodic checking for evidence of recertification is a requirement to avoid liability for physician errors in the hospital.

In addition, in many states there is a statutory requirement for continuing medical education (CME). Hospital staff privilege renewal may also, as a hospital requirement, call for a number of hours of accredited CME.

[b]   Specialty Societies

Many specialty societies, notably those in pediatrics, anesthesiology, obstetrics, orthopaedic surgery, thoracic surgery, radiology, and internal medicine, have established standards of practice for certain procedures. Ordinarily, these standards refer only to practice by specialists within that particular specialty. However, they may be applied to doctors of other specialties who perform procedures in the area. For instance, family physicians who practice obstetrics are held to the standards set by obstetricians.

The standards are established by special committees and approved by the governing boards. They are subject to constant review and frequent change, as medical technology changes. For this reason, quality assurance mechanisms and committees must constantly monitor these standards. The American College of Obstetricians and Gynecologists issues periodic publications that inform its members and others of important changes in its standards.

A problem arises when the standards promulgated by different societies appear to be at variance with each other. The Council of Medical Specialty Societies (CMSS) has established a mechanism for resolution of such conflicts.

[c]   Joint Commission (Formerly the Joint Commission on Accreditation of Healthcare Organizations or JCAHO)

This authoritative source for hospital standards requires medical staff evaluation of physician performance within the hospital. To this end, The Joint Commission has "clinical indicators," which are used as benchmarks for comparing the performance of different physicians on a given procedure.

[d]   Other Standard-setting Mechanisms

There are other organizations that have become involved in setting guidelines for the practice of medicine. These include the Rand Corporation, The Institute of Medicine, The American Medical Association, Professional

Review Organizations (PROs), and The American Medical Quality Review Association. Discrepancies between standards set by these groups among themselves and with those set by the specialty societies can create difficulties for quality assurance committees and, thus, for the finders of fact in medical malpractice cases.

Different organizations use different titles for standards such as practice policies, guidelines, practice parameters, etc. In general, however, they have the same purpose. They are yardsticks against which to evaluate clinical performance.

[4] Application of Standards

The application of standards to the individual physician is a hospital responsibility, which is delegated to its hospital staff. The hospital, in order to be accredited by the Joint Commission, must have in place a peer review procedure that reviews all of the medical practice within the hospital. This is a part of each hospital's quality assurance program. The exact mechanism of review varies from hospital to hospital.

[a] Quality Assurance Committees

A hospital's quality assurance program may be a part of the risk management program, but is usually separate. One of the important distinctions is that the quality assurance program is chiefly composed of physicians. There may be non physician staff members, but the committees themselves are largely, or entirely, made up of physician members. These Committees vary from hospital to hospital, but have in common certain audit functions that are called for by the Joint Commission.

[b] Medical Records

The process of reviewing medical records is a mixed physician and non physician activity. Completeness, coding, promptness of filing, etc., are duties of the medical record librarian. The physician members of the committee are responsible for the conduct of other staff physician in making sure that the charts are accurate reflections of the actual patient care. Writing operative notes long after a procedure is performed and the patient is discharged is unacceptable professionally and indefensible legally. Amending entries is even less defensible. Medical records are the business records of the hospital and are discoverable in a malpractice action. Discussions of the review committee are usually not discoverable in civil actions, however. Poor medical records are often the single most important factor in determining the outcome of a malpractice action. Their critical review is crucial to successful quality assurance.

[c] Surgical Committee

The surgical committee reviews the results of surgery and obstetrics as part of the quality assurance review. The committee should review both process and outcome, and, at least annually, should make recommendations regarding the function of the department and the individual physician's performance. The surgical committee either advises a credentials committee or directly regulates each physician's surgical privileges.

[d] Other Monitoring Committees

The total number of committees devoted to monitoring the quality of patient care, depends upon the size of the hospital. In addition to surgical use and medical records, the Joint Commission standards require monitoring of drug and blood utilization, infection control, nursing services, emergency services, special care units (e.g., intensive care and recovery rooms), anesthesia, and laboratories. The nature of these reviews is described in the Joint Commission *Accreditation Participation Requirements (APRs)*. All of the necessary requirements can be found on the web site: http://www. jointcommission.org/. These publications set out in detail how hospital quality assurance program reviews should be conducted by the various committees.

[5] Physician Performance outside Hospital

An Ohio hospital summarily suspended a doctor from its staff after his felony conviction for illegally distributing drugs at his office outside the hospital. The doctor sued the hospital, asking for reinstatement because the action which caused his suspension did not concern "patient care." The Supreme Court of Ohio upheld the hospital suspension because it found the action to be in the best interest of patient care, which includes the "perceived integrity" of the attending physician[43]

A Wisconsin court, however, found that a hospital which had granted a physician hospital staff privileges was not responsible for his malpractice in his own office.[44] The court held that the hospital did not owe the duty of supervision of this non-employee physician to a person who was not also a

---

[43] Bouquett v. St. Elizabeth Corp. 43 Ohio St. 3d 50, 538 N.E.2d 113 (1989).
[44] Pedrosa v. Bryafil, 101 Wash. 2d 226, 677 P.2d 166 (1984).

patient of the hospital. Thus, there is no general duty to the community on the part of a hospital to assure that staff members perform satisfactorily in offices outside the hospital limits.

§ 1.12 Conclusion

This chapter gives an overview of hospital liability concerns. Attorneys tasked with the legal responsibilities of hospitals must also familiarize themselves with a large and rapidly growing number of other issues, many of them unique to these institutions. It is not a field where one can come in from the outside and expect to be able to handle litigation competently in a short time. Furthermore, this chapter relates primarily to tort law. Hospital law covers many other areas, including antitrust, administrative regulations and law, contracts, and patents. There are also an increasing number of serious ethical issues, especially around the two ends of life—birth and death. This thesis is only intended to point the way toward identifying the exposure of a hospital to liability litigation.

CHAPTER 2

CARDIOLOGY

S. Sandy Sanbar, MD, PhD, JD

SYNOPSIS

———————————————

"All clinicians need good judgment. Judgment comes from experience. Experience comes from bad judgment."

C. Walton Lillehei, MD, MACC

§ 2.01 Introduction

[1] Cardiology Competency Statements and Guidelines

The American College of Cardiology (ACC) and the American Heart Association (AHA) are two of the best sites to obtain information about *competency statements* and *guidelines* specifically targeting cardiovascular disorders.[1] They include among others:

- ACC/AHA 2005 Guideline Update for the Diagnosis and Management of Patients with Chronic Heart Failure in the Adult;

- ACC/AHA/ACP-ASIM Practice Guidelines for Management of Patients with Chronic Stable Angina;

- Management of Patients with Unstable Angina and Non-ST-Segment Elevation Myocardial Infarction;

- ACC/AHA 2006 Revised Guidelines for the Management of Patients with ST-Elevation Myocardial Infarction;

- ACC/AHA Guideline Update for Perioperative Cardiovascular Evaluation for Noncardiac Surgery;

- ACC/AHA/SCAI 2005 Guideline Update for Percutaneous Coronary Intervention;

- ACC/AHA 2004 Guideline Update for Coronary Artery Bypass Graft Surgery;

- ACC/AHA 2006 Revised Guidelines for the Management of Patients with Valvular Heart Disease;

- ACC/AHA/ASE 2003 Guideline Update for the Clinical Application of Echocardiography;

- ACC/AHA/ESC 2006 Guidelines for the Management of Patients with Atrial Fibrillation (and Supraventricular arrhythmias);

- ACC/AHA/ESC 2006 Guidelines for the Management of Patients with Ventricular Arrhythmias and the Prevention of Sudden Cardiac Death;

- ACC/AHA 2006 Revised Guidelines for the Management of Patients with Peripheral Arterial Disease;

---

[1] http://www.acc.org/qualityandscience/clinical/pocket_guidelines.htm

- ACC/AHA Practice Guidelines for Implantation of Cardiac pacemakers and Antiarrhythmia devices;

- Clinical Competence Statement on Invasive Electrophysiology Studies, Catheter Ablation, and Cardioversion was published by the ACC/AHA in 2000;[2]

- The ACC/AHA/AAP Recommendations for Training in Pediatric Cardiology were published in 2005.[3]

§ 2.02   Training and Board Certification of Cardiologists

Cardiologists fall into two major categories, clinical or research. Fellowship in *clinical* cardiovascular diseases generally involves a 3-year training program that encompasses a 6-month research experience. Many cardiologists pursue a fourth year in interventional cardiology or electrophysiology, which are recognized subspecialties of the American Board of Internal Medicine.

Clinical training in cardiovascular diseases involves rotations in the following categories:

1. Adult and Pediatric Cardiology Consultation Service and Ambulatory Care;
2. Coronary Care Unit;
3. Diagnostic Cardiology: Electrocardiography; Nuclear Cardiology, Echocardiography, Magnetic Resonance Imaging and Positron Emission tomography and Ultrasonic Tissue Characterization;
4. Heart Failure, Cardiac Transplantation Service and Pre- and Post-Cardiac Transplantation Clinic;
5. Electrophysiology: Arrhythmia Service and Pacemaker/Arrhythmia Clinic;
6. Invasive cardiology: Cardiac Catheterization/Interventional Service; and
7. Preventive cardiology.

Subspecialty cardiology fellowships are offered in clinical electrophysiology, cardiac catheterization/intervention, echocardiography, cardiac computed tomography and cardiovascular magnetic resonance imaging.

---

[2] American College of Cardiology/American Heart Association Clinical Competence Statement on Invasive Electrophysiology Studies, Catheter Ablation, and Cardioversion, *Circulation.* 2000;102:2309. http://circ.ahajournals.org/cgi/content/full/102/18/2309

[3] ACC/AHA/AAP RECOMMENDATIONS FOR TRAINING IN PEDIATRIC CARDIOLOGY, PEDIATRICS Vol. 116 No. 6 December 2005, pp. 1574-1575. http://aappolicy.aappublications.org/cgi/content/full/pediatrics;116/6/1574

Fellowship in cardiovascular *research* is a training program designed for individuals who are interested in a career in academic cardiology. These individuals complete 24 months of in-depth clinical training in cardiovascular diseases, followed by 2 to 3 additional years devoted exclusively to research, thereby giving the trainee the necessary tools in the techniques of investigator-initiated clinical and/or basic research. The *research* training program aims at developing independent cardiovascular scientists competent to use principles of basic and applied clinical cardiovascular research, and to delve in the fields of cardiovascular bioengineering, biomedical and biological imaging, cell and tissue engineering, computational neurosciences and genome analysis.

Cardiologists are trained and certified first as internists then become certified in general cardiology and sometimes in a cardiology subspecialty. The general liability of internal medicine specialists may apply to *board certified* cardiologists.

§ 2.03 Cardiovascular Evaluation

The clinical evaluation of the cardiovascular system generally involves the following four categories:

1. Determination of the cardiovascular anatomy and pathology;
2. Performance of cardiovascular tests and procedures, both non-invasive and invasive;
3. Establishing the residual cardiovascular function, dysfunction or malfunction; and
4. Management modalities, both medical and surgical.

In order to determine the presence or absence of cardiovascular dysfunction/malfunction or impairment, whether caused by disease or as a consequence of negligence, it is important not only to determine the etiology or cause of the cardiovascular disorder, the anatomy and pathology, but also to document dysfunction or malfunction of the heart or blood vessels. When evaluating a patient following an acute cardiovascular event, such as an acute myocardial syndrome, angioplasty, coronary artery bypass surgery, heart valve surgery, or drug therapy following an acute episode of heart failure, a longitudinal clinical record which would cover several months of observation and therapy is usually necessary for the assessment of the severity and the expected duration of the cardiovascular impairment. The persistence of abnormal cardiac findings, which are uncontrolled with standard therapy, as well as recurrent episodes of acute cardiac dysfunction represents significant medical evidence when evaluating cardiovascular disorders. Additionally, where a patient is a worker and wage earner, the cardiovascular evaluation should include the impact of the cardiovascular impairment on the functional ability to perform work.

The primary consequences of cardiovascular disease may be classified into four major categories:

- *Failure* of the heart (dysfunction or malfunction),

- *Ischemia* (restriction of blood supply to the heart muscle),

- *Syncope* or near syncope (fainting), and

- *Cyanosis* (bluish discoloration, for example from a right-to-left shunt).

Dysfunction of the ventricles of the heart, often referred to as cardiomyopathy, may lead to heart failure. The latter may either be left, right or combined left and right ventricular heart failure. Heart failure may be "acute" lasting a few days if treated, or may be "chronic" lasting weeks, months or years. Ventricular dysfunction may be associated with the following cardiac abnormalities:

1. Abnormal heart size, either dilated (cardiomegaly) or hypertrophied (thickening of the heart muscle wall), abnormal wall-motion (hypokinesis, dyskinesis or akinesis); systolic or diastolic ventricular dysfunction with abnormal ejection fraction. The normal ventricular ejection fraction is 55-70%, while 41-50% is mildly abnormal, 31-40% is moderately abnormal, and less than 30% is severely abnormal;
2. Abnormal cardiac valves, with stenosis or regurgitation;
3. Coronary ischemia, usually due to obstructive coronary artery disease; or
4. Electrical conduction abnormality resulting in cardiac arrhythmia or dysrhythmia.

Cardiomyopathy causes myocardial malfunction. *Dilated* cardiomyopathy is associated with an enlarged heart size, i.e. cardiomegaly. *Hypertrophic* cardiomyopathy is associated with thickening of the heart muscle, i.e. myocardium. *Ischemic* cardiomyopathy is the result of obstructive coronary artery disease, in contrast with *non-ischemic* cardiomyopathy where the coronary arteries appear normal. *Infective* and *drug-induced* cardiomyopathy may result from a variety of viral, fungal and bacterial infections, and from chronic alcohol and drug abuse.

Cardiac valve abnormalities may result from a congenital defect, infection or coronary disease, and they may require surgical treatment and placement of a prosthetic heart valve. Congenital heart disease, often referred to as birth defects, manifests itself by abnormal cardiac walls and chambers, defective valves or abnormal great vessels. These defects include coarctation of the aorta, hypoplastic left heart syndrome, patent ductus arteriosus, transposition of the great vessels, atrial and ventricular septal defect, atrio-ventricular canal defect, stenosis of aortic or pulmonic valves, Epstein's anomaly, tricuspid atresia, and Tetralogy of Fallot (blue baby).

The manifestations of symptomatic congenital heart disease may include cyanosis at rest, with an increase in the hematocrit greater than 55%, oxygen saturation less than 90% at room air or pO2 less than 60. Cyanosis may occur only following exertion in some patients, and the pulmonary arterial systolic pressure may be markedly increased. Some patients with congenital heart defects may not be discovered until adulthood, for example atrial septal defect and Marfan's syndrome. The latter is a genetic connective tissue disorder that affects the eyes, bones, skin, lungs and heart, causing mitral or aortic regurgitation, and aortic aneurysm which may rupture resulting in sudden death.

Coronary artery disease, and irregular heart rhythm, in adults are two of the most commonly encountered cardiovascular disorders. Myocardial coronary ischemia may result from coronary spasm (e.g. Prinzmetal angina and catheter-induced spasm), stenosis of the coronary artery due to an atherosclerotic plaque, sclerosis or fibrosis, or complete occlusion resulting from a coronary thrombus or embolus.

Coronary artery disease is the leading cause of death in men and women in the United States, accounting for one in five deaths, and a major cause of the health care expenditures, with annual costs estimated at $142 billion in 2005. Although the gold standard for CAD diagnosis remains conventional, invasive coronary angiography, it is associated costs and morbidity, including a 1.7% rate of major complications, which led to the development of noninvasive modalities for CAD diagnosis. Death from coronary disease may occur either suddenly in previously asymptomatic patient or after a period of manifest symptoms of chest pain or heart failure.

§ 2.04 Symptoms and Signs of Cardiovascular Disorders

[1] Heart Failure

Heart failure symptoms result either form congestion or limited cardiac output. They include shortness of breath, fatigue, orthopnea, nocturnal paroxysmal dyspnea, and chest pain or angina pectoris. The patient may complain of significant limitations in performing activities of daily living, walking, climbing stairs or working. The patient may have symptoms of inadequate cerebral perfusion, such as ataxia, paresis or confusion. The signs of heart failure may include abnormal heart sound, irregular heart rhythm, abnormal blood pressure, pulmonary rales, increased pulmonary markings on chest x-ray, and presence of pleural effusion, pulmonary congestion and peripheral edema.

[2]   Chest Pain Syndrome

The *chest pain syndrome* represents any constellation of symptoms that the cardiologist feels may represent a complaint consistent with obstructive CAD.   Examples of such symptoms include: chest pain, chest tightness, burning, dyspnea (shortness of breath), shoulder pain, and jaw pain.

Angina pectoris, as defined by the ACC/AHA 2002 Guideline Update on Exercise Testing,[4] may be one of the following:

- *Typical Angina* is *definitely* caused by myocardial ischemia. It is (a) substernal chest pain or discomfort that is (b) provoked by exertion or emotional stress and (c) relieved by rest and/or nitroglycerin.[5]
- *Atypical Angina* may *probably* be ischemic in origin. The term represents chest pain or discomfort that lacks one of the characteristics of definite or typical angina.
- *Non-Anginal Chest Pain* or discomfort meets one or none of the typical angina characteristics.

Cardiac chest pain may result from:

1. Ischemic Causes:
   a. Stable Angina Pectoris, due to stenosis or spasm of the coronary arteries;
   b. Unstable Angina Pectoris, with greater stenosis causing a compromise in coronary flow;
   c. Myocardial infarction, which may be non-transmural or transmural;
2. Non-Ischemic Cardiac Causes: e.g. in mitral valve prolapse; pericarditis; and aortic dissection.

---

[4] Gibbons RJ, Balady GJ, Bricker JT, et al. ACC/AHA 2002 guideline update for exercise testing: summary article. A report of the American College of Cardiology/American Heart Association Task Force on Practice Guidelines (Committee to Update the 1997 Exercise Testing Guidelines). J Am Coll Cardiol 2002;40:1531–40.

[5] Diamond GA. A clinically relevant classification of chest discomfort. J Am Coll Cardiol 1983;1:574–5.

The *types of ischemic "angina"* include:

1. Silent (No Angina) – No pain, often discovered on an EKG or Holter monitor;
2. Typical Angina - Exertional, and prompt relief with nitroglycerin;
3. Atypical Angina – Pain that is felt in places *other* than the chest;
4. Angina Equivalent – Dyspnea *without* chest pain
5. Variant Angina (Prinzmetal) – ST elevation, paroxysmal ventricular tachycardia; exercise tolerance test (ETT) normal;
6. Drug-Induced Vasospasm – e.g. Cocaine and Ergotamine drugs;
7. Catheter- or Trauma-Induced coronary spasm.

Non-cardiac chest pain may result from:

1. Heart burn: Pain from esophagus or stomach;
2. Panic Attack;
3. Chest Wall Pain: Musculo-skeletal; costochondritis; Rib or thoracic vertebral fractures; Fibromyalgia
4. Lung Disease: Pleurisy; Pulmonary embolism or hypertension; Pneumothorax;
5. Nerves: Pinched thoracic nerves;
6. Shingles (Herpes Zoster);
7. Gallbladder diseases;
8. Cancer in the chest, for example bronchial, lungs and esophageal.

[3]   Heart Rhythm

The normal and abnormal *types of heart rhythm* include:

1. Rhythmic: Regular;
2. Arrhythmic: Irregular;
3. Normocardia: Normal heart rate (60-100 bpm);
4. Bradycardia: Slow heart rate (below 59 bpm), which may be regular or irregular;
5. Tachycardia: Rapid rate (above 100 bpm), which may be regular or irregular;
6. Fibrillation: Chaotic or irregularly irregular; and
7. Heart block: First, Second, or Third degree. The symptoms of complete heart block include fainting spells, unconsciousness, which may occur suddenly, at times associated with convulsions, requiring permanent cardiac pacemaker implantation.

§ 2.05 Assessment of the Cardiac Patient

[1] Determination of "Pre-Test Probability of CAD"

Once the cardiologist determines the presence of symptoms that may represent obstructive CAD (chest pain syndrome present), then the pre-test probability of CAD[6] should be evaluated, as recommended by the American College of Cardiology/American Heart Association (ACC/AHA) 2002 Guideline Update for Exercise Testing and the ACC/AHA 2002 Guideline Update for Management of Patients with Chronic Stable Angina. Multiple-Risk-Factor Assessment, which includes consideration gender, blood pressure, lipid levels and other factors, is accomplished utilizing the 1999 Framingham Risk Score calculation.[7] Based on these criteria, *Coronary Heart Disease (CHD) Risk* is calculated as one of three categories:

1. *Low CHD Risk*
   This category is defined by the age-specific risk level that is below average. In general, low CHD risk will correlate with a 10-year absolute CHD risk less than 10%.
2. *Moderate (or Intermediate)CHD Risk*
   This category is defined by the age-specific risk level that is average or above average. In general, moderate, or intermediate, risk will correlate with a 10-year absolute CHD risk between 10% and 20%.
3. *High CHD Risk*
   This category is defined as the presence of diabetes mellitus or the 10-year absolute CHD risk of greater than 20%.

[2] "Perioperative Risk Predictors" of Cardiac Patients

Cardiologists are frequently called upon to evaluate surgical candidates preoperatively. There are three categories of cardiac risk factors:

1. *Major risk predictors*
   These include unstable coronary syndromes, decompensated heart failure (HF), significant arrhythmias, and severe valve disease.

---

[6] Diamond GA, Forrester JS. Analysis of probability as an aid in the clinical diagnosis of coronary-artery disease. N Engl J Med 1979;300:1350–8.

[7] Grundy SM, Pasternak R, Greenland P, et al. ACC/AHA scientific statement: assessment of cardiovascular risk by use of multiple-risk factor assessment equations: a statement for healthcare professionals from the American Heart Association and the American College of Cardiology. J Am Coll Cardiol 1999;34:1348–59.

2. *Intermediate (or moderate) risk predictors*

These include mild angina, prior myocardial infarction (MI), compensated or prior HF, diabetes, or renal insufficiency.

3. *Minor risk predictors*

These comprise advanced age, abnormal electrocardiogram (ECG), rhythm other than sinus, low functional capacity, history of cerebrovascular accident, and uncontrolled hypertension.

[3] Surgical Risk Categories for Non-Cardiac Surgery

The 2002 ACC/AHA Guideline Update for Perioperative Cardiovascular Evaluation of Non-Cardiac Surgery[8] provides three surgical risk categories:

1. *High-Risk Surgery* — cardiac death or MI greater than 5%. This includes emergent major operations (particularly in the elderly), aortic and peripheral vascular surgery, prolonged surgical procedures associated with large fluid shifts and/or blood loss.

2. *Intermediate-Risk Surgery* — cardiac death or MI of 1% to 5%. This includes carotid endarterectomy, head and neck surgery, surgery of the chest or abdomen, orthopedic surgery, prostate surgery.

3. *Low-Risk Surgery* — cardiac death or MI less than 1%, as occurs in endoscopic procedures, superficial procedures, cataract surgery, and breast surgery.

§ 2.06 Cardiovascular Diagnostic Procedures

[1] Tests

Cardiologists are under a duty to utilize a variety of tools in diagnosing cardiac patients, including:

1. For *Acute cardiac disorders such as myocardial infarction and heart failure*: EKG, cardiac enzymes, such as troponin, creatine kinase, and B-Natriuretic peptide; An *uninterpretable ECG* refers to ECGs with resting ST-segment depression (greater than or equal to 0.10 mV), complete left bundle-branch block, pre-excitation (Wolf-Parkinson-White syndrome), or paced rhythm.

---

[8] Eagle KA, Berger PB, Calkins H, et al. ACC/AHA guideline update for perioperative cardiovascular evaluation for noncardiac surgery - executive summary report of the American College of Cardiology/ American Heart Association Task Force on Practice Guidelines (Committee to Update the 1996 Guidelines on Perioperative Cardiovascular Evaluation for Noncardiac Surgery). Circulation 2002;105:1257–67.

2. For *Presence of EKG Abnormalities*: Check the electrolytes – Na, K, Mg, Ca levels;

3. For *Syncope*: Check for anemia by measuring Hemoglobin and Hematocrit;

4. For *Cardiac Arrhythmia*: Check thyroid function – TSH, T3, T4; Perform Electrocardiographic Tests: ECG (EKG) – Electrocardiogram; Ambulatory Holter Monitor; Event Monitor; and EPS – Electrophysiology Studies;

5. For *Cardiac Risk Factors*: Check Lipids & Lipoproteins, Hbg A1c; hsCRP.

6. *Pathology Tests*: Include myocardial biopsy and Genetic DNA Testing for Downs syndrome and Marfan's;

7. *Echocardiographic Tests*: Trans-Thoracic; Trans-Esophageal (Endoscopic TEE); Intra-Vascular Ultrasound (IVUS); M-Mode, 2-Dimensional (and 3-D); Doppler Flow Velocity, Color Doppler; Micro Bubble Perfusion.

8. *Provocative Stress Tests*: Exercise Treadmill Tolerance Test (ETT); Bicycle ergometer; Arm exercise. All exercise tests may include either echocardiography or nuclear cardiac imaging.

9. *Radiologic Tests*: Chest X-ray: Lungs, heart, major vessels; EBCT - Electron beam computed tomography, and Ultrafast CT scan, for signs of calcium; CT of Chest – Computed Tomogram and CT angiograms; MRI – Magnetic resonance imaging and MRI angiogram: uses magnetic fields and radio waves to create cross-sectional images of the heart; Nuclear scan (cardiac imaging): Resting Ventriculogram and Stress (thallium or sestamibi); Nuclear Imaging with Exercise Stress or Chemicals such as Adenosine, Persantine, or Dobutamine;

10. *Invasive Procedures*: Cardiac catherization and coronary arteriography; Pulmonary Arteriography; Peripheral Angiography – Arteriogram, Venogram, or Phlebogram; EPS – Electro-Physiologic Studies; IVUS – Intravascular ultrasound;

11. *Ultrasound and Plethysmography Studies*: Resting Doppler or Duplex, which may be Arterial for Aneurysm, Stenosis, Obstruction; AVM – arterio-venous malformation, or Venous for Thrombi and Valve Insufficiency; Exercise Doppler Arterial, Legs for PVD; and Plethysmography, Toes & Fingers for Raynauld's disease; Buerger's syndrome and Diabetes.

Both invasive and noninvasive cardiovascular tests may pose significant cardiovascular risks to a particular patient, especially where the test is provocative (such as exercise tolerance tests, injection of any drug or nuclear radioactive isotope), cardiac catheterization, coronary arteriography, venography, phlebography, cardiovascular electrophysiologic studies, or CT and MRI angiography. The *informed consent* of the patient undergoing such tests becomes very important.

Exercise tolerance tests, for example, are frequently performed to diagnose cardiovascular disease. They are contra-indicated in patients with unstable angina, uncontrolled and symptomatic cardiac arrhythmias, presence of overt heart failure, severe systemic hypertension with a blood pressure >200/110 mm of mercury or pulmonary hypertension with pulmonary systolic arterial pressure > 60 mm of mercury, stenosis of the left main coronary artery, moderate or severe aortic stenosis with a gradient > 50 mm of mercury, presence of symptomatic hypertrophic cardiomyopathy, presence of aortic dissection, and in some patients with implantable cardiac defibrillators and chronic heart failure.

§ 2.07   Cardiac Imaging Techniques

Around the year 2000, some cardiologists began using words like "holy grail," "gold standard" and "promised land," to describe the coronary angiography that can be obtained with the latest generation of CT scanners. Presently, in 2007, both cardiologists and radiologists are confronting a barrage of new choices of tests that clinicians may order.[9] *Advanced Cardiac Imaging techniques* (See Table 1 for abbreviations) include:

1. Contrast-Enhanced Echocardiography (CEE);
2. Cardiac Nuclear Single Photon Emission Computed Tomography (SPECT) imaging;
3. Cardiac Nuclear Positron Emission Tomography (PET) imaging;
4. Cardiac Magnetic Resonance (CMR) imaging, which is utilized for myocardial structure, function, and viability;
5. Cardiac Computed Tomography (CCT), Electron Beam Computed Tomography (EBCT), 64-slice and Multi-detector CT (MDCT) scanners, capable of acquiring ECG-gated high-resolution images of the heart at extremely high speed;
6. Hybrid systems: (a) SPECT/CCT and (b) PET/CCT;
7. Three-dimensional rendering technique;
8. Dynamic cine-MRI sequences;
9. Pharmacological stress procedures;
10. Quantitative analysis of ventricular wall motion and cardiac function.

---

[9] Schuijf JD, Shaw LJ, Wijns W, Lamb HJ, Poldermans D, de Roos A, van der Wall EE, Baxter JJ; Cardiac imaging in coronary artery disease: Differing modalities. *Heart* 2005; 91:1110-1117.

Cardiac imaging may be categorized into five dimensions:

1. *Single cardiac images* are very useful in the evaluation of cardiac patients, for example, the chest x-ray and the M-Mode echocardiogram.
2. *Two-dimensional images* have greatly improved the diagnosis of cardiac disease, for example, the two-dimensional echocardiogram.
3. *Three-dimensional (3-D), high-resolution, dynamic images* of the heart may be acquired in a single breath-hold by the latest generation of multi-detector *computed tomography (CT)* and *magnetic resonance imaging (MRI)* scanners. The *3-D* cardiac images provide exquisitely detailed, *anatomical* information.
4. *A Fourth Dimension* is achieved when the cardiac images are displayed in a *dynamic mode* adding a *temporal dimension* to the images. The *fourth dimension* is obtained by acquiring images of the heart at different phases of the cardiac cycle allowing a better assessment of cardiac motion and function. More recently, cardiac imaging modalities have incorporated *molecular* imaging procedures.
5. A *Fifth Dimension* represents the addition of "functional or molecular" data to the anatomical images. The perspectives of functional imaging modalities are obtained by techniques based on molecular imaging, including *positron emission tomography (PET) and cardiac MRI.* These modalities are complementary to classic conventional and anatomical imaging like CT and MRI. The dramatic expansion of non-invasive diagnostic tools has coincided with innovations in contrast agents and molecular radionuclide imaging. The visualization of the two sets of images by PET and CT requires graphic tools allowing progressive blending of the two for better localization of metabolic alterations, depicted by PET over the corresponding anatomical structures obtained from the CT images. In cardiac cases, the dynamic property of the heart requires additional, temporal discrimination of the cardiac motion. This results in an additional dimension to the data where the linear correlation from CT to PET represents the fifth dimension.

[1] The AHA Statement regarding the Utilization of Cardiac Imaging

The American Heart Association (AHA) believes that the development of imaging modalities must strike a proper balance between the development of their scientific potential, and their premature clinical use.[10] The AHA supports the following principles in the development and use of existing and emerging cardiac imaging modalities:

1. Imaging studies should be performed by physicians who meet *published standards of training and experience* from medical societies accredited by the Accreditation Council for Graduate Medical Education.

2. These procedures should be performed in *high-quality laboratories* with appropriate facilities and technical personnel who are adequately trained in imaging procedures and related safety standards.

3. Rigorous scientific research should continue to *critically examine these emerging modalities* and define both their advantages and limitations. The AHA would encourage studies comparing emerging techniques to existing, less expensive technology.

4. Emerging imaging modalities should be fully incorporated into ongoing efforts to *improve the overall quality of cardiovascular care and compliance* with existing clinical practice guidelines. For example, the identification of asymptomatic intermediate-risk patients (10% to 20% risk of cardiovascular death/myocardial infarction in 10 years) with atherosclerosis *must* be followed by appropriate risk factor treatment according to existing AHA guidelines.

5. *Clinical investigation of the application of these modalities* should not examine their use in isolation, but rather in association with all other available clinical data about the patient, to determine not only their true *incremental* effect on clinical decision making, but also their potential for additional downstream risks and costs.

6. *Rigorous criteria for appropriateness* should be developed for all cardiac imaging techniques by expert committees that include imaging experts, healthcare quality experts, practicing cardiologists and experienced subspecialists who are not imaging experts, practicing general physicians, and third-party payers.

[2] National Appropriateness Criteria for CCT and CMR

Cardiac CT (CCT) is especially useful in evaluating the myocardium, coronary arteries, pulmonary veins, thoracic aorta, pericardium, and cardiac masses, such as thrombus of the left atrial appendage. However, CCT (and

---

[10] *Gibbons, RJ, Robert H. Eckel, RH, Jacobs, AK, for the Science Advisory and Coordinating Committee- The Utilization of Cardiac Imaging* http://www.americanheart.org/presenter. jhtml?identifier=3023366. *(Last accessed on May 6, 2007)*

CMR) tests are relatively expensive technologies, especially with regards to imaging equipment. The potential for uncontrolled utilization and stimulation of downstream testing and treatment such as unwarranted coronary revascularization has raised substantial concern, not only from government and private payers, but also clinical thought leaders of evidenced-based cardiovascular medicine. The health care community needs to understand how to incorporate these advances in CCT into acceptable clinical care. This process entails the development of appropriateness criteria by the medical community for CCT.

In an effort to respond to the need for the rational use of newer imaging techniques, the *ACCF/ACR/SCCT/SCMR/ASNC/NASCI/SCAI/SIR* (See Table-2 for abbreviations) jointly developed in 2006 Appropriateness Criteria for Cardiac Computed Tomography (CCT) and Cardiac Magnetic (CMR) Resonance Imaging.[11]

The *primary objective* of the reported criteria is to provide guidance regarding the perceived suitability of the two imaging techniques for diverse cardiovascular clinical scenarios. The *ultimate objective* of the appropriateness criteria is to improve patient care and health outcomes in a cost-effective manner based on current understanding of the limits of the CCT and CMR imaging modalities.

The *principal conclusions* of the 2006 appropriateness criteria for CAT and CMR were:

    a. The use of CCT, and CMR, tests for structure and function and for diagnosis in *symptomatic, intermediate coronary artery disease (CAD) risk patients* was deemed appropriate.

    b. On the other hand, *repeat testing and general screening* uses were viewed less favorably.

Based on these appropriateness criteria, it is anticipated that the reported results will have a *significant impact on*:

- Physician decision making and performance when providing quality and cost-effective cardiovascular care;
- Payers pre-authorization and reimbursement policy;
- Quality review by facilities, and
- Future research directions.

A total of 39 indications for CCT were reviewed; 13 were found to be appropriate, 14 were inappropriate, and 12 were uncertain.

---

[11] Hendel et al. Journal of the American College of Cardiology Vol. 48, No. 7, 2006.

The Appropriate Indications for CCT are:

1. Symptomatic chest pain syndrome, with intermediate pre-test probability of CAD; ECG uninterpretable or patient unable to exercise.
2. Symptomatic CAD — Evaluation of suspected coronary anomalies.
3. Symptomatic acute chest pain — Intermediate pre-test probability of CAD; No ECG changes and serial enzymes negative.
4. CAD Patient with prior test results—Evaluation of Chest Pain Syndrome — Uninterpretable or equivocal stress test (exercise, perfusion, or stress echo).
5. Assessment of complex congenital heart disease including anomalies of coronary circulation, great vessels, and cardiac chambers and valves.
6. Evaluation of coronary arteries in patients with new onset heart failure to assess etiology;
7. Evaluation of cardiac mass (suspected tumor or thrombus) - Patients with technically limited images from echocardiogram, MRI, or TEE.
8. Evaluation of pericardial conditions (pericardial mass, constrictive pericarditis, or complications of cardiac surgery) — Patients with technically limited images from echocardiogram, MRI, or TEE.
9. Evaluation of pulmonary vein anatomy prior to invasive radiofrequency ablation for atrial fibrillation;
10. Noninvasive coronary vein mapping prior to placement of biventricular pacemaker;
11. Noninvasive coronary arterial mapping, including internal mammary artery prior to repeat cardiac surgical revascularization;
12. Evaluation of suspected aortic dissection or thoracic aortic aneurysm;
13. Evaluation of suspected pulmonary embolism.

The Inappropriate Indications for CCT are:

1. Symptomatic chest pain syndrome with a high pre-test probability of CAD.
2. Symptomatic—Acute Chest Pain a high pre-test probability of CAD - ECG—ST-segment elevation and/or positive cardiac enzymes.
3. Asymptomatic patient with low CHD risk (Framingham risk criteria).
4. Asymptomatic patient with moderate CHD risk (Framingham).
5. Risk Assessment: General Population—Asymptomatic (Calcium Scoring) in patients with low CHD risk (Framingham).

6. CAD patients with prior test results indicating evidence of moderate to severe ischemia on stress test (exercise, perfusion, or stress echo).
7. Asymptomatic patients with prior calcium score within previous 5 years.
8. Risk Assessment with Prior Test Results—Asymptomatic with High CHD risk (Framingham) — Within 2 years prior cardiac CT angiogram or invasive angiogram without significant obstructive disease.
9. High CHD risk (Framingham) with prior calcium score greater than or equal to 400.
10. Risk Assessment: Preoperative Evaluation for Non-Cardiac Surgery — Low-Risk Surgery - Intermediate perioperative risk.
11. Detection of CAD: Post-Revascularization (PCI or CABG) — Asymptomatic — Evaluation of bypass grafts and coronary anatomy Less than 5 years after CABG.
12. Evaluation of bypass grafts and coronary anatomy - Greater than or equal to 5 years after CABG.
13. Evaluation for in-stent restenosis and coronary anatomy after PCI.
14. Structure and Function—Evaluation of Ventricular and Valvular Function - Evaluation of LV function following myocardial infarction OR in heart failure patients.

The Uncertain Indications for CCT are:

1. Symptomatic patients with chest pain syndrome with Intermediate pre-test probability of CAD, ECG interpretable AND able to exercise.
2. Symptomatic acute chest pain with low pre-test probability of CAD, no ECG changes and serial enzymes negative.
3. Symptomatic with high pre-test probability of CAD, but no ECG changes and serial enzymes negative.
4. "Triple rule out" to exclude obstructive CAD, aortic dissection, and pulmonary embolism: Intermediate pre-test probability for one of the above — ECG—no ST-segment elevation and initial enzymes negative.
5. Asymptomatic patient with high CHD risk (Framingham).
6. Risk Assessment: General Population—Asymptomatic (Calcium Scoring) in patients with moderate CHD risk (Framingham).
7. Asymptomatic with high CHD risk (Framingham).
8. Risk Assessment: Preoperative Evaluation for Non-Cardiac Surgery with intermediate or High Risk Surgery (Use of CT Angiogram) with intermediate perioperative risk.

9. Detection of CAD: Post-Revascularization (PCI or CABG) — Evaluation of Chest Pain Syndrome (Use of CT Angiogram) — Evaluation of bypass grafts and coronary anatomy.
10. History of percutaneous revascularization with stents.
11. Structure and Function — Evaluation of LV function following myocardial infarction OR in heart failure patients.
12. Patients with technically limited images from echocardiogram.
13. Characterization of native and prosthetic cardiac valves in patients with technically limited images from echocardiogram, MRI, or TEE.

[3] Risk/Benefit Trade-off

The development of appropriateness criteria for CCT, and other cardiac imaging modalities, requires the determination of a reasonable course of action for clinical decision-making based on a *risk/benefit trade-off* as determined by individual patient indications. The following aspects of CCT should be considered:

1. *Cost*
2. *Radiation exposure (See Table 3)*
3. *Contrast adverse effects*
4. *Impact of the image* on clinical decision making when combined with clinical judgment.
5. *Whether the test is reasonable* for the patient;
6. *Local availability*
7. *Type and variation of equipment, techniques and protocols;* (i.e. the number of detector rows, spatial and temporal resolution, and acquisition protocols)
8. *Performance by qualified individuals in a facility that is proficient in the imaging technique*
9. Indications for *CT angiography*
10. Indications for *coronary calcium scoring* (CCS by EBCT or multi-slice CT)

[4] CCT Imaging in Asymptomatic Individuals

In 2000, the AHA/ACC stated that EBCT testing for CAC was *not* superior to alternative noninvasive imaging techniques at diagnosing CAD and therefore could not be recommended for this purpose.[12] But in 2006, the

---

[12] O'Rourke RA, Brundage BH, Froelicher VF, et al. American College of Cardiology/American Heart Association expert consensus document on electron-beam computed tomography for the diagnosis and prognosis of coronary artery disease. *Circulation* 2000; 102:126-140.

AHA issued a statement on coronary calcium and CT and concluded that, "Coronary-artery calcified plaque, as determined by cardiac CT, documents the presence of coronary atherosclerosis, identifies individuals at elevated risk for myocardial infarction (MI) and CVD death, and adds significant predictive ability to the Framingham Score".[13] In 2000, an EBCT test cost around $400, while in 2006 a high-quality test could be obtained for $100.

In 2006, O'Malley[14] presented an argument that opposed the practice of screening for atherosclerosis in asymptomatic individuals. His argument was consistent with the US Preventive Services Task Force review that there was insufficient evidence to support the routine use of CCT.[15] O'Malley pointed out that before concluding that CCT testing is ready for widespread use, three considerations should be addressed:

1. Does the test information provide *additive prognostic value* to conventional risk prediction?

    Cumulative EBCT data suggest an independent prognostic value associated with high coronary artery calcium (CAC) scores. However, most published peer review data have not sufficiently included full, rigorous multivariate comparisons using other emerging and much cheaper risk prediction tools such as family history, C-reactive protein, metabolic syndrome, other markers of cardiovascular risk and the effects of age, gender and race.

2. Are there *improved outcomes* associated with use of the technology?

    There is no peer reviewed evidence that atherosclerosis imaging improves outcomes to date. There is, however, widespread implementation of the CCT technology, some of which is available on a self-referral basis and without systematic risk assessment prior to performing the test. Consequently, this practice makes it distinctly possible that net harm may be occurring despite the best intentions.

---

[13] Budoff MJ, Achenbach S, Blumenthal RS, et al. Assessment of coronary artery disease by cardiac computed tomography, a scientific statement from the American Heart Association Committee on Cardiovascular Imaging and Intervention, Council on Cardiovascular Radiology and Intervention, and Committee on Cardiac Imaging, Council on Clinical Cardiology. *Circulation* 2006; DOI: 10.1161/CIRCULATIONAHA.106.178458. Available at: http://www.circulationaha.org.

[14] O'Malley, PG. Atherosclerosis Imaging of Asymptomatic Individuals - Is the Sales Cart Before the Evidence Horse? *Arch Intern Med.* 2006;166:1065-1068.

[15] US Preventive Services Task Force. Screening for coronary heart disease: recommendation statement. *Ann Intern Med.* 2004;140:569-572.

3. Are there *reasonable costs* associated with the test itself and with the
    downstream *induced costs* that result from the abnormal findings?

    Current available data indicates that it is impossible to conclude that
    screening for CAC could be cost-effective at the present time.

    Therefore, as of 2006, there was insufficient evidence on all three counts
    of added prognostic value, improved outcomes, and cost-effectiveness to
    advocate for noninvasive atherosclerosis imaging in most *primary prevention
    populations*.

[5] Sensitivity and Specificity of CTA

CT angiography has a high sensitivity, and low specificity for detection of
significant CAD. Whereas 64-slice scanners have substantially improved the
ability to accurately image the coronaries, many people are still using 16-
detector machines in their practice. In 2006, Garcia et al[16] reported a multi-
national study on the accuracy of *16-row multi-detector computed
tomography* for the assessment of coronary artery stenosis in 187 patients
with suspected coronary artery disease (CAD) who underwent multi-
detector CT (MDCT), followed by conventional angiography within 14 days;
sensitivity and specificity for the detection of >50% stenosis (based on
quantitative coronary angiography) were calculated on a patient basis and on
the basis of arterial segments, of which a total of 1629 were imaged in the
study. Only 71% of the 1629 segments imaged on CT were evaluable by the
core lab. In patient-based analyses, sensitivity for detecting at least one
segment with >50% stenosis was 98%, but the specificity was 54%. Based on
their findings, the authors stated that:

1. CT should not be used indiscriminately, because if it is too widely
    applied, without having good clinical indication, it could lead to
    overdiagnosis.
2. The best use of CTA would be for patients who have equivocal stress-
    test results, such as a result that is uncertain or suspected to be false
    positive or false negative; then the CT is a good test to confirm or
    exclude coronary disease.
3. As a first test CT should be used only in a selected population,
    perhaps in patients of younger age in whom the likelihood of having
    a lot of calcium in the coronaries is low.

---

[16] Garcia MJ, Lessick J, Hoffmann MHK et al. Accuracy of 16-row multidetector computed
tomography for the assessment of coronary artery stenosis. *JAMA* 2006; 296:403-411.

4. The people who should go straight to angiography are those in whom it is very clear, based on clinical grounds, that they have coronary disease: patients who present with typical angina symptoms and multiple risk factors and perhaps ECG changes. They have such a high probability of CAD, they should go directly to coronary angiography without utilizing CT.

[6] CAD in Asymptomatic Patients with Left Bundle-Branch Block (LBBB)

The first study comparing 64-slice CT and conventional coronary angiography (CCA) in 66 patients with LBBB and sinus rhythm, showed that LBBB is commonly associated with CAD, and identification of chronic CAD in such patients is important to stratify the risk and manage the therapy.[17] The investigators reported that:

1. MSCT correctly identified the absence of significant stenosis in 35 of 37 patients (95%), and the presence of significant stenosis in 28 of 29 patients (97%).
2. MSCT correctly identified all 15 patients with multivessel disease, the results indicate.
3. Out of 94 significant stenoses detected by conventional coronary angiography in 990 coronary segments, MSCT correctly detected 68 (72%). The remaining stenoses were either missed or underestimated.
4. On a patient-based analysis, MSCT had an overall accuracy of 95%, the report indicates. On a lesion-by-lesion analysis, its overall accuracy was 97%.
5. Conventional coronary angiography could have been avoided in 57% of the cases (35/66 patients) with a negative predictive value of 97%.
6. MSCT had a low sensitivity for detecting lesions in the left circumflex artery (59%) and in the right coronary artery (52%).

[7] Cardiac Imaging in Symptomatic Patients with Coronary Artery Disease (CAD)

Cardiac imaging is frequently utilized in symptomatic cardiac patients, as noted in the following hypothetical case:

Rafia BJS, a 77-year-old female, was referred by her Internist to an Orthopedist because of severe low back pain with radiation to both lower extremities, which has not responded to medical management. X-rays, CT

---

[17] *J Am Coll Cardiol* 2006;48:1929-1937.

and MRI of the lumbar spine revealed two herniated discs in the lumbar region, with central canal stenosis, and the orthopedist recommended disc surgery. However, in addition to the low back pain, Rafia has been complaining of *chest pain* and occasional dizziness without syncope. She has hypertension, hyperlipidemia, premature ventricular contractions (PVCs), and a cardiac murmur. The orthopedist requested a *pre-operative evaluation* by a cardiologist.

The cardiologist conducted on Rafia a comprehensive cardiac evaluation. Her *EKG* was uninterpretable with ST-segment abnormalities and PVCs. [*Uninterpretable ECG:* Refers to ECGs with resting ST-segment depression (greater than or equal to 0.10 mV), complete left bundle-branch block, pre-excitation (Wolf-Parkinson-White syndrome), or paced rhythm.]

The *chest x-ray* revealed borderline cardiomegaly. *Transthoracic echocardiogram* revealed left atrial enlargement, mitral valve prolapse with moderate mitral regurgitation and LV diastolic dysfunction. *Ambulatory Holter monitoring* revealed frequent, unifocal premature ventricular contraction. *Nuclear (Adenosine Cardiolite) stress test* revealed normal LV wall motion and systolic function, with questionable apical reversible ischemia. *Cardiac CTA* revealed normal coronaries. *Cadiac magnetic resonance imaging* (MRI) confirmed the mitral valve prolapse and moderate mitral regurgitation. However, Rafia continued to complain of chest pain for which he went to the emergency room. Cardiac enzymes were normal. *Coronary arteriography* revealed no evidence of occlusive CAD.

The cardiologist's *diagnoses* were: abnormal EKG with frequent, unifocal premature ventricular contractions, left atrial enlargement, mitral valve prolapse with moderate mitral regurgitation, and left ventricular diastolic dysfunction. The cardiologist opined that Rafia's chest pain was atypical, that her hypertension and hyperlipidemia were well controlled with medications, that her PVCs were unifocal and benign requiring no anti-arrhythmic drug therapy, that she had a moderate risk for CAD, that her peri-operative predictor risks were minor, and that her surgical risk category was intermediate. Therefore, Rafia was cleared for surgery. She underwent lumbar disc surgery successfully and without complications.

In determining the need for cardiac imaging, the cardiologist evaluates the patient's cardiac symptoms, the probable risk of CAD, and in surgical patients the perioperative risk predictors of cardiac patients and the surgical risk categories for non-cardiac surgery, as discussed above. The limitations of cardiac imaging are also considered.

[8] Limitations of CCT Angiography

Single detector CCT angiography is of limited use in certain patients with the following conditions:

1. *Irregular rhythm* (e.g., atrial fibrillation/flutter, frequent irregular premature ventricular contractions or premature atrial contractions, and high grade heart block);
2. *Level III* (morbidly) *obese patients*, body mass index greater than 40 kg/m2;
3. **Renal insufficiency**, creatinine greater than 1.8 mg/dL;
4. *Heart rate greater than 70 beats/min* which is refractory to heart-rate-lowering agents (e.g., a combination of beta-blocker and calcium-channel blocker);
5. *Metallic interference* (e.g., surgical clips, pacemaker, and/or defibrillator wires, or tissue expander.
6. Can not *hold still*;
7. Can not *follow breathing instruction*;
8. Can not *take nitroglycerin* (for performing coronary CT angiography only);
9. Can not *take iodine* (despite steroid prep for contrast allergy);
10. Can not *lift both arms* above the shoulders.

Multi-Detector CCT has resolved some of the above limitations.

High-speed helical or spiral, non-contrast enhanced Cardiac CT scans are being used more frequently to detect calcium deposits found in atherosclerotic plaque in the coronary arteries before symptoms develop. They are referred to as Calcium-Score Screening Heart Scan. The predictive value of coronary calcium score screening is not fully defined. However, more coronary calcium indicates more atherosclerosis, and a greater likelihood of arterial narrowing and future cardiovascular events.

Advanced helical CT is being used more and more to allow the identification of both calcified and non-calcified plaques within the coronary artery walls or to exclude the possibility of significant stenosis due to atherosclerosis. When contrast-enhanced 3-dimensional versions of this type of scanning are performed, early stages of atherosclerosis of the coronary arteries can be seen before the development of arterial narrowing. It allows early detection of potentially unstable "soft plaque" and non-calcified plaque during a potentially reversible phase of development, making it possible to non-invasively monitor plaque regression with various therapies.

Techniques are being developed to combine the data acquired by Cardiac CT angiography of the coronary arteries and the data regarding myocardial viability acquired by Cardiac MRI. Based on the co-registration of the CT Angiography and MRI data, a spatial relationship can be directly established between the diseased coronary artery distribution and the myocardium at risk. With the advancement of these imaging modalities, patients may expect to realize improved pre-revascularization planning and reduced invasiveness of the diagnostic process.

Helical CT scans are being used to look at peripheral blood flow, e.g. through the carotid arteries and blood distribution in the brain. As with an acute myocardial infarction, during an acute stroke, the doctor can see if the patient actually has cerebral arterial obstruction, and if so, what vessel is affected, the amount of blockage, and what areas of the brain are not receiving enough blood. In addition, helical CT is providing an alternative to catheterization techniques for angiographic evaluation of the peripheral arteries of the arms and legs.

[9] Cardiac Imaging to Assess Hibernating Myocardium

Currently, MDCT is probably the best overall diagnostic modality for assessing left ventricular dysfunction due to viable but hibernating myocardium. Coronary revascularization by angioplasty or coronary bypass surgery should be based on the presence of left ventricular dysfunction and viable or hibernating myocardium, but *not* on myocardial scars. Viable myocardium may be determined non-invasively by:

- *Nuclear scintigraphy*[18] – originally using thallium 201, both at rest and redistribution study with delayed imaging, combined with exercise or injection of Adenosine, Dobutamine or Persantine. More recently, nuclear studies with 18-FDG-positron emission tomography (PET) have been utilized to locate and define hibernating viable myocardium.[19] However, these studies are complex and lack adequate reimbursement.
- *Contrast enhanced echocardiography (CEE)* – coupled with the infusion of the beta agonist dobutamine (Dobutrex, Lilly), has been

[18] Mheta D, Iskandarian A. Myocardial viability: Nuclear assessment. *Echocardiography: A Jrnl of CV Ultrasound & Allied Tech.* 2005;22:155-164.

[19] Ghesani M, DePuey EG, Rozanski A. Role of F-18 FDG positron emission tomography (PET) in the assessment of myocardial viability. *Echocardiography: A Jrnl of CV Ultrasound & Allied Tech.* 2005;22:165-177.

used to assess myocardial viability.[20] The presence of a ventricular wall motion abnormality, without wall thinning, indicates viable but an ischemic myocardial segment.

- *Cardiac Magnetic Resonance (CMR)* – allows both accurate assessment of wall motion and wall thickness, and the presence of myocardial scar.[21]
- *Multi-Detection Computed Tomography (MCDT)* – provides as good data as CMR regarding wall motion, thickness and scarring, at a relative low cost, with quicker acquisition, less motion artifact, and not limited by the presence of implanted pacemakers and cardiac defibrillators.

[10]   MDCT Coronary Angiography in Cardiac Transplant Recipients

Long-term survival of adult heart transplant recipients is limited by the development of late coronary lumen loss, due to coronary allograft vasculopathy, as determined by serial quantitative coronary angiography[22] and by serial intravascular ultrasound studies.[23]

In 2005, Romeo et al[24] and in 2006, Gregory and co-workers[25] (cardiologists and radiologists at Massachusetts General Hospital and Harvard Medical School) compared in 20 heart transplant recipients the image quality of the 64-slice MDCT coronary angiography with that of invasive coronary angiography with intravascular ultrasound. Patient with high serum creatinine levels were excluded from the study due to risk of contrast-induced nephropathy. The radiation exposure from the MDCT coronary angiographic examination was 13-18 mSv, compared with routine diagnostic cardiac catheterization. The radiation dose can be reduced by 30-

---

[20] Yao S, Chaudhry F. Assessment of myocardial viability with dobutamine stress echocardiography in patients with ischemic left ventricular dysfunction. *Echocardiography: A Jrnl of CV Ultrasound & Allied Tech.* 2005;22:71-83.

[21] Schmidt A, Wu K. MRI assessment of myocardial viability. *Semin Ultrasound CT MRI.* 2006;27:11-19.

[22] Mills, RM, Jr, *et al*, Serial quantitative coronary angiography in the assessment of coronary disease in the transplanted heart. *J Heart Lung Transplant* 11(suppl):S52-S55 (1992).

[23] Tsutsui, H, *et al*, Lumen loss in transplant coronary artery disease is a byphasic process involving early intimal thickening and late constrictive remodeling: results from a 5-year serial intravascular ultrasound study. *Circulation* 104:653-657 (2001).

[24] Romeo, G, *et al*, Coronary stenosis detection by 16-slicw computed tomography in heart transplant patients: comparison with conventional angiography and impact on clinical management. *J Am Coll Cardiol* 45:1826-1831 (2005).

[25] Gregory, SA, *et al*, Comparison of sixty-four-slice multidetector computed tomographic coronary angiography to coronary angiography with intravascular ultrasound for the detection of transplant vasculopathy. *Am J Cardiol* 98:877-884 (2006).

50% using tube current modulation, which is limited to subjects with high heart rates. Finally, the evaluation of MDCT coronary angiograms was limited to vessels with diameter of 1-1.5 mm; small vessel involvement of coronary allograft vasculopathy may not be reliably recognized by MDCT. For the detection of coronary allograft vasculopathy, the results showed that MDCT had a:

(a) Sensitivity of 70%;
(b) Specificity of 92%;
(c) Positive predictive value of 89%; and
(d) Negative predictive value of 77%.

The authors concluded that MDCT coronary angiography provides:
(a) Good to excellent quality in heart transplant recipients;
(b) Has moderate to excellent test characteristics for the detection of coronary allograft vasculopathy; and
(c) Measurements of lumen diameters correlated well with quantitative coronary angiography.

[11] Cardiac Imaging Quality

The definition of quality in cardiovascular imaging is being addressed number of organizations from the medical and non-medical sectors. Quality measures across imaging modalities are being achieved through a process culminating in the development, dissemination, and adoption of quality measures for all cardiovascular imaging modalities. Two cardiology groups, the Society for Cardiac Computed Tomography (SCCT) and the Society of Cardiovascular Computed Tomography, are the "principal" voice for cardiac CT overseeing and fostering the development of cardiac CT, including training, credentialing, and reimbursement deliberations.

The mechanisms for training and credentialing of physicians who provide these services have become more complex and expensive. Documentation and maintenance of competency in cardiac imaging now entails many hours of continuing medical education, achievement, and subsequent renewal of sub-sub-specialty board certification and participation in ongoing programs for continual quality improvement as part of cardiac imaging accreditation. And, a continuing increase in the demand for formal documentation of competency will be expected despite a notable lack of current evidence documenting a positive effect of these expensive and time-consuming activities on patient outcome.

In 2003, a model state Consumer Assurance of Radiologic Excellence act was developed for states that do not have licensure laws for individuals who perform medical imaging and radiation therapy and for states that need to revise the existing laws to reflect current practices by medical imaging and radiation therapy personnel.[26]

§ 2.08   Economic Aspects of Cardiac Imaging

Economic concerns have been voiced about the contribution of medical diagnostic imaging costs in general, and cardiac imaging in particular, to the overall increase in societal healthcare costs. In the United States, more than 40 million noninvasive cardiac tests are being performed annually, with a growth rate greater than 20% per year. The annual cost to Medicare alone is about ¾ billion dollars. In fact, the diagnostic imaging services reimbursed under *Medicare's physician fee schedule* grew more rapidly than any other type of physician service during the past decade.[27] The financial scope of the global illness burden that is attributable to cardiovascular disease, the leading cause of death in the U.S., has been higher than any other single disease entity and is projected to continue to remain as such until at least 2020. What is fueling this runaway cardiac health expenditure, and what is being done about it?

The Medicare Payment Advisory Committee's report to Congress in 2005 expressed concern about the recent apparent increase in the use of imaging services within the Medicare program and suggested several steps for reform.[28] In Medicare, the mantra is *reasonable and necessary*.

[1]   Deficit Reduction Act

Beginning January 1, 2007, reimbursement for imaging procedures were cut by 30-50%, under the provisions of the Deficit Reduction Act.[29] The Act was passed by Congress in February 2006, and it caps the payment rate for

---

[26] http://www.crcpd.org/PET-CT_Fusion_Imaging/Model_state_licensure_law_103003.pdf.

[27] Medicare Payment Advisory Commission (MedPAC). Report to the Congress: growth in the volume of physician services. December 2004. Available at http://www.medpac.gov/publications/Congressional_reports/December04_PhysVolume.pdf.

[28] February 10, 2005, Chairman, Medicare Payment Advisory Commission, Statement of Glenn M. Hackbarth, Available at waysandmeans.house.gov/hearings.asp?formmode=printfriendly&id=2483 - 31k *See also*, MedPAC Recommendations on Imaging Services, Miller, Executive Director of the Medicare Payment Advisory Commission (MedPAC) ... Diagnostic imaging services paid under Medicare's physician fee schedule. Available at, www.medpac.gov/publications/congressional_testimony/031705_TestimonyImaging-Hou.pdf

[29] S. 1932 Deficit Reduction Act of 2005, signed January 27, 2006. http://www.cbo.gov/ftpdocs/70xx/doc7028/s1932conf.pdf.

critical imaging services, provided by physicians and independent imaging centers, under the Medicare Physician Fee Schedule and the Medicare Outpatient Emergency Department rates. However, both the House and the Senate introduced the Access to Medicare Imaging Act of 2006,[30] which would place a moratorium on the implementation of these cuts.

[2] Coalition for Patient-Centered Imaging (CPCI)

The Coalition for Patient-Centered Imaging (CPCI) is a coalition of nearly 30 specialty and physician groups dedicated to ensuring that patients continue to have access to diagnostic imaging services in their physicians' offices. CPCI was formed to respond to allegations that diagnostic imaging performed by physicians other than radiologists is "substandard" and "unnecessary" and that the growth in utilization is principally attributable to in-office testing by physicians other than radiologists.

The CPCI advocates that office-based imaging services offer important advantages to patients. Advantages include expediting the correct diagnosis and treatment of the patient's medical condition, patient convenience and limiting Medicare spending by reducing the number of office visits and other physician encounters that are billed to the program.

The CPCI is concerned the MedPAC recommendations on diagnostic imaging may have a detrimental impact on non-radiologists who perform diagnostic imaging in their offices. The CPCI is in the process of educating MedPAC, Congress and CMS that the growth in imaging services is due to shifts in the *site of service*, not necessarily because of inappropriate utilization or self-referral by non-radiologists. The coalition recently presented testimony to the House of Representatives Committee on Ways and Means Health Subcommittee on imaging issues.

In March 2005, CPCI informed Congress that it should not endorse any particular set of credentialing or accreditation standards.

[3] Third-party Payers

Other *third-party payers* have expressed similar economic concerns about diagnostic imaging techniques and have taken some remedial action. For example, Massachusetts Blue Cross and Blue Shield announced in 2005 a new program for prescreening of certain imaging tests in the face of a 20% increase within one year in the use of CT and MRI.

---

[30] H.R. 5704: Access to Medicare Imaging Act of 2006. http://www.govtrack.us/congress/bill.xpd?bill=h109-5704.

Patients and physicians alike have been the subjects of *advertising campaigns*, particularly for freestanding imaging centers, that have often included marketing claims that may overstate the currently available scientific evidence supporting these new techniques. Like many other areas of evolving biomedical technology, the scientific evidence is still under development.

Heart disease has been the leading cause of death in the United States.[31] The *scope of global illness burden* that is attributable to cardiovascular disease has been higher than any other single disease entity and is projected to continue to remain as such until at least 2020.[32]

[4]   MDCT and Life Insurance Medical Directors

In 2006, Davidoff and Ruberg[33] reported an update of new developments with multidetector computed tomography (MDCT) coronary angiography. They noted that similar to what has occurred with the introduction of other new technologies such as electron beam computed tomography (EBCT) life insurance medical directors are expected to evaluate a technology before there are sufficient data from large clinical trials. The authors stated that MDCT applications include:

- Exclusion of significant coronary disease; and MDCT will perhaps be useful in emergency room "rule-out" situations, such as acute coronary syndrome, pulmonary embolism and thoracic aortic aneurysm dissection;
- Diagnosis of significant coronary obstruction (>75% stenosis); as well as for the evaluation of bypass grafts.

Limitations of MDCT include:

- MDCT does not provide information on atheroma morphology;
- Requirement for radiologic contrast administration; and
- Significant radiation exposure.

---

[31] National Vital Statistics Reports, April 19, 2006. http://www.cdc.gov/nchs/data/nvsr/nvsr54/nvsr54_13.pdf.

[32] Murray CJL, ed, Lopez AD, ed. The Global Burden of Disease: A Comprehensive Assessment of Mortality and Disability From Diseases, Injuries, and Risk Factors in 1990 and Projected to 2020. Boston, Mass: Harvard School of Public Health; 1996.

[33] Davidoff, R, and Ruberg, FL. Newer Cardiac Imaging Techniques: Multidetector CT Angiography, *Journal of Insurance Medicine:* Vol. 38, No. 2, pp. 116–125 (2006).

[5] Cardiac CT Liability

Cardiac CT liability issues includes:

1. Failure to diagnose
   a. Perception error – missed diagnosis
   b. Interpretation error – cognitive error
2. Failure to timely communicate results
3. Failure to correct discrepancy
4. Failure to suggest next appropriate procedure
5. Failure to refer
6. Improper documentation, and
7. Negligent hiring – negligent employee credentialing.

§ 2.09 Liability of Cardiologists

The cardiologist, like any other physician, is expected to evaluate a patient in a manner that will make possible the formulation of effective treatment. Although a cardiologist is not expected to insure the correctness of a diagnosis, a patient is entitled to as thorough and careful cardiac evaluation as the attending circumstances will permit, with the utilization of cardiovascular diagnostic methods approved and implemented by similarly situated cardiologists. In recent years, the cardiovascular diagnostic and therapeutic modalities have vastly expanded, as discussed above, particularly in the areas of preventive, non-invasive and interventional cardiology.

[1] Unstable Angina

[a] Case 1 Presentation

On July 26, a 67-year-old white male, 5′ 10″ tall, weighing 210 pounds, ate a taco salad with hot sauce for supper. Two hours later, he developed chest pain and indigestion. Rolaids relieved his indigestion but not the chest pain. One month earlier he had indigestion after eating Fritos and spicy bean dip. Two years previously he had experienced a 10-15 minute episode of chest pain. Fifteen years previously, the patient developed mild hypertension that was controlled with Chlorthiazide. Prior levels of serum cholesterol were 250 mg% to 284 mg%, and triglycerides ranged from normal to 484 mg%. He stopped smoking cigarettes at age 57. His father died at age of 75 years of heart disease and his mother had hypertension and died of old age.

On July 27, about seven hours after the onset of chest pain, the patient drove himself to the emergency room of a community hospital. His condition upon arrival was non-urgent, pulse and respirations were normal, and the BP was 182/112 mm Hg. His chest pain was substernal, without radiation, sharp, and constant. He had nausea, but no vomiting or diaphoresis. He had bilateral inspiratory rales in the lung bases. His heart rate was regular and rhythmic with no murmurs and no third or fourth heart sounds audible. The rest of the physical exam proved to be negative.

The initial electrocardiogram revealed no acute changes with sinus bradycardia, rate 52 bpm. The chest x-ray, total CPK, CPK-MB fraction, Troponins and arterial blood gases were all normal. The patient was treated at the emergency room with oxygen; nitroglycerin, three sublingual and one-inch transdermal; nifedipine, 10 mg by mouth; and morphine sulfate, 2 mg intravenously; after which he was admitted to the intensive care unit with the diagnosis of "rule out acute myocardial infarction". His chest pain persisted and was not relieved after two more tablets of sublingual nitroglycerin, as well as two IV injections of Demerol.

[i] Thrombolytic therapy

About nine and a half hours after the onset of chest pain, the patient prophylactically received cortisone and lidocaine IV; followed by a bolus of heparin, 5,000 units IV; and then streptokinase, 1,500,000 units infused over a 40-minute period. Immediately after streptokinase administration, heparin was infused at a rate of 1,000 units IV per hour. Despite the administration of streptokinase, the patient's chest pain increased, and he became slightly restless; he then received Demerol. There were no reperfusion arrhythmias.

Three hours after the administration of streptokinase, the patient ate a meal, after which he complained of nausea, mid sternum chest pain, and vomited his food; he received compazine, nitroglycerin, Riopan Plus, and Zantac. Repeat electrocardiogram and cardiac enzymes were normal.

Six hours after streptokinase, the patient's pulse increased to 116 and respiration to 36 per minute. His temperature rose to 99.2°F. His eyes were deviated to the left, and he had right hemiplegia. Heparin was discontinued, and 10 mg of Decadron were given intravenously. One hour later, he became aphasic, then he vomited approximately 200 mL of "golden" liquid. The CAT brain scan revealed a massive, left intracerebral hemorrhage.

About nine hours after streptokinase, he became unresponsive, his BP was 200/96, pulse 64, and his respirations were "snorting" at a rate of 60 per minute. His pupils were pinpoint and nonreactive. One hour later, he became cyanotic, and had complex ventricular cardiac arrhythmias, with poor response to lidocaine. He was in moderate respiratory distress. Pupils were mid-range and nonreactive to light. Corneal and Doll's eyes reflexes were absent. He had papilledema, flaccid paralysis, and no response to painful stimuli. He was intubated, hyperventilated, then placed on a respirator. Bretylol was given for the cardiac dysrhythmia.

Approximately six hours after heparin was discontinued and 12 hours after streptokinase, the partial thromboplastin time was 69 seconds, and the prothrombin time was 17 seconds. White blood count was 12,500, hemoglobin 15.2 g/dL, hematocrit 47.7%, and platelet count 290,000. Serum electrolytes, BUN and creatinine were normal. EKG revealed sinus tachycardia with a rate of 161 bpm, and the cardiac monitor showed multi-focal ventricular premature beats, with couplets and volleys of ventricular tachycardia. The patient was then declared "brain-dead"; and permission was granted by his wife and son to disconnect the respirator-which was done.

[ii] Postmortem findings

Autopsy was performed on July 28. The brain had a large, intracerebral hemorrhage of the left hemisphere. The hemorrhage began with the occipital lobe and extended forward approximately 7 cm. It involved the basal ganglia. The hemorrhagic cavity reached a maximum of 5 cm. There were scattered areas of subarachnoid hemorrhage noted over the left cerebral hemisphere and over the left portion of the cerebellum. The cerebral vessels showed scattered foci of minimal, non-occlusive atherosclerosis. No intracranial aneurysms were found.

The heart weighed 520 g. There was left ventricular hypertrophy. The pericardium and heart valves were normal. The coronary arteries were normal in distribution. There was a significantly stenotic lesion, approximately 75% luminal narrowing, of the left anterior descending branch of the left coronary artery. No fissuring, thrombosis, subintimal hemorrhage, or eccentricity was noted. The circumflex and the right coronary arteries were normal. The aorta had numerous, slightly raised, ulcerated and non-ulcerated atherosclerotic plaques.

The gallbladder contained about 30 mL of viscous bile. It revealed chronic cholecystitis with cholelithiasis. There were approximately 10 calculi, each of which measured 5 mm in diameter.

The gastrointestinal tract, liver, and spleen were normal. The lungs had moderate, bilateral atelectasis. The left kidney had a benign cortical cyst. The prostate was slightly enlarged and nodular.

(This is an actual case which did not get to trial; it was settled shortly after depositions were completed for a six-figure settlement.)

[b] Issues in Case 1

[i] *Failure to prevent coronary artery disease (CAD)*

The patient was a hypertensive, hyperlipidemic, obese, male, in his 60's, whose father had heart disease. The hypertension was treated with medications, but not his lipids and obesity. From the preventive cardiology standpoint, treating all the cardiac risk factors would in all likelihood have resulted in a more favorable outcome, vis-à-vis the coronary artery disease. A jury might find that it is more likely than not that the failure to treat cardiac risk factors (in hopes of preventing the development of an acute coronary syndrome) was negligent; the issue of causation may pose a difficult hurdle for the plaintiff to cross. Nevertheless, care should be exercised when treating all cardiac factors in accordance with guidelines by the American College of Cardiology/American Heart Association,[34] and other national guidelines for the treatment of hypertension, hyperlipidemia, diabetes and obesity.

[ii] *Failure to detect or diagnose CAD*

The treating physician knew or should have known that the patient had a high risk of developing CAD. In addition to not preventing CAD, the physician had never performed an exercise tolerance test (ETT) on the patient prior the event of July 27, despite the fact that the patient had prior episodes of chest pain. Because the left anterior descending coronary artery had a significant stenosis of 75%, in all likelihood an ETT might have been positive in the months preceding the terminal event. The jury may conclude that the failure to detect or diagnose the CAD was negligent. Failure to diagnose is one of the most common allegations made by plaintiffs in malpractice lawsuits.

[iii] *Failure to properly conduct a differential diagnosis*

Because the patient had a normal EKG and normal cardiac enzymes, the treating physician was under a duty to search for and rule out other causes of chest pain, including gastro-intestinal and gall bladder disease, prior to the administration of thrombolytic therapy.

The patient's chest pain could have been due to unstable angina, diffuse esophageal spasm, gastroesophageal reflux, chronic cholecystitis and cholelithiasis, and less likely musculoskeletal chest wall pain, pneumonia,

---

[34] AHA/ACC Guidelines for Preventing Heart Attack and Death in Patients with Atherosclerotic Cardiovascular Disease: 2001 Update. *Circulation.* 2001;104:1577.

pneumothorax, peptic ulcer disease, myocardial infarction, cardiac trauma, pericarditis, cardiomyopathy, mitral valve prolapse, aortic dissection, pulmonary hypertension, or pulmonary embolism.

An ultrasound test of the gall bladder in the case above would have revealed the evidence of cholelithiasis and cholecystitis, but would not have negated the concomitant presence of CAD; the treating physician was convinced that the patient had unstable angina, with proof of significant CAD at autopsy. The jury may conclude that the failure to conduct a proper differential diagnosis of the chest pain was negligent.

[iv] Failure to follow hospital protocol

Should thrombolytic therapy be administered to a patient who has clinically unstable angina; with no prior history of known coronary disease; who presents with new chest pain at rest of over nine hours duration; who has no cardiac abnormalities on physical exam; and who has no objective, diagnostic, abnormalities in the initial electrocardiogram or cardiac enzymes and isoenzymes?

With the help of the cardiology department, the hospital where the above case was treated had developed specific criteria for the use of thrombolytic therapy within 6-8 hours of onset of chest pain and in the presence of EKG evidence of ST elevation. In the case above, thrombolytic therapy was begun 9 ½ hours after the onset of chest pain ant there was no ST elevation on the EKG.

It behooves the treating physician to review the hospital policy and procedure regarding the proposed treatment. If the cardiologist elects to choose a course of treatment that is different from the hospital procedure, then the patient's informed consent should be obtained for that deviation, and the cardiologist should note the reasons for electing the chosen treatment.

In addition, the hospital nurse in charge of the patient may refuse to comply with the treatment that is against hospital policy. The hospital becomes liable when its own employees fail to follow hospital policy and procedure with resultant detriment to the patient.

[v] Failure to perform myocardial perfusion studies and coronary arteriography

Should the cardiologist have performed myocardial perfusion studies, nuclear or echocardiographic, or coronary arteriogram prior to the administration of thrombolytic therapy?

Unstable angina, as compared to *stable angina;* denotes a more serious stage of angina pectoris, and it is managed differently.[35] The pain lasts over 15 minutes and is not relieved by rest. There is a change or acceleration of the coronary arterial disease process. It is a stage before heart muscle damage, or myocardial infarction. Unstable angina is a syndrome and does not represent one disorder. It depicts the myocardial ischemic chest pain syndrome of patients with differing pathologic findings in the coronary arterial system, which vary from pure coronary spasm without thrombotic or atherosclerotic disease to stenotic lesions that may be fixed, smooth, or ulcerated, with or without thrombi, fissuring, eccentricity of plaque, or subintimal hemorrhage. It is no wonder that the prognosis of patients with unstable angina is variable and depends on the type, extent, and severity of the underlying coronary disease process.

During the pain of unstable angina, patients may demonstrate paroxysmal hypertension and sinus tachycardia and/or ischemic S-T segment depression on electrocardiogram, and coronary artery arteriography demonstrate 50% or greater narrowing of one or more of the major coronary arteries. Patients with unstable angina pectoris of recent onset may not develop myocardial infarction or die unexpectedly of a cardiac arrhythmia.

The degree of coronary stenosis is critical. Resistance to flow is normally maximal at the level of the coronary arterioles. It requires more than a 75% reduction of the lumina in the conduit major arterial trunks to effect the volume flow through the arterioles. This important hemodynamic fact must be kept in mind when interpreting the functional significance of atherosclerotic narrowing of lesser severity.

In the case above, the left anterior descending had 75% stenosis, which is significant and may have been a contributing cause of the chest pain. Myocardial perfusion studies and coronary arteriography would have justified angioplasty with stent placement in the left anterior descending coronary artery, which would have been a prudent course of treatment prior to cholecystectomy for cholecystitis and cholelithiasis. Neither the specific lesion of CAD nor the gall bladder disease was diagnosed prior to death.

Proper diagnosis is the foundation for rational therapy. Both noninvasive and invasive procedures should be utilized in the evaluation of coronary artery disease. The legal standards are set both by the medical profession and by the courts, for the diagnosis and treatment of coronary artery disease. In the case above, the failure on the part of the treating physician to obtain

---

[35] Braunwald et al., Management of Patients With Unstable Angina And Non-St-Segment Elevation Myocardial Infarction Update. http://www.acc.org/clinical/guidelines/unstable/incorporated/index.htm (ACC/AHA 2002 Guideline Update for the Management of Patients With Unstable Angina and Non-ST-Segment Elevation Myocardial Infarction).

appropriate tests represented a departure from the national standard of accepted medical practice by internists and/or cardiologists under similar circumstances.

[vi] Treatment of unstable angina

Aspirin, antiplatelet agents, intravenous nitroglycerin, beta- and calcium-blockers, and heparin have been shown to have significant beneficial effects in patients with unstable angina.

Intravenous nitroglycerin has been sanctioned by the Food and Drug Administration for use in unstable angina. Oral nitrates, beta blockers, calcium blockers, and heparin have all been shown effective in the treatment of unstable angina, in combination with rest, sedation, and oxygen. Some patients with unstable angina syndromes may benefit from intra-aortic balloon counterpulsation, coronary angioplasty, and bypass surgery.

Thrombolytic therapy is a well-recognized modality for the treatment of patients with acute myocardial infarction. To be most successful, thrombolytic therapy should be administered during the first four hours after the onset of the infarction. A number of thrombolytic (or fibrinolytic) agents, so-called "clot busters" are currently approved by the Food and Drug Administration for acute myocardial infarction, including streptokinase, urokinase, tissue-type plasminogen activator and others.

Thrombolytic therapy in unstable angina involving the intravenous and intracoronary thrombolysis has in some instances shown clinical benefit, but generally no angiographic improvement. There may also be an advantage in giving aspirin and thrombolytic therapy simultaneously.

[vii] Complications of thrombolytic therapy

Thrombolytic therapy may result in severe internal bleeding involving gastrointestinal, genitourinary, retroperitoneal, or intracerebral sites. Fatalities due to cerebral and other internal hemorrhage have occurred during intravenous thrombolytic therapy. Other complications of streptokinase include fever, allergic reactions, occasional nausea and vomiting, and headache. In addition, drug-induced, life threatening "reperfusion arrhythmias" may develop in a significant number of patients in whom the occluded coronary artery is reopened with thrombolytics.

Most bleeding complications from thrombolytic therapy can be avoided with proper patient selection, minimizing invasive procedures, limiting the duration of therapy, and using judicious anticoagulation methods.

[viii] Negligence standard set by the judge

Ordinarily, in medical malpractice cases, the standards set by the medical profession are generally accepted by the courts as being the standards imposed by law. But under certain circumstances the judge and not the physician determines the professional standard of care as a matter of law, and this may differ from common medical practice.

In the famous case of *T.J. Hooper,*[36] the court held that: "In most cases reasonable prudence is in fact common prudence; but strictly it is never its measure. ... Courts must in the end say what is required; there are precautions so imperative that even their universal disregard will not excuse their omission. Relying on T. J. Hooper, the Washington State Supreme Court rejected in *Helling v. Carry*[37] the standard set by common medical practice. In Helling, the physician did not test the patient for glaucoma; she became blind. The court held that the physician was negligent as a matter of law for not testing the patient for glaucoma. In 1979, the same court held that the doctrine of Helling requiring a higher standard of care than the prevailing standard of care applied in *Gates v. Jensen,*[38] and it could not be abrogated by enacted legislation. In *Keogan v. Holy Family Hospital,*[39] the Washington Supreme Court again held both the physician and the hospital negligent as a matter of law for not utilizing a simple and safe diagnostic tool, the EKG, in a patient presenting with chest pain due to myocardial infarction. The Keogan Court also relied on *Hicks v. United States*[40] and *Steeves v. United States* in reaching its decision; these cases are cited in *Keogan.*

The case presented above did not have an ultrasound of the gallbladder. Had the latter been done, thrombolytic therapy and the patient's death from intracerebral hemorrhage probably might have been avoided. The physician's conduct in this case could conceivably be construed by some courts as negligence as a matter of law.

When considering treatment, the physician should first utilize safer drugs in the treatment of unstable angina-that is, aspirin and nitroglycerin IV, among others, before utilizing FDA approved thrombolytics for unapproved uses. Unapproved uses of drugs should be in accordance with the manufacturer's recommendations; otherwise, the physician's deviation from

---

[36] *TJ Hooper*, 60 F.2d 737 (1932).

[37] Helling v. Carey, 83 Wn.2d 514, 519 P.2d 981, 67 A.L.R.3d 175 (1974). 519 *Pacific Rep 2nd Series*: 981-5.

[38] Gates v. Jensen, 92 Wn.2nd 246, 595 P.2d 919

[39] Keogan v. Holy Family Hospital, 95 Wn.2d 306

[40] Hicks v. United States, 368 F.2d 626 (4th Cir. 1966)

the latter is *prima facie* evidence of negligence. Such was the holding of the Minnesota Supreme Court in *Mulder v. Parke Davis & Co.*[41]

[ix] Survival strategy

"First, do no harm." Second, "The burning candle of life is such a precious light in anyone's existence that no one has a right to extinguish it before it flickers out into perpetual darkness and oblivion:" *(Valdez v. Lyman Roberts Hospital, Inc.*, 1982).[42]

[2] Myocardial Infarction

[a] Case 1 Presentation

The Reverend Allan David McKellips[43] was brought to the emergency room of St. Francis Hospital in Tulsa, Oklahoma, at 2:30 p.m., complaining of chest pain. The physician diagnosed his condition as gastritis and released him at about 4:15 p.m. A few hours later, he suffered cardiac arrest and was returned to the hospital. He died at 9:30 p.m.

The survivors of Mr. McKellips brought a wrongful death action against (1) St. Francis Hospital, (2) the company under contract with the hospital to provide physicians for the emergency room, and (3) the physician who had been on duty in the emergency room when Mr. McKellips was seen.

The plaintiffs expert witness, a board certified emergency physician, testified at the trial that the defendants had been negligent in failing to diagnose the patient's heart attack and in releasing him from the hospital. The expert said that admitting Mr. McKellips to the hospital would not have prevented his attack. As to ultimate chances of survival if admission had taken place, he testified:

> I think unquestionably his chances would have been significantly improved. As to whether or not it would have, in fact, changed the outcome, I think this is a statistical probability statement that is difficult to answer. But as far as improving his chances, there's no question that that's true.

---

[41] Mulder v. Parke Davis & Co., 288 Minn. 332, 181 NW2d 882, 887 (1970)

[42] Valdez v. Lyman-Roberts Hosp., Inc., 638 SW2d 111

[43] McKellips v. Saint Francis Hosp., Inc. 1987 OK 69 741 P.2d 467 58 OBJ 2229

[i]   Questions on appeal

The case was appealed and two questions were certified for consideration by the Oklahoma Supreme Court:

(1) In a medical malpractice action under Oklahoma law, absent evidence that the patient more likely than not would have survived with proper treatment, may a plaintiff establish causation under the loss of chance doctrine by presenting evidence that the alleged negligence lessened the chance of survival?

(2) If the loss of chance doctrine is recognized in Oklahoma, is expert testimony that "unquestionably [the patient's] chances would have been significantly improved" sufficient under the doctrine to create a question for the jury, even though the expert cannot quantify the increased chance of survival?

The Oklahoma Supreme Court answered *"yes"* to both questions.

[ii]   The court's reasoning

The court reasoned that the general principles of proof of causation in medical malpractice cases were the same as in ordinary negligence cases. It recognized, however, a developing trend to relax the traditional standard for sufficiency of proof of causation necessary for a jury to consider causation in lost chance of survival cases. The court reasoned that, in the typical loss of chance case, the plaintiff patient maintains that negligence has helped increase the risk of harm by either hastening or aggravating the effect of a preexisting medical ailment, condition, or risk-as for example, in negligent failure to diagnose cancer or myocardial infarction in a timely manner.

In adopting the loss of chance doctrine, the court limited its application to medical malpractice cases in which the duty breached was one imposed to prevent the type of harm that occurred. The court considered the Restatement 2nd of Torts, Section 343, as the most rational approach to follow:

> Health care providers should not be given the benefit of the uncertainty created by their own negligent conduct. To hold otherwise would in effect allow care providers to evade liability for their negligent actions or inactions in situations in which patients would not necessarily have survived or recovered, but still would have significant chance of survival or recovery.

The court also noted that, although the plaintiff's burden of production has been lowered, it only allows the plaintiff to establish more easily a jury question on the issues of causation-thereby giving the jury a greater role in the decision-making process. When the case does reach the jury, however, the plaintiff still has the burden of persuading the jury by a preponderance of the evidence.

[iii] Apportionment of damages

When applying the loss of chance doctrine in medical malpractice cases, courts commonly limit damages to those proximately caused by the defendant's breach of duty owed. A total recovery of all damages would be unfair to the negligent party. A simple formula is therefore used, based on statistical evidence of the plaintiffs reduced chance of recovery or survival. Damages equal the percentage of chance lost multiplied by the total amount of damages that would have been allowed in a wrongful death action.

The jury selects the original percentage of chance and the percentage of diminished chance from the defendant's negligence. Then the trial court multiplies the total amount of damages by the net reduced figure to determine the final damages. If, for example, the jury determines from statistical findings combined with specific relevant facts that the patient originally had a 40% chance of cure and that the physician's negligence reduced that chance to 25% then the patient's loss of chance was 15%. Thus, if the total amount of damages proved by the evidence is $500,000, the damages caused by the defendant are 15% of $500,000, which is $75,000.

The loss of chance doctrine allows compensating an injured patient for being deprived of a chance to recover or survive. The doctrine also recognizes that the chances of survival may be less than even to begin with. It reflects the growing trend to hold health care providers liable if they increase the seriousness of a patient's existing illness or injury by their acts or omissions. If liability is predicated on the lost chance for cure or survival, and it is imposed when the health care provider has been a concurrent or intervening cause of the loss.

[iv] The difference an hour makes in myocardial infarction

Where there is no contraindication, the intravenous administration of thrombolytic therapy during the first two or three hours following the development of acute, anterior, transmural, myocardial infarction is life-saving. Therefore, with the passing of every hour there is a gradual, albeit significant, loss of the chance to survive or recover from the complications of complete occlusion of the left anterior descending branch of the left coronary artery. The same may not be true, however, in cases of acute inferior myocardial infarction – since here there is no consensus as to mortality reduction.

From a medico-legal perspective, if a patient develops an acute anterior myocardial infarction and seeks medical attention in time to benefit from the administration of thrombolytic therapy, failure to administer such therapy may form a basis of liability.

[v] Loss of chance in unstable angina

If the traditional burdens of proof of negligence cannot be met by a preponderance of the evidence, failure to diagnose and hospitalize patients with unstable angina for treatment may be the basis for liability on grounds of loss of chance of survival or recovery.

A trend has been emerging nationally in recent years to relax the traditional burdens of proof in medical malpractice cases. The traditional view required an injury to have been the "probable" result of a negligent act or omission-with greater than 50% likelihood. In contrast, the "loss of chance" doctrine is related to a loss of the plaintiff's chance of recovery and may allow compensation for an injury that resulted even when the chance of recovery may have been less than 50% to begin with.

This doctrine does not depend on the patient's ultimate injury. Instead, it focuses on the loss of an opportunity for recovery or survival. Compensation may be given as long as the proximate cause of the loss of chance is proven. For the plaintiff to prevail, the medical expert does not necessarily have to state that the injury was the probable result of negligence.

When considering the loss of chance doctrine, the courts have basically taken three different approaches:

(1) Several jurisdictions still hold to the traditional "all or nothing" view--in which the plaintiff must go forward with the burden of proof and show that it is probable or more likely than not that the unstable angina patient would have recovered or survived with appropriate care. Courts that have held to the all-or-nothing approach state three concerns about adopting the loss of chance doctrine. First, the courts feel that jurors would have to speculate as to the lost chance of survival. Second, defendants in medical malpractice cases would be subject to a far lesser standard of proximate cause than other malpractice defendants. Third, a loss of chance recovery eliminates the requirement of proximate cause.

(2) The second theory is the "substantial possibility" of survival doctrine based on the opinion that if there was any substantial possibility of survival and the defendant has destroyed it, he is answerable. Courts have applied the "substantial possibility" inconsistently, and consequently this lack of uniformity has resulted in some confusion.

(3) The third theory pertaining to the loss of chance of survival follows the *Restatement 2nd of Torts,* Section 323 (1965). This section pertains to those who provide service necessary for protection of others. In medical malpractice cases, the application of Section 323(a) would relax the degree of evidence required of the plaintiff. It would also allow the jury to determine loss of chance on a showing of increased risk of harm to the patient. The task of balancing probabilities is left to the jury. Liability is imposed if the defendant proximately caused the harm. In medical malpractice cases, uncertain evidence may often be the only available evidence.

Courts have held that a caretaker could be liable for negligence if the patient's death is accelerated by even an hour, minutes, or seconds. One Texas court eloquently stated the reasoning involved in the loss of chance doctrine as follows: The burning candle of life is such a precious light in anyone's existence that no one has a right to extinguish it before it flickers out into perpetual darkness and oblivion. (*Valdez*) This may indeed describe a patient in acute, evolving myocardial infarction, where time matters. Whether or not this can be translated into a legal remedy, however, will depend on the jurisdiction.

[3] Implantable Cardiovascular Devices

Some of the most astounding advances in implantable devices involve artificial cardiovascular implants, including artificial hearts, artificial valves, pacemakers, defibrillators, prosthetic vessels, and vascular stents. In 1960, Chardack and his colleagues implanted the first successful internally powered pacemaker in a human.[44] There have been rapid strides since then, with continuous growth in the number of patients with pacemakers, attributable to improvements in our knowledge of cardiac arrhythmias, more accurate diagnosis, and the availability of better pacing systems.

More recently, the automatic implantable defibrillator has been utilized successfully to terminate ventricular fibrillation and ventricular tachycardias, and its improved performance capabilities allows for biventricular cardiac

---

[44] Greatbatch, W. http://www.greatachievements.org/?id=3839

pacing, cardioversion, monitoring and storage of information and extensive noninvasive interrogation.

[a] Permanent Pacemaker Implantation

The indications for permanent artificial cardiac pacing are continually being revised for both symptomatic and asymptomatic patients, but there are some clear indications and national guidelines.[45] Cardiologists involved in the implantation of permanent pacemakers must be thoroughly familiar with the accepted indications for their use. Bradyarrhythmias are among the most commonly found indications. In contrast, pacemaker implantation may be considered inappropriate under certain clinical circumstances. For example, the so-called "overdrive suppression" of ventricular arrhythmias often has been unsuccessful and the use of implantable pacemakers for this purpose also may be considered inappropriate.

[b] Implantable Defibrillators

Implantable defibrillators, which may combine pacemaker functions, deal primarily with ventricular tachycardias and fibrillation. Initially, criteria for defibrillator implantation were very strict. Recently, however, the criteria have been relaxed to require only a single episode of ventricular fibrillation or hemodynamically unstable ventricular tachycardia.[46]

[c] Liability Issues of Implantable Devices

A physician will be liable for negligent failure to implant a pacemaker, defibrillator, or other cardiac device when such a device is indicated, as well as for negligently implanting such a device that is not medically indicated. Undue delay in implantation of the cardiac device may also constitute negligence.

The soaring health-care cost has become a significant factor in the physicians judgment as to the need for pacemakers, defibrillators, and other implants, and in determining whether the implant is justified. The benefit versus risk rule is particularly critical in the decision to recommend an implantable cardiac device.

Physicians are becoming sensitized to cost-containment. There has been greater scrutiny of implantable devices due to concerns of patients, government, and health-care insurers over the cost of such devices. And, it is

---

[45] ACC/AHA Guidelines for Implantation of Cardiac Pacemakers and Antiarrhythmia Devices: Executive Summary. *Circulation*. 1998;97:1325-1335.

[46] ACC/AHA/NASPE 2002 Guideline Update for Implantation of Cardiac Pacemakers and Antiarrhythmia Devices: Summary Article. *Circulation*. 2002;106:2145.)

conceivable that an "affordable" type of care may become a determinant of the legal "standard of medical care" for implantable devices, thereby redefining the traditional standard of care set by the medical profession.

[d] Informed Decisions

The patient should be fully informed of and involved in each phase of the diagnosis and treatment of cardiac arrhythmias, heart failure and the need for implantable cardiovascular devices. This legal duty of informed decision making is being imposed by all courts in all aspects of medical care. If a patient's differential diagnosis includes cardiac arrhythmia, and the physician decides not to confirm the diagnosis by further testing, the patient must be fully advised of this decision and its implications. Also, if the patient refuses additional testing or implantation of a pacemaker, defibrillator, or other device, the patient must be advised of all the material risks of his or her decision, i.e., an informed refusal by the patient. Permanent pacemakers, for example, are generally not indicated unless the patient has a potentially life-threatening arrhythmia. Failure to inform the patient as to this decision carries potentially serious legal liability, at least for the failure to obtain informed consent.

A patient who undergoes implantation of a permanent device must give a fully-informed consent to the procedure. Otherwise, the attending or consulting physician may be subjected to allegations of "technical battery" on grounds of lack of informed consent. This is particularly likely to happen if complications occur and the plaintiff proves proper warning of the material risks involved in the procedure was not provided by the physician.

A physician may also be found negligent for failing to properly advise the patient of the signs of device malfunction. Patients should be warned about the possibility of pacemaker malfunction due to microwave ovens, magnetometers, or radar systems. Patients should be taught how to monitor their own heart rates at home and should know what their own rate should be. They should be advised about which changes in heart rate may signal malfunction. Generator malfunction can lead to sudden death. Every physician clearly has a duty to fully inform and educate patients on how to recognize possible warning signs.

[e] Economic Considerations

Cardiologists should consider non-medical determinants among the indications for the use of implantable cardiac devices. The third-party reimbursements, cost-effectiveness, government intervention, case law legislation as well as individual and public considerations, all help to determine the standard of care for the use of cardiac devices in patients.

[f] Legal Implications

What are the legal implications of implantable cardiac pacemakers, defibrillators, and other cardiac devices? As the number of patients with cardiac implants has increased, there has been a concomitant increase in the number of malpractice lawsuits. These actions have been based on the tort of negligence, breach of expressed or implied warranty, and strict product liability. They have been brought against the manufacturer, the hospital, the cardiologist, the attending physician and the cardiovascular surgeon.

The implantation of a pacemaker, defibrillator, or other cardiac device is burdened with the usual legal problems inherent in any other medical or surgical procedure. In addition, several areas of unique liability can be identified.

[g] Tort Actions

A patient who is injured during the implantation procedure may bring a medical malpractice action in tort against the attending and consulting physicians, the hospital, and the device manufacturer. The plaintiff may allege any of the following: Negligent failure to reach a decision on whether to implant a device when such is clearly indicated medically; Negligent failure to warn the patient of potential material risks, side effects and complications; Improper selection of the appropriate type of pacing system needed; Negligent post-implantation care; and improper design and manufacture of the device.

[h] Cardiovascular Product Liability

A tort action may be brought against the manufacturer of a device for defective design or manufacture of the cardiovascular product.[47] Manufacturers of defective implantable devices may be held liable under several legal theories. Recovery may be based on negligent failure to conform to the appropriate standard requiring due care in design, manufacture, assembly, packaging, inspection, or testing. However, an action in negligence poses difficulty in proving each of the necessary elements.

These difficulties have led to the development of the doctrine of strict product liability. Under this doctrine, the manufacturer can be held liable for

---

[47] Lehv, M. Medical Product Liability. In Legal Medicine / American College of Legal Medicine, - 7th ed. /editor S. Sandy Sanbar...[et al.]. – Philadelphia, PA : Mosby, cop. 2007.

a defect despite the exercise of all possible due care in design and manufacture of the product. No proof of negligence is necessary. Liability is based on the theory that the manufacturer owes a duty of care to the ultimate consumer to protect that consumer from defects. No contractual relationship or privity between the consumer and the manufacturer need exist. The trend has been toward "increased and widespread" application of this doctrine.

Difficulty in applying §402(a) of the Second Restatement of Torts arises when the defendant is not the manufacturer. The section applies to the "one who sells" the product and is "engaged in the business of selling" the product. Most courts have held that neither physicians nor hospitals fall within the scope of §402(a). However, hospitals and physicians may incur liability for failure to inspect the device for discoverable defects.

Failing to warn of dangers may result in a manufacturer's liability regardless of whether a defect exists. The manufacturer may not be subject to strict product liability if adequate warnings of all potential hazards are given to the physician/purchaser. In such cases, the physician's failure to heed and disclose the dangers to the patient is deemed a superseding cause that relieves the manufacturer from liability. However, if the dangers and warnings are minimized or downplayed, the manufacturer may be found negligent. If the physician's acts were reasonably foreseeable in light of the warnings, a manufacturer will not be exonerated from liability.

Generally, the manufacturer will be held to a "reasonable man" standard in determinations of whether the warning is inadequate. Five relevant standards concerning the adequacy of warnings have been identified.

1. The warning must adequately indicate the scope of the danger;
2. The warning must reasonably communicate the extent or seriousness of the harm that could result from misuse;
3. The physical aspects of the warning must be adequate to alert a reasonably prudent person to the danger;
4. A simple directive warning may be considered inadequate when it fails to state the consequences that might result from failure to follow it;
5. The means of conveying the warning must be adequate the drug manufacturer must bring the warning home to the doctor.

[i] Breach of Contract

As in any doctor-patient relationship, the cardiologist may be liable for breach of contract if the physician guarantees a specific result or cure. Physicians should avoid making any statements that could be misunderstood as an implied or expressed guarantee of a specific outcome. Generally, the "reasonable man" standard is used to determine whether a contract was made. Would a "reasonable man" in the patient's situation understand the physician's words as a guarantee? If so, legal liability may result for failure to obtain the promised results.

[j] Breach of Warranty

Most suits against manufacturers are based on an expressed or implied warranty. Generally, pacemakers and other devices carry an expressed, albeit limited, warranty for replacement in the event of a defect. Rarely, however, does the patient see this warranty. This, coupled with the fact that the physician selects the brand of implant to be used, makes it very difficult for the patient to prove reliance on an expressed warranty. To succeed in an action for breach of expressed warranty, the plaintiff must prove the existence of the expressed warranty, the scope of coverage of the warranty, and reliance on the warranty.

In some situations, the implantation of a particular pacemaker generator without appropriate prior electrophysiologic studies may constitute negligence on the part of the cardiologist or surgeon.

The types of negligence discussed above all involve failure of the physician, hospital, or both, to adhere to the appropriate standard of care in treatment of the patient. These types of claims deal with the service aspect of implantation as distinguished from the product aspect. None of the actions discussed so far would include allegations of a defective product.

[k] Implied Warranties under the Uniform Commercial Code Include Fitness for Purpose or Use and Merchantability

To recover under a theory of implied warranty, the plaintiff must prove that the cardiovascular product was defective when it was sold, that because of the defect the device did not conform to the implied warranty, and that the defect was the proximate cause of injury.

Expert medical testimony would be necessary for a plaintiff in an implantation case to succeed on a breach of warranty cause of action. In a New York case, the plaintiff brought an action against Medtronics[48] for breach of the expressed and implied warranty. At trial, evidence showed that there were at least three possible reasons why the pacemaker electrode in question broke, causing the plaintiffs injury. The court held that a finding by

---

[48] Medtronic Inc. v. Lohr, 518 U.S. 470 (1996).

the jury as to the cause of the break would be highly speculative and presumptuous without the aid of medical testimony. Without such testimony, the jury would have no grounds upon which to base a finding of breach of warranty.

Literature supplied with a cardiovascular device is not an expressed warranty as a matter of law. In one case, the literature dealt with the "life-expectancy" of the power pack. Although there may have been an expressed warranty as to the power pack, there was none with respect to the electrode. Since there was no allegation that the battery failed, the expressed warranty was found to be irrelevant. In general, a breach of warranty cause of action for a defective device cannot be sustained against a physician or hospital. The courts generally have held that the sale of the device by the health care provider is incidental to the services provided by the hospital and physician and, therefore, that they are not subject to a warranty cause of action.

[l] Class Actions

A plaintiff who desires to bring a class action suit based on a defective cardiovascular implantable product may have difficulty. The court may consider medical device cases as ill-suited for prosecution as a class action and may refuse to allow their trial as such because:

1. The defendants' liability could vary from claim to claim;
2. The extent of damages could range from essentially nonexistent to wrongful death;
3. The pleadings might not suggest a preponderance of common questions of law; and
4. Issues related to statute of limitations, contributory negligence, and assumptions of risk could vary from state to state and would require diverse rulings by the court.

The plaintiff also may have a potential problem in obtaining personal jurisdiction over the defendant. The plaintiff must establish that the manufacturer has sufficient "minimum contacts," i.e., business dealings, to allow the court to exercise jurisdiction. Merely placing the implant device into the stream of commerce with no knowledge about where the patient who ultimately receives it will reside, may not be adequate to allow jurisdiction over the defendant in the plaintiffs' home state.

Well documented records are essential. The patient's record must include pertinent data such as manufacturer, model, serial number, and measure physiologic data. Equally important is documentation regarding the patient's understanding of the device and compliance with recommended follow-up procedures. Failure or refusal to keep appointments, take medications, or participate in trans-telephonic monitoring all should be noted. Contributory negligence or assumption of the risk may prevent a plaintiff-patient's recovery on a negligence cause of action. The physician should attempt to inform the patient who refuses follow-up of the possible consequences of refusal.

[4]   Determination of Cardiovascular Impairment under SSA[49]

About 40% of cardiovascular (CV) patients who submits claims for disability determination to the Social Security Administration (SSA) are approved or allowed. Physicians play a vital role in the disability determination process under SSA, particularly in evaluating the patient's impairment. This section deals with the disability determination of CV patients, which is based on two criteria. First, whether the patient has a medically determinable CV impairment which has lasted or can be expected to last for a continuous period of not less than twelve months or is expected to result in death. Second, whether the patient is unable to engage in any substantial gainful activity due to the CV disorder. The first criterion, the subject of this article, is determined on the basis of medically acceptable clinical and laboratory diagnostic techniques. The second criterion is determined on the basis of laws and SSA criteria.

As with all patients, fundamental to evaluation of CV impairment are adequate documentation in the medical records of symptoms, physical findings, appropriate testing, treatment, prognosis and how the disorder impacts the patient's ability to function, i.e. functional cardiac classification (e.g. NY or Canadian Heart Association Classification). The medical records must include the longitudinal history of the cardiac impairments and be sufficient and current. There is a requirement for documenting persisting or continuing CV symptoms and signs despite a regimen of prescribed medical treatment.

[a] List of Cardiovascular Impairments

Under SSA, cardiovascular impairment is viewed as a consequence of one or more of the following: (1) Ventricular dysfunction or chronic heart failure; (2) Angina pectoris due to myocardial ischemia or infarction; (3) Syncope, or near syncope, due to inadequate cerebral perfusion; and (4) Cyanotic heart disease. SSA provides a "listing" of common CV disorders or impairments

---

[49] http://www.ssa.gov/disability/professionals/bluebook/Entire-Publication1-2005.pdf.url.

that are severe enough to prevent a patient from engaging in gainful activity. If the listing is met, the patient would qualify for disability benefits. The following represent some of the CV disorders which meet the "listing":

1. Heart transplant patients qualify for disability benefits for one year post-transplant, after which the cardiac impairment is reevaluated.

2. Chronic heart failure (CHF) patients with symptoms, signs and test results indicating objective cardiac decompensation, systolic or diastolic dysfunction, with ejection fraction of 30% or less, and inability to perform an exercise tolerance test (ETT) at 5 METS or less, qualify.

3. Ischemic heart disease patients qualify if their activities of daily living are very seriously limited, because of persistent angina pectoris due to myocardial ischemia, despite a regimen of treatment, with an abnormal ETT, or three separate episodes of acute coronary syndrome in 12 consecutive months, or angiographic evidence of significant coronary artery or bypass stenoses (>50-70%).

4. Patients qualify if they have syncope, or pre-syncopal attacks, due to recurrent cardiac dysrhythmia, not related to reversible causes (e.g. drugs or electrolyte imbalance), uncontrolled by treatment, documented by Holter or other monitoring, and coincident with syncopal episodes.

5. Patients qualify if they have symptomatic congenital heart disease, with cyanosis at rest or on exertion, or with pulmonary hypertension (pulmonary artery systolic pressure equal to 70+ % of systemic systolic BP).

6. Certain patients with symptomatic vascular aneurysms or symptomatic chronic venous insufficiency may qualify.

7. Patients with peripheral artery disease qualify if they have intermittent claudication and one of the following abnormal findings: resting ABI (ankle-brachial index) is 0.5 or less; exercise ABI decreases by 50% or more; resting toe systolic pressure is less than 30 mm Hg, or Toe/Brachial systolic pressure ratio is less than 0.40.

If a patient does not have an impairment that meets the SSA list, consideration is made of the combined effects of two or more impairments which might "equal" or approximate a listing. And, where the patient's impairments neither meet nor equal any listing, a determination is made by comparing the vocational factors (age, education and work experience) to the claimant's remaining residual functional capacity to perform work related tasks.

[5] End-Stage Heart Failure: Ethical Considerations

End-stage heart failure (ESHF) patients deserve end-of-life considerations, according to the ACC/AHA 2005 *Guideline* Update for the Diagnosis and Management of Chronic Heart Failure in the Adult.[50] The Guideline states that all professionals working with heart failure (HF) patients should examine current end-of-life processes and work toward improvement in approaches to palliation and end-of-life care. Professionals caring for patients with ESHF should have realistic expectations for survival and communicate those accurately to patients and families. They should also ensure continuity of medical care between inpatient and outpatient settings.

Before the HF patient becomes too ill to participate in decisions, the Guideline recommends educating and informing the patient and family about the prognosis for functional capacity, survival, treatment preferences, resuscitation, option of inactivating implanted cardiac devices, living wills, advance directives, and the role of palliative and hospice care services. Contemplation of resuscitation options, as required by the Patient Self-Determination Act, at the time of hospitalization for worsening HF may heighten patient and family anxiety without revealing true preferences. The ESHF patient should be encouraged to choose in advance a person to assume legal authority (i.e. designated power of attorney or healthcare proxy) for health-care matters when the patient cannot be involved in decisions. Hospitalization and/or resuscitation may no longer be desired by the patient when the limitations imposed by HF alone or in combination with other severe conditions become intolerable.

The Guideline states that it is inappropriate to perform aggressive procedures within the final days of life in patients with NYHA functional class IV symptoms who are not anticipated to experience clinical improvement from available treatments (including intubation and implantation of a cardioverter-defibrillator). Opiates are appropriate and recommended hospice care therapy for relief of suffering and symptom palliation for patients with HF at the end of life; inotropes and intravenous diuretics are optional. Greater attention needs to be devoted to the provision of comfort measures in the final days of life, including relief of pain and dyspnea.

It is important to understand which aspects of further care the ESHF patient wishes to forego. Some patients may want full supportive care while conscious without resuscitation; others may decline hospitalization or any intervention. Furthermore, the decision to forego resuscitation should

---

[50] www.acc.org/clinical/guidelines/failure/index.pdf.

lead to possible deactivation of the life-saving function of an implanted defibrillation device.

Hospice services, originally developed for patients with end-stage cancer, have recently been extended to provide compassionate care to patients dying of HF. While ESHF patients characteristically suffer from breathlessness, many patients dying of HF do describe pain during the final days. Physicians caring for these patients should, according to the Guideline, not only utilize optionally inotropes and diuretics, but also become familiar with the prescription of anxiolytics, sleeping medications, and narcotics to ease distress during the last days.

The utilization of hospice care, which traditionally required a prediction by the physician of death within 6 months, for patients with ESHF is acceptable even though the health-care providers are generally unable to accurately predict the end of life in patients with HF. Current hospice guidelines and policies are being revised to allow patients with HF to benefit from the type of care that can be provided through hospice services.

Finally, with regard to end-of-life considerations of patients with HF, the ultimate decisions regarding when end-of-life is nearing reflect a complex interaction between objective information and subjective information, emotions, and patient and family readiness. All professionals involved with HF care should make it a priority to improve recognition of end-stage disease and provide care to patients and families approaching this stage. And, as physicians "become more familiar with the steps in progression to end-stage HF in this era, the current abrupt transition from aggressive intervention to comfort and bereavement care will be softened by a gradual and progressive emphasis on palliation until it dominates the final days of care."

[6] Tables

Table 1 - Abbreviations

ACS	-	Acute coronary syndromes
CABG	-	Coronary artery bypass grafting surgery
CAC	-	Coronary artery calcium
CAD	-	Coronary artery disease
CCT	-	Cardiac computed tomography
CHD	-	Coronary heart disease
CMR	-	Cardiac magnetic resonance imaging
CT	-	Computed tomography
CTA	-	Computed tomography angiography
EBCT	-	Electron beam computed tomography
ECG	-	Electrocardiogram
HF	-	Heart failure
LV	-	Left ventricle
MDCT	-	Multi-Detector computed tomography
MI	-	Myocardial infarction
MPI	-	Myocardial perfusion imaging
MRA	-	Magnetic Resonance Angiography
MSCT	-	Multi-Slice computed tomography
NSTEMI	-	Non–ST-segment elevation myocardial infarction
PCI	-	Percutaneous coronary intervention
PET	-	Positron emission tomography
PET/CT	-	Combined PET and CT scanners
RV	-	Right ventricle
SPECT	-	Single-photon emission computed tomography
SPECT/CT	-	Combined SPECT and CT scanners
SPECT/MPI	-	SPECT myocardial perfusion imaging
STEMI	-	ST-segment elevation myocardial infarction
TEE	-	Trans-esophageal echocardiography

Table-2 – Organizations/Societies

ACCF - American College of Cardiology Foundation (Quality Strategic Directions Committee Appropriateness Criteria Working Group)
ACR - American College of Radiology
SCCT - Society of Cardiovascular Computed Tomography
SCMR - Society for Cardiovascular Magnetic Resonance
ASNC - American Society of Nuclear Cardiology
NASCI - North American Society for Cardiac Imaging
SCAI - Society for Cardiovascular Angiography and Interventions
SIR - Society of Interventional Radiology

Table 3 – Radiation Dose Comparison[51]

Diagnostic Procedure	Typical Effective Dose (mSv)	Number of Chest X rays (PA film) for Equivalent Effective Dose	Time Period for Equivalent Effective Dose from Natural Background Radiation
Chest x ray (PA film)	0.02	1	2.4 days
CT head	2.0	100	243 days
CT abdomen or chest	10.0	500	3.3 years

---

[51] http://www.fda.gov/cdrh/ct/risks.html

CHAPTER 3

CARDIOVASCULAR SURGERY[*]

Thomas D. Maher, MD

SYNOPSIS

---

[*] An earlier version of this chapter was written by Richard J. Lescoe, MD, JD.

          [ii]   Associated carotid artery disease
          [iii]   Associated valvular heart disease
      [e]   Ejection Fraction of 0.2 or Less
      [f]   Left Ventricular Aneurysm
      [g]   Trash Heart
      [h]   Right Ventricular Saphenous Vein Graft Fistula
  [6]   Surgical Treatment of Ventricular Arrhythmias
  [7]   Heart Transplantation
  [8]   Structural Failure of Heart Valves

---

§ 3.01 The Subspecialty of Cardiovascular Surgery

[1] Qualifications of the Surgeon

Adult cardiac surgery is a part of thoracic surgery. The specialty of thoracic surgery includes operative, peri-operative and surgical critical care of patients with acquired and congenital conditions within the chest. This includes the heart, lungs, esophagus, chest wall, great vessels, tumors of the mediastinum and disease of the diaphragm and pericardium. Also included is management of the airway and injuries to the chest.

Those who specialize in thoracic surgery may choose to limit their practice and this specialization which is common described using different terms. General thoracic surgery often implies surgery of the chest contents exclusive of the heart. The practice of cardiac surgery may be limited to the heart with further specialization into adult and pediatric practices. Cardiovascular surgery may imply the addition of general vascular surgery, that is, surgery of the peripheral arteries and veins along with the aorta and visceral vessels. Obviously many permutations of this exist.

Physicians practicing the specialty of thoracic surgery are usually certified by the American Board of Thoracic Surgery (ABTS). This Board was organized under the American Board of Surgery (ABS) in 1948 and became an independent primary Board in 1971. The ABTS has established qualifications for examinations and procedures for certification and recertification. The candidate for thoracic surgery certification must also have previously completed an approved general surgery program (board certification in general surgery is not required for those candidates beginning their thoracic residency from July 2003), or successfully completed a six year categorical-integrated Thoracic Surgery Residency developed along guidelines established by the Thoracic Surgery Director's Association.[1] A passing score on the

---

[1] The American Board of Thoracic Surgery Booklet of Information (Jan 2007).

examination acknowledges that the candidate possesses certain qualifications that are necessary to be competent in thoracic surgery. Certification is not intended to define the requirements for membership in hospital staff or to gain special recognition or privilege for the diplomat. Nor does certification define the scope of specialty practice or state who may or may not engage in the specialty. Certification does not relieve hospital governing boards from responsibilities in determining the hospital privileges of such specialists. Applicants who are now certified in thoracic surgery are issued a certificate that is valid for 10 years. They can be renewed before expirations by fulfilling the requirements for recertification as outlined by the ABTS.[2]

The cardiovascular surgeon is usually certified in general vascular surgery, which is defined as "surgery of the arterial, venous and lymphatic systems, exclusive of the intracranial vessels and those vessels intrinsic to and immediately adjacent to the heart." Certification is offered to board certified general and thoracic surgeons, but not to those who for practical purposes limit their activities to other surgical specialties such as neurology, orthopedic, urologic and plastic surgery.

The American Board of Surgery believes properly educated surgeons who are diplomates of the American Board of Surgery or the American Board of Thoracic Surgery are expected to possess qualifications in general vascular surgery. The board therefore intends certification for special qualifications in general vascular surgery of only those who, by virtue of intensive or additional training, dedicated practice characteristics, and contributions to this discipline, have demonstrated qualifications which are very special, and above and beyond those expected of other certified general or thoracic surgeons.

The board understands that there are certified surgeons who have been dedicated to the discipline of general vascular surgery from before July 1, 1978, when no endorsed or approved training programs existed, and who therefore do not meet the specified education or training requirements. Such persons, if they can document their major commitment to general vascular surgery by virtue of their practice characteristics and contributions to the discipline, and if they have thus demonstrated special qualifications, may apply to the board for individual consideration. They must, however, have been in practice five or more years since completion of residency in general and thoracic surgery before they may apply for consideration of the special certificate. After June 30, 1989, no applications will be accepted from this group, and all applicants shall be required to have completed an accredited residency in general vascular surgery.

Applicants must demonstrate to the satisfaction of the board that they

---

[2] The American Board of Thoracic Surgery Booklet of Information (June 2001).

have managed, as the responsible surgeons, approximately 100 cases with major vascular reconstructive procedures within a recent twelve month period of practice (cases from fellowship or residency are not acceptable). The cases must represent a wide spectrum of vascular disorders, and not be limited to one or two entities. The indications for surgery, the morbidity-mortality statistics, and outcomes must be within the standards established by the board.

The requirement of having made contributions to the discipline of general vascular surgery, which are considered to be special to the board, covers the multitude of research publication and teaching situations. The applicants then must have the endorsement of their program director or chief of surgery of the hospitals where they practice. They must successfully pass all examinations prescribed by the board. The first examinations were given in November, 1984. Examinations since 1985 have included an oral component.

Each candidate may take the examination no more than three times within the five years following approval of his application. If he wishes to be reconsidered after that time, he must fulfill such additional requirements as the board shall prescribe, and submit a new application.

All certificates issued on or after January 1, 1976 shall bear a time limited validity of approximately ten years. Opportunity for recertification will be offered in the 7th year to allow for reexamination before the ten year period is up.

Revocation will occur if the board decides the certificate was received, and the holder in some respect was not properly qualified. The directors may revoke the certificate after opportunity for a full and fair hearing by the medical staff of the hospital, by a state or county medical society, by a court of law, or by the directors of the American Board of Surgery, if the certificate holder has been found guilty of, or pleaded guilty to, a felony, professional misconduct, professional incompetence or unethical conduct.

Comment. Currently in community hospitals fewer than a hundred cases are being accepted for consideration of privileges in general vascular surgery. The special certification in general vascular surgery may unfortunately lead to an impression that super-specialists are better than those who have practiced for decades with excellent results.

[2] Introductory Comments on Surgical Mishaps

In evaluating adverse events involving surgical management, it may be difficult to separate complications resulting from management from those resulting from disease. We can get an idea of the magnitude of the problem from the study of randomly selected admissions to selected hospitals in Utah and Colorado from 1992.[3] Adverse events were no more likely in surgical care than in nonsurgical care. Surgical adverse events were not infrequent and often preventable. In their opinion an adverse surgical event was considered preventable "if it was avoidable by available means unless those means were not determined standard of care." Adverse surgical events occurred in approximately 1.9% of hospital admissions in this study, 54% were considered preventable. In this review, certain types of surgery were noted to be more likely to be involved with adverse events and have a higher proportion of preventable adverse events. In this short list were coronary artery bypass surgery and cardiac valve surgery. The reason for this is not known but may be related to the complexity of the operations in general. Clinical risk scores and in particular age were pointed out as the only individual factors which were found to be statistically significant as causes of surgical adverse events. As interventional cardiology and medical therapy have become more frequent and improved in recent years, those patients who now come to adult cardiac surgery are older and sicker.

Because the patients are usually in such desperate condition when undergoing cardiovascular surgery, it is difficult to differentiate the risk of the procedure from negligence on the part of the people involved. There are some areas where gross negligence does not require medical knowledge, such as creating a massive air embolus in the patient from knocking the oxygenator off the stand, or tripping on the tubes and disrupting the system.[4]

There have been heart valves sutured in upside down, which is incompatible with survival. They have to be excised, and a new valve properly inserted. This added time on cardiopulmonary bypass most likely has resulted in the death of some patients. Failure to unclamp the line, or clamping the line inappropriately, also is simple carelessness which may cost the patient his life.

Defective equipment can always be a problem. The alert perfusionist has to be able to determine defects, and be prepared for rapid changes. Changing a ruptured pump head tube should be accomplished in a matter of a couple of minutes, especially if it has been practiced. Simple things, like knowing where the fuse is for the equipment or the entire operating suite, as well as an emergency power source, can be lifesaving. A means of mechanically maintaining the circulation with a hand crank should be available, in this writer's opinion, on all cardiopulmonary bypass equipment.

---

[3] Gouerde et al., *The Incidence and Nature of Surgical Adverse Events in Colorado and Utah in 1992 Surgery*, 126:66-75 (1999).

[4] Stoney, et al., *Air Embolism and Other Accidents Using Pump Oxygenators*, 29 ANN. THORAC. SURG. 336 (1980).

Human error in using the wrong solutions, parts and medications will always be with us, and if proven, would be difficult to defend in a professional liability case.

New techniques also bring new hazards. One Texas heart team had two major technical bleeds in their first ten heart transplants. At the beginning of heart surgery, one of the first pediatric cases had the pump run dry while the pump technician looked over the surgeon's shoulder. In a second case, there was such haste that the surgeon not only sutured the septal defect and cleft mitral, but the entire mitral valve, with disastrous results.

The safety of new implantable material, such as prosthetic devices, requires not only laboratory tests but a track record before they can be evaluated. Obviously, if we knew of a superior valve, we all would be using it. There are some dozen valves on the market at the present time. The tissue valves were championed, because anticoagulation was felt not to be necessary. Experience has now taught us that atrial fibrillation and a mitral prosthesis are fraught with a high risk of embolization, so that anticoagulation is used in the mitral valve cases. The efforts of anticoagulating the patient properly has created many problems, with major bleeding occurring in most large series. Degeneration of tissue valves and calcification, particularly in the young, has led to avoiding tissue valves in children and anybody with a prognosis of more than ten years.

Strut fracture led to a general warning of the medical profession to observe these patients closely; however, when a strut fractures, it does so suddenly, and there is nothing that can be done in advance to anticipate it. The risk of bringing all these patients in and replacing their valves may prove to be the lesser risk, but at the present time it is a matter of watchful waiting.

What liability should be imposed for application of experimental techniques is going to take time to develop. The total mechanical heart was implanted at a time when sheep were dying in nine months. Somewhere back in 1964, a baboon heart was transplanted into a human, before they had done many heart transplants within the animal species. How one can believe that a cross-species transplant is going to work in humans when it has not worked in the animal kingdom is hard to understand.

[3] Surgical Anatomy

[a] The Heart and Coronary Arteries

The heart is located in the middle mediastinum covered by the sternum and costal cartilage of the third to fifth ribs. One third of its mass is located to the right and two thirds of the mass to the left of the mid line. The heart is covered by the pericardium, a fibrous sac that surrounds the heart. It has two layers. A visceral layer attached to the heart and a parietal layer, the outer layer, with a small amount of fluid in-between. The heart is in effect two pumps in series. The right heart receiving the venous return from the body through the inferior and superior vena cava into the right atrium across the tricuspid valve and pumped by the right ventricle through the pulmonic valve into the pulmonary artery into the lungs. After being oxygenated it returns to the heart via the pulmonary veins, into the left atrium across the mitral valve and into the left ventricle. It is pumped out of the ventricle through the aortic valve into the rest of the body. The first branches of the aorta are the coronary arteries.

Normally there is a left main coronary artery, so called left main trunk (LMT), which divides into the left anterior descending and the circumflex coronary artery. The other major branch is the right coronary artery. No two patients have the exact same coronary artery pattern, so there are many variations. They vary in size, position and the amount of myocardium that they supply. Coronary arteries are located on the surface of the heart. They are usually seen but may also be buried in fat or in the myocardium itself. This can make identification difficult. It may also be difficult to expose. This could lead to bypassing a different artery than was intended or to not bypassing an artery at all. Coronary anomalies are not rare. The circumflex artery may come from the right side with the right coronary artery. The take off from the aorta may vary in its location or a coronary artery may anastomose with a vein or enter directly into a cardiac chamber creating an arterial venous fistula. The heart has a complex venous drainage system usually composed of 3 parts: 1) the coronary sinus and its tributaries accounting for about 80% of the venous drainage; 2) right ventricular vein; and 3) the thebesian veins. Coronary arteriography is the standard means of delineating the coronary artery anatomy and identifying the locations of blockage with the vessels. Coronary arteriography is performed by the cardiologist in the catheterization laboratory and provides a map for the surgeon for his procedures on the heart.

[b] The Aorta

The aorta is the main trunk from which the systemic arterial circulation proceeds. It begins just after the aortic valve as the ascending aorta. The aortic arch is next giving branches to the head including the brain and the upper extremities and thorax. This proceeds then as the descending aorta localized in the posterior chest next to the spine. From this arise the intercostal vessels. The thoracic aorta ends at the level of the diaphragm where it becomes the abdominal aorta.

[c] The Pulmonary Artery

The pulmonary artery is the equivalent to the aorta but it is located on the right side of the heart. It begins just above the pulmonic valve as the main pulmonary artery dividing rather quickly into the right and left branches going to the right and left lungs.

The venous drainage of the heart comes from the head, thoracic, upper extremities via the superior vena cava and the venous drainage from the lower body below the diaphragm comes via the inferior vena cava, both emptying directly into the right atrium. In discussing anatomy, one must always be aware of anomalies, which are not uncommon and introduce variability.

[4] Procedures Performed by Cardiac Surgeons

[a] Incisions

Sternotomy is the most common incision used today in cardiac surgery. The sternum is divided in the midline with a saw. It gives excellent exposure to the anterior mediastinum, pericardium, heart and ascending aorta. The sternum is usually closed with stainless steel wire, but other materials may be used. Precise sternal closure is important not only for wound healing, but also for reducing the incidence of infection. The thoracotomy incision which is made between the ribs to the right or left side may be either anterior posterior, lateral or some combination of the three. Thoracotomy incisions are commonly used to approach the descending aorta and for so called minimally invasive approaches to the coronary arteries, cardiac valves or pericardium.

[b] Valvular Repair and Replacement

This refers to surgery on the valves of the heart. It may be one valve or a combination of valves. It may be in association with other procedures in the heart or great vessels, commonly the coronary arteries or the aorta. The combination of coronary bypass surgery and the valve surgery is particularly common. The two major valve procedures are repair and replacement. Repair has the advantage of leaving the patient with his own valve tissue. As long as it provides good function it may be used, thus avoiding complications associated with an artificial valve. Although much progress has been made over the years in valve design and materials, there are still valve associated problems particularly thrombo-embolic disease, infection, and valve failure that have not been eliminated. Valve repair as mentioned leaves the patient with his own tissue. It may require excision of some portion of the valve leaflet or leaflets or reducing the size of a dilated annulus allowing the leaflet edges to come together thus correcting valvular insufficiency. Replacing the surrounding supporting tissue such as the chordae tendonae and the mitral valve may be required in valve repair. Opening the stenotic leaflets of a valve by separating the leaflet edges that have been attached as a result of chronic inflammation for example then relieving stenosis is another form of valve repair.

Valve replacement means relying totally on an artificial prosthesis for valve function. The native valve is usually removed in part or in whole and a new prosthesis is inserted. Choosing an artificial valve for a patient involves many factors. It must be done with the individual patient in mind and also with the individual patient's participation in the decision. The different types of valves to choose from are explained to the patient. Characteristics most commonly considered are durability, need for anti-coagulation, ease of insertion and sometimes availability. Prosthetic valves fall into main categories, mechanical valve and tissue valve.

Aortic valve replacement is probably more common than aortic valve repair. Repair is less often possible and in many circumstances less reliable than say in the mitral valve repair. If possible though repair will allow the patient to retain his own aortic valve. Aortic stenosis is unlikely to be repairable while insufficiency may be repairable in some circumstances in experienced hands with good results. Often when aortic insufficiency occurs in association with aortic pathology such as some aortic aneurysms with dilatation of the sindtubular junction repairing the aortic pathology may allow the valve to be spared.

For aortic valve surgery the valve is exposed by an incision in the aorta above the valve. One must expose the valve without coming too close to the annulus or coronary artery ostium. On occasion, there can be an anomalous takeoff of one of the coronary arteries and it may be damaged on opening if not seen. The normal valve has three leaflets. One associated with the left coronary ostia, one associated with the right coronary ostia and a third so called non-coronary sinus. The common variant is a bicuspid aortic valve, really a congenital anomaly that has usually one large leaflet with a central raffe and a smaller leaflet. It may be insufficient or develop stenosis. For valve replacement the leaflets are removed. Insufficiency with thin pliable leaflets that can be excised without much difficulty.

In aortic stenosis the leaflets are often calcified along with the annulus, which can make removal more difficult. Excision too close to the annulus may leave too little tissue to secure the sewing ring of the prosthesis to be inserted resulting in increased incidence of insufficiency or later a perivalvular leak. Debridement of calcium in the annulus must be done with caution. The calcium should be removed to provide room for the largest possible prosthesis and allow proper seating of the valve. Too vigorous debridement can lead to detachment of the anterior leaflet of the mitral valve just below the non-coronary cusp or separation of the aorta from the ventricle posteriorly. When recognized during debridement, these disruptions can generally be corrected by adjusting placement of the sutures to reattach the separated tissue and these are the same sutures used to attach the aortic valve to the annulus. If not detected, severe bleeding or mitral valve dysfunction may become apparent as the patient is weaned from cardiopulmonary bypass. Then re-opening and re-replacement of the valve with annular repair is necessary at that time. This represents some increase risk to the patient. One must be careful of the calcium particles during debridement. They can be a source of embolization.

Once removal is complete, the aortic annulus is sized with a valve sizer specific for the type of valve to be used. In general the largest size valve that can be placed is used without oversizing. The larger the size, the less likely there is impediment to flow. The valve may be seated intra-annular or supra-annular. Placing the valve above the annulus may allow a larger prosthesis to be inserted but you must be careful not to interfere with the coronary ostia obstructing flow to the coronary arteries. This could cause difficulty weaning from bypass. With a mechanical prosthesis, one must be aware of the tissue below or around the prosthesis that may interfere with the popit motion. A tissue valve is less likely to be affected by surrounding tissue since it does not have a mechanical pop it to interfere with. The tissue valve leaflets are essentially located above its sewing ring and with a mechanical valve the leaflet or pop it protrudes often below the plane and the suture line and it can be interfered with by surrounding tissue.

The valve is secured to the annulus with permanent suture material usually interupted sutures, multiple in nature and independently tied. Teflon felt on the suture is often helpful particularly with fragile annular tissue to prevent the suture from pulling through causing a leak. This could become apparent immediately or in the future. Deeply placed sutures at the area of the right and non-coronary cusp can produce heart block. Interruption of the conduction system may require permanent pacemaker post-operatively. When tissue is extremely friable and/or extremely calcified this complication may be inevitable. The sutures as they are being tied are cut, being careful not to leave the ends too long or it may interfere with a mechanical prosthesis or irritate the tissue valve. Closure of the aortotomy may require thin strips and reinforcement with Teflon felt to prevent bleeding or disruption if the tissue is friable.

[c] Mechanical Valve

The most commonly used mechanical valve are tilling disk valves, either bileaflet or single leaflet with a Dacron sign ring attached to the metal housing. The principal valve material is pyrolite carbon at the present time. In the past, so called ball and cage valves were quite common. Over the years many different prosthetic designs existed. Various complications were associated with each of these valves but the variety of valves used today is much less than the past. Present day mechanical valves in general are more durable, have better hemodynamic properties. The perfect replacement heart valve, however, does not exist. Mechanical valves still require anti-coagulation, which is usually Coumadin therapy. This decreases the risk of thrombo-embolic events. Thrombo-embolism is intrinsic to a mechanical prosthesis. Durability of the valve is quite good and they are unlikely to wear out, for the patient usually will not out live his mechanical prosthesis. They are often the preferred valve in the younger patient. Good durability does not necessarily mean the valve won't need to be replaced at some time. Infection, tissue ingrowth or perivalvular leak cause a valve to need replacement.

[d] Tissue Valves

The term tissue valve covers a slightly broader spectrum at this time. This includes porcine valves, which are actually the heart valve leaflets of the pig heart. They can be either stented or a stentless valve. A stent is a stiff frame, which holds the valve in a given position, whereas a stentless valve relies more on the insertion technique for maintaining its position. The stented porcine valve is easy to insert, more rigid and requires one suture line. The stentless valves without the added support have good hemodynamics particularly at the small sizes but are a little more difficult to insert requiring two suture lines and precise placement to prevent leakage through the valve. The pericardial valve is made from bovine pericardium. The pericardial tissue is used to constrict a valve from non-valve tissue. It is supported on a frame like the stented porcine valve. The pericardial valve seems somewhat more durable than some of the other tissue valves and have improved hemodynamics over the standard porcine valve. Some porcine valves have also been modified to improve their hemodynamics and durability.

The xenograph valve that is the porcine and pericardial valve are very commonly used today. They are readily available in multiple sizes and are easy to insert. They do not normally require long term anti-coagulation in patients in normal sinus rhythm. The down side of tissue valve is its durability. They are used primarily in older individuals, that is more than 65-

70, and generally last about 10-15 years, those in the aortic position tend to last longer than those in the mitral. In the young patient less than 60 years of age tissue valve may be used with the understanding that the patient may need a valve replacement. They seem to fail earlier in the younger patient than in the older population, but the patient is spared Coumadin therapy.

The third type, the homograph valve, is taken from human donors. They are preserved and they are a type of a tissue valve. They may come as a valve alone or as a valve conduit, that is, with attached aorta. They have low thrombo-embolic rates, good hemodynamics and do not require Coumadin. They too are less durable than the mechanical valve. They are often used to replace an infected aortic valve or the extra tissue that comes can help repair the tissue that has been destroyed by the infection. All prosthetic valves are subject to infection. The risk associated with prosthetic valve endocarditis is generally higher than native valve endocarditis.

A primary factor leading to valve choice is the patient's life expectance. More durable valves are used in the younger patient. That is a mechanical prosthesis as long as anticoagulation is not a problem. In older patients or those with an increased risk of bleeding, who need to avoid anti-coagulation, some type of tissue valve may be better for them. Independent of the valves anticoagulation carries its own risks, which must be included when selecting a valve. Young women who are still at child bearing age and who require valve replacement may elect a tissue valve to avoid Coumadin with its risks of bleeding and terotegenetic effects. The tissue valve will likely need to be replaced and redo surgery performed in the future.

[e] Aortic Composite Graft

This refers to replacement of the aortic valve in association with the proximal ascending aorta. This is required for patients with associated aneurysmal disease involving the coronary sinuses. For example, a myxomatous degeneration associated with Marfan's syndrome. The option to replace the aorta and valve separately using the coronary ostia with a small rim of aortic tissue is used in some situations. If this tissue is diseased, however, as in most patients with Marfan's syndrome, it may become aneurysmal requiring higher risk surgery later on. So a composite graft is best in this situation. Aortic dissection associated with the disruption of the aortic valve continuity and surrounding tissue may also require a composite graft. This technique uses a so-called valve conduit that is a premade product in which the valve comes already sewn to the Dacron graft.

The homograft comes with an aortic valve attached to the aorta and is also a type of composite graft. In this case the surrounding aortic tissue is removed leaving a ring of tissue around each of the coronary ostia, so called coronary button, for the reimplantation. The remaining aortic tissue and valve are removed. The new valve conduit is sewn to the aortic annulus and the coronary buttons are then attached to the new graft, either directly or via an additional interposed piece of graft. Direct cannulation is preferable and produces more durable results but it may not always be possible. Composite graft replacement is somewhat more complex than aortic valve replacement associated with an additional separate graft replacement in the ascending aorta because of the need to transplant the coronary ostia. Care must be taken not to kink or twist the coronary artery that may interfere with coronary blood flow to the heart.

[f] Ross Procedure

This refers to replacing the ascending aorta and aortic valve with a pulmonary autograft that is the patient's own pulmonary artery and valve as a valve conduit. Then a separate homograft is used to replace the patient's pulmonic valve and pulmonary artery. This is primarily used in pediatric cardiac surgery and occasionally in young adults but it is much more complex and can be associated with complications including insufficiency of the new aortic valve or injury to branches of the coronary artery as the pulmonary autograft is excised. Good results can occur in experienced hands.

[g] Mitral Valve Replacement

The mitral valve can be replaced or repaired but is more often repaired than aortic valve. There are multiple approaches to the mitral valve. It is often via median sternotomy but it can also be approached through a right thoracotomy and this may be an easier approach in some redo situations. Once the heart has been exposed then there are also different approaches through the heart into the left atrium to see the valve. The left atrium can be opened directly once it is separated from the right atrium posteriorly. In some situations the surgeon may find it necessary to open the right atrium and go through the intra-atrial septum and then visualize the mitral valve.

The second is a little bit more complex. Patients may have heart block but also in some situations it may produce better visualization. Mitral stenosis has become less common with the decreasing incidence of rheumatic fever. Mitral insufficiency, which is more amenable to repair is more frequently seen by the cardiac surgeon now. Mitral stenosis early on in its course, before the presence of a calcification, can some times be repaired by so-called commissurotomy avoiding replacement. More commonly mitral stenosis with fibrosis and calcification is seen. This requires mitral valve replacement and excision of at least a portion of the valve leaflets. It has become apparent over the years that in mitral valve surgery leaving as much of the supporting apparatus as possible in place, i.e., the chordae tendonae is important for maintaining cardiac function. Excision of the chordae entirely has led to ventricular dilatation and progressive deterioration of ventricular function.

Sparing as many chordae as possible is preferred. Heavy calcification of the mitral annulus can make replacement quite difficult. Excessive debridement of the calcium may lead to disruption of the annulus in the atrial ventricular continuity. A complication that can be difficult to repair and fatal. It may be necessary to leave some calcium and use only the leaflet tissue to support the valve. Peri-valvular leaks are more common in general in this situation with the heavily calcified annulus. Again, the conduction system can be in jeopardy with deep bites. The aortic valve may be injured as can the circumflex coronary artery. One is balancing secure valve placement with the risk of injury to the surrounding structures.

[h] Mitral Valve Repair

Mitral valve repair is commonly used for a mitral insufficiency of various etiologies. This often involves resection of a redundant or diseased portion of the valve. Usually a portion of the posterior leaflet and accompanied with an annuloplasty using a prosthetic ring to support the repair and usually decrease the size of the annulus. Again suture placement is important as mentioned above. Extensive calcification is usually a less commonly encountered problem. The transesophageal echocardiogram (TEE) is critical to mitral valve repair. The probe of the esophagus gives an excellent view of the mitral valve. This allows the surgeon to assess the valve in the operating room, both pre and post repair.

Once the valve is repaired and the patient is being weaned from cardiopulmonary bypass, the surgeon must use the TEE to assess the results of his repair. Adequate blood pressure is obviously necessary and if low the anesthesiologist can pharmacologically raise the pressure to observe for regurgitation. Ideally there will be no leaks. A small leak may be acceptable. Surgical judgment is required as far as evaluating the results, weighing the risks of re-repair or valve replacement if one deems the repair initially unsatisfactory. TEE is also good for evaluating all valve replacement surgery assessing the function of the prosthesis and looking for any peri-valvular leaks.

[i] The Tricuspid Valve

The tricuspid valve requires surgical intervention less often than the aortic or mitral valve. Tricuspid stenosis is quite rare and tricuspid regurgitation is much more common. It is often associated with mitral valve disease. The most common tricuspid valve procedure is tricuspid valve repair using annuloplasty alone. Regurgitation is usually secondary to annular dilatation and shrinking of the annulus may be all that is necessary to reduce the regurgitant lesion to an acceptable level. Leaflet excision or exclusion may be necessary and in the case of infection debridement of vegetations may be indicated. Briefly, the gold standard in endocarditis surgery is removal of all infected tissue. Occasionally the entire tricuspid valve has been excised and no prosthesis re-inserted. This is done to avoid complications of prosthetic valves and re-infection. These patients may then require replacement at a later date.

The three leaflets of the tricuspid valve are anterior, posterior and septal. Septal leaflet is adjacent to the conduction system, again care is taken to avoid passing sutures through the conduction system creating heart block as in other valve surgery. The right side of the heart is usually a lower pressure system and some residual tricuspid insufficiency is often well tolerated. Tricuspid valve replacement is not often necessary but when required tissue valve are commonly used although a mechanical valve may be satisfactory but then will require anticoagulation.

The pulmonic valve is rarely replaced or operated on in the adult, especially those without congenital heart disease. Tissue valves are often used in replacement which is not complex. The pulmonic valve replacement is usually not complicated. The valve can be easily excised. There are no coronary ostia and the conduction system does not seem to be in jeopardy.

[5] Valvular Pathology

Valvular pathology in general includes rheumatic disease, degenerative disease and infection. Degenerative disease of the aortic valve leads to calcifications of valve leaflets, leading to stenosis and usually occurs in the age group of 8th or 9th decade and is a process associated with aging. Myxomatous degeneration of the mitral valve frequently causes mitral insufficiency. Leaflets are redundant and prolapsed into the atrium.

Rheumatic fever occurs in childhood and young adults, usually is acute, often recurrent inflammatory disease associated with beta hemolytic streph infection of the pharynx that leads to chronic progressive deforming valve disease, most frequently the mitral and then the aortic and tricuspid valve in decreasing frequency. These symptoms have declined significantly in the United States and developing countries with the advent of antibiotic treatment.

Infection of the heart valves and endocardium or blood vessels including the aorta is referred to as infective endocarditis. Any of the infectious agents can cause this problem, but it is usually bacterial. The infection can form vegetations or clumping of the infected material in the valve. These vegetations can embolize causing stroke and abscesses elsewhere in the body. Infection can destroy tissue causing severe regurgitation leading to congestive heart failure. Endocarditis can be lethal both from the infectious standpoint and the cardiac decompensation standpoint. It is also associated with pulmonary and renal insufficiency. Prolonged therapy for endocarditis is essential. Some infections can be treated with antibiotics alone achieving tissue sterilization. Those patients with valve complications often require surgery. Congestive heart failure, abscess formation, uncontrolled infection are often indicators. Heart block is a symptom of aortic ring abscess formation and is evidence of tissue destruction and severity of disease.

[6] Pre-op Evaluation

[a] History and Physical

Pre-op evaluation is an essential part of surgery. Patients who are healthy with few other problems unrelated to the anticipated surgery are less likely to have complications. Co-morbidities-a diagnosis unrelated to the primary diagnosis-increase the risk of procedure. They may change the balance of the risks to benefits ratio for the patient, even to the point where the procedure is not recommended. The co-morbidity may not change the surgeon's decision to proceed but may help the patient better understand the risk he is undertaking. Emergency situations arise often in cardiac surgery and it may be necessary to proceed in the presence of significant co-morbidities and without defining them fully as a less extensive evaluation is necessary: The severity of the patient's present condition being such that the increased risk is justified.

A pre-op evaluation consists of a history and physical that helps define co-morbidity and associated disease. For example, diabetes, smoking, chronic obstructive pulmonary disease, renal disease or history of bleeding are all important. History of previous surgery may be particularly important and it is critical to know what medications the patient has been on. Often times the patients are taking herbal drugs, which they don't view as medication. Even aspirin sometimes is not viewed as a medication.

Physical examination is important. For example, carotid bruits may indicate carotid artery obstruction that might need to be addressed. Lung disease, cardiac arrhythmias may all be detected. The physical exam is particularly important in coronary artery disease because one is also searching for possible conduits. Finding varicose veins may mean a search for additional conduits. A bedside Allen test may indicate that the radial arteries are not satisfactory for a graft. Body habitus, presence or absence of peripheral pulses are all clues to risk and are important to assessing the patient. Basic lab data are critical. A CBC may show an abnormal red cell mass, unexplained anemia may be present indicating a malignancy or occult GI bleeding. Elevated white counts may indicate infection. Renal function is important to assess by looking at the BUN and creatinine. Renal insufficiency is a particularly important risk factor in cardiac surgery. Basic bleeding parameters including a platelet count, protime, and partial thromboplastin time can help as screening tests along with a history. As long as the basic lab tests are unremarkable, along with the physical exam and history, a good assessment of the patient can be made.

[b] Other Pre-op Testing

The chest x-ray may reveal infection or occult malignancy and the lateral film is particularly helpful in redo surgery in identifying a clear space behind the sternum helping assess the risk of re-entry. CT scan may further delineate the intra-thoracic structures especially prior to redo aortic surgery. An EKG is part of the routine evaluation, cardiac catheterization is critical to rule out coronary disease as in valve patients or to identify the obstruction in known coronary disease prior to the coronary artery bypass surgery. Echocardiography either transthoracic (TTE) or transesophageal (TEE) are standard prior to peri-valvular heart disease. The TEE is particularly helpful in evaluation of mitral valve disease. Aortography and MRA are useful for aortic anatomy. Carotid doppler ultrasound examination is a useful screening element for carotid obstructive disease.

[c] Risk Stratification

All of the above help assess the risk of surgery for a particular patient. This then allows risk stratification: The ability to predict outcome for a particular procedure by defining the severity of illness. One wants to account for the difference in outcome based on pre-existing condition. At least four outcomes are particularly important to the surgeon: morbidity, mortality, cost (so-called resource utilization) and patient satisfaction. This requires sophisticated statistical analysis. One must be careful not to equate necessarily risk adjusted mortality with quality of care. Risk analysis data is to be used with caution. Many institutions have developed their own risk score. Assigning numbers to various co-morbidities and arriving at a total score to give an estimated risk of procedure to the patient. The risk usually being evaluated in these circumstances is mortality. Transferring these scoring methods from one institution to another without validating the data may not be accurate. Needless to say, risk analysis and outcome analysis are here to stay. The goal is to improve outcome.

§ 3.02   Problems Associated with Congenital Lesions

[1]   Pneumopericardium

Emery[5] recommended aspiration by an anterior tube inserted under direct vision, until positive end-expiratory pressure (PEEP) is discontinued. Five of fourteen patients who were not treated died. Two deaths occurred from laceration of the heart of five patients who had tubes placed without direct vision. Of 33 treated by aspiration or tube, there were thirteen recurrences with five deaths. Ten recurrences resulted because of tube or aspiration failure, and three recurred when the tube was removed before PEEP was discontinued. The author recommends direct visualization for the insertion of a tube into the pericardium to relieve pneumopericardium.

[2]   Patent Ductus Arteriosus[6]

In 1958, the FDA approved indomethacin therapy for patent ductus arteriosus. Routine therapy is suggested during the first 48 hours, during which time a clear-cut diagnosis is established (characteristic murmur, respiratory distress, hyperactive precordium, cardiomegaly, increased pulmonary circulation on chest X-ray). Indomethacin is contraindicated with bleeding intracranially or gastrointestinally, thrombocytopenia, coagulation defects, necrotizing enterocolitis and significant impaired renal function. Of 460 pre-term infants under 1,750 grams, a placebo resulted in closure in 25-30/%. Treated cases resulted in closure in 75-80/% of the cases.

---

[5] Emery, et al., *Neonatal Pneumopericardium: A Surgical Emergency*, 37 ANN. THORAC. SURG. 128 (1984).

[6] Kron, et al., *A Simple Rapid Technique For Operative Closure of Patent Ductus Arteriosus in the Premature Infant*, 37 ANN. THORAC. SURG. 422 (1984); Mikhail, et al., *Surgical and Medical Experience with 734 Premature Infants with Patent Ductus Arteriosus*, 83 J. THORAC. CARDIOVASC. SURG. 349 (1982); Yeh, et al., *Intravenous Indomethacin Therapy in Premature Infants with Persistent Ductus Arteriosus: A Double-Blind Controlled Study*, 98 J. PEDIATR. 137 (1981).

Mahoney[7] recommended surgical interruption in prematures over 1,000 grams. In Wagner's reported series of 268 pre-term infants below 1,750 grams from thirteen centers,[8] there were no operative deaths; however, eight died within six hours postoperatively. Only one death was directly attributable to the operative procedure. There was a 23/% hospital morbidity (bronchopulmonary dysplasia, pneumothorax and sepsis). Mavroudis[9] expressed his preference for ligation. He had no operative deaths or deaths related to the operation, but he reported two tears and one phrenic injury. He recommended early diaphragmatic plication for phrenic paralysis. He felt a single 3-0 tie was adequate. He used a clip in seven cases; two with severe bleeding who survived; however, three with severe coagulation and two unstable cases died. He recommended against using the chest tube routinely in cases without a pneumothorax, to reduce the likelihood of lung compression or sepsis. Oxnard[10] actually recommended doing the surgical procedure in the pediatric ICU, to minimize risks of transportation to the operating room.

[3] Coarctation of the Aorta

Coarctation of the aorta is surgically corrected by either end-to-end resection as preferred by Metzdorff,[11] in infants under eight weeks of age, or by patch[12] or subclavian aortoplasty.[13] Arm growth was normal in most cases of subclavian arterioplasty. Sade[14] reported growth of the aorta after prosthetic patch angioplasty, but indicated there was a high incidence of aneurysms opposite the patch. Coarctations treated late in life are frequently

---

[7] Mahoney, et al., *Prophylactic Indomethacin Therapy for Patent Ductus Arteriosus in Very Low-Birth-Weight Infants*, 306 N. ENG. J. MED. 506 (1982).

[8] Wagner, et al., *Surgical Closure of Patent Ductus Arteriosus in 268 Preterm Infants*, 87 J. THORAC. CARDIOVASC. SURG. 870 (1984).

[9] Mavroudis, et al., *Management of Patent Ductus Arteriosus in the Premature Infant: Indomethacin Versus Ligation*, 36 ANN. THORAC. SURG. 561 (1983).

[10] Oxnard, et al., *Ligation of the Patent Ductus Arteriosus in the Newborn Intensive Care Unit*, 23 ANN. THORAC. SURG. 564 (1977).

[11] Metzdorff, et al., *Influence of Age and Operation on Late Results with Subclavian Flap Aortoplasty*, 89 J. THORAC. CARDIOVASC. SURG. 235 (1985).

[12] Bergdahl & Ljungqvist, *Long-Term Results After Repair of Coarctation of the Aorta by Patch Grafting*, 80 J. THORAC. CARDIOVASC. SURG. 177 (1980).

[13] Cobanoglu, et al., *Coarctation of the Aorta in Patients Younger than Three Months: A Critique of the Subclavian Flap Operation*, 89 J. THORAC. CARDIOVASC. SURG. 128 (1985); Moulton, et al., *Subclavian Flap Repair of Coarctation of the Aorta in Neonates*, 87 J. THORAC. CARDIOVASC. SURG. 220 (1984); Penkoske, et al., *Subclavian Arterioplasty: Repair of Coarctation of the Aorta in the First Year of Life*, 87 J. THORAC. CARDIOVASC. SURG. 894 (1984).

[14] Sade, et al., *Growth of the Aorta After Prosthetic Patch Angioplasty for Coarctation in Infants*, 38 ANN. THORAC. SURG. 21 (1984).

bypassed to avoid the surgical hazards of exposure of the friable area, particularly the aneurysmal formation.

[4] Congenital Valvular Stenoses[15]

Balloon catheter valvotomy has been used in neonates to relieve pulmonic stenosis in 39 patients, and as a palliative procedure in 27 patients, by Walls.[16] Brown[17] reported two successes with the transventricular approach using a #6mm Gruntzig balloon catheter. A 77mm-Hg gradient was reduced to 48mm-Hg when restudied a year later. The second patient had only a 15mm-Hg residual gradient, but died on the 18th postoperative day from renal failure.

Messina[18] reported successful aortic valvotomy in eleven newborns less than thirty days old, with only one operative death. There were no late deaths during 2.2 years of followup. Three patients had mild residual aortic stenosis, and the fourth had a large gradient of 70mm-Hg, which was successfully corrected the second time. The average cardiopulmonary bypass time was 21 minutes, and the cross-clamp time was 6.4 minutes. Inoue[19] reported five of six successes in mitral stenosis with a #9 Fr. balloon by way of the saphenous, leaving a 5mm transeptal hole. He felt it was contraindicated in cases with calcification or thrombus formation.

[5] Cushion Defect

Stewart[20] reported 22 patients repaired, using the single patch technique. Initially, four had severe mitral insufficiency after repair. He recommends pledget buttressed sutures in repairing the mitral area. Two patients died before the second operation and two survived reoperation. Pulmonary hypertension was relieved in nineteen of the twenty survivors.

---

[15] Coles, et al., *Surgical Management of Critical Pulmonic Stenosis in the Neonate*, 38 ANN. THORAC. SURG. 458 (1984).

[16] Walls, et al., *Assessment of Percutaneous Balloon Pulmonary and Aortic Valvuloplasty*, 88 J. THORAC. CARDIOVASC. SURG. 352 (1984).

[17] Brown, et al., *Transventricular Balloon Catheter Aortic Valvotomy in Neonates*, 39 ANN. THORAC. SURG. 376 (1985).

[18] Messina, et al., *Successful Aortic Valvotomy for Severe Congenital Valvular Aortic Stenosis in the Newborn Infant*, 88 J. THORAC. CARDIOVASC. SURG. 92 (1984).

[19] Inoue, et al., *Clinical Application of Transvenous Mitral Commissurotomy by a New Balloon Catheter*, 87 J. THORAC. CARDIOVASC. SURG. 394 (1984).

[20] Stewart, et al., *Complete Endocardial Cushion Defect: The Late Results of Repair Using the Single-Patch Technique*, 39 ANN. THORAC. SURG. 234 (1984).

[6] Palliative Procedures[21]

Cleveland[22] reported 71/% five years survival after the Fontan procedure for tricuspid atresia. He felt there was good palliation, but many patients needed additional surgery in five years. Lamberti[23] reported two late deaths, probably shunt-related, of 44 systemic-pulmonary shunts in infants and children. Karpawich[24] found that polytetrafluoroethylene modified Blalock-Tausig shunts in 19 infants. Two of the nine 4mm shunts failed after one year.

[7] Surgical Injuries

[a] Phrenic Paralysis

Hong-Xu[25] reported 19 phrenic nerve injuries complicating 891 closed cardiovascular surgical procedures for congenital heart disease. Fifteen of those 19 had major complications. He and Shoemaker[26] recommended early diaphragmatic plication. Phrenic nerve injury can occur from transection, stretch, electrocautery and cold.[27] Adults compensate with the use of accessory muscles. Opinions are divided as to whether prolonged ventilatory therapy alone or diaphragmatic plication is optimal for adults.

[b] Chylopericardium

Chylopericardium was reported by Delaney[28] after a Glenn procedure for truncus arteriosis, and after a repair for an interrupted aortic arch.

---

[21] Ilbawi, et al., *Modified Blalock-Tausig Shunt in Newborn Infants*, 88 J. THORAC. CARDIOVASC. SURG. 770 (1984); Kutsche, et al., *Hemolytic Anemia Secondary to Erosion of a Silastic Band into the Lumen of the Pulmonary Trunk*, 55 AM. J. CARDIOL. 1438 (1985); Sanchez, et al., *The Surgical Treatment of Tetrology of Fallot*, 37 ANN. THORAC. SURG. 431 (1984); Zhao, et al., *Surgical Repair of Tetrology of Fallot*, 89 J. THORAC. CARDIOVASC. SURG. 204 (1985).

[22] Cleveland, et al., *Surgical Treatment of Tricuspid Atresia*, 38 ANN. THORAC. SURG. 447 (1984).

[23] Lamberti, et al., *Systemic-Pulmonary Shunts in Infants and Children*, 88 J. THORAC. CARDIOVASC. SURG. 76 (1984).

[24] Karpawich, et al., *Modified Blalock-Tausig Shunt in Infants and Young Children*, 89 J. THORAC. CARDIOVASC. SURG. 275 (1985).

[25] Hong-Xu, et al., *Phrenic Nerve Injury Complicating Closed Cardiovascular Surgical Procedures for Congenital Heart Disease*, 39 ANN. THORAC. SURG. 445 (1985).

[26] Shoemaker, et al., *Aggressive Treatment of Acquired Phrenic Nerve Paralysis in Infants and Small Children*, 32 ANN. THORAC. SURG. 251 (1981).

[27] Benjamin, et al., *Left Lower Lobe Atelectasis and Consolidation Following Cardiac Surgery: The Affect of Topical Cooling on the Phrenic Nerve*, 142 RADIOLOGY 11 (1982).

[28] Delaney, et al., *Chylopericardium with Cardiac Tamponade after Cardiovascular Surgery in Two Patients*, 69 CHEST 381 (1976).

Jacob[29] recommends avoiding ligation of the thoracic duct, if possible, and stresses medical treatment.

[8] Valves

Although Antunes[30] reported on the mitral porcine bioprosthesis in a young population group, most surgeons prefer mechanical prostheses. Kersten [31] reported on a six-month-old child receiving a #19 St. Jude's valve in both the aortic and mitral position. A mitral clot developed, but was dissolved with Urokinase and heparin. The patient did well. Iyer[32] wrote of his experience with the Bjork-Shiley prosthesis in patients under twenty years of age. He had no thromboses with an overall operative mortality of 10.3/%, and a late mortality of 4.4/% (up to eight years). Schaff[33] reported his experience with the Starr-Edwards valve in children, indicating a low rate of thromboembolism. Biological valves required reoperation in five years in 41/% of his cases. Cotrufo[34] prefers the Starr-Edwards valve in the mitral position in young patients with an adequate outflow tract. He stressed the importance of anticoagulation. Pass[35] reported on 34 children, followed one to fifty months without anticoagulation, and found no thromboembolic complications. He indicated that this approach was still investigational, however.

§ 3.03 Problems Associated with Trauma

[1] Mediastinum

Woodring[36] indicated a mediastinal width over 0.25 of the thoracic ratio should raise suspicion of major vascular injury.

---

[29] Jacob, et. al., *Chylopericardium as a Complication of Aortopulmonary Shunt*, 108 ARCH. SURG. 870 (1971).

[30] Antunes & Santos, *Performance of Glutaraldehyde-Preserved Porcine Bioprosthesis as a Mitral Valve Substitute in a Young Population Group*, 37 ANN. THORAC. SURG. 387 (1984).

[31] Jones, et al., *Combined Carotid and Coronary Operations: When Are They Necessary?*, 87 J. THORAC. CARDIOVASC. SURG. 7 (1984).

[32] Iyer, et al., *Valve Replacement in Children Under Twenty Years of Age: Experience with Bjork-Shiley Prosthesis*, 88 J. THORAC. CARDIOVASC. SURG. 217 (1984).

[33] Schaff, et al., *Late Results after Starr-Edwards Valve Replacement in Children*, 88 J. THORAC. CARDIOVASC. SURG. 583 (1984).

[34] Cotrufo, et al., *Intermediate Term Evaluation of Starr-Edwards Ball Valves in the Mitral Position*, 12 TEXAS HEART INST. J. 43 (1985).

[35] Pass, et al., *Cardiac Valve Prostheses in Children Without Anticoagulation*, 87 J. THORAC. CARDIOVASC. SURG. 832 (1984).

[36] Woodring & Dillon, *Radiographic Manifestations of Mediastinal Hemorrhage From Blunt Chest Trauma*, 39 ANN. THORAC. SURG. 171 (1985).

[2] Heart

Cuadros[37] reported laceration of a mitral papillary muscle and aortic root from blunt chest trauma, and stated that cardiac trauma occurs in 10-20/% of fatal motor accidents. Unusual injuries associated with CPR have included traumatic ventricular septal defect,[38] as well as an aneurysm of the left atrium.[39]

[3] Aorta

Acute traumatic disruption of the thoracic aorta is frequently associated with major head and abdominal bleeding. Pate[40] reported the twenty year experience of the University of Tennessee, where they had 59 patients operated within the first week. Forty-seven required cardiopulmonary bypass. Seven patients had simple aortic cross-clamping. One patient died of his head injuries after heparinization and cardiopulmonary bypass. Four patients were paralyzed: three of them following only cross-clamping the aorta and cutting and sewing. One had femoral-to-femoral support, and ended up with flaccid paralysis. All but two had other associated injuries. Two patients were hemiparetic on admission and one died without regaining consciousness. Fourteen had variable levels of consciousness, of which only two had later proven head injury.

Because of associated injuries and continued bleeding with heparinization, efforts to avoid cardiopulmonary bypass or pump support led Wakabayashi and Connelly[41] to develop a heparinless left heart bypass pump. Olivier[42] reported the use of the BioMedicus centrifugal pump for this problem. Of nine patients using the pump, only one died, and none were paralyzed. Gott shunts are used to bypass blood from the proximal to the distal portion of the body while repairing these tears. Paralysis is the major concern, other than survival. Rarely does one have time to establish

---

[37] Cuadros, et al., *Laceration of a Mitral Papillary Muscle and the Aortic Root as a Result of Blunt Trauma to the Chest*, 88 J. THORAC. CARDIOVASC. SURG. 134 (1984).

[38] Engleman, et al., *Traumatic Ventricular Septal Defect Following Closed-Chest Massage: A New Approach to Closure*, 38 ANN. THORAC. SURG. 529 (1984).

[39] Romfh & Paplanus, *Dissecting Aneurysm of the Left Atrium Following External Cardiac Massage*, 241 JAMA 1151 (1979).

[40] Pate, *Traumatic Rupture of the Aorta: Emergency Operation*, 39 ANN. THORAC. SURG. 531 (1985).

[41] Wakabayashi & Connelly, *Heparinless Left Heart Bypass for Resection of Thoracic Aortic Aneurysm*, 130 AM. J. SURG. 212 (1975).

[42] Olivier, et al., *Use of BioMedicus Centrifugal Pump in Traumatic Tears of the Thoracic Aorta*, 38 ANN. THORAC. SURG. 586 (1984).

somatosensory reflex monitoring[43] to assist in attempting to avoid spinal ischemia and paralysis.[44]

[a] Aortic Aneurysms[45]

Residual weakness from aortic tears and arteriosclerosis, with or without dissection, is probably the most common cause of thoracic aneurysms. Bullaboy[46] found a false aneurysm secondary to an esophageal foreign body. An open safety pin had been removed fourteen months previously.

Pressler and McNamara[47] reported a 47/% rupture of 135 thoracic aneurysms. Their 1985 report contained 260 cases of which 126 were operated. Sixty-seven emergency procedures carried a 33/% mortality, while 59 elective cases carried an 8/% mortality. Over the last five years of the study, mortality was reduced to 16/% and 5/% respectively. The five-year survival without surgery was 21/%. The five-year survival after elective surgery was 50/%. DeBakey, in his 1978 report[48] of 500 patients, did not believe that bypass or shunt was necessary, and felt paralysis was determined by anatomy of the spinal artery.[49]

Laschinger[50] believed that maintaining the distal aortic pressure between 60 and 70 systolic was safe in the absence of critical intercostal artery occlusions. The seven of nine patients who had a pressure above 60 and adequate somatosensory evoked potentials had no paralysis. Of two patients with pressures 40 or below, paralysis occurred in a patient who had 85 minutes of cross-clamp time.

---

[43] Coles, et al., *Intraoperative Detection of Spinal Cord Ischemia Using Somatosensory Cortical-Evoked Potentials During Thoracic Aortic Occlusion*, 34 ANN. THORAC. SURG. 299 (1982).

[44] Laschinger, et al., *Prevention of Ischemic Spinal Cord Injury Following Aortic Cross-Clamping: Use of Cortio steroids*, 38 ANN. THORAC. SURG. 500 (1984).

[45] Hirose, et al., *Use of the Balloon Catheter for Distal Occlusion of the Aorta in Prosthetic Replacement of Aortic Arch Aneurysms*, 39 ANN. THORAC. SURG. 538 (1985).

[46] Bullaboy, et al., *False Aneurysm of the Aorta Secondary to an Esophageal Foreign Body*, 39 ANN. THORAC. SURG. 275 (1985).

[47] Pressler & McNamara, *Aneurysm of the Thoracic Aorta*, 89 J. THORAC. CARDIOVASC. SURG. 50 (1985).

[48] DeBakey, et al., *Surgical Treatment of Aneurysms of the Descending Thoracic Aorta: Long-Term Results in 500 Patients*, 19 J. THORAC. CARDIOVASC. SURG. 571 (1978).

[49] Wadough, et al., *Arteria Radicularis Magna Anterior as a Decisive Factor Influencing Spinal Cord Damage During Aortic Occlusion*, 88 J. THORAC. CARDIOVASC. SURG. 1 (1984).

[50] Laschinger, et al., *Experimental and Clinical Assessment of the Adequacy of Partial Bypass in Maintenance of Spinal Cord Blood Flow During Operations on the Thoracic Aorta*, 36 ANN. THORAC. SURG. 417 (1983).

Crawford[51] and Najafi[52] replaced the descending thoracic aorta without bypass or shunting.

Comment. Although all aortic aneurysms are not traumatic, they will be discussed here.

Ottino[53] reported on 26 patients with ascending aortic aneurysms treated by composite conduit replacement. Fourteen were the result of acute dissection, and twelve were chronic. Causes included Marfan's, annuloaorticectasia, arteriosclerosis, luetic aortitis, and acute or chronic dissection. Ottino stated: "Their surgical treatment is a technical challenge, and their optimal management is controversial." In one case in which he wrapped the aneurysm sac around the graft, hematoma external to the graft caused decrease in cardiac output, with cardiac arrest.

Merrill[54] reported on two patients with low porosity teflon graft and silk sutures who developed false aneurysms at 13 and 23 years postoperatively. He felt the causes of this type of complication included wound infection, suture line stress, degenerative native vessels and the method of constructing the anastomosis. Bergsland[55] found mycotic aortic aneurysms in children to be a complication of infected umbilical artery catheters. He recommended aggressive medical and surgical treatment.

[b] Aorta — Aortic trauma

Traumatic aortic disruption occurring from a deceleration injury as a motor vehicle accident or fall occurs most often just distal to the left subclavian artery and is probably one of the most common traumatic injuries seen by the cardiac surgeon. Technical considerations are almost the same as surgery on the descending aorta. The primary concern as mentioned is paraplegia. In addition, we have an emergency situation often in the patient with other injuries. The aortic injury is approached as an emergency. The patient is taken for immediate replacement. On occasion, there may be other more life threatening injuries that need to be taken care of first, of course this

---

[51] Crawford, et al., *Graft Replacement of Aneurysm in Descending Thoracic Aorta: Results Without Bypass or Shunting*, 89 SURGERY 73 (1981).

[52] Najafi, et al., *Descending Aortic Aneurysmectomy Without Adjuncts to Avoid Ischemia*, 30 ANN. THORAC. SURG. 326 (1980).

[53] Ottino, et al., *Ascending Aortic Aneurysms: Composite Conduit Replacement*, 11 TEXAS HEART INST. J. 338 (1984).

[54] Merrill, et al., *Late False Aneurysm Following Replacement of Ascending Aorta: The Problem of the Teflon Graft in Combination with a Silk Suture Anastomosis*, 39 ANN. THORAC. SURG. 271 (1985).

[55] Bergsland, et al., *Mycotic Aortic Aneurysms in Children*, 37 ANN. THORAC. SURG. 314 (1984).

can be done. Left atrial femoral bypass is used to try to decrease the incidence of paraplegia. On occasion the aorta can be anastomosed directly end to end which would decrease cross clamp time when the vast majority of cases sees an interposition graft is necessary.

[c]   Aorta — Aortic dissection

Aortic dissection is a specific diagnosis. As mentioned above, it arises from a tear in the media of the aortic wall and usually occurs in the setting of hypertension. The patient usually presents with severe chest or back pain, worse than he has ever experienced. It may also be confused with myocardial infarction. The aortic dissection is classified according to the part of the aorta that is involved. If the dissection begins in the ascending aorta just above the aortic valve as it does commonly and proceeds through the aortic arch and into the descending aorta it is called a Type I aortic dissection, according to DeBakey classification. If it stops before the inominant involves only the ascending aorta it is called a Type II and if it involves only the descending aorta beginning beyond the subclavian and going distally it is called a Type III aortic dissection. Aortic dissection of other portions of the aorta have been identified but are rare, for example in the abdominal aorta.

Aortic dissections may also be classified according to the Stanford criteria Type A or Type B. Type A involves the ascending aorta and Type B involves the descending aorta. If both are involved it is still a Type A aortic dissection. The importance of ascending aortic involvement rests in the fact that this constitutes a surgical emergency and involvement of the ascending aorta with dissection can often lead to death from rupture into the pericardial cavity and cardiac tamponade. Aortic dissection involving the descending aorta is less lethal. Surgical intervention is usually done only for complications such as persistent unremitting pain, evidence of leak or critical organ malperfusion. Along with chest pain, aortic dissection can present with other symptoms. It can be the great masquerader since as the aortic wall tears, it may interrupt any of the branches along the course of the dissection beginning with the coronaries all the way down to the lower extremities. Such patients may present with a cold ischemic leg, which diverts ones attention, feeling that it is just a local problem where in fact this came from a tear in the ascending aorta. It can present as a myocardial infarction or stroke. So one must maintain a high index of suspicion. A wide mediastinum may be seen on initial chest x-ray. A diagnosis will require additional studies. CT scans are excellent for the diagnosis of dissection, as are MRAs and transesophageal echocardiography. Once the diagnosis of dissection is made involving the ascending aorta, emergency surgery is usually recommended.

[4] Endovascular Stent Grafting

Endovascular stent grafting is a recent technology that can be applied to disease of the aorta. A fabric supported as a metal stent is placed with in the lumen of the aorta supporting as covering for the weakened area. It is usually introduced from a more peripheral site as the femoral or iliac artery with introducer system. Initially used for the abdominal aorta, it has become a mainstay of therapy for treatment of aneurysmal disease there. [56] Now in thoracic aortic disease this technology is being used more frequently.

Currently, one stent graft device is FDA approved for descending thoracic aneurysms, although new devices are expected soon. They are also used "off label" or under a physician IDE (Investigational Degive Exemption) for other problems, such as traumatic disruption, aortic dissection, false aneurysm and penetrating ulcers, to name a few. Although morbidity associated with endovascular technique may be lower initially when compared to open procedures, the long-term results of this therapy are uncertain.

Indications now for stenting are based on predicted operative risk that is lower than the risk of conventional surgery or medical treatment. Other considerations are age, comorbidities, symptomatology, aortic size, other anatomic features, and experience of the operator.[57]

Associated complications of endovascular therapy include stroke, paraplegia, dissection, graft collapse, strut fracture, kinking and migration. They also require continued surveillance for the lifetime of the graft. This is usually done with CT scanning. Checking for graft integrity, position and endoleaks is needed. Radiation induced cancer, especially in younger patients requiring multiple studies is a concern.[58]

§ 3.04 Cardiac Tumors

[1] Cardiac Tumors — Generally

Cardiac tumors are not a common part of adult cardiac surgery, but the average cardiac surgeon may see several cases during the course of a year, but it would not be unusual to see none. Cardiac tumors may be benign or malignant, but the most common cardiac tumor encountered is the myxoma, which is a benign tumor. They may present with constitutional symptoms

---

[56] Schermerhorn, et. al., *Endovascular vs. Open Repair of Abdominal Aortic Aneurysms in the Medical Population.* 358 New Engl J Med 464 (2008).

[57] Sverrson, et al., *Expert Consensus Document on the Treatment of Descending Thoracic Aortic Disease using Endovascular Stent-Grafts*, 85 Ann Thorac Surg 31-41 (2008).

[58] Brenner, et al., *Computed Tomography — An Increasing Source of Radiation Exposure*, 357 New Engl J Med 2277 (2008).

secondary to obstruction from the tumor with decreased flow. They may present with an embolic event where a portion of the tumor has embolized to a peripheral part of the body and with the frequent use of echocardiography now it may even be found incidentally. Surgery really is the only treatment and, once found, the surgery should be done expeditiously. Tumors can lead to death or significant disability.

[2] Intracardiac Fungal Mass

Foker[59] reported on the surgical management of intracardiac fungal masses in premature infants with the use of inflow occlusion. Prolonged antifungal treatment had not helped.

[3] Myxoma[60]

In 1985, Hanson[61] reported surgical experience with mitral myxomas at the Cleveland Clinic. There were 33 cases, of which 31 involved the septum and two involved the annulus. Twenty-nine were pedunculated. Seventeen were shaved from the septum. One each presented with angina, peripheral embolus, hemoptysis and pleural effusion. One patient died on the 8th postoperative day with a coronary embolus. Follow-up with echocardiography was recommended.

[4] Other Tumors[62]

Reece[63] reported on the experience of the Texas Heart Institute, where there were twenty tumors other than myxoma between 1961 and 1983. There were two operative deaths and two late deaths. All pediatric cases were benign, including five fibromas and five Rhabdomyomas. Three cases involved incomplete excisions with survival up to 18 years. Ten adults had five benign lesions that were completely excised. Four patients with unresectable malignancies died from metastases in eight months. Corno[64] reported on two neonates with Rhabdomyoma who survived surgical

---

[59] Foker, et al., *Management of Intracardiac Fungal Masses in Premature Infants*, 87 J. THORAC. CARDIOVASC. SURG. 244 (1984).

[60] Semb, *Surgical Considerations in the Treatment of Cardiac Myxoma*, 87 J. THORAC. CARDIOVASC. SURG. 251 (1984).

[61] Hanson, et al., *The Surgical Treatment of Atrial Myxomas*, 89 J. THORAC. CARDIOVASC. SURG. 298 (1985).

[62] *Poole, et al., Surgical Implications in Malignant Cardiac Disease*, 36 ANN. THORAC. SURG. 484 (1983).

[63] Reece, et al., *Cardiac Tumors*, 88 J. THORAC. CARDIOVASC. SURG. 439 (1984).

[64] Corno, et al., *Cardiac Rhabdomyoma: Surgical Treatment in the Neonate*, 87 J. THORAC. CARDIOVASC. SURG. 725 (1984).

excision. Without surgery, the mortality rate is 50/% in the first month, and 80/% in the first year. In one of his cases, a 0.5 X 0.5 X 0.5 mass had to be left under the left anterior descending coronary artery.

§ 3.05 Problems Associated with Heart Surgery[65]

[1] Pregnancy

In 68 cases of intracardiac surgery in pregnant women, Becker[66] reported one death and 80/% viable fetuses. He recommended avoiding systemic hypothermia and anticoagulants. Larrea[67] reported on 38 pregnant females, including three patients with acute valve thrombosis. One died postoperatively. Major problems occurred with oral anticoagulation.

[2] Jehovah's Witnesses

The Jehovah Witness presents a unique problem to the cardiac surgeon. The refusal on religious grounds to accept any blood or blood products increases the risk of cardiac surgery. Although it is not unusual to perform cardiac surgery, both valve replacement and coronary bypass without needing blood, it does handcuff the surgeon in some respects. Should that unusual situation occur when there is significant unexpected blood loss and a transfusion is life saving. It is important to evaluate these patients pre-operatively should they be anemic and the surgery can be delayed, it is often best to send the patient home and stimulate the bone marrow pharmacologically. As with the drug Epogen, and increase their red cell mass to make the risk of surgery less. They should be taken off anti-platelet drugs like aspirin and Plavix and they should be off for at least 5-7 days to allow the effect of these drugs to wear off.

Most Jehovah witness patients will allow the use of a cell saver, which is a scavenger system for retrieving the shed blood and returning it immediately to the patient or heart/lung machine avoiding storage of the blood. Once the surgeon has chosen to accept the Jehovah witness patient for surgery, I think it is advisable to sit down with the patient and the family to go over all the risks. It is especially important in these patients and families in which all of the members of the family may not subscribe to the same religious beliefs. There can be that unforeseen situation in which the patient would ordinarily be

---

[65] Pennington, et al., *Coronary Artery Stenosis Following Aortic Valve Replacement and Intermittent Coronary Cardioplegia,* 33 ANN. THORAC. SURG. 576 (1982).

[66] Becker, *Intracardiac Surgery in Pregnant Women,* 36 ANN. THORAC. SURG. 453 (1983).

[67] Larrea, et al., *Pregnancy and Mechanical Valve Prosthesis: A High Risk Situation for the Mother and the Fetus,* 36 ANN. THORAC. SURG. 459 (1983).

given blood in a peri-op or post-op situation where he is not awake to make a decision and a family member who is not Jehovah witness finds it quite difficult to perhaps have someone die from lack of blood and then perhaps they are the guardian and they may decide that blood be given to the patient. Carmichael[68] reported cardiac surgery in children of Jehovah's Witnesses. Of 73 patients, nine died. In only three, death was due to blood loss.

[3] Antibiotics

Antibiotics should be used with caution.[69] Depression of cardiac function by streptomycin, kanamycin, tetracycline, erythromycin and colistin sulfate has been reported.[70] Also, Dajee[71] has pointed out that rapid intravenous infusion of vancomycin can cause hypotension. However, Newfield gave one gram of the drug in diluted form over a 30-60 minute period with no drop in blood pressure.[72]

[4] Anesthesia

In 1985, Keenan and Boyan[73] studied 422 cardiac arrests with 27 deaths over a fifteen-year period involving 163,240 anesthetics. Risks in emergencies were sixfold, and in pediatric, threefold that of the adult. Failure to ventilate accounted for half of the deaths. One-third of the deaths were secondary to overdose. Hemodynamic instability was associated in 22/% of the cases. Identifiable errors that could be managed were found in 75/% of the cases. Progressive bradycardia occurred in all but one patient. Of the eleven deaths secondary to decreased ventilation, four had esophageal intubation and one had an endotracheal tube dislodged.

Comment. The overdose and hypoventilation from dislodgement and esophageal placement should not require detailed medical testimony; however, the records probably will not be clear-cut.

---

[68] Carmichael, et al., *Cardiac Surgery in Children of Jehovah's Witnesses,* 12 TEXAS HEART INST. J. 57 (1985).

[69] Austin, et al., *Vancomycin Blood Levels During Cardiac Bypass Surgery,* 24 CAN. J. SURG. 423 (1981).

[70] Cohen, et al., *Depression of Cardiac Function by Streptomycin and Other Antimicrobial Agents,* 26 AM. J. CARDIOL. 505 (1970).

[71] Dajee, et al., *Profound Hypotension from Rapid Vancomycin Administration During Cardiac Operation,* 87 J. THORAC. CARDIOVASC. SURG. 145 (1984).

[72] Newfield & Roizen, *Hazards of Rapid Administration of Vancomycin,* 91 ANN. INTERN. MED. 581 (1979).

[73] Keenan & Boyan, *Cardiac Arrest Due to Anesthesia,* 253 JAMA 2373 (1985).

[5] Median Sternotomy

[a] Surgical Experience

In reporting sternal wound complications, Breyer[74] indicated that 0.8/% of 870 patients had major complications related to operating room time and inexperience of the resident (in comparison to the attending physician). Other factors included prolonged ventilation, reoperation and CPR. He preferred wire over dacron for sternal closure. Higher risk was found associated with prolonged ventilation in females. Age and weight were statistically less significant.

[b] Ruptured Brachiocephalic Vein

Boer[75] believes rupture of the bracheocephalic vein is usually due to overstretching of the divided sternum.

[c] Rib Fractures

Woodring[76] has called attention to fractures of the upper ribs following median sternotomy, and has recommended keeping the upper retractor blade below the 4th innerspace.

[d] Pericardial Closure

Because of the possibility of re-exploration, closure of the pericardium is recommended. Pericardial substitutes can reduce adhesions.[77]

Johnston[78] indicates a preference for Mersilene ribbon over wire sutures for closing the sternum.

[e] Infection

Grmoljez[79] found a higher infection rate with internal mammary artery graft procedures over those in which the saphenous vein was used.

---

[74] Breyer, et al., *A Prospective Study of Sternal Wound Complications*, 37 ANN. THORAC. SURG. 412 (1984).

[75] Boer, et al., *Interposition of a Composite Venous Autograft for the Treatment of Ruptured Left Bracheocephalic Vein*, 36 ANN. THORAC. SURG. 607 (1983).

[76] Woodring, et al., *Upper Rib Fractures Following Median Sternotomy*, 39 ANN. THORAC. SURG. 355 (1985).

[77] Revuleta, et al., *Implantation of Pericardial Substitutes*, 39 ANN. THORAC. SURG. 190 (1985).

[78] Johnston, et al., *Mersilene Ribbon Closure of the Median Sternotomy: An Improvement over Wire Closure*, 39 ANN. THORAC. SURG. 88 (1985).

[79] Grmoljez, et al., *Major Complications of Median Sternotomy*, 130 AM. J. SURG. 679 (1975).

Culliford[80] indicated an 8/% infection rate when both internal mammary arteries were used as grafts. And Sarr[81] found the incidence of mediastinal infection after cardiac surgery, as reported in the literature, to be from 0.4-5.0/%.

[f] Iodine Toxicity

Glick[82] has cautioned about iodine toxicity in irrigation of these wounds. He reported on a 34-month-old patient who developed unexplained metabolic acidosis followed by mental confusion and death. The blood levels of iodine were extremely elevated.

[g] Muscle and Omentum Flaps

Pairolero[83] studied the management of the recalcitrant median sternotomy wounds over a seven-year period. Thirty-eight patients controlled by muscle flaps required 67 operations. One omentum flap was used. Both muscle flaps and omentum were used in four cases. There were no early deaths, and all patients healed. Nine patients had significant early complications. None of five late deaths were related to sepsis or reconstruction. Four of these five patients required debridement. One refused surgery. Thirty-three of the 38 patients were alive after the seven years. Thirty-two of the 33 had excellent results.

[h] Reoperation

Reoperation is fraught with danger, particularly hemorrhage. Akl[84] reported on the use of a Sagittal oscillating saw for repeat sternotomy. In 1985, Oropeza[85] surveyed 131 cardiac surgeons who reported 144 hemorrhages in median sternotomies. An alternate approach to repeating a median sternotomy is right anterior-lateral thoracotomy with femoral arterial cannulation for cardiopulmonary bypass. Exposure through the 4th interspace gives excellent operating position for the mitral and tricuspid valve.

---

[80] Culliford, et al., *Sternal and Costochrondal Infections Following Open-Heart Surgery: A Review of 2,594 Cases*, 72 J. THORAC. CARDIOVASC. SURG. 714 (1976).

[81] Sarr, et al., *Mediastinal Infection after Cardiac Surgery*, 38 ANN. THORAC. SURG. 415 (1984).

[82] Glick, et al., *Iodine Toxicity in a Patient Treated by Continuous Povidone-Iodine Mediastinal Irrigation*, 39 ANN. THORAC. SURG. 478 (1985).

[83] Pairolero, et al., *Management of Recalcitrant Median Sternotomy Wounds*, 88 J. THORAC. CARDIOVASC. SURG. 357 (1984).

[84] Akl, et al., *Use of a Sagittal Oscillating Saw for Repeat Sternotomy: A Safer and Simpler Technique*, 38 ANN. THORAC. SURG. 646 (1984).

[85] Oropeza, *Hemorrhage During Redo Sternotomy*, 39 ANN. THORAC. SURG. 196 (1985).

[6] Surgical Care[86]

[a] Intensive Care

Kron[87] surveyed 576 Thoracic Society members, and reported that the cardiac surgeon retained overall responsibility in the ICU in 95/% of the cases. Intensivists were doing more, especially with the respirator, in teaching institutions. Intensivists were directors of the ICU in about 24/% of the surveyed reports.

An American College of Surgeons bulletin in 1985 indicated that 53/% of the directors of the thoracic surgical training programs felt that ICU training was necessary.[88] At that time only five of the 64 fellowships in clinical care were directed by surgeons. The report cited a concern about "abandonment" where the cardiac surgeon does not retain control. Salm and Blair[89] reviewed efforts to reduce postoperative days in the ICU following coronary artery bypass. Among 37 random cases, one or two days less ICU stay yielded no noticeable change in results.

Comment. I believe the study is too small to be of any statistical significance.

[b] Cricothyroidotomy

O'Connor[90] recommends cricothyroidotomy in patients requiring prolonged ventilation support who have had median sternotomy for cardiac surgery. Although the stoma was contaminated, there were no sternotomy problems. Two of the patients later required resection for tracheal stricture. One required bronchoscopy for stomal granulations.

---

[86] Kopman, *Pressure Monitoring During Cardiopulmonary Bypass*, 87 J. THORAC. CARDIOVASC. SURG. 319 (1984).

[87] Kron, et al., *Who Manages the Postoperative Cardiac Patient?*, 87 J. THORAC. CARDIOVASC. SURG. 629 (1984).

[88] American College of Surgeons, *Pre- and Postoperative Care Committee: The Surgeon and Intensive Care*, 5 AM. COLL. SURG. BUL. 25 (1985).

[89] Salm & Blair, *Effect of Reduction of Postoperative Days in the ICU after Coronary Artery Bypass*, 88 J. THORAC. CARDIOVASC. SURG. 558 (1984).

[90] O'Connor, et al., *Cricothyroidotomy for Prolonged Ventilatory Support after Cardiac Operations*, 39 ANN. THORAC. SURG. 353 (1985).

[c] Catheters[91]

The longer intravascular catheters are in place, the higher the incidence of infection.[92]

Rowley[93] reported on 55 autopsies in which nineteen had positive blood cultures at some point. Eleven of the nineteen occurred while the catheter was in place. Four of these eleven developed infective endocarditis.

Thrombosis,[94] perforation[95] and intracardiac knot[96] have been reported. Concern with monitoring during surgery has led Stone[97] to advise pulling the Swan-Ganz catheter back until the first R-Wave is detected, and then just advancing into the pulmonary artery before putting the patient on cardiopulmonary bypass. This technique is recommended to reduce the incidence of pulmonary hemorrhage.

Tremper[98] recommends transcutaneous monitoring of oxygen tension to reduce the need for another catheter. The sensor usually correlates at about 80/% of the arterial PO_2 level.

[7] Complications

[a] Tamponade

Cardiac tamponade is compression of the heart from blood or fluid in the pericardium. It usually results in decrease in the cardiac output and can lead to cardiac arrest in the acute situation, if not immediately recognized.

---

[91] Foote, et al., *Pulmonary Complications of the Flow Directed Balloon-Tipped Catheter*, 290 N. ENG. J. MED. 927 (1974); Henzel & DeWeese, *Morbid and Mortal Complications Associated with Prolonged Central Venous Cannulation*, 121 AM. J. SURG. 600 (1971); Katz, et al., *Pulmonary Artery Flow Guided Catheters in the Perioperative Period: Indications and Complications*, 237 JAMA 2832 (1977).

[92] Ducatman, et al., *Catheter-Induced Lesions of the Right Side of the Heart*, 253 JAMA 791 (1985); Lange, et al., *Local Complications Associated with Indwelling Swan-Ganz Catheters: Autopsy Study of 36 Cases*, 52 AM. J. CARDIOL. 1108 (1983).

[93] Rowley, et al., *Right-Sided Infective Endocarditis as a Consequence of Flow-Directed Pulmonary Artery Catherization: A Clinical Pathological Study of 55 Autopsy Patients*, 311 N. ENG. J. MED. 1152 (1984).

[94] Bradway, et al., *Thrombosis after Pulmonary-Artery Catherization Via the Internal Jugular Vein*, 306 N. ENG. J. MED. 1486 (1982); Becker, et al., *Bland Thrombosis and Infection in Relation to Intracardiac Catheters*, 46 CIRCULATION 200 (1972).

[95] Chun & Ellestad, *Perforation of the Pulmonary Artery with a Swan-Ganz Catheter*, 284 N. ENG. J. MED. 1041 (1971).

[96] Lipp, et al., *Intracardiac Knotting of a Flow-Directed Balloon Catheter*, 284 N. ENG. J. MED. 220 (1971).

[97] Stone & Khambatta, *Pressure Monitoring During Cardiopulmonary Bypass*, 87 J. THORAC. CARDIOVASC. SURG. 319 (1984).

[98] Tremper, et al., *Transcutaneous Monitoring of Oxygen Tension During One-Lung Anesthesia*, 88 J. THORAC. CARDIOVASC. SURG. 22 (1984).

Cardiac tamponade can also occur over a longer period of time as fluid accumulates slowly in the pericardium from various causes. It is likely to occur post-operatively from bleeding in the pericardial cavity. One should have a high index of suspicion when one is faced with a hypertensive patient with poor distal perfusion, high right-sided pressures cardiac tamponade should be considered. Delayed tamponade may be more insidious, echocardiography may be relied upon for a diagnosis, and again drainage in a symptomatic patient is necessary.

Although Alcan[99] suggested that the subxiphoid surgical approach is the safest for diagnosis and treatment, Callahan,[100] in a report on pericardiocentesis directed by 2D echocardiography, found in a series of 132 patients that prolonged drainage was accomplished in 29 patients for up to thirteen days without complications. A teflon sheath was passed over a wire with a 6 or 8 Fr. introducer.

The subxiphoid approach has been used since 1911. The polyethelene catheter was being suggested in 1955. Monitoring the aspirating and exploring needle with the EKG was suggested in 1956. Reported complications have occurred with the lung, pleura, liver, stomach and heart.

Stark and deLeval[101] reported on experience with fibrin seal[102] to reduce surgical bleeding in congenital heart defects. Of 38 children, there were excellent results in 31, good results in six and satisfactory results in one. It is best used on a collagen substrate, and it is useful where bleeding is hard to control. Blood pressure should be brought down with nitropresside. Fibrin seal is used to preseal dacron conduits, and to control bleeding from multiple suture lines, or bleeding near a major coronary artery. It also was used on Gore-Tex in high pressure areas and on raw areas.

[b] Chylopericardium

In 1981, Pollard[103] recommended dietary treatment with medium chain triglycerides and free fatty acids for isolated chylopericardium following cardiac operations. In his series, ligation was necessary for four failures. One

---

[99] Alcan, et al., *Management of Acute Cardiac Tamponade by Subxiphoid Pericardotomy*, 247 JAMA 1143 (1982).

[100] Callahan, et al., *Cardiac Tamponade: Periocardiocentesis Directed by Two-Dimensional Echocardiography*, 60 MAYO CLIN. PROC. 344 (1985).

[101] Stark & deLeval, *Experience with Fibrin Seal (Tissel) in Operations for Congenital Heart Defects*, 38 ANN. THORAC. SURG. 411 (1984).

[102] Rousou, *Fibrin Glue: An Effective Hemostatic Agent for Nonsuturable Intraoperative Bleeding*, 38 ANN. THORAC. SURG. 409 (1984).

[103] Pollard, et al., *Isolated Chylopericardium after Cardiac Operations*, 81 J. THORAC. CARDIOVASC. SURG. 943 (1981).

failure each occurred following surgery for pulmonic stenosis, ventricular septal defect, vein grafting and myotomy, and myomectomy for idiopathic subaortic stenosis. One patient developed tamponade. Three patients still had tubes in and were being treated medically. Only one was ligated at the time of the report.

[c] Nerve Injuries

Ulnar nerve injury is minimized, according to Wey and Guinn,[104] by the use of elbow pads, and by having the arms above the head rather than at the side. VanderSalm and Welch[105] discussed brachial plexus injury after open heart surgery. Internal jugular probing with the older introducer may well have injured the brachial plexus in their series. Phrenic nerve injury can occur from direct interruption, but also from topical cooling.[106] Markand[107] has pointed out an increase in respiratory problems postoperatively following phrenic nerve injury.

[8] Phrenic Nerve Paralysis

Phrenic nerve paralysis can occur as a complication of cardiac surgery. This is reflected in elevation in paralysis of the diaphragm. In some with impaired pulmonary function it may cause some difficulty in respiration. The frenic nerve runs from the thoracic inlet down through the mediastinum along the outside of the pericardium. In this location, the frenic nerve can be injured if a sufficient amount of ice used to cool the heart is placed in the pericardial cavity, since it can lie directly up against the frenic nerve can cause cold injury. Most of the time this can be reduced by insertion of an insulation pad in the pericardium. Frenic nerve can also be injured during the take down of the internal mammary artery. It is in close proximity to the internal mammary artery on the left as it comes into the thoracic inlet. This is quite unusual but can occur as the electrocautery is used to take down the internal mammary artery in the usual manner. Frenic nerve paralysis may be temporary or permanent. In a temporary situation it may take as long as six months to resolve. With less use of pericardial ice solution the incidence of this seems to be decreasing.

---

[104] Wey & Guinn, *Ulnar Nerve Injury with Open-Heart Surgery*, 39 ANN. THORAC. SURG. 358 (1985).

[105] VanderSalm & Welch, *Brachial Plexus Injury after Open Heart Surgery*, 38 ANN. THORAC. SURG. 660 (1985).

[106] Benjamin, *supra* note 24.

[107] Markand, et al., *Postoperative Phrenic Nerve Palsy in Patients with Open Heart Surgery*, 39 ANN. THORAC. SURG. 68 (1985).

§ 3.06 Problems Associated with Cardiopulmonary Bypass[108]

[1] Cardiopulmonary Bypass

[a] Basic Circuit and the Perfusionist

The development of cardiopulmonary bypass (CPB) is really what allowed modern cardiac surgery to be performed. The blood could be diverted from the heart and lungs allowing visualization of the heart and its internal structures while cardiopulmonary bypass maintained delivery of oxygenated blood to the rest of the body. The surgeon also had a still field to do his procedure. During cardiopulmonary bypass the blood comes into contact with various biomaterials of the perfusion circuit. This activates blood proteins and components of the body's defense mechanism initiating a so-called inflammatory response. Much research has gone into defining this response. During the procedure the cardiopulmonary bypass is run by the perfusionist under the direction of the surgeon. The perfusionist is specifically trained and certified for his job. They also work in close communication with the anesthesia team. The perfusionist is responsible for setting up the system, maintaining the system, adequate oxygen and CO_2 levels and adequate perfusion to the body. Along with the activation of protein and the inflammatory response, the bypass circuits tend to be thrombogenic. Administration of Heparin is essential to decrease clotting. Monitoring the Heparin therapy is done by the perfusionist. They also monitor electrolytes, blood gases, and red cell volume. Flow rates, temperature and cardioplegia (a solution for protecting the heart and keeping it arrested during surgery) are monitored in conjunction with the surgeon. The perfusionists are also responsible for maintaining the composition, temperature and infusing the cardioplegia solution. The cell saver, a means of scavenging shed blood, reprocessing it and returning it to the patient is under the control of the perfusionist.

The heart lung machine consists of a system of cannulas to remove blood from the body and return it to the arterial system. Venous cannulas are positioned to remove blood from the right atrium or the vena cava and the arterial cannulas are positioned to return blood to the arterial system, either through the aorta or possibly the femoral or axillary arteries. The secondary vessels are used in some situations where the aorta may be diseased or

---

[108] Akins, *Noncardioplegic Myocardial Preservation for Coronary Revascularization*, 88 J. THORAC. CARDIOVASC. SURG. 174 (1984); Kluge, et al., *Sources of Contamination in Open Heart Surgery*, 230 JAMA 1415 (1974); Thomas & McGoon, *Isolated Massive Chylopericardium Following Cardiopulmonary Bypass*, 61 J. THORAC. CARDIOVASC. SURG. 945 (1971).

perhaps the aorta being replaced. In the cardiopulmonary bypass circuit is an oxygenator to provide gas exchange for delivery of oxygen to the blood and removal of CO2. A heat exchanger to both cool the body when necessary and rewarm it is also in the circuit. During the course of surgery, the body temperature usually drifts down without active cooling. A blood pump is part of the circuit, either a roller pump or centrifugal pump is commonly used. Both are safe and reliable. The system also contains filters for removal of particulate matter and gas assemboli. The suction system for returning Heparinized blood from the field through the heart lung machine is also part of the system.

[b]   Aortic and Venous Cannulation

Aortic cannulation is most commonly used for general heart surgery. The aorta is first checked for areas of atherosclerotic disease, emboli from the aortic cannulation can be a source of stroke. Calcium seen in the aorta on chest x-ray or on a catheterization film can be a clue to a diseased aorta. Direct palpation being careful not to cause embolization can also reveal a diseased aorta. If there is a TEE probe in place, a probe can pick up atherosclerotic disease of the aorta.

A most useful way to view the entire ascending aorta is with the epi-aortic echo probe placed directly over the aorta in the operative field by the surgeon. The surgeon can use this probe to locate diseased areas in the aorta and see if cannulation is possible or desirable and to locate the side of this cannulation. The aorta may need to be avoided completely if severely diseased changes the conduct and possibly the extent of the operation. An additional cannulation site is the femoral artery. Retrograde perfusion from the groin can be safely done. If the descending aorta and iliofemoral arterial systems are severely diseased it may not be satisfactory to use the femoral artery. Aortic dissection is more common complication of femoral artery cannulation than aortic cannulation.

A second peripheral site is the axillary artery, usually the right side is used. Since this artery is often smaller and less durable closure after cannulation may be difficult. To help this, instead of directly cannulating the axillary artery with a perfusion cannula, the perfusion cannula is commonly inserted into a prosthetic graft, which has been sewn in the side to the axillary artery. Closure is then facilitated by leaving a rim of graft on the vessel and then this is closed making it much easier. Perfusion of any arterial site can cause aortic dissection, a tear in the wall of the artery, requiring repair and removal of the cannula to another site. Aortic dissection can lead to malperfusion of any of the body organs.

[c] Venous Cannulation

Venous cannulation is much simpler and usually uncomplicated. However the right atrium or either the superior or inferior vena cava can be torn with placement of sutures for the cannulas.

[d] Cardioplegia

Cardioplegia is the solution used to preserve the heart and keep it arrested during cardiac surgery. The solution usually blood or may be crystalloid, is cool thus decreasing the heart temperature and oxygen demand and usually carries a high concentration of potassium to arrest the heart in diastole allowing surgery on a still relaxed field. There is no one uniform cardioplegic solution, various additives that may help myocardial protection are used by some.

Once surgery is underway, the patient has been cannulated for cardiopulmonary bypass. The aorta is usually clamped, thus no blood is flowing to the coronary arteries from the aorta, and the cardioplegic solution is administered, producing the desired still operative field. The heart may be stopped for hours with cardioplegia having been given intermittently. The cardioplegic can be delivered antegrade into the aorta down the coronary arteries or it may be given retrograde, that is back through the venous system, particularly the coronary sinus. This is particularly effective if there is coronary artery disease with obstructed arteries that may limit distribution of the cardioplegia. Surgery on the aortic valve and aorta is also facilitated since the coronary sinus cannula is away from the field. Coronary sinus intubation requires a special cannula to be inserted.

Complications of administration of cardioplegia are damage to the aorta, though unusual, damage to the coronary sinus. The coronary sinus is a thin vein on the back of the heart. It can be damaged by direct catheter perforation or from over inflation of the balloon on the catheter. This can usually readily be repaired. One can no longer deliver retrograde cardioplegia by this route. Cardioplegia can also be delivered indirectly into the coronary arteries with a special hand-held cannula if the aorta is open as during aortic valve surgery. There can be direct injury to the coronary ostia from this cannula but this is rare.

[e] Cardiopulmonary Bypass as Adjunct to Aortic Surgery

Cardiopulmonary bypass can be used for procedures not on the heart and not performed via sternotomy. So-called femoral bypass (femoral vein to femoral artery) and left atrial femoral artery bypass are often used during procedures on the descending thoracic aorta. In cases where the surgeon is operating through a left thoracotomy the aorta is clamped at or near the distal aortic arch, thus decreasing blood flow to the distal body. Not only the abdominal organs but the spinal cord may be affected. By supplementing the distal flow with the pump, complications can be decreased. The pump without an oxygenator or venous reservoir bypassing from the left atrium to the femoral artery or distal aorta can provide distal perfusion using oxygenated blood from the atrium. In trauma one advantage of the left atrial femoral bypass is the possibility of reduced Heparin dosage since there is no oxygenator or reservoir in the system and problems with clotting are reduced. Femoral vein to femoral artery bypass can also be used but since deoxygenated blood is taken from the right heart there is an oxygenator and venous reservoir in the circuit and full Heparinization is needed. Femoral bypass can also be used for total circulatory support. This can be used to initiate circulatory arrest if necessary.

[f] Heparin

As the heart/lung machine has allowed modern cardiac surgery, Heparin, an anticoagulant, is an integral part of cardiac surgery allowing us to use cardiopulmonary bypass safely. As the blood outside the normal vasculature comes in contact with the biomaterials of the perfusion circuit, emboli and small clots can form. Heparin can prevent this and is critical to the procedure. Heparin is reversed or neutralized, after cardiopulmonary bypass has been completed, with protamine. Protamine can cause marked hypotension, rarely an antiphylactic type reaction with profound hypothension that actually may require the resumption of cardiopulmonary bypass. Reaction to Protamine is more common in patients allergic to fish and with a history of previous exposure.

[g] Heparin-induced Thrombocytopenia

Heparin-induced thrombocytopenia also called HIT occurs in a small percentage of patients who receive Heparin. A small percentage of the HIT patients may develop a more severe complication involving thrombosis, which can be catastrophic. It is characterized by a drop of 40-50% in the platelet count, and this should raise suspicion of possible Heparin reaction. If this occurs, Heparin must be stopped and this includes small doses of Heparin that are in flush solutions that are attached to cannulas usually a lab test is ordered to detect the Heparin induced thrombocytopenia response. Other complications of cardiopulmonary bypass include air-embolization, most cardiopulmonary bypass circuits are equipped with air sensors that immediately shut down the pump before air can be pumped into the patient. Bleeding may occur from any surgical site, including suture lines and anastomotic sites. Nonsurgical bleeding can be related to Heparin platelet dysfunction and/or thrombolysis. Pre-op medications such as aspirin and Plavix can cause a significant increase in post-operative bleeding.

[h] Aprotinin

Intraoperative blood loss and postoperative bleeding are frequent and can lead to serious complications in cardiac surgery. Three drugs have been in common use to decrease blood loss in clinical practice: Epsilon Amino-Caproic Acid, Tranexamic acid and Aprotinin. The first two are lysine analogous that has been extensively evaluated. The third drug, Aprotinin, a serine protease inhibitor has been widely used, but on October 19, 2007, the FDA was notified of a possible increased risk of death with this drug. A study being carried out in Canada: *Blood Conservation using Antifibrinolytics: A randomized trial in a cardiac surgery population (BART) study* was designed to test the hypothesis that Aprotinin was superior to Epsilon Amino-Caproic Acid and Tranexamic acid in decreasing bleeding associated with cardiac surgery. At the FDA's request Bayer Pharmaceuticals Corporation suspended marketing of Aprotinin (Trasylol) pending a detailed review of preliminary results of the BART study.

A previous meta-analysis comparing these three antifibrinolytic agents showed all to be effective in reducing blood loss and transfusion requirements. There was no significant risk or benefit for mortality, stroke, myocardial infarction, or renal failure. High dose Aprotinin was associated with a statistically significant increase in renal dysfunction. [109]

Aprotinin reduces post-op bleeding by reducing fibrinolysis during cardiopulmonary bypass and it also has a platelet sparing effect. It attenuates the inflammatory response. When using Aprotinin care must be taken to the appropriate Heparin amount to maintain good anti-coagulation on bypass because Aprotinin interferes with some of the usual methods of assessing Heparin response. Patients are also usually given a test of Aprotinin to test for allergic reaction, which may be antiphylactic. There is an association of increased adverse reactions on re-exposure especially within six months.

---

[109] Brown, et al. Meta-Analysis Comparing the Effectiveness and Adverse Outcomes of Antifibrinolytic Agents in Cardiac Surgery. 115 Circulation 2801 (2007).

[2] Redo Cardiac Surgery

Redo cardiac surgery is a special class, particularly because it is complicated by the fact that intra-thoracic adhesions have occurred since the previous operation, which make re-entering the chest some times more difficult and dangerous. The presence of open, but diseased grafts from previous coronary bypass surgery also increases the risk. Surgery on a valve or aorta may also have led to cardiomegaly which may cause the cardiac structures, including the cardiac chambers and the aorta in close approximation to the sternum. Re-entry may make injury possible and if it occurs catastrophic. Pre-operatively one may find it helpful to review the operative report from the previous surgery to know exactly what was done and any unusual circumstances that may have occurred. Reviewing the pre-operative chest x-ray, particularly the lateral view, may be helpful. If there is a free space behind the sternum it may imply that there is separation between the cardiac structures and the chest wall, which may facilitate reentry. If there is any question, CT scan may be more helpful to better delineate the position of the aorta and cardiac chambers and their relationship to the sternum.

Cardiac catheterization can reveal the presence of old vein grafts. All occluded grafts are less of a problem than open or partially opened diseased vein grafts. On entering the sternum, if they cross the field they can be cut, they can be damaged leading to embolization or ischemia, which can cause acute decompensation. The presence of an internal mammary artery graft is looked for. Since the internal mammary artery graft is so beneficial to the patient because of its long-term patency rate, one likes to avoid the chance of injuring this graft, since if injured on the way in it may not be able to be replaced. Since it is often patent, if a circumflex coronary artery needs bypass, for example, an alternate approach is a left thoracotomy may be better in allowing you to avoid the internal mammary artery. It is for this reason that when doing the first coronary bypass operation the internal mammary is placed off to the left side so if the reentry into the sternum is necessary it is less likely to be injured. In doing a redo sternotomy, the oscillating saw is used in order to divide the sternum.

It is often beneficial to divide the anterior table and the mid portion of the sternum leaving the posterior portion intact and begin at the inferior pole and gradually open the sternum from bottom to top, gradually removing adhesions laterally and from the under surface of the sternum. If it is determined by the pre-operative studies, perhaps the aorta is densely adherent to the back of the sternum or other cardiac structure, it may even be advantageous to make a small right thoracotomy incision and from the side under direct vision take down the adhesions from the back of the sternum. An alternative approach too may be cannulation of the femoral artery and vein and place the patient on cardiopulmonary bypass to decompress the cardiac structures and hopefully make injury less likely and if it does occur you are on bypass and you can support the patient. The first redo cardiac surgery has some increased risk as the number of redo procedures increases the risk dramatically.

[3] Cannulae

Brodman[110] reported results of a survey of 500 members of The Society of Thoracic Surgery in which he obtained 120 responses. Twenty arterial cannulae were compared for flows, at rates from 1-5 1/m. The line pressure at 5 1/m went as high as 271 in some cases. One style of 24 Fr. catheter had a gradient of under 55mm-Hg at 5 1/m flow. Some of these kink easily. The material and design affect the function.

In 1981, Arom[111] found the single stage venous cannula to be preferable over two separate vena cannulae. Nicoloff[112] found that a soft silicone rubber coronary perfuser that cupped over the osteum reduced the likelihood of osteal damage from coronary perfusion.

[4] Left Ventricular Decompression

Breyer[113] reported delayed ventricular rupture, secondary to transatrial left ventricular venting, and debated its necessity. Roberts[114] found six frequently used techniques to be equally effective. He believed the pulmonary artery pressure needed monitoring to keep it below 15mm-Hg. Little[115] recommended venting the left ventricle through the pulmonary artery, which has the added advantage of eliminating the risk of air embolization.

---

[110] Brodman, et al., *A Comparison of Flow Gradients across Disposable Arterial Perfusion Cannulas*, 39 ANN. THORAC. SURG. 225 (1985).

[111] Arom, et al., *Objective Evaluation of the Efficacy of Various Venous Cannulas*, 81 J. THORAC. CARDIOVASC. SURG. 464 (1981).

[112] Nicoloff, *Atraumatic Coronary Perfusion Cannula*, 37 ANN. THORAC. SURG. 428 (1984).

[113] Breyer, et al., *Delayed Left Ventricular Rupture Secondary to Transatrial Left Ventricular Vent*, 33 ANN. THORAC. SURG. 189 (1982).

[114] Roberts, et al., *Relative Efficacy of Left Ventricular Venting and Venous Drainage Techniques Commonly Used During Coronary Artery Bypass Graft Surgery*, 36 ANN. THORAC. SURG. 444 (1983).

[115] Little, et al., *Use of the Pulmonary Artery for Left Ventricular Venting During Cardiac Operations*, 87 J. THORAC. CARDIOVASC. SURG. 532 (1984).

[5] Aortic Dissection

In 1947, Benedict[116] reported on five dissections of 836 femoral arterial cannulations, and no dissections in 114 aortic cannulations. Three of the aortic cannulations had severe bleeding at the cannulation site, and two patients subsequently died.

[6] Central Nervous System Complications

Aberg[117] evaluated adverse effects on the brain from biochemical, psychometric and radiological methods, and found two cerebral infarcts in asymptomatic patients. Gravlee[118] reported two cases of bilateral brachial paralysis from "watershed infarction" after coronary bypass. He postulated that these were secondary to global cerebral hypoperfusion during bypass, although high perfusion (2-3 1/m/m²) and a pressure of 50-90 were maintained. He concluded that traditional flow and pressure monitoring do not guarantee protection. In 1983, Bojar[119] studied 32 major central nervous defects over a five-year period among 3,206 bypass patients. Two resulted from massive air embolization (one recovered and one died). Mechanisms for the neurological complications were air embolism with cannulation, cardiopulmonary bypass, and partial occlusion clamping; arteriosclerotic emboli; inadequate cerebral perfusion; and prolonged cardiopulmonary bypass. He felt contributory causes were equipment malfunction and inattention of operating room personnel.

[a] Coma

In 1985, Levy reported on prediction of outcome from hypoxic ischemic coma.[120] In 52 patients with absent pupillary reflex on initial evaluation, none returned to normal activity. Of 27 patients evaluated 24 hours later who had light reflex and spontaneous eye movement, eleven (41/%) regained normal activity. By 24 hours after onset, 93 poor outcome patients were identified by absent extensor or reflexor motor responses, and/or by spontaneous eye

---

[116] Benedict, et al., *Acute Aortic Dissection During Cardiopulmonary Bypass*, 108 ARCH. SURG. 810 (1974).

[117] Ronquist, et al., *Adverse Effects on the Brain in Cardiac Operations as Assessed by Biochemical, Psychometric and Radiologic Methods*, 87 J. THORAC. CARDIOVASC. SURG. 99 (1984).

[118] Gravlee, et al., *Bilateral Brachial Paralysis from Watershed Infarction after Coronary Artery Bypass: A Report of Two Cases and Review of the Predisposing Anatomic and Physiological Mechanisms*, 88 J. THORAC. CARDIOVASC. SURG. 742 (1984).

[119] Bojar, et al., *Neurological Complications of Coronary Revascularization*, 36 ANN. THORAC. SURG. 427 (1983).

[120] Levy, et al., *Predicting Outcome from Hypoxic-Ischemic Coma*, 253 JAMA 1420 (1985).

movements that were neither orienting nor roving conjugate. Only one patient regained independent function. In contrast, there were 19 of 30 (63/%) at 24 hours who showed improvement in eye-opening responses, obeyed commands, or had motor responses that were withdrawal or localizing.

Comment. It is disturbing to realize that these criteria may be used to deny even that one patient (out of 93) the opportunity for recovery.

[7] Air Embolism[121] and Other Accidents[122]

In 1980, Stoney[123] reported on one of the most extensive series of air embolism and other accidents using the pump oxygenator. Three-hundred-forty-nine usable responses from cardiac surgeons surveyed over a six-year period through 1977 revealed 1,419 accidents resulting in 100 permanent injuries and 264 deaths. Ninety-two deaths were from air embolism from the arterial line, 163 deaths from disseminated intravascular coagulopathy, and nine deaths from mechanical, electrical, or oxygen failure. Permanent injury was also reported from 61 cases of air embolization, 28 cases of disseminated intravascular coagulopathy, and eleven cases of electrical, mechanical, or oxygen failure. Low-level alarms were used by only 42/% of the respondents, and activated clotting time by 63/%. Of the perfusionists 66.5/% were certified; however, they felt rigorous monitoring could have reduced the number of accidents.

Accidents included rupture of the arterial line or connector in nineteen cases, air pumped into the left ventricle through reversed vent tubing in eighteen, oxygenator leak in sixteen, oxygenator clot in four, pressurized oxygenator in one, burst oxygenator in one, oxygenator contamination in one, oxygenator chemical injury in one, overheated blood in three, unable to rewarm in three, rupture of a pulsatle device in three, and reversed arterial and venous line in one, for a total of 71 cases. The larger capacity of disc oxygenators were associated with fewer massive emboli. The bag oxygenators, which collapse, are safer than the rigid ones that could be pumped dry in thirty seconds. Rigid oxygenators have a handicap in that one is not able to see the blood level. Alarms included photoelectric cells for air in the line, as well as oxygenator weight mechanisms and air-activated ball valves at the outlet.

---

[121] Beckman, et al., *Risk Factors for Air Embolization During Cannulation of the Ascending Aorta,* 80 J. THORAC. CARDIOVASC. SURG. 302 (1980).

[122] Robinson, et al., *The Potential Hazard of Particulate Contamination of Cardioplegic Solutions,* 87 J. THORAC. CARDIOVASC. SURG. 48 (1984).

[123] Stoney, *supra* note 1.

Comment. I believe bypass pumps should not be sold without the outflow air-activated ball valve or a monitoring device.

In discussion of the above article, three pump related deaths were reported from St. Thomas. One pump ran dry on rewarming. One death was due to inadequate heparinization. One death occurred because the alarm was turned off and the arterial line was allegedly "inadvertently advanced when reaching" across the controls.

Mills and Ochsner[124] reported eight cases of massive air embolism. Five of these had successful outcomes. Carbon dioxide flooding was not used in any operation, but all patients were fully heparinized. Five accidents resulted from inattention to the blood level. One patient had bilateral transient radial nerve paresis. Two patients were slow on awakening, and two returned to normal activity. Two had the vent tube reversed, one returned to normal, and one died immediately. A case of aortic valve replacement had sudden resumption of heart beat, with resultant coma, but eventual recovery. One patient died immediately when the oxygenator was knocked over. One pulmonary valvotomy was associated with a sucker wedged in the pulmonary artery. This patient had a normal recovery. One ventricular aneurysm was inadvertently pumped full of air, with immediate death. One death resulted from pressurizing the reservoir while trying to clear a clot.

Spencer, in discussing Mills' case, reported two cases of massive air emboli that had alarm levels. One was turned off. In Spencer's other case, the alarm system tested properly earlier, but failed during the run. That patient vegetated fifteen months before he died.

Treatment for massive air embolization includes deep Trendenlenberg, stopping the pump, venting the aorta with removal of the cannula, increasing the blood pressure, and retrograde perfusion[125] by way of the superior vena cava. Only one-third[126] to slightly less than one-half[127] of the air is removed by retrograde perfusion. Maximum removal occurs within the first 10-15 minutes.[128] Hypothermia, steroids,[129] barbiturate anesthesia afterwards, and hyperbaric oxygen[130] are suggested.

---

[124] Mills & Ochsner, *Massive Air Embolism During Cardiopulmonary Bypass,* 80 J. THORAC. CARDIOVASC. SURG. 708 (1980).

[125] Hendriks, et al., *The Effectiveness of Venoarterial Perfusion in Treatment of Arterial Air Embolism During Cardiopulmonary Bypass,* 36 ANN. THORAC. SURG. 433 (1983).

[126] Mills & Ochsner, *supra* note 117.

[127] Hendriks, et al., *supra* note 118.

[128] Mills & Ochsner, *supra* note 117.

[129] *Id.*

[130] Tomatis, et al., *Massive Arterial Air Embolism Due to Rupture of Pulsatile Assist Device: Successful Treatment in the Hyperbaric Chamber,* 32 ANN. THORAC. SURG. 604 (1981).

§ 3.07 Assist Pump Problems

[1] Intra-aortic Balloon Pump

A commonly used cardiac assist device is the intra-aortic balloon pump. It is a large balloon catheter placed percutaneously usually from the femoral artery into the aorta just below the level of the subclavian. The action of the balloon inflating and deflating is advantageous to cardiac function. The inflation during diastole increases coronary blood flow and may help in obstructive coronary disease with relief of angina and in such a way increase myocardial perfusion and cardiac function. With balloon deflation it decreases the resistance and is timed such that the balloon deflates when the heart contracts. In this way cardiac output is improved. As mentioned, the balloon is inserted percutaneously through the femoral vessel. If the femoral vessel is diseased, placing this catheter there may cause ischemia to the leg. Then the balloon will need to be removed and perhaps placed on the other side. In some dire situations, the choice between life and limb may be made. The balloon pump is contraindicated in the face of aortic dissection as might be anticipated since the aortic wall is torn and the balloon in such a position may worsen the situation with aortic insufficiency the balloon pump is usually not indicated.

Akins[131] documented the higher incidence of complications with the percutaneous approach, but reported it was faster, easier and less expensive. The incidence tapered off with the experience of the cardiologist. The author proposed a small incision with a purse string suture in the femoral artery before insertion.

Injury cannot be avoided in arteriosclerotic vessels. Rose[132] reported paraplegia following percutaneous insertion, probably from a small dissection or arterial embolus to the spinal cord artery.

[2] Right Ventricular Assist Pump[133]

Flege[134] reported the successful use of the distal one-third of a 40cc Datascope Percor in the pulmonary artery, with the rest in a graft secured with

---

[131] Akins, *Percutaneous Balloon Pump (Reply to Dr. Spodick)*, 87 J. THORAC. CARDIOVASC. SURG. 944 (1984).

[132] Rose, et al., *Paraplegia Following Percutaneous Insertion of an Intra-Aortic Balloon*, 87 J. THORAC. CARDIOVASC. SURG. 788 (1984).

[133] Miller, et al., *Pulmonary Artery Balloon Counterpulsation for Acute Right Ventricular Failure*, 80 J. THORAC. CARDIOVASC. SURG. 760 (1980); O'Neill, et al., *Successful Management of Right Ventricular Failure with the Ventricular Assist Pump Following Aortic Valve Replacement and Coronary Bypass Grafting*, 87 J. THORAC. CARDIOVASC. SURG. 106 (1984).

[134] Flege, et al., *Successful Balloon Counterpulsation in Right Ventricular Failure*, 37 ANN. THORAC. SURG. 167 (1984).

a ligature around the catheter and brought out through the linea alba. By the third day, the left ventricle took over, and operative removal was accomplished. The patient went home on the 29th day, and was well at the end of one year.

[3] Pacemakers and Implantable Cardiac Defibrillators

Pacemakers and defibrillators are implantable devices. Once solely inserted by the surgeons are now inserted by both surgeons and those cardiologists specifically trained to do so. The evaluation for the need of insertion of these devices is primarily done by the cardiologist. The surgeon's role is usually technical. He is involved in the insertion of the device but often called upon to deal with complications of the procedure. Pacemakers and defibrillators are inserted in a similar fashion. They usually require one or two leads inserted via peripheral vein, either cephalic or subclavian and passed into the heart. Vascular injury or cardiac perforation can occur but are very unusual. Cardiac perforation rarely results in tamponade. Once the device is in place, the leads are secured with an accompanying sleeve at the insertion site and then along with the generator for the pacemaker or defibrillator are placed in the carefully created subcutaneous pocket. They should be placed between the muscular layer and fatty tissue layer and not within the fatty tissue layer alone. If they are too superficial, they may be more prone to erosion.

If patient's present with infection or erosion of the device, this usually means that the device and the leads must be removed. In the face of infection in recently inserted devices, the leads can be withdrawn easily. If, however, the device has been in for many years, it may be difficult to remove the leads from the heart, particularly if the leads contained tines at the end. They are encased in fibrous tissues. This has led to the use of lead extraction devices that are mechanical or assisted with either laser or electrocautery. One must use extreme care in extracting chronic leads because the devices can lead to perforation of the vessels or the heart and can place the patient in sudden jeopardy, even to the point of requiring emergency surgery to relieve cardiac tamponade and repair of the bleeding.

§ 3.08 Problems Associated with Acquired Heart Lesions

[1] Valves

[a] Commissurotomy

Nakano[135] reported long-term results in 53 cases of mitral commissurotomy for mitral stenosis with severe subvalvular changes. There were two early and one late deaths, but 78.6/% of the patients were free of death or reoperation at the end of ten years. Maximum postoperative gradients were 5-9mm-Hg. Ninety-three percent of the procedures were done using cardiopulmonary bypass. Sixteen valves had to be replaced.

[b] Mitral Prolapse

In 1976, Jerestay[136] reported ten sudden deaths in patients with mitral valve prolapse. Reece and Cooley[137] reported surgical treatment of the "click syndrome" in 37 patients. They believe surgery probably has a place in a selected group of patients; however, many discussants were uncertain whether surgery should be offered.

[c] Replacement

[i] Elderly patients

Arom[138] raised the question as to whether valve replacement or related procedures should be performed in elderly patients. He reported an 8/% mortality of 135 patients, 70 years of age or older. Early deaths were related to infection, and to cardiac, renal, and multi-organ failure. He believed that early mortality compared favorably to 312 younger patients with a 5.2/% mortality. The only measurable increased risk appeared to be in the cerebral vascular accident complication rate of 5.2/% compared to 2.8/% for the younger group. Arom concluded that surgery could be done with an acceptable operative mortality, with improved function and low mortality in the median term follow-up.

---

[135] Nakano, et al., *Long-Term Results of Open Mitral Commissurotomy for Mitral Stenosis with Severe Subvalvular Changes: A Ten-Year Evaluation*, 37 ANN. THORAC. SURG. 159 (1984).

[136] Jerestay, *Sudden Death in Mitral Valve Prolapse — Click Syndrome*, 37 AM. J. CARDIOL. 317 (1976).

[137] Reece, et al., *Surgical Treatment of Mitral Systolic Click Syndrome: Results in 37 Patients*, 39 ANN. THORAC. SURG. 155 (1985).

[138] Arom, et al., *Should Valve Replacement and Related Procedures Be Performed in Elderly Patients?*, 38 ANN. THORAC. SURG. 466 (1984).

[ii] Mitral valve

Bonchek[139] suggested leaving the chordae in reconstructions for mitral regurgitation to avoid dilation of the left ventricle. David[140] believed this procedure improved left ventricular function as assessed by radionuclear ventriculography. Bjork[141] reported eight cases of left ventricular rupture complicating mitral valve replacement.

[iii] Aortic valve

Aortic valve replacement had a 4.5/% mortality in 912 consecutive cases according to Cohn in 1984.[142]

Associated vein graft carried only a 4.2/% mortality; however, associated surgery for ascending aortic aneurysm carried a 17/% mortality in 46 patients.

[iv] Infection

Nelson[143] found a favorable ten-year experience with valve procedures for active infective endocarditis. Forty-seven cases of native valve endocarditis and five cases involving prosthetic valves were reported. Twenty-seven were drug addicts. Thirty-seven required operative procedures during the active phase. Surgical indications were congestive heart failure, refractory infection and major emboli. All prostheses cases were actively infected at the time of replacement. Periannular abscess was associated most frequently with native endocarditis of the aortic valve. There were six preoperative strokes that were no worse postoperatively. There were two ruptured cerebral mycotic aneurysms in the series.

Antibiotic resistance is an expected phenomenon. Staphylococcus epidermidis resistant to Rifampin was reported in 1985.[144]

---

[139] Bonchek, et al., *Left Ventricular Performance after Mitral Reconstruction for Mitral Regurgitation*, 88 J. THORAC. CARDIOVASC. SURG. 122 (1984).

[140] David, et al., *Mitral Valve Replacement for Mitral Regurgitation with or without Preservation of Chordae Tendineae*, 88 J. THORAC. CARDIOVASC. SURG. 718 (1984).

[141] Bjork, et al., *Left Ventricular Rupture as a Complication of Mitral Valve Replacement: Surgical Experience with Eight Cases and a Review of the Literature*, 73 J. THORAC. CARDIOVASC. SURG. 14 (1977).

[142] Cohn, et al., *Early and Late Risk of Aortic Valve Replacement*, 88 J. THORAC. CARDIOVASC. SURG. 695 (1984).

[143] Nelson, et al., *Favorable Ten-Year Experience with Valve Procedures for Active Infective Endocarditis*, 87 J. THORAC. CARDIOVASC. SURG. 493 (1984).

[144] Chamovitz, et al., *Prosthetic Valve Endocarditis Caused by Staphylococcus Epidermitis: Development of Rifampin Resistance During Vancomycin and Rifampin Therapy*, 253 JAMA 2867 (1985).

Rumisek[145] reported native valve endocarditis resulting in valve dehiscence, intracardiac fistula, ventricular septal defect, aortic root aneurysm and aortoventricular discontinuity. Femoral arterial cannulation was required. Rumisek believed that subsequent suture laxity or pull-through could result in immediate uncontrollable hemorrhage, aneurysm or fistula. He advocated an approach by a vertical incision in the right ventricular outflow tract.

[d] Prostheses

Autologous grafts were used before mechanical valves were available. Robles[146] reported on experience with 202 autologous pulmonary valves that were excised and reimplanted in the aortic position between 1967 and 1982. The patients ranged in age from nine to sixty years. Anticoagulation was not required, and there were no thromboembolic problems. Freedom from valve-related deaths at fourteen years was 82/% plus or minus 6/%. Early in the series there were deaths and reoperations for technical failures or infective endocarditis. There had been no calcification of the valves. In cases with major right ventricular outflow compromise, reconstruction with an aortic homograft has led to a 81/% twelve-year freedom of problems. The authors' first success was in 1967. They believe that this is the most ideal approach, and is used in anyone with a life expectancy of forty or more years.

Lau[147] reported the surgical treatment of prosthetic endocarditis by aortic root replacement using a homograft. Six patients with uncontrolled bacteremia had the aortic root replaced with a preserved homograft aortic valve. This permitted exclusion of the weakened aorta and associated root abscess. There were no deaths. The longest survivor was alive and well at ten years. Two patients had conduction disturbances related to their malfunctioning valves. An additional four were alive and well at five years without further infection. Aortic root infection is associated with abscess, fistulization, ulceration, and perforation of the anterior mitral leaflet.

[i] Thromboembolism

Edmonds[148] estimated the incidence of thromboembolism with the Lillehei-Kaster valve in the mitral area to be between 0-6.7 per hundred

---

[145] Rumisek, et al., *Transeptal Control of the Difficult Aortic Annulus*, 39 ANN. THORAC. SURG. 385 (1985).

[146] Robles, et al., *Long-Term Assessment of Aortic Valve Replacement with Autologous Pulmonary Valve*, 39 ANN. THORAC. SURG. 238 (1985).

[147] Lau, et al., *Surgical Treatment of Prosthetic Endocarditis: Aortic Root Replacement Using a Homograft*, 87 J. THORAC. CARDIOVASC. SURG. 712 (1984).

[148] Edmonds, *Thromboembolic Complications of Current Cardiac Valvular Prostheses*, 34 ANN. THORAC. SURG. 96 (1982).

patient-years. He believed the actual rate might be 5.7 times the detected rate. McGoon[149] challenged the adequacy of valid information on thromboembolism in the literature, and felt that none of the 51 reports were completely adequate. On the scale of 0-17, Edmonds felt the average was 7.6. McGoon suggested that there was need for improved future reporting to assist in choosing the correct procedure for managing valvular heart disease. He felt that many minor complaints were the result of thromboembolism, such as blurred or double vision, dizziness, numbness, weakness, inability to speak or move, blackout, stroke and other symptoms.

[ii]   Embolectomy of prostheses

Early thrombectomy of mechanical valves once was abandoned in favor of replacement; however, thrombectomy is now being reconsidered. In 1982, Ayuso[150] reported on thrombectomy of seven Bjork-Shiley prostheses and reviewed the literature. Clot was peeled with vascular forceps and a high vacuum suction with a very thin, 9-11 Fr. tip. The valve was rotated. Disc freedom was checked, and the major orifice was placed in the opposite position. Antiplatelet medication and warfarin were required postoperatively. Moulton[151] was concerned with Ayuso's report because he had reported on only four mitral valves. Moulton knew that old clot was harder to remove. Ayuso's reply added two more cases where the mitral valve was declotted with success. Ayuso's conclusion was that removing the clot was less hazardous than valve replacement.

[iii]   Bioprosthesis

Zussa[152] studied the long term results of 990 patients with porcine cardiac bioprosthesis from 1974 to 1980. There were 27 patients requiring reoperations. Twelve reoperations were required for perivalvular leak, with no reoperative deaths. Five patients required reoperations because of endocarditis. Six reoperations were for valve thrombosis and four because of tissue failure. There were no operative deaths in the tissue failure cases. The author and his associates concluded: "The intrinsic durability of the

---

[149] McGoon, *The Risk of Thromboembolism Following Valvular Operations: How Does One Know?*, 88 J. THORAC. CARDIOVASC. SURG. 782 (1984).

[150] Ayuso, et al., *Thrombectomy: Surgical Treatment of the Thrombosed Bjork-Shiley Prosthesis: Report of Seven Cases and Review of the Literature*, 84 J. THORAC. CARDIOVASC. SURG. 906 (1982).

[151] Moulton, *Thrombectomy for Clotted Bjork-Shiley Prosthesis: Is It Really a Proven Procedure?*, 87 J. THORAC. CARDIOVASC. SURG. 147 (1984).

[152] Zussa, et al., *Porcine Cardiac Bioprosthesis: Evaluation of Long-Term Results in 990 Patients*, 39 ANN. THORAC. SURG. 243 (1985).

bioprosthesis appears to be very satisfactory over the long term (6-7 years), and the risk of failure appears to be well balanced by the advantage of low incidence of thromboembolism and no mandatory anticoagulation therapy."

Imamura[153] reported on the open position for fixation of the bioprosthesis for more physiological performance. He showed that fixation while partially open resulted in the valve in the open position 60/% of the time, compared to 49/% by the previous method.

[iv]   Mechanical valve versus bioprosthesis

Joyce and Nelson[154] compared porcine valve xenografts with mechanical prostheses over a 7½-year experience. They had 311 Carpentier-Edwards and 118 Hancock valves with an overall mortality of 5.6/%. There were 94 Bjork-Shiley and six other mechanical valves. The mortality in the aortic position was 2/%, and in the mitral position, 4.4/%. The Hancock valve required explantation in 5.9/%, while none of the Carpentier-Edwards or Bjork-Shiley valves had to be replaced.

[v]   Other complications of prostheses

Dhasmana[155] reported on increased perivalvular leaks that were thought to be secondary to the use of 2-0 running sutures. Maeda[156] studied the successful surgical treatment of dissecting left atrial aneurysms after mitral valve replacement. Maeda reported that during resection of the thrombosed valve "the posterior part of the mitral annulus was inadvertently incised too deeply." The incision extended to the posterior wall of the left ventricle and was repaired with three mattress sutures with teflon pledgets. Early postoperative trouble led to angiograms on the third day, at which time the aneurysm was diagnosed. Left thoracotomy by way of the fifth innerspace was required because of the aneurysm's close proximity (5mm) to the left circumflex coronary artery. Periprosthetic leaks were also studied by Newton.[157]

---

[153] Imamura, et al., *Open-Position Fixation of Bioprosthesis for More Physiological Performance,* 88 J. THORAC. CARDIOVASC. SURG. 114 (1984).

[154] Joyce & Nelson, *Comparison of Porcine Valve Xenografts with Mechanical Prostheses: A 7½ Year Experience,* 88 J. THORAC. CARDIOVASC. SURG. 102 (1984).

[155] Dhasmana, et al., *Factors Associated with Periprosthetic Leakage Following Primary Mitral Valve Replacement with Special Consideration of the Suture Technique,* 35 ANN. THORAC. SURG. 170 (1983).

[156] Maeda, et al., *Successful Surgical Treatment of Dissecting Left Atrial Aneurysm after Mitral Valve Replacement,* 39 ANN. THORAC. SURG. 382 (1985).

[157] Newton, et al., *Evaluation of Suture Techniques for Mitral Valve Replacement,* 88 J. THORAC. CARDIOVASC. SURG. 248 (1984).

Repeat replacement of 89 valves was reported by Bosch.[158] There were 39 cases of primary prosthesis failure. Sixteen were associated with endocarditis, sixteen with systemic valve related complications, and thirteen with leaks. Five were replaced with the insertion of a new valve in another position. The early mortality of 29.2/% was reduced to 7.4/% in the last two years. Eight patients required a third replacement.

Currie[159] found left ventricular outflow tract obstruction in a low profile mitral prosthesis. He reported that some of these may not be diagnosed before catherization, and some may actually require direct surgical visualization for conclusive information. Potential intrinsic prosthetic dysfunction is said to result from incorrect suture placement, inadequate tissue clearance from the annulus, and impedence of the disc by impaction on the struts or left ventricular myocardium.

[vi]   Types of prostheses

Marshall[160] reported on thirty Bjork-Shiley converoconcave valves, and was impressed with the absence of valve thrombosis in contrast to the spherical disc valve reports. Longer follow-up was felt to be necessary.

Abdulali[161] studied the late outcome of patients with Brunwald-Cutter mitral valve replacement.[162]

The overall mortality was high in their eighty patients. Aortic poppet escape occurred as late as 101 months. Only 34/% of mitral valve replacements were expected to be alive at ten years. Five of the seventeen mitral valves examined showed cloth wear at the ring, with fraying of the polypropylene cloth and its retraction from the distal strut. Two had fibrin clots on struts attached to the frayed cloth. One had transient left hemiplegia. Two aortic poppets escaped. Three reoperations were required; one each for endocarditis, leak and valve dysfunction. Schoen[163] reported ball wear to be greater in the aortic than in the mitral position. Focal mitral calcification was

---

[158] Bosch, et al., *Early and Late Prognosis after Reoperation for Prosthetic Valve Replacement*, 88 J. THORAC. CARDIOVASC. SURG. 567 (1984).

[159] Currie, et al., *Left Ventricular Outflow Tract Obstruction Related to a Valve Prosthesis: Case Caused By a Low-Profile Mitral Prosthesis*, 60 MAYO CLIN. PROC. 184 (1985).

[160] Marshall, et al., *Early Results of Valve Replacement with the Bjork-Shiley Converoconcave Prosthesis*, 37 ANN. THORAC. SURG. 398 (1984).

[161] Abdulali, et al., *Late Outcome of Patients with a Braunwald-Cutter Mitral Valve Replacement*, 38 ANN. THORAC. SURG. 579 (1984).

[162] Schoen, et al., *Implications of Late Morphology of Braunwald-Cutter Mitral Heart Valve Prosthesis*, 88 J. THORAC. CARDIOVASC. SURG. 208 (1984).

[163] *Id.*

reported in all mitrals adjacent to the strut or cloth. Jamieson[164] found excellent 81-month follow-up for Carpentier-Edwards porcine bioprostheses.

A thirteen-year appraisal of the Hancock bioprosthesis in isolated mitral valve replacement was conducted by Galluci.[165] Thirty-seven of 476 patients had valve failure. Only 58/% were free of trouble by thirteen years. There were 45 embolic accidents, thirteen of which were fatal. Forty-nine required reoperation; four were for valve endocarditis with three deaths; six were for perivalvular leak with no deaths, and two were for left atrial thrombus. Thirty-seven valve failures were secondary to primary tissue failure, with calcification. There were five operative deaths in this group. Calcific degeneration of the cusps was the major problem.

Ravuelta[166] expressed his preference for the pericardial xenograft of the Inoscu-Shiley valve for the small aortic valve root problem.

Burckhardt conducted a two-year follow-up of the St. Jude medical heart valve prosthesis, and Chaux reported a five-year experience on this bileaflet valve, with only fourteen valve-related complications in 233 valves.[167]

Nine had thromboembolism, which was more frequent after double valve replacement. Reoperation was required for valve thrombosis and erosion in one case each, and two patients required reoperation for perivalvular leaks due to endocarditis. Three of the four patients survived reoperation. They reported no structural failure or hemolysis, and recommended anticoagulation in all.

Miller[168] reported on the performance characteristics of the Starr-Edwards model 1260 aortic valve prosthesis beyond ten years. There were 13/% hospital deaths and 18/% late deaths. The structural durability and performance were acceptable. By ten years there were 12/% patients dead of valve-related causes, and 49/% patients with serious valve-related complications. These 449 non-consecutive patients were operated on between 1968 and 1975.

---

[164] Jamieson, et al., *Five-Year Evaluation of the Carpentier-Edwards Porcine Bioprosthesis*, 88 J. THORAC. CARDIOVASC. SURG. 324 (1984).

[165] Gallucci, et al., *Isolated Mitral Valve Replacement with the Hancock Bioprosthesis: A 13-Year Appraisal*, 38 ANN. THORAC. SURG. 571 (1984).

[166] Revuleta, et al., *The Ionescu-Shiley Valve: A Solution to the Small Aortic Root*, 88 J. THORAC. CARDIOVASC. SURG. 234 (1984).

[167] Burckhardt, et al., *Clinical Evaluation of the St. Jude Medical Heart Valve Prosthesis: A Two Year Follow-up of 150 Patients*, 88 J. THORAC. CARDIOVASC. SURG. 432 (1984); Chaux, et al., *The St. Jude Medical Bileaflet Valve Prosthesis: A 5-Year Experience*, 88 J. THORAC. CARDIOVASC. SURG. 706 (1984).

[168] Miller, et al., *Performance Characteristics of the Starr-Edwards Model 1260 Aortic Valve Prosthesis Beyond Ten Years*, 88 J. THORAC. CARDIOVASC. SURG. 193 (1984).

[2] Surgery on the Thoracic Aorta

Surgery on the aorta largely involves aneurysmal disease or aortic dissection. An aortic aneurysm is a localized enlargement or dilatation of the aortic wall and can affect any portion of the aorta. The primary risk from an aneurysm is rupture. As the aneurysm increases in size the risk of rupture also increases. Once the risk of rupture is greater than the risk of the operation intervention is recommended and this is usually in the 5-6 cm range for aortic aneurysms. At the present time, surgical resection of the thoracic aorta is still a primary therapy for aneurysms although progress is being made in intra-luminal graft technology. It is now regular therapy for abdominal aortic aneurysms and is still investigational for thoracic aortic aneurysms.

Aneurysms can also be the source of an aortic dissection, which is a longitudinal separation of the aortic wall in the medial layer of the aorta. A dissection may occur in an aorta that is not aneurysmal. It is often associated with hypertension. Chronic aortic dissection may lead also to aneurysm formation. Aortic aneurysms thus may rupture or dissect. These are two separate phenomenons. Operation on the ascending aorta approached through the sternotomy incision. Cardiopulmonary bypass is used. If the aneurysm involves the aortic arch where the cerebral vessels arise, repair may require hypothermic circulatory arrest to create a clear operative field, and also allow surgery at the point of arterial supply to the brain. The pump is shut off after adequate cooling of the cerebral tissue is achieved. By decreasing the metabolic demand of the brain with cooling, circulation can be interrupted for a period of time. Perfusion to the brain is shut off. The longer the circulatory arrest time the more chance of injury. At least 30 minutes of cooling is required prior to circulatory arrest and circulatory arrest is usually not begun until the nasopharyngeal temperature is equal to or below 18 degrees centigrade and if longer operating time is anticipated perhaps 15 degrees centigrade. Shorter periods of circulatory arrest may be tolerated at higher temperatures.

The safe duration of circulatory arrest is not precisely known. With nasopharyngeal temperatures of less than 18 degrees, 30 minutes is generally agreed to be the safe, with longer time the chance of injury increases. Most surgeons try to keep the arrest time below 60 minutes. It is also necessary to take care of the problem for which circulatory arrest is initiated, which can also be lethal. One is constantly balancing the risk and benefits of the procedure. Antegrade cerebral perfusion may also be used in aortic arch surgery but this does not eliminate the risk of stroke. Aneurysms of the descending aorta are usually approached through the left chest.

Other than the usual surgical complication, a primary concern of surgery on the descending thoracic aorta is paraplegia. This is due to interruption of the blood supply to the spinal cord. Adjunctive procedures to reduce the risk are distal aortic perfusion during the cross clamp period as described with left atrial femoral and femoral femoral bypass. Spinal fluid drainage has been shown to be effective in reducing pressure from edema and probably reducing paraplegia. Despite all these measures, paraplegia cannot definitely be prevented today. Paraplegia in this situation is also related to ischemic or clamp time. Keeping the clamp time as short as possible is necessary.

[a] Coronary Artery Aneurysm

Coronary artery aneurysms occurred in 36 of 175 cases of Kawasaki syndrome between 1979 and 1983 at Children's Hospital of Los Angeles.[169] The Public Health Department recommended that "[e]very child diagnosed as having Kawasaki syndrome should have a coronary artery evaluation by 2-D echocardiography." Other cardiovascular complications included myocarditis, pericarditis, hypertension, congestive heart failure, femoral and axillary artery aneurysms.

[3] Ischemic Heart Disease

[a] Normal Coronary Angiograms

In Salem's study of 528 consecutive coronary angiograms after acute myocardial infarctions, ten had normal coronary arteries.[170] Eight of the ten were 45 years of age or younger and were predominantly asymptomatic female smokers. Three patients recannulized with streptokinase. Nine lacked a history of variant angina. Seven had a negative ergonovine provocation test. Salem speculated that they may have been secondary to thrombus formation.

Richardson[171] reported ventricular septal rupture in a patient with normal coronary arteries.

---

[169] Finn, *Kawasaki Syndrome,* Public Health Letter (L.A. County Dept. Health Services) Vol. 7, No. 3, p. 1 (1985).

[170] Salem, et al., *Acute Myocardial Infarction With "Normal" Coronary Arteries: Clinical and Angiographic Profiles, with Ergonovine Testing,* 12 TEXAS HEART INST. J. 1 (1985).

[171] Richardson & Neiss, *Ventricular Septal Rupture with "Normal" Coronary Arteries,* 12 TEXAS HEART INST. J. 93 (1985).

[b]   Evolving Myocardial Infarction

Krebler,[172] in a study in the management of infarction by intracoronary thrombolysis and subsequent aorta-coronary bypass, did not see increased bleeding after streptokinase. Collen[173] reported tissue-type plasminogen was superior, for dissolving intracoronary thrombus, as it had no systemic effect.

Many institutions are using percutaneous transluminal coronary angioplasty (PTCA) in these situations if a clot does not dissolve, or if a significant stenosis is present. If all the above fail, emergency coronary artery bypass grafting is being done with increasing frequency in an increasing number of centers. Sudden blowout of ruptured myocardium after infarction is said by McMullan to account for 4-13/% of the mortality secondary to myocardial infarction.[174]

He was able to collect 22 cases with previous leak from the literature. He had four patients treated surgically with femoral-femoral cardiopulmonary support, all of whom survived the surgery. Two died of brain death in the hospital.

[c]   Percutaneous Transluminal Coronary Angioplasty (PTCA)

Acinapura[175] compared the efficacy of PTCA with single vessel bypass and concluded that it was an acceptable alternative in patients with localized lesions sufficiently serious to cause symptoms warranting coronary artery bypass grafting. He cautioned it may be associated with increased myocardial infarction and early recurrence of symptoms. Mills[176] cited a 2/% mortality at reoperation at the Cleveland Clinic. He feared that PTCA might delay the initial bypass graft, and that reoperation might carry a higher risk because of the increased number of arteries requiring grafting, and because of the decrease in ejection fraction of the left ventricle between the two procedures, and a possible increase in central venous system defects at the time of the second procedure.

---

[172] Krebler, et al., *Management of Evolving Myocardial Infarction by Intracoronary Thrombolysis and Subsequent Aorto-Coronary Bypass*, 83 J. THORAC. CARDIOVASC. SURG. 187 (1982).

[173] Collen, *Coronary Thrombolysis with Tissue-Type Plasminogen Activator: Prospective Review*, 11 TEXAS HEART INST. J. 344 (1984).

[174] McMullan, et al., *Sudden Blowout Rupture of the Myocardium after Infarction: Urgent Management*, 89 J. THORAC. CARDIOVASC. SURG. 259 (1985).

[175] Acinapura, et al., *Efficacy of Percutaneous Transluminal Coronary Angioplasty Compared with Single-Vessel Bypass*, 89 J. THORAC. CARDIOVASC. SURG. 35 (1985).

[176] Mills, *Trends in Selection and Results of Coronary Artery Operations*, 36 ANN. THORAC. SURG. 373 (1983).

Dorros[177] reported on 61 patients over a 53-month interval who had 105 attempts at PTCA for saphenous vein or coronary artery lesions following initial bypass grafts. Eighty lesions were dilated. A 20/% reduction in the diameter of the stenosis with clinical improvement was considered "success." Twenty-six of 39 (79/%) vein graft stenoses in the body of the graft were successfully dilated. Nineteen of 25 (76/%) anastomotic sites were successfully dilated. Seven of eight stenoses in the body of the graft were successfully dilated. Thirty-seven of 52 (71/%) patients with arterial stenoses were successfully dilated. Dorros found no difference in success in dilating saphenous vein grafts or the native coronary artery stenosis. He reported success in 18 of 22 left anterior descending, 13 of 22 circumflex, 21 of 26 right coronary artery, and two of two left main coronary arteries. Complications included one emergency coronary artery bypass graft, three myocardial infarcts, and two deaths.

Caralps[178] had three successes in four patients with intraoperative angioplasty, for left main coronary disease. Of patients with left anterior descending lesions considered unsuitable for bypass grafting, intraoperative angioplasty through a limited aortotomy produced improvement in three of the four cases studied.

Jones[179] reported on percutaneous saphenous vein graft angioplasty to avoid reoperative bypass surgery. A 20/% reduction occurred in 35 of 37 patients. The gradient was reduced from 58 to 15mm-Hg at the end of one year in the 28 cases studied. Fourteen of fifteen stenoses in the body or proximal vein graft were successfully dilated, but seven recurred within the first year. Two of the seven had no signs or symptoms. Only three of 22 distant stenoses restenosed, and twelve were symptom free at one year. There were no deaths, but two patients required emergency bypass grafting, two developed myocardial infarctions, and one developed ventricular tachycardia. Jones indicated the cost of bypass grafting was 2.8 times the cost of angioplasty.

Hastillo[180] reported successful percutaneous transluminal coronary angioplasty in donor hearts at 46 and 16 months.

---

[177] Dorros, et al., *Percutaneous Transluminal Coronary Angioplasty in Patients with Prior Coronary Artery Bypass Grafting*, 87 J. THORAC. CARDIOVASC. SURG. 17 (1984).

[178] Caralps, et al., *Intraoperative Transluminal Balloon Catheter Dilation*, 36 ANN. THORAC. SURG. 610 (1983); Caralps, et al., *Combined Aortocoronary Bypass and Intraoperative Transluminal Angioplasty in Left Main Coronary Disease*, 37 ANN. THORAC. SURG. 291 (1984).

[179] Jones, et al., *Percutaneous Saphenous Vein Angioplasty to Avoid Reoperative Bypass Surgery*, 36 ANN. THORAC. SURG. 389 (1983).

[180] Hastillo, et al., *Serial Coronary Angioplasty for Arteriosclerosis Following Heart Transplantation*, 4 HEART TRANSPLANT. 192 (1985).

[4] Coronary Artery Bypass Surgery

One of the most common procedures performed by the adult cardiac surgeon is coronary bypass surgery (CABG). The incidence of coronary artery disease (CAD) is high. Advances in medical therapy and interventional cardiology have decreased the number of patients coming to surgery with CABG still a very frequently performed procedure. It is literally a bypass using a vein or artery to direct blood around the blockage in the coronary artery.   The decision to operate is based on coronary anatomy, myocardium in jeopardy, the symptoms and the patient's risk factors. Usually the cardiologist has evaluated the patient and performed the catheterization.   They also assess candidacy for medical therapy or interventional radiology. Coronary arteries are generally on the surface of the heart and are easily accessible. The surgeon has reviewed the angiogram, localized the obstruction and decides where to place the grafts. Studying the films is essential. Arteries may not be as obvious on the surface as may be anticipated.

They may be buried in fat or located within the myocardium, so called intra-myocardial vessel. There may be multiple arteries in one area. You want to be sure that you identify the correct vessel. Most coronary bypass surgeons use cardiopulmonary bypass. However, in an attempt to eliminate consequences of CBP and possibly decrease complications, so called off pump CABG has come into practice.

[a] Off Pump Coronary Bypass

Off pump coronary bypass procedure is performed on the beating heart. An external stabilizing device is used to isolate a segment of the coronary artery to be bypassed on the surface of the heart. Adjunctive measures such as proximal artery snaring internal shunt and suction or blowing and misting devices are used to keep field free of blood for better visualization. By manipulating the heart in the pericardial cavity, even the posterior circulation may be accessible. There is a learning curve to this procedure, as it requires more patience on the part of the surgeon to obtain satisfactory exposure. The anesthesiologist needs to be closely involved in the procedure to monitor the patient as the heart is being manipulated. Concerns are obvious. Doing a precise anastomosis on a small vessel is easier on a still arrested heart. Though with improved technology and experience at least the short-term results are good in some hands with off pump surgery.

The benefits of not using cardiopulmonary bypass are still being debated. Clearly, there are those patients who benefit from off pump surgery and some patients who require cardiopulmonary bypass to be used for satisfactory operation. There is a large group in-between that can be done by either method and done satisfactorily. Those patients who are hemodynamically unstable have small diffusely diseased arteries that may be extensively intra-myocardial are probably better done on bypass. Patients with extensive atherosclerotic disease of the aorta may be best done off pump. Large vessels on a normal heart that are superficial are ideal for doing off pump surgery. I feel today that most coronary bypass surgery is still being done on bypass, but overall the percentage being done off bypass seems to be increasing as technology and experience improve. Long term results, particularly graft patency and survival are still pending. Without the effects on clotting secondary to cardiopulmonary bypass, there has been some suggestion of increased thrombosis in off pump surgery patients. The significance of this has yet to be determined.

[b] Conduits for CABG

The conduits for cardiopulmonary bypass largely fall into two categories, arteries and veins. Synthetic conduits are generally not used. Saphenous vein grafts from the legs are still the commonly used conduits. They are usually available and in sufficient quantity perform multiple bypass grafts. They are relatively easy to harvest but can vary in quality. They are subject to obstructive disease over time. In general 70-80% are patent in 5 years and 50% in 10 years. Arm veins and cryopreserved veins for the most part have been abandoned. The left internal mammary artery (LIMA) is an excellent conduit for cardiopulmonary bypass. It is located inside the left pleural cavity just to the left of the sternum and is harvested through the same sternotomy incision. It is used primarily as a pedicle graft based on its origin from the left subclavian artery and anastomosed to the left anterior descending coronary artery after being transected distally from the chest wall. It may also be used to bypass other vessels but the left anterior descending is its primary use. The LIMA to LAD bypass has been shown to improve survival and decrease the risk of re-operation for patients. This is based on long-term patency. This is the conduit of choice in LAD bypass. The right internal mammary artery similar structure is to the right of the sternum. It is less commonly used, as an in-situ graft primarily because of its location. It does not easily reach many of the coronary vessels, but when possible it can be used satisfactorily and it can also be used as a free graft. In using bilateral internal mammary arteries, you can decrease the blood supply to the sternum. There is a report of increased incidence of wound infection, particularly in the obese diabetic patient when both mammary arteries are used.

Success of the internal mammary arterial conduit has led to the investigation of other arterial grafts. The radial artery had been used in the remote past. Recently the recognition of some prolonged patency has caused a resurgence in its use. It is an artery with a more muscular wall than the internal mammary artery and is more prone to spasm. By using anti-spasmodic agents the hope was to produce long-term patency. It does not compete well in arteries where the degree of stenosis is not severe and tends to go into spasm but in arteries with stenoses greater than 70% it may be a good alternative graft. It is at least as good as vein grafts, maybe slightly better than some but it is not as satisfactory as the left internal mammary artery. In considering the use of the radial artery graft, there are two arteries to the hand and the forearm, the ulnar and radial artery. As long as there is good communication in the palmar arch, one can remove one of these arteries and still preserve adequate circulation to the hand. An Allens test is a bedside test that can be used to test for patency of this. It can also be done in the vascular laboratory. As long as there is good communication, the radial artery can be harvested. Other arterial grafts such as the gastro-poploric or epigastric artery have been used and are used occasionally but are not as useful as the mammary or the radial artery.

[5] Coronary Artery Bypass Grafting (CABG)[181]

[a] Threatened Myocardial Infarction

Roberts[182] reported on twenty cases, three of which were related to coronary artery catheterization, and seventeen followed PTCA. There was a 20/% incidence of new Q-wave myocardial infarction.

Losman[183] reported on myocardial revascularization after streptokinase treatment for acute myocardial infarct. Eighty-six cases of evolving myocardial infarct within six hours of symptoms were treated with streptokinase on an average of 4.4 hours. Thirty-nine received intracoronary streptokinase for sixteen anterior lateral and seven inferior infarcts. In seven the treatment failed to open the obstruction, and the patients had severe

---

[181] Bourassa, et al., *Factors Influencing Patency of Aortocoronary Vein Grafts*, 45 CIRCULATION (Suppl. 1) 79 (1972); Breuer, et al., *Central Nervous System Complications of Coronary Artery Bypass Graft Surgery: Prospective Analysis of 421 Patients*, 14 STROKE 682 (1983); Frey, et al., *Serial Angiographic Evaluation 1 Year and 9 Years after Aorto-Coronary Bypass*, 87 J. THORAC. CARDIOVASC. SURG. 167 (1984); Spray & Roberts, *Changes in Saphenous Veins Used as Aortocoronary Bypass Grafts*, 94 AM. HEART J. 500 (1977).

[182] Roberts, et al., *Emergency Coronary Artery Bypass Surgery for Threatened Acute Myocardial Infarction Related to Coronary Artery Catheterization*, 39 ANN. THORAC. SURG. 116 (1985).

[183] Losman, et al., *Myocardial Surgical Revascularization after Streptokinase Treatment for Acute Myocardial Infarction*, 89 J. THORAC. CARDIOVASC. SURG. 25 (1985).

hypokinesia. Twenty-three of 39 patients underwent vein bypass grafting. An additional 47 patients received intravenous streptokinase for anterior lateral infarct in fourteen and for inferior infarct in four. Twenty-eight of these 47 were subjected to coronary artery bypass grafting. In spite of recannulization, nine of fourteen patients showed severe hypokinesia and there was one apical aneurysm. Intracoronary instillation led to 69.5/% patients being angina free, while the intravenous route relieved 75/%. The intravenous route was felt to be as effective in relieving pain and salvaging myocardium. Skinner[184] reported 24-hour emergency coronary bypass graftings for severe triple vessel disease and moderate ventricular dysfunction. Eight of these patients required intra-aortic balloon pump assist preoperatively; there were four operative deaths and two late deaths. Thirteen patients had normal clotting postoperatively, but two had frank coagulopathy (hyperfibrinolysis). Four required reexploration; two for coagulopathy, one for surgical bleeding, and one to rule out tamponade which was not found.

Sterling[185] found no increased risk in coronary artery vein bypass grafting accomplished three to ten days after streptokinase thrombolysis. He found the restored flow to infarcting myocardium improved its function. Reul[186] recommended coronary artery bypass for unsuccessful PTCA, and reported 571 lesions in 518 patients, of which 184 had coronary artery bypass grafting because of PTCA failure. Thirty-seven patients were delayed a week or more, with no deaths. There were 87 patients operated on immediately with two deaths. Seven procedures were urgent because the patients had cardiac arrest. Murphy[187] discussed surgical management of acute myocardial ischemia following PTCA, and pointed out that the myocardial infarct may be delayed up to 22 hours. Of sixteen cases supported with intra-aortic balloon pump, 80/% were protected. Only 50/% were protected without pump support.

FitzGibbon[188] reported 118 patients without angina over an eight-year period who had coronary artery bypass grafts. This group of patients had more preoperative infarcts and abnormal ventriculograms. The group with angina had a higher reoperative rate.

---

[184] Skinner, et al., *Immediate Coronary Artery Bypass Following Failed Streptokinase Infusion in Evolving Myocardial Infarction*, 87 J. THORAC. CARDIOVASC. SURG. 567 (1984).

[185] Sterling, et al., *Early Bypass Grafting Following Intracoronary Thrombolysis with Streptokinase*, 87 J. THORAC. CARDIOVASC. SURG. 487 (1984).

[186] Reul, et al., *Coronary Artery Bypass for Unsuccessful Percutaneous Transluminal Coronary Angioplasty*, 88 J. THORAC. CARDIOVASC. SURG. 685 (1984).

[187] Murphy, et al., *Surgical Management of Acute Myocardial Ischemia Following Percutaneous Transluminal Coronary Angioplasty*, 87 J. THORAC. CARDIOVASC. SURG. 332 (1984).

[188] FitzGibbon, et al., *Aorto-Coronary Bypass in Patients with Coronary Artery Disease Who Do Not Have Angina*, 87 J. THORAC. CARDIOVASC. SURG. 717 (1984).

[b] Graft Choice

Liddle[189] reported on early angiographic follow-up with 354 patients, and found skip vein grafts to have a higher mean patency rate than single vein grafts for 70-90/% lesions in arteries less than 2mm in diameter. He found no difference in patency when coronary arteries were in excess of 2mm diameter with obstructions greater than 70/%. Most reports indicate a higher patency rate with internal mammary bypass grafting than when veins are used for a conduit.[190] Kamath[191] reported 93/% patency at one year with sequential internal mammary artery grafts compared to 90/% for vein grafts. Singh and Sossa[192] indicated that the internal mammary artery changes calibre in response to changes in the size of the coronary artery vascular bed. Puig[193] described a method of positioning the right internal mammary artery behind the heart by cutting the pericardial sac to reach the circumflex artery and its branches. He reported that complications included one mediastinal infection leading to death, one temporary dysphonia, and one possible phrenic nerve injury.

In Lytle's[194] long-term results of bilateral internal mammary artery grafting, 76 consecutive cases were studied in 1983 with no hospital deaths, but there were five late deaths, two of which were not related to the heart. Lytle recommended that when saphenous veins are unsuitable for grafting, bilateral internal mammary artery grafts should be utilized before other conduits.

Seifert[195] reported 21 cases of coronary artery bypass grafting with 44 arm vein grafts studied at eight months in which only 66/% of the 35 grafts were

---

[189] Liddle, et al., *Conditional Probability of Multiple Coronary Graft Failure*, 87 J. THORAC. CARDIOVASC. SURG. 526 (1984).

[190] Kay, et al., *Internal Mammary Artery Bypass Graft Long Term Patency Rate and Follow-Up*, 18 ANN. THORAC. SURG. 269 (1974); Lytle, et al., *Long-Term (5-12 Years) Serial Studies of Internal Mammary Artery and Saphenous Vein Coronary Bypass Grafts*, 89 J. THORAC. CARDIOVASC. SURG. 248 (1985); Singh, et al., *Long-Term Fate of the Internal Mammary Artery and Saphenous Vein Grafts*, 86 J. THORAC. CARDIOVASC. SURG. 359 (1983).

[191] Kamath, et al., *Sequential Internal Mammary Artery Graft*, 89 J. THORAC. CARDIOVASC. SURG. 163 (1985).

[192] Singh & Sossa, *Internal Mammary Artery: A "Live" Conduit for Coronary Bypass*, 87 J. THORAC. CARDIOVASC. SURG. 936 (1984).

[193] Puig, et al., *A Technique of Anastomosis of the Right Internal Mammary Artery to the Circumflex Artery and its Branches*, 38 ANN. THORAC. SURG. 533 (1984).

[194] Lytle, et al., *Multivessel Coronary Revascularization Without Saphenous Vein: Long-Term Results of Bilateral Internal Mammary Artery Grafting*, 36 ANN. THORAC. SURG. 540 (1983).

[195] Seifert, et al., *Aorto-Coronary Bypass Grafts Using Cephalic Veins*, 30 J. THORAC. CARDIOVASC. SURG. 15 (1982).

patent. Andros and Harris[196] preferred cephalic and basilic arm veins over synthetic grafts if leg veins were not adequate. Murtra[197] reported a patent 4mm polytetrafluoroethylene graft at 53 months.

Anticoagulation therapy postoperatively is beneficial according to McEnany;[198] however, there is no uniform agreement as to its benefit. Although warfarin improved patency at six months, in McEnany's report there were four major hemorrhages with one death. Occlusion was said to be related to an imperfect anastomosis, vein handling, size difference causing turbulence and slow flow, inadequate runoff, progressive disease, and alterations in the vein secondary to systemic pressures.

Cosgrove[199] studied mortality trends in 24,672 isolated vein bypass grafts between 1970 and 1982. He reported 66.2/% of the deaths were cardiac, and 9.6/% were related to neurological deficits. Risk factors included emergency, congestive heart failure, left main coronary artery disease, female sex, age, normothermic arrest, number of grafts, poor left ventricular function, and incomplete revascularization.

[c] Without Cardiopulmonary Bypass

Buffolo[200] reported 68 coronary artery bypass grafts (CABG) without cardiopulmonary bypass, representing 30.2/% of 225 patients needing such grafts. The left anterior descending and distal right coronary arteries were the most frequent arteries grafted. The thirty-day hospital mortality was 1.5/%. There were two perioperative myocardial infarcts; 84.2/% of the grafts were patent when studied. Buffolo believes this technique avoids cerebral and pulmonary complications of cardiopulmonary bypass.

---

[196] Andros & Harris, *Arm Veins — Durable Autogenous Alternatives to Arterial Bypass,* 142 WEST. J. MED. 537 (1985).

[197] Murtra, et al., *Long-Term Patency of Polytetrafluorethylene Vascular Grafts in Coronary Artery Surgery,* 39 ANN. THORAC. SURG. 86 (1985).

[198] McEnany, et al., *The Effect of Antithrombotic Therapy on Patency of Saphenous Vein Coronary Artery Bypass Grafts,* 83 J. THORAC. CARDIOVASC. SURG. 81 (1982).

[199] Cosgrove, et al., *Primary Myocardial Revascularization Trends in Surgical Mortality,* 88 J. THORAC. CARDIOVASC. SURG. 673 (1984).

[200] Buffolo, et al., *Direct Myocardial Revascularization Without Extracorporal Circulation: Technique and Initial Results,* 4 TEXAS HEART INST. J. 33 (1985).

[d]   Added Risk Factors [201]

[i]   Elderly patients

Knapp[202] reported 3.3/% strokes and 7.6/% psychoses in patients who were over 70 years of age. This compared to 0.7/% and 1.8/% for those younger. Roberts[203] compared a group of patients who were 65 or older with those 60 or younger, and found the mortality the same, but the older group required longer hospitalization. He concluded: "After coronary artery bypass graft procedures, the highly symptomatic elderly patient may experience dramatic relief of symptoms. Another goal of such surgery should be to optimize the quality of life. If these aims can be achieved, the greater utilization of hospital resources and the expense associated with coronary artery bypass grafting in the elderly may be justified." Montague[204] reported on 597 consecutive patients older than 70 years, with 16 being between 80 and 87. There was an average of 3.4 grafts with a 2.7/% hospital mortality and a 10.6 day hospital stay. There were 23/% major complications. He concluded coronary artery bypass grafting can be safely performed in the elderly at only slightly higher risks.

[ii]   Associated carotid artery disease [205]

Ivey[206] reports that patients with asymptomatic bruits can be safely screened with ultrasonic carotid duplex screening, and do not require arteriography. Jones,[207] in discussing when combined carotid operations may be necessary, pointed out the past temptation to recommend the combined operation when the stenosis was greater than 75/% and the patient was

---

[201] Breyer, et al., *Late Postoperative Tamponade Following Coronary Artery Bypass Grafting in Patients on Antiplatelet Therapy*, 39 ANN. THORAC. SURG. 27 (1985); Pluth, *Operative Mortality and Morbidity for Initial and Repeat Coronary Artery Bypass Grafting*, 38 ANN. THORAC. SURG. 552 (1984).

[202] Knapp, et al., *Efficacy of Coronary Artery Bypass Grafting in Elderly Patients with Coronary Artery Disease*, 47 AM. J. CARDIOL. 923 (1981).

[203] Roberts, et al., *Mortality, Morbidity, and Cost-Accounting Related to Coronary Artery Bypass Graft Surgery in the Elderly*, 39 ANN. THORAC. SURG. 426 (1985).

[204] Montague, et al., *Morbidity and Mortality of Coronary Bypass Grafting in Patients 70 Years of Age and Older*, 39 ANN. THORAC. SURG. 552 (1985).

[205] Keagy, *Combined Carotid and Coronary Operations: Discussion of Jones et al.*, 87 J. THORAC. CARDIOVASC. SURG. 7 (1984); Webster, *Carotid Endarterectomy: Indications and Techniques*, SURG. ROUNDS, May, 1985, p. 57.

[206] Ivey, et al., *Management of Patients with Carotid Bruit Undergoing Cardiopulmonary Bypass*, 87 J. THORAC. CARDIOVASC. SURG. 183 (1984).

[207] Jones, *supra* note 28.

symptomatic. The risk of carotid embolization is greater if the patient had a previous stroke. Symptomatic carotids are operated first if the angina is stable. Simultaneous surgery is recommended by Jones for bilateral symptomatic carotid disease, or if a symptomatic bruit is associated with left main coronary or diffuse multivessel coronary artery disease.

[iii]   Associated valvular heart disease

Mitral valve replacement: Kabbani[208] reports that mitral valve replacement for regurgitation in association with coronary artery bypass grafting has the highest mortality of any bypass grafting surgery. One should reconsider replacing the mitral valve. Kabbani feels the risk is less with annuloplasty. Magovern[209] reported a 21.7/% mortality in 23 patients. His mortality in 130 consecutive patients with mitral stenosis was 7.1/%, with mitral insufficiency 5.4/%; for mixed stenosis and insufficiency, it was 8.1/%. Four of Magovern's patients with mitral valve replacement and coronary artery bypass grafting needed a left ventricular assist device. Three of these survived. Of eleven emergency operations for shock, there was a 45/% mortality. Of the non-emergency group over sixty years of age, there was 15/% mortality. Those with a left ventricular diastolic pressure in excess of 15mm-Hg had 16/% mortality. Pinson[210] reported the use of wall motion score and severity of regurgitation in deciding which mitral valve should be replaced. Of 120 patients, 56/% were graded mild, 18/% moderate and 26/% severe. If regurgitation is only moderate, one may avoid valve replacement with acceptable results.

Aortic stenosis: Green[211] did coronary angiograms routinely in 103 cases of isolated aortic stenosis. Twenty-five of the patients without angina had significant coronary artery disease, and 70/% of those were in a single vessel.

[e]   Ejection Fraction of 0.2 or Less

Zubiate[212] reported twelve-year results (between 1973 and 1981) in 232 patients with ejection fractions of 0.2 or less. There were ten deaths of 150

---

[208] Kabbani, et al., *Risk of Combined Coronary Artery Bypass and Mitral Valve Replacement,* 11 TEXAS HEART INST. J. 348 (1984).

[209] Magovern, et al., *Risks of Mitral Valve Replacement and Mitral Valve Replacement with Coronary Artery Bypass,* 39 ANN. THORAC. SURG. 346 (1985).

[210] Pinson, et al., *Late Surgical Results for Ischemic Mitral Regurgitation: Role of Wall Motion Score and Severity of Regurgitation,* 88 J. THORAC. CARDIOVASC. SURG. 663 (1984).

[211] Green, et al., *Relation of Angina Pectoris to Coronary Artery Disease in Aortic Valvular Stenosis,* 55 AM. J. CARDIOL. 1063 (1985).

[212] Zubiate, et al., *Myocardial Revascularization for Patients with Ejection Fraction of 0.2 or Less: 12 Years' Results,* 140 WEST. J. MED. 745 (1984).

patients, or 7/% mortality. Congestive heart failure was an important factor related to five-year survival. If the patients never had congestive failure, there was 60/% five-year survival. In those that responded to treatment, there was 40/% survival. Of those who had congestive failure at the time of surgery, there was 24/% five-year survival. Zubiate believes that this is better than the outlook for heart transplant.

[f]   Left Ventricular Aneurysm

Barratt-Boyes[213] reported 113 patients with 22 hospital deaths and 24 late deaths. He indicated aneurysm occurs in 4-20/% of myocardial infarctions. He recommends surgery for continuous angina, congestive heart failure, intractable ventricular arrhythmias, and arterial embolism. Olearchyk[214] reported on 224 left ventricular aneurysms with 218 survivors. Surgical indications included angina in 61/%, congestive heart failure in 9.8/%, arrhythmia in 7.8/%, and combinations, 20.9/%. Resection of the aneurysm alone was done in 24 cases with a 7.7/% operative mortality and a 56.8/% ten-year survival. Left ventricular aneurysm resection was combined with valve or ventricular septal defect operations in 8.2/% of the cases. The operative mortality in this group was 20/% with a ten-year survival of 60/%.

[g]   Trash Heart

In 1980, Robicsek[215] recommended aortic patch with dacron or Gore-Tex for a calcified thickened aortic wall. The proximal graft can be made from this patch. Parsonett[216] reported a case of trash heart along with thirteen in the literature, all of which had been fatal. He recommends avoiding the ascending aorta if it is pasty. Alternate methods of dealing with this problem include using the innominate artery[217] and internal mammary artery graft,[218]

---

[213] Barratt-Boyes, et al., *The Results of Surgical Treatment of Left Ventricular Aneurysms: An Assessment of Risk Factors Affecting Early and Late Mortality*, 87 J. Thorac. Cardiovasc. Surg. 87 (1984).

[214] Olearchyk, et al., *Left Ventricular Aneurysm*, 88 J. Thorac. Cardiovasc. Surg. 544 (1984).

[215] Robicsek & Rubenstein, *Calcification and Thickening of the Aortic Wall Complicating Aortocoronary Grafting: A Technical Modification*, 29 Ann. Thorac. Surg. 84 (1980).

[216] Parsonett, et al., *Atheroemboli Complicating the Pre- and Postoperative Course of Aortocoronary Bypass (The Trash Heart): Case Report with Comment*, 12 Texas Heart Inst. J. 87 (1985).

[217] Weinstein & Killen, *Innominate Artery-Coronary Artery Bypass Graft in a Patient with Calcified Aortitis*, 79 J. Thorac. Cardiovasc. Surg. 312 (1980).

[218] Murphy & Hatcher, *Coronary Revascularization in the Presence of Ascending Aortic Calcification: Use of an Internal Mammary Artery-Saphenous Vein Composite Graft*, 87 J. Thorac. Cardiovasc. Surg. 789 (1984).

or doing the distal anastomosis without crossclamping the aorta by controlling the coronary artery. Robicsek reported two cases, one of which occurred spontaneously two weeks prior to admission, and one that occurred during the operation.

Grondin[219] recommended tying arteriosclerotic vein grafts that are to be replaced at the start of the cardiopulmonary bypass in patients requiring reoperation, if the arteriosclerotic vein grafts are patent.

[h] Right Ventricular Saphenous Vein Graft Fistula

Riahi[220] reported coronary artery steal ten months postoperatively with successful repair.

[6] Surgical Treatment of Ventricular Arrhythmias[221]

Ostermeyer[222] reported on forty electrophysiologically guided encircling endocardioventriculotomies for recurring sustained ventricular tachycardia secondary to coronary artery disease and previous myocardial infarct. Of twelve patients who had complete encirclement, there was one death, but eight were free of ventricular tachycardia without medication. In the second group of 28 with partial encirclement, including the earliest electrical activation sites, there were two deaths with nineteen being free of ventricular tachycardia without medical treatment. Ostermeyer recommends partial encirclement with complete obliteration of the mapped area to avoid the decreased left ventricular function found with complete encirclement procedures. Isner[223] reported the advantage of carbon dioxide or Argon laser in avoiding the difficulty in establishing tissue planes.

---

[219] Grondin, et al., *Reoperation in Patients with Patent Arteriosclerotic Vein Grafts*, 87 J. THORAC. CARDIOVASC. SURG. 379 (1984).

[220] Riahi, et al., *Right Ventricular-Saphenous Vein Graft Fistula*, 87 J. THORAC. CARDIOVASC. SURG. 626 (1984).

[221] Brodman, et al., *Results of Electrophysiologically Guided Operations for Drug-Resistant Recurrent Ventricular Tachycardia and Ventricular Fibrillation due to Coronary Artery Disease*, 87 J. THORAC. CARDIOVASC. SURG. 431 (1984).

[222] Ostermeyer, et al., *Surgical Treatment of Ventricular Tachycardia: Complete Versus Partial Encircling Endocardial Ventriculotomy*, 87 J. THORAC. CARDIOVASC. SURG. 517 (1984).

[223] Isner, et al., *Laser Photoablation of Pathological Endocardium: In Vitro Findings Suggesting a New Approach to the Surgical Treatment of Refractory Arrhythmias and Restrictive Cardiomyopathy*, 39 ANN. THORAC. SURG. 201 (1985).

[7] Heart Transplantation[224]

Cyclosporine has rekindled interest in human heart transplantation because of the control of the rejection phenomenon. Most groups have benefited from the pioneer work done by Shumway in the knowledge of improved selection, better management of donors, and improved graft preservation. One now expects 80/% one-year survival and 50/% five-year survival. Legionnaire's disease has been reported in at least one transplant patient.[225] Cardiopulmonary transplantation[226] is being used with increased frequency for patients with associated lung disability.

[8] Structural Failure of Heart Valves

Jaumin[227] reported an outlet strut fracture and disc embolis postoperatively in a patient who had a 23mm aortic Bjork-Shiley valve. The patient died. Previously, only the 29mm and larger sizes reported fractures, and these were usually in the mitral position. Patel[228] described a successful outcome following disruption of such a valve, and emphasized the benefit of 2-D echocardiography in diagnosis. Ibarra[229] reported an emergency operation for fracture of the outlet strut of a Bjork-Shiley mitral prosthesis ten months postoperatively. Until 1975, there were only three strut fractures, and these were at the inlet. A recent new case in a 31mm mitral valve six years postoperatively has been reported. The manufacturer changed its process from welding the strut to making it an integral part. Shiley recalled all their 29, 31, and 33mm prostheses. Only one disc fracture was reported. X-ray of the left anterior oblique from 45-70 degrees was recommended to try to pick up this fracture. The president of Shiley in a "Dear Doctor" notification stated: "We recommend close monitoring of patients with these sizes until

---

[224] Frazier, et al., *Cardiac Transplantation at the Texas Heart Institute: Comparative Analysis of Two Groups of Patients (1968-1969 and 1982-1983)*, 39 ANN. THORAC. SURG. 303 (1985); Novitzky, et al., *The Surgical Technique of Heterotropic Heart Transplantation*, 36 ANN. THORAC. SURG. 476 (1983).

[225] Fuller, et al., *Legionnaire's Disease after Heart Transplantation*, 39 Ann. Thorac. Surg. 308 (1985).

[226] Baldwin, et al., *Bronchoscopy After Cardiopulmonary Transplantation*, 89 J. THORAC. CARDIOVASC. SURG. 1 (1985).

[227] Jaumin, et al., *Strut Fracture of the Bjork-Shiley Aortic Valve*, 88 J. THORAC. CARDIOVASC. SURG. 787 (1984).

[228] Patel, et al., *Successful Outcome Following a Disrupted Bjork-Shiley Prosthetic Mitral Valve*, 12 TEXAS HEART INST. J. 111 (1985).

[229] Ibarra, et al., *Fracture of the Outlet Strut of a Bjork-Shiley Mitral Prosthesis: Emergency Operation with Survival*, 87 J. THORAC. CARDIOVASC. SURG. 315 (1984).

we develop data on the rate of strut fracture. Shiley will continue to update you on any significant changes in the status..."[230]

The Ionescu-Shiley pericardial xenograft has been reported to fail suddenly.[231]

According to Brais,[232] five out of 497 valves inserted through July 1983 were removed for secondary intrinsic failure. Gabbay[233] reported seven valve failures of forty patients with mitral valves. He found complete absence of neoendothelial lining of the dacron-covered frame in lesions similar to previous fatigue studies. He believed it was related to the continuous trauma of the tissue against the bare dacron cloth during closure of the valve. He recommended close follow-up with 2-D echocardiography after the third clinical year.

The Omniscience valve has caused the most recent concern. Rabago[234] discontinued use of the valve because of a high incidence of dysfunction at eighteen months. Only 73/% were free of valve problems by thirty months. There were six emboli with no deaths. There were additional thromboembolic obstructions of the valves requiring reoperations: five in the mitral position, and one patient with a double valve in the mitral and aortic areas. These occurred in an average of nine months. The mitral was replaced. The aortic clot was removed by turning the valve with a holder.

There were five perivalvular leaks with one operating room death. There were two cases of infection requiring emergency surgery. Both patients died. There were eight deaths in all, but no autopsies. Gradients with exercise increased from 8 to 21mm-Hg. Of 26 cases studied at six months, none of the valves opened to their maximum distance. Rabago felt that the stiffness of the polyester sewing ring predisposed to perivalvular leaks. In "Letters to the Editor," many theories were proposed for the failure. Some felt that the running of monofilament suture might be a cause; however, the aortic valves were placed with interrupted sutures. It was observed that the dacron cloth did not have new endothelium.[235]

---

[230] Dear Doctor letter from B. E. Fettel, President of Shiley, Feb. 18, 1985.

[231] Gabbay, et al., *Fatigue-Induced Failure of the Ionescu-Shiley Pericardial Xenograft in the Mitral Position*, 87 J. THORAC. CARDIOVASC. SURG. 836 (1984).

[232] Brais, et al., *Ionescu-Shiley Pericardial Xenografts: Follow-up of Up to 6 Years*, 39 ANN. THORAC. SURG. 105 (1985).

[233] Gabbay, et al., *Long-Term Follow-up of the Ionescu-Shiley Mitral Pericardial Xenograft*, 88 J. THORAC. CARDIOVASC. SURG. 758 (1984).

[234] Rabago, et al., *Results and Complications with the Omniscience Prosthesis*, 87 J. THORAC. CARDIOVASC. SURG. 136 (1984).

[235] Fananpazir, *Results of Valve Replacement with Omniscience Prosthesis*, 87 J. THORAC. CARDIOVASC. SURG. 939 (1984); Fananpazir, et al., *Reflections on the Omniscience Heart Valve*, 87 J. THORAC. CARDIOVASC. SURG. 941 (1984).

The sewing ring material was changed to teflon, and this problem was overcome. Panebianco[236] also recommended discontinuation of the valve. The same problem with the sewing ring had been reported in the Lilliehi-Kaster valves.[237] The most recent communication from the manufacturer indicated the FDA has approved it for use, and they consider the valve to be safe.

---

[236] Fananpazir, *Results of Valve Replacement, supra* note 228.

[237] Alstrup & Rygg, *Experiences with Omniscience and Lillehei-Kaster Valves,* 87 J. THORAC. CARDIOVASC. SURG. 940 (1984).

CHAPTER 4

EMERGENCY MEDICINE*

Darren P. Mareiniss, MD, JD, MBe

SYNOPSIS

---

* An earlier version of this chapter was written by James T. Zimmerly, MD, JD, MPH.

§ 4.01 Introduction

This chapter is divided into four sections. Section 4.01 introduces the subject of Emergency Medicine and provides a broad overview of the specialty, the core medical content, qualifications required and administrative guidelines for emergency departments. Section 4.02 gives a brief description of the different types of emergency medicine practices. Section 4.03 describes selected diseases that may pose a liability risk for practicing emergency medicine physicians. Finally, section 4.04 considers the current trend in malpractice cases and focuses on diagnostic errors as a source of medical liability. In conclusion, this final section gives some recommendations for future research and strategies for avoidance of liability.

[1] Qualifications of the Emergency Physician

Prior to development as a specialty in itself, with recognized board certification, the emergency department was often viewed as the retirement community of general practitioners and other physicians who were interested in set hours in a controlled environment. The physicians who were, on occasion, the least well trained for emergency medicine practice found themselves managing emergency rooms. The development of emergency medicine as a specialty has changed all of that. Presently, emergency physicians typically enter the practice of emergency medicine upon completing a three- or four-year residency program after medical school. As of 2007, there were 143 emergency medicine programs in the United States. In 2006, these programs graduated over 1287 residents. There are, however, many emergency physicians who have not completed an emergency medicine residency and have entered emergency medicine from other medical fields. These physicians are no longer eligible to sit for the American Board of Emergency Medicine boards due to the residency requirement but still provide competent emergency medical care and may retain eligibility for one of the other emergency medicine boards.

[2] The Specialty of Emergency Medicine

The American College of Emergency Physicians defines "emergency medicine" as the medical specialty with the principal mission of evaluating, managing, treating and preventing unexpected illness and injury. In 2003, approximately 114 million patients were treated in emergency departments in the U.S. Emergency departments have become the health care safety net in the U.S. and provide access for everyone who needs medical care.

Along with the recognition of emergency medicine as a medical specialty and the establishment of emergency medicine residency programs, the development of the specialty required a delineation of the body of knowledge required of emergency physicians. As a result, the American College of Emergency Physicians, American Board of Emergency Medicine, the Council of Emergency Medicine Residency Directors, the Emergency Medicine Residents' Association, the Residency Review Committee of Emergency Medicine and the Society for Academic Emergency Medicine jointly developed the core content for emergency medicine.

The following is an outline of the core content for emergency medicine:

[a]   Core Content for Emergency Medicine

1.0   Abdominal and Gastrointestinal Disorders – disorders of the esophagus, liver, gallbladder, pancreas, stomach, small bowel, large bowel, rectum, anus, abdominal wall, spleen and peritoneum

2.0   Cardiovascular Disorders
   2.1   Acquired diseases of the myocardium – congestive heart failure, cardiomyopathy, ischemic heart disease, coronary syndromes, myocardial infarction, myocarditis, ventricular aneurysm, cardiac failure
   2.2   Diseases of the pericardium – pericarditis, pericardial tamponade
   2.3   Disturbance of cardiac rhythm – cardiac dysrhythmias, conduction disorders
   2.4   Disorders of the circulation – arterial, venous
   2.5   Congenital abnormalities of the cardiovascular system
   2.6   Cardiopulmonary arrest
   2.7   Hypertension
   2.8   Tumors of the heart
   2.9   Valvular disorders
   2.10 Endocarditis

3.0   Cutaneous Disorders
   3.1   Dermatitis
   3.2   Infections – bacterial, viral, fungal
   3.3   Maculopapular lesions
   3.4   Cancers of the skin – basal cell, Kaposi's sarcoma, melanoma, squamous cell
   3.5   Decubitus ulcers
   3.6   Papular/nodular lesions
   3.7   Vesicular/bullous lesions

4.0 Endocrine, Metabolic, and Nutritional Disorders
    4.1 Acid-base disorders
    4.2 Adrenal disease
    4.3 Fluid and electrolyte disorders – sodium, calcium, potassium, magnesium, water
    4.4 Glucose metabolism – diabetes mellitus, type I and II
    4.5 Nutritional disorders
    4.6 Endocrine gland disorders – pituitary, thyroid, parathyroid
    4.7 Endocrine manifestations of cancer

5.0 Environmental Disorders
    5.1 Dysbarism
    5.2 Submersion incident
    5.3 Electrical injury
    5.4 High altitude illness
    5.5 Radiation emergencies
    5.6 Temperature illnesses – frostbite, hypothermia, heat stroke
    5.7 Bites and envenomation

6.0 Head, Eye, Ear, Nose, and Throat Disorders
    6.1 Ear – infections, foreign bodies, Meniere's Disease, eardrum perforation
    6.2 Nose – epistaxis (nosebleeds), infections, foreign bodies, sinusitis, rhinitis
    6.3 Throat – foreign bodies, gingivitis, epiglottitis, laryngitis, oral candidiasis, pharyngitis, tonsillitis, stomatitis
    6.4 Eye – external eye (e.g., conjunctivitis, corneal abrasions, foreign bodies), anterior pole (e.g., glaucoma, hyphema), posterior pole (e.g., retinal detachment, vascular occlusion), orbit (e.g., cellulitis, purulent endophthalmitis).
    6.5 Tumors

7.0 Hematologic Disorders
    7.1 Clotting disorders – hemophilia, platelet disorders, disseminated intravascular coagulation
    7.2 Lymphomas
    7.3 Red blood cell disorders
    7.4 Transfusions
    7.5 White blood cell disorders – leukemia, multiple myeloma, leukopenia

8.0 Immune System Disorders
    8.1 Collagen vascular disease

8.2 Autoimmune diseases – rheumatic fever, rheumatoid arthritis, sarcoidosis, lupus
8.3 HIV and manifestations
8.4 Hypersensitivity/allergic reactions
8.5 Kawasaki syndrome
8.6 Sarcoidosis
8.7 Transplant-related problems
8.8 Rheumatic fever

9.0 Systemic Infectious Disorders
9.1 Bacterial
9.2 Fungal
9.3 Viral
9.4 Biologic weapons
9.5 Tick-borne
9.6 Emerging infections/pandemics

10.0 Musculoskeletal Disorders (Nontraumatic)
10.1 Bony abnormalities
10.2 Joint abnormalities
10.3 Disorders of the spine – herniated discs, sciatica, tumors
10.4 Overuse syndromes – tendinitis, bursitis, strains, carpal tunnel
10.5 Muscle abnormalities
10.6 Soft tissue infections

11.0 Nervous System Disorders
11.1 Hemorrhagic/ischemic stroke
11.2 Cranial nerve disorders – Bell's Palsy, trigeminal neuralgia
11.3 Demyelinating disorders – multiple sclerosis
11.4 Infections – meningitis, encephalitis
11.5 Neuromuscular disorders
11.6 Movement disorders
11.7 Seizure disorders
11.8 Headaches
11.9 Tumors
11.10 Stroke
11.11 Spinal cord compression
11.12 Hydrocephalus
11.13 Transient cerebral ischemia
11.14 Other conditions of the brain – dementia, pseudotumor cerebri

12.0 Obstetrics and Disorders of Pregnancy
12.1 Female genital tract

12.2   Pregnancy – uncomplicated and complicated (e.g., ectopic pregnancy, miscarriages, toxemia)

12.3   Labor – uncomplicated and complicated (e.g., preterm labor, premature membrane rupture, fetal distress)

12.4   High-risk pregnancy

12.5   Normal labor and delivery

12.6   Complications of labor

12.7   Complications of delivery

12.8   Postpartum complications

13.0 Pediatric Disorders

13.1   Gastrointestinal – appendicitis, congenital lesions, gastroenteritis

13.2   Cardiovascular – congenital heart disease, acquired heart disease

13.3   Endocrine/metabolic – diabetes

13.4   Hematologic – anemias, leukemias

13.5   Neurologic – meningitis, seizures, tumors

13.6   Orthopedic

13.7   Head, eye, ear, nose, and throat – epiglottitis, croup, otitis media, pharyngitis

13.8   Psychiatric – behavioral disorders, depression, eating disorders

13.9   Respiratory – asthma, pneumonia, cystic fibrosis

13.10 Skin and soft tissue infections

13.11 Genitourinary

13.12 Sudden infant death syndrome

13.13 Neonatal/pediatric resuscitation

14.0 Psychobehavioral Disorders

14.1   Thought disorders – schizophrenia

14.2   Mood disorders – depression/suicidal thoughts, bipolar disorder

14.3   Neurotic disorders

14.4   Addictive behavior

14.5   Personality disorders

14.6   Organic psychoses

14.7   Addictive behavior

14.8   Factitious disorders

14.9   Patterns of violence/abuse/neglect/sexual assault

14.10 Psychosomatic disorders

14.11 Personality disorders

15.0 Renal and Urogenital Disorders

15.1   Acute and chronic renal failure

15.2   Complications of renal dialysis

15.3   Infections

15.4 Male genital tract
15.5 Nephritis
15.6 Structural disorders
15.7 Tumors

16.0 Thoracic-Respiratory Disorders
16.1 Acute upper airway disorder
16.2 Disorder of pleura, mediastinum, and chest wall
16.3 Noncardiogenic pulmonary edema
16.4 Obstructive/restrictive lung disease
16.5 Physical and chemical irritants/insults
16.6 Pulmonary embolism/infarct
16.7 Pulmonary infections
16.8 Tumor – breast, chest wall, pulmonary

17.0 Toxicologic Disorders
17.1 Principles – toxidromes, treatment modalities (e.g., antidotes, decontamination, cathartics, diuresis, dialysis)
17.2 Drug and chemical class

18.0 Traumatic Disorders
18.1 Principles of care – prehospital, triage, resuscitation, injury prevention
18.2 Radiologic evaluation – plain x-ray, CAT scan, ultrasound, angiography
18.3 Diagnosis and treatment by anatomic area
18.4 Cutaneous injuries – lacerations, burns, puncture wounds, bites, chemical
18.5 Trauma in pregnancy
18.6 Pediatric trauma

19.0 Urogenital/Gynecologic Disorders
19.1 Female – ovarian disorders (e.g., torsion, cysts, tumors), vagina, uterus (e.g., bleeding, tumors), cervix (e.g., cancer, cysts), infections
19.2 Male – testicular torsion, epididymitis, hernias, prostate enlargement, infections
19.3 Sexual assault

[3]   The American Board of Emergency Medicine

The American Medical Association and the American Board of Medical Specialties officially recognized emergency medicine as the 23rd medical specialty in 1979. It achieved primary board status in 1989. The American Board of Emergency Medicine administers the board examination, which consists of a comprehensive written examination. After successfully passing the written examination, an oral examination must be completed. When board certification in emergency medicine first became available, candidates might have completed an approved emergency medicine residency or worked a certain number of hours in an emergency department. However, the latter option has expired for this particular board. Now the only candidates allowed to sit for the examination are those that have completed an approved Emergency Medicine residency. The written board examination is given once per year and the oral board examination is given twice per year. Every ten years an examination must be passed to maintain board certification. As of 1999, there were over 16,000 physicians certified by the American Board of Emergency Medicine. The American Osteopathic Board of Emergency Medicine also certifies emergency physicians.

[4] Principles of Emergency Care

The American College of Emergency Physicians has developed planning and resource guidelines for emergency departments. These guidelines include administration, staffing, design, and essential material requirements for modern emergency medicine departments ("EDs"). The following is a brief synopsis of these requirements:

[a] Administration

- The emergency facility must be organized and administered to meet the health care needs of its patient population. A written organizational plan for the ED consistent with hospital bylaws and similar to the organizational plan of other clinical departments should be created.
- Operation of the ED must be guided by written policies and procedures.
- The medical director of an ED, in collaboration with the director of emergency nursing and with appropriate integration of ancillary services, must ensure the quality, safety and appropriateness of emergency care. This care should be continually monitored and evaluated.
- All new staff members working in an ED should receive a formal orientation that addresses the mission of the institution, standard operating procedures of the ED and the responsibilities of each member of the ED staff.

- All emergency care personnel must maintain and enhance their professional knowledge and skills. All personnel should have the goal of providing optimal care to patients.
- The duties and responsibilities of physicians, nurses and ancillary staff in the ED must be defined in writing. The ED quality assurance program should provide for the evaluation and monitoring of each member of the emergency care team.
- In accordance with applicable laws, regulations and standards, the triage and screening of each patient who enters the facility must be performed by a physician or by a specially trained registered nurse, nurse practitioner or physician assistant. Such triage and assessment should be in accordance with Emergency Medical Treatment and Active Labor Act ("EMTALA") policies and medical staff bylaws. Policy guidelines should be developed collaboratively by the medical director of emergency services and the director of emergency nursing.
- Each patient who presents with an emergency medical condition should be immediately evaluated and stabilized, to the degree reasonably possible.
- The emergency physician is responsible for the medical care provided in the ED. This includes the medical evaluation, diagnosis and recommended treatment and disposition of the emergency patient, as well as the direction and coordination of all other care provided to the patient. Medical care responsibility for a particular patient in the ED may be transferred to another physician if said responsibility has been assumed unambiguously. A registered nurse is responsible for the nursing care of each emergency patient. This includes assessment, planning and the evaluation of a patient's response to an intervention.
- The ED must maintain a control register or "log" identifying each individual who presented to the facility seeking emergency care.
- A legible and appropriate medical record must be established for every individual who presented for emergency care. As required by law, this record must be retained and should remain available to the emergency staff when needed.

[b] Staffing

- Appropriately educated and qualified emergency care professionals shall staff the ED during all hours of operation.
- An emergency medical director shall direct the medical care provided in the ED. The medical director of the ED should:

- be certified by the American Board of Emergency Medicine or the American Osteopathic Board of Emergency Medicine or possess comparable qualifications as established through the privilege delineation policy;
- possess competence in management and administration of the clinical services in an ED;
- be a voting member of the executive committee of the hospital's medical staff;
- be knowledgeable about EMS operations and the regional EMS network;
- be responsible for assessing and making recommendations to the hospital's credentialing body related to the qualifications of emergency physicians with respect to the clinical privileges granted to them; and
- ensure that the emergency staff is adequately qualified and appropriately educated.

- All physicians who staff the ED, including the medical director, should be subject to the hospital's customary credentialing process and must be members of the hospital medical staff with clinical privileges in emergency medicine. Emergency physicians should have the same rights, privileges and responsibilities as any other member of the medical staff.

- Each physician should be individually credentialed by the hospital medical staff department in accordance with criteria contained in ACEP's policy on physician credentialing. All emergency physicians who practice in an ED must possess training, experience and competence in emergency medicine sufficient to evaluate and initially manage and treat all patients who seek emergency care. This training should be consistent with the physician's delineated clinical privileges.

- The nursing care provided in the ED shall be directed by a registered nurse. The director of emergency nursing services should:
  - demonstrate evidence of substantial education, experience and competence in emergency nursing;
  - show evidence of competence in management and administration of the clinical services in an ED; and
  - ensure that the nursing and support staff are appropriately educated and qualified.

- Each nurse working in the ED should:
  - provide evidence of adequate previous ED or critical care experience or have completed an emergency care education program (the CEN credential is an excellent benchmark); and

   ○ demonstrate evidence of the knowledge and skills necessary to deliver nursing care in accordance with the Standards of Emergency Nursing Practice.

- The medical director of the ED and the director of emergency nursing must assess staffing needs on a regular basis. Patient census, injury/illness severity, arrival time and availability of ancillary services and support staff are factors to be considered in the evaluation of emergency scheduling and staffing needs. Staffing patterns should accommodate the potential for the unexpected arrival of additional critically ill or injured patients. A plan should exist for the provision of additional nursing, mid-level practitioners and physician support in times of acute overload or disaster.

[c] Facility

- The ED should be designed to provide a safe environment in which to render care and should enable convenient access for all individuals who present for care.
- The ED should be designed to protect, to the maximum extent reasonably possible consistent with medical necessity, the right of the patient to visual and auditory privacy.
- Radiological, imaging and other diagnostic services must be available within a reasonable period of time for individuals who require these services.
- Laboratory services must be available within a reasonable period of time for the provision of appropriate diagnostic tests for individuals who require these services.
- Appropriate signs consistent with the applicable regulations and laws should indicate the direction of the ED from major thoroughfares and whether the facility is designated as a specialized emergency care center.
- Adequate provisions for the safety of the ED staff, patients and visitors must be designed and implemented.

[d] Equipment and Supplies

- Equipment and supplies must be of high quality and should be appropriate to the reasonable needs of all patients anticipated by the ED.
- Necessary equipment and supplies must be immediately available in the facility at all times.

• Evidence of the proper functioning of all reusable direct patient care medical equipment must be documented at regular intervals.

[e] Pharmacologic/Therapeutic Drugs and Agents

Necessary drugs and agents must be immediately available. A mechanism must exist to identify and replace all drugs before their expiration dates.[1]

§ 4.02 Types of Practice

[1] The Hospital Emergency Department

Since the early 1970s, there has been an increasing trend in emergency medicine practice to staff hospital emergency departments with full-time emergency physicians. Over the past decades, there has been a gradual but definite trend away from the physician who maintains a part-time practice in the community and a part-time practice in the local hospital emergency room. Emergency physicians now must demonstrate experience in emergency medicine prior to receiving credentials to work in the department. The credentialing process consists of proof of either prior experience in emergency medicine or residency training in emergency medicine or other specialties with a sufficiently adequate exposure to emergency medicine patients.

The development of full-time emergency medicine specialists has increased the level of care provided in emergency departments; prior to 1970, many patients received excellent care, but many did not.

The number of patient visits to emergency departments rose sharply from the early 1970s to 1980. The 1980s saw the number continue to rise very slowly, plateau or even dip in some hospitals. In many hospitals, the emergency department was once a back room or two, always crowded, and always active. The 1970s witnessed the development of larger, more spacious, better equipped departments, staffed by better-trained and more experienced physicians. As noted above, emergency department patient visits have increased yearly as these departments have become more important to both hospitals and patients.

[2] Free-standing Ambulatory Care Clinics

The early 1980s saw the growth of urgent care, medical walk-in clinics whose purpose it is to capture the walking-well patients who do not require

---

[1] Adapted from - American College of Emergency Physicians. Emergency Department Planning and Resource Guidelines. *Ann Emerg Med.* 2005;45(2):231-38.

the services of a fully staffed emergency department. Many of these patients would ordinarily be treated in a physician's office. Those who do not have personal physicians are especially attracted to these clinics.

These ambulatory care clinics capitalize on mass advertising and relatively long hours of operation. They advertise that they are available when the family physician is not, generally on evenings, weekends and holidays. The development of walk-in clinics has skyrocketed in recent years. In addition to private physicians and corporations, many hospitals have developed outreach clinics to capture patients and preempt other groups from infringing on what they consider to be their territory.

By 1982, it was estimated that there were 600 minor emergency centers in the United States. As of July 2006, the Association for Ambulatory Care reported 500 members representing 1,700 clinics in 46 states. Most of these clinics are owned by physicians, while the rest are run by hospitals and corporations.

[3] Other Emergency Medicine Positions

[a] Teaching

The growth of emergency medicine residency programs has required the development of faculty to teach in these programs. A greater number of emergency physicians now serve as professors of Emergency Medicine.

[b] Administrative

With the growth of emergency medicine generally, there has also developed the need for emergency physicians experienced in business to manage, market, promote and develop this aspect of various health care delivery systems. A growing number of emergency physicians have found themselves well-suited to move into the increasing number of administrative positions.

§ 4.03 Medical Negligence Problem Areas — Selected Diseases

The following section summarizes some selected disease pathologies that may create liability issues for a practicing emergency medicine physician. Of note, some of the most common claims for malpractice involve the missed diagnoses of myocardial infarction, fractures, infections and appendicitis. Accordingly, the following section highlights these disease pathologies and other specific illnesses that may be sources of malpractice litigation for emergency medicine physicians.

However, the author would like to caution the reader that the following descriptions of diseases, diagnostic strategies and recommended courses of treatment are not meant to be an exhaustive medical review. Such a review is far beyond the scope of this chapter which primarily concerns liability issues and the avoidance of medical error. Rather, the following are simply "snapshots" of different types of diagnostic dilemma and disease pathologies that an emergency medicine physician should be aware of when considering medico-legal liability. For a more complete clinical review of each topic, the author refers the reader to Rosen's Emergency Medicine: Concepts and Clinical Practice, sixth ed. Philadelphia: Mosby Elsevier, 2006.

[1] Evaluating Abdominal Pain

One of the most frequent conditions seen by the emergency physician is abdominal pain. Patients who present with abdominal pain may have infectious causes, chronic disease causes or acute/emergent causes of disease. In such cases, the emergency physician is challenged to arrive at a clinical impression as promptly as possible. The impression or diagnosis should be based on a complete history, thorough physical examination and laboratory tests and diagnostic imaging as indicated. The emergency physician may not be able to arrive at a specific diagnosis but should be able to quickly determine which patients have potentially life threatening conditions and require immediate surgical consultation.

[a] The Patient's Medical History — Abdominal Pain

The history is the most important aspect of diagnosing the cause of acute abdominal pain. Patients should be allowed to give a full history before physicians ask a specific question. The history should include a full history of the present illness, a complete medical history, a complete surgical history and a list of current medications. The clinician should ask about any previous similar symptoms, the presence of prodromal symptoms and prior abdominal surgery. In addition, the physician should inquire about bowel function, the presence or absence of flatus, anorexia, nausea, vomiting, coffee ground vomit, diarrhea, melena, fever and bloody stool. For female patients, a complete gynecologic history, menstrual history and pregnancy history should be taken. Of note, gynecological causes of abdominal pain, such as ectopic pregnancy, mittelschmerz and ovarian torsion, must be considered in the differential and ruled out.

The history should include an inquiry into how long the pain has been present and both the onset and the character of the pain (e.g., constant or colicky). Of note, inflammatory process such as appendicitis and diverticulitis are often characterized by a gradual worsening of constant pain. In contrast, intermittent colicky pain is usually indicative of an obstructive process such as intestinal obstruction, ureteral calculus or acute biliary colic. Further, a sudden onset of severe abdominal pain may signal the rupture of a hollow viscus, aortic aneurysm (also presenting as back pain) or mesenteric thrombosis.

In addition to the character and onset of pain, the location of the pain can be critical to the diagnosis of an abdominal pathology. Abdominal pain often becomes localized over the involved organ or viscus. Based on the location of the pain, the differential may be narrowed to specific disease pathologies. By example, in a patient with epigastric pain, one may consider pancreatitis, gastritis, peptic ulcer disease, cholecystitis, reflux esophagitis, myocardial ischemia and pericarditis as potential causes. Further, with right upper quadrant pain a clinician may consider acute cholecystitis, choledocholithiasis, retrocecal appendicitis, pancreatitis, subdiaphragmatic abscess, peptic ulcer, pneumonia, myocardial ischemia, pleuritis, pulmonary infarct or empyema. Right lower quadrant pain may indicate appendicitis. However, the differential for pain in this location may also includes mesenteric lymphadenitis, Meckel's diverticulum, ruptured peptic ulcer, cholecystitis, intestinal obstruction, diverticulitis, inflammatory bowel disease, leaking abdominal aortic aneurysm, ectopic pregnancy, ovarian cyst, salpingitis, ovarian torsion, endometriosis, mittelschmerz, renal calculi and psoas abscess. Left upper quadrant pain may indicate splenomegaly, splenic infarct, splenic artery aneurysm, splenic rupture, rib fracture, gastritis, pancreatitis, peptic ulcer disease, pneumonia, myocardial ischemia, pericarditis, pleuritis, empyema and pulmonary infarct. Left lower quadrant pain can be consistent with diverticulitis, colon cancer, intestinal obstruction, inflammatory bowel disease, leaking abdominal aortic aneurysm, ectopic pregnancy, ovarian cyst, salpingitis, ovarian torsion, endometriosis, mittelschmerz, renal calculi and psoas abscess.

[b] The Physical Examination — Abdominal Pain

Beyond a thorough abdominal exam, a complete physical examination of a patient with abdominal pain includes other areas of the body as well. Female patients should always have a gynecologic exam to check for cervical motion tenderness, adnexal mass, and tenderness on bimanual exam. Physical examination should always include evaluation of vital signs — blood pressure, the presence or absence of fever and the respiratory rate and character and heart rate.

The abdominal exam includes inspection, auscultation, percussion and palpation. In addition, a rectal exam should be performed and stool sample checked for blood. The first and most important aspect of the physical exam is to inspect and observe the patient's body habitus and facial expressions. A patient who lies still on the stretcher and is unwilling to change position suggests peritonitis. In addition, such patients may flex their hips and draw their knees up to maintain comfort. This suggests abdominal wall and possible peritoneal irritation. In contrast, patients with intermittent colicky pain seen in acute cholecystitis and renal calculi will writhe on the stretcher attempting to find a comfortable position.

Auscultation of the abdomen should be performed and bowel sounds recorded. Absent bowel sounds are consistent with illeus and peritonitis. Hyperactive bowel sounds may be heard in obstruction. In addition, the examiner should listen for bruits and examine the lung fields for evidence of consolidation. Percussion of the abdomen is less important but may reveal the presence of shifting fluid ascites.

Palpation of the patient's abdomen should begin in the areas of the least discomfort. This is because once a painful area is palpated, the abdominal wall may spasm making additional information difficult to obtain. The presence of "guarding," which is tensing of the abdominal muscle wall, should be noted. Voluntary guarding is the tensing of the patient's abdominal muscles on palpation. In contrast, involuntary guarding is the presence of abdominal muscle spasm where the abdomen continually remains tense and board-like. This is indicative of peritonitis. In addition, rebound tenderness should be determined. This is tenderness that results from increased pain when the examiner releases pressure after palpation. It is indicative of potential significant intraabdominal surgical disease. In addition to the above, the patient should be examined for evidence of inguinal herniation, ventral hernia, femoral hernia and umbilical hernia. As noted above, pelvic examinations are essential in determining the exact cause of abdominal pain in female patients.

Diffuse abdominal tenderness, without guarding, is often found in gastroenteritis and other diseases of the intestines where peritonitis has not developed. Palpation and percussion of the back in the area of the costovertebral angle will result in pain in patients with pyelonephritis and patients with nephrolithiasis, and sometimes with retroperitoneal abscesses or retrocecal appendicitis. There are a number of maneuvers that the physician uses to help localize acute abdominal pain; these are covered in detail in the various textbooks on physical examination.

[c]   Laboratory Examinations — Abdominal Pain

Laboratory examinations include a white blood cell count with differential. This should include the number of polymorphonuclear leukocytes and immature band cells. A left shift and elevated white blood cell count would be indicative of acute infection. An urinalysis, serum electrolytes survey, liver function tests, lipase and amylase should also be performed. The amylase, lipase and liver function tests are particularly important for patients with epigastric and right upper quadrant pain for ruling out liver, biliary disease and pancreatitis. Elevated lipase and amylase indicates pancreatitis. Further, elevated alkaline phosphotase is indicative of ductal obstruction in gallbladder disease, while elevated bilirubin may indicate a common duct obstruction. If pancreatitis is suspected, a lactic dehydrogenase ("LDH") level should also be added. The stool should be examined for occult blood. Examination of the urine is important in differentiating urinary tract infection (white blood cells or nitrate positive), kidney or ureteral stones (blood) and diabetes (glucose), as well as providing clues to other disease processes. For female patients of childbearing age, a human chorionic gonadotropin level must be taken in order to rule out ectopic pregnancy. Finally, depending on the history and risk factors, an ECG should be considered to evaluate for potential myocardial infarction/ischemia.

[d]   Radiologic Tests — Abdominal Pain

Radiologic examination of patients with abdominal pain should be directed by history. In these patients, an abdominal x-ray has limited utility in the evaluation of abdominal pain. Suspected bowel obstruction, foreign body and perforated viscus are the main indications for these studies. In addition, a chest x-ray may be useful and diagnostic for lung pathologies (i.e., pneumonia or empyema) responsible for the patient's symptoms. Ultrasound should be considered in all female patients presenting with abdominal pain. This is a necessary step to evaluate for gynecologic causes of abdominal pain (e.g., ovarian torsion, ectopic pregnancy).

Additional studies should be dictated by the specific patient's history. Of note, the helical CT scan of the abdomen has become the imaging modality of choice for evaluation of nonobstetric abdominal pain. This imaging is typically establishes a diagnosis in more than 95% of cases in one study. Ultrasonography is also useful in all patients for evaluating right upper quadrant pain, as it can assist in the diagnosis of biliary disease. Ultrasound can also be useful in diagnosis of renal calculi, as can helical CT.

In addition, the diagnosis of abdominal pain may not be determined by one of the above studies. Such patients often require repeated examinations over a period of time. Patients may be held in the emergency department or admitted to the hospital for care. The emergency physician, upon completion of his or her examination, is forced to make a decision on treating the patient either in-hospital or out and/or consulting with another specialist. When the patient is considered to have a non-life-threatening condition that may be treated on an outpatient basis and the patient is discharged only to return later with the same complaint, serious consideration should be given to hospitalization for further diagnostic evaluation and consultation.

Early surgical consultation is often helpful in establishing the diagnosis and treatment of the cause of abdominal pain. The surgeon, like the emergency physician, may be forced to rely on observation and repeated examinations. Usually, the earlier the surgeon is involved in the assessment of a potential surgical abdomen, the better for all concerned. Delay in consultation may allow worsening of the patient's condition with possible disastrous consequences and subsequent malpractice claims.

[e] Appendicitis

Failure to diagnose appendicitis is a common allegation in emergency medicine malpractice claims. The failure to timely diagnose the condition may result in increasing morbidity and mortality in all age groups. The diagnosis is more commonly missed in the very young and very old patients. Appendicitis is the most common cause of emergent abdominal surgery in the United States with a lifetime incidence of 7%.

The classical presentation of appendicitis consists of nausea, vomiting and anorexia with intermittent and crampy pain in the periumbilical area. This progressive cramping pain typically migrates to a constant pain in the right lower quadrant of the abdomen typically within 24 hours. Patients frequently have a low-grade fever and the white blood count may be moderately elevated (> 10,000/mm) in 80% to 90% of patients. There are many variations on the classic clinical picture, and variations are especially common in the case of a retrocecal appendix. Further, gynecologic pathologies may present similarly and must be considered in women presenting with similar symptoms. For such patients, a pregnancy test should be administered as an ectopic pregnancy should always be considered in women of childbearing age. On physical exam, patients classically will have localized abdominal tenderness in the right lower quadrant over McBurney's point (2 cm from the anterior iliac spine). The patient may exhibit Rovsing's sign (tenderness in the right lower quadrant when the left lower quadrant is palpated). Further, they may have psoas or obturator sign. See Rosen's Emergency Medicine: Concepts and Clinical Practice, sixth ed. Philadelphia: Mosby Elsevier, 2006 for a more complete discussion.

Patients with low risk of appendicitis—minimal physical findings, are hungry, have strong alternative diagnosis, have multiple previous episodes of similar pain or have symptoms for more than 3 days—may not require diagnostic imaging. These patients often are educated about worsening symptoms and sent home. Arrangements are usually made to have these patients reassessed immediately with worsening symptoms or in 12 to 24 hours if they do not improve.

Equivocal patients, or moderate risk patients, should have diagnostic studies performed. Such patients may have suspicious presentations but lack at least one classic finding. In pregnant women, women with abnormal pelvic exams, and slender children, ultrasound examinations may be obtained. This is a preferred study in pregnant women and children as it does not involve the risk of radiation exposure. For women, this exam also allows assessment of gynecological causes of disease. Such exams may be positive if the appendix is visualized, noncompressible and greater than 6 mm in diameter. However, a negative study that does not visualize a normal appendix does not rule out appendicitis. After such a study result, either a limited helical CT with enteric contrast or hospital admission with serial abdominal exams should be considered if symptoms do not abate and no other cause is found.

For women not of childbearing age and adult men with equivocal signs of appendicitis, an enteric contrast enhanced CT scan is likely the best study to evaluate for appendicitis. However, it is important to reiterate that negative study results for these patients are not 100% sensitive. Patients with a negative study and continued symptoms may require continued observation and serial abdominal exams to assess for disease progression. Further, if these patients are discharged, adequate follow-up should be arranged. In addition, patients should be instructed to return upon worsening or persistent symptoms. For high-risk patients with a classic presentation of appendicitis, no diagnostic studies are necessary and surgical consultation should be immediately sought.

Treatment of appendicitis typically requires immediate removal of the inflamed appendix prior to rupture. Because the diagnosis is not always straightforward, the competent surgeon will remove a certain number of normal appendices in his or her practice. If every appendix that is removed is inflamed, the surgeon is not operating often enough. It is not uncommon or outside the standard of practice to find up to 20% of the appendices removed to be normal, non-inflamed structures.

If surgery is necessary, the patient should be given nothing by mouth and posted for an emergent exploratory laporotomy. Nasogastric suction may be started, and intravenous fluids are given to replace volume deficits. Preoperative treatment with antibiotics covering anaerobic bacteria is standard (Cefoxitin or Cefotetan). If perforated appendicitis is suspected, broader preoperative antibiotic coverage is administered (i.e., gentamicin and metronidazole, levofloxacin or combination B-lactam/B-lactamase inhibitor therapy). For nonperforated appendicitis, post-operative antibiotics should be given for 24 hours.

[f] Volvulus

Failure to diagnose an intestinal volvulus (twisted intestine, causing obstruction) may result in rapid patient demise. This diagnosis also has generated medical malpractice claims with some frequency. A volvulus may develop when a loop of bowel becomes twisted upon itself or under a postoperative adhesive band. The majority of colonic volvulus cases involve the sigmoid colon, whereas cecal volvulus accounts for the remainder of these cases.

Sigmoid volvulus may result in patients with high-residue diets, chronic constipation or laxative abuse. This pathology is most often encountered in elderly bedridden or institutionalized patients, many of whom have a history of prior abdominal surgery. Sigmoid volvulus classically presents with acute abdominal pain, abdominal distention and constipation. Diagnosis is typically made via sigmoidoscopy, plain abdominal x-ray or radiographic exam with a gastrografin enema. Prolonged volvulus may result in strangulation of the bowel, necrosis, gangrenous bowel and sepsis. If emergent strangulation or gangrenous bowel is suspected, the patient must undergo immediate resection. If there is no strangulation or necrosis, sigmoidoscopic reduction can be performed. However, there is a very high recurrence rate for volvulus in these patients (up to 60%). Accordingly, elective resection of the redundant section of sigmoid colon is recommended after the resolution of the patient's acute episode.

Patients with cecal volvulus may have poor fixation of the right colon. Typically, these patients present with an acute onset of colicky right lower quadrant pain that becomes constant. These patients may have vomiting, obstipation and abdominal distention as well. Of note, pregnant women make up around 12% of these cases. Abdominal x-ray may show a large ovoid viscus in the right lower quadrant with an air fluid level forming a classic "coffee bean" sign with the apex aiming towards the LUQ or the epigastrium. If the abdominal x-ray does not demonstrate this, colonoscopy or a gastrografin contrast enema should be diagnostic. The treatment for cecal volvulus is emergent surgery and detorsion of the cecum. Redundant cecum is then resected or the cecum is surgically fixed to the abdominal wall.

Severe steady pain in a patient with intestinal obstruction and distention should raise a high index of suspicion of a potentially severe condition such as volvulus, strangulation of an incarcerated hernia or intussusception. The potential for vascular compromise dictates immediate surgical management. As with appendicitis and other abdominal pain conditions, the diagnosis is not always easy. The emergency physician is not expected to be able to establish the diagnosis in every case but is expected to recognize those potentially life-threatening conditions that require early consultation with the appropriate surgeon.

[g] Intussusception

Intussusception (one segment of an intestine invaginates within another) is a potentially disastrous condition that must be considered in any infant or small child who presents with episodes of crampy abdominal pain alternating with periods of well-being. Typically, patients will have alternating lethargy and irritability ("grumpy baby"). This is the most common cause of small bowel obstruction in toddlers (< 2 years old). While the disease most commonly occurs in young children and youths, it also can occur on occasion in adults. "Currant jelly" stools are considered diagnostic. Abdominal x-rays are often completely normal. Intussusception is occasionally reduced during the performance of an air or barium enema, but surgical exploration is usually necessary to correct the cause of the intussusception and to prevent recurrence.

For adults, an ultrasound or CT scan is the preferred study. This is because reduction of the intussusception may result from barium enema. Such reduction is not desirable in adult patients because 90% of adult intussusceptions involve a malignancy in the lead point of the invaginating small intestine. As a result, reduction in these patients with a barium enema is thought to potentially allow for the spread of malignant cells from the lead point. Physical examination may be non-productive because of the patient's discomfort. In pediatric patients, a mass may be palpated on occasion, but the location of the mass is variable. Rectal examination is essential to check for blood in the stool.

[h] Ruptured Abdominal Aortic Aneurysm

Patients with ruptured abdominal aortic aneurysms ("AAA") classically present with the triad of pain, hypotension and a pulsatile abdominal mass.

Patients with a ruptured AAA will complain of pain in their abdomen, back or flank. The pain typically has an acute onset and is severe and constant. Further, the pain may radiate to the chest, thigh, inguinal area or scrotum. Patients frequently will develop hypotension and syncope as a result of the blood loss. However, hypotension is the least consistent part of this symptomatic triad and may only be seen in half to two-thirds of these patients.

The condition is uniformly fatal without immediate surgical repair. Accordingly, quick identification and treatment of this disorder are of great importance. In addition, patients who are diagnosed and taken to the operating room for surgical repair soon after presentation to the emergency department have a much higher survival rate than in patients in which surgical care is delayed. However, even with immediate surgical intervention, the mortality rate for these patients is very high. Patients with a ruptured AAA progress to shock in short order in the absence of immediate vascular surgical treatment. Time is of the essence. If the patient is to have any chance of survival, the emergency physician must mobilize the vascular surgery team while the patient is being prepared for surgery. Delay in mobilizing the surgeons has resulted in a number of malpractice claims involving this diagnosis.

Any patient with a previously-diagnosed AAA who presents with acute abdomen, flank or back pain must prompt consideration of a potential or impending rupture. Further, with respect to radiologic imaging, hemodynamically unstable patients in which AAA is strongly suspected should be taken to the operating room as soon as possible. With a strong presumptive diagnosis, such patients may be taken to the OR without a definitive diagnostic imaging. In general, diagnostic testing in suspected AAA ruptures should be kept to a minimum. Bedside ultrasound may be used to quickly confirm a diagnosis. Further, a CT scan may only be appropriate if it can be obtained very quickly without compromising a patient's care.

[2] Evaluating Chest Pain

Chest pain is a frequent cause of patient visits to emergency departments and can be a difficult diagnostic problem for the emergency physician. Separating those patients with severe life-threatening conditions who require urgent treatment from those experiencing chest pain from a more benign disease is not always easy. Failure to diagnose and treat patients with certain of these life-threatening conditions has resulted in frequent claims of medical negligence. Some of these conditions are: 1) myocardial infarction; 2) pulmonary embolism; 3) pneumonia; and 4) cardiac tamponade. Such malpractice concerns continue to affect the practice of medicine. In a recent study in the *Annals of Emergency Medicine*, Katz et al determined that malpractice fears correlated with significant variability in the treatment of patients with symptoms of acute coronary syndrome. *See* Katz DA et al. Emergency Physicians' Fear of Malpractice in Evaluating Patients with Possible Acute Cardiac Ischemia, *Ann Emerg Med* 2005; 46(6): 525-533. This may be due in part to the fact that missed myocardial infarction has resulted in the highest mean payout for malpractice claims against emergency medicine physicians.

[a] Myocardial Infarction

The vascular supply of the heart is provided by the right coronary artery and the left coronary artery (dividing into left anterior descending and left circumflex), and their branches supply blood to the heart muscle. A heart attack is caused by an obstruction in one of these arteries. This causes blood to stop flowing past that obstruction to the portion of the heart muscle supplied by that artery and results in death to those heart muscle cells, or myocardium. The death of cells due to lack of blood supply is called infarction. This results in the term "myocardial infarction" ("MI"). Anterior, inferior or lateral MI refers to the area of the heart that has died due to a blockage in the corresponding artery supplying that portion of the heart. These blockages are caused by atherosclerosis, which is a buildup of fatty deposits in coronary arteries. The event that causes an acute MI is a clot in a coronary artery that previously had an atherosclerotic plaque. There are several well-known risk factors that increase the probability of developing coronary artery disease. These include: smoking, diabetes mellitus, hypertension, hyperlipidemia, obesity, sedentary lifestyle, male sex, increased age, family history of coronary artery disease, artificial or early menopause and cocaine use.

Patients who present with an acute MI typically report chest pain. Most often this pain is described as a substernal heaviness, tightness, pressure or a squeezing sensation. The chest pain can radiate to the left shoulder, down the left arm or to the back, neck or jaw. Occasionally the pain occurs in other areas, including the right arm or abdomen. The chest pain usually lasts two to twenty minutes. Deep breaths, pressing on the chest, twisting or bending should not worsen the chest pain caused by an MI. Other symptoms frequently associate with an MI include shortness of breath, nausea, vomiting, profuse sweating (diaphoresis), dizziness, excessive fatigue or anxiety.

Of note, many patients do not present with the typical chest pain symptoms. In fact, a recent study of 450,000 patients ultimately diagnosed with MI showed that one-third did not present with these symptoms. Risk factors for atypical presentation include: diabetes mellitus, older age, female gender, nonwhite ethnicity, dementia, no prior history of MI or hypercholestoremia, no family history of coronary artery disease and previous history of congestive heart failure and stroke. Atypical presenting symptoms include dyspnea, nausea, diaphoresis, syncope or pain in the arms, epigastrium, shoulder or neck. Also, many patients older than 85 may present with atypical symptoms.

The diagnosis of an acute MI is typically based on a combination of the patient's history, the electrocardiogram ("ECG") and serial enzyme changes. If the history is suspicious for an MI, even in the face of a normal electrocardiogram, the patient is generally admitted for monitoring and further diagnostic tests. Many emergency rooms now have special units to rule out MIs called "chest pain centers" ("CPC"s) where patients can be monitored while they are ruled out with serial cardiac enzymes and ECGs.

In a standard 12 lead ECG, each lead corresponds to the electrical activity in various areas of the heart. The electrocardiogram abnormalities of an MI may only occur in some of these leads. A physician can tell which region of the heart is involved and often which coronary artery is involved based on which electrocardiogram leads are abnormal. The electrocardiogram may or may not have abnormalities during an MI. One of the initial ECG findings may be a hyperacute T wave. This is a T wave that is taller and more pointed than the normal T wave and is a transient abnormality. However, though many different abnormalities may be seen, ST segment elevation is the hallmark abnormality of an acute MI. When this occurs with an appropriate history, it is termed "ST elevation myocardial infarction" ("STEMI") and must be addressed immediately. However, not all patients with an MI have abnormal ECGs. In fact, the ECG may not show ST elevation in a large portion of patients having an MI. This is termed non-ST elevation MI. Of note, one study showed nondiagnostic and normal ECGs in up to 20% of patients eventual diagnosed with an acute MI. In patients being evaluated for acute coronary syndrome, only serial ECGs, combined with serial cardiac enzymes can be used to rule out an acute MI.

Cardiac enzymes are also useful in the diagnosis of an MI. Such enzymes include CPK, CPK-MB, Troponin and Myoglobin. Some of these chemicals can occur in other cells and can limit their value in determining if an MI has occurred. Of these markers, Troponin I is one of the most sensitive and specific laboratory test to aid in the diagnosis of MI. This enzyme rises within three to four hours following cardiac injury and remains elevated for seven or more days. The sensitivity of this enzyme approaches 50% within three to four hours of symptoms and increases to 75% in 6 hours and to 100% in 12 hours. As noted above, for patients with concerning histories without a clear diagnosis of MI, serial enzymes and ECGs should be used to rule out an MI.

Patients being evaluated for MI should be placed on oxygen and intravenous lines should be started. Also, aspirin should be given to all these patients and beta blockers and nitroglycerin should be used as indicated. For patients with STEMI, reperfusion should be sought as soon as possible. Either fibrinolytic therapy or percutaneous coronary intervention should be pursued depending on available resources, time from onset of symptoms, history and clinical contraindications (contraindications for fibrinolysis). Both reperfusion techniques have shown significant benefit if pursued with 12 hours of the onset of symptoms. Of note, the American Heart Association ("AHA") recommends that fibrinolytic therapy, for appropriate candidates, be initiated within 30 to 60 minutes of patient's arrival in the emergency department. Further, the AHA also recommends that primary PTCA be initiated within 90 minutes of arrival for appropriate STEMI candidates. Delay in initiating these therapies could create allegations of untimely treatment and malpractice claims.

In patients with non-ST elevation MI, aspirin, nitroglycerin, and heparin should be administered (barring contraindications). Also, supplemental oxygen via nasal canula should be provided and beta blockers and/or morphine, depending on the clinical history, may be considered as well.

Finally, the emergency physician should always be thinking about a potential diagnosis of acute MI. Approximately 2-8% of patients who present to emergency departments with an acute MI are discharged without the diagnosis being made. As noted above, the failure to diagnose this condition has resulted in the highest mean payout for medical malpractice claims against emergency medicine physicians. Atypical presenting symptoms are a major cause of misdiagnosis. Typically patients who are not diagnosed are significantly younger, more likely to be women and nonwhite. These patients have atypical complaints and often do not have ECG findings. Among these patients, women younger than 55 have been shown to have the highest risk for inappropriate discharge. Fifty-three percent (53%) of the patients with missed acute MIs had no ECG finding. However, in 11% of cases, emergency department physicians missed ST segment elevations of 1 to 2 mm. In addition, the risk-adjusted mortality ratio for all patients with acute cardiac ischemia was 1.9 times higher among non-hospitalized patients compared to hospitalized patients. Finally, some factors identified with misdiagnosis of acute coronary syndrome and MI in medical malpractice closed claim analysis have included physicians with less emergency department experience, physicians who admit fewer patients and physicians who have difficulties with ECG interpretation.

[b] Pulmonary Embolism

Pulmonary embolism (PE) is a common disease that causes a significant number of deaths. Approximately 500,000-700,000 cases occur each year in the U.S. A pulmonary embolus is a piece of clotted blood that has broken off from a larger blood clot (thrombus) typically present in the deep venous system of the legs. This embolus travels to the lung and causes an obstruction to the blood flow to a portion of the lung. These clots often start in a vein in the calf. Within the calf, such clots usually do not cause clinically significant emboli. If the clot spreads to the veins of the ileofemoral system they can become sources of pulmonary emboli. Over 90% of PE cases are caused by emboli from the lower extremity. The factors that increase the likelihood of a thrombus forming in the legs are venous stasis, tissue trauma and hypercoagulability. As a result, the most common risk factors of pulmonary embolism are prolonged immobilization, surgery, cancer, thrombophlebitis, leg trauma, advanced age, congestive heart failure, smoking, acquired or inherited thrombophilia, pregnancy and the use of birth control pills.

Pulmonary embolisms often occur in the presence of other debilitating diseases and for that reason are not always suspected. The signs and symptoms are often non-specific, making diagnosis difficult at times. The most common symptoms of pulmonary emboli are chest pain and shortness of breath. The chest pain is often pleuritic or made worse with deep breaths and lateral in location. Purely substernal chest pain is rare in PE and should point the clinician towards another origin of pain and potential diagnosis. A cough is frequently present and can produce blood-tinged sputum or hemoptysis. Leg pain and asymmetrical swelling can also be present and is due to the thrombosis in one of the legs. Signs of pulmonary embolism on physical examination can be scant. Tachypnea (rapid breathing) and tachycardia (rapid heart rate) are often present but are not specific to pulmonary embolism. Lung sounds called rales can also be present. A loud pulmonic component of the second heart sound can be heard as well as a fourth heart sound.

The diagnosis of a pulmonary embolism can be quite difficult. The most definitive test for a pulmonary embolism is the pulmonary angiogram. However, this test is quite invasive and may cause either minor complications or some possible fatal complications. An arterial blood gas ("ABG") is a frequently ordered test to help diagnose a pulmonary embolism and often shows a lowered level of oxygen in the arterial blood. However, this is not specific for a pulmonary embolism as many other conditions can cause this. A chest x-ray is frequently obtained in the evaluation of a patient complaining of chest pain or shortness of breath. The chest x-ray can be normal but may show atelectesis (partial collapse of some lung tissue), pleural effusion (fluid in the space between the lung and pleura), decreased blood in the pulmonary blood vessels or elevation of the diaphragm on the affected side, as well as some other abnormalities. The ventilation/perfusion ("V/Q") nuclear lung scan and CT angiography ("CTA") are probably the most frequently used tests to diagnose a pulmonary embolism. The V/Q scan is a nuclear scan and is positive when a perfusion defect is present during normal ventilation. While the nuclear scan is fairly sensitive, small emboli may be missed. Sometimes an ultrasound of the legs is performed to determine if a deep vein thrombosis ("DVT") is present in one of the legs. A pulmonary embolism is often assumed to be present if the pulmonary signs and symptoms are present in a patient with a definite DVT. However, if a lower extremity ultrasound is negative, it does not necessarily rule out a pulmonary embolism.

Each year, 16 million patients present to emergency departments with chest pain or dyspnea. In light of this huge number, a method of screening patients for pretest probability has been formulated in order to maximize the benefit of work-ups. Accordingly, physicians may use an objective PE rule-out criteria in order to determine whether a work-up is warranted in a patient. If a patient is less than 50 years old, has a heart rate < 100, an oxygen saturation > 94% on room air, no hemoptysis, no unilateral leg swelling, no history of recent surgery or trauma, no prior PE or DVT and no history of hormone use, then it is unlikely that the patient will benefit from a work-up. However, barring this rule-out, patients with clinical presentations consistent with this disease pathology should be assessed.

Currently, there are algorithms to guide this work-up. In light of the diverse patient populations and multiple modes of work-up, it is not possible to relate a single algorithm that covers all possibilities. The following is just one suggested method. In patients with less than a 40% pretest probability of PE, D-dimers should be tested. If the quantitative D-dimers are positive, the patient should then have either a ventilation perfusion lung scintigraphy ("V/Q scan") or computer tomography angiography ("CTA") performed to diagnose a PE. (Of course, other diagnostic tests are available including MRI, venous duplex US, and pulmonary angiography.) Positive D-dimers are not diagnostic of a PE in such patient groups. This is because D-dimers are a very sensitive test, but not specific. If the quantitative D-dimers are negative (i.e., < 500 ng/dl), PE is ruled out in low-risk patients. If the D-dimers are positive, further studies are indicated. A CTA or a V/Q scan should be performed. A negative CTA will rule out PE and positive CTA is diagnostic in this patient group. With respect to V/Q scans, a normal result also rules out PE. However, a result consistent with low, moderate, intermediate or high probability of PE requires additional testing in patients with < 40% pretest probability. Further testing with CTA, pulmonary angiogram or venous duplex should be pursued.

Patients with a likely PE by signs, symptoms and history (> 40% pretest probability) should have a CTA or V/Q scan. D-dimers are not necessary in this higher risk group. A positive CTA or high probability V/Q scan reading confirms the diagnosis in these patients, while a normal V/Q scan rules out PE. However, a low, moderate or intermediate probability V/Q scan requires further testing. Similarly, a negative CTA scan in a patient with high pretest probability requires additional testing as well. One final note: with respect to V/Q scans for patients with chest x-ray findings of air space disease, a CTA or alternative study should be pursued as pre-existing pulmonary pathology affects the accuracy of a V/Q scan read.

Patients with PEs are usually kept at bed rest and given supplemental oxygen. Treatment of pulmonary embolism is usually carried out in an intensive care unit. The standard treatment for pulmonary embolism is intravenous Heparin. This is an intravenous medication that prevents further clots from forming and is continued for five to ten days. The patient is then started on an oral anti-clotting medication called Coumadin. This is begun several days prior to discontinuing Heparin so that the anti-clotting effect of Coumadin has time to begin before intravenous heparin is stopped. Coumadin is usually continued for three months. In seriously ill patients with PE, a surgical embolectomy to remove the clot or thrombolytic medications such as streptokinase, urokinase or tissue plasminogen activator ("t-PA") can be used to dissolve the clot. Thrombolysis is usually given to patients with a massive pulmonary embolism who are unstable. It can improve symptoms quickly but is associated with more complications, specifically bleeding. In patients with recurrent pulmonary emboli, a filter can be placed in the vena cava to prevent clots in the legs from traveling to the lungs.

[c] Cardiac Tamponade

Cardiac tamponade results from the accumulation of fluid or blood in the pericardial space (as little as 15-20 ml of fluid in the pericardial sac can cause tamponade). This results in compression of the heart and interferes with the heart expanding to its full normal degree in order to pump adequate volumes of blood. The restriction on the diastolic filling of the ventricles lowers the amount of blood that can be pumped, reducing the cardiac output and eventually resulting in death. Cardiac tamponade should be suspected in patients with penetrating chest wounds. Also, 10% of all patients with cancer will develop tamponade. In cardiac tamponade, tachycardia develops early to compensate for decreased cardiac filling during diastole. Beck's triad is indicative of this life-threatening cardiac tamponade—hypotension, muffled heart sounds and jugular venous distension. Also, patients will typically have pulsus paradoxus. As the tamponade becomes severe, it presents a life-threatening condition requiring immediate treatment. Echocardiography is the most sensitive and specific non-invasive test to measure the presence of pericardial fluid. Routine chest radiographs may suggest the diagnosis by demonstrating sudden marked increase in the apparent heart size.

Cardiac tamponade requires hospitalization in an intensive care environment with immediate cardiology and cardiothoracic surgical consultation. With hemodynamic instability, pericardiocentesis and subsequent surgical exploration is indicated. While in the emergency department, the patient's blood pressure should be monitored every five to ten minutes, oxygen should be given, and continuous electrocardiograph monitoring should be begun. A peripheral intravenous line is started along with a central venous pressure catheter to continuously monitor the central venous pressure. Echocardiography should be scheduled immediately and the patient transferred to the intensive care unit. It is dangerous to administer diuretics or nitrates to patients with cardiac tamponade because these drugs will further reduce the blood pressure and can cause sudden death. As noted above, patients who are already decompensated from the cardiac tamponade require immediate pericardiocentesis in the emergency department. These patients cannot tolerate the delay in transfer to the intensive care unit.

[3] Evaluating Testicular Pain

The painful scrotal mass is not an uncommon emergency medicine diagnostic problem. Various conditions, including the relatively benign hydrocele, the more severe epididymitis, torsion of the testis, torsion of the appendix testis, incarceration of an inguinal hernia and testicular tumor all must be distinguished. Torsion of the testis must be diagnosed as early as possible in order to facilitate surgical correction. Immediate urologic or general surgical consultation is indicated in any male where torsion is a possible diagnosis. Detorsion, either manual or surgical, must be performed within six to eight hours to prevent loss of the testicle from infarction. Even if the patient is not examined within the critical six-to-eight-hour period, it is still worth surgical exploration because of the possibility of intermittent torsion, and a testicle may be saved even though definitive surgery is delayed for a much longer period of time. It falls below the standard of emergency practice for an emergency physician to fail to obtain an immediate urologic consultation in a patient where the diagnosis may be torsion of the testicle.

[a] Torsion of the Testicle

Torsion usually occurs in prepuberal boys and young men and is uncommon over the age of twenty; however, it can occur at all ages. Testicular torsion is a twisting of the spermatic cord resulting in venous occlusion and subsequent arterial occlusion and infarct of the testicle. Most often there is a sudden onset of severe scrotal pain, followed by swelling of the involved side, making diagnosis very difficult. This complaint may fallow vigorous activity or minor trauma. The most common error is treating the patient for a presumed epididymitis when, in fact, the diagnosis is torsion. This error is almost impossible to excuse in the prepuberal age group, yet it occurs all too often. Nausea and vomiting may occur and the pain may not be limited to the scrotal area. The patient may complain of abdominal pain. A careful history is important to rule out trauma as the cause of the scrotal pain and swelling, although torsion can occur following trauma. Incarcerated hernia may result in scrotal pain and swelling; however, signs of intestinal obstruction are found in such cases.

Patients who develop torsion often give a history of having had similar episodes of scrotal pain that spontaneously resolved. The involved testicle may be found in an elevated position, and it may be positioned horizontally. If the examination is not performed at an early point in the development of the condition, the entire scrotal contents become so swollen and tender that examination is virtually useless. Epididymitis is more commonly found in sexually active men over 20 years of age; however, torsion is also seen in this age group.

Physical examination may reveal a tender epididymis with a normal testis, but a physical examination cannot be relied on in most cases. The Doppler ultrasonic stethoscope, however, provides a simple and quick aid to diagnosing torsion. The absence of sounds of pulsatile flow in the testicular artery is suggestive of testicular torsion, but false negative results can occur. The non-involved testis is usually examined as a control. Radionucleide scanning, using technetium TC 99M sodium pertechnate, will reveal increased scrotal uptake on the affected side in the patient with epididymitis and will demonstrate decreased technetium uptake in the patient with a torsion. Ultrasonography is also useful in distinguishing between epididymitis and an incarcerated hernia and may also demonstrate the presence of varicoceles and other testicular cysts and masses. An x-ray may also be helpful in distinguishing an incarcerated hernia by demonstrating bowel gas within the scrotum. Urologic consultation is always indicated when the diagnosis is in doubt.

Patients with torsion of one testicle have a greater incidence of developing torsion of the contralateral side, and therefore standard procedure consists of performing a bilateral orchiopexy (tacking down both testis). Recent studies tend to suggest that the longer the delay in surgically correcting or removing the infarcted testicle, the greater the chance that the patient will be sterile as a result of an autoimmune response affecting the contralateral testicle. If this theory is proven correct, then the patient with a missed torsion has potentially very significant damages as a result of the resultant sterility. Previously, the majority of physicians were of the opinion that loss of one testicle did not have any effect on the other testicle, and therefore the patient had relatively minimal damage since fertility was thought to be not affected. Finally, as noted above, time is a factor in the treatment of this disease pathology and the best results will be obtained if the testicle is detorsed within 6 hours of the onset of symptoms. This results in approximately a 90% salvage rate. However, delay of greater than 24 hours will likely result in less then 10% of involved testicles being salvaged.

[b] Epididymitis

Epididymitis is uncommon in the prepuberal age group unless it is associated with mumps. The treatment is medical, while the treatment of torsion is surgical. Hydrocele can often be differentiated by transillumination and is not necessarily tender on palpation. Epididymitis is an infection of the epididymis. These patients present with swollen, tender testicles and dysuria. These patients can also have fever and/or chills and a scrotal mass. As noted above, the major differential diagnosis is testicular torsion, which must be ruled out. In the elderly, the cause of these infections is most commonly *E. coli*. In younger patients, it is *Gonorrhea* or *Chlamydia*. The treatment consists of antibiotics treatment for the most likely causative organism.

[4] Evaluation and Treatment of Life-threatening Infections

Life-threatening infections and fevers of unknown origin are frequent emergency medicine diagnostic problems. Failure to establish the appropriate diagnosis oftentimes leads to malpractice claims. There are a number of life-threatening infectious diseases that may result in a rapid demise of the patient if the diagnosis is not suspected and appropriate treatment begun early. Those diagnoses that most commonly result in litigation involve alleged failures to diagnose meningitis, epiglottitis, toxic shock syndrome and other overwhelming septic conditions such as pneumonia and Rocky Mountain spotted fever.

[a] Bacterial Meningitis

Meningitis is an infection of the covering of the brain and spinal cord called the meninges. Organisms reach the meninges by either traveling through the blood, by spreading from nearby sites such as the sinuses or ear infections (rarely) or through penetrating wounds caused by trauma or surgery. Many different organisms can cause bacterial meningitis. Causative organisms can be viral, bacterial or fungal. In neonates, *Group B streptococcus*, *Escherichia coli* and *Listeria monocytogenes* are the most common bacterial organisms. In infants and children, *Haemophilus influenzae*, *Streptococcus pneumoniae* and *Neisseria meningitidis* are the most common organisms. In adults, *Streptococcus pneumoniae* is the predominant bacterial pathogen followed by *Neisseria meningitidis* and *Listeria monocytogenes*. *N. meningitides* is the predominant organism in adults younger than 45. A vaccine to prevent certain serogroups (A, C, Y and W 135) of meningococcal meningitis has been available since 1974 and has been used in the military since 1970s. In December 2000, the American Academy of Pediatrics recommended the routine immunization of students living in dormitories because of their increased risk of this potentially fatal disease. Of course, viral meningitis is a frequent cause of meningitis and the spinal fluid obtained from the lumbar puncture can distinguish this. Risk factors for the development of meningitis include otitis media, altered immune status, alcoholism, pneumonia, sinusitis, endocarditis, diabetes mellitus, head injury and a cerebrospinal fluid leak. Other predisposing factors include age > 50 or < 5, male gender, low socioeconomic status, crowded living conditions, past splenectomy, sickle cell disease, African-American race, household contact with meningitis patient, IV drug abuse, VP shunt and malignancy.

Prompt recognition and immediate treatment of bacterial meningitis with appropriate antibiotics is essential to reduce morbidity and mortality. The early diagnosis of bacterial meningitis is sometimes very difficult and may border on the impossible, especially in the younger age group. The symptoms of meningitis include fever, headache, stiff neck, abnormal mental status, nausea and vomiting, seizures, photophobia and weakness. On physical examination the signs of meningitis include nuchal rigidity and other meningeal signs (Kernig and Brudzinski), fever, petechial rash and focal neurological defects. However, focal neurologic defects and seizure are more commonly seen in encephalitis than in meningitis. Infants may present with a bulging fontanel. However, many of these signs and symptoms may be difficult to detect or absent in the very young or very old. These age groups have difficulty in verbalizing their symptoms. In addition, young infants may not develop nuchal rigidity and may sometimes present with non-specific symptoms such as irritability and poor feeding. With respect to geriatric and immunosuppressed patients, classic signs and symptoms of meningitis may not be present. In elderly patients, an altered mental status may be the only presenting sign of meningitis.

A lumbar puncture (LP) should be performed to determine if meningitis is present and should be performed early so that the diagnosis can be made and treatment started as soon as possible. If the diagnosis is suspected, empiric broad spectrum antibiotics can be started before an LP is performed. Further, before performing an LP, some patients require a head CT in order to assess for intracranial mass or increased pressure, as an LP in such patients can be extremely harmful or fatal. A screening CT is indicted in patients who are immunocompromised, have a history of stroke, mass lesion, focal infection or head trauma. Further, patients who have had seizures within the last seven days, have abnormal level of consciousness, focal neurologic deficits or abnormal speech should have a screening CT. The cerebrospinal fluid obtained during a lumbar puncture is tested for white blood cell ("WBC") count and differential, a gram stain to determine if any bacteria are present, a culture to determine which bacteria, if any, are present and sensitivity to determine the antibiotic sensitivity of any bacteria that do grow. In addition, glucose, protein and latex agglutination test for specific bacteria can be performed. Further, PCR can provide a highly sensitive and specific test. However, such testing should likely be reserved for unclear presentations, patients who are pre-treated with antibiotics and when less common causes of meningitis are suspected. The cerebrospinal fluid in a patient with bacterial meningitis typically shows an elevated WBC count with primarily polymorphonuclear cells, a gram stain that shows the presence of bacteria, a decreased glucose, an elevated protein and cultures that eventually grow bacteria. In viral meningitis, the WBC count in the cerebrospinal fluid may be elevated, (but not typically as dramatically as in bacterial meningitis), the WBCs are primarily mononuclear cells, the gram stain shows no bacteria, glucose is normal to slightly decreased, protein is normal to slightly increased and bacterial cultures show no growth.

Patients are hospitalized, often in the ICU, and the treatment of bacterial meningitis with intravenous antibiotics should be started rapidly. Minutes count in the treatment of bacterial meningitis. A number of malpractice claims have alleged a delay in treatment once the diagnosis was suspected. It falls below the standard of practice to suspect the diagnosis and then send the patient to a distant larger hospital for definitive treatment without beginning antibiotics first. Broad spectrum antibiotics may be administered empirically in suspected bacterial meningitis. Many authorities recommend ceftriaxone or cefotaxime, plus vancomycin to cover potential resistant organisms. Once the causative organism is cultured and sensitivity is determined, antibiotic treatment can be further targeted. In addition, corticosteroid treatment is currently recommended in these patients. Treatment with dexamethasone has been shown to decrease long-term neurologic deficits in adults and children. In adults, absolute risk reduction of 10% for unfavorable outcomes was seen when this corticosteroid was administered concomitantly with antibiotics and continued for four days. Finally, chemoprophylaxis of household contacts for patients with meningococcal meningitis is recommended. For *H. Influenza type b* meningitis, chemoprophylaxis is recommended for non-pregnant household contacts when there are children younger than 4 years of age in the house.

The treatment of viral meningitis is often symptomatic. However, patients are often treated with antibiotics because the distinction between viral meningitis and bacterial meningitis may be difficult and may even require a repeat lumbar puncture. Complications of meningitis include deafness, developmental delays, focal neurologic deficits, cranial nerve deficits, seizures and hydrocephalus. These neurologic sequelae are common even under the best of treatment and circumstances and more commonly result from certain organisms.

[b] Epiglottitis

Epiglottitis (inflammation of the mouth of the wind pipe) is most commonly seen in young children (between 3 and 7 years of age), but is also known to occur in adults. However, the incidence of epiglottis in the pediatric population has markedly declined in the last 15 years as a result of the widespread use of *Haemophilus influenza type b* vaccine. Of note, the failure to diagnose this condition in adults has led to a number of successful lawsuits. The most common etiologic agent is the bacteria *Hemophilus influenzae type b*. The condition is a severe life-threatening condition that may result in complete upper airway obstruction if not recognized and treated immediately. Because the physical examination or attempted intubation may precipitate an airway obstruction, it is essential that the appropriate otolaryngology consultant and anesthesiology specialist are available at the patient's bedside and prepared to perform an immediate cricothyroidotomy or tracheostomy if complete obstruction occurs. Hospitalization with constant monitoring is required, and empiric parenteral antibiotics are normally prescribed. A lateral soft tissue x-ray of the neck is helpful in establishing the diagnosis by demonstrating a swollen epiglottis that is displaced posteriorly. The condition is also referred to as supraglottitis because, in addition to the epiglottis, other structures around the area of the epiglottis are often inflamed.

Epiglottitis usually has a very rapid progression, following an abrupt onset. Of note, 85% of children with epiglottis in one study were symptomatic for less than 24 hours before presentation. The patient may first develop a fever and sore throat, followed by dysphagia, aphonia and stridor. As the disease progresses, the edema of the involved structures interferes with the ability to swallow secretions. Patients presenting to the emergency department who are unable to swallow their own saliva should never be discharged and will likely need a definite airway. A complaint of a sore throat is a common presenting symptom. The respiratory rate increases, and the accessory muscles of respiration are called upon to help the patient breathe. This results in suprasternal and subcostal retracting. Laboratory data may show an elevated white blood cell count with an increase in the percentage of leukocytes. Blood culture may demonstrate the offending organism, although by the time the blood culture results are available, the condition has either run its course, been treated successfully or the patient has expired. The lateral neck x-ray is very diagnostic. In adults, lateral cervical soft tissue x-ray films have a reported sensitivity of up to 90%. The normal epiglottis has a thin curve silhouette that looks like a bent finger, convex on one side and concave on the other. The swollen, inflamed epiglottis assumes a configuration that is convex on both sides. As soon as the clinician suspects epiglottitis, immediate consultation with appropriate otolargyngologists or other surgical and anesthesia personnel and preparation for the insertion of an artificial airway should be made. Time is of the essence. The patient with epiglottitis should never be left unattended in the emergency department, radiology department or other area of the hospital. Antibiotics are essential to treat the local infection in the supraglottic area, to limit the spread to other sites and to treat concurrent infections such as pneumonia. First-line agents pending culture and sensitivity results are cefotaxime and ceftriaxone. Alternative antibiotics include ampicillin-sulbactam and trimethoprim-sulfamethoxazole. Some physicians add steroids to the treatment regimen. However, there is some debate about their usefulness. Mortality in adults is higher than in children, probably because of its misdiagnosis and undertreatment.

[c] Toxic Shock Syndrome

Toxic shock syndrome ("TSS") is a toxin-mediated systemic inflammatory response syndrome. It is caused by toxins released either by *Staphylococcus aureus* or *Group A Streptococcus* bacteria. This disease most commonly is found in menstruating women, although the disease can occur in both sexes and at all ages. In the 1980s, the majority of TSS was found in menstruating women where TSS resulted from bacterial colonization of tampons. However, changes to the absorbency of tampons and use have significantly decreased the number of these cases. The CDC reported a total of 200 cases per year from 1994-2001. The etiologic organisms are *Staphylococcus aureus* and *Group A Streptococcus* bacteria. *Group A Streptococcus* causes toxic shock less frequently in menstruating women and is more typically caused by toxin-secreting bacteria in wound infections, burns and bruises. In addition, while Staphylococcal TSS carries a mortality of less than 3%, Streptococcal TSS can result in a mortality of 30-70%.

It is not known how many patients have a subclinical illness associated with the toxin produced by the *Staphylococcus aureus* bacteria. It is known, however, that many patients do develop a mild form of the condition and do survive untreated. In fact, recurrent toxic shock syndrome has been known to occur in menstrual forms, and a patient may expire with the second or third bout of the illness.

TSS patients typically present with fever, chills, muscle aches and pains, vomiting, diarrhea and sore throat. Patients go on to develop shock with a systolic blood pressure of less than 90 millimeters of mercury, with a fever greater than 102° F and signs of multiple organ involvement. A diffuse, blanching, macular erythematous rash appears over the first few days of illness. This rash is common in Staphylococcal TSS, but only present in 10% of patients with Streptococcal TSS. The rash fades after a few days, and the skin of the hands and feet desquamates approximately one to two weeks later. Patients with Staphylococcal TSS frequently are using a tampon at the time of the illness; if so, it should be removed. Regarding patients with wound infections with toxin-secreting bacteria, surgical consultation and debridement may be required.

In TSS, abnormal laboratory tests reflecting dysfunction of multiple organ systems may be found. The white blood count is frequently elevated with an increase in the percentage of leukocytes and thrombocytopenia (low platelet level). Other laboratory abnormalities occur, including elevation of liver enzymes, blood urea nitrogen, bilirubin and creatinine levels, as well as lowering of the serum calcium, serum albumin and total protein levels. Bacteremia is not typically seen in Staphylococcal TSS but is often seen in

Streptococcal TSS. Patients with TSS should receive aggressive fluid resuscitation with crystalloids and may require up to 20 L/day. Antibiotics may not affect the course of Staphylococcal TSS but are recommended in Streptococcal TSS. Regardless, antibiotics should be started early in the treatment of TSS, as the clinical presentation of the disease is similar whether the source is Staphylococcal or Streptococcal. Clindamycin is considered the first line agent in this disease because of its inhibitory effects on bacterial toxin synthesis. Also, this antibiotic has been shown to decrease cytokine synthesis. Corticosteriods are not currently recommended in TSS as their value has not been determined.

[d]   Bacterial Pneumonia

Pneumonia is a common emergency department condition that requires prompt diagnosis and treatment. As of 2003, pneumonia was the sixth leading cause of death in the United States and the leading cause of death from infectious disease. The annual incidence of community-acquired pneumonia ranges from 2 to 4 million, resulting in approximately 500,000 hospital admissions.

Pneumonia may be caused by many different organisms, with a few bacteria and viruses being the cause in most of the cases. The organisms that cause pneumonia differ with the age, immune status, and comorbidities of the patient. As a result, presumptive antibiotic coverage and treatment are typically guided by the age of the patient and their comorbidities. Pneumonia is often divided into "typical" pneumonia caused by bacteria such as *S. pneumoniae* or *H. Influenza* and "atypical" pneumonia caused by organisms such as *Mycoplasma pneumoniae, Chlamydia pneumoniae, C. burnetii, Legionella* species or viruses. Of all the bacterial causes of community-acquired pneumonia, *S. pneumonia* is the most common cause. In patients with HIV and AIDS, respiratory infections are the most common type of opportunistic infection. In these patients, other causes of pneumonia must also be considered including: *P. carinii*, CMV virus, *M. tuberculosis*, *M. avium* complex, *Cryptococcus neoformans* and *Rhodococcus equi.*

Bacterial pneumonia often follows an upper viral respiratory tract infection. Patients with bacterial pneumonia may appear very severely ill, or they may appear to be relatively clinically well. They often will present with cough productive of purulent sputum, shortness of breath and fever. Pleuritic chest pain and chills may also be noted. In most healthy older children and adults, the diagnosis can be reasonably excluded on the basis of history and physical examination, with suspected cases confirmed by chest radiography. The absence of any abnormalities in vital signs or chest auscultation substantially reduces the likelihood of pneumonia. Elderly or debilitated patients with pneumonia often present with nonspecific complaints and may not show classic symptoms.

Typically, patients with pneumonia have an elevated white blood cell count that usually reveals an increase in the number of polymorphonuclear leukocytes. The chest x-ray findings can be variable. Some patients with pneumonia caused by certain organisms may have a single dense infiltrate (*S. pneumoniae* and *H. Influenzae*), an infiltrate in several locations, an interstitial pattern (*Mycoplasma pneumoniae*) or tiny nodules disseminated throughout both lungs (TB or fungal disease).

Systemic complications can be expected in inadequately treated patients. These include overwhelming sepsis, meningitis and septic conditions in other areas of the body, such as the joints. A Gram stain of the patient's sputum may be obtained to aid identification of the causative organism, but the American Thoracic Society guidelines recommend an empiric approach and starting broad antibiotic coverage as soon as possible. The antibiotic chosen must cover the likely etiologies based on clinical, laboratory, radiologic and epidemiologic information. Empiric antimicrobial therapy should be started in the emergency department for patients admitted with pneumonia. Unless otherwise indicated by clinical, laboratory, radiologic and epidemiologic information, empiric therapy should treat the most likely pathogens, including *S. pneumoniae*, *H. influenzae*, *M. pneumoniae* and *C. pneumoniae*. Blood cultures should be obtained in seriously ill patients and, if drawn, should be obtained before the initiation of antibiotics (although antibiotics should not be delayed for this reason). Oxygen may be required for the comfort of the patient, and arterial blood gas levels are monitored if the patient is in respiratory distress. All patients with suspected significant disease should have initial pulse oximetry to determine oxygenation.

Many patients with pneumonia are treated as outpatients. Patients considered the lowest risk who should be treated as outpatients are younger than 50, without significant comorbid conditions and without certain physical exam findings (altered mental status, pulse of 125 beats/min, respiratory rate > 30, systolic blood pressure < 90 or temperature < 35° C or > 40 ° C). These patients can be treated with a macrolide or doxycyline antibiotic. Further, respiratory fluoroquinolones should be considered if such patients have a risk for drug resistant *S. pneumoniae*. For patients with underlying disease processes, comorbidities and those at the extremes (the very young or very old) hospitalization should be considered. Currently, there are guidelines to assist clinicians in assessing risks based on demographics, comorbid conditions, physical examination and laboratory results for a patient. However, good clinical judgment should supersede a strict interpretation of such scoring systems. Patients older than 60 years of age and those with comorbidities require different antibiotic coverage than younger patients. Such regimens may include second or third generation cephalosporins plus a macrolide, amoxicillin-clavulanate plus a macrolide, or a respiratory fluoroquinolone.

Frequent allegations of substandard medical practice in the diagnosis of pneumonia include allegations of failure to closely follow a suspected pneumonia, failure to order appropriate chest x-rays and failure to hospitalize the patient to insure appropriate and adequate treatment of the disease process.

[e]   Rocky Mountain Spotted Fever

Rocky Mountain spotted fever is a regional disease, most common in the middle and south Atlantic states, but also seen in the Rocky Mountain states. Fewer than twenty cases a year are reported in the Rocky Mountain states, while over 300 cases per year are reported in the mid-Atlantic and southeastern states. The disease is caused by *Rickettsia rickettsii* carried by a tick vector. The disease is seasonal, with the peak incidence occurring in the summer.

Approximately three to twelve days following a bite by an infected tick, the patient develops fever, chills, generalized muscle aches, malaise, and headache. In addition, these patients may have nausea and vomiting. Typically around the third to fifth febrile day, the patient develops a pink blanchable macular rash, usually beginning on the wrists and ankles and spreading to the palms and soles. The rash then spreads centripetally and migrates over the entire body. After two to three days, the rash becomes maculopapular and a deeper red. By the fourth day the rash typically becomes petechial. The patient's temperature is usually elevated and may be in the 103°-104° F range. Laboratory tests are often non-specific. The white blood cell count may or may not be elevated. Rocky Mountain spotted fever may cause significant cardiopulmonary and neurologic manifestations in patients. Of note, severe cases may result in non-cardiogenic pulmonary failure or ARDS. Further, neurologic manifestations can range from mild headache and lethargy to seizure and coma.

When the disease is suspected, the treatment consists of either doxycycline or chloramphenical (for pregnant populations), started early. The patients usually require hospitalization, although the disease may be self-limiting, and mild cases do not require hospitalization. Serologic titers will confirm the disease. Specifically, immunofluorescent antibody staining of skin biopsies in rash regions can confirm a diagnosis as soon as four hours after obtaining a specimen. However, as Rocky Mountain spotted fever may present without rash, such biopsies cannot always be obtained. The presumptive diagnosis, however, should be made on clinical grounds, and treatment should be dispensed in the emergency department. Failure to diagnose Rocky Mountain spotted fever creates malpractice claims each year in the regions of the country where the disease is prevalent.

Delayed or missed diagnosis of Rocky Mountain spotted fever is the principal cause of the significant mortality rate associated with the disease. Complicating the diagnosis is the wide variety of similar infections that can be confused with the disease. Of note, the differential in these patients includes meningococcal infection, measles, atypical measles, gonococcemia, infectious mononucleosis, toxic shock syndrome and enteroviral infections. The rash of Rocky Mountain spotted fever may mimic the rash of fulminant meningococcemia, and failure to diagnose meningococcemia also has been the subject of numerous malpractice claims. The diagnosis is oftentimes difficult in that the clinical presentation of the patient—often an infant, youth, or young adult—frequently mimics other less serious illnesses early in its course. In addition, a certain number of patients with meningococcemia develop a rapidly fulminant course that is probably not alterable by any treatment, no matter how promptly the diagnosis is established and how early appropriate treatment is started.

While failure to diagnose meningococcal disease results in claims of alleged substandard treatment each year, many of these cases are defensible. The defensible cases are usually characterized by a thorough, well-documented examination carried out by an experienced emergency physician who is sensitive to the diagnosis of this disease. Even under the best of circumstances, the disease will be missed on certain occasions.

[5] Treatment of Lacerations and Similar Injuries

Lacerations are one of the most common types of trauma seen in emergency practice, and improper treatment is not an uncommon claim in medical negligence cases. The term laceration most commonly refers to any cut in the skin caused by either a sharp or blunt object. Lacerations are further described by their shape and configuration. A "through-and-through" laceration extends through all layers of the skin or other soft tissue. A linear laceration is relatively straight. A stellate wound is a star-like laceration with the various legs of the star radiating from a center core. An avulsion, which may be partial or complete, is the tearing away of skin from its attachments. A flap avulsion is a partial avulsion with a portion of the skin remaining hinged to the surrounding skin. An amputation is a complete severing of an appendage or limb from the body. A puncture wound is a type of laceration with a relatively small entrance wound. Animal bites, needlesticks and nails cause the majority of puncture wounds.

Treatment of lacerations consists of cleaning, irrigation, debriding and closing the wound. Not all wounds are closed, however. There are certain types of wounds that do better if they are left open, either to heal by granulation or to be closed at a later date. The primary closure of certain types of wounds increases the risk of infection and should be avoided. Wounds that are usually not closed include human bites, certain animal bites, non-facial wounds that are over eight hours old, facial wounds that are over twelve hours old (unless a significant cosmetic deformity will result), obviously contaminated wounds and certain gunshot wounds and puncture wounds. Further, some linear lacerations to the face may be closed greater than 24 hours after injury.

Regardless of the area of the body involved, the evaluation of any laceration begins with an assessment of damage to important structures, including arteries, nerves, veins, tendons and joints. The testing for nerve injury includes testing of the distal skin for presence or absence of sensation and testing the bodily area for muscle strength by examining movement. Arterial pulses are checked distal to the wound, and capillary filling is tested by compressing the skin or the nail to blanch the capillary bed and by observing the rate of blood return. The bones are palpated for evidence of tenderness, swelling or deformity that might indicate a fracture. X-rays are often ordered in puncture wounds and lacerations to rule out the presence of a retained foreign body. The foreign body may be located quite distal to the site of entrance. The wound is also explored and probed in an attempt to assess the degree of damage, repair injured vital structures and remove any foreign bodies. The use of fluoroscopy can be helpful in extracting such foreign bodies.

Routine antibiotic prophylaxis for lacerations does not have a scientific basis. However, antibiotics usually are used for lacerations with a high potential for infection. Of note, antibiotics are usually prescribed for patients with through-and-through intraoral lacerations, cat bites, human bites, dog bites and puncture injuries to the foot. Open fractures, wounds with exposed tendons or joints also require prophylaxis. Also, antibiotics should be considered in immunocompromised patients, patients with grossly contaminated wounds and those with severe crush injuries. All patients who present with lacerations and report a greater than ten-year span of time since their last booster should be given a dose of either tetanus toxoid or diphtheria/tetanus. For burn patients, contaminated wound sites and patients without an immunization history, treatment with tetanus immune globulin should be considered.

[a] Bites

Human and animal bites are common and occur in all areas of the body, most often the hand. Typically these bites are at the metocarpophalangeal joint and are assumed to be human "fight bites." Treatment consists of debridement and thorough irrigation. Animal bites are almost always left open and closed secondarily. Exceptions include animal bites of the face where a serious cosmetic deformity might result if the wound were left open. Systemic antibiotics are often used in an attempt to prevent an infection, although there is not uniform agreement on the need prophylactically to prescribe antibiotics.

Bites of certain animals carry a higher probability of rabies. Bat (17%), skunk (31%), raccoon (36%) and fox bites (17%) account for most cases of rabies encountered in the United States, but nearly all other animals have been found to have rabies at some time. Where the animal cannot be sacrificed to rule out rabies, the bite must be evaluated with the possibility of human rabies immunoglobulin being added to the treatment regimen.

Snake bites are not uncommon and are most reported in the southern U.S. Poisonous snake bites must be observed closely; in a hospital inpatient setting, the degree of ecchymosis and swelling adjacent to the wound is measured. Pit vipers (including rattlesnakes, copperheads, water moccasins, pygmy and Massasauga rattlesnakes) account for 98% of snakebites in the United States. Antivenin may need to be administered depending on the grade of envenomation. Any patient with moderate or severe envenomation should likely receive antivenin. The choice of antivenin depends on the species of snake. Wyeth laboratories previously produced a polyvalent antivenin derived from four species of U.S. pit vipers that can be used. Snake bite victims with clinical evidence of envenomation should have a large bore IV placed in an unaffected extremity and receive crystalloid resuscitation. Further, these patients must have their vital signs monitored closely. An ECG, CBC, U/A, coagulation studies, electrolytes and BUN, fribrin split products and fibrinogen levels should be obtained. In addition, the patient's blood should be typed and cross-matched for 4 units of packed red blood cells.

In addition to snake bites, human bites and mammalian bites, both venomous arthropods (e.g., spider and scorpion bites) and marine animal bites may occur. As treatment of this topic exceeds the scope of this chapter and cannot be completely addressed in this section, the author encourages the reader to consult other sources dealing with these specific types of bites for further information.

[b] Hand Injuries

Hand injuries are the most common type of injuries that result in litigation involving alleged improper wound treatment. An open hand injury is a true emergency and must be treated as soon as possible. The examination for injury to the blood supply and nerves distal to the wound, as well as an evaluation of tendon function, must be carried out and documented in the emergency record. The physician should note, if possible, the position of the hand at the time of injury. This is especially important in determining the level of tendon lacerations. Adequate radiologic examination is essential to determine the presence and degree of severity of bone and joint injury.

Tendon lacerations are best treated by surgeons with training and experience in the repair of tendons; they are rarely repaired in an emergency department setting. However, many extensor tendon injuries are more commonly repaired by emergency physicians. Depending on the zone classification and extent of injury, primary closure by the emergency physician and splinting can be performed. However, flexor tendon repairs require the expertise of a hand surgeon. Repair of flexor tendons may be delayed for as long as four to six weeks. In these cases, the wound is often closed in the emergency department and the nerve and tendon repair scheduled for several weeks later to be carried out by an appropriate specialist. Nerve injuries do better if the repair is not delayed too long, however. The patient should be referred to the appropriate specialist at the earliest point in time. The specialist will then design and prescribe the follow-up treatment. Since hand injuries can often result in loss of some function, it is important that the emergency physician be extremely careful in offering an opinion to the patient regarding an expected good result.

[c] Tetanus

As noted above, tetanus prophylaxis must be considered in any laceration. The treatment is 100% effective if administered properly. Because allergic reactions have been recorded, the overutilization of tetanus toxoid is now discouraged. Lacerations that are heavily contaminated by soil, barnyard lacerations and those involving a crush injury to the surrounding tissue are at higher risk of developing tetanus.

Patients who have received the standard primary immunization, followed by boosters every ten years, are well-protected. Passive immunization with human tetanus immune globulin may be necessary in patients over 50 years of age, patients who are foreign-born, burn patients,

patients with contaminated wounds and those who are unable to provide a history of prior tetanus immunization. Tetanus toxoid combined with diphtheria toxoid is considered to be preferable to tetanus toxoid alone.

[d] Foreign Bodies

Emergency department patients with lacerations should always have a thorough physical evaluation to determine the presence or absence of foreign bodies. Probing the wound may detect a foreign body, but it is not always the best approach. Additional damage may be caused by the probing, and the foreign body might be some distance from the entrance wound in the skin. Radiographs are indicated whenever the physician suspects a possible foreign body. Many emergency physicians and other physicians still labor under the false impression that radiographs are not of value in the case of lacerations caused by glass. Their belief is that glass will not show up on a radiograph. To the contrary, most glass does show up on radiographs. Further, fluoroscopy can be of great utility in the location and removal of foreign bodies. One ex vivo model showed that fluoroscopy had 100% sensitivity for gravel, metal and glass. The sensitivity for graphite was 90%. However, the sensitivity for wood and plastic was 0%. In cases where wood or plastic are suspected as foreign bodies, emergency medicine physicians should consider using ultrasound or CT to locate these objects. A great advantage to fluoroscopy is the ability to use fluoroscopic images to guide removal of objects and then confirm the absence of foreign bodies after removal.

It is not always possible to remove a foreign body and on some occasions, particularly with metal fragments located deep in non-critical areas, it may be best to leave them alone. The physician must weigh the possibility of causing more harm by attempting removal against the detriment of leaving the foreign body in place. Some foreign bodies that are close to the skin may migrate to the surface and can be removed at a later time.

If the foreign body is in a weight-bearing area, such as the sole of the foot, reasonable attempts at removal should be made as early as possible. After foreign bodies are removed, the emergency physician should consider tetanus prophylaxis and antibiotic coverage when warranted by the clinical circumstances. Patients with contaminated hand wounds and wooden splinters may be candidates for such antibiotic coverage and tetanus treatment. The physician must also thoroughly evaluate each patient for evidence of injury to adjacent vital structures, including tendons and nerves. Patients with suspected vascular or neurologic injuries require early evaluation by appropriate specialists.

[6] Problem Cases in Orthopedics

Orthopedic trauma contributes a significant proportion of emergency department patient visits. The patient with an orthopedic injury may also have additional soft tissue injuries that may be more immediately life-threatening than the fracture or the dislocation. Shock from blood loss is a significant problem in the multiple traumatized patient, and large volumes of blood may be lost. This occurs more commonly in fractures of some bones than others. Fractures of the pelvis, followed by fractures of the femur may result in the largest volume of blood loss from a closed fracture. Injuries to peripheral nerves often accompany injuries to bones, and must be evaluated in every case. Neurovascular function is critical.

Standard practice requires documentation at the earliest point in the evaluation of the patient with an extremity injury. The history, including the mechanism of injury, also is extremely helpful in assessing the degree of damage. Extremities are splinted and early radiologic studies are obtained. In addition to the standard anteroposterior and lateral views of the injured extremity, in some instances special films of a particular bone or a stress film are indicated.

[a] Spinal Fractures — Trauma Assessment

In any patient who has sustained significant traumatic injury to the neck or head, the emergency physician should presume a spinal cervical injury until proven otherwise. In fact, 15% of patients who sustain a traumatic injury above the clavicle will have a c-spine injury. Cervical spine injuries are the most common spinal injuries in trauma patients and account for 55% of such injuries. Trauma patients with suspected spinal injury should be immobilized with a c-collar and proper spinal precautions. However, these patients should not be left on a backboard more than 2 hours as this can result in decubitus ulcer formation. Of note, such a morbidity may result in claims of negligence against a treating physician.

With respect to spinal trauma in a conscious and alert patient, the entire spine should be palpated during the trauma assessment. Typically, pain on palpation, discernable step offs, altered neurologic exams or decreased sphincter tone are indicative of spinal injury and require radiologic assessment and neurosurgery consultation. Cervical spine x-rays should be obtained early in the trauma assessment. The standard trauma series for cervical spine evaluation consists of an AP view, lateral view and odontoid view. The combination of these x-rays results in an approximately 92% sensitivity for the identification of c-spine fractures. With respect to the lateral view of the c-spine, the base of the skull to the top of the T1 vertebrae must be visualized to have an adequate study. Patients who are involved in high-speed motor vehicle accidents, falls from tremendous heights, multiple trauma victims and those who have any head, facial or neck injuries are at particularly high risk for developing a cervical spine injury and should be assessed for this injury. If a patient is awake, alert, sober, neurologically normal, has no distracting injury and no neck pain, cervical spinal injury may be ruled out by exam. Otherwise, the screening AP, odontoid and lateral x-rays must be obtained.

Unconscious patients are particularly difficult to assess and require immobilization until such time that their mental status permits them to participate in the evaluation. Further, these patients may require radiographic screening of the entire spine. Finally, it should be noted that spinal cord injury may occur in the absence of a cervical vertebral fracture. Bony instability from ligamentous tears may result in serious, and even fatal, spinal cord injury in the absence of a demonstrable fracture or dislocation. In patients without neurological deficits who have continued neck pain in spite of negative c-spine radiographic studies, flexion and extension films should be obtained to evaluate for ligamentous injury. Such films must be obtained only under the direct supervision and control of a knowledgeable physician.

[b] Compartment Syndromes

Injuries to nerves, muscles, and other soft tissue within a closed fascial compartment occasionally occur as a complication of a fracture, trauma or crush injuries to an extremity. Compartment syndrome may occur at any site where muscle is contained within a closed fascial space. The mechanism by which this occurs is an increase in pressure within the osteofascial compartment of muscle that causes ischemia and subsequent necrosis from inadequate arterial flow. This ischemia can be caused by increased compartment size/swelling secondary to trauma or revascularization of an ischemic extremity. Further, the compartment may be constricted by a tight dressing or cast. Common areas where compartment syndrome occur are the lower leg, forearm, foot, hand, the gluteal region and the thigh. Accordingly, certain extremity injuries have an increased risk of compartment syndrome. These include: tibial and forearm fractures, injuries immobilized in tight dressings or casts, severe crush injuries, localized prolonged external pressure to an extremity, circumferential burn injuries and reperfusion injuries. The longer the elevated compartment pressure persists, the greater the degree of irreversible damage to the vital structures.

Patients who develop this complication, unless unconscious, normally have the following signs and symptoms: 1) pain greater than expected and that typically is increased by passive stretching of the involved muscle; 2) paresthesia in the distribution of the involved peripheral nerve; 3) decreased sensation or loss of function of the peripheral nerves that traverse the involved compartment; 4) tense swelling of the involved region. Of note, a palpable distal pulse is usually present. However, loss of the distal pulse and paralysis of the involved muscle is a late finding.

All nerves in the involved extremity must be tested, even though the damage might initially be limited to one localized area. Repeated examinations are essential to monitor the development of this potentially disastrous condition. The diagnosis of compartment syndrome is based on the history of the injury and clinical signs coupled with a high index of suspicion.

Intracompartmental pressure measurements may be helpful. Tissue pressures of 35-45 mm Hg suggest decreased capillary blood flow and anoxic damage to the muscles and nerves. However, patients with lower systemic blood pressures may develop compartment syndrome at lower pressures. The treatment of the syndrome requires a fasciotomy. The longer the delay in performing the fasciotomy, the less chance of a good result. Further, such patients may develop myoglobinemia with resultant decreased renal function. Accordingly, surgical consultation for suspected compartment syndrome must be obtained early. Failure to promptly diagnose and refer the patient with compartment syndrome has resulted in more than a few allegations of substandard medical practice. The loss of the extremity and neurovascular functioning in many of these cases is completely avoidable.

[c] Open Fractures

Open fractures are potential disasters for emergency physicians and a true orthopedic emergency. Osteomyelitis is a grave concern and all of these patients should be treated with IV antibiotics. First-generation cephalosporins are recommended for all open fractures. In addition, aminoglycosides should be added to the regimen for patients with Grade II and III open fractures. The wound should be irrigated, gross debris removed and the wound covered with a sterile dressing. In addition, hemorrhage should be controlled and the extremity should be splinted without reduction, unless vascular compromise is present. Further, tetanus prophylaxis should be administered to these patients and tetanus immune globulin given to patients with large crush injuries.

Even the smallest puncture wound is potentially a very significant injury. Whenever a laceration or puncture wound is found in a fractured extremity, the emergency physician must assume that that wound communicates with the fracture. The perforating portion of bone may have been retracted to a more normal position, and there may not be an obvious connecting injury, especially if the puncture wound is some distance from the fracture location. In addition to the great potential for serious bacterial infection, open fractures also carry a high risk of injury to adjacent neurovascular structures. Distal pulses should be checked and signs of arterial disruption in the distal extremity should be monitored for pain, pulselessness, polkiothermia, parathesia, paralysis and pallor. In addition, ABIs can be helpful in the assessment. Most of these patients will require hospitalization and appropriate surgical management that is beyond the scope of most emergency physician practices. Any laceration (or even abrasion) located adjacent to a fracture can complicate the condition and demands close treatment, and in most cases, referral to the appropriate orthopedic specialist at the earliest opportunity.

[d] Extensor Tendon Injuries

Injuries to the fingers, which include avulsion or tearing of the extensor tendons, are common in emergency medicine practice. Unless the patient is adequately examined by the emergency physician, the tendon injury may go undiagnosed. Radiographs will not show the injury, and in the absence of a fracture, the patient may be summarily dismissed with a diagnosis of a contusion or a sprain. The disrupted tendon may result in a loss of function in the finger if not treated appropriately. Timely, appropriate splinting of tendon injuries may bring about a good result, but inadequate splinting may cause the patient to develop a deformity that can never be adequately repaired and may require a fusing of the finger.

[e] Rib Fractures

Rib fractures may be relatively simple closed injuries that heal without complication, or they may result in severe injury and even death. Simple rib fractures are the most common form of significant chest injury and account for half of the cases of nonpenetrating thoracic trauma. The fourth through ninth ribs are most commonly fractured. The diagnosis in an awake patient is usually determined by history and localized chest pain and tenderness. The pain is typically aggravated by deep breathing or any movement. Ecchymosis, crepitus and muscle spasm over the site of injury may also be seen. Further, on exam, pain at the fracture site may be produced by bimanual compression of the patient's thoracic cage remote to the site of injury. The true danger with these injuries is the potential for penetrating injuries to underlying structures such as the pleura, lung, liver and spleen. Further, fractures of the first or second rib raise suspicion of underlying major vascular injury in the chest. Patients with such fractures and suspected intrathoracic injuries—clinical evidence of distal vascular insufficiency, a widened mediastinum on plain films, large hemothorax or apical lung hematoma, brachial plexus injury, intercostal artery injury or significant displacement of the fracture—should undergo a contrast-enhanced helical chest CT to asses for major vascular injury.

Chest x-rays of the involved area may not demonstrate the fracture. However, chest x-rays assist clinicians in locating or ruling out the presence of a pneumothorax from a punctured lung or a hemothorax from a lacerated vessel; both conditions require treatment depending on the severity of the pneumothorax or hemothorax.

Closed rib fractures were once treated with a rib binder or taping. Current medical opinion advises against such taping because it precludes the patient from the required deep breathing that helps prevent the development of lung atelectasis and pneumonia. Pain medication should be given for one to two weeks, and the patient should be encouraged to breath deeply and cough. Most rib fractures will heal within three to six weeks. Elderly patients who are unable to cough and breathe deeply may require hospital admission.

Of note, open rib fractures often signal significant internal injuries because of the force that is required to produce the fracture. Contusion of the lung is commonly associated with fractures of more than three ribs, although it may be seen in patients with three or fewer rib fractures. Lung contusion is of concern because of the possibility of atelectasis and pneumonia as a result of the patient's resistance to deep breathing and coughing. Fractures of the costochrondral junction or sternum are commonly associated with myocardial contusion, and this must be considered in patients with injury to the center of the chest. Fractures of the left lower ribs are associated with rupture of the spleen in a significant number of cases, while fractures of the right lower ribs are sometimes associated with injuries to the liver. Both injuries can be life-threatening and must always be considered. As noted above, fractures of the first and second ribs require significant force and may be indicative of other underlying thoracic injuries. Accordingly, such fractures raise clinical suspicions and may require additional studies as noted above.

[f] Skull Fractures

While a skull fracture may signal a severe brain injury, it does not necessarily mean that the brain is injured. On the other hand, absence of a skull fracture does not mean that the patient has not sustained a substantial brain injury. Open skull fractures are all serious and require antibiotic treatment at the earliest possible time in the emergency department. The patient should then be admitted for appropriate surgical treatment.

Depressed fractures of the skull may be noted on x-ray or detected by gentle palpation. X-ray evaluation or a CT scan with bone windows can aid the diagnosis. When examining such a fracture, the clinician must be gentle so as to avoid pushing the depressed fracture deeper within the cranial cavity. The most frequent location of such factures is over the temporal and parietal bones. Further, the typical mechanism of such fractures is secondary to injury with a small blunt object such as a baseball bat or hammer. Depressed skull fractures more likely have underlying contusions and TBI injury and should be evaluated with this in mind. These injuries also require immediate hospitalization for appropriate operative repair. Fractures of the basilar skull are frequently not detectable on standard x-rays but may be suspected if physical examination demonstrates ecchymosis in the mastoid area, bilateral periorbital ecchymosis (so-called "raccoon eyes"), hemotympanum, hearing loss or a facial palsy on the side of the fracture. Patients with basilar skull fractures require hospitalization and close observation for signs of cerebrospinal fluid leak. Persistent cerebrospinal fluid leak may require surgical closure. The potential for central nervous system infection is great and must be watched for at all times.

[7] Obstetric and Gynecologic Emergencies

Obstetric and gynecologic emergencies are common in emergency medicine practice. Several of the conditions are life-threatening, including profuse vaginal bleeding and ruptured ectopic pregnancies. Certain other conditions, while not immediately life-threatening, still may result in increased morbidity and malpractice claims if not managed properly.

[a] Ectopic Pregnancy

An ectopic pregnancy is a pregnancy that occurs outside the uterus. By far the most common site for an ectopic pregnancy is the fallopian tube (97% of the time). As the ectopic pregnancy grows it may rupture the fallopian tube, causing significant internal bleeding. The diagnosis of ectopic pregnancy is usually considered in a female in her childbearing years who presents with abdominal pain or vaginal bleeding. Unfortunately, this condition is becoming more frequent and occurs in up to 2% of all pregnancies. The reasons for the increased frequency of ectopic pregnancies include an increase in sexually transmitted diseases, the increased use of tubal ligation for sterilization and the improvement in diagnosis. Risk factors for ectopic pregnancy include fallopian tube disease, previous ectopic pregnancy, IUD use, pelvic inflammatory disease ("PID"), smoking, advanced age, prior spontaneous abortions, medically-induced abortions and a history of infertility. However, many patients with an ectopic pregnancy have no obvious risk factors. In fact, up to 50% of patients who present with an ectopic pregnancy may not have any of the above risk factors.

Unfortunately, many of the symptoms of an ectopic pregnancy are non-specific. As a result, the diagnosis is sometimes missed at the time of the initial visit. The most common symptoms are abdominal pain with missed menstrual period, often followed by vaginal bleeding. Patients also have symptoms of pregnancy such as nausea, vomiting, breast tenderness, fatigue and urinary frequency. If enough blood loss occurs, patients may have a syncopal episode. On physical examination, patients can have abdominal tenderness, cervical motion tenderness and an adnexal mass. The uterus is usually normal in size or not as enlarged as predicted by the last menstrual period. If a patient's blood loss is significant, then orthostatic hypotension, hypotension or even shock can develop.

Although the ability to diagnose an ectopic pregnancy has improved, it is still a condition that is often missed initially. A positive pregnancy test establishes the existence of a pregnancy. A pregnancy test measures the level of B-hCG (human chorionic gonadotropin) in the urine or blood. B-hCG is a hormone produced by the developing pregnancy. The level of B-hCG rises dramatically in early pregnancy and doubles every two to three days. If the B-hCG level does not increase as predicted, then an abnormal pregnancy exists (although not necessarily an ectopic pregnancy). An ultrasound can help locate the pregnancy. A positive diagnosis of an ectopic pregnancy is made when the ectopic pregnancy is seen on ultrasound. However, the absence of an intrauterine pregnancy in a patient with a positive pregnancy test is highly suspicious of an ectopic pregnancy, especially if the B-hCG levels are high enough to predict that an intrauterine pregnancy should be seen. Progesterone is another hormone produced during pregnancy. A low serum progesterone level usually means that an abnormal pregnancy is present. Culdocentesis is a procedure performed, less often than in the past, to determine if a ruptured ectopic pregnancy is present. This procedure is not typically used in a stable patient. A positive culdocentesis occurs when non-clotting blood is obtained. A negative culdocentesis is the aspiration of clear fluid. Occasionally however, the presence of blood can be due the presence of a ruptured corpus luteum cyst.

The treatment of an ectopic pregnancy depends on the stability of the patient. In the case of an unstable patient with a ruptured ectopic pregnancy, intravenous fluids, blood and immediate laparoscopic surgery are required. Stable patients may have laparoscopic surgery with an attempt to preserve future fertility by preserving the fallopian tube. However, this can lead to a recurrence of an ectopic pregnancy with the next pregnancy. Non-operative treatment is usually reserved for stable patients with small ectopic pregnancies and minimal symptoms. These patients can receive methotrexate to end the pregnancy. This medical treatment is most often used for tubal masses less than 4 cm in diameter and without sonographic evidence of rupture.

[b] Spontaneous Miscarriage

Spontaneous miscarriages are common in pregnancy. Reports vary, but spontaneous miscarriage occurs in around 25% of all pregnancies less than 6 weeks after the patient's last menstrual period. Further, 80% of spontaneous miscarriages occur during the first trimester. In addition, it is estimated that 20% to 25% of clinically pregnant patients experience some bleeding. Further, it is widely estimated that about 50% of all women who have bleeding during early pregnancy will miscarry.

The assessment of a patient with reported vaginal bleeding during the first trimester should include an abdominal exam and assessment of potential peritoneal signs from an ectopic pregnancy and an assessment of the size of the uterus. Of note, ectopic pregnancy is a major concern in such patients and must always be considered in the differential. For this reason, early ultrasonography is imperative to locate the pregnancy within the uterus of these patients and rule out an ectopic pregnancy.

Physical exam of these patients should include a pelvic exam to determine if the cervical os is open or closed and assess for the products of conception. If products of conception are present, the miscarriage is termed "incomplete." Further, if the internal cervical os is open, the miscarriage is considered "inevitable." While the spontaneous miscarriage is usually not life-threatening, the possibility of a postpartum infection and septic shock may be. Occasionally, the fetus will die but will not be expelled. This is termed a first or second trimester fetal death.

The diagnosis of a spontaneous miscarriage may be supported by signs of an enlarged uterus and evidence of recent bleeding. In addition, the pregnancy tests are positive in most cases. The tissue expelled, when brought to the emergency department, is normally sent to the pathologist for confirmation that it contained products of conception. However, unless an intact gestational sac or fetus is visualized, it is rarely clear whether the miscarriage is "complete."

Studies have shown that in women presenting with a history consistent with miscarriage and with minimal intrauterine tissue by ultrasound, expectant management is safe if an ectopic pregnancy has been excluded. In the "incomplete" or "inevitable miscarriage," the patient may require hospitalization, especially if she is beyond the first trimester. Treatment of patients with inevitable miscarriage (open os and bleeding) can include observation, dilation and evacuation, or D&C. For incomplete miscarriage, the uterus may not be able to contract adequately to limit bleeding from the implantation site. Bleeding may be brisk, but removal of remaining fetal tissue may serve to slow such hemorrhage. Patients with either incomplete or inevitable miscarriages who have an RH-negative blood type should be administered Anti-D immunoglobin.

Patients presenting with a threatened miscarriage (bleeding and a closed os) are usually instructed to rest in bed, and are sent home. Otherwise, there is very little specific medical treatment. Patients who have an Rh-negative blood type are administered Anti-D immunoglobin. Further, ultrasonography should be employed to confirm a viable intrauterine pregnancy. If this cannot be confirmed, the patient should be given warnings related to ectopic pregnancy and scheduled for serial B-hCG and a follow-up ultrasound.

[c] Pelvic Inflammatory Disease

Pelvic inflammatory disease ("PID") refers to a spectrum of infections of the female upper genital tract which may include endometritis, salpingitis, peritonitis or tubo-ovarian abscess. Serious complications of PID include infertility, ectopic pregnancy and chronic pelvic pain. PID is the most common serious infection in women of reproductive age. The infection may be either acute or chronic and may be found on only one side or bilaterally. The most common etiologic organisms are *Chlamydia trachomatis* and *Nieisseria gonorrhoeae*. However, the cause of PID is often polymicrobial and various microorganisms have been recovered from patients with acute PID. Such organisms have included genital mycoplasma and both aerobic and anaerobic bacteria from endogenous vaginal flora. The disease is normally found in young, sexually-active patients. Risk factors for PID include young age, multiple sexual partners, smoking and menses. Intrauterine devices had previously been thought to carry a risk of PID, but this increased risk is only present for the first month after insertion.

These patients may present with a wide variety of signs and symptoms. As a result, the diagnosis is often challenging. The most common presenting symptom is lower abdominal pain. Other common symptoms include dyspareunia (pain with intercourse), abnormal bleeding and abnormal cervical or vaginal discharge. Common signs include lower abdominal tenderness, cervical motion tenderness, fever greater than 38° C and adnexal tenderness on bimanual exam. An adnexal mass may be found if the patient has progressed to the point of abscess. Laboratory evaluation may demonstrate an increase in the white blood count, an elevated C-reactive protein level or an elevated erythrocyte sedimentation rate. Further, wet mount evaluation of vaginal secretions usually shows WBCs. If WBCs are not present on a wet mount evaluation, diagnosis of PID is less likely. Further, ultrasonography may be helpful in the diagnosis of PID, especially in locating and measuring the presence of a tubal abscess. The differential diagnosis in these patients includes ectopic pregnancy, acute appendicitis, endometriosis, ovarian cyst, diverticulitis and functional abdominal pain. In patients with an unclear diagnosis with fever and peritoneal signs, an abdominal CT in addition to ultrasound evaluation may also be helpful to rule out diverticulitis, appendicitis or other intra-abdominal pathologies.

Once a diagnosis is made, the goal of treatment is to prevent the chronic sequelae of infection. Treatment consists of broad-spectrum antibiotic coverage of likely pathogens, including *Gonorrhea*, *Chlamydia*, anaerobes, gram-negative bacteria and streptococci. Depending on the degree of the severity of the symptoms, the patient may or may not be hospitalized. Pain relief is often required, and the patient should have any intrauterine device removed as soon as possible. As the clinical diagnosis of PID is fairly insensitive, the CDC recommends the empiric treatment of PID in sexually active women if uterine tenderness or adnexal tenderness or cervical motion tenderness are present without other identifiable causes. Other criteria that support the diagnosis of PID include: oral temperature greater than 38° C, abnormal cervical or vaginal discharge, the presence of WBCs on wet mount, elevated ESR, elevated C-reactive protein or laboratory documentation of cervical infection with *Chlamydia* or *Gonorrhea*. With each additional criteria, the specificity of the diagnosis increases while the sensitivity decreases. As noted above, the absence of WBCs on wet mount of vaginal secretions makes the diagnosis of PID unlikely. Accordingly, if no WBCs are seen, other causes of the symptoms should be sought.

[d] Intrauterine Devices

Complications of intrauterine devices ("IUD"s) have not infrequently resulted in litigation. The most common problem rising to the level of litigation involves the development of IUD-related uterine and tubo-ovarian infections.

(In August of 1985, as a result of an outstanding claim volume in excess of 5,000 cases, the A.H. Robins Co. of Richmond, Virginia, filed for protection under the bankruptcy statutes in order to consolidate and resolve the claims arising out of complications associated with the use of the Dalkon Shield IUD.)

In addition to the development of endometritis, salpingitis, and pelvic peritonitis, IUDs have also resulted in persistent pelvic pain and have perforated the wall of the uterus, ending up either partially or entirely in the peritoneal cavity. Many patients have retained extrauterine IUDs for long periods of time prior to surgical removal. The IUD may or may not result in a complication once it is outside the uterus. Pregnancies have occurred with the IUD in place (both within the uterine cavity and ectopic) and require early referral to an obstetrician for treatment.

[e] Preeclampsia-eclampsia

Preeclampsia-eclampsia most commonly occurs in patients in the third trimester of pregnancy. These are vasospastic diseases of unknown cause that are unique to pregnant women. Vasospasm, ischemia and thrombosis associated with preeclamptic changes can cause damage to maternal organs such as the liver, kidney and brain. In addition, these vascular changes can result in placental infarcts, abruption and fetal death.

Patients with preeclampsia typically have increased blood pressure, protein in the urine (> 300mg/24 hours), and peripheral edema during pregnancy. In severe preeclampsia, diastolic blood pressures can exceed 110 mm Hg. Central nervous system symptoms may include headaches or visual disturbances. Further, thrombocytopenia (a low platelet level) may be present and liver enzymes may be elevated. Also, renal dysfunction may present as oliguria or increased creatinine levels. Of note, these patients can have hematologic abnormalities, renal dysfunction and liver ischemia. As a result, patients with preeclampsia should have a CBC, platelet count, liver function test and BUN/creatinine level taken. Of concern, as noted previously, these patients can progress to eclampsia, the hallmark of which is seizure and coma.

The most dangerous complication of preeclampsia is eclampsia, which is the occurrence of seizures or coma in the setting of signs and symptoms of preeclampsia. The failure to recognize and treat a patient with preeclampsia may result in eclampsia and complications of pregnancy, including death of the fetus and/or the mother. Of note, the maternal mortality for eclampsia is around 1% while prenatal mortality is around 4% to 8 %.

Management of patients with preeclampsia depends on whether the patient has mild preeclampsia, severe preeclampsia or fulminant disease. Patients with mild preeclampsia may not require hospital admission. However, obstetrical consultation prior to their discharge from the emergency department and appropriate follow-up should be arranged. Patients with sustained hypertension above 140/90 mm Hg and signs of severe preeclampsia should be hospitalized. Further, patients with fulminant or severe preeclampsia with marked blood pressure elevations (160/110 mm Hg) associated with epigastric or liver pain, severe headache and visual disturbances must be admitted and managed like eclampsia. The goal in these patients is to prevent seizures and permanent damage to maternal organs. Magnesium sulfate should be given for seizure prophylaxis. Definitive treatment for all of these patients is delivery of the fetus.

Finally, it should be remembered that a failure to intervene at an appropriate time may result in fetal and/or maternal demise as a result of these disorders. Whenever possible, patients with this complication of pregnancy should be treated in a hospital capable of managing high-risk obstetric patients.

[f] Third Trimester Bleeding

Bleeding in the second half of pregnancy occurs in only about 4% of pregnancies. Further, only about 20% of miscarriages occur after the first trimester. The most important differential diagnoses for vaginal bleeding after 12 to 14 weeks of gestation are placenta previa and abruptio placentae. Both are potentially life-threatening emergencies for mother and the fetus, and they require immediate obstetric consultation and hospital admission. The patients must be treated for any resultant hypovolemia and blood must be available for rapid replacement should it become necessary.

Placenta previa (implantation of the placenta over the cervical os) may result in small amounts of relatively painless bleeding (typically bright red blood) over a period of time. Since the blood loss seems relatively minor, the physician may develop a false sense of security. This is a mistake, because the possibility for a sudden massive hemorrhage exists at all times. Of note, digital or instrumental probing of the cervix should never be attempted in these patients as it may precipitate severe hemorrhage. This diagnosis can usually be made on vaginal or abdominal ultrasound. In many cases, the mother can be managed expectantly until term and then a caesarean section can be performed.

Abruptio placentae (premature separation of the placenta from the endometrium) usually results in abdominal pain and tenderness. The separation also results in hemorrhage into the space between the uterus and placenta and will often present as vaginal bleeding (80% of patients). Unlike placenta previa, the blood is more typically dark. There is a wide spectrum of the severity of this disease. Fetal distress and death occurs in approximately

15% of cases. Further, abruptio placentae may result in life-threatening hypotension, disseminated intravascular coagulation, amniotic fluid embolus and feto-maternal transfusion. Unfortunately, ultrasound is not a reliable means of detecting abruption. For both abruptio placentae and placenta previa, anti-D immunoglobin should be administered to RH-negative mothers.

[g] Sexual Assault

Victims of rape and sexual assault are normally brought to an emergency department for examination. The emergency physician is best advised to have on hand a standard medical report form to be used in any cases of alleged sexual assaults. The form should have the approval of the local district attorney or prosecutor for routine use. The advantage of the standard form is that it is complete and will enable the emergency physician to record all important positive and negative aspects of the examination. In addition to a thorough physical examination and documentation of the results, the physician should consider the possibilities of venereal disease exposure and pregnancy.

Hospital emergency departments normally maintain a standard procedure for the examination of the sexual assault victim, which includes a list of the proper authorities to be notified. Appropriate follow-up treatment of the patient should always be made and may include further examination for venereal disease and pregnancy. In addition, psychological consultation is often necessary.

[8] Problems in Headache Evaluation

Evaluation of the patient with a severe headache, a relatively common complaint, is one of the most difficult tasks faced by the emergency physician. The cause of the headache might range from simple tension to infections resulting in meningitis or a brain abscess, to intracranial hemorrhage. The emergency physician's task is to separate the relatively benign causes from the more serious and to channel the patient with the serious conditions to the proper consultants for definitive treatment.

As with other complaints, the emergency physician relies heavily on the patient's history. Questions are directed toward whether the headache is of recent onset or has been present for some time, duration of the headache, whether it involves one side or both sides of the head, whether it is similar to past headaches, whether there is a history of head trauma and whether the patient has had any seizures either recently or in the past. Also, the presence of photophobia or fever should be assessed. The physical examination should focus on whether the patient demonstrates any focal neurologic abnormalities and whether signs of meningeal irritation are present. The patient's blood pressure should be checked and recorded, and evidence of trauma and tenderness should be sought. The patient's mental status should also be evaluated.

[a] Subarachnoid Hemorrhage

Subarachnoid hemorrhage ("SAH") is an acute life-threatening condition that requires immediate recognition and hospitalization. A SAH refers to the extravasation of blood into the subarachnoid space of the brain. This pathology accounts for 10% of strokes and has an incidence of up to 44% of all cases of severe head trauma. This makes SAH the most common CT scan abnormality seen after head trauma. In traumatic causes, SAH is thought to be caused by intimal tears of small subarachnoid vessels.

In nontraumatic SAH, 80% of these patients have a ruptured cerebral aneurysm. The risk of aneurysmal SAH increases with age and the majority of patients are between 40 and 60 years old. Risk factors include hypertension, smoking, excessive alcohol consumption and sympathomimetic drugs.

Patients may present in coma, making it difficult to obtain a history. If the patient is awake, he or she usually will complain of a severe headache of sudden onset. Typically, this is described as the "worst headache of their life." Further, these patients may have nausea, vomiting, neck stiffness and/or seizure. In addition, up to 50% of these patients are restless on presentation or have an altered level of consciousness. Loss of consciousness is not unusual. Patients may have focal neurologic findings, cranial nerve palsy or may demonstrate decerebrate posturing on presentation. Diagnosis is established by CT scan or lumbar puncture, which will demonstrate grossly bloody cerebral spinal fluid or xanthochromia. Patients with subarachnoid hemorrhage require hospitalization and immediate neurosurgical consultation. They are normally sedated, if agitated, while in the emergency department. Regardless, all of these patients should be placed on bed rest in a quiet and dark environment. Further, nimodipine may be administered to patients with aneurysmal SAH to decrease the likelihood of ischemic stroke. However, hemodynamic monitoring is required during this administration. In addition, both ICP and hemodynamic monitoring are required in the majority of these patients.

[b] Subdural and Epidural Hemorrhages

Subdural and epidural hemorrhages are often amenable to surgical treatment by decompression of the bleeding if the diagnosis is established in a timely manner. In the absence of a timely diagnosis, the patient may very well expire.

Epidural hematomas are blood clots that form between the inner table of the skull and the dura and comprise .5% of all head injured patients. Most of these injuries are caused by traumatic impact that results in a forceful skull deformity. Eighty percent (80%) are associated with skull fractures across the middle meningeal artery or across a dural sinus. The majority of these injuries are located in the temporoparietal region. The high arterial pressure of the artery dissects the dura from the skull, forming a convex or lenticular-shaped hematoma that can be identified by non-contrast CT. Classically, on presentation, these patients are described as have a "lucid interval" after a period of decreased consciousness followed by significant worsening of symptoms. These patients may also complain of headache, sleepiness, dizziness, nausea and vomiting. With rapid detection by CT, surgical consultation and evacuation, the functional outcome is usually excellent.

Subdural hematomas are blood clots that form between the dura and the brain and account for up to 30% of patients with severe head trauma. This injury is usually secondary to trauma and often caused by acceleration-deceleration injury. Movement of the brain relative to the skull causes tension and injury to superficial bridging veins, resulting in a venous bleed in the subdural space. Patients with brain atrophy, such as alcoholics or elderly patients, are at higher risk for this injury. Patients with subdural hematomas normally have sustained trauma, which may precede the development of the symptoms of an increasing intracranial mass by as little as several hours to as long as several weeks. The patients may become difficult to arouse, have a change in mental status, motor deficits or pupil inequality on examination. Posterior fossa SDH may present with nausea, vomiting and decreased level of consciousness. A non-contrast CT scan normally will demonstrate the area of bleeding as a crescent-shaped hyperdense area that lies between the calvaria and the cortex. Neurosurgical decompression may be life-saving, and suspicion of a subdural hemorrhage requires immediate neurosurgical consultation in every case.

[9] Nasal Trauma

Nasal trauma is frequently seen in emergency medicine practice. Fractures are usually closed, but may be open. Deformity of the nose may be difficult to assess because of localized swelling and tenderness to palpation. Some emergency medicine texts suggest that x-rays of the nasal bones are not useful and are not recommended for routine use. Despite this advice, many emergency physicians routinely order x-rays in any case of nasal trauma.

Patients with nasal fractures are typically referred to otolaryngologists for definitive treatment. Many otolaryngologists will not reduce a nasal fracture on the day of injury, preferring to wait until the swelling has been reduced with the use of ice packs, and the engorgement has dissipated to the point where local anesthesia will be more effective. The nose can be better manipulated when it has reduced to a more normal size. Typically, these patients are referred to otolaryngology for follow-up in three to five days when the swelling likely will have subsided.

A complication of any nasal injury is a septal hematoma. This may result regardless of the presence or absence of a fracture. Patients must be followed closely for a few days to be certain that a septal hematoma has not developed. When this complication is found, immediate drainage and antibiotic therapy is essential to prevent the development of a septal abscess. A septal abscess can cause a perforation of the septal cartilage, resulting in a saddle nose deformity that is extremely difficult to correct. Patients are rarely hospitalized with nasal fractures and are usually treated on an outpatient basis with follow-up in the emergency department or an otolaryngologist's office.

[10] Intoxicated Patients

Alcohol-intoxicated patients are frequent visitors to emergency departments, and they present difficult problems in diagnosis and management for the emergency medicine team. The intoxicated patient is not always able to appreciate pain and describe his or her symptoms. Also, these patients are often belligerent and uncooperative. Attempting to establish an accurate diagnosis in the face of an obstinate patient is never easy. In addition, intoxicated patients are often disruptive, and they interfere with the orderly management of the emergency department. They frequently require several attendants to monitor and control their behavior. Few emergency departments can spare the required attendants on a regular basis, and the staff is tempted to move the patient from the emergency department as soon as possible.

Intoxicated patients do sustain serious injuries, and frequently these are difficult to detect. When the patient is not cooperative, and in some instances assaultive, it is easy to understand how the emergency physician might not be able to provide a thorough examination. Nevertheless, the patient must be controlled and should not be permitted to leave the emergency department prematurely. Significant serious head injuries have been missed in intoxicated patients because of the inability to adequately assess them during their inebriated state. The only safe course is to retain them in the emergency department or somewhere in the hospital until such time as their senses have cleared. These patients should always be released in the care of a competent adult family member or friend, the police department, or a person from Alcoholics Anonymous or an alcohol detoxification program.

[11] Mentally Ill Patients

Certain mentally ill patients are dangerous to themselves because of suicidal ideation. Some are dangerous to other parties. The emergency physician's difficult task is to recognize the dangerousness of the patient, either to himself or to others, and to refer the patient for appropriate treatment. This may be referral to a psychiatrist or to an inpatient ward for psychiatric treatment. The ability to predict dangerousness with certainty is rare indeed. The safest practice for the emergency physician is to request consultation from an appropriate psychiatrist.

Certain patients are at higher risk of committing suicide than others. Depression in the elderly is generally more serious than in teenagers, although teenage suicide has reached epidemic proportions in some areas of the country. Patients who have a history of a prior suicide attempt are at a greater risk of another attempt. Patients who have attempted suicide by violent means, as opposed to drug overdose, are often more serious in their suicidal intent. Patients who have a chronic sense of hopelessness, have very little support from family or friends, are lonely, and reach the depths of their depression during the holiday season are at a higher degree of risk of suicide.

[12] Mentally Retarded Patients

The treatment of a mentally retarded patient is often difficult. In general, it may be obvious that the patient is ill, but the patient is often not able to fully participate in the diagnostic evaluation. In these evaluations, family members are frequently of great help to the emergency physician in examination and providing history.

[13] Munchausen Syndrome

Munchausen's syndrome consists of a personality disorder in which the patient claims false symptoms or simulates an acute illness, then obligingly undergoes any and all laboratory and hospital testing that is suggested. In addition, the patient will often readily accept surgical treatment and will on occasion mutilate his or her body in order to obtain continuing medical or surgical treatment. When the health care team discovers the true nature of the illness and refers the patient to psychiatric care, the patient usually leaves the hospital—often without notice—and moves on to a new location to challenge a new group of health care providers.

[14] Splenectomized Patients

A patient can lose his or her spleen through surgical removal from trauma or because of certain hematologic diseases. Also, the presence of sickle cell disease can result in an autosplenectomy. Patients who no longer possess a spleen are at higher risk of complications from bacterial infections; most prominently, infections caused by encapsulated bacteria. While vaccines have been available for several years that provide a good deal of protection against infection from certain bacteria, many patients with splenectomies have not received these vaccines.

A fever in a splenectomized patient signals a potentially dangerous condition. The emergency physician must be constantly on the alert for patients in this category. The failure to detect the problem and begin appropriate antibiotic treatment in a splenectomized patient may result in sepsis and rapid demise.

[15] Patients with Sickle Cell Disease

Patients with sickling hemoglobinopathies, which include the sickle cell disease ("HbSS"), are frequently seen at emergency departments in various crises. The majority of patients exhibiting this inherited disease are of African-American descent. This disease is caused by a homozygous recessive defect in the hemoglobin beta chain that results in a sickled erythrocyte (red blood cell). The sickled erythrocyte causes greater blood viscosity and sludging. Typically, infection, cold, stress or hypoxia can precipitate a sickle cell crisis. These painful crises are thought to result from deoxygenated hemoglobin that causes the formation of sickled cells. The erythrocytes then cause sludging of blood, resulting in tissue ischemia and microvascular obstruction and pain. Patients in crisis often present with deep aching pain in the abdomen, chest, back and extremities.

Aplastic crises that may be life-threatening can occur post-infection or as a result of folate deficiency and must be recognized and treated. Further, patients with sickle cell disease are susceptible to the following organ system injuries: stasis ulcers, stroke, retinal hemorrhage/retinopathy, congestive heart failure, pulmonary embolisms/pneumonia, hepatic infarct, gallstones, impotence and priapism, bone infarcts and osteomyelitis. Of note, acute chest syndrome is a leading cause of death in these patients and accounts for 25% of premature deaths associated with sickle cell disease. This pathology is thought to be caused by vascular sludging and resulting damage to the lung parenchyma. Patients have fever, cough, chest pain, dyspnea and new infiltrates on chest x-ray on presentation.

An additional life-threatening complication in these patients is the possibility of a sudden overwhelming sepsis. As mentioned above, patients with sickle cell disease are at an increased risk of the complications of infection. They lack the ability to fight common offending organisms and are particularly susceptible to septicemia caused by *Streptococcus pneumoniae* or *Haemophilus influenzae* bacteria. Infarction of various organs also occurs and may result in significant disability. All of the aforementioned crises may require hospitalization and appropriate treatment. These patients can rarely be managed in the emergency department. However, in uncomplicated sickle cell crisis, patients can often judge the severity of their pain and frequently advise the emergency physician as to whether they feel they can tolerate treatment as an outpatient. Treatment of uncomplicated crises may include hydration, supplemental oxygen and analgesics.

[16] Discharge against Medical Advice

Occasionally patients will disagree with or refuse treatment prescribed in an emergency department. Under these circumstances, if the patient is competent and an adult, he or she should be permitted to sign out of the emergency department "against medical advice" ("AMA").

Six steps should be undertaken in such a situation. First, the patient should be informed of the hospital's obligation under the law to treat and stabilize regardless of a patient's ability to pay. Second, the physician should determine if the patient has capacity and is legally competent to refuse care. Third, the risks and benefits of refusing treatment should be explained to the patient. These risks and benefits should be tailored to the patient's presenting illness. Fourth, the patient should be asked to sign a written consent form detailing the competence of the patient, the fact that the risks and benefits were discussed and noting whether the patient's family was available. If the patient refuses to sign the form, a second person in the emergency department who has witnessed the discussion should note this fact on the chart and sign along with the emergency physician and nurse.

Fifth, the patient should be offered alternative care or referral to another physician. In addition, the patient should be told to return to the emergency department with worsening symptoms or if he/she changes their mind. Sixth, all of the above information should be documented including the patient's medical work-up, why the patient decided to leave, and the fact that the risks and benefits were discussed. Finally, it should be noted that patients should not be dismissed from further care based on a disagreement over proposed treatment or any financial concerns.

[17] Drug Reactions

Drug reactions result in considerable patient morbidity, occasional mortality and a large number of malpractice claims filed each year. Alleged errors in drug prescribing account for many of the claims filed against emergency physicians and other primary care practitioners.

One of the most common, and preventable, complications is allergic reaction. Emergency patients always should be asked whether they have a drug allergy, and all emergency department record forms have a place for recording the patient's response. When an emergency physician prescribes a drug to which a patient has a recorded allergy because the physician either overlooked the allergy or decided that it was not a dangerous condition or a true allergy, the physician's liability carrier will end up paying damages.

Failure to observe a patient for a reasonable period of time following the administration of drugs also has resulted in malpractice claims. Patients have been prematurely discharged and have suffered allergic reactions after leaving the emergency department.

[18] Drug Interactions

Prescribing medication that potentiates or neutralizes the effect of other medications the patient is taking also has resulted in negligence claims against emergency physicians. It is important that the emergency physician obtain a complete drug history on every patient before prescribing medication.

[19] Overdose

An additional area of liability involves the patient who is given a large amount of a medication and later uses it to attempt or commit suicide. Emergency physicians should refrain from prescribing a large amount of medication for patients with whom they are not going to be able to follow up on a regular basis.

§ 4.04   Diagnostic Error in the Emergency Department

Diagnostic errors have become the most prevalent type of malpractice claim over the last decade. Accordingly, it is important to consider the causes of such error and ways in which it can be avoided by emergency physicians.

In 2007, Kachalia et al. addressed this subject in a review dealing with 122 closed malpractice claims concerning diagnostic error arising from outpatient evaluations in emergency departments. The reviewers obtained malpractice claim files from four insurance companies covering 21,000 physicians, 46 acute care hospitals, and 390 outpatient facilities. Of the 122 closed claims reviewed, Kachalia et al identified 79 cases where diagnostic errors occurred in emergency departments and led to adverse patient outcomes. A review of these cases revealed that fracture (19%), infection (15%) and myocardial infarction (10%) were the most commonly missed pathologies. Further, 39% of these errors led to death while 48% resulted in adverse outcomes that were considered significant or major.

The results of this study indicated that the four leading breakdowns in the diagnostic process were: failure to order proper tests (58%), inadequate medical history and physical exam (42%), incorrect interpretation of tests (37%) and failure to request consultations (33%). The study determined that the majority of physicians failed to order tests because they did not recognize that they were required (93%) and/or lacked knowledge that the test was indicated (52%). In cases where tests were misinterpreted, the lead causes were errors in clinical judgment (63%) and inexperience (23%).

In all, the three most common contributing factors to errors were mistakes in judgment (87%), lack of technical competence or knowledge (58%), and lapses in vigilance or memory (41%). Of note, 96% of missed diagnoses involved at least one of these cognitive errors. Other leading contributing factors included patient-related factors (34%), lack of appropriate supervision (30%), inadequate handoff of information (24%) and excessive workload (24%).

Missed diagnosis frequently involved multiple breakdowns in the diagnostic process and contributing factors. Of note, there were at least two process breakdowns in 81% of cases resulting in diagnostic errors. Further, two-thirds of errors involved more than one physician. Kachalia et al concluded that the causes of missed diagnoses in emergency departments are the result of a complex interplay of factors and often involve multiple physicians. Key among the forms of avoidable error highlighted was cognitive error. In an effort to address these errors, there is ongoing research into systems that can support clinical decision in emergency department and, thus, avoid such error. However, the logistical and efficiency concerns of the modern emergency department make the creation of such systems challenging. Until such systems can be instituted, emergency medicine physicians will need to continue to strive to offer thorough evaluations for each presenting patient. Performing complete histories and physical exams should be emphasized. In addition, the use of flow sheets and algorithms denoting indicated tests for presenting symptoms may serve to minimize the risk of both cognitive and diagnostic errors. *See* Kachalia A. Missed and Delayed Diagnoses in the Emergency Department: A Study of Closed Malpractice Claims from 4 Liability Insurers *Ann Emerg Med* 2007;49(2): 196-205.

CHAPTER 5

PATHOLOGY

Cyril H. Wecht, MD, JD, FCAP, FASCP
Paraluman Q. Ravano, MD, FCAP, FASCP

SYNOPSIS

[2]   Urinalysis
    [a]   Improper Collection or Preservation of Specimens
    [b]   Incorrect Labeling of Specimens
    [c]   Incorrect Testing or Misinterpretation of Results
    [d]   Failure to Recognize Special Disease Characteristics
    [e]   Failure to Correlate Test Results with Clinical History and Previous Tests
    [f]   Failure to Report Test Results in a Timely Manner
[3]   Chemistry Tests
    [a]   Improper Collection or Preservation of Specimens
    [b]   Incorrect Labeling of Specimens
    [c]   Incorrect Testing or Misinterpretation of Results
    [d]   Failure to Recognize Special Disease Processes
    [e]   Failure to Correlate Test Results with Clinical History and Previous Tests
    [f]   Failure to Report Test Results in a Timely Manner
    [g]   Failure to Report Diseases to Health Authorities
[4]   Microbiology
    [a]   Improper Collection or Preservation of Specimens
    [b]   Incorrect Labeling of Specimens
    [c]   Incorrect Testing or Misinterpretation of Results
    [d]   Failure to Recognize Special Disease Processes
    [e]   Failure to Collect Sterile Specimens
    [f]   Failure to Correlate Test Results with Clinical History and Previous Tests
    [g]   Failure to Report Test Results in a Timely Manner
    [h]   Failure to Report Venereal and Other Specified Diseases to Health Authorities
[5]   Immunology and Serology
    [a]   Improper Collection or Preservation of Specimens
    [b]   Incorrect Labeling of Specimens
    [c]   Incorrect Testing or Misinterpretation of Results
    [d]   Failure to Recognize Special Disease Processes
    [e]   Failure to Correlate Test Results with Clinical History and Previous Tests
    [f]   Failure to Report Test Results in a Timely Manner
    [g]   Failure to Report Venereal and Other Specified Diseases to Health Authorities
[6]   Blood Bank
    [a]   Improper Collection or Preservation of Specimens
    [b]   Incorrect Labeling of Specimens
    [c]   Incorrect Testing or Misinterpretation of Results
    [d]   Failure to Correlate Test Results with Previous Blood Type or Crossmatch Tests
    [e]   Failure to Report Test Results in a Timely Manner

---

§ 5.01   Training and Certification of Pathologists

[1]   Premedical Education

In the United States, pathologists normally require completion of four years of medical education through either a homeopathic or an osteopathic school after four years of undergraduate degree. The major course of study prior to medical school will be in the natural sciences, biology, chemistry, physics or biomedical engineering. Some universities offer a shorter intensive six-year medical course inclusive of the premedical and medical education.

Increasing public demand for protection, coupled with the growth and sophistication in the number of fraudulent practitioners over the past two decades has resulted in stronger and more complex licensing boards and licensing statutes throughout the country. Requirements vary from state to state, depending on the resources of each jurisdiction, on the Medical Practice Act, on legislation, the media and on public expectations. Nonetheless, all medical boards have continued to improve licensure processes, and a trend toward uniformity among licensing boards exists to enhance both the initial licensure process and licensure portability.

A number of states have passed legislation giving medical boards jurisdiction over the practice of medicine across state boundaries or over the treatment decisions made by medical directors of managed care organizations. This provision may hinder to some degree a physician seeking an initial licensure or a subsequent application to practice in other states. Investigation of credentials and past practice in addition to the need to satisfy necessary license standards could cause delays for a physician seeking to obtain a license in a particular state.

[2] Medical School

Enrollment in an approved medical school or school of osteopathy, is the next step in becoming a pathologist. This program should provide a general grounding in all areas of medicine, and is normally completed in four years.

[3] Internship

A one-year internship is required in most states following the completion of medical school. This program may be a broad-based rotating one, or it may involve work in only one or a few clinical areas.

[4] Residency Training

Pathology is the only discipline in Medicine that can be classified as both a basic and a clinical science. For medical students, it is an indispensable bridge between the basic science forming a large part of the first two years in school and the clinical relevance of the application of such science during the third and fourth years of medical school.

Following medical school, a year of internship is required for prospective pathologists prior to undertaking a pathology residency program. This may either be a broad-based rotating internship that involves work in various clinical areas or a straight internship in Pathology.

There are two major branches of Pathology – Anatomic Pathology and Clinical Pathology. Pathologists may either train in both branches, taking a total of four years, not including the one year of internship or elect to train in only one of the two branches and spend three years in addition to the year of internship. Most Pathologists in practice are trained in both branches. Many of those Pathologists who anticipate engaging in academics elect to undergo training in only one of the two branches.

Anatomic Pathology is concerned with the diagnosis of diseases based upon the gross and microscopic examination of various bodily fluids, tissue washings, and fine needle aspiration of various organs and body sites. Visual examination is entailed on gross while special stains and immuno-histochemistry are employed to visualize specific proteins and other substances present either in or around cells. More recently, molecular biology techniques have been employed to gain additional information from the same specimen.

Anatomic Pathology includes three special areas, namely Autopsy Pathology, Surgical Pathology and Cytopathology. *Autopsy Pathology* deals with the performance of postmortem examinations. *Surgical Pathology* deals with tissues removed during surgery. *Cytopathology* deals with smears obtained from secretions such as vaginal swabs, sputum and urine as well as body fluids, washings and fine needle aspirations from solid and cystic masses.

Clinical Pathology involves the testing of various body fluids, mainly blood and excreta in the effort to correlate changes in those samples with the development of disease processes. The special areas in Clinical Pathology include *Chemistry, Urinalysis and Endocrinology* (diseases related to special organs such as the pancreas in diabetes, the thyroid and adrenal glands in other diseases), Hematology (blood diseases), *Microbiology* (diseases produced by bacteria, viruses, fungi, and parasites), *Blood Banking* (the transfusion, indications and adverse effects of blood, its products and substitutes), *Immunology* (special proteins involved in diseases) and *other special laboratory procedures.*

[5]   Subspecialty Areas

In addition to the two broad divisions of Anatomic and Clinical Pathology, it is possible for a Pathologist to specialize further in any of the subspecialty areas listed above in conjunction with their clinical application and correlation. A few examples in Anatomic Pathology are Forensic Pathology (determination of the manner and mechanism of death such as in violent, unexpected, unexplained or medically unattended deaths), Neuropathology (a specific study of disorders of the central nervous system, peripheral nerves and muscle), Ophthalmic Pathology (the study of diseases of the eyes and related organs), and Dermatopathology (a study of skin diseases).

A few examples in Clinical Pathology are subspecialties in Hematology, Microbiology, Chemistry, Endocrinology and Blood Banking. In connection with these subspecialties, a clinician such as an internist may elect to subspecialize in blood transfusions and blood banking; as a Neurologist may undertake Neuropathology; a Dermatologist may take Dermatopathology; an oncologist, hematopathology; an Infectious Disease specialist, Microbiology, etc.

[6] The American Board of Pathology

The American Board of Pathology is the organization responsible for setting specific requirements for each of the specialties. It also serves as the examining and certifying body for those seeking specialist ratings. It further coordinates with the American Board of Internal Medicine in regard to the clinical subspecialties mentioned before.

§ 5.02 Types of Pathology Practice

[1] Hospital Pathology

Most hospital Pathologists are board certified in both Anatomic and Clinical Pathology. They have active responsibilities in all areas of service, but chiefly in Surgical Pathology and Cytopathology, in which areas, the pathologists result the tests. The declining number of hospital autopsies makes this latter function secondary and lumped with the resulting of specific tests such as bone marrow examination, interpretation of esoteric tests like protein immune electrophoresis and investigation of transfusion reactions and adverse effects of blood and blood products. It is also the chief responsibility of the pathologists to serve as consultants to the medical staff and to direct and supervise all the activities of the hospital laboratory's technical staff. The pathologists are also involved in teaching in institutions where residency programs are existent.

[2] Private Laboratories

Private laboratories, big and small, are usually directed by a certified pathologist, not uncommonly a pathologist associated with hospital practice as well. There are some private laboratories that perform only certain tests pertaining to a highly specialized area and may not require direction or administration from a pathologist. Most of these laboratories are required to satisfy strict regional, state and often national regulations in order to satisfy the standards of laboratory practice.

For example, a private laboratory such as a toxicology laboratory strictly performing tests pertaining to detection of drugs and their concentration in blood, body fluids, and certain tissues may be supervised by a specialist in that specific area, not necessarily a pathologist. On the other hand, there are private laboratories with a non-pathologist administrator that perform as a reference laboratory with a host of consultants in various fields of specialization, who commonly serve also as faculties of private hospitals, teaching centers or universities.

[3] Consulting

Pathologists serve as consultants in a variety of roles. Pathologists with recognized training in a subspecialty will frequently be called upon by hospital pathologists to render opinions on tissue slides that fall within their area of expertise. These specialists may also be asked by members of the legal profession to render opinions in malpractice litigation, and they often testify in court as expert witnesses. They also may serve as consultants to various governmental agencies. In some counties where the office of coroner is held by a hospital-based pathologist, consulting pathologists are used in death cases on an "as needed" basis. Consulting pathologists also frequently serve as medicolegal consultants to district attorneys and public defenders.

[4] Governmental Agencies

In many areas the pathologist may be an employee of a governmental agency, serving as a county coroner, medical examiner, member of the department of health, health department director, etc. In these situations the pathologist might be employed full-time, or in smaller and more rural areas, as a part-time employee.

[5] Academic Positions

In large university hospitals there are often pathologists specifically devoted to the training of pathology residents and students in medical technology programs. These individuals normally will be board-certified, and their primary responsibility will be teaching in their special areas.

[6] Research

Large university-based hospitals generally provide a site for research pathologists. These individuals usually are involved in basic and applied research, and in investigation into the underlying findings of disease states. Special techniques such as radioimmunoassay, fluorescence polarization immunoassay, immunofixation, polymerase chain reaction, flow cytometry, immunocytochemistry, electron microscopy and many others have been developed for application to clinical laboratory practice. Some large teaching hospitals, private and governmental facilities, and a few major commercial laboratories also operate programs that involve the pathologist in research studies.

§ 5.03 Scope of Practice: Anatomic Pathology

[1] Examination of Surgical Specimens

Surgical specimens received by the anatomic pathologist for examination are those portions of excised tissue or devices removed during a surgical procedure. Samples of material that are extruded from a patient's body are also examined as surgical pathology specimens. Explanted devices are similarly treated as surgical pathology specimens. Tissues removed in the hospital operating rooms represent the primary source of such specimens but equally important are specimens obtained bedside, from free-standing surgery centers and those removed in relatively minor surgical procedures in physician's offices or clinics, especially from dermatologists and gastroenterologists. Finally other specimens, such as bone marrow biopsies, can be obtained on the general hospital floors.

The purpose of submitting a specimen for review by an anatomic pathologist is to confirm a strongly suspected diagnosis, establish a diagnosis where several possibilities are likely, or to document the existence of a foreign material, whether intentionally or accidentally introduced.

[a] Handling and Processing the Specimen

From the site of surgery to the final destination of a test result, surgical pathology specimens are given the same attention and care as any laboratory sample. The correct identification is maintained throughout the steps at which the specimen is handled. Proper stickers carrying the name, date of birth and medical record number (replaced in some institutions by the individual's social security number) are attached to the specimen container and the test requisition slip. The source of the tissue, the clinical impression and a brief history are provided by the more responsible clinicians for better communication with the pathologist.

Once surgical removal of the tissue, or a part of it, or a foreign body or device has been completed, it is the responsibility of the surgeon to ensure that the specimen is properly handled until it reaches the site where the examination is to occur. The specimen should be clearly identified and indisputably assigned to an individual patient. As previously mentioned, the source of the specimen and the preoperative diagnosis should be included. In certain complicated cases, an open discussion between the surgeon and the pathologist could provide a more meaningful approach to difficult diagnostic problems.

The specimen should be preserved properly prior to examination. Preservation requirements may vary according to the nature of the investigation and the amount of time that will lapse from the time of collection to the time of processing. The great majority of specimens are collected in containers with buffered formalin. Formalin also should be used if a specimen is taken later in the day and will not be examined for a prolonged period of time. Preservation in this fixative will prevent drying or shrinkage during transport of the tissue as well as avoid distortion of the tissue architecture and cellular structure.

If the specimen will be examined shortly after it is sent to the pathology department, or special studies are required, then the specimen may either be sent fresh or in normal saline. There are some specimens which need to be kept fresh in normal saline solution to keep from drying. These are the very large specimens that need to be dissected fresh or photographed fresh. Examples are resected tumors of the breast, lung, or bowels. Portions of specimens that need to be cultured for bacteria, viruses or fungi also require to be submitted fresh or in appropriate culture media. Others, such as placenta for chromosome studies, kidney, skin, or muscle may require special care such as submitted in a muscle clamp or fresh frozen or in some transport medium.

[b]   The Routine Examination

On receipt of the specimen in the laboratory, the first step is the confirmation of the identity and the assignment of a specific identification number. This "surgical pathology" number is carried throughout from the requisition slip that accompanies the specimen, the label on the specimen container, through the processing steps of the plastic cassette (tissue holders) where the entire specimen or representative sections have been placed, to the paraffin block where thin ribbons (usually six microns thick) of tissue are cut onto the microscopic slides, which are then passed through a set of stains.

The initial step in the routine examination of a surgical pathology specimen is the gross examination. In most places, this function is performed by the pathologist. In larger institutions with a greater load, specially trained pathology assistants perform the gross examination. The description is usually dictated to the transcriptionist. It includes the condition of the specimen upon receipt, the preservative it was received in, the nature and specified source and the clinical information whenever provided. The description will include the size, color, and consistency. Small specimens are totally submitted in a cassette after sectioning when necessary.

Larger specimens are weighed and measured along three planes. Representative sections are taken from the larger specimens and submitted in multiple cassettes. The sectioning process can be of vital importance. For example, multiple sections of a tumor may show different types in different areas. The number of sections is dictated by the nature of the specimen and the anticipated diagnosis. The specific location or site from where a particular section has been taken is assigned a sub of either number or letter. The pertinent areas are stained with India ink. This does not wash away during processing such that the inked surfaces will mark the edges of surgical resection and will determine the adequacy of the surgical procedure most important in tumor surgery.

The tissue holders that contain thin, usually half a centimeter thick specimen section are passed through a series of fixative and clearing solutions in an automatic processor starting from the end of the day and continuing through the night. The histology technicians are then ready the following morning to do the embedding by covering the tissue sections with paraffin wax that forms a rectangular block in the cassettes when cooled. From this block, ribbon sections averaging six microns thick are cut and placed onto glass slides. These tissue sections are now ready for automatic staining with the routine Hematoxylin and Eosin stain.

The glass slides containing the sections of the tissue sample for microscopic examination are first etched with the identification number, then affixed with printed labels. The microscopic slides are then brought to the anatomic pathologist for interpretation. A diagnosis is made based on the structure of the cells and the architecture or pattern the cells form. This diagnosis is made from the correlation of facts gathered from the clinical data provided, the gross appearance and the microscopic findings. The initially assigned identification number is carried through to the final surgical pathology report.

[c] Special Techniques, Special Stains and Immune Histochemical Stains

In special cases, there may be a need for an extra step in tissue processing in order to be able to prepare routine sections. Bone, for example and calcium deposits need to undergo "decalcification" to soften the tissue and make it suitable for sectioning.

Others require special stains to make certain objects not easily identified on routine Hematoxylin and Eosin stain be more easily visible. Examples are: PAS (periodic acid Schiff stain)—most useful in the demonstration of fungi parasites, glycogen, and intracytoplasmic crystals; gram stain to accentuate specific groups of bacteria (gram-positive or gram negative forms); acid fast stain to demonstrate mycobacteria in suspected tuberculosis; silver stain to show certain organisms such as pneumocysts and various fungi; Sudan or Oil Red O for fat; mucicarmine for mucin and many others.

Trichrome, reticulin and iron stains—these are routinely used in liver biopsies. The main value of these stains is in the evaluation of the type and amount of extracellular material, the demarcation of individual cell membrane and the hemosiderin content in the tissue in the case of the special stain for iron. Other stains such as argentafin, amyloid, mucin, myelin, etc are used for the demonstration of specific substances that will help identify a pathologic entity or confirm the exact nature of the tissue.

Further, immune histochemical stains are now commonly utilized to aid in the differentiation of tumor nature and origin.

In Surgical Pathology, many immune histochemical stains are now standard tests to identify the specific nature of the tissue, the disease that the tissue is involved in, or the precise pathology in many instances. Immune histochemistry has revolutionized the field during the past 50 years. On the principle of antigen-antibody reaction, remarkable sensitivity and specificity have greatly improved diagnosis precision. The advantages, in addition to aiding in the particular diagnosis, include the applicability of the test to processed materials including those that have been processed for a long period of time. The tests are also compatible with most preservatives.

However, cross-reactivity between various antigens may be encountered frequently. Due to the considerable occurrence of false positive and false negative results, the surgical pathologist is expected to be trained, have become sufficiently experienced, and qualified in the interpretation of the results.

Different panels of immune histochemical stains are used for identification of undifferentiated malignant neoplasms, carcinomas of unknown origin, urinary bladder versus prostate carcinoma, adenocarcinoma versus mesothelioma, and various other tests specific to an organ. Specific immune histochemical stains can be used to determine the origin of the culprit cell.

A tumor can be identified as to have originated from the tissue lining (carcinoma) or supporting connective tissue (sarcoma). In identifying the tumor type, a cancer specialist who will treat the cancerous patient, will be able to prescribe the best appropriate treatment, either by plain surgical removal of the tumor, or radiation with x-ray by external beam or radioactive seed implantation, or by the use of systemic oral or injected chemotherapeutic agents.

Whether the tumor originated from the lung, for example or has just spread to that organ, a set of immune histochemical stains on the tissue slides prepared from the tumorus tissue, such as cytokeratin (CK AE1/AE3 or CK5/6), thyroid transcription factor 1 (TTF-1), calretinin, and thrombomodulin could narrow down the diagnosis. The type of primary lung cancer can also be divided into small or non-small cell type. Specific histochemical stains such as chromogranin, synaptophysin and non-specific enolase (NSE) will confirm a small cell carcinoma. Small cell carcinoma requires radiation and chemotherapy initially as opposed to surgical removal of a non-small cell carcinoma as the first line of treatment.

Widely used examples are the LCA (leukocyte common antigen) and other lymphoid immune stains used for the diagnosis of lymphomas such as CD3 (for T cells), CD20 (for B cells) and CD15 and CD30 (for Reed Sternberg Cells in Hodgkin's Disease). Also popular are the cytokeratins as the AE1/AE3 and CAM5 to establish the epithelial nature of the tumor and the GFAP (Glial fibrilllary acid protein) for neural tissue.

In conditions involving the lymphatic system the immune histochemical stains are very helpful in the diagnosis of whether a lymph nod is due to tumor involvement by lymphoma (a malignant condition developing primarily in lymph nodes) or just a reactive process as in infection, or even HIV process. Various lymphoma (malignancy of the lymphatic system) markers are commonly used to diagnose Hodgkin's disease and non-Hodgkin's lymphoma.

PSA (prostatic specific antigen) or thyroglobulin immune stain or other specific immune stains are sometimes employed to identify the origin of an undifferentiated metastatic tumor. Some immune stains are used for prognostication or as an aid in the chemotherapy of certain malignancies. Estrogen receptor (ER) and progesterone receptors (PR) and herceptin (Her2Neu) are well known examples of tumor markers for breast cancer now routinely quantified from the percentage of positive staining cells from microscopic examination of the tissue sectioned from the paraffin block of the tumor sampled. Less than a decade ago, these markers had to be performed on fresh tumor tissue requiring a specified size with minimum weight requirement. Epidermal growth factor receptor (EGFR) is another histochemical stain that is commonly associated with colon cancer, its presence leading to a specific monoclonal antibody treatment.

[d] Frozen Sections

The average time required to process a surgical specimen and issue a diagnosis from examination of the microscopic slides is approximately one day that could extend to three days when additional procedures are obtained. There are instances when the anatomic pathologist is called upon to assist while the patient is still undergoing the operation. It may be necessary for the pathologist to provide an *intraoperative* consultation. A needle localization biopsy of breast tumor may require the anatomic pathologist to obtain a rapid specimen x-ray with the assistance of the

Radiology Department to determine if the abnormality found in the patient's mammogram has been removed.

At times, the anatomic pathologist could advise the surgeon about the nature of the lesion just from gross examination, thus aiding in the immediate termination or extension of the surgical procedure. A common example will be the determination of the completeness of bowel resection in the presence of a tumor. The completeness of excision may need a frozen section examination of the resection margins. This request usually comes from the plastic surgeon who wants to take as little skin as possible in removing a facial skin cancer.

Others may require a frozen section examination to determine whether a lesion is malignant or not. The surgeon may have planned and advised the patient of a staging procedure should a lesion turn out to be malignant, thus avoiding for the patient to undergo anesthesia once again in a future second operation. Occasionally, frozen sections are requested to determine the adequacy of the sample for diagnosis. The surgeon would want to avoid subjecting the patient to another operation if the sample had not been sufficient for diagnosis.

A frozen section abbreviates the tissue processing by the use of the cryostat, a machine that quickly freezes the specimen sample in a special medium at or lower than -20 degrees C. The sample is sectioned with the mounted blade in the cryostat at a thickness averaging 8 to 10 microns, substantially thicker than the sections that can be obtained from routine processing. Touching the section with a glass slide kept at room temperature will transfer the section ready for fixing, clearing and rapid staining in approximately three minutes. The College of American Pathologists requires the anatomic pathologist to render a frozen section diagnosis in 15 to 20 minutes after receipt of the specimen. In rare instances, the anatomic pathologist may defer to give a diagnosis until permanent sections are available.

Frozen sections have been utilized to determine tissue margins in many forms of cancer, to insure that the entire tumor has been removed. A modern utilization of this is in Mohs' micrographic surgery, which may be used in the treatment of recurrent basal cell carcinoma or for the initial presentation of this type of carcinoma. The carcinoma is excised along with a tiny margin of non-involved tissue. The entire margin is frozen and multiple levels are made and examined. If any portion of the margin still has tumor present that are of the margin is re-excised and the process is repeated until the entire margin is tumor free.

Radiography may be utilized to assist the pathologist while making frozen sections. The most common use of this is with breast biopsies where microcalcifications are present with no obvious tumor also present. A faxitron (small self-contained x-ray machine) is utilized to isolate the area of these microcalcifications in the specimen and they are then assessed by frozen and/or permanent sections.

[e] Photography, Gross and Microscopic

In addition to the gross and microscopic description, there may be an occasional need to photograph the gross specimen and perform microphotography for documentation. Photographs provide a permanent record of unusual pathology and also provide a simple means of documenting a complete structure prior to sectioning. The final official report makes a reference when this has taken place. The photographs also provide excellent teaching material or for publication purposes. Also, when slides are received from an outside source and must be returned following examination, photographs can provide a relevant record for future reference or study.

[f] Electron Microscopy

Electron Microscopy is now used sparingly as an adjunctive technique in certain specimens. Its main applications are in the fields of tumor and kidney pathology. Ultrastructural examinations are useful in determining the genesis or differentiation of various malignant tumors. The role of diagnostic electron microscopy has, however diminished considerably as a result of the advent of immune histochemistry and other techniques. In kidney diseases, changes in the thickness of the basement membrane, the changes in the structure of the cells, and the presence of deposits and inclusions are best demonstrated by electron microscopy. The usual fixative used is glutaraldehyde and semi-thin plastic embedded tissue sections of approximately one micron thick are stained with toluidine or methylene blue and double-stained with uranyl acetate and lead citrate for electron microscopic examination. Documentation is by photography.

[g] Direct Immunofluorescence

Direct immunofluorescence performed on fresh or frozen tissues is the most satisfactory method for the routine assessment of a renal biopsy. Antisera most frequently used are the immune globulins IgG, IgA, IgM, Clq, C3, C4, fibrinogen and fibrin. Immunofluorescence for a variety of other complement factors, light chains and various cell markers is performed for selected diagnostic purposes. The procedure involves the use of antigens and specific antibodies tagged with fluorescent material forming a complex that is visible with the use of a fluorescent microscope.

Direct immunofluoresence testing of tissue is indicated in the evaluation of autoimmune bullous diseases, lichen planus, urticarial eruptions, vasculitis and a variety of other dermatoses or skin diseases outside of tumors. Indirect immunofluorescence (IIF) on serum for endomyseal anibody and tissue transglutaminase (enzyme-linked immunosorbent assay (ELISA) is used for gluten-sensitive enteropathy, dermatitis herpetiformis, or celiac disease.

[i] Molecular pathology

Fluorescence in situ hybridization (FISH) DNA probe technology has evolved into a mainstream technology in the pathology laboratory. FISH is used to detect chromosome, gene and locus copy changes in paraffin-embedded and cytological preparations from a variety of solid tumor and hematological samples. FISH DNA Probes for HER-2 gene amplification have been approved in breast cancer. It is in FDA consideration for its broad utility in bladder, prostate and hematological cancer pre-disposition, detection and monitoring.

[ii] Immunohistochemistry

The various cell types of the body have different antigens on their surfaces that distinguish them from one another. Immunohistochemistry utilizes antibodies to identify the antigens that make them unique. Unlike immunofluorescence, immunohistochemistry does not require a special ultraviolet microscope to look for fluorescence. Instead the antigen has an unlabelled antibody bound to it, which in turn has an enzyme labeled antibody that utilizes color change to illustrate antigen positivity. This can be seen using a light microscope. This label may be a peroxidase, alkaline phosphatase, biotin-avidin or a gold-silver technique.

The number of antigens that can be utilized is large and ever increasing. Examples of antigens that can be used include: Actin for smooth muscle, Carcinoembryonic antigen (CEA) for adenocarcinomas, Keratins for epithelial tumors, Prostatic-specific antigen (PSA) for prostatic adenocarcinoma, and S-100 which can be used in the diagnosis of malignant melanoma. These antigens have allowed pathologists to more accurately diagnose specific cancers, differentiate between cancers that appear similar utilizing normal staining techniques and to better delineate subsets of specific cancers, such as lymphoma.

[iii] Flow cytometry

Flow cytometry allows the analysis of from 5,000 to 10,000 cells per second by passing the single cell through a light source into light detectors and converting the electronic signals into a digitized computer to produce a histogram. The technique can evaluate the cell size, the granularity of the cytoplasm, cell viability, the cell cycle time, DNA content and enzyme content and the phenotype of the surface marker. While this technique may assist in diagnosing malignances, such as specific types of lymphomas, the role of flow cytometry in the initial diagnosis of tumors is limited. It appears that flow cytometry is more useful in determining the prognosis of a specific malignancy. Its main role is in the prognostication of breast, colorectal, urinary, prostatic, non-Hodgkin lymphomas and endocrine neoplasms. DNA ploidy (the rate of cell division) and S-phase fraction (indication of cell proliferation) correlate with prognosis in many tumors. The faster growing the cells are, the more aggressive the tumor behaves.

DNA content (ploidy) is the most common factor measured. In a normal human cell there are 46 chromosomes, consisting of 22 pairs or autosomal chromosomes and 2 sex chromosomes. One of each pair of autosomal chromosomes and one sex chromosome make up the haploid number (i.e., 23 chromosomes) and all 46 chromosomes represents the diploid number. When 46 chromosomes are not present then the cell is said to be aneuploid. Aneuploidy is felt to cause genetic instability and to give rise to the clonal cells that form malignant tumors. The exact number of chromosomes present can be used to determine how aggressive some malignant tumors will be.

Flow cytometry can also be used to determine the CD4 T-lymphocyte count in individuals infected by the human immunodeficiency virus (HIV). If this lymphocyte subset has a concentration less than 500/ul then retrovirus therapy is recommended to slow the disease's progress.

[iv] Other techniques

To facilitate the surgical pathologist and clinicians in diagnosing and treating specific tumors, cytogenetics and molecular pathology have been employed. In some forms of cancers, especially those involving the blood, cytogenetics will determine which chromosomal translocations are present in the malignant cells, facilitating the diagnosis and susceptibility to treatment. The nature of the chromosomal defect is also found with the use of cytogenetics in individuals with congenital anomalies. Numeric and sex chromosome abnormalities have also been identified in disease entities.

In cytogenetics the chromosomal characteristics (i.e., karyotype) of tumor cells is determined to assess for genetic abnormalities that have been found to be unique for specific tumors. Examples of this include the Philadelphia chromosome in chronic myelogenous leukemia, where there is a reciprocal translocation between chromosomes 9 and 22, the translocation between chromosomes 11 and 22 in Ewing's sarcoma and the deletion of a portion of chromosome 11 in Wilms' tumor. It may also be utilized to determine the karyotype of a fetus or infant or adult to examine for specific chromosomal abnormalities. The cells obtained to produce a karyotype can come from fetal cells in the amniotic fluid, chorionic villus sampling from the placenta, fetal blood sampling, peripheral blood and skin fibroblasts. Chromosomal abnormalities that can be found include various trisomies, such as trisomy 13 or 18 or 21, with the latter found in Down syndrome, and Turner's syndrome. In Turner's syndrome (also known as 45 XO) there is only one sex chromosome meaning that there are only 45 chromosomes, rather than the normal 46.

Molecular pathology looks at the genetic basis for disease and malignancies, by identifying specific gene abnormalities. There are a number of techniques utilized in molecular pathology including filter hybridization, in situ hybridization, polymerase chain reaction, and oncogenes and tumor-suppressor genes. These techniques can be utilized in a number of ways including: identification of specific viral infection in a surgical specimen (such as specific human papilloma virus in cervical dysplasia), detection of tumor cells in the blood, and gene rearrangements/amplifications.

DNA typing is frequently used in Forensic Medicine and will be discussed further under § 5.05 in Forensic Pathology. DNA profiles are widely used for parentage in man and are rapidly replacing serologic analysis. Additionally, DNA testing is an indispensable tool for positional cloning, a technique by which a previously unknown gene is identified by finding association or links between DNA markers and the inheritance of a disease.

[h]   The Final Report

A final report is prepared for the patient's permanent medical record. As previously indicated, the report should clearly identify the patient, and all pertinent information such as the preoperative diagnosis, source of tissue, date of collection and receipt, surgical identification number and the submitting or ordering physician or surgeon. The diagnosis rendered whenever an intraoperative consultation has been obtained is clearly stated within the body of the gross and microscopic examination of the sample. The official date of issue is included and the handwritten signature of the interpreting pathologist is incorporated if the electronic signature is not routinely used.

The pathologist reviews previous reports and slides whenever applicable to the patient's current disease. This is especially important in evaluating the progression or regression of the patient's disease. Computerized laboratories make the tracking of all patients simple while smaller laboratories maintain logs of all procedures.

[i] Supplemental, Revised, or Corrected Reports

After the initial written report has been issued, there may be occasion to prepare a supplemental, revised, or corrected report. A supplemental report generally will provide further information, such as corroborative findings from special stains or other clinical pathology examinations. An example would be confirmation of a lung biopsy diagnosis of tuberculosis through the use of culture techniques.

A revised report may be necessary as a result of additional findings. For example, an examination with special techniques and stains may change a lung biopsy diagnosis from one of tuberculosis to that of another causative agent, such as a fungus. Such a revision would involve a change in the patient's clinical management.

In certain cases it will be necessary to issue a corrected report. A corrected report is not intended to replace the original report, which will remain a part of the patient's record, but to correct an error that has been made. When a corrected report is issued, the attending physician must be made aware of the change.

[j] Preservation and Retention of Specimens

The College of American Pathologists is the governing body that decides the length of time tissue samples, prepared paraffin blocks, microscopic slides and final reports are to be stored. Gross specimens are generally stored in proper preservatives for at least two weeks after a final report has been issued. More complex specimens are retained for a longer period until the involved pathologist is absolutely sure that there will be no further need to take additional sections.

The College of American Pathologists, with sanctions from other accrediting institutions such as the Joint Commission on Accreditation of Hospitals, and individual state licensing health boards require the paraffin blocks to be retained and stored in properly controlled temperature for a minimum of five years. Microscopic glass slides and reports are stored in the laboratory for ten years. The patient's medical record will have the final report permanently in micro fiche.

[k] Office Records

It is necessary to retain complete office records of all functions performed in the practice of anatomic pathology. All documentation of the steps and procedures up to and including issuance of the final report should be retained in a manner that will allow one to easily track a specimen from receipt in the pathology department to final disposition of the case. All log books should be retained to permit identification of time of receipt, tissue submitted, condition of tissue, individuals who performed work on the tissue, etc. Additionally, records should be maintained for all quality control functions; i.e., procedures carried out to ensure that all protocols are working properly, that equipment is functioning correctly, etc. Failure to retain these records can raise serious questions in the event of a malpractice suit.

[l] The Data Bank

A complete data bank should be maintained on patients that will allow the pathologist to access information on past surgical admissions. The actual structure of the data bank can be as simple as an index card file that lists patients together with their surgical reports and surgical specimen numbers. Or, the data bank might consist of a fully computerized system that allows virtually instant retrieval of all relevant surgical pathology information on a given patient. There is no standard method, but the method used should be relatively error-free and allow retrieval of the needed information in a timely manner.

[m] Requests for Consultation

In cases where the pathology of a tissue is of an unusual nature, it is not uncommon for the anatomic pathologist to submit tissue slides to a consultant pathologist for a second opinion. Generally, the consultant chosen will be determined by his or her expertise on the type of tissue under examination (e.g., renal pathology, dermatopathology, bone pathology, etc.) Additionally, the pathologist may find it necessary to consult with experts in fields outside the area of anatomic pathology. For example, an expert could be consulted to determine the effect of a drug on a given tissue, for the evaluation of a bone marrow specimen, or to correlate clinical data to the anatomic findings in a tissue specimen. The purpose of such consultation usually is to provide a firm and well supported diagnosis.

[n] Special Evaluations or Opinions

In some cases the surgeon may request the anatomic pathologist to enter the operating room for an in situ evaluation of a suspicious tissue. In these cases the pathologist will be requested to give an opinion as to the nature of the tissue based on gross findings, not unlike the gross examination of tissue performed prior to sectioning.

Other cases will arise where the surgeon, prior to an operation, will request the pathologist to make arrangements for special procedures to be done on tissue samples, e.g., electron microscopy or immunoflourescent studies.

Situations also arise where the pathologist is approached by the patient's family to render an opinion on the disease process from a review of the patient's medical records. These reviews frequently relate to the appropriateness of treatment, cause of death, cause of an injury, or correctness of a diagnosis.

[o] The Role of the Histopathology Technologist

The histopathology technologist is responsible for performing the specimen processing required to obtain finished microscopic sections. His or her routine duties involve recording of specimens, assignment of surgical specimen numbers, preparation of required stains, tissue fixation following gross description and sectioning by the pathologist, preparation of paraffin embedded tissue blocks, microtome sectioning of tissue blocks, preparation and staining of microscopic sections, special staining procedures, and storage and retrieval of all tissue blocks and slides. These individuals are also responsible for equipment maintenance. They are normally under the direct supervision of the pathologist. At no time should they be responsible for gross descriptions, sectioning, or microscopic examination of tissue slides, all of which are supposed to be carried out solely by the pathologist.

[i] Quality control

Quality control of all the activities of the pathologist and all technical personnel is required for accreditation. The technical staff keeps a daily log of all solutions, instruments and equipment in use in the histology laboratory. The quality of the end-product, that is, the microscopic slides and staining daily evaluates the performance of the technical staff. This is achieved by the pathologist reviewing the slides for interpretation and diagnosis. The quality of the sections and the clarity of the routine and special stains are graded daily.

On the part of the pathologist, quality assurance is undertaken by regular and periodic review of certain aspects of anatomic pathology practice. The accuracy of rapid diagnoses can be determined by assessing the agreement between the frozen section diagnosis with the final diagnosis after permanent sections. A review of the agreement between the cervical biopsy diagnosis and the diagnosis on cytological smears constitutes another quality assurance. The variance between the intra-departmental or extra-departmental diagnosis from an individual pathologist's diagnosis is another section. Any disagreement between the diagnosis from an open biopsy with a non-gynecology cytology diagnosis is another quality assurance criterion. Major disagreements must not exceed 3% of the total for quality assurance.

Quality assurance on the part of the clinician is also assessed. Technical or procedural competency question involves evaluation of specimen samples which are non-diagnostic on the basis of inadequate size, type of tissue, preservation or location. Also falling under this category are incomplete excision of a lesion and specimens suggestive of technical surgical misadventure. Clinical judgment questions include cases where the pathologic diagnosis is substantively different from the pre-operative or post-operative diagnosis, in cases where the surgical procedure is possibly inappropriate for the clinical diagnosis and where there are discrepancies between the pre-operative and post-operative diagnosis, raising questions about the work-up or clinical judgment.

[2] Cytology Studies

[a] Papanicolaou Smears

The Papanicolau smear, commonly referred to as the PAP smear is the most common cytological examination designed for early detection of cancer in women. A cervical/vaginal swab is collected during the second half of the menstrual cycle to avoid contamination by obscuring blood. The patient is instructed not to use douche or engage in sexual intercourse within 24 hours of collection.

The specimen is collected before the bimanual examination and an unlubricated speculum is utilized to visualize the cervix. The specimen is promptly smeared on a glass microscope slide and immediately fixed. Commercially prepared spray is used and properly identified slide and requisition are processed with great care like tissue specimens. Many laboratories around the country are converting to the use of "Thin Preps". This preparation allows better preservation and clarity in cellular detail.

The PAP smears are screened by specially trained cytotechnologist. The College of American Pathologists limits the number of slides a cytotechnologist is allowed to screen in one day. The maximum is 80. All slides with any degree of abnormality, from benign reactive changes to frankly malignant cells, are reviewed by the pathologist. Ten percent (10%) of the normal smears are also reviewed by the pathologist as part of quality assurance.

[i] Non-gynecologic specimens

Respiratory. Properly collected sputum from a deep cough must be at least a teaspoon in volume. Bronchial epithelial cells or alveolar macrophages need to be identified in order to classify the specimen as satisfactory. A lung specialist may obtain specimens from the respiratory tract by use of the bronchial brush smeared directly to the slide or by leaving the detached bronchoscopy brush in a fixative, either Saccomanno or 50% alcohol. At least 10 ml of fluid used to wash the bronchi during the scope procedure is needed for microbiology or for examination for pneumocyts and cytological evaluation. A post-bronchoscopy sputum is also submitted for cytological examination. These specimens could provide material from a less invasive procedure in the diagnosis of certain tumors that shed cells into the surface of the respiratory tract.

Gastrointestinal smears. A fiberoptic scope designed to examine the gastrointestinal tract from the esophagus and farther can be utilized to obtain a brushing or washing specimen. The scope is passed through the mouth or through the anus depending on what specific abnormality is anticipated. Bile drainage may also be submitted for cytopathological examination. This examination can provide materials in the diagnosis of precancerous conditions such as Barrett's esophagus, yield organisms such as fungal infections or malignant cells in the presence of cancer.

Fluids. Body fluids are routinely submitted for cytological examination. The sources are the chest (pleural fluid), the heart (pericardial), the abdomen (either peritoneal or pelvic) or any washing of a specific cavity during surgery. The specimen is submitted for cytological examination of tumor or infection with a specific agent.

Urine, cerebrospinal fluid and vitreous humor. The urine specimen may either be voided or obtained through a catheter. The washing of the urinary bladder, the ureters or the kidney can also be submitted for cytological evaluation.

Cerebrospinal fluid is usually obtained from a lumbar tap. The presence of a large number of white blood cells could diagnose an infection. Tumor cells, either from a primary or metastatic malignancy may occasionally find their way in the cerebrospinal fluid.

On occasions, when orbital tumor is suspected, fluid from the posterior chamber of the eye may disclose tumor cells. Hemorrhage can also be detected in this specimen.

Fine needle aspirates, superficial and deep. Fine needle aspirates from superficial organs include specimens obtained by needle from the neck, thyroid, salivary gland or breast. Aspiration from lesions deep in the body may be obtained through guidance with computed tomography.

Other specimens submitted for cytological examination include breast discharge, oral scraping, skin scraping (Tzanck smears), conjunctival scrapings and aspirated joint fluid.

Tissue imprints. Direct touch preparations from fresh tissue samples are helpful in some instances. Touch preparations are processed like standard cytological specimens. This is specially useful in lymph node pathology like in Malignant Lymphoma because the cell structure is better visualized although the architecture is not preserved. Touch imprints also take less preparation time. It can be used in sentinel node biopsy for metastatic tumor, most specifically in breast cancer where they want to avoid dissection of all axillary lymph nodes when there is no metastasis to the sentinel node.

Processing and preparation of slides. The actual processing and preparation of slides will vary among different specimen types. The laboratory may receive prepared smears from the doctor's office. When no prepared smears are submitted of fluids, smears may be prepared in the laboratory by cytospin to concentrate the cells in a button on a slide and simultaneous preparation of a cell block, also a button of cells that is processed like the routine tissue section.

The smears are routinely stained with the Papanicolau stain. At times, Giemsa or May Grunwald stain is employed. All stains that are used on tissue sections may be applicable to smears as well. Proper specimen identification is maintained as in the routine sections of tissue samples.

Smears are evaluated as to the adequacy of the preparation and the presence or absence of diagnostic cellular material. Obscuring material is specified. The report contains comments and relevant recommendations as well as correlation with previous samples.

Laboratory reports. Following microscopic examination of the smears, a final report is issued. The full identification information, cytologic diagnosis, additional comments where necessary, date, the identification of the screening cytologist and reviewing pathologist are all indicated on the final report.

Follow up examinations. In cases where a suspicious classification was reported by the pathologist, it is the responsibility of the attending physician to decide whether there is a need to review the slides, either by the involved pathologist or by other members in group practice, to request an outside consultation or to repeat the procedure for a more appropriate sample, or even excise the entire lesion when feasible.

[b] Sputum and Bronchial Washings

Properly collected specimens of sputum or bronchial washings can provide a non-invasive method of establishing a diagnosis of pulmonary disease. Proper specimen collection and preparation are important. The actual method used, however, will vary from laboratory to laboratory. Not all pulmonary diseases are detectable by cytologic techniques. Some of those that can be detected are:

1. Invasive squamous carcinoma
2. In situ squamous carcinoma
3. Small cell anaplastic carcinoma
4. Bronchogenic adenocarcinoma
5. Bronchio-alveolar carcinoma
6. Large cell undifferentiated carcinoma

The responsibility of the cytotechnologist in pulmonary cytology studies is to prepare and stain the slides. The slides themselves should be evaluated by the pathologist.

[c] Gastric Washings

One of the common methods of collecting specimens for gastric cytology studies is through the directed gastric washing technique. A fibergastroscope is used to survey the stomach for suspicious areas. When such areas are found they are lavaged (washed) with saline. The saline is then aspirated for use in the preparation of the cytology slide. (Various other techniques for obtaining the specimen also are used, including blind gastric lavage and gastric brushing.)

Following aspiration of the specimen, it is normally concentrated, and the slides are prepared from the concentrate. These slides are evaluated by the pathologist. Cells that are characteristic for the following conditions usually can be identified:

1. Peptic ulceration
2. Chronic superficial gastritis
3. Atrophic gastritis and gastric atrophy
4. Benign neoplasms
5. Well-differentiated papillary adenocarcinoma
6. Mucous-producing adenocarcinoma
7. Poorly differentiated adenocarcinoma
8. Undifferentiated adenocarcinoma
9. Surface carcinoma
10. Malignant lymphoma
11. Malignancy that has spread from other organs
12. Malignancy that may have originated in the esophagus, bronchus, or mouth as a result of swallowed cells.

[d]   Examination of Other Body Fluids

Other body fluids can be used for cytologic examinations. Specific methods will vary from site to site, but in most cases the general technique described in § § 5.03 [2][a] to 5.03 [2][c], above, will apply. Frequently sampled fluids include urine, cerebrospinal fluid, breast discharges, thoracentesis fluid, and paracentesis fluid. These specimens are prepared by the cytotechnologist, and the slides are evaluated by the pathologist.

[i] Cytology studies – Fine needle aspiration

Cytology is not limited to the various sites that have been previously described. Now many organs or other body sites can be accessed utilizing small bore needles and modern imaging techniques, such as ultrasound or computed tomography. Lesions in the breast and thyroid may be sampled without the use of radiological intervention at the time of the aspiration. The aspirate can be dropped onto glass slides in order to prepare smears that can be fixed or air dried. The air dried specimens may be stained by the Romanowsky method or the Diff-Quik stain, while those that are fixed can be stained by a rapid hematoxylin and eosin stain or a Papanicolaou stain. In cases where the aspirate is low in cellularity a cytospin preparation may be undertaken to concentrate the cells. Also aspirates may be turned into cell blocks, which can be treated like other surgical pathology specimens and can even be used for immunohistochemical studies or electron microscopy. This technique can be used to diagnose benign lesions, malignancies and even infections without having to utilize more invasive procedures, so this procedure can be done in a timelier manner. As such the diagnosis and treatment can begin much faster that in the past.

[e] Processing and Preparation of Slides

The actual processing and preparation of slides will vary among different specimen types. In general, specimens not obtained by direct cellular scraping will need to be concentrated prior to examination. This can be accomplished through centrifugation or by using a cell-trapping vacuum filter. Following concentration, a small cell "button" can be removed to prepare the smear. Care must be taken to ensure that the cells will properly adhere to the microscope slide. This can be accomplished by coating the slides with albumin (egg white) prior to smearing the cells. Failure to obtain adherence will result in the cells being washed away during subsequent processing steps. Following smear preparation, a fixative is added to preserve cellular structure, and the slide is then stained to allow cellular detail to be visualized.

[f] Routine and Special Stains

Routine staining of PAP smears is accomplished using the Papanicolaou stain, which is usually purchased commercially and is a combination of several different stains. Other smears are normally stained with a modified PAP stain.

The actual staining process involves introducing the fixed smears into a series of solutions that will, as a final result, differentially color the various cellular components present in the smear. The finished smear is then evaluated by the cytotechnologist or pathologist.

In addition to the standard and modified PAP stains there are special stains that can be used to identify specific cellular elements. Some of these are: Schorr's stain (used to evaluate hormonal status in smears from the female reproductive tract); Biebrich scarlet-fast green (used to evaluate buccal mucosa for sex chromatin determinations); Mowry's alcain-blue-periodic acid-Schiff's stain (used to evaluate for the presence of carbohydrates); and oil-red O stain (used to evaluate smears for the presence of fat droplets).

Throughout the entire staining procedure it is necessary to ensure that proper specimen identification is maintained. This is usually done by affixing the cytology specimen number to the microscope slide with indelible markings. Failure to do so can result in serious errors occurring during the reading phase of the test.

[g] Classification of Smears

The way the description and diagnoses are given in the PAP report began to be modified in 1988 with the introduction on the Bethesda System, which main aim was towards specimen adequacy. This system also deals with interpretation/results of any PAP smear. It has been modified since its introduction. Overall this system separates the PAP smear report into a specimen adequacy section and an interpretation/results section. The main subheadings of the results section are 'Negative for intraepithelial lesion or malignancy" and "Epithelial cell abnormalities." The latter section deals with squamous cells, glandular cells and other. In squamous cell lesions the most important diagnoses are include: Atypical squamous cells (ASC), low grade intraepithelial lesion (LSIL), and high grade intraepithelial lesion (HSIL). This system can be seen in total by reviewing moderate textbooks in cytology.

[h] Laboratory Reports

Following microscopic examination of a smear, a final report is issued by the laboratory. These reports should provide full patient identification information, a classification of the smear, additional comments as indicated, date of completion of the work, the initials of the cytotechnologist performing the screen (where appropriate), and the initials of the pathologist who has either read or reviewed the smear.

[i] Follow-up Examinations

In cases where a suspicious classification has been reported to the attending physician, follow-up examinations are indicated. In these cases it is suggested that the current smear be evaluated against all prior smears to determine disease progression or remission. In cases that suggest the need for a biopsy or surgical intervention, a similar procedure should be followed. A complete file should be maintained by the cytotechnologist that will allow the rapid indexing of individual patient smears.

[j] Tissue Imprint Examinations

Direct tissue imprint examinations are a variation of the standard cytologic technique. In this procedure, which usually involves a lymph node, the tissue is sectioned and pressed directly to the surface of a glass microscope slide. The specimen is then fixed, stained, and evaluated. This technique takes less time and has a high degree of correlation with standard tissue techniques, but it is used infrequently since the frozen section will provide similar data in even less time.

[3]   Postmortem Examinations

[a]   External Examination

Each postmortem examination will begin with an external examination of the body. Weight and height should be determined, and the pathologist should make a general comment relating the deceased's stated age to his apparent age. The examination should continue with a description of clothing, approximate body temperature, and presence of postmortem lividity and rigidity. The head should be fully described, including hair color, eye color and condition, and ears and external auditory canals. Nostrils are examined for the presence of foreign material, and dentition is evaluated. The lips, tongue, and mouth are examined, and appropriate notations should be made. The neck is examined and described.

The breasts are examined for masses. The abdomen is examined, including palpation for masses. External genitalia are described. The back and extremities are examined and described. Throughout the procedures, special note is made of any identifying scars, marks and surgical incisions. Hospital identification bands also are noted.

[b]   Internal Examination

For examination of the head, an incision is made on the scalp from the back of the ear to the other side. It is then folded back to examine the undersurface for any evidence of trauma. The outer surface of the skull is examined before a cap of the skull is removed with the aid of an electric saw. The membranes of the brain consisting of the dura and arachnoid are examined along with the spaces between the skull and between membranes. The brain is examined in-situ, removed and weighed. It is usually fixed in formalin for an average of two weeks prior to dissection and sectioning for microscopic examination. In cases of neuropathological disease/disorder the brain may be fixed in formalin for examination by a neuropathologist.

The neck is examined and notes are made on the condition of the musculature, subcutaneous fat, thyroid gland, vascular structures and the larynx.

The body cavities are examined next. The relationship of all organs in-situ is noted as well as the amount and nature of the fluid in each cavity. The organs may be eviscerated as a whole in what is termed Rokitansky method or individually. The organs are separated from each other, noting deviations from normal anatomy, weighed and sectioned. Depending on the need, cultures for bacteria, fungi, or viruses must be taken in the fresh state. Great care must be taken to ensure that no contamination is introduced. Representative portions are retained in fixative for microscopic examination.

The musculature is dissected in certain instances when trauma or some abnormality is anticipated. For example, the lower extremities are frequently dissected to explore for possible source of pulmonary embolism as these are the most frequent site where deep vein thrombosis is found.

[c] Photographs

If during the course of the external or internal examination unusual pathology is noted, there may be a need for photographic documentation of the specific details. The photograph will serve to supplement the verbal descriptions that comprise the final written report.

[d] Identification, Collection and Preservation of Body Tissues

Portions of vital organs are taken, fixed in formalin, labeled and processed in much the same fashion as tissues obtained during surgery. The paraffin blocks and microscopic slides are retained for the same length of time as the surgical cases: five years for paraffin blocks and ten years for microscopic slides. Gross specimens are retained for a longer period, usually two months since the College of American Pathologists allows 30 days for completion of the final autopsy report.

For legal purposes, when toxicological examination will be employed, blood, urine and bile, and in certain cases, portions of brain, liver or kidney tissue are collected and retained. This sampling may be necessary in cases where a drug overdose, reaction or interaction is implicated in the cause of death. These specimens should be fully identified and retained until final disposition of the case has been made.

[e] Microbiology Specimens

In the event that a bacterial, fungal, or viral infection is suspected, appropriate sites should be cultured. Great care must be taken to ensure that as little contamination as possible is introduced. Following collection of the specimens, routine microbiologic procedures are carried out if required.

[f] Review of Medical Records

A complete review of all available medical records on the deceased should be conducted by the examining pathologist. All procedures, test results (both laboratory and other), and medication records should be correlated with any diagnosis established prior to death, and this information in turn should be correlated with the findings made at autopsy.

[g] Clinical-pathologic Correlation

The deceased's medical records are made available for the examining pathologist. All procedures performed before death, the results of the tests performed and the medications administered are part of the complete medical records necessary to correlate with any diagnosis established prior to death. This information is in turn, correlated with the findings made at autopsy.

In the great majority of cases, the clinical course and diagnosis will be confirmed by the findings during the postmortem examination. Unsuspected contributing causes to death of a patient may be uncovered during the postmortem examination. An incidence of as high as 13 to 15% of missed diagnoses has been reported in institutions where postmortem examinations are conducted practically as a routine procedure on all deaths in the medical care intensive unit.

[h] Preliminary Report ("Gross Tentative Diagnoses or Provisional Anatomic Diagnosis")

A presumptive cause of death is issued within 24 hours after completion of the gross examination and review of the available records. These findings are provisional and subject to revision following microscopic examination and availability of ancillary tests. The presumptive findings are communicated to the attending physician during the same period while the tentative diagnosis is attached to the medical record.

[i] Examination of Microscopic Slides

Upon completion of the tissue processing, a microscopic examination should be conducted of all tissues sectioned during the internal examination. A review of these slides should lead to the issuance of a final microscopic diagnosis. This should be much more detailed than the gross tentative diagnosis. While it usually tends to confirm the gross diagnosis, it should provide additional details on the secondary and contributing causes of death.

[j] The Final Report

The microscopic slides should be ready for examination by the pathologist within 30 days after the gross postmortem examination. The report will be completed by 30 days. The final report should list all information gathered during all phases of the postmortem examination. It should include a list of all diseases and pathologic processes that have been identified, contain a conclusion as to the final cause of death along with any secondary or contributing causes. A copy of the final report is sent to be incorporated with the patient's medical record, to the attending physician, and may be provided to the family of the deceased when so requested. The pathologist should make him or herself available to answer questions pertaining to the findings from all interested parties.

[k] The Role of the Autopsy Technologist

During the postmortem examination the pathologist is assisted by an autopsy technologist. It is the responsibility of this individual to provide assistance as directed by the pathologist. These duties are normally limited in scope, consisting principally of opening the body cavities prior to internal examination, removing and weighing the individual organs after the pathologist has examined them in situ, and closing the body upon completion of the internal examination.

The certified pathology assistant is usually trained to take sections for stock and for microscopic examination and collect specimens for ancillary tests.

[l] DNA Testing

The focus of most criminal investigations is on linking evidence from the crime scene. Fingerprinting has been applied to criminal investigations since the 1880s. It was followed by ABO blood typing in 1900. Human leukocyte antigen (HLA) became the principal tool in 1960. The 1980s ushered in the age of DNA testing. DNA testing permits the investigator to perform almost unbelievable feats of identification.

The purpose of DNA typing in Forensic Medicine is to match a sample from the crime site with a suspect. Testing does not actually determine whether the sample came from the suspect. Because statistical analysis of the test results yields a probability that the sample did not come from a given suspect, DNA testing has proven to be as powerful for exonerating suspects as it has for convicting them. In about one in three cases of those reported by FBI laboratories, DNA testing has proven that the current suspect could not have committed the crime.

DNA testing has been especially valuable in rape and murder cases as well as in solving robbery, assault, kidnapping, car accidents, extortion and blackmail cases. As previously discussed, it has also been applied to parentage determination and has proven useful in settling certain immigration disputes that hinge upon proving family relationships.

§ 5.04 Scope of Practice: Clinical Pathology

[1] Hematology

[a] Complete Blood Count

Erythrocytes (red blood cells) leukocytes (white blood cells) and thrombocytes (platelets) represent the three populations of cells normally present in the blood. Each of these blood cell populations is bestowed with specific morphologic characteristics and functions essential to normal life. Basic hematologic measurements are commonly performed as an automated procedure and ordered as a complete blood count.

a. Red blood cells (RBCs) are mature cells that contain, but no longer able to synthesize pink-staining hemoglobin. These cells circulate in the blood throughout the body to deliver oxygen to the tissues. The normal count ranges from four to six million per cubic millimeter. Due to blood loss during menstruation, women tend to have a lower RBC count than men. When the count is lower than the range established by each laboratory, the condition is called anemia. A higher than normal count may be due to either concentration as in an individual who is dehydrated or due to increased production such as in the condition called polycythemia or even in a malignant condition called erythroleukemia. Various anemias are termed according to the size, shape or presence of inclusions in the red cells.

b. White blood cells (WBCs) are composed of mature granulocytes (neutrophils, eosinophils and basophils), lymphocytes (the major cell population involved in the development of immune response) and monocytes (which remain in the blood for a short period of 16–36 hours) and then migrate to tissues, where they transform into macrophages or histiocytes. The usual normal range is from 5,000 to 10,000. An increase in the WBC count may be brought about by a reaction to a stimulus, usually an infection or leukemia where there is a malignant increase in immature white blood cells.

c. Hemoglobin is the oxygen-carrying protein contained in the red blood cells. The usual range is 14 to 16 grams per deciliter. A low hemoglobin level is present in anemia and usually has a proportionate increase or decrease as the hematocrit below.

d. Hematocrit is a measure of the portion of the blood occupied by the red cells in relation to the liquid plasma in the blood. It is usually three times the hemoglobin value and is reported in percent. The normal range is 36 to 52%. It approximates the total red cell volume and estimates the functional oxygen-carrying capacity and bulk viscosity of blood.

e. Mean corpuscular volume (MCV) is a measurement of the volume of an individual red cell. The anemia can be classified as normocytic (normal cell size), microcytic (small size) or macrocytic (large cell) using this parameter. The normal range is 80 to 99 cubic microns.

f. Mean corpuscular hemoglobin concentration (MCHC) is a measure of the hemoglobin content of an individual red cell. It is linearly related to the MCV and is a redundant parameter. It is also of little diagnostic value although part of the routine automated test result.

g. Red cell distribution width (RDW) is based on either the coefficient of variation or the standard variation of the volume of the volume of the red cell population. This parameter is a measure of variation in RBC size or anisocytosis. It is most clinically useful in detecting early iron deficiency anemia, discriminating thalassemia trait (normal or increased RDW) from iron deficiency anemia (increased RDW), indicating a combined small/large cell process, and indicating response to Vitamin B12, folate or iron therapy.

h. Platelet count can be determined simultaneously with many cell counters. This test result is important in patients with a suspected bleeding disorder or as a part of a screen for bleeding abnormalities before surgery. An estimation of the platelet count can be made from the peripheral blood smear in an area where the red cells barely overlap. The average range is 150 to 400,000 per cubic millimeter in adults and children.

The data provided by the complete blood count is often supplemented with data provided by the differential count. It is a microscopic classification of the various WBC subtypes. In this procedure, a thin smear of the peripheral blood is prepared on a glass slide and stained with Wright's or Giemsa stain. Most larger automated hematology instruments are used to perform a screening WBC differential with the other hemogram parameters. The percentage and absolute values of total neutrophils (bands and segmenters) and lymphocytes are reported. The WBC differential is an appropriate diagnostic test in the patient with a suspected primary blood disease or with unexplained high or low WBC count, high or low RBC count, or high or low platelet count.

The peripheral blood smear also allows evaluation of the red cells. Anemia is one of the most frequently encountered medical problems. It is a sign of many disorders of either primary or secondary blood disease. Anemia could be a result of either decreased production, loss from bleeding or from increased destruction of the red blood cells.

Red cell size variation is called anisocytosis. Microcytosis (small RBCs) occurs when there is insufficient hemoglobin production in the developing RBC. This can be produced by insufficient iron, by hereditary hemoglobin abnormalities or by impairment of enzymes involved in the production or synthesis of hemoglobin. The most common causes of microcytic anemia are iron deficiency, chronic disease and thalassemia.

Macrocytosis (large RBCs) occurs when mitotic divisions are skipped during maturation in the bone marrow. It can be caused by vitamin B12 deficiency, folate deficiency or by bone marrow dysplasia. The last mentioned condition is a precursor of leukemia (malignant blood disease), indicating an arrest in the maturation of any of each cell line. All blood cells are derived from a common ancestor cell in the bone marrow that differentiates as it matures into a specific category: a red blood cell, a white blood cell (either as a neutrophilic granulocyte, eosinophilic granulocyte, basophilic granulocyte, lymphocyte, monocyte, plasma cell) or platelet.

Normocytic (normal sized RBCs) anemia comprises the most common category. Most patients with chronic infection, inflammation, or malignancy develop a mild to moderate degree of anemia. This is thought to be caused by a combination of decreased RBC life span and of decreased RBC production. RBC production may be severe in patients with chronic kidney failure. RBC destruction is increased in hemolytic anemia, which may be a hereditary or acquired disorder.

Just as the size of the red cells is evaluated and graded from 1+ to 4+ as microcytic or macrocytic when different from the normocytes, the shape is also reviewed. Variation in shape is known as poikilocytosis. Red blood cells may take many different shapes under various conditions, including a resemblance to teardrop, helmet, bull's eye and fish mouth. A specific pathologic process may be characterized by the preponderance of an abnormal-shaped red cell. Examples are crescent-shaped cells in sickle cell anemia and fragmented RBCs produced by the arrest of their passage through the circulation by fibrin strands, damaged prosthetic valves, altered vessel walls, or increased shear force.

The red cell color is altered by the amount of hemoglobin present in the red cell. With decreased hemoglobin, there is hypochromia and when increased, the cell is called hyperchromic. Polychromasia is a blue gray coloration of RBCs that indicates the presence of an admixture of RNA and hemoglobin as seen in reticulocytes. Normally, about 1% of RBCs in an adult are polychromatophilic. The percentage significantly rises in severe anemias with increased activity in red cell production.

The reticulocyte count is a part of the initial evaluation of any unexplained anemia. It is particularly useful in classifying whether a normocytic anemia is due to increased production or destruction. It may also be used to follow the response of a nutritional deficiency anemia to replacement therapy. A recticulocyte is a developing RBC that has extruded its nucleus. This term is derived from the reticulin-like network of RNA that remains in the cell for the next 3–4 days as hemoglobin production continues. Normally, the reticulocyte spends 2–3 days in the bone marrow, passes through the sinus into the peripheral circulation, and matures in the peripheral blood for 1 day. These less hemoglobinized and larger sized cells have a bluish or polychromatophilic appearance on Wright's or Giemsa stain.

Various other tests are performed in the Hematology laboratory. These tests deal with cell morphology or structure. Body fluids such as those from the pleural and pericardial fluid obtained through thoracentesis, peritoneal, joint and cerebrospinal fluid are examined in the Hematology laboratory. Cell counts are performed on these fluid specimens. Sperm analysis and eosinophil count are also performed in this section of the laboratory. Sedimentation rate, sickle cell screening, and hemoglobin electrophoresis are also part of Hematology testing.

[b] Bone Marrow Examination

The bone marrow, though largely interpreted by the pathologist is jointly prepared in the Hematology laboratory and in Histology. The set of samples for evaluation of a blood disease, whether primary or secondary consists of the bone marrow needle biopsy, the particle sections obtained from a spun washing of the syringe used to aspirate the bone marrow, smears prepared from the aspirate of the bone marrow and the peripheral blood smear along with the complete blood count.

The sample is usually obtained by a hematologist or an oncologist. In certain institutions, the pathologist who had special training in the procedure may be requested to perform the sample procurement. The usual site is the posterior iliac crest (the back of the hip), or an area that may be clinically suspected to harbor a tumor, or less frequently, the sternum or breast plate.

The special needle is introduced under local anesthesia. The needle aspirate is smeared into an average of four glass slides and allowed to air dry. The biopsy core and the washing of the syringe are expressed into a small container with Zenker's solution fixative. The biopsy and the particle sections are processed in the Histology laboratory while the smears are stained with Wright's stain in Hematology. Additional stains routinely performed are iron and Giemsa.

[c] Hemostasis and Coagulation Tests

Hemostasis is a multicomponent system that serves two major functions. The first is to stem blood loss from a site of vascular disruption. The second is to prevent pathologic clotting by limiting the plug formation at the site of vascular damage. When the vessel wall is damaged, the initial response is the arrival of platelets that stick to the site of disruption. Chemical mediators are released to recruit additional platelets, resulting in the formation of a plug or platelet aggregate. As the platelet plug is forming, thrombin is generated and converts fibrinogen to fibrin. Factor XIII is activated by thrombin to make the fibrin clot stable.

Abnormalities of hemostasis may present clinically as a bleeding disorder, as a thrombotic or clotting disorder, or as a complex disorder involving simultaneous bleeding and microvascular thrombosis. A thorough clinical history, physical examination, and a few screening tests of hemostatic system is usually sufficient for a presumptive diagnosis or limited differential diagnosis. The objective is to determine whether the patient has a significant bleeding problem, the problem is congenital or acquired, or the problem is due to platelet defect or to abnormal fibrin clot formation.

Platelet count may be increased (thrombocytosis) or decreased (thrombocytopenia). Reactive increase in platelets is usually clinically silent. By contrast, primary thrombocytosis is seen in leukemias and may be associated with bleeding or thrombosis. Conversely, platelet counts lower than 50,000/cu mm could result in excessive bleeding during surgery or trauma. Spontaneous bleeding occurs when the platelet count goes lower than 10,000–20,000.

Factor level assays may be utilized on inpatients with vitamin K deficiency as in liver disease. Factor VII and Factor II are vitamin K dependent. Factor V or Leiden factor may be assayed for presymptomatic evaluation of at risk thrombosis or for patients with deep vein thrombosis.

Qualitative platelet disorders may be either hereditary or acquired. Von Willebrand's disease is the most common hereditary bleeding disorder due to abnormal platelet adhesion. The von Willebrand factor also functions as a carrier of Factor VIII. Tests to assess this disease include the bleeding time, activated plasma thromboplastin time, platelet aggregation with ristocetin, VWF antigen, ristocetin cofactor assay, factor VIII and other esoteric tests. Other hereditary disorders are the Bernard-Soulier syndrome (a rare autosomal recessive disorder characterized by mild thrombocytopenia, giant platelets and deficient VWF binding site) and the Glanzmann's thrombasthenia (a rare autosomal recessive disorder of platelet secretion and aggregation).

Acquired qualitative platelet disorders are the most common cause of abnormal platelet function. The most common culprit is drug therapy. The most common associated drug is aspirin. Aside from aspirin, other drugs that may cause bleeding due to abnormal platelet function are anti-inflammatory drugs and antibiotics.

Hereditary disorders of fibrin clot formation most commonly present early in childhood. The two most common disorders are hemophilia A (caused by factor VIII deficiency) and hemophilia B (caused by factor IX deficiency).

Some patients have a hereditary predisposition to thrombosis or formation of blood clots. An autosomal dominant trait has a relatively high rate of expression. The disorder may be an antithrombin III or heparin cofactor II deficiency, a protein C or S deficiency, plasminogen of its activator deficiency and various other factors that will not be discussed here. The demonstration of familial transmission of the abnormality is helpful in the diagnosis of a hereditary thrombotic tendency.

Hypercoagulation tests for inherited thrombotic disorders include the following. The so-called lupus anticoagulant tests consist of the Prothrombin/plasma thromboplastin time, dilute Russell Viper venom time (for screening) and confirmatory cardiolipin antibodies. Additionally, activated protein C resistance, anti-thrombin III and specific tests for factor V Leiden mutation, homcysteine and prothrombin gene variant.

A number of acquired systemic disorders are associated with an increased risk of thrombosis. Recurrence of thrombosis during oral anticoagulant therapy may be a clue to the presence of an occult tumor. Recurrence of thrombosis during heparin therapy should raise the possibility of a heparin dependent antiplatelet antibody. An unexplained prolongation of the APTT in a patient with thrombosis should suggest the possibility of a lupus anticoagulant. This depends on the demonstration of phospholipid dependence of the inhibitory activity.

The classic example of a complex acquired disorder of hemostasis presenting with simultaneous bleeding and microvascular thrombosis is disseminated intravascular coagulation. The diagnosis depends on the clinical setting and on laboratory documentation of excessive thrombin and plasmin activity. Excessive thrombin generation results in consumption of fibrinogen, presence of circulating fibrin monomers, consumption of antithrombin III and protein C, and thrombocytopenia. Excessive plasmin generation results in formation of fibrin degradation products (D-dimer), and consumption of fibrinogen, factor V and factor VIII. The tests for DIC (disseminated intravascular coagulation) include prothrombin time, plasma thromboplastin time, fibrinogen, D-dimer and platelet count.

[d] Types of Blood Tests

Hematology is that subdivision of clinical pathology that deals with the cells found in various body fluids. The primary fluid examined is whole blood, but examinations also are conducted on spinal fluid, seminal fluid, joint fluids, as well as fluids removed from a variety of other locations. The most commonly performed tests are the Complete Blood Count (CBC) and Cell Differential. The CBC is actually composed of a group of subtests (see below). Taken together, they present a comprehensive evaluation of an individual's hemapoetic state.

1. White Blood Cells (WBCs). These normally present at levels of 5,000 to 10,000. Increasing numbers are present in most infections, and can reach into the hundreds of thousands in the leukemias. The WBCs are comprised of a variety of subpopulations that will be discussed later.
2. Red Blood Cells (RBCs). These are the cells that contain hemoglobin, and are responsible for delivering oxygen to the tissues of the body. The red cells are normally present at levels of 4,000,000 to 6,000,000 per cubic millimeter. Females usually have fewer red cells than males. When present in lower than expected numbers, the condition is called anemia; when present in higher than expected numbers the condition is called polycythemia.
3. Hemoglobin. This is the oxygen-carrying protein contained in the red cells. It is normally present at levels of 12 to 18 grams per deciliter. As with the red cells, females have lower levels than males. Insufficient amounts of hemoglobin result in anemias and excessive amounts present as polycythemias.
4. Hematocrit. This is a measure of the plasma contained in whole blood, and is reported in percentages. The normal range will be approximately 37 to 52%, with females having lower levels.
5. Mean Corpuscular Volume (MCV). This is a measurement of the volume of an individual red cell. The presence of a larger or smaller than expected volume can provide guidelines in determining the

source of anemias. The reporting units are cubic microns and the expected range is approximately 80 to 99.

6. Mean Corpuscular Hemoglobin (MCH). This is a measure of the hemoglobin concentration of an individual red cell. It is reported as picograms, and the average value is 29 plus or minus 2.

7. Mean Corpuscular Hemoglobin Concentration (MCHC). This is a measure of the hemoglobin concentration in the red cell mass. It is reported in grams per deciliter, with an average value of 33 g/dl.

8. Red Distribution Width (RDW). This is a measure of the size differences encountered when the red cell population is measured. The number is presented as a percentage, and is seen only in CBCs performed on the newer automated cell counting instruments. This dispersion measure is useful when evaluating specific aspects of red cell morphology.

9. Platelets. These cells are, in part, responsible for clotting. They are normally present at levels of 130,000 to 400,000/cubic millimeter. Depressed levels are of particular concern because spontaneous hemorrhage may occur if the level becomes too low. A lack of platelets is called thrombocytopenia. This test is a part of the CBC on the newer automated cell counters.

10. Mean Platelet Volume (MPV). This is a measure of the actual volume of the individual platelets in circulation. Normally, this will range from approximately 7.2 to 10.5 cubic microns. This parameter is included only with the newer instruments.

11. Lymphocyte Percent. This is an evaluation done on the white blood cell population, and provides a very general guide to the make-up of this population.

12. Lymphocyte Number. This is an absolute measurement of the lymphocyte population, and is reported in thousands/cubic millimeter. Normal ranges from 1,000 to 3,000. Both lymphocyte percent and lymphocyte number are provided only with the newer automated cell counters.

The data provided by the Complete Blood Count is often supplemented with data provided by a Cell Differential Count. In this procedure a drop of blood is placed on a glass microscope slide and a thin smear is made. This smear is allowed to air-dry, and is then stained with a Wright's, Giemsa, or Wright's-Giemsa stain. A microscopic examination and count is made of the white blood cell population and an evaluation is made of the size and shape of the red cells present. Normally 100 WBCs are counted in sequence as they are encountered, and the percentage of each cell type is reported. In a similar fashion, the red cells are visually evaluated for size, color, and shape, while the WBC differential is being performed. The white blood cells normally encountered are:

1. Segmented neutrophils
2. Bands
3. Monocytes
4. Eosinophils
5. Basophils
6. Lymphocytes

Various pathologic conditions will cause other white cells to appear in circulation. Some of these are:

1. Atypical lymphocytes
2. Metamyelocytes
3. Myelocytes and promyelocytes
4. Myeloblasts
5. Prolymphocytes
6. Lymphoblasts
7. Promonocytes
8. Monoblasts
9. Plasmacytes
10. Proplasmacytes
11. Plasmablasts

The evaluation of red cell populations is known as red cell morphology, and usually is performed as a scaled grading, ranging from 1+ (least notable) to 4+ (most notable). Size variations are known as anisocytosis or aniso, and this measurement represents the range of size difference between the largest and the smallest of the red cells seen.

For aniso to be present, there must be at least two distinctly sized cell populations. These could be very small cells and normal cells, very large cells and normal cells, or very small cells and very large cells, with the later yielding the highest grading of aniso.

The aniso grade generally will correlate with an increased RDW from the CBC. Smaller than normal cells are called microcytes, and larger than normal cells are called macrocytes. The number of cells that are either microcytic or macrocytic are also graded 1+ to 4+. It is possible to have no aniso and 4+ microcytes or macrocytes present. This will occur if only one category or the other is present; that is, where all cells are uniformly large or small. The anemias are frequently identified as either macrocytic or microcytic, and subsequent investigations into the underlying cause of the anemia can be based on this distinction.

Just as size is evaluated, shape is reviewed as a part of red cell morphology. Variation in shape is known as poikilocytosis, and there are numerous specific poikilocytes that can be identified. The presence of certain poikilocytes can be linked to a specific pathologic process. This is best illustrated by the correlation between sickle cells and sickle cell anemia. Others encountered are ovalocytes, target cells, echinocytes, acanthocytes, crenated cells, spur cells, burr cells, and helmet cells, among many others. This particular area of hematology lacks standardization, and there are many nomenclature systems in use.

As with the size and shape, red cell color is evaluated. The terms most frequently encountered here are polychromasia (excessive color) and hypochromasia (depressed amount of color).

Along with evaluations of size, shape, and color, numerous other comments and notations may appear on blood test reports with regard to the presence of certain red and white cell inclusions. A few of these might be toxic granulation in neutrophils, basophilic stippling of red cells, Howell-Jolly bodies in RBCs, hypersegmented neutrophils, and many others.

Other tests frequently performed in the Hematology laboratory include:

1. Reticulocyte counts
2. Sedimentation rates
3. Red cell fragility
4. Sperm counts
5. Cerebrospinal fluid cell counts
6. Synovial fluid examinations
7. Sickle cell screening
8. Hemoglobin electrophoresis
9. Eosinophil counts

[e] Methodologies

The actual methodologies used to perform the tests listed in § 5.04 [1][d], above, will vary greatly from laboratory to laboratory. In the case of the CBC, the number of parameters evaluated will vary depending upon both the manufacturer of the instrumentation and on the age of the equipment. In smaller laboratories and in many physicians' offices, a complete blood count is not available, and only portions of the examination will be done. These are normally the hemoglobin and hematocrit, and the WBC and RBC counts.

Methods here can vary from simple procedures that entail nothing more than placing blood obtained by finger prick onto a special reagent stick, allowing a color to develop, and then performing a visual comparison against a color chart to determine the hemoglobin value. A simple multiplication by 3.0 of this number may be used to obtain the hematocrit. A microscopic count of the red and white cells can be performed in a specially designed counting slide. Small, semi-automated instruments exist that will allow these determinations to be completed with considerably less risk of error than that associated with the manual procedures.

In larger laboratories, these tasks are performed by large, automated cell-counting instruments. These instruments will take a small sample of blood and, through the use of pneumatic systems, split the sample into various sections of the instrument for further manipulations. Via the use of electronics, the instruments count, size, and provide quantitation for the parameters discussed in § 5.04 [1][d], above. These instruments are capable of processing a patient's sample approximately every sixty seconds.

In the case of the differential count, all smears should be stored for a period of time following the completion of the work to allow a review of the slide should it become necessary.

The methodologies for the other tests vary considerably from laboratory to laboratory.

In small laboratories and many physicians' offices, a certain fraction of the panel of tests are performed manually. While these test results may provide a rough aid in the clinical evaluation by the physician, unless the laboratory is approved to operate in this capacity, the values obtained are not acceptable as true laboratory results. A series of guidelines for evaluating performance are available from the National Committee for Clinical Laboratory Standards (NCCLS).

Automated cell counters are used to perform the set of tests by larger hospital and private laboratories. The instruments take a small sample of blood and, through the use of pneumatic systems and electronics, previously discussed quantitative parameters are obtained. Laboratory methods have improved in sensitivity and specificity over time. Introduction of new methods and new treatment require ongoing vigilance of laboratory personnel and clinicians to prevent problems.

[f] Collection and Preservation of Specimens

EDTA-anticoagulated blood is the preferred specimen. Blood is promptly mixed in an anticoagulant to prevent clotting. Heparinized blood may be acceptable for some of the hemogram parameters, depending on the type of laboratory instrumentation. Newer instruments use very small sample volumes (.25 ml or less). Capillary blood from newborns or children can be collected directly into EDTA-coated microcollection vials.

In the case of large automated instruments, great care must be taken to ensure proper specimen identification. The risk of handling errors increases due to the high volume of samples being run through the system. A method of cross-checking patient results should be in place and should be incorporated into the laboratory's policy and procedure manual.

[g] Special Considerations

In evaluating any hematologic examination it is of vital importance to consider both the method and the instrumentation used. A full disclosure of this information should be sought prior to making an evaluation, and the evaluation should be made only after an understanding of the idiosyncracies and possible shortcomings of the method and instrument combination.

In any hematologic examination, quality control procedures are important. These procedures should be developed in accordance with the instrument manufacturer's guidelines. A failure to adhere to such procedures can make it difficult if not impossible to validate the results.

In the case of large automated instruments, great care must be taken to ensure proper specimen identification. The risk of handling errors increases due to the high volume of samples being run through the system. A method for cross-checking patient results should be in place, and should be incorporated into the laboratory's statements of policy and procedure.

[2] Urinalysis

[a] Types of Urine Tests

Test of urine specimens can range from very simple evaluations of basic chemical constituents up to exceedingly complex evaluations for urine hormones and various metabolic products. The most frequent test is a routine and microscopic urinalysis. It is composed of four parts: (1) a visual description of the specimen; (2) specific gravity; (3) chemical examination; and (4) microscopic examination of the formed elements.

The visual description provides information on both the color and appearance of the specimen. Commonly used terms for color are yellow, amber, and red. Other colors that can be encountered include orange, green, blue, brown, and black. These are "aberrant" colors that can be caused by drugs or certain pathologic conditions.

The determination of specific gravity gives some index of the concentration of the urine. This test is commonly performed with a T.S. meter or a urine refractometer. Results can range from a low value of 1.003 to high values in excess of 1.035.

Chemical determinations normally are performed by the urine dipstick method, and include:

1. pH (measure of the acidity of the specimen)
2. Protein (normally negative)
3. Glucose (normally negative; can be used as a diabetic screening test)
4. Ketones (normally negative)
5. Urobilinogen (normally negative)
6. Bilirubin (normally negative)
7. Blood (normally negative)
8. Nitrite (normally negative; certain types of pathogenic bacteria will cause it to be positive)

Upon completion of the chemical examination, the urine specimen is placed in a centrifuge to allow the formed elements to be concentrated as a sediment "button." This sediment is then resuspended in a small amount of urine, placed on a microscope slide, and examined. All formed elements are identified, and a semi-quantitative count is done using a 40x microscope objective. Results are reported as the average number of each element encountered per high-power field (HPF). Commonly encountered formed elements include:

1. White blood cells
2. Red blood cells
3. Epithelial cells
4. Mucous and mucous threads (quantitated as light, moderate, or heavy)
5. Amorphous crystals
6. Bacteria (quantitated as light, moderate, or heavy)
7. Casts (type is specified and reported per low-power field)
8. Yeast cells (quantitated as light, moderate or heavy)
9. Parasites (type specified)
10. Crystals (type specified)
11. Spermatozoa

The clinical significance of the above elements can vary, with some (epithelial cells, mucous) being normal and others (parasites and casts) being associated with significant pathologic findings.

Other urine tests are more closely related to chemistry determinations, and are discussed in § 5.04 [3][a] *et seq.*

[b] Collection and Preservation of Specimens

The specimen most frequently used for urine testing is random urine. This is collected by simply having the patient void into a container. Specimens should be delivered to the testing facility within thirty minutes of collection, and processing should begin as soon as possible to prevent degradation of formed elements.

Special urine chemistry examinations frequently require the use of 24-hour collections. Preservatives are necessary for many of these assays, with the specific preservative being dictated by the test requested, and in some cases by the test method used by the facility. Care must be taken in the collection of 24-hour urine specimens to ensure that a true 24-hour volume has been collected. Failure to obtain the full volume can lead to serious errors in test interpretation.

[c] Special Considerations

Even in the simple urine dipstick test, care must be exercised. There are numerous causes for both false positive and false negative results, especially in the presence of drugs and other interfering compounds. The technologist performing the assay must be aware of atypical color reactions, and care should be exercised to ensure that the values reported are correct. Also, the results of both the chemistry testing and the microscopic examination can be significantly influenced by the concentration of the urine. Specific gravity should be used to judge concentration, and specimens with low specific gravity should be evaluated carefully, because the chemical constituents may be too dilute to detect.

In the 24-hour collection, the presence of an unexplained low volume of urine, coupled with unexpectedly abnormal urine creatinine results, are sufficient grounds to question the validity of the test, and it should be repeated on a new specimen.

[3] Chemistry Tests

[a] Types of Tests

The chemistry section of the clinical pathology laboratory is by far the largest, both as to the number of specimens tested and the variety of tests. There are hundreds of possible assays that can be performed, and many tests can be done using a variety of different methods. Testing can range from simple blood-glucose determinations of diabetic patients to large, multi-channel instruments that can perform 25 or more different individual determinations on a single specimen. Between the two extremes, nearly every conceivable combination exists. The following is a condensed list of common chemistry tests:

1. Glucose
2. BUN (blood urea nitrogen)
3. Sodium
4. Potassium
5. Chloride
6. CO_2
7. Creatinine
8. Calcium
9. Phosphorus
10. Bilirubin (total and direct)
11. Uric acid
12. Amylase
13. Lipase
14. Alkaline phosphatase
15. Prostatic acid phosphatase
16. Gamma GTP
17. SGOT (serum glutamic-oxaloacetic transaminase)
18. SGPT (serum glutamic-pyruvic transaminase alanine aminotransferase)
19. LDH (lactate dehydrogenase)
20. CPK (creatine phosphokinase)
21. Total protein
22. Albumin
23. Serum iron
24. Total iron binding capacity
25. Triglycerides
26. Cholesterol
27. Vitamin B-12
28. Folic acid
29. Therapeutic drug levels
30. Drugs of abuse (both blood and urine)

[i] Urinalysis

Urine examination, by convention, means the gross and microscopic examination of urine for formed elements such as cells and casts and for crystals and amorphous material. The visual process is integrated with a chemical assessment of the urine that is now achieved by the use of strips that carry dried reagents for multiple chemical tests (dipsticks). Both of these analytic processes have now been automated, although the majority of laboratories retain the conventional visual microscopic examination with manual or semiautomated chemical testing. The first morning specimen is the most concentrated and is the specimen of choice for urinalysis.

The tradition of reporting the color, appearance and odor of urine is disappearing. However, specific urine color may suggest possible causes such as pink to red from blood, blue through green from drugs, pseudomonas infections, and bile and brown through black from homogentisic, melanin, etc.

The urine specimen must be examined less than six hours after voiding or significant loss of formed elements may occur. The specimen is centrifuged to allow the cells to concentrate as a sediment. Formed elements are identified and reported in semi-quantitative counts per high power field.

a. Erythrocytes or red blood cells are increased in the urine in the presence of kidney disease, diseases of the urinary tract or even in some diseases unrelated to the renal system. The reference range is less than 3 per high power field.

b. Leukocytes or white blood cells are increased in the urine in the presence of inflammation in the urinary tract. Large numbers of leukocytes (greater than 50/high power field) are suggestive of acute infection. The presence of moderate numbers (5-50/hpf) is indicative of a localized inflammation that may either be acute or chronic. The normal range is less than 5/hpf.

c. Epithelial cells may be renal tubular, transitional, or squamous type. Renal tubular epithelial cells are increased in situations where tubular damage has occurred, such as pyelonephritis, acute tubular necrosis or following ingestion of many drugs including aspirin. Transitional cells are derived from the ureter, bladder, urethra or prostate. Healthy individuals may have a few. When large numbers are present, a full cytologic examination must be done. Squamous cells are derived from the distal portions of the urethra, but in females may be derived from the vulva or vagina.

d. Casts are protein precipitate in the renal tubule. Factors that contribute to cast formation include decreased urine flow, increased acidity, concentrated urine and the presence of proteinuria. Casts may be hyaline, red blood cell type, white blood cell casts, epithelial cell casts, granular, waxy or fatty.

e. Crystals may have diagnostic significance. However, some crystals may be present in the urine of individuals without disease. Calcium oxalate in acid urine arise from diet constituents such as spinach, tomatoes rhubarb, tea and vitamin C. Uric acid crystals may increase in the presence of gout. The crystals associated with abnormalities are cystine, leucine in severe liver disease, tyrosine and sulfonamides.

f. The reporting of the presence of bacteria in the urine is still made and semi-quantitatively reported as light, moderate or heavy. However, it has been found by many researchers that the great majority of patients with bacteria in their urine were asymptomatic and did not have significant urinary tract disease.

It is standard procedure to include in routine urinalysis a semi-quantitative assessment of as many as nine analytes by the use of a reagent strip. The usual tests performed are the pH, protein, glucose, ketones, hemoglobin, bilirubin, urobilinogen, nitrite, leukocyte esterase and occasionally, the specific gravity.

[ii] Chemistry panels

The Medicare insurance program is under the Social Security Act. Blood testing necessary for diagnosis or treatment of an illness or injury will be reimbursed by Medicare. Medicare will not pay for check-ups or most blood screening tests. Blood testing laboratories have been assigned the responsibility of certifying that the blood testing that they perform is in compliance with current Medicare guidelines.

Reimbursement schedules differ substantially by state, county, date, eligibility, and qualification requirements. The Blood testing laboratory must be able to identify a qualified provider as defined by Medicare. Documentation must be made of the reason for ordering the test. Title XIII of the Social Security Act section 1862 (a)(7) excludes routine physical checkups from the Medicare program. Screening is defined as diagnostic procedures performed in the absence of signs or symptoms. A diagnosis code should reflect the reason for the requested blood laboratory test.

Limited Coverage Blood Tests

The Health Care Finance Administration (HCFA) requires Medicare carriers to establish policies to ensure the medical necessity of services being paid for by the Medicare program. Local area carriers have the authority to establish their own list of tests and procedures, which may be reimbursed as those they have determined to be medically necessary.

The Medicare program will allow the laboratory to bill the patient for denied services if an Advanced Beneficiary Notice is completed, appropriate places checked and signed by the patient, and forwarded to the laboratory. If there is a failure to complete an acceptable requisition form or signed Advance Beneficiary Notice, the physician may be charged for the denied services.

[iii] Pulmonary and cardiac function

Respiratory system — Arterial blood gases are used to evaluate the respiratory function. It is divided into three functional components: ventilation, respiration and oxygen delivery. Clinical blood gas analyzers measure the pressure of oxygen (pO2), pH, and the pressure of carbon dioxide (pCO2). Additional acid-base parameters are calculated from the values of those three. These include bicarbonate concentration (HCO3-), base excess and oxygen saturation (SO2).

Tests for cardiac disease — Measurement of serum enzyme activity is important in the diagnosis of myocardial infarction. The most important enzymes are creatine phosphokinase (CPK) and lactate dehydrogenase (LDH). The measurement of these cardiac enzymes at specified intervals could determine the presence of an ischemic heart disease or an acute myocardial infarction.

CPK is an enzyme found in high concentrations in skeletal muscle, cardiac muscle and brain tissue. It is a sensitive indicator of cardiac muscle damage. A serial testing of this enzyme, in conjunction with troponin can determine the presence of an acute myocardial infarction. Different laboratories, in association with cardiologists in the facility determine the panel of testing of cardiac markers. An example includes CK-MB (fraction for cardiac muscle), total CPH and Troponin-I on arrival in the Emergency Department, followed by CK-MB and total CK at 4 hours, then CK-MB, total CK and Troponin-I at 8 hours and CK-MB and total CK at 16 hours. If the CK-MB is greater than 6.0 ng/ml and the Troponin-I greater than 1.5 ng/ml, an acute myocardial infarction is diagnosed.

[iv] Renal function

Urea, the major product of protein catabolism is synthesized in the liver, excreted by the kidney trough the glomeruli, and reabsorbed to a degree by the tubules. Measuring urea is probably the most popular laboratory procedure for assessing renal function. Normal range is 8–20 mg/dl.

Creatinine is derived from the catabolism of creatine in skeletal muscle. It is removed from the blood by filtration in the glomeruli of the kidney, thus the most popular analyte for the determination of glomerular filtration rate and the most important clinical measurement of renal function.

Sodium is the most important cation in fluid and electrolyte balance. The average diet provides between 8 and 15 grams of sodium but the body requires only between 1–2% of the intake such that the excess is excreted in urine. As with sodium, renal function constitutes the major mechanism for potassium homeostasis. Chloride is the major anion in extracellular fluid balance. Excess chloride is excreted in the urine.

[v] Liver function

Serum alanine aminotransferase (ALT or SGPT) is useful for determining inflammation and necrosis of the liver. It is used for screening for blood donors for hepatic disease including possible viral hepatitis. The usual reference range is 10–40 IU/L.

Aspartate aminotransferase (AST, SGOT) is also useful for identifying inflammation and necrosis of the liver. Because it is also present in heart, skeletal muscle, pancreas, kidneys and red blood cells, it is less specific for liver disease than ALT. The reference range is usually 10–40 IU/L.

Alkaline phosphatase (AP) is useful for diagnosing cholestatic hepatobiliary disease with highest levels found in extrahepatic biliary obstruction and in osteoblastic bone disease. The reference range is 25–100 IU/L.

Bilirubin is useful for diagnosis, screening and follow up of liver diseases and when jaundice is present not attributable to liver problems. Patients with hepatic injury, as found in alcoholic, viral or toxic hepatitis have increased unconjugated and conjugated bilirubin.

Ammonia, lactate dehydrogenase, gamma glutamyl transferase are supplemental tests of liver function. Miscellaneous tests such as alpha fetoprotein, albumin, ceruloplasmin, alpha anti-trypsin, anti-smooth muscle and antimitochondrial antibodies are esoteric tests for liver disease.

[vi] Pancreatic function

The pancreas has the highest amylase concentration and largest total amount of amylase of any organ in the body. Amylase is also found in the salivary glands such as the parotid glands, submaxillary and submandibular glands. Amylase is elevated in the presence of inflammation or obstruction of the ducts.

The only organ containing significant lipase activity is the pancreas. Thus, elevated lipase should be more specific for pancreatitis than elevation of total amylase activity. As with amylase, the reference range varies with the substrate and assay used. Diagnosing pancreatitis remains one of the many medical areas that relies more heavily on clinical judgment and the art of medicine than an objective science.

[vii] Lipids, lipoproteins, and apolipoproteins

One of the recent major advances in lipid biochemistry is a better understanding of the relationship among lipids, especially the roles of cholesterol and lipoproteins in coronary heart disease.

Evaluation of the lipoprotein profile is recommended for determining the existence and the type of lipoprotein abnormality. The test battery includes total cholesterol, total triglycerides, electrophoresis of the serum and serum fractions, very low density lipoprotein, beta low density lipoprotein, alpha-1 high density lipoprotein (alpha-1 HDL). The last mentioned fraction is favorable in relation to coronary heart disease. It is essential that the patient fast for 12–14 hours before the test.

[viii] Therapeutic drug monitoring

Because individuals vary in their response to a prescribed drug dose as a result of a variety of factors, individualization of drug dosage is desirable to ensure therapeutic effectiveness without undue toxicity. Measurement of serum drug concentrations may be helpful for drugs, for which the dosage should be individualized or the therapeutic and toxic action cannot be quantified adequately by other means.

Specimens for serum drug levels should be drawn when steady state is reached. Therapeutic drug monitoring is done in certain groups such as anticonvulsants, anti-arrhythmics, cardiac glycosides, psychotropic agents, xanthines and miscellaneous drugs such as cimetidine, cyclosporine, gold, and methotrexate.

[ix] Toxicology and drugs of abuse

Analytic methods in toxicology include immunoassays, thin layer chromatography, high performance liquid chromatography, and gas chromatography. Alcohol is the most commonly encountered drug ingestion observed in the clinical setting. It may be seen as an acute intoxication or its complications, as synergistic effects in combination with other drugs, or in connection with accusations of operating a motor vehicle while intoxicated.

Non-narcotic analgesics such as aspirin, acetaminophen (Tylenol), and benzodiazepine may be found in the blood and levels can be ordered. Barbiturates such as phenobarbital, mephobarbital and a closely related compound primidone are used primarily for treating seizures. Methadone is used to counteract opiates.

Drug abuse is an increasing public health problem. Drug screening programs have been instituted in the workplace for pre-employment, random testing, or job-related incidents, at drug rehabilitation centers, and by the criminal justice system to monitor compliance with abstinence programs. Urine drug screens are reported as "positive" or "none detected". Positive urine samples are tested for phencyclidine, benzodiazepine, cocaine, amphetamines or antidepressants, THC/cannabinoids, opiates, barbiturates and tricyclics.

[b] Methodologies

The methodologies used in chemistry testing are widely diverse, and are selected according to the specific analyte to be quantitated.

Spectrophotometric analyses are used where it is possible to measure the analyte of interest by causing the material, or a closely associated material, to produce a color change that can be measured. This color change is proportional to the amount of analyte in the original specimen. Common constituents that are assayed using this method include calcium, triglycerides, uric acid, total protein, albumin, and many others.

A subdivision of spectrophotometric analysis, kinetic reaction, is used to quantitate enzyme levels. Enzymes are biological catalysts that react with a very specific substrate to produce an end product. In the great majority of cases there is a need for a cofactor. If the cofactor is NADH (nicotinamide-adenine dinucleotide phosphate) or NADPH (a reduced form of NADH), the rate of conversion can be monitored by following the change in absorbance at 340 nanometers. This mechanism, and others that are closely related, form the basis for the majority of the enzyme measurements done today. These include tests for CPK, LDH, SGOT, SGPT, and others.

A third method widely used is radioactive immunoassay (RIA). In these studies the analyte of interest is usually a drug, vitamin, or hormone. RIA is the method of choice for these compounds because they are present in minute amounts in the body, and RIA can provide detection down to the picogram range. Here the analyte of interest is mixed with the same material that has been tagged with a radioactive tracer, and the mixture is reacted with a nonradioactive antibody. A proportional binding of the radioactive material will occur, and when compared with the radioactive binding that occurs in a series of standards of known concentration, the concentration of the analyte in the patient's serum can be determined. The radioactive material most commonly used is Iodine-125. Tests currently performed using the RIA assays include digoxin, folic acid, Vitamin B-12 FSH (follicle-stimulating hormone), LH (leuteinizing hormone), and many others.

The measurements of certain other materials are done by flame photometry. Here, the analytes measured are principally the inorganic ions, sodium and potassium, and the antidepressant drug lithium. With this technique the analyte of interest is burned in a gas flame. As the material is heated, a characteristic color is produced. Measurement of the intensity of the color, and comparison against a standard concentration, will allow one to determine the amount present in the unknown. To a large extent, however, flame photometry measurements of sodium and potassium have been replaced with ion-specific electrode techniques.

Electrophoresis provides still another approach to determining certain analyses. In this technique a mixture of serum containing the substance being assayed is applied to a support medium (usually cellulose acetate or an agarose gel), and then subjected to an electric current. The mixture will separate into its component parts according to size, shape, and net electrical charge. This separation process allows the identification of the individual components of the mixture, provided that proper post-separation identification techniques are used. The isoenzymes of CPK and LDH are often identified and quantitated by this method. This technique is also used in hemoglobin identification and in serum protein electrophoresis, where whole serum is separated into five fractions that can be quantitated and compared to normal populations.

Chromatography is another method widely used in toxicology and drug analysis. Methods here range from simple paper chromatography, where mixtures are separated into individual components based on relative solubilities in different organic solvent mixtures, to gas and high pressure liquid techniques. The gas and high pressure liquid methods are very sensitive, and can provide quantitative results.

Many other methodologic techniques and method variations are currently available, and new techniques are being introduced on a regular basis. It is the responsibility of the testing facility to provide information on the specific method that has been used for any given analyte. The importance of obtaining this information cannot be overstated. (*See* § 5.04 [3][d].)

[c] Collection and Preservation of Specimens

Specimen collection methods for the various chemistry tests vary widely because many tests require special handling procedures. The most commonly used specimen is serum. To obtain serum, one collects whole blood in an evacuated tube and allows the specimen to form a clot. After the blood has clotted, which usually requires about fifteen minutes, the tube is placed into a centrifuge and rotated at high RPMs for approximately ten minutes. This will allow the liquid portion of the blood (the serum) to separate from the formed elements. The serum is subsequently harvested, and it is this material that is used for the great majority of chemistry tests. Other specimens used include plasma, urine, body fluids, cerebrospinal fluid, and whole blood.

Each chemistry test should be performed according to a specific set of requirements or guidelines. These should include the type of tube to use for collection, proper post-collection storage if the test is not to be done immediately, length of time the analyte is stable under proper storage conditions, special diet restrictions, proper timing, postural influences, and other specimen collection factors that can influence test results. In the event that a specimen is not suitable, a special notation should be made on the final report form.

[d] Special Considerations

Due to the great diversity of methods and tests performed in the chemistry section of a laboratory, it is imperative that care be used in interpreting the results of any analysis. Each method will have its own normal ranges, and these normals will vary from laboratory to laboratory, from method to method, and from instrument to instrument. It may be important to know: From what population was the normal range derived? What units were used in the reporting of the results? At what temperatures were the tests performed? When two different machines could be used, were they, and were the results equivalent? These are all relevant questions in evaluating test results.

With the rapid increase in automated instrumentation, the need for quality control procedures is greater than ever. Can the testing laboratory provide documentation that the result obtained was correct? Was the test procedure controlled over the entire analytic range of the instrument or method?

Even with simple tests such as a glucose determination, results can be influenced by numerous external factors. There are in excess of 350 references that have been cited relating to the effects of drugs on blood glucose determinations. Some simply cite an expected therapeutic effect, others point out method interferences that can be seen, and still others illustrate an effect in a specific instrument. When one adds to this the nearly 100 diseases that can influence glucose levels, one becomes aware that even so-called simple tests can become highly complex.

[4] Microbiology

[a] The Four Divisions

In the typical laboratory, microbiology is divided into four divisions or subsections:

1. Bacteriology. This subsection deals with true bacteria. Its primary function is to identify the bacterial agents from any specified culture site and determine the organisms' sensitivity to antibiotics.
2. Mycology. This is the study of fungi, and the subsection's primary function is to identify fungi from cultured sites.
3. Virology. The virology subsection is responsible for the identification of viral agents by identifying viral antibodies developed by the infected individual or through the identification of viral antigens found in tissues. Isolation and identification of the virus itself is done less frequently, and in a great many cases the proof is of a secondary or inferential nature.
4. Parasitology. This subsection is responsible for the isolation and identification of parasites.

Virtually any site suspected of containing pathogens (organisms that can cause disease) can be cultured. The following are common sites and the most likely pathogens:

1. Oral and Respiratory tract (Beta-hemolytic Streptococcus) (Mycobacterium tuberculosis) (Bordetella pertussis) (any mycotic agent)
2. Ophthalmic fluid (Hemophilus influenzae) (Staphlococcus aureus) (Beta-hemolytic Streptococcus) (Neisseria gonorrhoeae)
3. Spinal fluid (Neisseria meningitidis) (Cryptococcus neoformans) (Mycobacterium tuberculosis)
4. Blood (E. Coli) (Staphylococcus aureus) (Staphylococcus pyrogenes) (Klebsiella pneumoniae)
5. Urine (E. Coli) (Klebsiella) (Proteus sp.) (Pseudomonas)
6. Wounds and punctures (Bacteroides sp.) (Clostridium perfringens) (Peptococcus) (Pseudomonas)

The above is not a comprehensive list. It does serve to illustrate the more commonly encountered pathogens, and the more commonly cultured sites.

[i] Bacteriology

Bacteriology deals with bacterial organisms. The upper respiratory tract is a common site of infection in humans. While most are caused by viruses, which are typically mild and self limiting, infection could progress into the sinuses or lower respiratory tract. Pneumonia is the most common cause of infectious mortality in the United States. The urinary and genital tracts, skin wounds, tissue and body fluids may harbor a bacterial infection. Blood harboring bacteria heralds a severe infectious disease. Blood cultures are screened for aerobic and anaerobic bacteria. Anaerobic cultures may be done on body fluids, deep abscess, tissue biopsies. Anaerobic bacteria are normal flora in urine, stool, skin, vagina, mouth, throat and sputum.

Smears for acid fast bacilli are reported immediately when positive while preliminary negative reports are issued at one week and held for eight weeks. Mycobacterium tuberculosis, the bacterial agent in TB may take up to eight weeks to grow in culture. It is a public health reportable infection.

[ii] Mycology

Mycology is a branch of Microbiology that deals with diseases caused by fungal organisms. Candida Albicans causes mucous membrane infections of the mouth and throat of newborns and patients with deficient immunity. Aspergillus may be a contaminant but can produce an opportunistic infection. Cryptococcus neoformans can cause meningitis, and be found in immunosuppression and AIDS. Geotrichum, Zygomycetes and Rhodotorula are also known to infect the blood of immune-deficient individuals.

[iii] Virology

The relationship between viremia and clinical disease varies widely from asymptomatic or mild transient infection to severe life-threatening disease. Some viruses such as herpesvirus, human immune deficiency virus and rubeola persist in leukocytes, in contrast to others such as enteroviruses, which are transient in the blood. Cytomegalovirus is an opportunistic virus in immune compromised patients. Since viruses are capable of causing the patient to develop antibodies against them, many viral infections can be diagnosed with serology.

[iv] Parasitology

Parasitology deals with examination of the specimen for parasites. Malaria, Babesia, trypanosomes and various species of microfilariae are important causes of parasites in the blood. Appropriate travel history is an important component of the diagnostic evaluation because parasitic infections are generally confined to specific geographic locations.

[v] Specimen collection

Virtually any site suspected of containing pathogens (organisms that can cause disease) can be cultured.

1. Sterile-obtained body fluids, respiratory tract specimens, cerebrospinal fluid, urine and wounds can be submitted for routine bacterial cultures.
2. Blood cultures are screened for aerobic (oxygen-loving) and anaerobic bacteria (independent of oxygen) and fungi. Anaerobic cultures may be done on body fluids, deep abscess, tissue biopsies and not on specimens where they are considered normal flora such as urine, stool, skin, vagina, mouth, throat and sputum. Positive results are reported as soon as growth becomes evident. Negative cultures are held for 5 days before reported negative.
3. Acid fast smears (tuberculosis agent) are reported immediately when positive. Preliminary negative results are reported at one week and cultures are held for eight weeks if negative.
4. Cultures for fungi may be submitted as one specimen for both bacteria and fungi. Urine, vaginal, stool and throat specimens are processed for yeast culture and held for four weeks if negative.
5. For ova and parasites, screening for Cryptosporidia and Microsporidia is done. Giardia antigen test is done first on patients without any history of foreign travel.
6. Nucleic acid probes (DNA probes) are the testing method performed for chlamydia and gonorrhea.
7. Other miscellaneous tests include fluorescent procedures of bacteria and viruses such as the test for Legionnaire's disease antibody and Epstein Barr virus antibody.

Unacceptable specimens include those that have been improperly collected, mislabeled specimens, inappropriate specimen for culture, those that are leaking or spilled and those specimens rejected because of age. Final reports have antibiotic susceptibility with minimum inhibitory concentration performed routinely on streptococcus species.

[b] Methodologies

The chosen site to be cultured is carefully swabbed, and the resultant swab (which will have picked up any microorganisms present) is streaked onto a Petri dish containing a nutrient agar. The dish is then incubated at an appropriate temperature, and examined for the appearance of colonies of bacteria. These individual colonies may in some cases be identified at this point based on characteristic biochemical reactions. In other cases, it will be necessary to subculture the original colonies further to ensure purity before undertaking identification procedures. Once a specific pathogenic organism has been identified, it is frequently tested against a panel of antibiotics to determine its relative sensitivity and resistance to each.

[c] Collection and Preservation of Specimens

The correct collection of microbiologic samples is critical to all other procedures performed on the specimen. Normally, specimens are collected into sterile containers with as little site contamination as possible. They should be promptly cultured onto or in an appropriate media. For growth to occur, a *live* organism must be placed onto the media. Many organisms are very fragile, and excessive exposure to a hostile environment will lead to negative findings.

All specimens should be identified as to site of collection and, if possible, as to the suspected infective organism. This will allow the microbiology laboratory to ensure that proper growth media are used, which in turn will provide the most rapid and accurate diagnosis.

[d] Special Considerations

The microbiology section, like all other sections of the pathology laboratory, must adhere to proper specimen identification procedures to ensure that correct results are obtained. Also, quality control procedures should be maintained to ensure that the growth media will support the appropriate organisms, and that antibiotic sensitivity disks are active.

[5] Immunology and Serology

Immunologic and serologic tests involve the identification of a specific antibody or antigen through the use of an antigen-antibody binding reaction. Tests performed that employ this method include:

1. RPR (screening test for syphilis)
2. FTA (confirmatory test for syphilis)
3. RA latex (diagnosis of rheumatoid arthritis)

4.   LE screen (screening test for lupus erythematosus)
5.   ANA (diagnosis of auto-immune diseases)
6.   Anti-mitochondrial antibody (diagnosis of auto-immune diseases)
7.   Mono screen (diagnosis of infectious mononucleosis)
8.   Anti-streptolysin O (diagnosis of streptococcal infection)

The above is not a comprehensive list, and many other tests fall into the general category of serologic and immunologic procedures.

[a] Methodologies

The basis for all these assays is the ability to detect an antibody through the use of a corresponding antigen. In some cases, patient serum is mixed with a latex reagent, and the mixture is gently rotated and observed for the presence of agglutination or clumping of the antigen-coated latex particles. In the ASO test, the hemolysis of blood group O red cells is observed at varying dilutions of test serum. The ANA procedure is based on reactions that occur between antibodies to nuclear antigens found in the patient's serum reacting with the tissue nuclei found in a slice of animal tissue. When coupled with a fluorescent tag, it is possible to do a direct microscopic examination for the presence of these antibodies. Test results can be reported as positive, as negative, as positive at a specified dilution, and as less than specific titer value.

[b] Collection and Preservation of Specimens

The great majority of these tests are performed using serum. (*See* § 5.04[3][c] for collection techniques.) Preservation requirements will vary from test to test, but in many cases the antibodies being sought are stable for an extended time at refrigerator temperatures.

[c] Special Considerations

Of the tests listed in § 5.04[4], above, the most commonly performed is the RPR. It should only be used for syphilis. It can produce a positive result in conditions totally unrelated to syphilis. No diagnosis of syphilis should be made, however, until the much more specific FTA test has been done. Great care should be exercised in confirming proper specimen identification when performing both the RPR and FTA tests. Specimen labeling errors can have serious psychological consequences.

As with many of the chemistry assays, care must be used in evaluating the results of any test, because many will have multiple pathologic causes for positive results. Similarly, sensitivity and specificity can vary greatly from one method to another.

[6] Blood Banks

Blood is the vital liquid in one's body. The function of the Blood Bank is centered in the collection and transfusion of blood and its components from one person into the circulatory system of another. Transfusions can be life-saving in situations such as massive blood loss from trauma or to replace blood loss during surgery. They are also used in blood diseases such as anemia, leukemia, hemophilia, sickle cell disease, and many others.

[a] Types and Classifications of Blood

Prior to the transfusion of blood to a patient, it is necessary to determine the recipient's blood type. "Blood type" is actually an evaluation of two separate groups of antigens, the ABO type and the Rh group. All individuals will fall into one of the following categories: Type A; Type B; Type AB; or Type O.

Testing the Rh antigen will further classify individuals in Rh positive or Rh negative categories. Thus, there are the following possible blood types:

1. Type A/Rh positive (A+)
2. Type A/Rh negative (A-)
3. Type B/Rh positive (B+)
4. Type B/Rh negative (B-)
5. Type AB/Rh positive (AB+)
6. Type AB/Rh negative (AB-)
7. Type O/Rh positive (O+)
8. Type O/Rh negative (O-)

[b] Methodology

Donor blood is available in different preparations. The most commonly used blood is the packed red cells, prepared as a unit of approximately 250 ml following removal of most of the donor plasma or liquid blood component. The liquid portion is separated, prepared, stored and transfused either as a fresh frozen plasma or a cryoprecipitate (stored liquid blood with concentrated blood clotting factors). Platelets are blood cells commonly separated from donor blood through a procedure called platelet pheresis. This blood component is commonly stored in fractions transfused as multiple units for bleeding conditions due to deficiency in the specific cells

An individual with blood group O has no A or B antigens but will have anti-A and anti-B antibodies in their plasma. The individual with blood group A has the A antigen and anti-B antibody. The individual with blood group B has the B antigen and anti-A antibody and the individual with blood group AB has both A and B antigens without anti-A or anti-B antibodies. Cross-matching involves the mixture of the recipient's serum and the donor red cells. Blood Group O is considered a universal donor due to the absence of either A or B antigen that can be destroyed by the recipient's serum. Conversely, an individual with the blood group AB is considered a universal recipient since no antibodies are normally present in the individual's plasma to destroy the cells being transfused.

After the recipient's ABO and Rh groups have been determined, usually only blood that is an exact match in ABO and Rh antigens is selected. Prior to the transfusion of blood cells to a patient, a cross-match is performed to ensure that the blood selected for transfusion will be compatible with the recipient's blood. Blood transfusion can result in adverse reactions ranging from hives and rashes, fever and chills, or death of the recipient.

[i] Trends

There is a slight downward trend in blood use and collection in the last twenty years. This has been brought about partly by the increasing public awareness of the risks of blood transfusion. Vigilance in the justification and documentation of the rationale for transfusion of blood and its components contributes significantly to this decline. In 1980, 10 million units were transfused of the 14 million units collected. In 1986, 12.2 million units of the 12.5 millions collected were transfused. In 1997, 11.4 million units were transfused of the 12.5 millions collected. In that same year of 1997, one third of the blood units collected from autologous donations (in which the patient's own blood is collected before surgery for possible use during or after surgery) was discarded, whereas only 7.4% of the units collected from allogeniec (volunteer and directed) donors was discarded.

Blood Group O (the blood group that can be transfused into any recipient regardless of the recipient's blood group) is highly desirable in situations requiring emergency transfusion. For this reason, this blood is habitually in short supply. Donor trends have also changed since the 1970s. Blood collection peaked in 1987 and declined by 9.3% from 1989 to 1994. This decline is due to the misconception that HIV can be transmitted by the process of blood donation and the enhanced screening and testing procedures that disqualify prospective blood donors.

[c] Collection and Preservation of Specimens

While specimen collection procedures are of vital importance in all areas of clinical pathology, the impact of incorrect specimen collection is the greatest in the blood bank. Failure to correctly identify a specimen or patient can lead to a recipient's death. No specimen should be removed from a patient until proper identity has been established, and all conflicts of identity must be fully resolved before testing begins.

[d]   Special Considerations

The principal causes of fatal blood transfusion are not technical error, but clerical errors. Prior to beginning any work on a patient, a back-check of records should be made to see if the individual has been previously tested. If this is the case, current test results must be consistent with prior results. Notations on the strength of any reactions, and interpretation of those reactions, should be made as the testing is done. Each unit of blood being crossmatched must be fully labeled with information that will identify it for a specific recipient. Prior to release of the blood for transfusion, each unit must be rechecked to ensure that it is being issued to the correct recipient. Before the start of transfusion, the identity of the patient must again be confirmed, and the intended blood unit is once again checked against the intended recipient. If all these steps are properly carried out, the probability of an error is remote.

[i] Risks of blood transfusion

The risks of blood transfusion are many. This is shown in the tabulation below:

Risk Factor	Estimated Frequency/million units	No. deaths/million units
Infections		
Viral		
Hepatitis A	1/1,000,000	0
Hepatitis B	1/30,000 – 1/250,000	0–0.14
Hepatitis C	1/30,000 – 1/150,000	0.5–17
HIV (AIDS)	1/200,000 – 1/2,000,000	0.5–5
HTLV – I & II	1/250,000 – 1/2,000,000	0
Parvovirus B19	1/10,000	0
Bacteria		
Red cells	1/500,000	0.1–0.5
Platelets	1/12,000	21
Acute hemolytic reaction	1/250,000–1/1,000,000	0.67
Delayed hemolytic Rx	1/1,000	0.4
Acute lung injury	1/5,000	0.2

§ 5.05 Scope of Practice: Forensic Pathology

Forensic pathology is the branch of Anatomic Pathology concerned with the determination of the cause, mechanism, and manner of death, usually for criminal or civic law cases. Derived from the Latin word, "forensic," "forensic" means public or forum.

The Forensic pathologist is an Anatomic pathologist who has had additional subspecialty training. These specialists are experts in establishing the cause of death, estimating the time of death, inferring the type of weapon used, distinguishing homicide from suicide, establishing the identity of the deceased, and determining the additive effect of trauma or pre-existing conditions.

[1] Coroners and Medical Examiners

Coroners are usually elected officials who are charged by law with the investigation of unnatural deaths (sometimes limited only to homicides and suicides), medically unattended deaths, and cases in which no physician is willing to sign the death certificate. Coroners need not have any medical training to qualify for their position. The lay coroner usually requests a pathologist to perform an autopsy in a suspicious death.

Medical examiners are appointed to their position, and usually must be pathologists. In some jurisdictions, medical examiners must be forensic pathologists. In most states that have adopted the system, the jurisdiction of a medical examiner is broadly defined. For example, the Medical Examiner Law of the State of Maryland gives the medical examiner authority to investigate deaths when "any person shall die in Baltimore City, or in any county of the state as a result of violence, or by suicide, or by casualty, or suddenly when in apparent good health, or when unattended by a physician or in any suspicious or unusual manner …"

The term "violence" includes all types of extraneous injuries (mechanical, chemical, thermal, electrical, etc.), drowning, rape, criminal abortion, etc. In questionable cases, the medical examiner has the authority to decide if he has jurisdiction and whether an autopsy should be performed.

Generally, both coroners and medical examiners are charged with the responsibility of investigating deaths of a suspicious nature, i.e., all cases of death where the cause is not known to be natural. This involves answering the following questions:

1. Who is the victim (sex, race, age, particular characteristics)?
2. When did the death and injuries occur (timing of death and injuries)?

3. What injuries are present (type, distribution, pattern, path and direction of injuries)?
4. Which injuries are significant and may have caused death (major versus minor injuries, true versus artifactual or postmortem injuries)?
5. Where did the death occur (scene and circumstances)?
6. Why and how were the injuries produced (mechanism and manner of death)?

[2] Determination of the Cause of Death

The determination of cause of death is normally made during the course of an autopsy, and is presented as a portion of the autopsy report. It consists of a factual description of the condition or injuries responsible for the death. Examples would include: "gunshot wound to the head," "pulmonary embolus," "blunt force injuries to the chest," "bacterial meningitis." These determinations are not to be confused with the "manner of death" discussed below.

[3] Determination of the Manner of Death

The determination of the manner of death takes into consideration the cause of death and other available information surrounding the death (i.e., scene investigation, witnesses' accounts, medical history, etc.), and places the death into one of five categories:

1. Natural (death due to natural pathologic processes)
2. Accidental (death resulted from an accident in which no individual or individuals can be held responsible or negligent)
3. Suicide (death resulted from the individual act of taking one's own life)
4. Homicide (death resulted from the act of another individual)
5. Undetermined (the circumstances are not sufficiently clear to arrive at a decision of any of the above)

Sometimes it is extremely difficult, even for an experienced forensic pathologist, to be certain about the manner of death. A thorough and complete review and evaluation of all the investigative data in the case, correlated with the postmortem anatomic and toxicologic findings, must be performed before expressing final and official opinions and rulings in questionable cases.

[4] Relationships with Attorneys

[a] District Attorneys and Prosecutors

The relationship of the forensic pathologist to the district attorney or prosecutor should always be on an impartial and professional basis. If an investigation shows that no crime was committed, this should be clearly stated, irrespective of how the prosecuting attorney feels about the criminality of the case. In cases that are somewhat equivocal, i.e., cases in which the medical findings could be interpreted in more than one way, the forensic pathologist should state these findings both verbally and in writing to the district attorney's office, and he should allow the district attorney to decide what legal applications will be made of the findings. It is not for the forensic pathologist to determine if a particular statute has been violated based upon equivocal medical findings.

Good lines of communications should be maintained between the forensic pathologist and the district attorney's office. There should be regularly scheduled homicide conferences, in which all deaths thought to be due to criminal negligence or acts of criminal intent are discussed prior to going to trial. The forensic pathologist should evaluate each case in which he will be called to testify, and review the testimony relevant to the particular case under consideration.

[b] Private Attorneys

The forensic pathologist can enter into several different relationships with private attorneys. The role will vary depending upon the specific relationship. The forensic expert can serve as an expert witness in both criminal and civil cases where he will be called upon to provide specific details that will help a jury better understand the medical aspects of the case. He also is frequently called upon to determine if the attorney's client has grounds to file a civil or criminal action. This is usually done by a review of medical records, tissue slides, etc.

[5] Other Relationships

[a] Families of the Deceased

The relationship of the forensic pathologist to a family or family member is most often one of medical advisor following the death or injury of a relative. Often, the family will request that the forensic pathologist review details of the case to determine if there are sufficient grounds to pursue legal action. In these cases, the forensic expert should act as an impartial reviewer.

[b] Physicians

Even though a member of the same profession as clinical physicians, the forensic expert should maintain a degree of independence from these fellow physicians. It is often the forensic pathologist's responsibility to provide impartial medical evidence as to the correctness or appropriateness of care rendered to a patient. In the event litigation is necessary, it usually will be the forensic pathologist who will provide testimony. At no time should the forensic pathologist let himself be influenced, either in a favorable or unfavorable fashion, in these cases. All opinions rendered must be based on the available medical evidence and nothing else.

[c] Hospitals

The relationship of the forensic pathologist to hospitals is similar to their relationship to physicians. In all cases, the opinions rendered regarding the appropriateness of care must be based solely on the available medical evidence. The behavior of the forensic expert must be totally impartial at all times.

[d] Law Enforcement Agencies

A forensic pathologist acting as a coroner or medical examiner should develop a working relationship with law enforcement agencies similar to that described in § 5.05[4], above, relative to district attorneys and prosecutors. It is sometimes easy to allow a law enforcement official to influence a pathologist's interpretation of findings. This cannot be allowed. The forensic expert must establish his role clearly in an investigation, and not allow the law enforcement official to hurry him into conducting anything less than a thorough investigation.

[e] Public Health Agencies

In the course of his investigations, the forensic pathologist may uncover deaths that have been caused by diseases that are of general concern to the population at large. This would be true in the case of highly communicable diseases. In these cases, the forensic expert is responsible for promptly identifying and reporting the disease to public health officials, and he should fully cooperate in any investigation they conduct.

[6]   Forensic Consultation — Medical Malpractice Cases

Private forensic consulting is limited to a small number of pathologists who are certified in forensic pathology. While the number of these consultants is small, their involvement in cases that involve medical testimony can be critical, since they can provide a high degree of expertise, and are widely recognized for providing impartial testimony on the medical evidence of a case.

These consultants can determine if there is sufficient evidence of professional negligence to warrant the filing of an action in a suspected case of medical malpractice. They can provide expert evaluation by reviewing all aspects of a case, and testify to these findings. They can aid both plaintiff and defense attorneys in establishing lines of questioning to be used during trial, and counsel attorneys as to what aspects of the case are most relevant. They can conduct autopsy investigations in an impartial atmosphere, uninfluenced by the hospital or physician involved in the case.

§ 5.06 Malpractice: Anatomic Pathology

[1] Surgical Specimens

[a] Misdiagnosis of the Specimen

The misdiagnosis of a surgical specimen by a pathologist does not automatically indicate that malpractice has occurred. The possibility of malpractice should be viewed against the following widely accepted criteria.

1. To render a correct diagnosis, the pathologist must first determine the adequacy of the tissue sample submitted, and ensure that it is representative of the suspected disease process. If specimen adequacy is questionable, this should be discussed with the submitting physician, and further samples should be submitted prior to rendering a diagnosis. A failure to do so may result in a finding of malpractice against the pathologist.

2. In examining the specimen, it is the responsibility of the pathologist to correlate the tissue findings with all other clinical data, laboratory findings, and radiology findings. If inconsistencies are present, they should be resolved prior to issuing a diagnosis. Failure to do so may result in the finding of malpractice against the pathologist.

3. If in the course of routine evaluation a diagnosis of the specimen cannot be reached without the use of special testing techniques and additional studies, these must be employed prior to issuing a final

diagnosis. Failure to utilize fully all necessary testing may be grounds for malpractice.

4. The diagnostic interpretation by a surgical pathologist should be based on established standard histologic criteria. Interpretations may vary from one individual to another pathologist. Regularly performed quality assurance by review of the pathologist's activities is standard practice by the hospital or facility that the pathologist provides the service. Failure to provide an ongoing quality assurance may be grounds for malpractice for both the pathologist and the hospital through its credentialing committee.

5. In the event that some doubt exists about the final diagnosis, it is the responsibility of the pathologist to consult with other pathologists regarding the true nature of the disease process present. Even though a consensus diagnosis is reached, the final report should include alternate diagnoses expressed as dissenting opinions, along with the reasons given by the dissenters in support of their findings. This will serve to alert the attending physician to the possibility of other diagnoses. A failure to consult and to provide all diagnostic possibilities may result in malpractice.

[b] Misdiagnosis of Frozen Sections and Inoperative Consultations

A misdiagnosis based on examination of slides prepared from frozen sections is not uncommon. A national error rate of 5% is acceptable to the College of American Pathologists. This failure rate to reach a diagnosis similar to one made from the examination of permanent sections results from the inherent deficiencies of the frozen section method: the sections prepared from a frozen section may not be representative due to large portions discarded during the actual preparation of thicker cuts than those made for permanent sections from the duly processed submitted specimen. It is also not uncommon that the surgeon may have submitted a sample that is not representative of the disease.

[c] Benign versus Malignant Tumors

The failure to differentiate between benign and malignant tumors may result in a malpractice action against the surgical pathologist. As previously discussed, frozen sections are ordinarily performed to guide the surgeon in determining whether the surgical procedure can be extended or concluded. A misdiagnosis of a malignant tumor may extend the surgery that is not necessary for a benign tumor. When the pathologist is in doubt of the frozen section diagnosis, it is prudent to defer the diagnosis until permanent sections are out, at which time, further surgery could be done at a later date. If reasonable care has been taken and a misdiagnosis has occurred, a malpractice suit can be defended.

[d] Classification, Grading, and Staging of Malignant Tumors

The correct classification, grade, and stage of a malignant tumor can significantly influence both the degree and extent of surgical intervention and type of postoperative therapy. The failure to provide this information correctly can result in a finding of liability against the anatomic pathologist if it can be proved that the correct information would have resulted in an improved therapeutic outcome.

[e] Failure to Consult Other Pathologists

Where the pathologist cannot adequately establish a diagnosis, there is a clear need to consult with other pathologists. Failure to do so can be a malpractice. Additionally, if an incorrect diagnosis was made on a specimen that is not normally within the range of expertise of the pathologist can be shown that there was a clear need for the specimen to be evaluated by a particular specialist, a malpractice action also may be well grounded. Examples are eye, muscle and bone specimens.

[f] Failure to Recognize an Inadequate Specimen

The failure to recognize the inadequacy of the tissue being evaluated can result in the negative findings in otherwise malignant tumor. This can cause a delay in the treatment, rapid progression of disease, and present a risk to the patient. This possibility should be clearly conveyed to the attending physician as a recommendation for a closer follow up. Communication with the clinician is important since most of the time, the pathologist is unaware of the clinical differential diagnoses. Mot specimens are submitted to the laboratory without any clinical information.

[g] Failure to Communicate with the Surgeon in a Timely and Proper Manner

On receipt of a surgical specimen for evaluation, the pathologist assumes the responsibility of providing the submitting surgeon with a diagnosis in a timely and proper manner. The failure to do so can result in a delay in starting treatment, and thus subject the patient to an increased risk. If the pathologist is unable to reach a diagnosis, this information should be transmitted to the surgeon, along with any information available about the tissue. In some cases, a provisional diagnosis can be rendered pending final results of other studies. In no case should the surgeon be expected to wait for an extended period of time without receiving some communication from the pathologist.

It is the responsibility of the pathologist to transmit the information to the surgeon that there are further studies being performed to reach a definitive diagnosis, especially in cases where there is urgency in providing a specific treatment. A good surgeon is also expected to be mindful of the pathologic diagnosis on tissue sample he or she has submitted.

[h] Failure to Resolve Conflicting Diagnoses

In the event two sequentially excised portions of the same lesion present different diagnoses, it is the responsibility of the pathologist to resolve and adequately explain this finding. It is also incumbent on the pathologist to correlate the current sample with previously diagnosed specimens.

A failure to do so is a deviation from the standards of good practice, and could result in a successful malpractice action.

[i] Failure to Report Revised Findings

There will be cases in which a revised report must be issued because of supplemental findings. (See § 5.03[1][i], above.) It is the responsibility of the pathologist to ensure that the surgeon is fully informed of any changes in findings and the reasons for such changes. Failure to do so can delay proper treatment and can be grounds for malpractice.

[2] Cytology Studies

[a] Misdiagnosis of a Cytology Preparation

The standards governing the diagnosis of PAP smears or other cytology preparations closely parallel the diagnosis of tissue specimens. Additionally, the pathologist has direct responsibility for the actions of the cytotechnologist in his supervision. The cytotechnologist can be held to the same general standards of professional conduct as the pathologist. The cytotechnologist screens PAP smears from the female genital tract and in some places, also screens non-gynecologic smears. He or she is allowed to screen a maximum of 80 slides in an 8-hour work day.

[b] Benign, Malignant, and Atypical Cells

The pathologist is expected to be able to classify cells as benign, atypical, or malignant. Malignant cells are usually easily differentiated from benign cells but there are occasions that cells do not appear frankly malignant. Many conditions could produce atypical cells. These may be due to the presence of infection, repair due to chronic irritation or trauma, or even when adjacent to where the sample has been obtained, there may be a malignant tumor. It is incumbent upon the pathologist to clearly state the various conditions that may have caused the presence of atypical cells. The clinician must be aware of what the pathologist wishes to convey in order to decide on the most appropriate treatment of the patient. Incorrect negative results when these atypical cells may be present can delay additional investigative procedures to diagnose and treat cancer.

[c] Classification and Grading of Smears

The classification and grading of cytology specimens present a situation similar to that described in § 5.06[1][d], above. The failure to make classifications based on standardized histopathologic features can result in a finding of negligence.

[d] Failure to Consult Other Pathologists

In the event that the classification of a cytology smear is in question, the pathologist has a responsibility to consult with other pathologists in an attempt to reach a diagnosis. The same rules that apply to surgical specimens (§5.06[1][e], above) will apply to cytology preparations, and similar findings of negligence can result from the failure to consult.

[e] Failure to Request Repeat Smears

The cytology smear, for the most part is obtained through a noninvasive procedure. However, smears are now also popularly prepared from fine needle aspiration of deeply located organs suspected to be involved by a disease process. The preparation may yield inadequate cells for critical evaluation. The pathologist is responsible for communicating to the attending physician the need for a repeat testing for more proper evaluation. A statement regarding the pathologist's recommendation must be included in the written report.

[f]   Failure to Communicate with the Physician in a Timely and Proper Manner

The pathologist is responsible for the timely and appropriate reporting of the results of the cytological examination. The attending physician is equally responsible in determining whether a result of the test he had ordered has been received and appropriately applied to his particular patient. Since the attending physician clearly has more information about his patient that he can correlate with all other tests, the pathologist can gain an aid in his interpretation of a result upon discussion of an uncertain case with the patient's attending physician.

[g]   Failure to Resolve Conflicting Diagnoses

The same care given by the pathologist in rendering a diagnosis on a tissue specimen obtained from surgery must be given to the interpretation of the disease process on smears examined cytologically. In cytology, there are some specific cell architecture changes produced by certain infections. The pathologist must be astute as to suspect certain specific organisms that may have caused the disease process and suggest the possibilities to the attending physician for a timely treatment.

[h]   Failure to Identify Specific Infectious Microorganisms

The identification of specific infectious micro-organisms can be relevant in certain cytology smears (especially the PAP smear), and the failure to properly identify these organisms can result in the delay of treatment. A successful malpractice action can be brought against the pathologist if these organisms are not identified and the pathologic process is allowed to reach advanced stages because of lack of treatment caused by this diagnostic failure.

[3] Autopsies

[a] Misdiagnosis of Disease Processes

The misdiagnosis of a disease process at autopsy is uncommon, but can occur and result in a malpractice action against the pathologist. When certain tests are not performed because specimens were not collected at the time of the autopsy and hence, not produce accurate results after a reasonable time has elapsed, the pathologist can be held liable for such failure. For example, since cultures for bacteria or virus require prompt and sterile collection of specimens, a high index of suspicion has to be present initially in order to collect the specimen properly. There could be a delay in the conveyance of a necessary information of a existence of a communicable infectious process that requires some form of isolation or treatment of contacts of the deceased.

[b]   Misdiagnosis of Injuries

The misdiagnosis of injuries also can lead to a malpractice action against the pathologist. For example, while performing an autopsy on a burn victim, the pathologist finds evidence of skull fractures and brain hemorrhage, in addition to the findings associated with the thermal injuries. The pathologist concludes that the death resulted from the skull fracture, and as a result homicide charges are filed against a suspect. However, testimony presented at trial showed that the skull fracture was in reality an artifactual injury caused by the intense heat of the fire.

[c]   Postmortem Artifacts versus Antemortem Pathophysiological Processes

The failure on the part of the pathologist to recognize postmortem artifacts, and instead attribute them to antemortem processes, has led to charges of negligence. For example, an individual was discovered dead in a swimming pool. On autopsy, it was found that the deceased had sustained injuries consistent with strangulation. The pathologist's finding was death by homicide, and a suspect was arrested. During the criminal trial, testimony was introduced that in the process of recovering the deceased's body from the swimming pool, the police dragged it out of the water with a pole and a strap around the neck. The cause of death was changed to accidental, and the accused suspect brought suit against the pathologist.

[d]   Failure to Diagnose an Infectious or Communicable Disease

The failure on the part of the pathologist to identify infectious or communicable diseases and notify interested parties can result in liability. *See* § 5.06[3][a], above.

[e]   Failure to Diagnose Genetic Defects

Failure to diagnose certain genetic central nervous system disorders in deceased newborns can lead the parents of the deceased child into a false sense of security with regard to future pregnancies. Should additional children suffer the same fate, the parents would have grounds for malpractice against the pathologist who performed the initial autopsy.

[f] Failure to Diagnose Homicide

The situation discussed in § 5.06 [3][b] could occur in reverse. By mistake, a pathologist could overlook evidence of a homicide, and in theory a legal action could be considered by a family member of the deceased.

[g] Failure to Diagnose an Accident

Mistaking postmortem artifacts for an antemortem finding (*see* § 5. 06[3][b]) also could lead to the failure to diagnose an accident, and result in a malpractice action against the pathologist.

[h] Failure to Diagnose an Industrial or Environmental Hazard

The pathologist's failure to recognize certain disease processes as having been caused by industrial or environmental exposure could lead to charges of negligence. An example would be a finding at autopsy of mesothelioma, a type of lung malignancy. Failure to recognize that this condition arose as a result of exposure to asbestos (a common cause of this cancer) could result in litigation against the pathologist.

§ 5.07   Malpractice: Clinical Pathology

[1] Hematology

[a] Improper Collection or Preservation of Specimens

In Hematology, one of the most common errors particularly in nonhospital based laboratories is a failure to obtain an adequately anticoagulated specimen that will give an accurate cell count. Both the phlebotomist who withdraws the blood specimen and the technician performing the actual procedure have a responsibility to follow the collection guidelines, proper preservation and performance of the test procedure to ensure an accurate test result.

The improper collection or preservation of specimens needed for hematologic analysis can result in serious problems. One of the most common errors is a failure to obtain an adequately anticoagulated specimen to be used for a complete blood count (CBC). The failure to properly anticoagulate the specimen will result in the specimen containing many small clots. When this is subjected to analysis, the result may be an incorrect diagnostic impression that may lead to therapeutic measures that would not otherwise be called for.

A failure on the part of the hematology section to recognize specimens that have been improperly preserved can result in misinterpretation of the final results. The problem of specimen preservation is of particular concern to the nonhospital based laboratory, or the hospital laboratory that accepts specimens from distant sites. In many cases, individuals obtaining the specimens may not be aware of proper preservation techniques. It is the responsibility of the testing laboratory to provide guidelines to collection sites, and to recognize the characteristics of a specimen that may have been improperly preserved. In all cases where specimen quality is questionable, the testing laboratory should make appropriate notations to this effect on the final report.

[b]   Incorrect Labeling of Specimens

The incorrect labeling of a specimen collected for any test performed in the hematology laboratory can have serious consequences that could lead to liability for negligence. The labels need to be affixed simultaneously since it is very easy to put labels from a wrong patient on either the requisition form or the tube or collection medium.

It is the responsibility of the testing laboratory to provide specific identification procedures and protocols to ensure that proper specimen identification is made. While the specific protocol will vary from laboratory to laboratory, the general principles remain the same. The patient's name should be clearly printed on the specimen, the date and time of specimen collection should be present on the request form that accompanies the specimen, and the initials of the individual collecting the specimen should appear on the request form. In the case of hospitalized patients, the laboratory technician should confirm the patient's identity by checking the information on the request form with the patient's identification band.

Even if all protocols are followed, errors will still occur. With proper protocols in place, the errors should be detectable. Errors in labeling can result in necessary treatment being withheld and unnecessary treatment being given. In some cases, the result can be relatively harmless, as where two normal results have been interchanged. When an abnormal result is given the wrong patient, the likelihood of it being detected is greater with follow up testing.

Errors in labeling can result in necessary treatment being withheld and unnecessary treatment being given. In some cases the result can be relatively harmless, as where the specimens of two normal individuals are mislabeled. The more serious the error, the greater the likelihood that it will be detected, since the patient's radical change in condition will not be supported by the results obtained.

[c] Incorrect Testing or Misinterpretation of Results

The incorrect interpretation of tests in the hematology laboratory can result in inappropriate therapeutic measures being instituted. In some cases, incorrect follow-up testing may be ordered as a result of the initial error. This will result in further delay recognizing the actual pathologic process that is occurring. It is on occasion the responsibility of the laboratory to alert the attending physician about severely abnormal test results such as the so-called "panic values."

The hematology laboratory has a responsibility in some instances to indicate to a physician that additional or different testing may be required. For example, in the case of an anemic patient who clearly presents a pattern consistent with macrocytic anemia, the laboratory has a responsibility to see that the attending physician orders follow-up testing for both Vitamin B-12 and folic acid deficiencies. If the physician chooses only to test for folic acid deficiency, the laboratory should advise the physician that Vitamin B-12 deficiency can result in a very similar anemia, and that the test for B-12 is clearly indicated. If the physician declines to test for the B-12, the laboratory should document this fact.

Another example might involve a physician who orders a hemoglobin and hematocrit determination on a patient. The testing laboratory, as a matter of policy, would likely perform this test on an instrument that provides several other tests, including a white blood cell (WBC) count. The WBC count is found to be greatly elevated, and appears to be consistent with a severe infection. Even though the only test ordered was the hemoglobin and hematocrit, the laboratory should inform the physician of the coincidental finding because it could significantly alter the treatment of the patient.

[d] Failure to Recognize Special Disease Characteristics

In acting as the testing agent for the attending physician, the hematology laboratory assumes the full responsibility for providing all relevant information that can be obtained from the test that has been ordered; this includes the recognition of unusual disease processes. By way of illustration, consider a patient with an intermittent fever and night sweats. As a part of the routine investigation, a complete blood count and white cell differential are ordered. The laboratory completes the tests and uncovers no unusual findings. The patient undergoes additional diagnostic measures, and only then does it become known that the patient has just returned from an endemic malaria zone. A blood smear for malarial parasites is requested, and proves to be positive. A review of the initially ordered blood film is conducted, and malarial parasites are identified. The testing laboratory can be held liable, even though malaria is not a common disease and is not frequently identified. A missed diagnosis has occurred, and the patient may have suffered as a result.

[e] Venipuncture Trauma

Litigation can arise as the result of obtaining blood from a vein (venipuncture). The most likely problems involve: (1) Local infections following venipuncture; (2) thrombophlebitis following venipuncture; and (3) injuries resulting from fainting following venipuncture.

In the case of infection, the most relevant issue is the sterilization technique used prior to and during the process of obtaining the specimen. How was the venipuncture site prepared prior to puncture? Also, was more than one puncture attempted with the same needle? Specific written laboratory policies should be available for inspection.

Also important and jointly borne by the laboratory and the attending physician who ordered the test is a patient's unexpected bleeding tendency that may require special precautions. Medications the patient may be taking could occasionally predispose to difficult venipuncture and should be known to the astute phlebotomist. Documentation of any untoward event during the procedure is an important aspect of sample collection.

The complication of thrombophlebitis also involves technique. How many attempts should the laboratory technician make to obtain a suitable specimen before the benefits of obtaining the test are outweighed by the potential harm to the patient? Was the attending physician contacted for an opinion on this issue? Was the patient questioned prior to the collection procedure about unexpected bleeding tendencies that might require special precautions? Is this documented? Was the patient receiving any medication that might result in unexpected bleeding? Was he questioned on this point?

With regard to injuries that result from a patient fainting, one should inquire about the collection site where the venipuncture occurred. What type of seating was provided? Was the patient assisted in getting off the table? Was the patient questioned about the outcome of previous venipuncture experiences? Was this documented?

[f] Failure to Correlate Test Results with Clinical History and Previous Tests

The failure on the part of the hematology laboratory to correlate test results with the patient's clinical history and previous test results invites a malpractice action. Failure in this area often causes other errors to go undiscovered, for example, in specimen collection, labeling, diagnostic misinterpretation, and failure to recognize special disease characteristics (§ § 5.07[1][a] to 5.07[1][d]).

Additionally, the failure to compare current tests with the patient's earlier tests and clinical history can result in the failure to recognize new disease processes that might be developing, which could have an important bearing upon the therapeutic measures being used.

Each department in the Clinical Laboratory has a responsibility to recognize test values that are critical in the care of a patient. The so-called "Panic Values" must be established and recognized by the technical staff so as to alert the Laboratory Director should repeat testing persist to yield the abnormal value. A "Panic Value" is a point, either numeric or a finding in which the patient is considered at serious risk of suffering life-threatening injury if his condition does not receive immediate medical attention. The Clinical Laboratory should have established values that need to be immediately reported to the clinician. The Laboratory Director should decide which abnormal values need to be discussed with the attending physician.

The failure to compare current tests with the patient's earlier test results can result in the failure to recognize new disease processes that might be developing, which could have an important bearing upon the therapeutic measures being used. It is not uncommon for an individual patient to have the same test repeated several times in a 24-hour period. The complete blood count will tell whether a bleeding condition has stopped or the patient may require a transfusion to replace blood loss.

A patient's blood gases could vary significantly within a short time interval. Values can change rapidly and dramatically. Developing organ or system failure such as respiratory and renal functions will show in repeated Chemistry test results that need to be correlated.

[g] Failure to Report Test Results in a Timely Manner

It is of little consequence that a test has been properly performed and carefully correlated with the patient's previous test results and clinical history if the current test result does not reach the attending physician in time to institute appropriate treatment. The amount of time that can elapse between the beginning of the testing procedure and the final reporting of the test result will vary greatly depending on the complexity of the test and the urgency of the request. In some instances, up to 48 hours is acceptable, but in other cases thirty minutes may be excessive. It is the responsibility of the testing laboratory to provide all test results in the most timely manner possible, and notification of the physician should occur in a manner that is appropriate to the medical urgency of the result.

Consider two patients who have had the same test requested by the same physician. Both individuals are seen in an outpatient setting, and the physician requests that a CBC be performed on both. The first patient shows a mild anemia, probably iron deficiency, and no other abnormalities. While these constitute abnormal results, it is considered acceptable merely to see that the physician receives the results within 24 hours. The CBC on the second patient reveals that the patient has a markedly reduced platelet count, with no other abnormalities. In the second case, 24 hours is much too long to wait. In this case, an immediate telephone call to the physician is indicated. Failure to do so could subject the testing laboratory to a successful malpractice action.

Each individual test should be evaluated at the laboratory, and a "panic value" should be established. A panic value is a numeric point at which the patient is considered at serious risk of suffering life-threatening injury if his condition does not receive immediate medical attention. Values that fall into this category should be immediately transmitted to the attending physician. The laboratory should document the transmission of this information to the physician with specific notations as to the time of the reporting.

[2] Urinalysis

[a] Improper Collection or Preservation of Specimens

Improper collection and preservation of specimens obtained for urinalysis can result in the tests being invalid and the attending physician being misled as to the proper treatment for the patient. There are many formed elements in the urine that can deteriorate if improperly preserved. Failure to detect these elements can result in a diagnosis not being established. Similarly, the chemical constituents of the urine can be broken down and not detected, leading to a delay in diagnosis and clinical problems. The general guidelines governing urinalysis are similar to those applicable to the collection and preservation of blood (§ 5.07[1][a], above).

The failure to obtain a *sterile* specimen can result in the misdiagnosis of bacterial infection. This can be a particular problem in the outpatient setting where a catheterized specimen is not obtained. One must rely on the patient to collect the specimen in an acceptable manner, and this is not always done because of the failure of the testing laboratory to adequately instruct the patient. This frequently results in the physician establishing a diagnosis of bacterial infection, when in fact the bacteria seen were merely a contaminant resulting from poor collection procedures.

[b] Incorrect Labeling of Specimens

The labeling and identification of urine specimens should be as stringent as those for blood (§ 5.07[1][b], above). The diagnostic significance is no less important than that of the most sophisticated hematology test.

[c] Incorrect Testing or Misinterpretation of Results

The potential for error in urine testing is much less than in other areas because there are fewer tests, and their interpretation is much less complex. There can still be problems in interpretation, however. One of the constituents in a routine test is the evaluation of protein. The finding of a positive urine protein can result from many pathologic and benign conditions, and yet in many cases, the cause of this abnormality is left uninvestigated. This can lead to a delay in the diagnosis of potentially damaging kidney diseases. The same basic principles with respect to a laboratory's general duty to inform and advise the attending physician are applicable here.

[d] Failure to Recognize Special Disease Characteristics

The urine testing section of a clinical laboratory has the same responsibility to recognize and identify uncommon or unusual disease conditions as the hematology section (§ 5.07[1][d], above). These conditions will most commonly be found during the microscopic examination of the urine sediment in characteristic but unusually formed elements. Examples would include tumor cells that have been shed into the urine from a urinary tract tumor, and amino acid crystals in patients suffering from inborn errors of amino acid metabolism.

A special problem exists regarding proof in these cases. Since the specimen usually is disposed of once testing is completed, there is no practical method of proving that the formed element in question actually existed in the specimen when evaluated.

[e] Failure to Correlate Test Results with Clinical History and Previous Tests

A failure to correlate current test results with the patient's clinical history and previous urinalysis tests will result in problems similar to those discussed in § 5.07[1][f], above.

[f] Failure to Report Test Results in a Timely Manner

Urinalysis test results need to be reported in a timely manner just as blood tests (*see* § 5.07[1][g], above), although the use of numeric trigger values for immediate reporting of abnormal results are not used. A series of general guidelines is used instead. A finding of tumor cells in a urine specimen would most certainly constitute a finding of sufficient importance to warrant an immediate notification of the attending physician, while the finding of formed elements consistent with a mild urinary tract infection would not, and routine communication channels would suffice.

[3] Chemistry Tests

[a] Improper Collection or Preservation of Specimens

Improper collection or preservation of specimens by the chemistry section of a clinical laboratory present a group of problems not unlike those discussed in § 5.07[1][a] under hematology. However, these problems can be much more serious because of the greater variety of testing done in the chemistry section. Each test should be accompanied by specific guidelines established for proper collection and preservation, and a failure to adhere to these guidelines can result in serious diagnostic errors.

Specific areas of concern include the time of the specimen collection, when the patient last ate, quality of the specimen obtained (non-hemolyzed), medications that could interfere with the test method in use, post-collection handling procedures, and many others.

In investigating a misdiagnosis arising from an erroneous chemistry test, it is essential that the investigation include a review of the collection and preservation policies and procedures of the laboratory. The specificity and highly individualized nature of those tests cannot be overemphasized. What is a perfectly acceptable specimen for a given chemistry test in one laboratory may prove to be totally inappropriate in a second laboratory, even though the test being performed is the same.

[b] Incorrect Labeling of Specimens

The discussion of the consequences of incorrect specimen labeling of blood (§ 5.07[1][b], above) are equally applicable in chemistry testing. An additional problem is the need to split the specimen to allow multiple tests on the same sample. This increases the chance of mislabeling, and specific criteria must be established and adhered to by laboratory personnel to reduce this risk.

[c]   Incorrect Testing or Misinterpretation of Results

With the current availability of so many possible chemical tests, the opportunity for incorrect selection or misinterpretation of a given test has been greatly increased. It is the responsibility of both the patient's physician and the testing laboratory to select the correct tests and correctly interpret the results. A failure to do so places both parties at risk of being found liable for a resulting therapeutic failure. In addition to the large array of tests now available, new and improved versions of old tests are being introduced. The courts have generally held that once a newer technology gains wide acceptance it is the responsibility of the physician to use this technology in keeping with acceptable standards of care.

Test interpretation is complex. With any set of basic chemistry tests, the possible number of patterns that can be seen becomes astronomical. Selecting the correct follow-up tests from initial findings also can be difficult, and as a result there is a tendency to over-order tests to ensure that no possible situation is missed. Follow-up testing is more the responsibility of the laboratory, because most physicians will order the correct basic tests. Similarly, the laboratory that fails to inform the clinician of new methodologies runs the risk of liability for resulting misdiagnosis.

[d]   Failure to Recognize Special Disease Processes

The failure of the chemistry section of a clinical laboratory to recognize and diagnose special disease processes results in problems similar to those encountered by the other sections of the laboratory.

[e]   Failure to Correlate Test Results with Clinical History and Previous Tests

Failure to correlate chemistry test results with the patient's clinical history and prior test results carries the same risks of liability faced by other departments of the clinical laboratory, only more so. It is not uncommon for an individual patient to have the same test repeated several times in a 24 hour period. The intent of the repeat testing usually is to monitor the progress of therapeutic measures being taken. It can be difficult to correlate previous results with current results for a patient on therapy. Values can change rapidly and dramatically, and every attempt must be made to consider how this therapy will influence the results being obtained. In these cases, the documentation is extremely important in determining possible negligence.

[f]   Failure to Report Test Results in a Timely Manner

Failure to report chemistry test results in a timely manner involves problems similar to those in hematology (*see* § 5.07[1][g]).

The so-called "Panic Values" are employed to indicate the need for immediate notification of the attending physician. The failure to report life-threatening values can be viewed as negligent.

[g]   Failure to Report Diseases to Health Authorities

Certain conditions are required to be reported to the appropriate public health agencies. For example, in the Common-wealth of Pennsylvania, the following diseases are to be reported if discovered by chemical testing: lead poisoning; neonatal hypothyroidism; and phenylketonuria.

Additional reportable conditions, usually diagnosed by the microbiology section of the laboratory, are listed in § 5.07[4][h].

[4]   Microbiology

[a]   Improper Collection or Preservation of Specimens

Improper collection and preservation of specimens submitted for testing by the microbiology section of the clinical laboratory can have serious consequences. Since microbiology deals with the recovery and identification of microorganisms, it is essential that the specimens be collected properly. Failure to collect and preserve the specimens properly will result in nonviable organisms reaching the laboratory, with the end result being no growth on culture media and a subsequent failure to isolate and identify infective agents. This failure to isolate and identify causative organisms will result in a delay in instituting the proper antibiotic therapy, and in severe infections can lead to the patient's demise. It is the responsibility of the microbiology section to insure that proper collection and preservation protocols are established, and that the proper collection equipment is available and correctly used.

Microbiology is unlike other sections of the laboratory in that many of the specimens are collected by other than laboratory personnel. Where the adequacy or appropriateness of a specimen is questionable, this information should be clearly included in the record transmitted to the attending physician.

[b]   Incorrect Labeling of Specimens

In addition to the specimen labeling precautions that laboratory personnel should observe generally, the microbiology section must additionally concern itself with proper identification of the site of culture collection. The site of collection directly influences the types of organisms that are sought, and the type of culture techniques that are used. In other words, one does not culture a throat specimen in the same manner one cultures a puncture wound. The puncture wound would be cultured for both aerobic and anaerobic organisms, while the throat specimen would be cultured for aerobic organisms only. The failure to identify a wound correctly could result in not finding a significant pathogenic organism, which could result in serious consequences for the patient.

[c]   Incorrect Testing or Misinterpretation of Results

Errors that can cause a misinterpretation of culture results include failure to identify the pathogenic organism, failure to interpret the results of antibiotic sensitivity testing, failure to identify mixed cultures of multiple pathogenic organisms, and similar occurrences.

Incorrect results also can arise from the use of inappropriate culture techniques and culture media for the site under investigation. Furthermore, failure to evaluate plates at the correct time intervals can result in overgrowth of pathogenic organisms by so-called normal flora, and failure to observe cultures for a sufficiently long period of time might result in slow-growing organisms not being identified.

[d]   Failure to Recognize Special Disease Processes

It is the responsibility of the microbiology section to recognize organisms that are currently considered major infective agents. The ability to recognize these agents must be made available to physicians. An example is best illustrated by the activity that ensued following the deaths of several individuals from what was eventually designated as Legionnaire's disease. When the disease first appeared, no one was aware of the causative agent, and thus no blame for failure to recognize it could be established. However, now that the causative agent has been identified and characterized, and appropriate culture techniques have been developed, a failure to recognize this relatively rare disease could constitute negligence on the part of a microbiology section.

[e]   Failure to Collect Sterile Specimens

The failure to collect a sterile specimen for the microbiology laboratory can result in the finding of a bacterial infection that in reality does not exist. This can result in the inappropriate, and perhaps harmful, treatment of a patient with antibiotics. While antibiotics are commonly used, their use is not without risk. This is especially true of the newer aminoglycoside antibiotics that carry the risk of renal damage and ototoxicity. Additionally, the failure of a microbiology laboratory to recognize the characteristics of nonsterile specimens can result in delays in obtaining properly collected specimens, and may thus delay the identification of serious pathogenic organisms.

[f]   Failure to Correlate Test Results with Clinical History and Previous Tests

The potential for liability resulting from the microbiology section's failure to correlate test results with the patient's clinical history and previous microbiology tests is similar to that encountered in the other sections of the clinical laboratory.

[g]   Failure to Report Test Results in a Timely Manner

The problems created by the lack of timely reporting of results obtained in the microbiology section of the laboratory most closely parallel those found in the urinalysis section (§ 5.07[2][f],above). There is no numeric data generated, and generally a listing of specific circumstances that require immediate notification is used. In the case of certain organisms, such as tuberculosis bacillus, a great deal of time may be required for growth to occur in the culture. The patient may have long since been discharged from the hospital. It remains the responsibility of the microbiology section to see that the attending physician is notified of positive findings, so that appropriate measures can be instituted. It is not sufficient to assume that the physician will remember to follow up every discharged patient's test to see that the final culture results are negative.

In Microbiology, detection of highly infectious agents constitutes "Panic Values." Bacterial meningitis is immediately reported to the physician so that prophylactic antibiotics could be given to close contacts of the patient. Mycobacterium tuberculosis detected on smears is reported urgently and even cultures that do not grow until 8 weeks after collection in many cases. Bacteria in blood poses a great danger to the patient and needs to be treated emergently.

[h] Failure to Report Venereal and Other Specified Diseases to Health Authorities

The microbiology section of the clinical laboratory is required to report certain infectious organisms to the public health authorities. These requirements normally are dictated by state law. The reportable diseases for the Commonwealth of Pennsylvania are listed below. Similar requirements exist in other states.

Acquired immune deficiency syndrome (AIDS)
Amebiasis
Anthrax
Botulism
Brucellosis
Cholera
Diphtheria
Encephalitis
Food poisoning
Giardiasis
Gonococcal infections
Hepatitis (viral, including types A and B)
Histoplasmosis
Legionnaire's disease
Leptospirosis
Lymphogranuloma venereum
Malaria
Measles
Meningitis (all types)
Meningococcal disease
Mumps
Pertussis (whooping cough)
Plague
Poliomyelitis
Psittacosis (ornithosis)
Rabies
Rheumatic fever
Rickettsial diseases (including Rocky Mountain spotted fever)
Rubella
Salmonellosis
Smallpox
Syphilis (all stages)

Tetanus
Toxoplasmosis
Trichinosis
Tuberculosis (all forms)
Tularemia
Typhoid
Yellow fever

[5]   Immunology and Serology

[a]   Improper Collection or Preservation of Specimens

Improper collection or preservation of specimens obtained for testing by the immunology and serology section involves the same risks incurred by other departments of the laboratory.

[b]   Incorrect Labeling of Specimens

The incorrect labeling of specimens collected for the immunology and serology section carries risks similar to those described for other areas of the laboratory.

[c]   Incorrect Testing or Misinterpretation of Results

Testing done in the immunology and serology sections of the laboratory is for antibodies that have a long-term persistence in the body (*see* § § 5.04[4] to 5.04[4][c], above). In most cases, this allows one to prove or disprove errors in interpretation through repeated testing. This is particularly true in syphilis tests, where a positive test result can have serious psychological and social consequences for the individual. (If the test was done incorrectly or misinterpreted, it is a relatively simple matter to prove through repeated testing, because a true positive test for syphilis will remain positive for a long time.)

[d]   Failure to Recognize Special Disease Processes

The failure of the immunology and serology sections to recognize and diagnose special disease processes poses problems similar to those found in the other areas of the laboratory.

[e] Failure to Correlate Test Results with Clinical History and Previous Tests

The problems that can arise from the failure of the immunology and serology section to correlate testing with the patient's clinical history and previous test results do not differ from those of other sections of the laboratory.

[f] Failure to Report Test Results in a Timely Manner

The failure to report testing done in the immunology and serology section in a timely manner will have consequences similar to those discussed in other areas of the laboratory, but generally the time element is not as critical. An exception would be in the case of certain infectious diseases that are identified through serologic techniques (e.g., Rocky Mountain spotted fever, psittacosis). Here the need to transmit the results of positive findings to the attending physician can be critical to the patient's survival, because appropriate therapy must begin as soon as possible after the causative agent has been identified.

[g] Failure to Report Venereal and Other Specified Diseases to Health Authorities

Certain diseases required by law to be reported to the proper authorities will be diagnosed in the immunology and serology sections of the laboratory. *See* § 5.07[4][h] for a list of these diseases.

[6] Blood Bank

[a] Improper Collection or Preservation of Specimens

In the blood bank, improper collection is seldom a problem because of the relatively stable nature of the antigens and antibodies that are studied during compatibility testing. However, preservation and storage of the blood and blood products are of extreme importance for a product to be effective and not be harmful to the recipient when transfused. Blood products are a fertile medium for the growth of harmful organisms that will kill the recipient. The temperature at which the blood and its component have to be stored needs to be kept at a specified temperature for each product. The products are stored in a refrigerator with an alarm to warn of any deviations in temperature control.

[b] Incorrect Labeling of Specimens

An incorrect labeling of a specimen collected for blood bank testing can have extremely serious consequences for the recipient of the blood. A patient may be given the wrong type of blood and result in a fatal acute hemolytic transfusion reaction. Transfusion of even a very small amount of incompatible blood can produce a rapid reaction with immediate anaphylactic shock and eventual death. This clerical mistake cannot be defended.

 Usually, the following information is required:

1. Patient's full first and last names
2. Hospital identification number
3. Date of collection
4. Time of collection
5. Initials of the technician collecting the specimen

The above information should be taken directly from the patient's identification band, and written onto the specimen container at the bedside. All information on both the specimen container and the identification band must reconcile fully with the information on the request form sent to the blood bank.

[c] Incorrect Testing or Misinterpretation of Results

An incorrect test or misinterpretation of a test performed in the blood bank can lead to a patient being transfused with incompatible blood, where the consequences can range from a shortening of the lifespan of the transfused cells to the death of the patient. The result will depend upon the nature of the incompatibility.

The receipt of incompatible blood will become obvious by a rapid deterioration in the patient's condition (hemolytic transfusion reaction). The number of such reactions that result from incorrect testing or misinterpretation of a test is small. The great majority of them are the direct result of clerical errors made during the process of transfusing the blood, i.e., the blood is given to the wrong patient.

[d] Failure to Correlate Test Results with Previous Blood Type or Crossmatch Tests

It is the responsibility of the blood bank to maintain a record of a patient's previous tests. An individual's blood type (for all practical purposes) never changes, and failure to review available records to confirm this information is negligence.

It also is necessary to review a patient's files for information on any previous identification of unexpected or atypical *alloantibodies*. These are antibodies that individuals can develop (as the result of previous blood transfusions, pregnancy, etc.) to specific antigens that can be present in the donor blood. The recipient with an alloantibody who is transfused with red cells containing the corresponding antigen will suffer a transfusion reaction. The severity of the reaction is highly variable, but death can result.

[e] Failure to Report Test Results in a Timely Manner

In an emergency, the failure of the blood bank section of a laboratory to report on a test in a timely manner could result in a delay in a patient receiving a life-saving transfusion. Otherwise, the failure to comply with a request for test results promptly will subject the department to risks similar in scope to those encountered by other laboratory sections.

[7] Special Studies

The tests performed in the special studies section of a clinical laboratory are virtually identical with those performed in the chemistry section. With regard to malpractice risks, *see* § § 5.07[3] to 5.07[3][g].

§ 5.08 Malpractice: Administrative Functions

[1] Laboratory Director

The pathologist, in his role as a laboratory director, can be held liable for the negligent actions of those in his employ, even though he may be innocent of personal fault, under the theory of respondeat superior.

[a] Employment of Incompetent or Inadequately Trained Personnel

It is the responsibility of the laboratory director to see that individuals in his employ are competent and properly trained to perform the tasks assigned to them. Failure on the part of the director to recognize incompetent or inadequately trained personnel could subject him to liability in the event that an employee's error could be proved to result from such failure.

The laboratory director should conduct periodic reviews of the work of all technical staff, and should judge their performance against objective performance-related criteria to insure that expected levels of competence are being demonstrated. Additionally, the director should insure that the technical staff is kept abreast of current developments in the field of laboratory medicine, and that technologists are using the most appropriate testing methods available.

If during the course of performance evaluations of the technical staff, the director discovers suboptimal performance that cannot be corrected through retraining and education, he has a responsibility to discharge the individual.

[b]   Failure to Monitor Physicians

The director of a hospital laboratory has the responsibility to indirectly monitor the actions of the staff physicians who use the laboratory in any capacity. The postmortem examinations can reveal some negligent physician treatment of a patient. The pathologist classifies autopsy findings into five categories:

1. Major discrepant autopsy findings with direct impact on survival;
2. Major discrepant autopsy findings with no direct impact on survival;
3. Minor discrepant autopsy findings without effect on survival;
4. Minor discrepant autopsy findings of epidemiologic or genetic interest only; and
5. No discrepant autopsy findings.

It is the responsibility of the laboratory director or his designee from the department to report a tally of the autopsies to the medical director and the hospital administrator. An attending physician's negligent act could involve the director in a litigation and the failure to notify could even be viewed as collusion, and as such, the director could be named a co-defendant.

The laboratory director is also involved in the indirect monitoring of the activities of the surgeons. The director submits to the hospital Credentials Committee a quality assurance report. The number of inadequate samples obtained by the surgeons is monitored monthly. A list is compiled of those apparent inappropriate procedures, technical complications, therapeutic misadventures, etc.

[2]   Hospital Committees

The hospital pathologist frequently serves on one or more of the following committees.

[a]   Tumor and Tissue Committee

The Tumor and Tissue Committee is usually chaired by the pathologist, and is responsible for evaluating the surgical procedures that are being performed. The name of the committee is somewhat misleading, since the members also review cases where no tissue is removed. In such cases, the appropriateness of the procedure performed is evaluated based on both the clinical history and the laboratory data present. In cases where tissue is removed, a review of the pre-operative diagnosis versus the tissue diagnosis is conducted, and differences are reconciled. It is through the actions of this committee that most of the incompetent actions of surgeons are discovered.

[b]   Transfusion Review Committee

The function of the Transfusion Review Committee is to evaluate the use of all blood and blood products by the hospital medical staff. Both the surgical and medical staff are included in this review. The committee evaluates utilization, insuring that blood and blood products are given only when appropriate, and that excessive amounts of blood are not being used by any individual staff member. (The use of excessive amounts of blood utilization on a regular basis by a surgeon might be an indication of incompetent surgical technique.)

[c]   Mortality Committee

The Mortality Committee is responsible for reviewing hospital deaths. The purpose is to ensure that appropriate medical care was rendered, and that the death did not result from a negligent act. An individual physician with an excessive mortality rate might be the subject of further scrutiny to determine that no inappropriate or incompetent care is being provided.

[d]   Infection Control Committee

The Infection Control Committee is responsible for evaluation of the rates and types of hospital-based infections. This evaluation includes both medical and surgical infections, and is designed to insure that proper infection control measures are being utilized by the hospital staff.

[e]   Medical Staff Executive Committee

The Medical Staff Executive Committee serves as the internal credentialing group for the hospital. It grants staff privileges to individual physicians after reviewing their qualifications. It also is responsible for reviewing any unfavorable reports generated on a physician by any of the committees discussed above. This committee is responsible for the decision to take action against an allegedly incompetent staff member.

[f]   Utilization Review Committee

The Utilization Review Committee is responsible for evaluating the appropriateness of care provided to a patient during the hospital stay. It evaluates length of stay, procedures performed, outcome of the procedures performed, laboratory tests and radiology procedures ordered and their appropriateness, etc. The committee evaluates the total care given to the patient, and identifies those areas or individuals providing less than optimal care according to the national standards.

[g]   DRG Review Committee

The DRG Review Committee came into being with the development of the DRG (Diagnosis Related Group) method of payment by the federal government. This committee seeks to ensure that the care given patients is appropriate for their DRG category, and more importantly, that individuals entering the hospital under the Medicare and Medicaid programs are not given suboptimal care because of the DRG fixed payment method.

§ 5.09 Malpractice: The Pathologist as an Expert

[1]   Review and Analysis of the Patient's Records

Utilization of the pathologist to review hospital and medical records in malpractice cases is often mandatory. There are few individuals better qualified to evaluate the care received by a patient. The pathologist can compare the defendant physician's findings against the findings presented by the records, and determine the appropriateness of both the diagnosis and treatment.

[2]   Review and Analysis of Opinions of Other Experts

When reviewing the reports and depositions of other medical experts, the pathologist frequently can present valuable alternative opinions. The pathologist can review these depositions and reports for errors of omission: relevant facts that may not have been presented or have been glossed over. The inclusion of a pathologist as a reviewer frequently assures that all material facts in the case are fully explored, and that all possible explanations are provided.

[3]   Review and Analysis of Laboratory Findings

The pathologist can usually provide information that will correlate the various laboratory test data, and provide insight as to how such data supports or does not support the clinical diagnosis. The pathologist usually can determine the appropriateness of the testing selected and evaluate the results for correctness. Where conflict appears to exist in the clinical diagnosis, he often can provide information that will relate the laboratory findings to the actual disease process, and suggest other possible diagnoses that should have been considered.

By the careful examination of microscopic surgical and autopsy tissue slides, a pathologist can make determinations relating to the correctness of tissue diagnosis, and where appropriate, the grading and staging of tumors. The pathologist is most useful when malpractice actions involve a missed diagnosis or misdiagnosis. His review may uncover findings that were overlooked during the initial evaluation of tissue studies, or may uncover additional or alternative disease processes that could have contributed to a patient's death.

In a similar manner, cytology slides, peripheral blood smears, bone marrow biopsies, and other special slide preparations can be evaluated for a missed diagnosis or misdiagnosis.

The examination of gross tissue specimens can be helpful in cases of malpractice. When these examinations are performed by the pathologist, tissue specimens are evaluated for appropriateness and completeness of sampling done. Sections must have been obtained from representative areas that depict the exact pathology of a disease process and be able to determine whether adequate uninvolved margins surrounding the area of concern have been taken. When questions are raised regarding a missed diagnosis, it may be that appropriate sections of tissue were not cut from the paraffin blocks in which the tissue sample has been stored. The pathologist can obtain this tissue block and cut additional and deeper sections to determine if this was the case. And if indicated, the pathologist can also perform special staining procedures that may prove a diagnosis was missed during the original examination. Special stains may not have been done, and the routine sections may not have provided conclusive evidence of the pathologic process at issue.

Examination of the specimen will also be able to determine if the extent of the surgical procedure had been appropriate. These issues of sampling can be relevant in malpractice cases, and if any questions are to be raised in this area, the tissue should be evaluated by a pathologist. The tissue obtained by the surgeon and submitted to the pathologist may have been inadequate to reach the appropriate diagnosis. In cases where the margins of normal tissue around a malignant tumor may not have adequately removed, the reviewing pathologist could raise the issue that the clinician taking care of the patient had not paid attention to the pathologist's report, if the latter had been appropriately addressed.

[4] Postmortem Examinations

Circumstances may arise in a malpractice case where members of the family feel that the care received by the patient contributed to his death. A private pathologist may be asked to perform a postmortem examination to determine the exact cause of death, or perhaps to offer an opinion as to the appropriateness of the care. This examination probably would not be performed by the hospital pathologist where the deceased was a patient because the family would feel that his opinion might be biased.

Cases may arise where malpractice litigation is instituted following the burial of the deceased. It may be necessary to retain a pathologist to perform an *exhumation* autopsy. In these cases the body is removed from the burial site and an autopsy is performed following the standard protocols. In some cases, vital tests will not be available, such as toxicology studies for certain drugs. Also, body fluids would not be available for chemical analyses. This will make the pathologist's job much more difficult, but nevertheless valuable information often can be obtained.

§ 5.10   Selected General References

Ackerman, A.B. Histologic Diagnosis of Inflammatory Skin Diseases.(Arbor Scribendi, New York 2005.)

American Cancer Society. Possible Risks of Blood Product Transfusions www.cancer.org 11/28/2006.

Anderson, Richard. Medical Malpractice. A Physician's Sourcebook, Doctor's Company, California 2004.

Anderson, Pathology (2 vols.) (C. V. Mosby Co. 1996).

Balows, Albert et al. Manual of Clinical Microbiology (Fifth Edition) (American Society for Microbiology 1991).

Beutler, Ernest et al. Williams Hematology (Fifth Edition) (McGraw-Hill, Inc. 1995.)

Bibbo, Comprehensive Cytopathology (W.B. Saunders Company 1997).

Bick, Rodger L. Hematology Clinical and Laboratory Practice (2 volumes) Mosby 1993.

Bigner, DD et al. Russell and Rubinstein's Pathology of Tumors of the Nervous System. Sixth edition. (Oxford University Press, 1998).

Cibas and Ducatman, Cytology Diagnostic Principles and Clinical Correlates (Saunders 2003).

Cornwall, Patricia. All That Remains. (Avon Books, March 1996).

Cotran, Kumar and Robbins. Robbins: Pathologic Basis of Disease. Fourth edition (W. B. Saunders Company 1989).

Coulson, Walter F. Surgical Pathology Second edition (2 volumes)(J. B. Lippincott Company 1988).

Dabbs, David. Diagnostic Immunohistochemistry. (Churchill Livingstone 2006).

Dalton, HP and Nottebart, HC. Interpretive Medical Microbiology (Churchill Livingstone 1986).

Damjanov, I and Linder, J. Anderson's Pathology (2 volumes)Tenth edition, (Mosby 1996).

Dana, S and DiMaio, V. Handbook of Forensic Pathology.(CRC Press 1999).

DiMaio, V. and DiMaio, D. Forensic Pathology. (CRC Press 2002).

Dodd, MM and Dodd, MJ. Anatomy of a Medical Malpractice Lawsuit. MD Med J 45:108-115, 1996.

Elder, David et al. Lever's Histopathology of the Skin (Eighth Edition) (Lippincott-Raven 1997).

Ellington, DP & Rosenthal. RS. The defense perspective. Med Malpractice. 94:323–327, 1997.

Enzinger, Franz M. and Weiss, Sharon W. Soft Tissue Tumors (C. V. Mosby Company 1988).

Epstein, Jonathan.I. Pathologists and the judicial process: How to avoid it. 25(4) 527–537 Amer. Jour. Surg. Path. 2001.

Finegold, SM, and Baron EJ. Bailey and Scott's Diagnostic Microbiology (CV Mosby Company 1986).

Forbes, BA et al. Bailey and Scott's Diagnostic Microbiology-Text and Study Guide Package, (Twelfth edition), Elsevier, 2007).

Henry, Richard J. et al. Clinical Chemistry Principles and Technics.(Second edition) (Harper and Row 1974).

Howanitz, Joan H. and Howanitz, Peter J. Laboratory Medicine Test Selection and Interpretation (Churchill Livingstone 1991).

Hutchins, Grover. Autopsy Performance and Reporting (College of American Pathologists 1990).

Kaplan, Lawrence A. and Pesce, Amadeo J. Clinical Chemistry Theory, Analysis and Correlation (C. V. Mosby Company 1984).

Knight, Forensic Pathology (Arnold 1996).

Kurman, Robert J. Blaustein's Pathology of the Female Genital Tract (Fourth Edition) (Springer-Verlag 1994).

Lowe, David Surgical Pathology Revision (Cambridge University Press 2006).

Lowe, D.G. and Jeffrey, I.J.M. Surgical Pathology Techniques. (B.C. Decker, Inc. 1990).

Mayo Medical laboratories Interpretive Handbook edited by Jane C. Dale, MD, January 2005.

McPherson, RA and Pincus, MR Henry's Clinical Diagnosis and Management by Laboratory Methods (Twenty-first edition)(Saunders 2006).

Medicare Reimbursement for Blood Testing . BloodBook.com, 11/2004.

Moenssens, A et al Scientific Evidence in Criminal Cases (Third edition) (Foundation Press 1986).

Riley, Donald E. DNA Testing. An Introduction for Non-Scientists. April 2005.

Rosai, Juan: Rosai and Ackerman's Surgical Pathology (2 volumes) (Ninth edition) (Mosby 2004).

Rubin, Emmanuel. Rubin's Pathology: Clinicopathologic Foundations of Medicine (Fourth edition) (Lippincott, Williams and Wilkins 2005).

Smith, Robert A. American Cancer Society Guidelines for the Early Detection of Cancer. A Cancer Jour for Clin Jan/Feb 2001.

Smith, Robert A. American Cancer Society Guidelines for the Early Detection of Cancer: Update of Early Detection Guidelines for Prostate, Colorectal, and Endometrial Cancers CA (A Cancer Journal for Clinicians Jan/Feb 2001).

Spitz, W (ed) Medicolegal Investigation of Death: guidelines for the application of Pathology to crime investigation. (Seventh edition) (Charles C. Thomas 2006).

Sternberg, Stephen S. Diagnostic Surgical Pathology (Second Edition) (2 vols.) (Raven Press 1994).

Sternberg, Stephen S Principles and Practice of Surgical Pathology and Cytopathology (Churchill Livingstone 2006).

Teitz, Norbert. Fundamentals of Clinical Chemistry (W.B. Saunders Company 1976).

Tubbs, Raymond et al. Atlas of Immunohistology (American Society of Clinical Pathologists 1986).

Wecht, Cyril. Forensic Sciences (Matthew Bender 1981).

Wecht,CH and Rago, JT. Forensic Science and Law: Investigative Applications in Criminal, Civil, and Family Justice. (CRC Press 2006).

Wecht, Cyril. Legal Medicine (Butterworth-Heinemann 1989).

Wecht, Cyril. Medicolegal Primer (American College of Legal Medicine Foundation 1991)..

Weiss, S and Goldblum, J. Enzinger and Weiss's Soft Tissue Tumors, (Fifth edition) (Mosby 2008).

Digital Pathology Archives, Rick Stouffer, Post Gazette June 5, 2008.

CHAPTER 6

PSYCHIATRY

Robert L. Sadoff, MD, and K. Ryan Connolly MS, MD

SYNOPSIS

§ 6.01 Training and Certification of Psychiatrists

[1] Premedical Education

As in other medical specialties, the psychiatrist's preliminary education consists of premedical courses taken over a period of four years. Most premedical curricula emphasize chemistry, physics, and other sciences. More recently, the curriculum has included the humanities and behavioral sciences as well. Occasionally, the premedical student will obtain a master's degree prior to entering medical school. In the past, applicants for medical school may have completed the premedical curriculum in two or three years, depending upon the requirements of the school, the need for accelerating their medical education, and the quality of the applicant. Most medical schools require, as a minimum, courses in organic and inorganic chemistry, physics, biochemistry, and calculus. Some require courses in genetics, psychology, English, and other humanities courses including philosophy and especially ethics. The emphasis recently has been on a more well-rounded education, including the arts as well as the sciences.

In addition to required coursework, applicants to medical schools are required to sit for the Medical College Admissions Test (MCAT).

[2] Medical School

All psychiatrists must have a medical school education, which consists of four years at an approved medical school in the United States or Canada, or the equivalent in a foreign country. Medical school education as a requisite for becoming a psychiatrist includes the M.D. (Doctor of Medicine) or the D.O. (Doctor of Osteopathy) degree. In addition to completing coursework in medical school, students must pass a series of examinations administered by the Federation of State Medical Boards and the National Board of Medical Examiners, the United States Medical Licensing Examinations (USMLE). Applicants from foreign countries must be certified by the Educational Commission for Foreign Medical Graduates and sit for the USMLE. A recent development is the USMLE Step 2 CS, which tests applicants on bedside manner, English proficiency and clinical decision-making, in addition to the more traditional testing of factual knowledge.[1]

---

[1] USMLE Bulletin 2007.

[3] Internship

The requirements for internship have varied over the past years, and are regulated by the Accreditation Council for Graduate medical education (ACGME). Traditionally, all physicians must have completed either a year of internal medicine internship or a "rotating" internship. More recently, the internship year in psychiatry has been blended with the first year of residency or specialty training. Thus, physicians may enter a psychiatry residency program at either the first or second postgraduate year. Physicians entering at the second postgraduate year will have completed one year of ACGME-accredited training in internal medicine, family practice, pediatrics or other specialty requiring continuous patient care. The "blended" programs require at least four months of internal medicine, family practice or pediatrics; a minimum of four months of neurology is also required.[2] During the intern year, and for most of residency, physicians will practice with a medical training license, requiring their work to be supervised by a fully-licensed physician. After the completion of internship, physicians must pass "Step 3" of the USMLE in order to apply for an unrestricted medical license.

The importance of the internship is to acquaint the prospective psychiatrist with the practice of medicine in other specialties, and to consolidate his education and experience in medicine before embarking on the specialty of psychiatry. This has become increasingly important as the neurobiologic substrates of mental illness are being appreciated with growing clarity. In parallel with these developments is the proliferation of psychotropic medications with diverse actions on the brain and body. In order to safely and effectively prescribe these medications, the psychiatrist must not only appreciate their psychotropic effects, but their effects on the body generally. Further, the diagnostic methods by which "organic" disease processes may be distinguished from purely psychiatric or functional illnesses are becoming more routine and available, and thus demand the psychiatrist to have a working knowledge of these procedures.

[4] Residency

Residency training programs in psychiatry consist primarily of three years after internship or four years if the internship is blended with the first year of residency. Thus, the trainee is not considered a fully trained psychiatrist until he or she completes four years following graduation from medical school.

---

[2] Program Requirements for Residency Training in Psychiatry, ACGME 2007.

Residency training programs vary throughout the country in both quality and emphasis. Many programs are geared toward training the psychiatrist to become an academic psychiatrist or professor of psychiatry. Other programs are directed toward research in psychopharmacology or biology and psychiatry. Still others heavily emphasize the psychoanalytic model of treatment (most programs consider themselves to take an eclectic approach and include training and experience in all phases of psychiatry).

Most programs begin with inpatient treatment experience during the first and second years. This is followed by outpatient experience in the third and fourth years, with increased time in the fourth year available for electives in the individual's particular area of interest. The fourth year may include electives such as psychosomatic medicine, (formerly consultation and liaison psychiatry), mood disorders, geriatric psychiatry, forensic psychiatry, administrative psychiatry, or research in any phase of psychiatric practice. Some programs demand individual research with a publishable paper as a requirement to completing the program. Most programs, however, do not have such academic requirements.

The resident in psychiatry is considered a trainee and not a fully trained psychiatrist with total responsibility for a patient. Although the resident in psychiatry is fully licensed to practice medicine, he is still considered as an apprentice in the field of psychiatry until he completes his training. He is under the supervision of various preceptors and supervisors during his period of residency. Each case that he undertakes is reviewed or discussed with his supervisor so that a responsible psychiatrist oversees the patient's treatment program.

Residents in psychiatry also gain experience in emergency psychiatry, handling commitment procedures, and testifying at various legal hearings regarding their patients.

[5] Administrative and Research Psychiatry

Following the completion of residency training, the psychiatrist may enter a number of fields of practice, including any of the subspecialties for which he has been trained. The three general areas of psychiatry, excluding the subspecialties, are administrative, research, and clinical psychiatry.

A number of psychiatrists do not maintain a clinical practice, or they maintain a very limited one at best. They devote considerable time to the operation and administration of psychiatry departments. They also practice by training others in medical schools and departments of psychiatry. Ultimately, their goal is to become chairperson of a department of psychiatry or to run a psychiatric hospital.

Research psychiatrists may similarly choose not to pursue clinical practice in order to focus on particular areas of interest: an example would be research on medications used in treating psychiatric illnesses. Basic work in neurophysiology and psychopharmacology would be included in these studies. Some of these psychiatrists eventually go to work for pharmaceutical or biotechnology companies, or become academic psychiatrists in an integrated medical school training program.

Other areas of special interest include research on the various types of mental illnesses. The causes of psychotic disorders and the treatment of mood disorders are currently popular fields of research. Research on the various forms of psychotherapy is another special interest, as is the comparison of the efficacy of psychotherapy, behavioural modification, and psychoanalytically oriented psychotherapy. Research has proliferated in the area of brain chemistry and its effect on mental illness. The implications in this field are vast, including the genetic determination of various illnesses, their neurobiologic substrates and developing specific medication for treatment of particular psychiatric illnesses.

[6] Clinical Psychiatry

By far the largest number of psychiatrists enter clinical practice. That is, they deal directly with patients either on a one-to-one basis or in groups. The clinical psychiatrist may conduct his or her research projects on clinical patients, but primarily he or she is interested in the treatment of people who come for help with psychiatric symptoms. The clinical psychiatrist may utilize medications, psychotherapy, behavioral therapy, and may treat people either as inpatients, outpatients, or both. Most clinical psychiatrists have hospital affiliations, and do some treatment of patients in private or community hospitals. Some clinical psychiatrists work exclusively for state or Veterans Administration hospitals. Others treat people exclusively in outpatient settings, either community mental health centers or community outpatient clinics. Most psychiatrists have at least a small, part-time outpatient clinical practice in addition to other affiliations. Many psychiatrists work alone in their outpatient offices, but some are in professional associations with other psychiatrists, or with other mental health professionals, including clinical psychologists, psychiatric nurses, and psychiatric social workers.

Clinical psychiatrists in private practice have found that managed care regulations have imposed significantly on professional income. In particular, managed care providers have become reluctant to reimburse the relatively high expense of psychotherapy provided by psychiatrists, favoring social workers and psychologists in their stead. Psychiatrists have reduced the frequency and length of psychotherapy visits, consistent with payment procedures, and spend increasing amounts of time monitoring medication given to patients who receive psychotherapy from non-medical psychotherapists. As in other fields of medicine, dwindling reimbursements have led many to see more patients in a shorter period of time to maintain income. Many psychiatrists have found it necessary to join groups of other psychiatrists in order to maintain clinical practice.

[7] Subspecialty Areas

There are some psychiatrists who specialize beyond the general treatment of adult psychiatric patients. These include the subspecialty of child and adolescent psychiatry, which has its own national associations and its own board certification approved by the American Board of Psychiatry and Neurology. Other recognized subspecialties with board certification include addiction psychiatry, forensic psychiatry, geriatric psychiatry, pain medicine, sleep medicine, hospice and palliative care medicine and psychosomatic medicine (formerly consultation and liaison psychiatry).[3] New but growing subspecialties include women's mental health, psychopharmacology and the advanced treatment of mood disorders, schizophrenia or other specific disorders. Some psychiatrists have obtained multiple board certifications in various subspecialties of psychiatry. Although it is not a recognized subspecialty of psychiatry, some psychiatrists have joined HMO groups and other managed care facilities regulating treatment of patients of other psychiatrists.

In the past, board certification was awarded on the basis of clinic experience and the passing of subspecialty-specific examinations. Increasingly, the completion of a fellowship program is required to obtain certification in many specialties.

[8] Board Certification

There are currently about 40,000 psychiatrists in the United States, most of whom belong to the American Psychiatric Association (APA). The APA is the recognized national group of psychiatrists dedicated to the improvement of psychiatric treatment and to the welfare of its members. It is not a certifying organization.

The APA has undergone a number of changes throughout the years, but currently functions as a broad-based organization dealing with the multiple problems confronting psychiatrists in all aspects of the profession. Recently

---

[3] Initial Certification in the Subspecialties, ABPN 2007.

the APA has begun to set policy standards in controversial areas, including civil rights, social welfare, the labeling of individuals as disordered, and the insanity defense in criminal cases. The APA has also changed its tax exempt status so that it may speak out politically on issues that affect patients, psychiatrists and families of mentally disturbed individuals.

The American Board of Psychiatry and Neurology is the certifying board for psychiatrists in this country. Fewer than half of the psychiatrists practicing today have board certification. Requirements for certification include the completion of a residency training program at an accredited institution, experience in the field, and the passing of both a written and a practical examination. A physician may call himself a psychiatrist even if he is not board certified in psychiatry. However, board certification indicates the successful completion of training, and the mastery of concepts and practices in the field. Hospitals are increasingly requiring board certification for psychiatrists to be granted admitting privileges. Since 1993, psychiatrists have been required to take a recertification examination every ten years to maintain board certification.

Subspecialty board certifications currently exist for the subspecialties listed in § 6.01[7]. The importance of certification lies in improved quality of care and the higher standards of practice demanded by the profession.

There have been changes in board certification in the subspecialty of forensic psychiatry. The American Board of Psychiatry and Neurology and the American Board of Medical Specialties have accepted a new classification in psychiatry, called "Added Qualifications in Forensic Psychiatry." This certification involves a new set of examinations, and since 1999 requires the candidate to have served as a full time fellow in forensic psychiatry for one year in an accredited forensic psychiatric program. Those forensic psychiatrists who had obtained board certification in forensic psychiatry from the American Board of Forensic Psychiatry will maintain certification, although that board has dissolved.[4]

§ 6.02 Types of Practice

[1] Hospital Psychiatry

Most practicing psychiatrists have some affiliation with a hospital in order to hospitalize their patients when necessary. Some psychiatrists are full-time employees of the hospital, and act in a supervising or administrative capacity as well as a therapeutic one. As to those psychiatrists who have both

---

[4] For a more comprehensive presentation of the education and training of psychiatrists, *see* Dattilio, F.M., and Sadoff, R.L., MENTAL HEALTH EXPERTS, ROLES AND QUALIFICATIONS FOR COURT, PA Bar Inst. Press, 2002, 2007, Mechanicsburg, PA.

outpatient and inpatient practices, the bulk of their time is spent in their offices treating outpatients. However, they do admit patients to community, private, or state hospitals.

Psychiatrists' affiliation with the community or private hospital allows them to treat their patients throughout the hospital as well as participate in decision-making on hospital policies. They may have some administrative or teaching responsibilities as well, depending upon the nature of the hospital and its affiliation with teaching centers or medical schools.

Often the psychiatrist with a community or private hospital affiliation is asked to volunteer time to the mental health clinic at the hospital, give "grand rounds" (a teaching experience at the hospital), or teach nurses and other mental health professionals. He may also be asked to be on call for consultation or liaison psychiatry with other specialties of medicine within the hospital.

Most staff positions at state hospitals or veterans hospitals are full-time positions. In that capacity, the psychiatrist has both administrative and treatment responsibilities. In the case of state hospitals, the psychiatrist may have to deal with involuntarily committed patients, which includes making recommendations to the court for change of status or release from the hospital. He will also work with the treatment team, which usually consists of the psychiatric nurse, psychologist, social worker, and mental health aides involved in the treatment process. In such capacity, he will help make decisions about levels of function and need for restraint, seclusion, or suicidal precaution.

At university hospitals, the staff positions are usually full time, but with some clinical appointments. A clinical professor is one who has a part time, often unpaid, position in which he serves primarily as teacher to medical students, psychiatric residents, and other staff. He may or may not have "patient privileges," which means he can admit a patient to the hospital and take direct care of him. More often he would transfer the patient to one of the full-time staff psychiatrists and consult with him. Psychiatrists at university hospitals also serve a liaison consultative role with other specialties of medicine throughout the hospital when there is no specifically employed psychiatrist to do so.

[2] Outpatient Practice

Most practicing psychiatrists in the United States work in an outpatient capacity either in their own private office or in a community mental health center or psychiatric clinic. Many psychiatrists combine their private outpatient work with clinic practice or community mental health center work. Often, the mental health center is attached to the community hospital with which the psychiatrist is affiliated.

A number of psychiatrists, for economic and tax reasons, have incorporated and function as a professional corporation in their offices. With the rise of managed care and HMOs, many psychiatrists have also joined together in groups with other non-medical psychotherapists in outpatients settings. Outpatient treatment in the psychiatrist's office usually includes psychotherapy, somatic treatments, behavior therapy, and other forms of psychiatric treatment that can be performed outside a hospital.

Psychiatrists often work in psychiatric clinics affiliated with hospitals or university teaching centers in addition to their own private psychiatric practice. In that capacity they may be agents of the clinic or the hospital entity that runs the clinic. Some are independent contractors.

A number of psychiatrists have chosen to work in community mental health centers as those centers have proliferated since the 1960s. Psychiatrists in community mental health centers usually work full time as employees of those centers and treat indigent or near indigent patients who cannot afford private psychiatric fees. If the patient requires hospitalization, he is referred to a hospital and is transferred to another therapist.

Frequently, psychiatrists working in an outpatient capacity consult with patients' families and spouses for more comprehensive treatment. Some psychiatrists working in community mental health centers make house calls to geriatric or homebound patients. With the rise of the National Health Alliance for the Mentally Ill (NAMI), primarily the families of the mentally ill, outpatient psychiatrists have begun to work more closely with families of their patients. Family members have demanded to know more about the illness and the treatment of their family members and psychiatrists have complied by sharing information with the consent of their patient.

[3] Psychosomatic Medicine and Consultation Psychiatry

A number of psychiatrists specialize in consulting rather than a treatment practice. Most psychiatrists working in a consultative capacity do so within a hospital, especially a teaching hospital or a university-affiliated setting. Their primary function is to consult with other physicians with respect to the total care of the patient. They also attempt through liaison efforts to bring physicians together when a number are involved in treating the same patient. This coordination of medical efforts is extremely important in many cases, such as apparently psychiatric disturbances manifesting in a medically ill patient. Previously called consultation-liaison psychiatry, this subspecialty is now known as psychosomatic medicine to emphasize the additional training and expertise that these physicians have in understanding the relationships between "medical" and "psychiatric" illnesses.

Examples of liaison or consultative psychiatry within large medical centers include consulting with surgeons on the competency of their patient to consent to operative procedures, and consulting with physicians on the use of psychotropic or other medications to help control or calm an individual on a medical ward. Psychiatric consultants are often also asked to evaluate the safety and advisability of combinations of medications, given the high degree of polypharmacy used to treat hospitalized patients. As many physicians are less familiar with the risks and benefits of psychiatric medications used in combination with other medications, advice from a consulting psychiatrist is often essential to assure patient safety in such cases. Consultation may also include advice regarding the transfer of a patient from a medical or surgical floor to a psychiatric ward for psychiatric treatment or to comment on the appropriate level of observation for behaviourally disturbed patients on a medical-surgical ward.

In addition to the expertise used by psychosomatic physicians in consultation with non-psychiatrists, experts within the field of psychiatry are often called by other psychiatrists to advise on particularly challenging cases. This may include "second opinions" by physicians with expertise in certain disorders or evaluation of a patient's suitability for electroconvulsive therapy by a psychiatrist experienced with this therapy.

In outpatients practice, a consulting psychiatrist may be called by other psychiatrists: to advise in difficult cases, with respect to a "block" in the therapeutic process, to advise on the use of medications, to confirm a diagnosis, to advise on forensic issues, or to help plan for future psychiatric care.

[4] Governmental Psychiatry

Psychiatrists working for government agencies (state, federal, or local) usually are full-time employees. The Veterans Administration psychiatrist is discussed in § 6.02[1], above. The military psychiatrist is on active duty in one of the branches of service. He will have a fairly high rank as an officer, and will work both in the hospital and in the mental hygiene consultation outpatient service. His responsibilities may include family therapy, drug and alcohol treatment, as well as adult and child psychotherapy. The military psychiatrist also may be responsible for assessing the mental state of the members of a military unit. The military psychiatrist also may work in a liaison and consultative capacity with other military physicians, and may have administrative, forensic, and correctional duties.

State hospital psychiatrists are discussed in § 6.02[1], above. Some municipalities maintain psychiatrists on the staffs of city hospitals. Municipal psychiatrists also may work with inmates in jails, usually part-time.

However, there are a number of psychiatrists currently working in county jails, state prisons and federal correctional institutions in what is known as correctional psychiatry. These psychiatrists working under the aegis of the security system have the responsibility for the mental health of inmates. The usual treatment is medication, but some group psychotherapy is also available. Some of the larger correctional institutions have mental health units (MHUs) which serve as psychiatric hospitals within the prison system. Correctional psychiatrists may have to effect a transfer of an extremely mentally ill individual from the correctional system to a state hospital if the clinical condition warrants such a transfer.

[5] Academic Psychiatry

Psychiatrists working in university settings are also discussed in § 6.02[1], above. The primary function of the academic psychiatrist is teaching; however, his duties also involve administrative and supervisory work. In his capacity as teacher, he may serve as preceptor for residents in psychiatry during their clinical training.

Many academic psychiatrists also engage in research. Currently, research in psychiatry is focusing on the pharmacological, neurobiological and genetic aspects of mental illness and treatment. Also, specialized research centers for the study of the neurobiology of schizophrenia, addictions, and mood disorders exist in a number of university settings. Work on genetic factors in mental illness is also a presently fertile area of research. Ongoing studies of clinical research, including effectiveness of various types of psychotherapy or therapeutic settings, also can be found. Some academic psychiatrists receive considerable grant support from the pharmaceutical industry, while others rely more heavily on the National Institutes of Health/National Institute of Mental Health (NIH/NIMH) to fund their research projects.

§ 6.03 Scope of Practice: Hospital Inpatient Psychiatry

[1] Care of Voluntary Patients

[a] Admission of the Patient

Voluntary patients in psychiatry are admitted to hospitals in the same way as patients on other services. They have agreed to come into the hospital for treatment, and that treatment has been explained to them by their psychiatrist. They are made aware of the rules of the hospital, as well as their privileges and rights. They are told what is expected of them and the obligations of the staff. Orders are written consistent with the patient's needs, and the patient is assigned a room, also consistent with his needs.

The Supreme Court of the United States has mandated that incompetent patients may not voluntarily sign themselves into psychiatric hospitals.[5] Formerly, psychiatric patients were encouraged to sign in voluntarily, as that was the preferable mode of treatment, rather than involuntary commitment. Some patients who are incompetent may not meet the criteria for involuntary commitment, since they are not deemed to be a "clear and present danger of harm to self or others." Thus, there needs to be determined a means by which such patients may be admitted or committed to psychiatric hospitals when they are not competent and do not meet the criteria for involuntary commitment. Recommendations include having next of kin sign for the incompetent patient and having the court assume jurisdiction as temporary guardian until a formal hearing can be held.

As a voluntary patient, the individual is told that he may sign out of the hospital when he wishes, since there is no coercive pressure for him to remain in the hospital unless his situation changes. In most hospitals, the voluntary patient must give 72 hours' notice before leaving by telling the psychiatrist and signing a form to this effect; however, there is no way the hospital can enforce the 72-hour hold unless the psychiatrist believes the patient has become a danger to himself or others, and should be involuntarily committed. In that event, the hospital will hold the patient until a court or other convening authority can hear testimony regarding involuntary commitment. Thus the 72-hour hold is a provision to allow for an urgent re-evaluation of the patient rather than an automatic extension of the patient's hospitalization.

[b] Examination and Assessment of the Patient's Needs

Upon admission, the voluntary patient is given both a psychiatric and physical examination. Laboratory studies are performed, including blood studies, urinalysis, and x-rays where indicated. Other tests on admission may include an EEG or neuroimaging such as MRI or CT scan if neurological damage is suspected.

Primarily, the evaluation focuses on the patient's mental state and degree of mental impairment. Assessment is made with respect to his potential for violent behavior. This is often termed an assessment of the patient's "dangerousness to himself or to others." Most voluntary patients are not considered a significant threat to others, but they may have suicidal potential. If so, their particular needs must be assessed and orders written consistent with those needs.

---

[5] Zinermon v. Burch, 110 S. Ct. 975 (1990).

Suicidal patients usually are placed on "suicide precaution" of various levels, depending on the assessment of the psychiatrist and the particular needs of the patient. Such suicidal levels may include total restraint or isolation in a "quiet" room where the patient cannot harm himself. Usually, under these circumstances the patient is stripped of belts, sharp instruments, and other materials that might be harmful to him.

Other assessments include need for medication, including type and dosage. Sleeping medication and medication for pain will be ordered if necessary. The patient's social needs will be assessed and orders written accordingly, often after review by a social worker. The patient may be allowed visits from some individuals and denied visits from others if they seem to be promoting or aggravating his mental disturbance. The patient may or may not be allowed phone calls, depending upon his condition.

Orders will be written for consultation with other physicians if warranted. These may include specialists in psychology, neurology, internal medicine, and surgery.

During hospitalization, the patient's needs may change. Modifications in orders and status should reflect these changes.

[c] The Right to Treatment

All patients admitted to psychiatric facilities have a right to adequate treatment. For the past two decades, the courts have confirmed this right, mainly for involuntarily committed patients, by holding that to hospitalize a person against his will without providing adequate treatment is tantamount to incarceration of an innocent person. Psychiatrists, however, do not distinguish between the voluntary and involuntary patient with respect to providing adequate treatment.[6] In some cases the courts have held that adequate treatment not only includes proper medication, proper security, and proper environment, but also the requirement that the staff maintain its continuing medical education to keep up with advances in the field of psychiatry.[7] The right to treatment was initially enunciated by Morton Birnbaum in 1960.[8] Several subsequent landmark cases have clearly defined that right for various purposes and in specific situations.[9]

---

[6] American Psychiatric Association, *Position Statement on the Right to Adequate Care and Treatment for the Mentally Ill and Mentally Retarded*, 134 AM. J. PSYCHIAT. 354 (March 1977).

[7] Davis v. Hubbard, 506 F. Supp. 915 (N.D. Ohio 1980).

[8] Birnbaum, *The Right to Treatment*, 46 A.B.A.J. 499 (May 1960).

[9] Wyatt v. Stickney, 325 F. Supp. 781 (M.D. Ala. 1971); Donaldson v. O'Connor, 493 F.2d 507 (5th Cir. 1974).

[d] The Right to Refuse Treatment

All patients have a right to refuse treatment if they are competent to so refuse, and if there is no emergency compelling forced treatment.[10] In the case of voluntary patients, the patient may leave treatment if he objects to the type of treatment offered. If the psychiatrist believes that the voluntary patient should remain in treatment, or should be converted to an involuntary patient because he poses a particular danger to himself or others, then such procedures should be instituted.

The involuntary patient cannot leave treatment voluntarily; however, the law does protect his rights by allowing him to refuse treatment that may be harmful to him if he is competent to so refuse, and if he does not pose an emergent threat to himself or others. Some courts have restricted the right to refuse treatment to treatment with psychotropic medication that may have long-term harmful side effects; e.g., tardive dyskinesia. Also, the courts have differed on the definitions of competency and emergency, as well as on whose responsibility it is to assess competency and the degree of emergency.[11] (Usually, the assessment of competency is made initially by the treating psychiatrist, and if challenged, it is determined by a court.)

Historically, the right to refuse treatment began as a religious right, wherein patients refused medication because such treatment was against their religious beliefs.[12]

[e] Confidentiality and the Right to Privacy

The patient's right to refuse treatment has often been considered a right of privacy against intrusion into his private thoughts, even if they are psychotic. Patients were deemed to have a right to the privacy of their hallucinations and delusions if they harmed no one as a result. Similarly, patients have a right to privacy of their medical records, in that such records may not be divulged without proper legal authority or without an *emergent* need to protect the patient or others.

The regulation of patient privacy has become even more stringently enforced by the Health Insurance Portability and Accountability Act (HIPAA) of 1996. As part of a broader act to regulate aspects of health insurance and the interchange of patient data in electronic form, the Privacy Rule (effective 2003) mandates: standardized formats for all patient health,

---

[10] Rogers v. Okin, 478 F. Supp. 1342 (D. Mass. 1979); Rennie v. Klein, 462 F.Supp. 1131 (D. N.J. 1979).

[11] *Id.*

[12] Winters v. Miller, 446 F.2d 65 (2d Cir. 1971).

administrative, and financial data; unique identifiers (ID numbers) for each healthcare entity, including individuals, employers, health plans and health care providers; and security mechanisms to ensure confidentiality and data integrity for any information that identifies an individual. This has led to the very close guarding of all patient information, including whether the patient is even in the hospital, released only to those whom the patient has designated or under special conditions. Exceptions include the exchange of information between physicians engaged in the treatment of the patient, as well as in emergencies and for the purposes of billing.

The patient's right to privacy dove-tails with the ethical requirement of confidentiality imposed upon practicing psychiatrists. The ethical standards of the American Psychiatric Association require the psychiatrist to maintain the confidentiality of the doctor-patient relationship unless he (1) is forced to divulge information because of an emergency that could lead to harm to the patient or to others, or (2) is compelled to divulge the information by order of the court.[13]

Patients are deemed in some states to waive their right to confidentiality when raising as an issue their mental state in criminal, personal injury, or domestic relations matters. In cases involving the treatment of drug and alcohol abuse, the courts have applied more stringent rules of confidentiality. Federal law protects the identity of, and information gathered from, such patients. More recently, standards of care in psychiatry have allowed greater flexibility in dealing with families of hospitalized psychiatric patients. The growing influence of the National Alliance for the Mentally Ill, comprised mostly of families, has become a major force in American psychiatry, encouraging more open communication about patients, including diagnosis, treatment, side effects of medication of patients where informed consent is given. This is especially important when patients are returned to live at home with families who need to know what to do about the day-to-day care of their family member.

[f] The Psychiatrist-patient Relationship

The psychiatrist-patient relationship is deemed to be a fiduciary one in which the psychiatrist "must do no harm to the patient." This is the first rule of both ethics and standard of care with respect to the psychiatrist's role.

The psychiatrist must not harm the patient by giving unnecessary or inappropriate medication or treatment. Further, the psychiatrist must not

---

[13] American Psychiatric Association, *Official Actions: Statement of Ethics*, 130 AM. J. PSYCHIAT. 1063 (September 1973).

maintain a social or sexual relationship with the patient during the course of active treatment. A psychiatrist cannot make proper medical decisions about a patient with whom he has such contact. (See § 6.06[2][d].)

Usually, there is a therapeutic "contract" created between the psychiatrist and patient that outlines the modalities of treatment and responsibilities of both parties. This contract may be modified when needs and situations change, but the modifications must be by mutual consent.

[g] Treatment Modalities

Treatment of the voluntary inpatient may consist of a number of different plans. Initially, the treatment is milieu; that is, the patient is removed from the community (and sometimes the source of his anxiety or depression) and placed in a safe, therapeutic environment. Next, the patient is given psychotherapy by an experienced, caring person—his psychiatrist. This treatment may include both individual and group psychotherapy, and may involve other mental health professionals in the hospital working in conjunction with the patient's psychiatrist. This team approach to therapy is quite common in most psychiatric hospitals.

A third form of treatment is medication, or a combination of medications. Often this therapy causes side effects that need to be counteracted by the use of still other medications. Traditionally, the use of dopamine-blocking antipsychotic medications (neuroleptics) has been the most problematic as these medications can result in the often-irreversible motor side effects of tardive dyskinesia. More recently the use of "atypical" antipsychotics with fewer movement side effects has become more common; increasingly these medications have been associated with alterations in blood sugar including frank diabetes mellitus. Thus, monitoring of a patient on medication must be continuous and stringent.

Electroconvulsive therapy is used in many hospitals for the treatment of refractory mood disorders and catatonia. Treatments are typically given every other day and for a variable length of time. Because of its controversial history, many states require a judicial order to administer this treatment when the patient lacks the capacity to give consent. Thus this treatment is usually given to such incapacitated or incompetent persons only when potentially life saving.

Other forms of treatment within the hospital for the voluntary patient may include occupational therapy, work therapy, music therapy, art therapy, and other such expressive therapies. This type of therapy is considered very important in many hospital treatment programs because it consumes most of the patient's in-hospital time. Further assessment of the patient's condition is made at this time by the specific therapists involved. Family therapy is often utilized as well, as is couple therapy, in helping the patient rehabilitate and prepare for his return to the community.

[h]   The Patient's Relationship with Other Members of the Professional Staff

In addition to the psychiatrist, the patient interacts with other members of the staff (as well as other patients). It is the responsibility of the staff to maintain the confidentiality of the patient's communications; however, there can be no secrecy in certain areas. Staff members should never agree with the patient to withhold information from other members of the treatment team. This creates dissidence and difficulty in maintaining coordinated treatment efforts. The treatment team should discuss the patient openly among themselves, but not beyond the team.

Consultation with other professionals may be essential to the well-being of the patient, but communication to third parties not directly involved in the treatment of the patient must be closely regulated. In most hospitals such communications are handled by a particular member of the treatment team, typically the primary physician.

[i]   Record-keeping

All patients must have adequate records of their hospitalization. These records must include an admission sheet, progress notes written regularly, physician's orders for medication and other treatment needs, nurses' notes, laboratory test results, consultation reports, and the discharge summary. All entries should be signed and dated. Most psychiatric records also contain a treatment plan that contains expectations of what the treatment should do for the patient. These treatment plans should be reviewed and revised on a regular basis, especially for long-term patients. The records also include a list of patients' rights for that particular hospital and signed consent forms.

Under the Freedom of Information Act, the patient now has a right to view his records. If the records are deemed to be harmful to the patient or likely to disturb his mental health, the psychiatrist may require that they be reviewed only with the psychiatrist present, so that he may help the patient deal with the information. Many psychiatrists now limit the information they put in the records because of the patients' right to review them. It would not be prudent to include damaging information unless absolutely necessary.

There should be only one set of records. Dual sets are not authorized. However, in teaching hospitals, a medical student's or resident's own notes about a patient may not necessarily be included in the official records. These should be destroyed or have information that may identify the patient removed after the teaching conference is over.

[j]   Security Measures for the Suicidal Patient

All patients admitted to psychiatric hospitals are assessed for suicidal ideation or potential, and the need for security measures. All hospitals have standards with respect to suicidal precautions. Many use a designation of *levels of care*. The highest level of suicidal precaution may be isolation and restraint with regular review by the physician or nurse.[14] Other levels might consist of confining the patient to his room or to the ward, placing an escort with him on a regular basis, or merely seeing that he has no access to dangerous objects.

It is not always possible to predict suicidal behavior, but the hospital psychiatrist must assess the potential for such behavior on a regular basis, especially when changes in levels of security are made. The most effective security within a hospital—and the most expensive—is one-on-one supervision; however, most hospitals cannot provide such a luxury for any extended period of time. In some cases, such a patient requiring close supervision may need to be transferred to a more secure facility. This is often the case when a patient on a relatively low-security medical or surgical floor is determined to be a suicide risk, in which case he is often transferred to a dedicated psychiatric ward as soon as is medically prudent.

Each staff member must be aware of the level of security of each patient for whom he is responsible, and must know his obligations to that patient within that level of security. These obligations are spelled out in rules available to all staff members.

[k]   Discharge Planning

Ideally, discharge planning begins at the time of admission. The patient's treatment program must be geared toward a successful discharge. Thus, all treatment developed for the patient should be directed toward rehabilitation with the goal of ultimate release from the hospital.

Goals beyond the hospital, however, may differ, depending on the patient's situation and the stress that led to the hospitalization in the first place. Discharge planning involves the social worker and other staff as well as the psychiatrist. Consultation with family members, employers, and

---

[14] TARDIFF, THE PSYCHIATRIC USES OF SECLUSION AND RESTRAINT (American Psychiatric Press 1984).

community agencies also may be necessary. Proper discharge planning will minimize the likelihood of the patient's return to the hospital.

As part of the discharge planning, families need to know, with the consent of the patient, what medication the patient is taking, what side effects may occur from the medication, and what effects may occur if the patient does not take his medication. Also, instructions to family members may include recommending locking away dangerous items such as guns, large knives, and toxic substances and poisons. [15]

Discharge of a voluntary patient must occur for clinical reasons and not for economic ones. Often, private hospitals will discharge a patient at the termination of his or her insurance coverage. This may coincide with the patient's clinical needs for discharge; however, if the patient requires further hospitalization, plans should be made for hospitalization at a state hospital or at a hospital that does not require private insurance.

In addition to the social and environmental planning, preparation for follow-up care in the community should be made. The patient should be referred to a therapist in the community or be followed by one of the staff psychiatrists who has cared for the patient in the hospital. Continuity of care is often important in psychiatric treatment. An outpatient visit shortly after discharge is advisable.

Discharge planning must be workable as well as theoretically sound. All discharge planning is done with the patient's informed consent.

[2] Care of Involuntarily Committed Patients

[a] Commitment Procedures

All states have rules regarding the involuntary commitment of mentally ill patients. All provide for emergency involuntary commitment, and for renewal of commitment status.

The emergency involuntary commitment laws require that the person be mentally ill, and as a result of the mental illness, that he clearly presents a danger of harm to himself or others. In most jurisdictions, the patient must have somehow demonstrated his violence or dangerousness. Danger to one's self may include suicide attempts, maiming or harming one's self directly, or passive neglect of one's self that leads to physical illness or disability. Such "danger" may include threats of harm to others with the ability to carry them out.

The patient who is committed to the hospital involuntarily has the right to hearings to determine if and when he can be released. A patient may be

---

[15] Petrila, J.P., and Sadoff, R.L., CONFIDENTIALITY AND THE FAMILY AS CAREGIVER, Hosp. & Comm. Psychiatry 4312 Feb. 1992 (pp. 136-139).

released from involuntary commitment prior to his designated period of confinement if the treating psychiatrist believes that his mental illness has remitted or improved to such a degree that he no longer poses a danger to himself or others.

The prior concept of the need for commitment, that the patient is mentally ill and in need of hospitalization, is no longer considered constitutional because of its vagueness. The requirement of dangerousness has now been added in almost all jurisdictions.

[b] The Concept of "Dangerousness"

"Dangerousness" is a poorly defined concept in the law, but it is a required element for a mentally ill person to be committed to a hospital against his will. Just possessing a serious mental illness is not sufficient for involuntary commitment. A person must be in danger of harm to himself or others.

Some jurisdictions define dangerousness as actually committing a violent act resulting in damage or injury. Other jurisdictions are not content to wait for the damage or injury to occur, and define dangerousness as the potential for causing violent or destructive behavior. In these cases, a psychiatrist is asked to make a prediction based on experience and reasonable medical certainty.

Some studies have shown that psychiatrists are seldom able to make accurate predictions of dangerousness in patients, [16] but more recent studies suggest that psychiatrists are able to make predictions with respect to imminent violent behavior or when violent behavior may occur within certain clinical conditions.[17]

[c] The Involuntary Patient's Rights

The competent involuntary patient has all the rights of the voluntary patient with respect to treatment, including the right to refuse medication if there is no emergency. Rights of the involuntarily committed patient include the right to due process of law with respect to the commitment. This includes the right to have regular hearings to determine the need to remain in the hospital, and the right to leave the hospital if the patient is no longer considered to be dangerous to himself or others.

---

[16] STEADMAN & COCOZZA, CAREERS OF THE CRIMINALLY INSANE: EXCESSIVE SOCIAL CONTROL OF DEVIANTS (Lexington Books 1974).

[17] J. MONAHAN, THE CLINICAL PREDICTION OF VIOLENT BEHAVIOR (U.S. Department of Health and Human Services 1981).

All the aspects of care of the voluntary patient (§§ 6.03[1] [a] through [k]) pertain to involuntarily committed patients as well.

[d]   Assessment of Competency

In most jurisdictions, patients who are involuntarily committed to the hospital are not deemed incompetent to manage their own affairs. There is no *presumption* of incompetency in any patient committed to the hospital except in Utah.

Competency can apply to various functions. Patients may be competent to vote, to hold property, to enter into business or contractual agreements, to marry, to divorce, to handle their children, or to make decisions about their treatment. It is the latter aspect of competency that is most relevant to the involuntarily committed patient. Can the patient aid in the decision-making about his treatment, and work with his psychiatrist in planning the treatment program? Also, can he give informed consent to the treatment offered? The patient can give his consent to such treatment only after being informed of its nature, side effects, and the expectation for improvement of his condition. Further, the patient must be told of alternative treatments and their side effects and expectations for improvement. The patient should be assessed for his competency to give such consent, and for his competency to refuse various types of treatment. If the involuntary patient is found to lack the capacity to refuse psychotropic medications in a non-emergency setting, a decision is made as to whether to treat over the patient's objection. In some states, a determination that the patient is incompetent to refuse and may be treated over objection is made judicially, while in others this determination is made by a number of physicians or a proceeding of hospital administrators.[18]

[e]   Discharge Planning

Discharge planning for involuntary patients proceeds similarly to the planning for the discharge of voluntary patients. From the time of admission or commitment, the treatment plan prepared for the patient is geared toward discharge. In some jurisdictions, a judge approves the discharge, but this is not necessary in most jurisdictions except in criminal cases where commitment follows a finding of not guilty by reason of insanity. However, some psychiatrists prefer to have judges make the decision about discharge.

---

[18] *See,* for example: Washington v. Harper, U.S. 110S.Ct. 1028, 108 L.Ed. 2d 178, 58 U.S.L.W. 4249 (February 27, 1990), rivers v. Kutz, 67 N.Y. 2d 485, 496 (1986). Newer relevant cases involving use of psychotropic medication in involuntary committed patients include U.S. v. Gomes, 289 F. 3rd 71 (2nd Cir. 2002) and U.S. v. Sell, 282 F. 3d 560 (8th Cir. 2002), vacated and remanded 123 S. Ct. 2174 (2003).

Some patients are not able to be discharged into the community immediately following their period of commitment to the hospital. They may be transferred to a less secure facility such as a minimum security hospital or a halfway house before final discharge. Such determinations are often informed by assessments by social workers and occupational therapists to determine the ability of the patient to safely live in increasingly unstructured settings.

Some states have enacted outpatient commitment statutes that allow for postdischarge involuntary treatment in the community. Unfortunately most of these statutes are not properly enforced, and there is no effective means of requiring a patient to comply with outpatient treatment short of a probation or parole system under which the psychiatrist has the option of calling the patient back to the hospital if he does not comply with outpatient treatment procedures.

If the psychiatrist is unsure about a patient's potential for violent behavior or self-destructive or suicidal behavior, the psychiatrist should defer discharge until the case is brought before the committing authority. In involuntary cases, it is the court that deprives the patient of liberty in the commitment. Psychiatrists may protect themselves from future lawsuits by bringing the case back to the committing authority for a comprehensive determination of potential violent or suicidal behavior by the patient when released — by having the court hear all testimony relating to the proposal for discharge. In many cases, the authority of the court to discharge the patient following such a comprehensive hearing will avert subsequent liability toward the psychiatrist or hospital if violent or suicidal behavior occurs following the court's order to discharge.

§ 6.04 Scope of Practice: Outpatient Psychiatry

[1] Private Practice

[a] Modalities of Treatment

The modalities of treatment in outpatient psychiatric practice include the same types of treatment rendered in the hospital except for certain ancillary therapies. There is no "milieu" therapy in outpatient psychiatry, unless one considers "day hospitalization" to fit this category. (Under this program, the patient returns home to sleep every night.) The usual modalities for outpatient practice are psychotherapy and medication. Electroconvulsive therapy may be given to outpatients, but it is not as usual today, as it was in the past. Family therapy, group therapy and couples therapy are common in outpatient treatment. Individual psychotherapy may take the form of supportive or psychodynamically-oriented psychotherapy of indefinite length or more time-limited modalities using cognitive, behavioural or cognitive-behavioral approaches.

[b] Frequency and Intensity of Treatment

Most outpatient treatment procedures call for weekly visits. Some patients are seen twice weekly, and those receiving psychoanalytic therapy may be seen four to five times a week. The frequency and intensity of treatment is determined by the nature of the illness and the needs of the patient. Depressed patients do better on weekly visits; however, in a crisis, some of these patients may need to be seen daily. Newer guidelines under managed care and HMO proposals have shortened the length of treatment and in some cases the frequency of treatment has decreased. Indeed, many psychiatrists that work under managed-care reimbursement have altered their practice to include only monthly visits to manage medications while delegating psychotherapy to non-physician therapists. As with the model of inpatient psychiatry, communication among the treating team is essential when the care is thus distributed among multiple therapists.

[c] Confidentiality

Outpatients require the same type of confidentiality as do inpatients. The psychiatrist should keep confidential that which he learns in the course of his treatment of the patient unless he is mandated to reveal this information by law or it becomes necessary to reveal it to protect the welfare of the patient or the community.

[d] Record-keeping

The psychiatrist's records should be written legibly and include the times the outpatient was seen, any changes in the patient's condition, the type and dosage of medication, and any side effects. Also, the records should contain information regarding payments of the psychiatrist's fees. Many psychiatrists with relationships to managed care companies find that their conformation to record-keeping standards provided by the insurer is a prerequisite to reimbursement.

[e] Termination of Treatment

Outpatient treatment usually terminates by mutual consent. Frequently, patients simply stop coming for treatment, but more often there is an agreement between the patient and the psychiatrist that therapy is finished. It is unlikely that the therapist would unilaterally terminate treatment without consent of the patient since that may constitute abandonment.

Occasionally, the psychiatrist believes that he can go no further with the patient, and will discuss this therapeutic "impasse" with the patient. In those instances, the therapist usually will refer the patient to another therapist or give the patient the names of three or four therapists from which to choose.

[2]   Community Mental Health Center Clinical Practice

Most community mental health clinics require financial eligibility for a patient to receive psychiatric treatment. They will not take patients who can afford private therapy. Some of these clinics, however, will consider patients eligible who require particular types of treatment that are not available elsewhere. These may include certain research efforts.

There are a number of mental health clinics in each community established by law to provide comprehensive mental health care to those unable to afford private care.

The methods and frequency of treatment in clinics are similar to those found in private outpatient practice. Here it is even more common to see the use of non-psychiatrists to conduct psychotherapy. Psychologists, social workers, psychiatric nurses and mental health specialists are often used as primary therapists, with the psychiatrist being utilized primarily for writing prescriptions and for brief visits with the patient in case of any difficulties with medication.

Record-keeping in clinics usually follows the same pattern as that in private outpatient treatment, although the requirements may be more stringent due to the greater number of staff members. The records should show the times the patient came for treatment, his responses, kinds, dosages, and side effects of medication, and changes in the patient's mental state or condition. Consultation with other professionals and utilization of ancillary therapy also should be noted in the records.

Confidentiality is maintained in outpatient clinic practice as it is in hospital practice and private outpatient care. The patient's right to privacy should be maintained throughout treatment. (Some state-affiliated clinics do have a computer system that records demographic data on the patients involved. No such data bank exists in the private outpatient sector.)

[a]   Commitment to Outpatient Treatment

Some jurisdictions have statutes under which patients can be committed to outpatient care (usually at clinics). The treatment is mandatory and the patient must attend or face contempt of court. In practice, however, there is very little enforcement of these statutes. Only if the therapist believes the patient is likely to become dangerous to himself or others will he ask a court to bring the patient in for medication or confinement.

Newer methods of aiding these patients are being developed, including house calls and longer-acting medication. The concept of forced outpatient commitment has become controversial following Kendra's law in New York State. Civil libertarians have challenged the concept as imposing on the civil rights of psychiatric outpatients.

[b]   Termination of Treatment

Termination of outpatient clinic treatment is similar to that in private outpatient treatment. The patient, with the assistance of the therapist, decides that treatment is no longer necessary. If the therapist believes the patient may be dangerous, however, he may have him committed to the hospital pending further investigation of his mental state. The therapist will not unilaterally discharge a patient who wishes to continue treatment.

Sometimes there may be personality conflicts that would suggest alternative therapeutic approaches. In these cases the psychiatrist will suggest to the patient that there is an impasse in therapy that probably can be overcome by referral to another therapist within the clinic or at another clinic.

§ 6.05   Malpractice Problems in Hospital Psychiatry

[1]   Administrative Procedures

[a]   Failure to Provide a Secure Environment

Patients admitted to a psychiatric hospital have the right to be treated in a secure manner. This means they have the right to be free of the violence of other patients, and also to be free from the effects of their own potential violence.

Individuals who show signs of violence will need to be confined or deterred from such behavior. Methods commonly used to control violent behavior include medication, seclusion, and restraint. Restraints vary in type, and may be either hard or soft. Hard restraints (leather straps) are rarely used except in extreme cases. They are usually placed on the four extremities. The soft restraint, or posey, is a cloth restraint that may be used on the extremities or around the chest or abdominal area. The old camisole or "strait-jacket" is rarely used today.

Regulations involve the careful monitoring of individuals who have been placed in seclusion or restraint.[19] Similarly, individuals who are restrained by medication require careful monitoring. Most hospitals have established guidelines for the utilization of such control procedures. Failure to follow these guidelines may be a deviation from the standard of care and grounds for malpractice.

Because of the concept of "least restrictive alternative of treatment consistent with the needs of the patient," the type of control mechanism must be carefully selected by the therapist. For example, one should not impose seclusion and restraint if one-on-one therapy or person-to-person counseling might suffice. Yet, brief periods of seclusion may be less restrictive than an injection of medication that could affect the patient for up to two weeks.

Suicide is by far the most frequent cause of lawsuits within a psychiatric hospital. Provision of a secure environment for the patient is geared toward the prevention of self-destructive behavior. Windows must be designed so that they do not break or push out. In some places, safety screens are used, and in others, a strong plastic window that cannot be broken. Doors remain locked at night on some wards to prevent patients from leaving inappropriately or in a confused manner. Where doors remain unlocked, there is often a psychiatric technician or aide whose job it is to see that nobody comes in or leaves unless authorized to do so.

Patients with grounds privileges must not be allowed to run off. A secure environment here involves an adequate number of escorts. Monitoring bathrooms is also important. Patients have killed themselves in hospital bathrooms by drowning, or by tying bathrobe belts around their necks and hanging themselves from pipes. In many hospitals, patients are not allowed alone in bathrooms if they are under "suicide watch."

The levels of observation and privilege must be established at the time of admission so that each staff member knows what his or her responsibilities are with respect to a particular patient.[20]

[b] Inappropriate Release of Records

The hospital staff has a duty not to divulge information about a patient unless the request is made by a duly authorized person. Such requests may come from the court or from third-party payers, as detailed in the Health Insurance Portability and Accountability Act Privacy Rule While the

---

[19] TARDIFF, *supra* note 10.

[20] *See generally*, Simon, R.I., Assessing and Managing Suicide Risk, APA Press, Wash. DC, 2004.

request must be responded to when mandated by law, the information given should be reviewed by the staff to be certain that it is appropriate. In most cases, the patient should be informed that the information is to be released.

Inappropriate disclosure of information may occur informally when staff members talk among themselves in non-secure areas of the hospital or outside the hospital. If the disclosure harms the patient, the hospital or staff may be liable.

Since patients have a right to the information in their records under the Freedom of Information Act, psychiatrists and staff members in psychiatric hospitals have become cautious about what information is put in the patient's records. It would be improper to withhold necessary information, but it would also be inappropriate to include unnecessary information that may be injurious to the patient. When the patient requests to see his records, he should be granted permission only after they are reviewed by the psychiatrist to be certain that the material will not harm the patient unduly. If the psychiatrist determines that there is potentially harmful material in the records, he may allow the patient to see the records, but only in the company of a responsible staff member who can deal with the possible emotional impact on the patient.

[c] Inappropriate Use of Seclusion or Restraints

For potentially violent or self-destructive patients, seclusion and restraint often may be necessary in the total treatment regimen. However, such methods must be properly administered. Monitoring by staff is necessary for all patients who are secluded or restrained.

Leaving a patient alone in a room for prolonged periods of time can lead to the patient's death. Other patients may come in and harm the patient, or the patient might harm himself (or someone else). Restraints themselves may also lead to adverse patient outcomes and so the restraints must be checked regularly and the patient must be monitored by a responsible staff member.[21] Federal regulation passed in 1999 requires the reporting of deaths proximal to restraint use for hospitals participating in the Medicare program; states have passed similar laws.[22]

---

[21] U.S. General Accounting Office. Mental health: improper restraint or seclusion places people at risk. (GAO publication Heh-99-176). Washington (DC): USGAO; 1999.

[22] Code of Federal Regulations at 42 CFR 482.13.

[2] Clinical Procedures

[a] Misdiagnosis

The psychiatrist can be liable for misdiagnosing a patient if that misdiagnosis leads to injury to the patient. However, many patients are given tentative diagnoses because their symptoms are not clear enough to fall into a particular pattern. Often, there is a differential diagnosis developed, and several possible "labels" may be given to the patient. The law allows the psychiatrist some clinical judgment in diagnosis.

Also, merely misdiagnosing a patient without causing him harm will not subject the psychiatrist to liability. The misdiagnosis has to result in negligent management that proves to be the proximate cause of any damage sustained by the patient. Such damage, however, would include delay in treatment that prolongs pain and suffering from the patient's mental illness.

[b] Medication Errors

If a patient is diagnosed as having anxiety, but in fact is depressed, and is given medication to help the anxiety, his depression may be worsened. Some psychiatrists do not believe in medication, only in long-term psychotherapy. Cases have been seen recently in which individuals with agitated depression, which is readily treated with antidepressant medication, were given only psychotherapy, which prolonged their illness.

A common problem today is tardive dyskinesia, a side effect of psychotropic medications used to treat schizophrenia. When using these medications, the psychiatrist has a duty to observe the patient regularly for this permanently disabling side effect. In order to avoid this side effect the newer generation of "atypical" antipsychotics has gained swift popularity. However, with their increased use it has become increasingly clear that while these medications offer significantly less likelihood of causing tardive dyskinesia, they have other possible adverse effects. In particular, and to varying degrees, the new antipsychotics have been linked to increased risk of sudden death and to elevations in blood glucose in some patients.[23] So, just as the monitoring of muscular movements of patients on older antipsychotics is essential to prevent progression of tardive dyskinesia, frequent monitoring of adverse effects is key to the judicious use of newer antipsychotics. The careful use of antipsychotics is increasingly necessary as these medications have gained popularity for use in a very broad number of clinical conditions, some unapproved by the FDA.

---

[23] Jeste et al. Neuropsychopharmacology. 2007 Jul 18; [Epub ahead of print].

Finally, the use of some medications to treat mental illness may be incompatible with the patient's occupation or lifestyle. Some patients should not be allowed to operate heavy machinery or drive while taking certain medications and should be so informed.

[c]   Failure to Obtain Necessary Consultation

Psychiatrists usually do not consult with other physicians as often as other specialists, mainly because of the problem of confidentiality. However, a number of organic illnesses may mask as psychiatric problems. The psychiatrist as a physician has the obligation to assess his patient from a total medical point of view, and is required to call in a medical consultant if the patient's symptoms or signs reflect the possibility of a metabolic, infectious or other organic disease process. It would be difficult to justify the inadequate treatment of a patient's non-psychiatric illness in a hospital where specialist consultation is available. Furthermore, a treating psychiatrist is expected to consult other psychiatrists if he does not have sufficient experience treating a particular mental illness. Usually there is a hierarchy in hospitals where the chief of service or supervisors are available to participate in the team treatment of such a patient. However, specific consultation may be required, especially in cases involving family, pediatric, adolescent, or forensic problems. One recent case involving the assessment of a 75 year old man with Dissociative Disorder NOS, led to a diagnosis of brain tumor when the symptoms changed abruptly and a neurological consult was obtained.

[d]   Communication Problems among Staff Members

One of the major problems in treating psychiatric patients involves the communication between members of the treatment team. There can be no favorites, no secrets, and no withholding holding of information from individual members. Also, the team members must be very clear in their communications with each other. Lawsuits frequently arise from miscommunications. Too often nurses do not call the psychiatrist when patients require a change in medication or security status. Also, malpractice claims frequently arise from psychiatrists and nurses failing to coordinate the patient's treatment program.

[e]   Improper Supervision of Psychiatric Residents

In most teaching hospitals, psychiatric inpatients are treated by psychiatric residents who are in training at the hospital. These residents are supervised by senior psychiatrists on the staff, and also by the psychiatrist who admitted the patient. However, much of the day-to-day treatment is performed by the resident without direct supervision. If the resident is negligent in his care of the patient, and the supervisor does not pick up on the problem, the patient may have a valid claim for malpractice. The resident in training is usually immune from such liability, but the attending psychiatrist or the supervisor is not immune.

All supervisors and preceptors in psychiatric training programs should be aware of their potential liability in supervising the work of a trainee. Often, preceptors do not actually see the patients they discuss with their students. It is advisable for the supervisor to have examined the patient on at least one occasion. It is difficult to defend the psychiatrist's position if he is supervising the work of a negligent resident involving treatment of a patient he has never seen.

[f] Disputed Charges

Patients should be told what the cost of their hospitalization or treatment will be. Patients become angry when they are sent high bills that they do not understand. Part of the informed consent doctrine may include telling the voluntary patient how much his treatment will cost so that he can consider it in making his decision to undergo therapy. In some cases, charges may be higher than the average for the particular community, and a board of physicians from the local medical society may have to be appointed to evaluate the charges.

[g] Failure to Obtain Informed Consent to Treatment

In psychiatric hospitals, the most commonly used treatments are drug therapy and psychotherapy. For the most part, psychiatrists do not obtain written informed consent from the patient for psychotherapy or for other milieu therapies (e.g., occupational therapy or rehabilitation therapy). Informed consent, however, is required for the use of somatic therapies including medications, electroshock, and other methods of treatment that might damage the patient physically.

Currently, psychiatrists in hospitals are clearly aware of the need for informed consent for electroconvulsive therapy, but many do not adhere to the usually strict rules of informed consent with respect to medication. Most medication can be given without harmful side effects; however, there are some psychotropic or neuroleptic drugs used in the treatment of schizophrenia that do have long-term, harmful side effects, specifically tardive dyskinesia. Patients should be informed about the potential for this particular side effect, as well as less serious problems such as dry mouth, constipation, slower urination and others that occasionally develop during drug therapy.

Failure to provide the proper information on which the patient can give a truly informed consent to such treatment may be the basis of a malpractice suit if the patient is damaged as a result.

[h] Failure to Prevent Suicide Attempts

All hospitals have established guidelines for treating patients who have suicidal potential. On admission, the patient is evaluated by the treatment team, including the psychiatrist whose responsibility it is to assign a level of security for that patient. If the patient is clearly suicidal, and is admitted as an emergency, he probably will need to be observed on the highest level of suicide precaution for the first twenty-four to forty-eight hours. The most dangerous time for suicidal patients is the first day or two when they are required to make an adjustment to the hospital. Once they have made such an adjustment, their suicidal potential is usually reassessed, and they may be placed on lower levels of security.

Levels of security on suicide precaution may range from one-on-one observation of the patient for the highest level, to placing him in a secure room without access to sharp instruments, belts, or similar objects. Sometimes a padded cell has to be used to prevent the patient from banging his head into the wall. Special duty nursing may be required in some cases.

As the patient traverses the levels of suicide precautions to the least restrictive, he should be reassessed before each change. It should be noted that some patients will successfully suicide even under the most stringent suicide precautions. Liability ensues when the hospital or its staff is negligent in implementing the appropriate suicide prevention measures.

[i] Failure to Place the Patient in a Secure Environment

As part of the psychiatrist's obligation to prevent harm to the patient, he is responsible for placing the patient in an environment appropriate to his condition. Attempting to treat a violent patient in a non-secure environment may lead to injury to other patients. It is the standard of care for psychiatrists in psychiatric hospitals to evaluate the mental condition of the patient on admission to determine where and how he should be treated within the hospital. The "doctrine of least restrictive setting for treatment" applies to those patients who are able to be treated in a non-secure environment. Cases of malpractice have occurred when a violent patient attacks other patients when his potential of violence was not adequately assessed or he was placed inappropriately.

[j] Failure to Warn Others about a Discharged Patient's Potential for Violence or Suicide

When a patient is returned to a family following hospitalization, the psychiatrist should discuss with them what they may expect of the patient. If there are any special requirements, such as regular medication to prevent regression and further violent or suicidal behavior, the family should be clearly informed. If the patient has doubts about himself, the family should be told how to deal with this, and should be given phone numbers to call for support in the event the patient becomes acutely disturbed or depressed.

If the patient has expressed hostile feelings toward members of his family of others in the community, under the doctrine of *Tarasoff v. Regents of the University of California*,[24] the psychiatrist has a duty to warn or protect these people. This would be necessary even if the patient has stopped making overt threats while in the hospital. More recent cases have expanded the psychiatrist's duty to warn individuals to a duty to protect the community. The cases require a specific threat of harm or an identifiable third-party victim.[25]

Some states have enacted legislation similar to *Tarasoff* where there is a duty to warn rather than a broader duty to protect. Since each state may have a variant of the *Tarasoff* concept, it is incumbent upon each psychiatrist to know the law regarding duty to warn or duty to protect in his particular jurisdiction.

[k] Improper Discharge

A number of lawsuits have been filed against hospitals and psychiatrists for negligently discharging patients who shortly thereafter commit suicide or harm someone. In these cases, the plaintiffs claim that since psychiatrists should be able to predict when their patients will cause harm, the discharge itself was negligent.[26]

---

[24] Tarasoff v. Regents of the Univ. of Calif., 551 P.2d 334 (Cal. 1976).

[25] *See, e.g.*, Schuster v. Altenberg, 144 Wis. 2d 233, 424 N.W.2d 159 (1988).

[26] *See, e.g.*, Naidu v. Laird, 539 A.2d 1064 (Del. 1988) (psychiatrist who discharged his patient without consulting the court was liable for the damages caused by the patient six months after discharge; because the patient was improperly discharged, the doctor should have known that he would likely cause damage in the community).

Violent behavior following discharge usually is presumed to have been caused by the patient's mental illness. This is not always the case. Some patients are treated effectively, and their illness abates or goes into remission; however, their potential for violence may remain.

In most cases where psychiatrists are uncertain about a patient's future behavior, they should bring the matter before an appropriate authority, such as a judge or mental health review officer, who can make the decision from a global point of view.

Many mental health acts have immunity doctrines for the treating psychiatrist and hospital that limit liability unless there is evidence of "gross negligence" or "wanton misconduct."

There are so many factors that determine a patient's future behavior that it is difficult to make such predictions accurately. If a psychiatrist believes a patient is no longer seriously mentally ill or not able to benefit from further hospitalization, and he can be treated effectively as an outpatient, under the doctrine of "least restrictive alternative of treatment," the psychiatrist is obliged to recommend discharge. However, the doctor must consider the clinical factors involved in future violent behaviour, including non-compliance with taking medication or the likely potential for the patient to return to drinking alcohol to excess or taking illicit drugs.

§ 6.06   Malpractice Problems in Outpatient Psychiatry

[1]   Administrative Procedures

[a]   Improper Disclosure of Information

Psychiatrists who treat outpatients are constantly bombarded with requests for information about their patients. Under ethical standards, the psychiatrist is obliged not to divulge information about a patient unless he is mandated by law or unless the information is needed to protect the patient or members of the community. An exception to this rule is the need for third party payers to have information about the patient to justify claims for benefits. It is also presumed in some jurisdictions that the patient waives his privilege to the psychiatrist's silence if he names the psychiatrist as a treating doctor in a lawsuit in which the patient's mental state is at issue. This includes personal injury, domestic relations, and criminal matters.

It is important for the psychiatrist to be aware of the circumstances surrounding a request for information on a patient. It also is important for the psychiatrist to obtain the patient's informed consent to release the information. This may be done either by having the patient sign a consent form or by sending the requested information to the patient with instructions that he send it on to the requesting party. Patients should be told at all times when such information is being released, especially in the current practice of managed care and HMO regulations which require disclosure of various information about the patient. To avoid the mishandling of information, psychiatric residency education stresses the knowledge of current regulations such as HIPAA.

[b] Failure to Keep Adequate Records

Psychiatrists have been criticized for failing to keep adequate records on outpatients. Often the records include only financial data or the fact that the patient came for therapy. Some psychiatrists purposely keep no records to avoid improper disclosure of information. Others, however, keep extensive notes that do contain information that may be damaging to the patient. Acceptable standards of record-keeping require the inclusion of the medication administered, changes in the patient's condition, side effects of medication, and similar important data. Even though the records may be inadequate, it is often difficult to prove in court that this was a proximate cause of any damage to the patient. It may look bad for the doctor, but it seldom is an issue in a lawsuit.

If records need to be changed, the changes also should adhere to acceptable standards. There should be no erasures or rubouts. One always should be able to see what has been changed. The proper method is to put one line through the erroneous record, correct it, and then date and initial the change.

[c] Failure to Obtain Proper Consultation

Psychiatrists often are loath to open their records to consultants. Psychotherapy is a very personal form of treatment that involves a one-on-one relationship. However, if the need arises, the psychiatrist must request consultation. He may require psychological tests to help him understand the psychodynamics of the patient. He may require a consultation with a psychopharmacologist who is more experienced in the use of a particular medication or combination of medications. More importantly, the psychiatrist may require a neurologic consultation to determine whether his patient has organic brain syndrome or brain tumor. He also may require other tests such as the EEG, CT scan, or MRI. In some cases, he may simply require consultation with a more experienced psychiatrist to help him deal more effectively with the patient generally.

Failure to obtain proper consultation when required may lead to damage to the patient and a successful malpractice claim.

[2] Clinical Procedures

[a] Improper Diagnosis

Psychiatrists are known to diagnose patients improperly. Most serious is the failure to make a diagnosis that requires immediate treatment. Failure to treat effectively and timely can result in injury to the patient, and would be grounds for malpractice. Diagnosing improperly can also lead to the wrong form of medication or treatment, and this may be harmful to the patient. For example, diagnosing a depressed patient as having anxiety and prescribing medication that is contraindicated in depression can result in suicide. Also misdiagnosing a bipolar patient as depressed and thus treating with an antidepressant with a mood stabilizer could result in a manic attack that could damage the patient.

This is important only if a misdiagnosis leads to faulty treatment and damage to the patient. However, it is common in the early stages of psychosis to confuse bipolar disorder with various forms of schizophrenia. One should perhaps be cautious in labelling a psychotic individual and perhaps remain with a more generic form of diagnosis such as "psychotic disorder not otherwise specified" until the illness begins to take clearer form either as schizophrenia or as bipolar disorder.

[b] Inappropriate Use of Medication

The psychiatrist may prescribe the wrong form of medication or wrong combinations of medication. Also, psychiatrists have been held liable for giving restricted medication too freely when a less addicting form would suffice. Some psychiatrists use methamphetamines to accelerate treatment in serious depression, and others will use narcotics to augment treatment of patients who are overly anxious and have low pain thresholds.

Some psychiatrists will use exceedingly high doses of a medication, well beyond the limits recommended in the *Physicians' Desk Reference (PDR)*. They tend to justify this by citing their own research experience or the particular needs of the patient. Use of a medication that does not conform to the recommendations in the *PDR*, or to the experience of colleagues in the community, can lead to malpractice if the patient is harmed in the process.

It is difficult to know the effect of combinations of medications sometimes used in psychiatric treatment. Some combinations have been shown to be risky, and warnings have been issued against their use. These include the concurrent use of several types of antidepressants, especially when tricyclic antidepressants or MAO inhibitors are among the agents used. Also, patients who use MAO inhibitors should be educated in how to adhere to a diet low in tyramine, a substance found in red wine and many aged foods. Such a combination can result in an elevated blood pressure and possibly a stroke.

Occasionally, dosages of medication must be geared to the individual needs of the patient, which in some cases might differ from established guidelines. Any deviation from the standards should be noted in the patient's record, together with an explanation. Also, there should be careful monitoring of any patient who is receiving any such medication.[27]

[c] Failure to Obtain Informed Consent

In outpatient psychiatric treatment, failure to obtain informed consent is not as much a problem as it is in inpatient psychiatry. Occasionally, electroshock therapy will be given on an outpatient basis, and drug therapy is common. Both require the patient's informed consent.

Obtaining informed consent for treatment must include providing the patient with all the information required for him to understand the purpose of his therapy. The discussion must be conducted in terms the patient understands. And if he is competent, he should sign the necessary forms. The information given must include alternate methods of treatment, if available, and their side effects and likelihood of success. And, of course, the patient must be informed of the anticipated side effects, morbidity rates, and treatment success of the procedure selected.

The psychiatrist also should outline at the beginning of any treatment (whether individual psychotherapy, group psychotherapy or other treatment) the limits of confidentiality. Basically, the psychiatrist must keep information as to the patient's treatment undisclosed unless he is mandated to reveal it by law or to protect the welfare of the community or the patient. These exceptions must be explained to the patient at the beginning so that he knows that there is no absolute secrecy in the relationship.

[d] Sexual Contact with Patients

The ethical standards of all professional therapy organizations prohibit sexual contact between therapist and patient. This includes the American Psychiatric Association, the American Psychological Association, and those associations of social workers and other professional therapists. Any sexual contact by the therapist that is inappropriate, will likely lead to damage to the patient, and therefore is grounds for malpractice.

---

[27] DiGiacomo, Joseph N. and Sadoff, Robert L., Managing Malpractice Risks during Psychopharmacologic Treatment in Essential Pharmacology, Volume Three, No. 1, 1999, pp. 65-89.

Sexual contact usually arises out of a mishandling of the *transference phenomenon*. In all therapy situations, it is presumed that some degree of this "phenomenon" develops between the patient and the therapist. The patient develops an unusually strong dependence upon the therapist, and a devout trust that the therapist would never do anything to harm her. Thus, if the therapist approaches the patient sexually, she may respond because she believes the therapist is treating her in her own best interests. Only after some time may the patient realize that she is not being helped by this relationship, but is actually being harmed.

Some psychiatrists admit to sexual contact with their patients because they "had little control over their urges," or because they "fell in love." More commonly, however, psychiatrists will attempt to justify sexual contact for "therapeutic reasons." They contend that the patient was sexually inhibited, and by this behavioral approach they could help the patient become less inhibited and more active sexually, thereby permitting the patient to lead a more complete and happier life. In fact, the contact almost always has a negative effect upon the patient. She develops a mistrust of persons in authority, and has difficulty returning to therapy, which she then needs even more.

Sexual relations with a patient became an issue in psychiatric malpractice actions with the 1976 case of *Roy v. Hartogs*.[28] Undoubtedly, there have been many instances of sexual contact, but since *Hartogs*, more patients have been surfacing to make such accusations.

Is a sexual relationship following the termination of therapy inappropriate? Some commentators say yes, in view of the psychiatrist's intimate knowledge of the patient and the potential for exploitation because of the authoritarian role the psychiatrist played in the patient's life. However, whether it should be the basis for a lawsuit may depend on the amount of time that has elapsed between the termination of treatment and the sexual contact. It is also more common for a lawsuit to occur, not as a result of the sexual contact following the termination of treatment, but because the sexual contact had been terminated by the former therapist. Some former therapists end up having long term meaningful relationships with former patients and some have even married former patients. Such cases must be assessed individually.

The American Psychiatric Association has declared that it is "almost always" unethical for a psychiatrist to have sexual relations with a former patient.[29]

---

[28]   Roy v. Hartogs, 381 N.Y.S.2d 587 (N.Y. Sup. Ct. 1976).

[29]   ADDENDUM TO STATEMENT ON ETHICS FOR PSYCHIATRISTS (American Psychiatric Association, Washington, D.C. 1991).

[e] Failure to Warn an Intended Victim of a Patient's Violent Intent

Under the *Tarasoff* doctrine,[30] the psychiatrist has a special relationship with the patient that creates a duty to protect an intended victim from the patient's violence. If the patient tells the therapist that he intends to harm a particular third party, and the therapist believes that the patient will do so, the therapist is obliged to protect that person. He may do so in several ways. The original *Tarasoff* rule required the psychiatrist to warn the intended victim; however, this could be a breach of confidentiality that could prove damaging to the patient. For example, the third party might be more violent than the patient, and upon being warned by the psychiatrist, might attack the patient. If time permits, other means of protecting the intended victim should be instituted before an actual warning. The doctor might try to influence the patient to come in for counseling. If the patient does not agree to come voluntarily, the psychiatrist might attempt commitment proceedings with the help of the patient's family or the police department.

In 1983, California expanded the *Tarasoff* rule to include a foreseeable victim even though the patient never issued a threat against that particular person.[31] Other courts have rejected *Tarasoff* where a patient issued a general threat rather than a particular threat against a particular individual.[32]

One of the difficulties in the *Tarasoff* situation is the ability to predict violent behavior. Psychiatrists are expected by the public to predict such behavior in their patients, and when they are not able to do so and the patient becomes violent, the psychiatrist is sued for negligence. In the case of *Brady v. Hopper,* [33]for example, the accusation was made that Dr. Hopper did not properly assess the potential violence of his patient, John W. Hinckley, Jr., in that he should have known that Hinckley would try to impress actress Jodie Foster by attempting to assassinate the President of the United States. The United States District Court in Denver found no basis in law to uphold such an accusation, and the Court of Appeals upheld the lower court's ruling, suggesting that the courts do not feel that psychiatrists can make these predictions without a proper foundation.

[f] Failure to Hospitalize Suicidal Patients

If a severely depressed patient commits suicide, the family often will sue the psychiatrist on the grounds that he was not carefully monitoring the

---

[30] Tarasoff v. Regents of the Univ. of Calif., 551 P.2d 334 (Cal. 1976).

[31] Jablonski v. United States, 712 F.2d 391 (9th Cir. 1983).

[32] Hopewell v. Adebimpe, 130 Pitt. Leg. J. 107 (1981). *See also* Bardini v. Kim, 390 N.W.2d 218 (Minn. App. 1986).

[33] Brady v. Hopper, 570 F. Supp. 1333 (M.D. Colo. 1983).

patient's condition. It is often difficult for the psychiatrist to know when a patient is going to attempt suicide. Patients frequently withhold this information from their therapists, yet discuss it openly with family or friends. It is important that this information is communicated to the psychiatrist.

If it can be shown that the psychiatrist clearly ignored a warning that the patient was suicidal, even though he claims the defense of "clinical judgment," the family could have a basis for a successful malpractice suit.[34]

The changes in the law that now prohibit involuntary commitment except when the patient is both mentally ill and dangerous inhibit some psychiatrists from attempting involuntary hospitalization of their patients. They may request a patient to admit himself into the hospital, but if the patient refuses, they often back down, concerned that if they attempt to commit the patient and are unsuccessful, they will lose the patient, who may then go without any therapy. Frequently, therefore, a psychiatrist continues to treat a person as an outpatient when hospitalization is obviously required. Psychiatrists should bring these patients to the attention of a court for determination of the criteria for involuntary commitment.

[g] Repressed Memories

In the 1980s, a number of cases arose of repressed memory of early sexual abuse. These are sometimes referred to as "False Memory Syndrome" cases.

Initially, patients were suing their parents and others whom they believed had sexually abused them when they were younger. The statute of limitations was tolled because the courts ruled the patient had repressed the memory until she learned of the abuse while in therapy and could not have filed suit within the required two years. Most of these cases were successfully defended as the memories were seen to be "false" and not able to be corroborated by external means.

The accusations then switched from the parents or the alleged perpetrators to the psychotherapists who were blamed for bringing out these "false memories." During the past several years, a number of psychiatrists have been successfully sued for initiating false memories that led to damage to parents and to patients. Psychotherapists have become increasingly cautious about encouraging female patients with eating disorders and/or sexual disorders from "remembering" the early sexual abuse that "must have been the cause" of such disorders. Most recently, these cases have disappeared as therapists have become more cautious with such patients.

---

[34] *See generally*, Simon, R.I. Assessing and Managing Suicide Risk: Guidelines for Clinically Based Risk Management. APA Press, Wash. DC. 2004.

CHAPTER 7

GENERAL SURGERY*
L. Jean Dunegan, MD, JD, FCLM

SYNOPSIS

---

* An earlier version of this chapter was written by John T. Burroughs, MD, JD.

[5]   Thyroid Surgery
[6]   Surgery on the Parathyroids
[7]   Surgery on the Submaxillary Glands
[8]   Breast Surgery
      [a] Surgical Options for Carcinoma of the Breast
[9]   Biopsies of the Cervical Lymph Nodes
[10] Gastric Surgery
[11] Surgery on the Biliary Tract
[12] Appendectomies
[13] Other Surgery Involving the Intestinal Tract
[14] Blunt Abdominal Trauma
[15] Shorter Hospital Stays

---

§ 7.01 Training and Certification

[1] Introduction

Surgery has been legally described as "the art or practice of healing by manual operation; that branch of medical science which treats by mechanical or operative measures for healing diseases, deformities or injuries."[1] The technical artistry that the early surgeons displayed was initially quite sufficient; soon, however, the added requirement of patient management (both pre and post-op) by the surgeon was embraced. Today, nowhere are the intellectual and technological advances in medicine more apparent than in the form and quality of care provided in operating rooms and intensive care units across the country.

The general surgeon once performed surgical procedures on any and all parts of the body, but the dramatic advances in medical knowledge and technology over the past four decades has resulted in infinitely more complex operative tools, techniques, and procedures. Minimally invasive surgery advances are being accomplished on a nearly daily basis and the general surgeon must continuously update his skills in order to remain competent. Many subspecialties, in addition to minimally invasive/ endoscopic surgery, are recognized: cardiac, thoracic, vascular, neurologic, orthopedic, obstetric and gynecologic, urologic, ophthalmologic, plastic, abdominal, colo-rectal, and otolaryngologic. Each of these specialties has a national board whose function is to certify those individuals who have satisfied certain specific programs of training and experience as described further in [2] and [3] of §7.01 below.

---

[1] BLACK'S LAW DICTIONARY (4th ed).

[2]   Medical Training

All physicians must attend and complete the required courses given at an accredited school of medicine or osteopathy and pass the examination given by the licensing board of either medicine or osteopathy in whatever jurisdiction he wishes to practice. This license gives him permission to practice medicine and surgery in that jurisdiction.

Allopathic and osteopathic medical schools, while distinct from each other in name, include identical subjects and substantive materials in their academic programs. For all practical purposes, the knowledge gained by the students is similar. As long as the two disciplines are separately recognized, there will be certifying boards for each; i.e., the American Board of Surgery and the American Board of Osteopathic Surgery. However, there are many graduates of osteopathic schools who obtain their specialty training from medical residency programs and become eligible for certification by the medical specialty boards upon successful completion. Also, some hospitals accept the osteopathic boards as indicia of formal training and experience in a specialty.

While a license to practice medicine gives the licensee the opportunity to perform surgery, the granting of clinical privileges to a physician to operate in a hospital is hospital-specific and based upon review and approval of his or her current competence in specifically defined treatment areas and procedures. Medical board certification is a recognized benchmark, but it cannot be the only criteria relied upon for granting privileges. Documentation of knowledge, skill, training, experience, competence and personal integrity are determinative.[2]

[3]   Surgical Training

This certification process is based upon postgraduate residency training in programs associated with accredited medical schools and specifically approved by each examining specialty board. Training requires five years, sometimes more, in a program where, year-by-year, the resident assumes more independence and responsibility in training those more junior until the final, senior year when he or she becomes the responsible, "senior" resident conducting all the affairs of the particular surgical service. The entire period of training is closely supervised and monitored by the attending surgeons on the particular service. The chief surgeon must submit written notification to the specialty board that the resident has successfully completed training and

---

[2] Johnson v. Misericordia Hosp., 99 Wis. 2d 708, 301 N.W.2d 156 (1981).

is qualified to sit for the boards. The examination may be oral, although frequently it is both written and oral, requiring several days to administer.

The American Board of Surgery (ABS) is an independent, non-profit organization founded in 1937 for the purpose of certifying surgeons who have met a defined standard of education, training, and knowledge. This board certifies surgeons in the fields of general, vascular and pediatric surgery as well as surgical critical care and surgery of the hand. The ABS is one of the 24 member boards of the American Board of Medical Specialties. As of July 1, 2008, applicants completing surgery residency in June 2009 who apply for the 2009 surgery qualifying examination must:

- have spent over 5 years in an accredited surgery program, no less than 42 months devoted to the essential content areas of surgery (general surgery)
- have completed all chief year rotations in the essential content areas, thoracic surgery or   transplantation, with no more than 4 months devoted to any one area
- Have been the operating surgeon for a minimum of 750 operative procedures in 5 years and for a minimum of 150 operative procedures in the chief resident year. Residents may count up to 50 cases as teaching assistant toward the 750 total; however, these cases may not be counted toward the 150 'chief year' cases

[4] The Status of Board Certification

As a rule, if the physician fails the examination three times within a designated period of years, he or she is no longer eligible to sit for the examination until he or she has received additional approved training in an accredited program. Such information may be important to explore in a medical malpractice action relative to the competence of a defendant or testifying medical expert witness.

[5] Importance of Certification

When a surgeon applies for hospital staff appointment, all JCAHCO (Joint Commission on Accreditation of Healthcare Organizations)-approved hospitals, and most of the remaining institutions, give primary consideration to board certification in granting surgical privileges. Also, there is a national standard for hospitals recognized by the courts, frequently phrased as the "reasonably prudent hospital operation under similar circumstances."[3]

---

[3] Shilkret v. Annapolis Emergency Hosp. Ass'n, 276 Md. 187, 349 A.2d 245 (1975).

Once staff appointment is contemplated, each surgeon must submit a specific list of operations for which he or she is requesting privileges to perform. The Medical Staff By-Laws will contain the specific committees and steps in the appointment procedure. Usually, they require that specific privileges will be determined by the Credentials Committee. The appointment will then proceed through the Medical Executive Committee and the governing board of the hospital. Hospitals are frequently named defendants in surgical negligence actions, and since they will be held responsible for negligent appointment of a surgeon whose training, knowledge, judgment, competence, experience, or skill is inadequate, great pains are taken to screen the physician and his specific capabilities. The Wisconsin Supreme Court, in *Johnson v. Misericordia Hospital* stated:

In summary, we hold the hospital owes a duty to its patients to exercise reasonable care in the selection of its medical staff and in granting specialized privileges. The final appointing authority resides in the hospital's governing body, although it must rely upon the medical staff and in particular the credentials committee (or committee of the whole) to investigate and evaluate an applicant's qualifications for the requested privileges. However, the delegation of the responsibility to investigate and evaluate the professional competence of applicants for clinical privileges does not relieve the governing body of its duty to appoint only qualified physicians and surgeons to its medical staff and periodically monitor and review their competency. The credentials committee (or committee of the whole) must investigate the qualifications of applicants. The facts of this case demonstrate that a hospital should, at a minimum, require completion of the application and verify the accuracy of the applicant's statements, especially in regard to his medical education, training and experience. Additionally, it should: (1) solicit information from the applicant's peers, including those not referenced in his application, who are knowledgeable about his education, training, experience, health, competence and ethical character; (2) determine if the applicant is currently licensed to practice in this state and if his licensure or registration has been or is currently being challenged; and (3) inquire whether the applicant has been involved in any adverse malpractice action and whether he has experienced a loss of medical organization membership or medical privileges or membership at any other hospital. The investigating committee must also evaluate the information gained through its inquiries and make a reasonable judgment as to the approval or denial of each application for staff privileges. The hospital will be charged with gaining and evaluating the knowledge that would have been acquired had it exercised ordinary care in investigating its medical staff applicants and the hospital's failure to exercise that degree of care, skill and judgment that is exercised by the average hospital in approving an applicant's request for privileges is negligence. This is not to say that hospitals are *insurers* of the competence of their medical staff, for a hospital will not be negligent if it exercises the noted standard of care in selecting its staff. (Footnotes omitted.)

In rural hospitals, surgical procedures are sometimes performed by practitioners without formal surgical training. In the past this was often routine but is much less prevalent in the recent decade. These practitioners were often the stalwarts of the hospital and performed many operations such as removing benign skin tumors, repairing a routine hernia, and the like. Some hospitals do allow more major surgery by such physicians with long-standing demonstration of competence. Whenever any physician, certified or not, performs a surgical procedure within the scope of a general surgeon, the standard of care to which he or she will be held is that of a board-certified general surgeon possessing ordinary knowledge, skill, training, and experience.

§ 7.02 Negligence

[1] Standard of Care

As the technological advances improve the environment of safety for surgical patients they raise the standard of care progressively. Intraoperative neurophysiological monitoring (IONM), for example, has made great strides in safety for those having spinal or intracranial operations. The need for hospitals to provide the latest equipment to meet the 'standard' (even for operations that may be much less risky) is one of the many issues that make medicine the multi-billion dollar industry that it has become.

The standard for acceptable care and treatment by a physician is based upon that care and treatment that would be given by a similarly trained doctor possessing ordinary knowledge, skill, training and experience under the same or similar circumstances. Since medical knowledge is not understood by the lay person, testimony establishing a standard of care must be given by a medical witness with specific expert qualifications relevant to the case at bar. Infrequently the doctrine of *res ipsa loquitur* may apply (*see* §7.02 [3]).

Evidence based medicine has made its mark on surgical care and education. Tradition-based care ("my old chief taught me that…") has now given way to evidence based behavior ("this study shows that…."). A competent surgeon in the 21st century must be able to apply the best of current surgical thinking to the practice of modern surgery.

There is a division among jurisdictions as to whether the applicable standard of care is specific to the locality in question or is a national standard. Because of the numerous *specialized* fields that are taught in all medical schools, in nationally uniform residency training programs and national seminars, the trend has been more and more to accept a national rather than a local standard. And since a patient relies upon the requirements of additional training for specialization, a physician who holds himself out as a specialist in a particular area of medicine will be held to the higher standard of care applicable to a board—certified specialist possessing ordinary knowledge, training, skill, and experience in that specialty. There are jurisdictional variations where locality rules are still observed to varying degrees. For example, in Idaho a national standard is applied, but an expert witness must have personal knowledge as to whether or not local, acceptable standards of care by the specialists in that particular locality differ from the national standards. In the absence of such personal knowledge, an expert is judged incompetent to testify.[4]

One of the most frequent defense arguments is that the physician used his "best judgment." There is confusion in court decisions as to the meaning of the "best judgment" rule, and misunderstanding of its true meaning has resulted in conflicting results. Conceptually, the standard should track the analysis applied in consideration of the respectable minority exception to a negligent act. The latter may be illustrated by demonstrating that, if there are two *acceptable* methods of treatment that a physician might use under a certain set of circumstances, there is no negligence in choosing the lesser-used method so long as it is shown that there is a respectable minority of practitioners whose application of that course of treatment would not be negligent, even though the outcome of applying the course of treatment in the case at bar was bad. But the confusion seems to be in an understanding by the court or jury that best judgment should only apply where the course of treatment did follow acceptable standards under the circumstances extant. It is a broad area and includes such aspects as consideration of an adequate data base for acceptable application of the course of treatment chosen, as well as the clear understanding of the application, in fact, of that choice of treatment under all of the clinical circumstances. The appropriateness of the best judgment rule was discussed in *Sewell v. United States.*[5]

In that case, Chief Judge Tom Stagg of the United States District Court of the Western Division of Louisiana found that there was inadequate basis to find for the argument that the physicians used their best judgment, after consideration and careful analysis of all the evidence. The case has been

---

[4] Buck v. St. Clair, 108 Idaho 743, 702 P.2d 781 (1985). *See also* Grimes v. Green, 746 P.2d 978 (Idaho 1987).

[5] 629 F. Supp. 448 (W.D. La. 1986).

widely applied in the Fifth Circuit and has been adapted as the lead case in a decision by the Supreme Court of Louisiana.[6]

The standard of care applied in any given medical trial may vary with the testimony of the defendant doctors and expert witnesses. Variations can create bad outcomes for either plaintiff or defendant, since the jury relies upon the testimony presented in the trial. There are persuasive (sometimes called expert witnesses who testify frequently on both sides — "hired guns") who can influence juries to reach unsound conclusions.

A significant development in the last several years is the establishment of practice standards or guidelines. Patient outcome analyses have helped to develop such standards and Congress, with the creation of AHCPR (Agency for Health Care Policy and Research) as a third major subdivision of Health and Human Services, has spurred their development in all medical disciplines. These standards will be admissible as some evidence of the applicable standard of care, but the specific applicable standard of care will depend upon all the evidence in each instance. However, there should be substantial improvement in consistency of decisions in medical negligence cases.[7]

Even when there is a national standard as established in a specialty, some courts have found the standard itself was not "reasonable." A higher standard was applied in two leading examples, *Helling v. Carey*[8] and *Incollingo v. Ewing*.[9]

In *Helling*, the Supreme Court of Washington held that ophthalmologists were liable in spite of the fact that they followed an established and stable standard in that specialty of not examining for glaucoma in patients less than forty years of age. The court, applying a risk-benefit analysis, concluded that this standard was unreasonable, since evidence presented at trial demonstrated that one in 25,000 persons developed asymptomatic glaucoma at an early age and that the testing for it carried no risk or discomfort. In *Incollingo*, the Pennsylvania Supreme Court ruled that the care by the defendant physician was unreasonable, even though he followed the local practice of prescribing chloramphenicol contradictory to some of the label warnings. Although neither case involved general surgery, there could well be similar judicial rulings in cases with similar fact situations.

[2] Proximate Cause

This element of the law of negligence is most difficult and confusing. Not infrequently it is the key area in negligence litigation, and very often it is the

---

[6] Martin v. East Jefferson Gen. Hosp., 582 So. 2d 1272 (La. 1991).

[7] J.T Burroughs, Practice Standards: Legal Implications, in LEGAL MEDICINE 179-90 (1992).

[8] 83 Wash. 2d 514, 519 P.2d 981 (1974), 67 A.L.R.3d 175.

[9] 444 Pa. 263, 282 A.2d 206, aff'd, 444 Pa. 299, 282 A.2d 255 (1971).

critical issue in medical malpractice actions. To compound the legal difficulties, proximate cause is a difficult theory for the jury to comprehend. Trials abound where the jury, totally confused over proximate cause, either ignored or misapplied the law, or came up with their own version, frequently with an inappropriate result. Lawyers and judges also struggle with the problem at trial. Many appeals center upon allegedly faulty and inappropriate jury instructions on proximate cause. The most important issue for the attorney is *clarity* regarding the different definitions that comprise its broad scope. The legal burden of proof subdivides into four general levels, which vary on the difficulty of proof spectrum from quite easy to complex and arduous. Jurisdictional variations also exist within these four identifiable levels as to the applicable law of proximate cause. A brief review, in order of decreasing difficulty, follows:

[a] *"But For"*

The large number of jurisdictions in the United States still follow this definition of proximate cause. The burden of proof of the elements of negligence in civil law is the preponderance of the evidence; i.e., just ever so slightly more likely than not that there was a breach of duty and the error proximately caused the harm. Frequently used phrases to describe this burden include "more likely than not," "reasonable degree of medical certainty," "49-51 percent," and "better than just 50-50." In those jurisdictions following the "but for" level of legally defined causation, the plaintiff must establish, by preponderance of the evidence, that the damages would not have occurred *but for* the negligent act, which might have been only one act among several that occurred.[10]

[b] *"Substantial Factor"*

In those jurisdictions following the substantial factor level of proximate cause, the same preponderance of evidence is applicable. But it is not necessary to prove that the damages would not have occurred *but for* the negligent act; more easily, harm would not have occurred unless the identified negligent act was a *substantial* (material) *factor* causing the harm, although there may have been other acts or omissions that could have also contributed or led to the injury or loss of life.

---

[10] Gooding v. University Hosp. Bldg., 445 So. 2d 1015 (Fla. 1984); Weimer v. Hetrick, 309 Md. 536, 525 A.2d 643 (1987).

[c]   *"Lost Chance Doctrine"*

The rule uniformly has been that proximate cause cannot be found for harm due to a negligent act unless it was more likely than not that the act caused the harm. This majority rule is known as the 'but for" test: the negligently injured patient must prove that the chance for recovery/survival was probable, was more likely than not, or was better than even. To find otherwise is thought to unfairly impose a liability burden based on unquantifiable possibilities. Under this rule a plaintiff with less than a 50/50 chance cannot be harmed to a compensable degree by negligent care.

A different doctrine is illustrated by the seminal case of *Hicks v. United States.*[11]

In *Hicks*, the patient died of acute high intestinal obstruction from an internal abdominal herniation caused by a congenital defect in the peritoneal lining. The court, in discussing whether or not causation was proven or was merely speculation, said:

> When a defendant's negligent action or inaction has effectively terminated a person's chance of survival, it does not lie in the defendant's mouth to raise conjectures as to the measure of the chances that he has put beyond the possibility of realization. If there is any *substantial* possibility of survival and the defendant has destroyed it, he is answerable.[12]
> (*Emphasis added*).

In *Hicks*, the plaintiff's two experts testified "categorically that if operated on promptly, Mrs. Greitens would have survived, and this is nowhere contradicted by the government expert."[13]

Thus, the burden of proof in *Hicks* was a substantial factor. In some jurisdictions, decisions espousing "lost chance" take the position that there is valid proximate cause even if the loss of a chance was less than probable.[14]

In *Thompson v. Sun City Community Hospital,*[15] the court said:

---

[11] 368 F.2d 626 (4th Cir. 1966).

[12] *Id.* at 634.

[13] *Id.*

[14] Waffen v. United States Dep't of Health and Human Servs., 799 F.2d 9112 (4th Cir. 1984); Thompson v. Sun City Commun. Hosp., 141 Ariz. 597, 688 P.2d 605 (1984); Roberson v. Counselman, 235 Kan. 1006, 686 P.2d 149 (1984); Evers v. Dollinger, 95 N.J. 399, 471 A.2d 405 (1984).

[15] 141 Ariz. 597, 688 P.2d 605 (1984).

[E]ven if the evidence permits only a finding that the defendant's negligence increased the risk of harm or deprived plaintiff of some significant chance of survival or better recovery, it is left for the jury to decide whether there is a probability that defendant's negligence was a cause in fact of the injury.[16]

[d] *"Increased Risk"*

Other jurisdictions have taken this relaxed burden of proof of proximate cause a step farther, allowing recovery when there was an "increased risk" as enunciated in Section 323(a) of the *Restatement (Second) of Torts*. There is considerable confusion in the application of this concept and in differentiating it clearly from cases citing *Hicks* but not requiring probability. It comes into play primarily in medical negligence cases where a patient who is already suffering from a pre-existing injury or illness claims treatment below the standard of practice. Such situations make it virtually impossible to prove causation through demonstrating a better-than-even chance of recovery if the negligent act had not occurred.

The leading case is *Hamil v. Bashline*.[17] Based upon its interpretation in Section 323(a) of the *Restatement*,[18] the court stated that

the effect of section 323(a) is to relax the degree of certitude normally required of plaintiff's evidence in order to make a case for the jury as to whether a defendant may be held liable for the plaintiff's injuries: Once a plaintiff has introduced evidence that a defendant's negligent act or omission increased the risk of harm to a person in plaintiff's position, and that the harm was in fact sustained, it becomes a question for the jury as whether or not that increased risk was a substantial factor in producing the harm.[19]

The court pointed out that, in these types of cases, the fact finder "must consider not only what *did* occur but what *might* have occurred" and that

---

[16] *Id.*, 688 P.2d at 614.

[17] 481 Pa. 255, 392 A.2d 1280 (1978); see also Hamil v. Bashline, 243 Pa. Super. 227, 364 A.2d 1366 (1976); Hamil v. Bashline, 224 Pa. 407, 307 A.2d 57 (1973).

[18] § 323. Negligent Performance of Undertaking to Render Services

One who undertakes, gratuitously or for consideration, to render services to another which he should recognize as necessary for the protection of the other's person or things, is subject to liability to the other for physical harm resulting from his failure to exercise reasonable care to perform his undertaking, if

(a) his failure to exercise such care increases the risk of such harm, or

(b) the harm is suffered because of the other's reliance upon the undertaking.

[19] Hamil, 392 A.2d at 1286.

"such cases by their very nature elude the degree of certainty one would prefer and upon which the law normally insists before a person may be held liable."[20]

The court also emphasized that:

> In light of our interpretation of Section 323(a), it follows that where medical causation is a factor in a case coming within that Section, it is not necessary that the plaintiff introduce medical evidence—in addition to that already adduced to prove defendant's conduct increased the risk of harm—to establish that the negligence asserted resulted in plaintiff's injury. Rather, once the jury is apprised of the likelihood that defendant's conduct resulted in plaintiff's harm, that Section leaves to the jury, and not the medical expert, the task of balancing probabilities. In so saying we do not intend to undermine the well-established standard of "reasonable degree of medical certainty" as the accepted norm for medical opinions on causation. But we think it would be unreasonable and unrealistic in this type of case to expect a physician to state with a "reasonable degree of medical certainty" what *might* have happened when the law (Section 323(a)) recognizes the contingencies involved.[21]

Subsequent cases have affirmed and bolstered this concept in the state of Pennsylvania.[22] And more recently, in *Mitzelfelt v. Kamrin*,[23] in discussing this relaxed standard as related to statistical chances of surviving a breast cancer where there was a negligent delay in diagnosis, the Pennsylvania Supreme Court pointed out:

> Legal commentators have noted this different standard in cases where there is a statistical uncertainty:

> It is often difficult for a patient-plaintiff to demonstrate that a physician's negligence was a substantial factor in causing injury, because a patient-plaintiff cannot prove the events which would have occurred, had the physician not acted negligently. If the physician proves that the injury would have been sustained without his or her negligence, then the physician is not liable for the injury.

---

[20] *Id.* at 1187.

[21] *Id.* at 1288.

[22] Gradel v. Inouye, 491 Pa. 534, 421 A.2d 674 (1980); Jones v. Montefiore Hosp., 494 Pa. 410, 431 A.2d 920 (1981).

[23] 584 A.2d 888 (Pa. 1990).

Since the burden is on the patient-plaintiff, however, this standard often treated patient-plaintiff unfairly. Accordingly, the Pennsylvania Supreme Court has held that once a patient-plaintiff shows that a physician-defendant's negligence increased the risk of harm and that harm actually occurred, sufficient evidence has been offered to submit the case to a jury. The jury must then decide whether the increased risk constituted a substantial factor contributing to the injuries sustained. Post, Peters and Stahl, *The Law of Medical Practice in Pennsylvania and New Jersey*, section 4:35, at page 416 (1984).[24]

One must not overlook the other issues involving proximate cause that may be pivotal, namely unforeseeable consequences, intervening causes, and responsibility shifting to another. A dramatic case illustrative of the last issue is *Thompson v. Lillihei*.[25] In that instance, a mother on another operating table was serving as the heart-lung circulation for her child whose heart was being operated upon by Dr. Lillihei, who was utilizing this cross- circulation technique before heart-lung machines were introduced. An anesthesiologist who was tending the mother allowed a glass intravenous bottle under pressure to run dry so that the mother received a fatal air embolus. Ultimately, the anesthesiologist, who had not been named in the lawsuit, was found liable. (The court succinctly referred to him as "Dr. X" in its opinion.)

[3] *Res Ipsa Loquitur*

Under the doctrine of *res ipsa loquitur*, there is no need for expert testimony as to breach of duty or proximate cause, if three criteria are met: 1) the outcome resulted by an instrumentality under the exclusive control of the defendant, 2) the plaintiff did not voluntarily contribute to the outcome, and 3) the injury was of the type that would not normally occur in the absence of negligence The burden of proof as to these issues, in many jurisdictions, shifts from the plaintiff to the defendant, at which time the defendant would need to give evidence that the outcome occurred without negligence.

In those jurisdictions where there is a shift of the burden to the defendant, this becomes a legal presumption, a "bubble" subject to easy bursting. The inference of negligence is left to the jury, who is permitted, but not compelled, to find it. But now there is the presumption of wrongdoing by the defendant. In the absence of any evidence to disprove negligence, the court is required to order a directed verdict against him. The defendant can

---

[24] *Id.* at 892, n.1.
[25] 164 F. Supp. 716 (D. Minn. 1958), *aff'd*, 273 F.2d 376 (8th Cir. 1959).

present whatever evidence is necessary to show why the injury happened in the absence of any negligent act by him.[26]

[4]   The Exclusive Control Doctrine

In an allied area, the doctrine of "exclusive control" is operative. Under this doctrine, the plaintiff alleges that he has no way of discovering who was liable, since all the facts are within the exclusive control of the defendant. The first important case asserting this doctrine was *Ybarra v. Spangard*.[27]

In Ybarra, a patient was taken to the operating room for surgery under general anesthesia on a part of the body other than an upper extremity. When he awoke, it was determined that he had an upper extremity weakness due to injury to the brachial plexus. The allegation was that this injury was unrelated to the site of the operation, would not have occurred if due care was given, and that who or what caused the injury was within the *exclusive control* and knowledge of one or all of the named defendants. The court ruled that it was for the defendants to prove who was liable, and they must go forward with evidence on this issue. Other courts have called this precept "conditional" *res ipsa loquitur*.[28]

[5]   Preoperative Events

Failure to follow established standards of care may occur during the initial visit. At this visit, the surgeon is required to take a proper history, perform a reasonable examination, order appropriate laboratory studies, and properly prepare the patient for an operation, if necessary. All of these areas have played prominent roles in cases alleging negligence. For example, in an unreported case, a female patient presented signs and symptoms suggestive of appendicitis. An exploratory laparotomy was performed. It was found that the patient's appendix had *already been removed* during a previous operation. The patient had been asked if she had ever undergone surgery, but she did not know that an incidental appendectomy had been performed during a hysterectomy, and no attempt was made by the examining surgeon to determine that fact. The previous operation had been performed in another hospital in the same city three years earlier. While the laparotomy was not

---

[26] W. PROSSER, LAW OF TORTS 257-8 (5th ed. 1984).

[27] 25 Cal. 2d 486, 154 P.2d 687 (1944). *See also* Jones v. Harrisburg Polyclinic Hosp., 437 A.2d 1134 (Pa. 1981).

[28] *See* Anderson v. Somberg, 67 N.J. 291, 338 A.2d 1 (1975), *cert denied*, 483 US. 92; Anderson v. Somberg, 158 N.J. Super. 384, 386 A.2d 413 (1978), *cert. denied*, 77 N.J. 509, 391 A.2d 522 (1978); *Someone Has To Be Guilty*, MEDICAL ECONOMICS, Jan 12, 1976, at 151.

technically negligent, it was unnecessary, and could have been avoided with a few phone calls.

Failure to ask about drug sensitivities has led to serious harm in surgical patients. However, most hospitals have now established a policy whereby this interrogation is routinely performed by the nursing staff. But proper record keeping *mandates* that such pertinent information be in the physician's history review. If any disciplinary action is contemplated, the lack of this information being appropriately recorded is very likely to be used against the doctor.

If a patient has been vomiting over a protracted period of time, the patient should be properly hydrated, and a profile of the electrolyte pattern be obtained, so that proper correction can be made prior to any operation. Rarely is it possible to delay surgical intervention to allow for proper fluid and electrolyte correction.

Failure to evaluate routine preoperative studies is definitely a breach of accepted medical standards. These studies are performed to help the physician arrive at a diagnosis and to determine whether the patient is in suitable condition for operation. The following case is an example of substandard care. A young female was diagnosed as having a symptomatic calculous gallbladder due to the surgeon's inability to visualize the gallbladder by oral cholecystography. Prior to operation, a routine chest X-ray was done. The X-ray was reported as showing the diaphragm on the right to be at the level of the second interspace, suggesting an eventration of the diaphragm. This finding was brought to the attention of the attending physician, surgeon and anesthesiologist. None of them, however, bothered to look at the X-rays. When the surgeon entered the abdomen through a right subcostal incision, the liver was not in its usual location, being dislocated into the right hemithorax. Because the biliary tract could not be visualized through this surgical approach, the contemplated operation could not be done and the incision was closed. The true nature of the abnormal biliary tract location and the proper surgical approach could easily have been ascertained by a simultaneous liver and lung scan or by a CT scan (computerized tomography). The latter was subsequently done at another hospital, and a successful cholecystectomy via a thoraco-abdominal approach was effected.

Prior to many operative procedures, special treatment may be necessary to decrease the incidence of postoperative complications. These are numerous and cannot be fully documented, but a number of the more common ones are worthy of mention. Elective colon surgery should not be performed unless the bowel is properly prepared. Mechanisms for cleansing the GI tract has evolved to the point where PEG, or electrolyte lavage solution by mouth in conjunction with a 24 hour clear liquid diet, is generally regarded as standard care. The PEG preparation is a high volume/4 liter ingestion and a lesser volume (2 liters) plus a bisacodyl or magnesium citrate preparation works equally well. A mechanically clean bowel with as low as possible a bacterial flora is generally recognized as making the surgery simpler. It is now thought that a mechanical bowel preparation prior to elective bowel resection does not reduce the risk of anastomotic leaks; rather it is the surgical technique that determines such post operative complications.

In small intestinal obstruction, unless there are signs suggesting bowel necrosis with imminent or actual perforation, the bowel should be decompressed by long-tube intubation (Cantor tube, Miller-Abbott tube or similar suction tubes) prior to operation. Frequently, this will totally decompress the dilated bowel and correct the mechanical problem (such as a torsion around an adhesive band) so that an operation can be avoided. If it does not correct the obstruction, the bowel will be decompressed, making operation simpler and, should a resection be necessary, the bowel will be more easily sutured, being less likely to leak in the postoperative period.

When a patient presents with marked pyloro-duodenal obstruction with gastric distention, the stomach must be decompressed prior to operation, since through decompression alone the surgeon may frequently avoid the operation.

When there is suspicion of cancer or other tumors, every effort must be made to obtain biopsy material for more complete planning of contemplated intervention. With present techniques, including small-needle biopsy with CT localization, ultrasound evaluation, sophisticated endoscopic instruments (permitting visualization of pancreatic and biliary ducts, and the inner walls of the esophagus, stomach, and entire colon), and cytologic techniques, biopsy specimens can and should be obtained from the gastrointestinal tract and most of the other internal organs. The pancreas is an exception because of possible leakage and pancreatitis. Kidney needle biopsy can lead to hemorrhage, especially in the hypertensive patient. Liver biopsies can lead to bleeding or bile leakage, but are generally safe and frequently accomplished without complications.

All chemical imbalances should be corrected prior to any operation, so that the patient will better be able to cope with the operation itself and progress more satisfactorily in the postoperative period. This is also true for pulmonary and cardiac function, impairment of which can be ascertained from a careful history, physical examination, and appropriate laboratory tests.

[6] Intraoperative Events

Minus the act of failing to correctly diagnose a patient with a condition calling for an operation in a timely fashion, most allegations of negligence involving general surgeons involve events that occur during the operation itself. These include inadvertent injuries to vital structures. The following have been the basis for negligence actions: (1) disruption of bile ducts during gallbladder removals; (2) unintentional ligation of important vessels producing necrosis of organs; (3) tearing of spleen during gastrectomy, requiring a subsequent splenectomy; (4)injury to pancreas during gastrectomy; (5) ligation of ureters during low sigmoid colon resection; (6) anastomosis of gastric stump to ileum instead of proximal jejunum during gastrectomy; (7) failure to identify all seriously injured intra-abdominal structures following traumatic injuries to abdomen; (8) failure to recognize that bowel edges anastomosed after bowel resection are devascularized; (9) failure to further explore for a Meckel's diverticulitis when a normal appendix is found during an appendectomy for suspected acute appendicitis; and (10) failure to remove sponges or instruments from the abdominal cavity prior to closure.

As yet unsettled is the risk of liability that can occur from the complications of laparoscopic abdominal procedures. With these new procedures, painful abdominal incision under general or spinal anesthesia, with concomitant loss of bowel function for several days, all requiring several days' stay in the hospital, is avoided. The number of acceptable procedures is increasing continuously, including but not limited to cholecystectomy, appendectomy, bowel resection, and hysterectomy, partial and total. Serious complications can occur, however, including injury to the common duct, perforations of major blood vessels with hemorrhage requiring laparotomy for control, and injuries to the bowel, liver, and spleen.

This is not to conclude that all such acts that occur are due to negligence on the part of the surgeon. They may occur in spite of ordinary care. Operations of all types are fraught with the possibility of injuries of one sort or another, and it is the surgeon's responsibility to be aware of their possible occurrence and to take measures to avoid them. For example: (1) When a low colon resection is performed, it must be recognized that the ureters anatomically run along a course close to the bowel prior to entering the bladder; unless the ureters are identified, they may be injured, even divided. (2) When the stomach is resected on the greater curvature up to the level of the spleen, the latter must be visualized to avoid tearing the capsule of the organ during traction in the area. (3) At the time that the cystic duct is ligated during a cholecystectomy, the point of its junction with the hepatic bile duct forming the common duct must be identified to avoid injury to the latter duct. There are essentially two schools of thought concerning the need to do a cholangiogram to best discern the anatomy of the biliary tree, prior to ligation of the cystic duct: one school mandating it in every case and one school requiring it only if one of the following criteria are met: 1) choledocholithiasis is suspected on clinical grounds or 2) the anatomy appears unclear at the time of the operation.   Generally, it may be stated that in every operation there are structures that must be identified and meticulously avoided to prevent injury to them. During the training of a surgeon, this principle is repeatedly stressed for every procedure.

[7] Postoperative Events

During the postoperative period, beginning immediately after an operation is completed, due care must be exercised in all aspects of management. This includes repeated examinations, proper medication orders, indicated consultations, proper laboratory study orders, and the institution of all ancillary aids to effect a proper result. These vary in number and intensity, depending upon the nature and complexity of the operation, and upon the development of any complications.

While each major surgical procedure requires specific postoperative orders, there are general principles of postoperative care that must be observed to insure a good result. The more common ones are:

1. Every major abdominal procedure involves a greater or lesser degree of trauma to the intestines, resulting in a paralytic ileus, wherein intestinal activity is markedly decreased. This permits fluid to accumulate in the bowel lumen, causing the bowel to become distended. In addition, swallowed air enters the bowel, aggravating the distention. Some form of a nasogastric (or longer) tube may have to be inserted to remove these contents, because if the distention becomes extreme before bowel activity returns, and the ileus extends over an excessively long period of time, it can lead to complications that may seriously jeopardize the outcome of the case. Recent progress in paralytic ileus recovery is the use of methylnaltrexone as an antagonist for the peripheral opioid related side effects. This medication given intravenously shortly after operation (within 90 minutes) is capable of avoiding the peripheral adverse effects of opioids (inhibition of GI motility) while sparing their central analgesic effects.

2. At least 25-30% of patients have nausea and/or emesis post-op and in high risk patients the figure is closer to 75%. Although prophylaxis for all patients is not cost-effective, the incidence increases for various factors such as the agents used for anesthesia, the length of the operation (> 60 minutes), the patient's state of hydration, etc. Propofol, a frequently used short acting agent, is a protective

antiemetic despite its unknown mechanism for this effect. All of the 5HT3 receptor antagonists are equally effective. If a patient vomits persistently after an operation, particularly after general anesthesia, and the repeated administration of antiemetic drugs does not promptly relieve the situation, nasogastric suction to empty the stomach to allow gastric tone to return to normal may be necessary. This is because gastric atony commonly occurs, resulting in the accumulation of large amounts of fluid and swallowed air in the stomach. This can only be removed mechanically by the nasogastric tube. (In either of the above situations, there frequently is a concomitant loss of essential electrolytes and fluid. These must be replaced, and constant monitoring is necessary to maintain the proper fluid and electrolyte balance until the condition is corrected.)

3. Elderly patients often have problems with urination following major surgical procedures. This is more common in males, and is usually due to some degree of hyperprostatism. The problem may manifest itself by the inability to void or by voiding small amounts frequently. In either event, a period of catheterization may be necessary, either periodically, or by leaving the catheter in the bladder. Failure to catheterize the patient may aggravate an already impaired urinary system, because of back pressure on the ureters and the kidneys.

4. An elevated temperature in the first 48 hours post-operatively is usually from a non-infectious etiology (atelectasis in the lung bases is thought to be the most likely etiology).A persistently febrile postoperative course however, beyond the first few postoperative days, may be due to infection somewhere, and its source should be meticulously sought out and proper treatment instituted. Fever elevation from day 5 to 8 is often an indication of a wound infection, although, if there are no clinical signs of this, a urinary tract infection or atelectasis which is now bacterial pneumonitis or pneumonia would also have to be considered.

5. Certain types of pain are common after most operations. Improvements in analgesia, from the patient controlled analgesia (PCA) with IV medications to epidural catheters for the first 48-72 hours post op, have markedly increased early ambulation, resolution of ileus and earlier discharge from the operative facility. Since postoperative pain should progressively decrease in the first 7-10 days, pain that requires increasingly higher doses of analgesics

should be an indication that there may be other problems such as an infection or a hematoma of the wound, which may require drainage, or there may be an intestinal obstruction (following an intra-abdominal procedure) that requires intensive measures to correct, including intubation (as previously described for an ileus) or, in extreme cases, reoperation.

[8] Medical Judgment as a Defense

The practice of medicine and its specialties is based upon scientific principles learned through all the years of formal education. However, at best, it is also an art in which judgment at each step in medical care plays a large part. Medicine is in no way an exact science. The reason is that while disease entities have similarities by which they may be identified, there are sufficient differences that demand individual application in varying situations. And people do not always react in exactly the same way to similar stimuli.

It is, therefore, recognized in all jurisdictions that the treatment of any two patients may not be the same, although the diagnosis may be identical. However, regarding of any deviation from a general manner of management, such deviation must be based upon sound medical and scientific principles.[29] The physician must keep abreast of improvements and developments in the field, since these may change the standard of care required.

Because it is recognized that the practice of medicine is not an exact science, and that there may be more than one way of treating a given condition, the surgeon has some leeway. In an action against a surgeon for improperly managing a case, where the plaintiff presents an expert who testifies that he would have acted differently under the circumstances, if the defendant can present evidence to show that he acted properly according to some surgeons, even though merely a *respectable minority*, the defendant should prevail. This principle applies to all aspects of medical and surgical care, including diagnosis, operation and postoperative management.[30]

[9] Borrowed Servant and Captain of the Ship Doctrines

The general laws of agency are applicable to surgical practice. A surgeon does not work alone. From the time he first sees a patient until the time he finally discharges the patient from his care, others participate in some way in the management of that patient.

---

[29] *See* Johnson v. Misericordia Hosp., 99 Wis. 2d 708, 301 N.W.2d 156 (1981).

[30] Furey v. Thomas Jefferson Univ. Hosp., 472 A.2d 1083 (Pa. Super. 1984).

The general rule regarding vicarious liability is that when an individual who is subject to the control of another person performs a service on behalf of that person in a negligent manner, then the one on whose behalf the service is being performed may be held liable for any resulting harm (respondeat superior). It follows that when a paid employee of a surgeon (nurse or other assistant) harms a patient for whose care the surgeon is responsible, the surgeon is vicariously liable.

Another agency principle applicable to the medical profession is known as the "borrowed servant doctrine." Under this doctrine, a master-servant (or principle-agent) relationship comes into existence only during the time when an individual actually performs acts subject to the control of another. A good example of the application of this "borrowed servant doctrine" to the operating room can be found in *McConnell v. Williams*,[31] which involved a case where an obstetrician was found liable for the negligent acts of a resident during the delivery of a child. The newborn was injured by the resident. The obstetrician was neither the employer nor preceptor of the resident. The only function of the resident was to take care of the newborn after delivery. When a negligence action was brought against the hospital and the obstetrician, based on the principle of vicarious liability, the lower court ruled that the hospital was immune from liability because of charitable (hospital) immunity. It also found, as a matter of law, that the obstetrician, being neither the employer nor the preceptor of the resident, was also not liable. The verdict was appealed to the Pennsylvania Supreme Court, which reversed, holding that the obstetrician was vicariously liable, based on the theory that during the time that the resident was caring for the newborn, he was, in fact, performing a function that the obstetrician owed to the newborn, and that the obstetrician borrowed the resident from the hospital for that purpose, and that during that period of time, the resident was the servant of two masters, the hospital and the obstetrician. The court stated that a failure to employ this reasoning would be a disservice to an injured innocent party. This reasoning also is the basis of the "captain of the ship doctrine," which many other courts subsequently adopted, and which remained a prominent part of a surgeon's liability for the acts of others in the operating room suite for many years. This doctrine, however, has now largely disappeared because of the increasing complexity of surgical procedures in which several doctors may be independently responsible for separate technical portions of the operation. Examples are open heart surgery, organ transplants, single and multiple. The seminal case overturning the doctrine was *Thompson v. Lillihei*.[32]

---

[31] 361 Pa. 355, 65 A.2d 293 (1949).

[32] 164 F. Supp. 716 (D.Minn. 1958), *aff'd,* 273 F.2d 376 (8th Cir. 1959).

The Pennsylvania Supreme Court, which was responsible for the "captain of the ship doctrine," abolished hospital immunity in 1965 in *Flagiello v. Pennsylvania Hospital*.[33]

Eleven years later it abandoned the "captain of the ship" theory in fact situations similar to those in *McConnell*.[34]

[10]   Direct Liability for the Acts of Others

The abandonment of the above doctrines does not mean that a surgeon today will not be held liable for the acts of others in the operating room or elsewhere merely because that other person is not an actual employee of the surgeon. For example, when a resident in training performing an operation under the supervision of a surgeon does so in a negligent manner, the surgeon may be held directly liable because of his own negligence in permitting the resident to commit such negligence. It is also possible that, in view of the fact that the resident is actually under the control of the surgeon, the surgeon may also be held vicariously liable. With proper reasoning and depending on the fact situation, a plaintiff will often be able to make out a case for a surgeon's liability, either directly or vicariously, if the surgeon was in the immediate vicinity of the negligent act.

A surgeon should not be held liable for the negligent acts of another (other than his employee) when a proper order written by him (the surgeon) is carried out in a negligent manner. When orders are written by the surgeon for a patient in the hospital, the established practice is that the order is carried out by a nurse or some other party who is not employed by him. If the order is executed negligently, resulting in harm, the surgeon will not be held vicariously liable. Should he be in a position where he observes the act, and is able to prevent it, and does nothing, he may be held liable for direct, not vicarious, negligence.

There are circumstances, however, that may lead to another conclusion. In a few jurisdictions, hospital immunity still exists, and in a few others, there is limited liability (only up to a certain maximum). In the latter, it is quite possible for the courts to look to someone to pay damages where the injury is serious, as was done by the Pennsylvania Supreme Court in *McConnell*. The court may still rule that the one performing the act was a "borrowed servant" during that period of time. This would require that the court conclude that if the one performing the ordered act did not do so, then the surgeon himself would have done so. This would appear to be quite a

---

[33] 417 Pa. 486, 208 A.2d 193(1965).

[34] Tonsic v. Wagner, 458 Pa. 246, 329 A.2d 497 (1974).

departure from a long-established practice, but not substantially different from what the Pennsylvania Supreme Court faced in *McConnell.* The same reasoning may be applied if the one performing the act is not a hospital employee (e.g., a private duty nurse).

§ 7.03 Consent and Informed Consent[35]

[1] Who May Consent

While the informed consent doctrine relates to all areas involving an invasive procedure, by the nature of the practice of surgery, it would appear that in almost every operation the surgeon should be deeply concerned with consent principles.

Determination of those who may give consent is usually governed by statute, but the statutes are similar in most jurisdictions. Generally, the following may give consent: those who are eighteen years-of-age or older; those who are married; females who have been pregnant; and emancipated minors. In each case, the person must be of sound mind. When a person is unable to give consent, consent must be given by a spouse, next-of-kin, or guardian.

When an operative procedure has been performed without consent, the surgeon has committed a battery, an intentional tort, for which money damages may be obtained, even in the absence of harm. However, such damages are generally nominal. An exception would exist where a surgeon removes the wrong extremity, the wrong lung or the wrong kidney. While these are truly *negligent* acts, they so go against one's sensibilities that they are considered more akin to an intentional tort. When such an action is brought, the pleadings are frequently those of battery. However, in most jurisdictions, the cause of action will be limited to negligence. Since such acts are considered egregious, a claim for punitive damages may be added to the pleadings because of willful and wanton disregard, although in some states, such as California, tort reform efforts have virtually precluded the ability to include any punitive damage claims in a medical malpractice action.

[2] Informed Consent

Consent in a surgical practice is a *process* rather then a piece of paper with signatures on it. A mere form with information on it cannot shield a surgeon

---

[35] For an excellent discussion of the doctrine, *see* F. Rozorsky, CONSENT TO TREATMENT: A PRACTICAL GUIDE (2d ed. Little, Brown 1990).

from liability for failing to give *informed* consent. The surgeon needs to document that, in addition to the filled out form, the patient and the surgeon had a discussion about the planned procedure, expected benefits, probable outcome, potential risks/complications, and that the patient requested that the operation be done.

The usual pleadings in actions against surgeons involving consent are that there has been a "lack of *informed* consent," namely, that the patient consented to an operation, but without being adequately informed as to the nature of the operation, the alternatives available, and the risks and complications of the procedure. In short, the theory is that while the patient consented to the operation, he did so only because he was not fully informed, and had he been informed, he would not have consented.

The principle that a person has a right to do with his body as he wishes was first promulgated in *Schloendorff v. Society of New York Hospital*.[36] This decision has been used as a basis for many court rulings, and is the basis for the theory of informed consent as applied to medical practice.

At first, when an action was brought based upon this theory, the manner of pleading and proof was similar to that for negligence, and for a plaintiff to prevail, it was necessary to present expert testimony as to the standard of care on disclosure of information to a patient (*See* §7.03 [6] below.) In 1971, a trend began in a number of jurisdictions wherein the courts ruled that in an action based on lack of informed consent, expert testimony was not necessary for the case to go to the jury.[37]

These decisions were based upon the principle that the *law*, not the medical profession, should set the standard of disclosure (nature of the procedure, risk of the procedure, and alternatives), and that a jury does not need input from the medical profession as to what a patient would need to know in order to arrive at an informed decision as to whether or not to undergo the recommended surgery. (*See* § 7.03 [5], below.)

In effect, this set a new standard for the surgeon to follow. However, in the opinions of the courts it was emphasized that it was not necessary for the physician to give the patient a *mini-course* in medicine, nor was it necessary for the physician to disclose *all* the possible risks involved. What the courts did state was that it was necessary to inform the patient as to "material" risks, namely, those that a reasonable person would need to know in order to make a decision. The purpose of the disclosure is to inform, not to frighten

---

[36] 211 N.Y. 125, 105 N.E. 92 (1914). *See also* Natanson v. Kline, 186 Kan. 393, 350 P.2d 1093 (1960).

[37] Cooper v. Roberts, 220 Pa. Super. 260, 286 A.2d 647 (1971); Canterbury v. Spence, 464 F.2d 772 (D.C. Cir. 1972); Cobbs v. Grant, 8 Cal. 3d 229, 502 P.2d 1, 104 Cal. Rptr. 505 (1972).

patients. Further, the disclosure should be made to the patient himself, or, if the patient is unable to give consent, to the person who would give the consent. In fact, there is no duty to give the required information to anyone other than the one who is to give consent.[38]

On the other hand, the patient frequently requests that a member of his family or a close friend be present during the disclosure. Since that party is privy to the information disclosed, he can help the patient in making the decision. This also is usually helpful to the surgeon. This is particularly true when the patient does not fully understand the surgeon. (Should the patient speak a language other than the surgeon's, it is imperative that an interpreter be engaged.)

Various aids are employed to help the surgeon satisfy the requirements to obtain an informed consent. Many are using video tape which depicts in a graphic manner the anatomical sites involved, and describes the risks and alternatives. This is often accompanied by having the patient answer questions from a prepared booklet. Video tape should not be a substitute for direct communication between surgeon and patient, however, its purpose is merely to assist the surgeon in his duty. The same may be said for written material that the surgeon may give to the patient.

All hospitals in which operations are performed require that a written consent form, signed by the patient or properly authorized party, be executed before an operation is performed. Prior to delivering the patient to the operating suite for pre-anesthesia medication, a nurse usually checks to see that a properly executed consent form appears in the patient's records. (No patient should be asked to sign such a form if he is under the effects of medication which may impair mental acuity.)

If a patient does not want to be informed, a notation to that effect should be made in the patient's chart and on the consent form that the patient signs.

[3] Extending the Scope of the Operation

Not infrequently, when a surgeon operates upon a patient he finds a condition other than what was anticipated. When this occurs, it is important that he have wide discretion to perform what is necessary to correct the pathologic state.[39] Generally, this does not present a problem since the patient expects to be made well. However, conditions may be found which are not life-threatening, but serious enough to lead to prolonged disability or to produce a state which will interfere with the patient's future desires and

---

[38] Nishi v. Hartwell, 52 Haw. 188, 473 P.2d 116 (1970).

[39] See Kennedy v. Parrott, 243 N.C. 355, 90 S.E.2d 754, 56 A.L.R.2d 686 (1956).

expectations. For example, assume that a female patient is operated upon for a possible perforated appendicitis with pelvic peritonitis. At operation, it is found that the patient has a diffuse primary pelvic inflammatory disease, that both fallopian tubes are acutely inflamed, and that the ovaries are sites of abscess formation. Under this circumstance, it is probably surgically wrong to remove the infected organs, and if the surgeon should do so, he may be liable in an action for lack of informed consent because removal of these reproductive organs will deprive the patient of the expectation of bearing children. On the other hand, if the patient is operated upon for appendicitis and is found to have a perforated tumor of the cecum, the proper course for the surgeon, acting in the patient's best interest, is to resect the right colon, an operation more serious than an appendectomy. If this operation is followed by complications not present in an appendectomy, such as breakdown of the suture line with leakage and fistulization, or even death, and an action is brought for lack of informed consent, the likelihood of a plaintiff prevailing would be slim.[40]

[4]   When the Surgeon Himself Does Not Operate

When a patient gives a surgeon consent to perform a given procedure, the expectation is that the surgeon himself will perform the operation. In teaching institutions, as part of his training, a resident must acquire operative experience. When one other than the surgeon will perform all or a great part of the operation, the patient *should be informed.* If he agrees, no problem exists. However, if he insists the surgeon himself be the operator, his desires should be respected, regardless of whether he is a paying or a non-paying patient. In this situation, should the trainee perform the operation, and whether or not harm results, the patient may have an action in battery. In addition, he may have an action for breach of contract against the surgeon.

There are times when consent is not necessary. These are limited to the situations which are immediately life-threatening (or limb-threatening) and where no one is able to give consent. Here the consent is implied by law. Ironically, should the surgeon fail to operate, an action in negligence may be brought against him.

[5]   "Reasonable or Prudent Patient" Standard

When an action is brought for lack of informed consent in jurisdictions that do not require expert testimony as to the standard of disclosure (the so-

---

[40] *See id.*

called "reasonable or prudent patient" standard jurisdictions), the case will go to the jury if the plaintiff alleges that he was not informed of the risk and harm that actually occurred. The jury must then decide whether or not a "reasonable or prudent" person in the situation of the plaintiff would have accepted or rejected the proposed procedure had he been informed of the risk. The basis for the reasonable or prudent patient splits into two variations depending upon whether the standard is the patient herself (a subjective "reasonable or prudent patient") or a patient in like circumstances as the plaintiff at bar (an objective "reasonable or prudent patient"). Quite different testimony may be adduced in these two different scenarios. If the jury decides that a reasonable or prudent person would have rejected the procedure, it may find for the plaintiff. If it decides that a reasonable person would have agreed to the procedure, it must find for the defendant.

[6] "Reasonable Physician" Standard

If an action is brought in a jurisdiction that follows the "reasonable physician" rule, the plaintiff must present expert testimony of the profession's standard of disclosure, that the surgeon failed to follow this standard, and that the plaintiff would not have consented had he been informed of the risk of injury that did, in fact, occur. The jury must then deliberate as it would in a negligence action.

While the action at first was brought on the theory of battery, a non-consensual touching, all courts have treated it as a form of negligence, and, therefore, have equated the elements of "lack of informed consent" with those of negligence. The duty is that the patient must be informed as to the nature of the procedure, the alternatives, the risks and the complications. Harm must be present, the harm being the undisclosed risks or complications. The proximate causation element is satisfied by the fact that the patient agreed to the procedure and suffered harm because of the fact that he was not informed, and therefore did not have the opportunity to forego the procedure. The reason for this is that the patient did actually agree to the operation, but without being adequately and properly informed. If the courts treated the action as a battery, an intentional tort, punitive damages could be imposed on the tortfeasor, and there might be a problem with the defendant surgeon's professional liability insurer denying coverage, since such policies of insurance generally insure only for negligent acts.

§ 7.04 Specific Problems in General Surgery

[1] Diagnosis of Surgical Diseases

While the general surgeon often is called in by the general practitioner after a diagnosis of a specific surgical condition has been made, frequently he is asked to see a patient because the diagnosis is in doubt. Under these circumstances, the surgeon has a duty to apply all his skill and experience, and request whatever diagnostic aids he believes are necessary to help establish the diagnosis. He must avail himself of all those modalities that may help differentiate one disease process from another. In recent years, ultrasonography of specific areas, and more recently, computerized tomography (CT) have proved to be of invaluable assistance in this regard. Also, the use of magnetic resonance imaging (MRI) is becoming recognized as an important additional diagnostic tool. Ultrasound, CT, and MRI are readily available in most hospitals. They should not be indiscriminately employed, but, as with any other laboratory aid, they should be ordered when the history, physical examination, blood laboratory studies, and indicated roentgenological studies do not give the surgeon all the information he needs.

In addition, although a diagnosis may be established that indicates that an operation may be necessary to remove a diseased organ, additional studies may indicate that an operation will neither "cure" nor even ameliorate the condition. This is true when a diagnosis of malignancy is established in one organ, such as the stomach or colon, but additional studies indicate extensive metastasis. In light of our present knowledge in the treatment of certain malignancies with metastases, surgery on the primary site, in the absence of obstruction or bleeding or perforation, might be a fruitless procedure, and might actually shorten the already limited life expectancy of a patient.

[2] Bleeding Problems

Frequently, the surgeon is called upon to treat severe bleeding from a specific organ. Generally, this poses no problem as to the necessity for the operation, but there may be some difficulty in establishing the exact site of the bleeding, particularly with internal organs. This is important, because the surgical approach should be a direct one, if at all possible.

Many bleeding organs will stop bleeding on their own, thus avoiding any emergency operation. On the other hand, some internal bleeding requires an immediate operation to prevent exsanguination and death. This is true of a rupture of a large blood vessel, such as an abdominal aneurysm which, when it ruptures, frequently bleeds freely into the abdominal cavity.

When a patient presents in a "shock" state, with abdominal or low back pain, rigidity and tenderness of the abdomen, decreased to absent pulses in the lower extremities, and especially a pulsatile mass in the abdomen, a presumptive diagnosis of a ruptured aneurysm is to be made. The operating room should be prepared, blood should be given, blood should be taken for laboratory studies, and, if conditions permit, an ultrasound of the abdomen should be done to confirm the diagnosis. However, if the patient's condition is precarious, the operation should not be delayed. Any unnecessary delay in taking the patient to the operating room might be considered negligence, since it is the delay that actually may be the cause of death.

If bleeding is coming from anywhere in the digestive tract, immediate endoscopy of the suspected area should be employed. This procedure can be performed expeditiously, and frequently provides all the information necessary to treat the patient, whether by operation or other measures. Endoscopy should be performed before any X-rays are done, since the former takes less time, can localize the site of bleeding more accurately, and may often even be used to stop the bleeding.

In all bleeding cases, frequent hemoglobin determinations are usually necessary to monitor the bleeding, and to aid in determining the amount of blood to be given to replace loss. It must be emphasized, however, that repeated hemoglobin determinations should not be a substitute for intensive and frequent clinical observations. It is not unusual for bleeding to continue in spite of a stable hemoglobin determination because there has not been sufficient time for hemodilution to be reflected in a lowering of the hemoglobin level. A patient is often brought in with a history of a massive hematemesis or melena and in shock with a normal or even elevated hemoglobin level. This is frequently because there has been insufficient time for hemodilution, or because of a contraction of the vessels, a normal physiologic response to sudden massive bleeding. Finally, after the patient is given intravenous fluids to stabilize his condition, the hemoglobin level will fall, sometimes quite dramatically. But this does not necessarily mean that bleeding is continuing or that it has started again after having stopped. Close clinical observation is necessary to assess the true state of affairs.

Prior to any operation, a careful history should be taken, and a bleeding and coagulation "profile" should be done to determine whether any bleeding tendencies are present. If they are, corrective measures should be immediately undertaken. Occasionally, in spite of normal routine preoperative studies, excessive "oozing" is noticed during and after the operation. Additional studies should be done, either during the operation or immediately after, to determine the cause.

When continuing bleeding occurs in the postoperative period, it may be necessary to reoperate. On occasion, this bleeding is due to a ligature failing to control a ligated vessel. When such bleeding occurs in spite of good surgical technique, there is no cause of action for negligence, but there might be if the bleeding is not recognized and corrected.

When blood replacement is necessary, if possible it should be by packed cells, rather than whole blood, to reduce the incidence of hepatitis. The remainder of the blood volume may be replaced with either lactate or saline solution.

[3]   Wound Healing and Infection

Not all incisions heal properly. For reasons not fully understood, abdominal incisions do occasionally dehisce (re-open), requiring reoperation. Even the use of nonabsorbable sutures does not completely overcome the problem of a wound dehiscence. However, the surgeon should do what he can to reduce the incidence of this complication. The wound should be closed meticulously, layer-by-layer. Material that absorbs slowly or not at all should be used. All gross bleeding in the incision should be controlled prior to closure, and all attempts to reduce or prevent abdominal distention should be undertaken. If, in spite of these measures, a wound does dehisce, the surgeon should not be held liable for any harm that results.

Any wound may become infected, in spite of meticulous technique. Nosocomial (hospital-caused) infections are common. If the measures employed to prevent dehiscence are taken, if all incisions are thoroughly irrigated after open bowel surgery prior to closure, if subcutaneous drains are employed in cases where infection is likely to occur (cases with gross soiling or those with peritonitis), and if appropriate antibiotics are prophylactically used in such cases, the acceptable standard of care has been met.

Wounds should always be redressed by sterile technique, and a wound in which an infection is believed to be present should be opened for drainage and cultures taken, so that the proper antibiotics can be administered.

[4]   Surgery on the Parotid Gland

Surgery on the parotid may result in injury to the contiguous facial nerve. To prevent this, the nerve and its branches must be meticulously avoided. If the tumor is a deep one necessitating extensive dissection, the nerve should be identified and kept under direct observation prior to cutting any structures. This complication should occur when a malignancy of the gland is so intimately associated with the nerve that some injury cannot be avoided.

[5] Thyroid Surgery

It is well known that it is possible to injure one or both recurrent laryngeal nerves during a thyroidectomy. This complication should be kept to a minimum if the posterior capsule of the thyroid lobe is preserved, since the course of the nerve is behind the capsule as it comes up in the groove between the trachea and the esophagus. Rarely is the nerve injured below the level of the thyroid cartilage. If it is injured, it is at the point where the nerve enters the larynx via the crico-thyroid membrane. It is here that the single-trunk nerve branches out to innervate the muscles of the larynx. When bleeding occurs at this point, clamps or sutures should not be blindly employed. It is usually safer to apply gentle pressure and use hemostatic agents such as gelfoam, surgacil or similar materials. In practically all cases the bleeding will stop without suturing.

The likelihood of injury to the nerves is greater when the operation is a secondary one, or when it is for a malignancy of the gland, because of distortion and excessive fibrosis in the former, and because of the extent of the excision in the latter. While injury cannot be absolutely avoided, its incidence can be lessened by slow and meticulous dissection, and identification of all structures prior to ligation or cutting.

The possibility of injury to a parathyroid gland during thyroid surgery is always present. Careful dissection can avoid inadvertent removal of the parathyroids (except for the few that are within the thyroid lobes); however, it is not unusual for a patient to exhibit signs of tetany in the early postoperative period as a result of traumatic edema of the glands. Every postoperative thyroid should be checked for early tetany by careful physical examination. At the earliest signs of this condition, intravenous calcium should be given. The calcium levels should be carefully followed. In almost all cases, these return to normal without any further treatment.

Major bleeding after thyroid surgery may lead to catastrophic results if not recognized early. Stridor and cyanosis are prominent early signs. As soon as these occur, and there is no evidence of parathyroid injury (tetany as determined by physical examination), the wound must be promptly opened and blood clots evacuated. The patient may then be taken to the operating room for permanent control of the bleeding.

[6] Surgery on the Parathyroids

The parathyroids are usually operated upon because of hyperfunction of the glands or because of a tumor, both of which usually produce symptoms of hypercalcemia. The surgical complications are the same as those associated with thyroid surgery, but the likelihood of hypocalcemia is much more likely, and when it does occur, it is much more persistent and requires a longer period of monitoring. Unless a surgeon is operating on a cancerous mass which obliterates the anatomy of the anterior neck, it is essential to prevent injury to the external laryngeal nerve which is responsible for tensing of the vocal cords. This nerve is the motor branch of the superior laryngeal nerve on (80%) or in (10%) the cricothyroid muscle and runs with the superior pole thyroid vessels (thus the thyroid vessels should be ligated near the thyroid capsule, low on the thyroid gland, to avoid injury to this nerve). It is also essential to avoid injury to the recurrent laryngeal nerve, a branch of the vagus/10th cranial nerve that supplies motor function and sensation to the larynx. This nerve is best identified by locating the inferior parathyroid gland which is just inferior to where the inferior thyroid artery enters the thyroid gland. This nerve lies posterior to the lower parathyroid and travels superiorly to enter the cricothyroid muscle at the level of the superior parathyroid gland.

[7] Surgery on the Submaxillary Glands

Patients with low grade stage III tumors of the salivary gland can be treated with surgery alone or surgery with post-operative radiation. Patients with high grade stage III tumors confined to the gland need operation plus post-op radiation. The most common surgical complication of these operations is trauma to the most inferior branch of the facial nerve, which results in weakness of the lower corner of the mouth. This branch must be meticulously avoided at all times during the operation, and the patient needs to have been pre-operatively informed of the possibility or probability of facial nerve damage.

[8] Breast Surgery

Operations upon the breast are performed for both benign and malignant conditions. Benign operations are done either to reduce the size of the breast (reduction mammoplasty) or to increase the size of the breast by the insertion of an implant. Negligence actions against surgeons have usually been because of marked distortions of the breast resulting from the operations.

Because of the undermining of the tissues necessary in the operations, the vasculature may be compromised, resulting in necrosis and sloughing. These possibilities should be explained in great detail to the patient.

Breast implants have brought a host of lawsuits for malpractice and product liability because of multiple illnesses thought to be immune reactions from leakage of silicone out of defective implants. In 1992 silicone breast implants were banned in the United States, although saline implants remained available. In 1997 Dow Corning admitted that their silicone implants caused "health complications" in some women whose implants ruptured, leaked, etc, BUT they did not admit to their causing any illnesses. The company did, however, offer $2.4 Billion as a settlement to >200,000 women worldwide for these "health complications." Despite this company's liability the public and medical profession (for breast reconstruction after mastectomies) has continued to put pressure on the FDA to allow silicone implants to stay on the market. In November of 2006 the FDA approved silicone gel breast implants once again. Now, however, the informed consent for women who choose these implants makes the known risks a liability for the patient instead of the surgeon.

Most operations upon the breast are for the treatment of tumors. It is generally agreed that solitary solid dominant masses of the breast should be removed for biopsy purposes, and that if a solitary mass is aspirated, any bloody fluid obtained should be subjected to microscopic evaluation. In addition, if a palpable mass remains in the breast following aspiration, it should be excised for microscopic examination. Examination of the breast should not just a physical examination by a clinician but also mammography or xerography to find lesions that are not clinically palpable.

If a mass is palpable a surgeon can do a core needle biopsy in the office using local anesthesia and a 14 gauge needle or a biopsy gun device.

For lesions that are not palpable some surgeons prefer the radiologist to localize the area for biopsy using a needle/wire localization prior to the patient coming to the OR. Again local anesthesia with or without IV sedation is sufficient. For these procedures radiography on the specimen site is mandated, to show that the actual tissue in question has been removed; only then can the operation come to an end. For equivocal results with the specimen x-ray, more tissue can be excised or repeat mammogram can be performed post healing.

A new generation of mammography equipment will substantially change the approach to biopsy and operations for tumor of the breast. Stereotactic Core Needle Biopsy Mammography combines CT X- ray with computerized control of a thin needle for biopsy of suspicious areas in the breast seen on the films. This is accomplished by x,y,z coordinate films being taken of the breast held in a stabilizer-compression device. After pinpointing a lesion, with one-millimeter accuracy, by this stereotactic localization, the images are analyzed by the computer, which then activates a guiding mechanism that advances the core needle. When the needle is in the correct position and computer verified, the gun controlling the needle is manually fired by the operator, piercing the target area. Further coordinate films are taken to verify that the material biopsied is that from the lesion.

Since the vast majority of breast procedures are biopsies and 80-90% of biopsies are benign, this very exact method, obviating the need for open breast biopsy, will drastically reduce the use of surgery, similar to the impact of laparoscopic techniques on open abdominal surgery

Not using this technique may lead to claims for unnecessary surgery and delay in diagnosing breast cancer. It is well known that better than 95% of these tumors are curable when found in the early stage and of small size. One can postulate that, with further sophistication of the technology, breast lesions may be routinely discovered at a very early stage and be ablated by insertion of an appropriate laser device, eliminating most incisional breast surgery.

[a]   Surgical Options for Carcinoma of the Breast

It is now recognized that standard care for breast cancer is no longer a radical operation! In nearly all patients, wide local excision with microscopically clear margins together with axillary dissection and radiation, will give equivalent long term survival to that associated with the formerly widespread modified radical mastectomy. However, even today, the ideal method of management for carcinoma of the breast is in a state of flux.

The recent diagnostic and treatment controversy is the use of sentinel lymph node biopsies and what to do with the results. The axillary sentinel lymph node is the first node to which extra cellular fluid from a tumor drains. It is a so-called 'gateway to the lymphatic system' and thus the evidence of tumor spread or progression. It was thought to be a way to avoid the often disabling effects of a formal lymph node dissection of the axilla (upper extremity edema, paralysis, pain, and inflammation) and to better stage the tumor for post-operative treatment. The issues left unanswered are 1) how to identify and treat micro metastasis in the axilla and 2) how important are lymphatic alternative lymphatic drainage patterns (internal mammary or supraclavicular drainage systems).

There are an increasing number of surgeons who recommend a lumpectomy for all solid tumors of the breast, unless the tumor is a massive one, requiring a complete simple mastectomy. The medical articles and lay press have drawn much public attention to the management of breast cancer, stressing the various options available. This has even led to legislation in some states requiring that a special informed consent form be provided to a patient prior to any operation on the breast to ensure that the patient has been fully informed of her options.

Most of the litigation involving the breast has concerned failure to make an early diagnosis. The only protection the physician has in this regard is to carefully physically examine the breasts, order mammography even if masses are not definitely palpable, and if there is a suspicion that a small mass may be present, to examine all breast aspirates or secretions from the nipples.

[9] Biopsies of the Cervical Lymph Nodes

There have been a number of lawsuits against surgeons following the removal of a cervical node in the posterior triangle of the neck. Nodes in this area (level V), when enlarged, can arise from nasopharyngeal and thyroid cancers as well as from carcinomas of the scalp or pinna of the ear. Usually, the reason for liability is that the branch of the cervical plexus innervating the supraspinatus muscles of the shoulder has been injured, resulting in paresis or paralysis and atrophy of the muscles. Anatomically this branch is in close proximity to the lymph nodes, and when one of the nodes must be removed, the nerve must be avoided to prevent injury. Many of these node excisions are performed under local anesthesia, and when the area is infiltrated with the anesthetizing agent, unless the nerve is actually seen, any manipulation of the nerve usually does not result in any contracture of the muscle. The only precaution to be taken in these procedures is to make sure that dissection is not done haphazardly or traumatically, and that it is done within the plane of the node itself.

[10] Gastric Surgery

Surgery for peptic ulcer is done much less frequently today because of new drugs that reduce the high acidity within the stomach. However, surgery is still being done for complications such as perforation, uncontrollable bleeding or obstruction. The former two may be surgical emergencies, but the latter rarely requires immediate operation. In fact, many cases of obstructing pyloric ulcer are due to edema, not fibrous stricture, and meticulous medical care, gastric decompression and careful electrolyte control will more often than not result in the subsidence of the edema, thus avoiding any operation. When operations have been performed for this complication and the end result has not been favorable, actions have been brought against the surgeon alleging that an unnecessary operation was performed. In some cases, this may have merit. The lesson to be learned is not to rush to operate for obstructing peptic ulcers.

When an operation is actually performed, whether for benign or malignant lesions, meticulous dissection in the region of the pyloric canal and duodenum is necessary to avoid injury to the underlying pancreas and to the structures of the biliary tract that lie in close proximity to the posterior portion of the duodenum. In fact, when the structures are obliterated by edema, dissection in this area should not be done unless the common bile duct is directly visualized or even cannulated.

When an operation is being performed for a duodenal or pyloric ulcer, and the surrounding structures are obliterated by inflammatory reaction, it is safest to avoid the area entirely and do an operation other than a gastrectomy, or if a gastrectomy is desirable, to allow the duodenum to remain, and ream out the mucosa. Only a foolhardy surgeon will attempt a standard gastrectomy under these conditions.

If the duodenal closure is difficult, or the suture line does not look secure, it is often best to insert a drainage tube into the lumen to create a fistula that will eventually close. An alternative is to insert a suction drain in the area surrounding the suture line, so that if leakage occurs, it may drain to the outside, and at least allow the surgeon the opportunity to determine whether or not the suture line is intact. Failure to follow these guidelines has led to lawsuits.

On occasion, because of mechanical and exposure problems, the spleen has been traumatized during gastric surgery, necessitating a splenectomy. This is not necessarily negligence. The important thing is to recognize it when it occurs. Failure to do so is generally negligence.

[11] Surgery on the Biliary Tract

Negligence actions have been brought against surgeons because of injuries to the common duct, retained common duct stones, and unrecognized hemorrhage from the gallbladder bed. With the laparoscopic approach being *de rigueur* for most procedures on the biliary tract for benign (non-cancer) disease, an additional liability is thought to be the unrecognized perforation of the bowel at the time of trocar insertion for the procedure. While not all common duct injuries during a planned cholecystectomy are due to negligence (because of anatomical variations, cystic dilatation of the common duct, etc.), once there is such injury, the patient will almost always sue the surgeon. Obviously, every attempt must be made at the time of the cholecystectomy to identify individually all structures at the hilum, and to separately ligate each one after the ductal structures are clearly identified. If the structures cannot be accurately identified, plans for a total cholecystectomy should be abandoned and a substitute operation, such as a submucous cholecystectomy or even a cholecystostomy and cholelithotomy, should be performed. Direct injury by cutting, ligating, or fulgurating the structure is culpable negligence, but there are some cases where there was no discernible injury and where questions of negligence remain open at this time. If jaundice is a symptom, then the common duct must be explored. In the hands of a gastroenterologist with excellent hand-eye coordination, this is most easily done pre-operatively. Should this not be feasible, at the time of operation a percutaneous cholangiogram or a transabdominal cholangiogram should be performed to determine whether or not the common duct is actually mechanically obstructed. In some cases, the jaundice is due to inflammatory changes and not a stone or other obstruction. In any event, if it is too precarious to explore the duct at this time, the catheter used for the cholangiography may be allowed to remain, to decompress the system and (it is hoped) allow the concomitant inflammatory process to subside, thus deferring surgical exploration to a more favorable time.

Cholangiography is done in a large number of cases scheduled for routine cholecystectomy for cholelithiasis. If common duct stones are demonstrated or even suspected, the duct must be explored. Failure to do so may be considered negligence, since the operation is not completed until such stones are removed In spite of all of the above, and even when the common duct lumen is visualized with a choledochoscope, there are cases in which retained stones subsequently cause colic or actual common duct obstruction. If all of the precautions have been taken, there is no negligence. A gastroenterologist may be able to do an ampullary sphicterotomy via the gastroduodenoscope (in adequately treated cases intraoperatively) but with retained common bile duct stones found post-operatively. On the other hand, if there was failure to explore suspected shadows, a cause of action does exist against the surgeon.

When the common duct is explored, in most cases a drainage tube is left in the duct. This should not be removed in less than two weeks, so as to allow a tract to the outside to form to prevent bile peritonitis from leakage of bile into the peritoneal cavity. In any event, it should not be removed until a cholangiogram through the tube demonstrates an unobstructed and tone-free duct. If retained stones are seen, the tube should not be removed, but allowed to stay until either the retained stones pass spontaneously or until a firm tract develops through which the instruments can be inserted to remove the retained stones. Failure to follow these precautions demonstrates a subminimal standard of care.

After any cholecystectomy, bleeding may occur because the cystic artery ligature becomes dislodged or because of massive bleeding from the gallbladder bed. Neither of these may be due to any breach in technique, but when they do occur, the complication must be promptly recognized and treated. After a short period of observation and necessary blood and fluid replacement, if the bleeding does not appear to have stopped, an operation should be performed to correct the condition. Failure to do so is negligence.

[12] Appendectomies

Many lawsuits have been instituted because of failure to make a timely diagnosis of acute appendicitis, and the patient eventually has to be operated upon for a ruptured appendicitis with peritonitis. A careful history, physical examination, review of pertinent laboratory studies, and the finding of point tenderness are the typical criteria diagnostic of acute appendicitis. If all of the above are present, an operation is indicated, since the risk of not operating is greater than that of operating. Most surgeons are now quite comfortable doing a laparoscopic exploration and (incidental) appendectomy even in those cases where the diagnosis is suspected but not clear and watchful waiting has not allowed clarification.

There are few complications following a simple appendectomy, while those following a ruptured appendicitis are many and serious. If the diagnosis of acute appendicitis is in doubt, frequent re-examination may be necessary, and if doubt still exists, an operation should be performed. The condition with which acute appendicitis is most frequently confused is acute mesenteric adenitis, a relatively benign condition for which operation is not necessary. However, it is not considered negligence when an operation is performed for acute appendicitis and mesenteric adenitis is found. The symptoms and physical findings are frequently identical.

In the female at the time of ovulation, there may be escape of blood into the peritoneal cavity (mittelschmerz). The signs and symptoms simulate appendicitis very closely. A careful history and physical examination and judicious watchful waiting, combined with frequent reexamination, will usually lead to the proper diagnosis. Ovarian cystic disease, twisting of an ovary, and pelvic inflammatory disease all can simulate appendicitis. Frequently there is need for gynecologic consultation to avoid an unnecessary operation. Failure to consider these conditions or failure to obtain an appropriate gynecologic consultation may lead to culpable harm.

[13] Other Surgery Involving the Intestinal Tract

One condition that is often almost impossible to diagnose prior to operation is mesenteric occlusion producing gangrene of the affected segments of bowel. The symptomatology is vague in the early stages, and even with the aid of repeated roentgenograms and computerized tomography, a diagnosis is frequently difficult to make. Not until sepsis or peritonitis appears is the operation performed. Frequently, by this time there is extensive gangrene of the small and even large intestine, and the mortality rate becomes prohibitive. As long as the patient is frequently seen and appropriate studies are ordered, the surgeon should not be held liable.

In colon surgery, when performing a right hemicolectomy, the duodenum should be identified and injury to this structure avoided. When a perforated obstructing sigmoid diverticulitis or carcinoma is found, it may be best to drain the area, perform a proximal colostomy, and do a definitive resective operation at a later date when the inflammatory process has subsided. Resection and anastomosis of an unprepared colon is generally associated with many and difficult postoperative problems, particularly leakage from the suture line. The ureters should be identified at the time of low colon resections. The spleen must be carefully observed during resection of the splenic flexure of the colon.

Operations for the treatment of morbid obesity have been gaining in prominence over the past decade. A disproportionately large number of lawsuits have been brought against surgeons performing this procedure. While some have alleged lack of informed consent, all have alleged negligence. The patients have been dissatisfied with the aftermaths of the operation and, in some, with the necessity to take down the anastomosis or stapling and restore the continuity of the alimentary tract. The early operations consisted of bypassing the greater portion of the intestinal tract by means of a jejunoileal anastomosis. Various technical modifications of the anastomosis were improvised, but all basically excluded most of the small intestine from the functional digestive system. The complications were many. In addition to usual complications of any intra-abdominal operation (intestinal obstruction, suture line disruptions, etc.), additional late complications often developed. These included hepatic dysfunction, arthritis, and excessive weight loss. As a result, other operations were devised to correct obesity. The most commonly performed operation today is the vertical-banded gastroplasty, which effectively limits the amount of food an individual may ingest at any one time. This has not been associated with the late serious sequelae mentioned; however, even this operation has led to lawsuits, most being based upon the allegation that the opening in the stomach was too small, or not small enough, or that the staples disrupted, effectively reversing the surgical attempt at limiting the proximal gastric pouch to a small volume. Neither of these may be due to faulty technique, and a lawsuit would be defensible.

To avoid problems in operations for obesity, several precautions should be followed: operate only if the patient is truly morbidly obese; avoid the jejunoileal bypass procedure; accept only patients who have earnestly attempted nonsurgical methods to correct the obesity; have the patient evaluated psychiatrically; and explain in meticulous detail the nature of the procedure, the risks, the complications and the alternatives.

[14] Blunt Abdominal Trauma

Every patient suffering from a blunt injury to the abdomen must be carefully observed for evidence of internal bleeding or rupture of an internal organ. This requires constant monitoring, X-rays of the abdomen and frequently computerized tomograms. It may be necessary to repeat these studies many times to follow the patient's progress. If a perforated viscus or bleeding is suspected, four-quadrant abdominal taps should be performed to look for blood or intestinal juices free in the peritoneal cavity. When there is trauma to the left upper quadrant, injury to the spleen should be suspected. With laparoscopic splenectomies or splenic repair for rupture being done in most trauma centers, the patient whose catastrophic diagnosis was sometimes missed in the past is often taken to the operating room earlier. Although many argue that the same procedure (once the laparoscope is inserted) carries the same risk, the luxury of a shorter operation with less need for analgesia equates to a quicker recovery, shorter hospital stay and perhaps a more aggressive stance on the part of the surgeon to 'take a look'!!

If free air is seen within the abdomen on initial X-ray examination, an immediate operation must be performed. If internal bleeding is diagnosed, and does not respond completely and rapidly to supportive therapy (blood and fluids), an operation becomes necessary.

When the abdomen is explored, the exploration must be complete, including not only the intraperitoneal structures, but the retroperitoneum as well. Injury to the retroperitoneal duodenum and pancreas are not uncommon in severe trauma cases, and special care should be used in examining those areas.

The same precautions must be taken when there is sharp instrument (stab wound) trauma to the abdomen. Fortunately, in these cases, the site of injury is generally quite clear. The same criteria should be employed in monitoring these cases and determining when surgical exploration becomes necessary.

Surgery for abdominal trauma has dramatically improved over the last several years. Rapid transportation to trauma centers is receiving critical attention. There have been remarkable improvements in the mortality and morbidity of hepatic and splenic trauma. Triage and resuscitation of the severely injured patient in severe shock has been significantly upgraded with increased survival of these patients. Better nutritional care has substantially reduced morbidity and altered the healing process. With these changes, complications such as postoperative infection and multisystem organ failure have been reduced. Lack of utilizing these advanced techniques may well be deemed substandard care.[41]

[15] Shorter Hospital Stays

Because of the changes that have occurred in the length of hospitalizations, due mainly to the method of reimbursement under Medicare, many operations are now being done as "short-procedures." When a patient is admitted to a hospital for operation, the postoperative lengths of stay have been dramatically shortened.

While a patient should not be discharged from the hospital unless the surgeon believes no problems will arise, some complications occur only after a period of time has passed. The patient and those responsible for his care should be fully apprised of the complications that may arise, and how to recognize them. No complaint should be considered trivial, and the surgeon must make his services available at all times, so that the patient can be seen quickly and his problem evaluated. Readmission to a hospital under these circumstances is not wasteful of resources, and may be necessary to insure good surgical care. It should not be fear of a lawsuit that guides the surgeon, but the well-being and condition of the patient.

---

[41] K.L. Mattox et al., TRAUMA (Appleton & Lange 1988); E.E. Moore et al., CRITICAL DECISIONS IN TRAUMA (C.V. Mosby 1984).

CHAPTER 8

ANESTHESIOLOGY*

Matthias I. Okoye, MD, JD, and Logan A. Griffin, AB, MD

SYNOPSIS

---

* An earlier version of this chapter was written by Valentino D.B. Mazzia, MD, JD.

---

§ 8.01   Introduction

[1]   The Standard of Care

Many states and the federal government have legislated various aspects of anesthesia delivery and medical care. New Jersey's legislation may well be most comprehensive in this regard. For specifics for each state, the reader should consult the annual publication *Healthcare Standards*, published by ECRI, 5200 Butler Pike, Plymouth Meeting, Pennsylvania 19462. This publication lists pertinent organizations and their standards, plus the law, legislation, and regulations at both the federal and state levels.

In addition, medical societies and professional groups have addressed the problem of delivery of quality anesthesia care. This effort has been particularly successful in reducing the incidence of iatrogenic injury. In this regard, the reader should consult the policy statements of The American Society of Anesthesiology, 520 N. Northwest Highway, Park Ridge, Illinois 60068 and the American Association of Nurse Anesthetists, 216 Higgins Road, Park Ridge, Illinois 60068. Also, a good discussion of the effect of standards on medical liability appears under "Medical News and Perspectives" in the *Journal of the American Medical Association*, Volume 267, No. 12 (March 25, 1992, at pages 575-583. Another important publication that spells out many standards is *Operating Room Risk Management*, which is also published by ECRI.

According to the American Society of Anesthesiologists (ASA), the practice of anesthesiology involves the following:

1. Production of unconsciousness and obliteration of pain during surgical, obstetrical, and other procedures. This requires preoperative, intraoperative and postoperative evaluation and care.
2. Prevention of damage to, and insurance of reversibility of depression of, the brain, heart, and lung function. Also, there should be no damage to the liver, kidneys, skin, nerves, eyes, or other body parts.

3. Management of pain. Avoidance of overdosage particularly by use of Patient Controlled Analgesia (PCA). There are anesthesiologists who specialize in this area.

4. Management of cardiopulmonary resuscitation. (This is an evolving field. If an anesthesiologist is in the operating room should the cardiac arrest team be called? Is open massage indicated? One of the major problems is delay in instituting resuscitation. Other problems are failure to perform external massage properly — in smaller hospitals, this duty was delegated to orderlies — inadequate record keeping, and failure to monitor adequacy of sternal compressions.) The cardiac arrest team should be called because they have the external cardiac defibrillator. It is even more important to establish NSR. One would suppose that 100% 02 is being administered plus external cardiac massage while awaiting the arrival of the defibrillator

5. Management of problems in pulmonary care. (But today, there are pulmonologists who specialize in this field.)

6. Management of critically ill patients in special care units. This has developed into a subspecialty in anesthesiology.)[1]

7. Management of various fluids, oxygen delivery and uptake, and carbon dioxide excretion disturbances.

Some idea of the present scope of anesthesiology may be gleaned from the journals relating to the field. These should be consulted regarding specific issues. Among the current journals are the following:

Canadian Journal of Anaesthesia
Critical Care Medicine
Anaesthesist (German)
International Anesthesiology Clinics
Seminars in Anesthesia
Acta Anaesthesiolol Scan
Anaesthesia
British Journal of Anaesthesia
Anesthesia and Analgia
Anesthesiology
Journal of Clinical Anesthesia

There are also several nurse-anesthetist journals.

---

[1] Many other subspecialties of anesthesiology have developed, and some even have their own societies and publications. There are societies and meetings for pediatric, neurosurgical, cardiovascular, and academic anesthesiologists, as well as "pain specialists," among others.

Although the publications listed above outline various standards of care, unless a judge takes judicial notice of their applicability (which is most unlikely), the standard must be elicited from a medical expert under oath. The standard may be circumscribed by the "locality rule," namely, that a healing arts practitioner is held only to that standard of care of the average conscientious practitioner in his geographic area at and before the time of the alleged negligence. The standard of care is constantly being upgraded. In many states the locality rule has been superseded by a national standard. Patient expectations with respect to the quality of the delivery of anesthesia care are high. Because of the nature of the delivery of anesthesia, good rapport with a patient and his family is difficult, if not impossible, to achieve. The attorney must be wary of the client who comes to his office with a complaint that may be principally an attempt to displace or shift guilt.

The intricacies and subtleties of highly specialized anesthesia for premature infants, open cardiotomy, neurosurgery, etc. should be sought in the texts listed in the bibliography at the end of this chapter.

[2] The Practice of Anesthesiology

The American Society of Anesthesiologists, in 1974, approved the following definition of anesthesiology.

Anesthesiology is a practice of medicine dealing with, but not limited to:
(1) The management of procedures for rendering a patient insensible to pain and emotional stress during surgical, obstetrical, and certain medical procedures;
(2) The support of life functions under the stress of anesthetic and surgical manipulations;
(3) The clinical management of the patient unconscious from whatever cause;
(4) The management of problems in pain relief;
(5) The management of problems in cardiac and respiratory resuscitation;
(6) The application of specific methods of inhalation therapy;
(7) The clinical management of various fluid, electrolytes, and metabolic disturbances.

Anesthestics may be administered by many routes: inhalation, intravenous, intramuscular, rectal, infiltration, spinal, epidural, caudal, and nerve blocks. Hypnosis may also be utilized.

While anesthesiology is a practice of medicine, nonphysicians such as nurse anesthetists and physicians' assistants probably administer the majority of anesthetics in the United States under the supervision of surgeons or obstetricians who usually know less about anesthesia than the nonphysician. Also, many surgeons administer local anesthesia without an anesthesiologist in attendance. Should a complication occur, they are held to the same standard of care as a trained anesthesiologist.

Any physician who is licensed as a physician and surgeon may practice anesthesia (or for that matter, any other specialty). However, certification by nongovernmental boards such as the American College of Anesthesiologists, the American Board of Anesthesiology, and the American College of Osteopathic Anesthesiologists may be required as a condition of being granted hospital privileges. Requirements for certification can be obtained directly from the various boards, and are often spelled out in medical directories.

Dentists are usually legally authorized to administer anesthesia sufficient to perform dental surgery. Some states have special requirements for dentists who administer anesthesia.

Outpatient surgical facilities, such as "surgicenters," may not require certification.

A license as a registered nurse (RN) may be sufficient for a nurse to administer anesthesia. A licensed practical nurse, licensed vocational nurse, operating room technician, and emergency medical technician, etc. are not legally authorized to administer anesthesia with or without supervision.

The Certified Registered Nurse Anesthetist (CRNA) certification is granted after completion of a privately approved course of training and the successful passage of an examination administered by the American Association of Nurse Anesthetists. As many as seventeen states have some definition by statute of nurse anesthesia. Attorney general opinions have also been issued regarding non-physician anesthesia. Statutes, attorney general opinions and the case law are in a constant state of flux, so the lawyer handling a medical negligence action must research the authority that governed at the time of the alleged negligence.

Some states recognize non-physician, non-nurse anesthesia practitioners. Podiatrists in some states may administer local anesthesia.

While in training, all of the above categories authorized to administer anesthesia may do so under supervision. Some states do not require full licensure for trainees.

To learn the privileges of a practitioner of anesthesia in a particular hospital, the by-laws, policy and procedure manuals, and job descriptions of that institution must be consulted. As a rule, no such procedural guidelines will be found governing office-based anesthesia practice.

Whether because of the stress of administering anesthesia, or because of the easy accessibility to controlled drugs, anesthesiologists and nurse anesthetists sometimes become addicted to narcotics and other substances.

Before administration of an anesthetic, a preanesthetic evaluation and appropriate preparation is mandatory. (See §§ 8.03–8.04.) During the administration of the anesthetic and until significant recovery from the depression caused by the anesthetic drugs, continuous moment-to-moment monitoring of the patient is also mandatory. (See § 8.06 [5].)

Regardless of the type of anesthetic administered, cardiopulmonary resuscitation and control of seizures may be required and therefore suitable equipment must be immediately at hand.

In general, any surgical procedure can be performed under any anesthetic technique, and with any FDA-approved drug. Which technique and which agent is actually utilized will depend on the preferences and biases of the patient, his family and friends, the surgeon or obstetrician, the anesthetist, the hospital, the insurers, and the community.

§ 8.02   Informed Consent

The anesthetist should, whenever possible, obtain from the patient his own informed consent for the type of anesthesia contemplated. The consent should be oral and after it has been obtained, memorialized in a writing and signed by the patient and witnessed. A printed form signed by the patient is not necessarily conclusive evidence that informed consent has been obtained.[2]

Informed consent consists of five elements that must be conveyed to the patient: (1) What is planned; (2) the significant or material risks of what is planned; (3) alternative techniques or drugs which might achieve satisfactory anesthesia; (4) the significant or material risks of the alternatives; and (5) what will happen if nothing is done.

In the mid 1970s some states, as part of the so-called malpractice reform, enacted statutes which prescribe the procedure for obtaining prima facie evidence of informed consent. Several of these statutes have already been repealed, principally because of lack of information regarding incidence of complications.

The purpose of informed consent is to enable the patient to make his own decision regarding his body after having been apprised of the potential risks and of the anticipated benefits.

The problems in obtaining informed consent are so great and so many, that for all practical purposes truly informed consent is an elusive and perhaps an unattainable goal. For example, should the anesthetist be held to an objective or to a subjective standard? Does the custom and practice in the

---

[2] *See* Cobbs v. Grant, 8 Cal. 3d 229, 502 P.2d 1, 104 Cal. Rptr. 505 (1972).

community determine whether failure to obtain informed consent is negligent? What does "material" and "significant" mean when the actual incidence of various anesthetic complications is unknown and unknowable? Can informed consent be obtained the night before surgery when the patient is apprehensive? Can informed consent be obtained the morning of surgery if the patient is fasting or premedicated? What does informed consent mean when the woman is in labor? (In a delivery at term, who represents the viable fetus?) Who is authorized, and by whom, to give informed consent when the patient cannot? What does informed consent mean if the patient requires an urgent, perhaps life-saving emergency operation and the patient refuses? What should be done when a Jehovah's Witness absolutely refuses blood when it is clear that if no blood is administered the patient will die?

No litigation should ever be begun solely on an informed consent issue. However, if upon analysis there is a reasonable allegation that a departure from the standard of care has caused damage, then an informed consent count may be added. It may be that the cases that have reached the appellate courts on an informed consent issue are those in which the plaintiff's attorney learned he could not prove a deviation from the standard of care after he invested a significant sum in the litigation. (Medical practitioners would be well advised to tape their informed consent discussions and also have witnesses present.)

No patient should be persuaded paternalistically to consent to a procedure that they have indicated previously they did not want performed. For example, if a patient refuses a spinal anesthetic he should not be persuaded to have a subarachnoid block (medical term for a spinal).

If the patient refuses a certain anesthetist or physician, that person should not administer care. Also, if the patient insists that a certain anesthetist or surgeon should administer care, elective anesthesia and surgery should not be performed unless the person desired is present. (Making a record of such disagreements may prove, in court, damaging to the defense.)

§ 8.03 Preanesthetic Evaluation

The Joint Commission on Accreditation of Healthcare Organizations requires that a preanesthetic note be recorded on the chart by a physician before elective surgery.[3] The physician need not be an anesthesiologist and often the operating surgeon's presurgical note includes comments regarding anesthesia and risk when no anesthesiologist may be on staff, as in small

---

[3] The Joint Commission revises its Accreditation Manual annually. The attorney should obtain the issue for the year of the alleged negligence. All hospitals must be approved by the Joint Commission to be eligible for Medicare payments.

hospitals. If the operating surgeon is a dentist or podiatrist, the preanesthetic note should be by an allopathic or osteopathic physician.

Although appropriate preanesthetic evaluation and preparation is crucial before emergency surgery, a preanesthetic note is not required by the Joint Commission. Legally, the note can, at most, be considered evidence of whatever preoperative evaluation has been performed. Failure to record a preanesthetic evaluation may have some value in arguments to the jury but obviously cannot be causally related to damage. Failure to perform a preanesthetic evaluation and to bring the patient into optimum condition to undergo anesthesia and surgery may be causally related to damage.

If the required surgical and anesthetic care is beyond the capability of the facility or skills of the personnel, and if there is time, the patient must be promptly stabilized and transferred to a suitable facility.

The preanesthetic evaluation should include a review of present and, if pertinent, past hospital records, a history and sometimes appropriate physical examination. The hospital chart should indicate the surgical procedure contemplated. This evaluation should prevent surgery on the wrong patient on the wrong side or organ. The chart would document the medical conditions from which the patient may be suffering as well as whether these conditions are under control by which medications. There may be a record of previous anesthetics and, most important, untoward reactions to previous anesthetics. There should be a record of a physical examination and appropriate laboratory, roentgenological, and other studies. A family history of untoward reactions to anesthesia is very important, since some susceptibilities (e.g., malignant hyperthermia) may be inherited.

A history of muscle cramps and of extreme soreness following exercise should alert the anesthetist to the possibility that this patient could be liable to develop malignant hyperthermia. Therefore all possible triggering agents should be avoided such as succinycholine, halothane, ethrane, forane, and desflurane. If general anesthesia is to be elected then a "fresh anesthesia machine "should be utilized and an IV narcotic technique used. Sufficient Dantrolene must be available in the department to treat the patient should the need arise.

Practically all hospitals require that the laboratory perform a complete blood count and a urinalysis. The hemoglobin and hematocrit are concentrations and do not necessarily indicate circulating blood volume. Oxygen is carried by hemoglobin so these determinations are indications of oxygen-carrying capacity. White cell counts may indicate infection. Urinalysis may indicate unsuspected diabetes or other disorders. These results should be recorded on the chart, and the anesthetist and surgeon should be aware of any abnormal results before beginning the administration of the anesthetic.

For procedures in which operative or post-operative bleeding (such as a tonsillectomy) may be a problem, preanesthetic tests of blood clotting should be performed and recorded. For patients who are over forty years of age, often an electrocardiogram is required by the hospital. Sophisticated laboratory studies to evaluate cardiac function are available today. These include stress tests followed by thallium or other radioactive studies, echocardiography, and coronary artery angiography. These can pinpoint coronary artery plaques, spasm, areas of myocardial damage, valvular malfunctions, etc. If significant heart disease is found, many elective procedures on other parts of the body should be postponed until after the heart disease is appropriately managed. Patients with third degree or complete heart block should have pacemakers inserted before administration of anesthesia.

Patients on diuretics or weight-losing regiments should have serum potassium determinations. If found to be low (hypokalemia), elective procedures should be postponed until the serum potassium has been brought into the normal range. The danger is that both low and high potassium can produce cardiac arrest, which may not be reversible.

Blacks and some Mediterraneans may have sickle-cell disease or sickle-cell trait. They are especially susceptible to hypoxic episodes which can precipitate sickle-cell crisis and death.

If there seems to be reason, a roentgenogram of the chest is also performed. In the past these were done routinely to rule out tuberculosis. Recently, resistant strains of tuberculosis, partially associated with the AIDS epidemic, have emerged in some parts of the country, making it likely that the routine chest X-ray will again be advisable. If done, they should be read carefully to rule out malignancy. A chest X-ray will not show bronchitis, bronchiostasis, or asthma.

Because of the ease with which various blood tests can now be done by automatic analysis and computers [SMA-12, SMA-18, etc.], often batteries of tests are done to indicate serum levels of glucose, urea nitrogen, creatinine, uric acid, calcium, phosphorus, sodium (Na^+), potassium (K^+), chloride (CI^-), cholesterol,[4] triglyceride, total bilirubin, alkaline phosphatoose, SGPT (ALT), SGOT (AST), LDH, CPK, total protein, albumin, and calculated globulin and ionized calcium. The computer printed report also indicates normals and deviations from normal.

Blood-typing and cross-matching with reservation of one or more units [a unit is about 500 cc] before an operation may be needed. It takes from 30 to

---

[4] While the total cholesterol is of some importance, the measurement of high-density and low-density lipoprotein fractions and their ratio is crucial in evaluating the risk of myocardial infarction.

50 minutes to type and cross-match blood, so if the need is anticipated an appropriate number of units should be reserved and placed in suitable refrigerator, usually in the operating room or obstetrical area.

Other tests are dictated by the patient's chief complaint, history, surgical procedure, etc.

The anesthetist's history should stress:

1. Previous anesthetics and reactions, if any, thereto, including outpatient surgical procedures;
2. Previous hospitalizations and significant visits to a doctor's office;
3. Family history of sudden death or untoward reactions to anesthetics and of significant medical conditions which might be inherited;
4. Prescription and over-the-counter drugs and medications [illicit drugs are, of course, also very important, as is alcoholism]; and
5. History of allergies.

Physical examination by the anesthetist is usually minimal. Overall impression of the patient's condition is obtained (alert, ambulatory, in no distress, etc.). Color of the skin is observed (cyanosis, pallor, jaundice, mottling, etc.). The mouth and teeth should be examined carefully for dentures, loose or chipped teeth, etc. If there is disease of the heart or lungs, auscultation and percussion of the chest and heart might be in order. Enlarged liver and abdominal distension may also be significant.

If the neck is short and thick, and the temperomandibular joint frozen, endotracheal intubation may be difficult.

It is partially the anesthetist's responsibility to determine that the patient is in the optimum condition possible to undergo elective surgery. In the case of emergency surgery, the anesthetist is responsible that adequate preparation has been performed considering the urgency of the surgical intervention.

Pulmonary function tests are of value to determine whether the patient's respiratory system is in the best condition possible before elective surgery.

Blood gases, measurements of arterial oxygen tension or pressure, carbon dioxide tension, pH or acid base status, and oxygen content and saturation can be valuable as indications of the overall functioning of the respiratory system, and also to some extent of the cardiovascular system.

Thyroid malfunctions, excessive or deficient, may be suspected on the basis of a good history and physical examination. Appropriate laboratory tests will confirm the presence of hyperthyroidism or hypothyroidism, both of which should be managed before elective surgery is undertaken.

The question that must be raised in every preanesthetic evaluation, bar none, is whether the stomach has contents which might be passively regurgitated or actively vomited and aspirated into the tracheobronchial tree. For elective surgery, it is routine to order nothing by mouth after midnight of the day before surgery because it is assumed that the stomach will empty itself during sleep. However, gastric acid may be secreted after awakening, and gastric acid can seriously damage the tracheobronchial tree. For emergency surgery, it must be assumed that the stomach is full because trauma and anxiety can produce gastric stasis. (Anesthetic management of the full stomach is discussed in § 8.09 [1].) If there is any doubt in regard to the possibility of a full stomach (especially emergency surgery) after aspiration of the stomach, an awake intubation should be performed after anesthetizing the tongue. After anesthesia is established, Versed should be given to prevent or at least dull the memory of this unpleasant procedure. Obstetrical patients at term also can be assumed to have gastric stasis so routinely upon admission nothing by mouth is ordered and an antacid is often administered if a general anesthesia is to be given. (Milk is a superb antacid but fat tends to produce gastric stasis.) Many anesthesia record forms have a preprinted space to indicate when food was last ingested.

[1] Preanesthetic Medication

Although preanesthetic medication is not mandatory, the surgeon or anesthetist will usually order such medication. Some of the purposes for which these medications are administered are:

1. To minimize salivary and gastric secretions;
2. To allay anxiety;
3. To alleviate pain;
4. To render somnolent;
5. To decrease (it is hoped) the incidence of nausea, retching, and vomiting;
6. Occasionally, to produce amnesia for ongoing events;
7. To facilitate uninterrupted sleep the night before elective surgery; and
8. To decrease the likelihood of serious cardiac dysrhythmia during anesthesia and surgery.

Infants and children present special problems and pre-anesthetic medication is often omitted.

If preanesthetic medication is believed to be necessary, and it has not been administered subcutaneously, intramuscularly or orally one-half to one hour before anesthetic induction, the anesthetist may administer appropriate drugs intravenously and expect peak action within five to ten minutes.

Unfortunately, individualization of preanesthetic medication is not common. Underdose or overdose is frequent. Possible complications include nerve injury, vomiting and aspiration, airway obstruction, and death.

[2] Medication for Pre-existing Medical Conditions

Specific management of all the various medical conditions from which patients suffer is beyond the scope of this chapter. In general, however, the surgeon, internist, family practitioner, and anesthetist should err on the side of caution, keeping in mind those conditions that can be recognized under anesthesia and managed most easily. For example, overdose of insulin resulting in hypoglycemia (low blood sugar) cannot be readily diagnosed under general anesthesia. The brain needs sugar (glucose) moment-to-moment just as it needs oxygen. The AM dose of insulin should be omitted to avoid this problem. An immediate blood sugar test in the recovery room and insulin given as required.

Low blood sugar can result in severe brain damage. If hypoglycemia is recognized, the treatment is easy. Rapid intravenous infusion of glucose will correct blood sugar deficit. It is recognition of the problem under general anesthesia that is difficult. On the other hand, moderately elevated blood sugar can be managed by administration of insulin and does not cause any immediate problem. Of course, very high blood sugar levels can result in increased blood viscosity and thrombosis, and in time ketoacidosis and death.

Overdose of digitalis can result in lethal cardiac dysrhythmias for which there is no specific treatment; these rhythm disturbances are particularly likely if serum potassium is low. Underdose of digitalis can result in congestive heart failure which will not cause sudden death and which can be managed by digitalis. Blood levels of digitalis can now be measured.

If the patient has been receiving steroids, he may not be able to respond to the stress of anesthesia and surgery by increasing his steroid production. Adrenocortical hypofunction can result in hypotension, fever, tachycardia and coma. The treatment is intravenous steroids. Prophylactically, if the patient has been receiving steroids, then steroids should be administered preoperatively and during surgery.

Although drugs administered for preanesthetic medication are almost never themselves the proximate cause of damage, a brief outline of their actions is presented below. Further details regarding these and other such drugs can be found in Good-man and Gilman, *The Pharmacological Basis of Therapeutics* (8th ed.), Pergamon Press 1990, and the latest edition of

Physicians' Desk Reference. Also, the American Medical Association publishes a three-volume set on drug evaluations that is updated quarterly.

The narcotics (morphine, fentanyl, sufentanil, meperidine, alfentanil, etc.) elevate the threshold for pain. If the patient has been addicted or has become tolerant to one of these drugs, it is important to administer it to avoid withdrawal crisis during anesthesia. Narcotics have no amnesic properties. Naloxone will reverse the respiratory depressant action of narcotics.

Barbiturates actually lower the pain threshold. They are soporifics and amnesics and tend to decrease anxiety. They were at one time recommended to decrease the likelihood of convulsions from the overdose of local anesthetics. Acute withdrawal in barbiturate addicts can be lethal. There are no pharmacologic antagonists to barbiturates and their dose response is unpredictable. In the rare disease porphyria, barbiturates may produce permanent central nervous system damage.

Mood-altering or neuroleptic drugs such as diazepam (Valium), Ativan (lorazepam) or droperidol may be administered as tranquilizers, sedatives, antiemetics and amnesics. There are no effective pharmacologic antagonists to these drugs.

Atropine may be administered to suppress salivary secretions and possibly counteract bradycardia and deleterious vagal reflexes. Scopolamine has the actions desired of atropine, but also may produce amnesia. Physostigmine will counteract the central nervous system actions of scopolamine.

Robinul (glycopyrrolate) has become popular as a preoperative antimuscarinic drug to decrease salivary and gastric secretion.

Anesthetists seem to like to prescribe and administer recently approved drugs in lieu of old tried and true standbys. The risk is that only a few thousand case reports are required by the Food and Drug Administration before approval of a drug, while the incidence of complications may be 1:100,000 or even one in several million, so the toxicity does not become apparent until the drug has been in use for several years. If a failure-to-warn issue arises, the attorney should examine the Drug Experience Reports of the drug's manufacturer.

[3] Respiratory and Cardiovascular Systems

The lungs have many functions other than delivery of oxygen to blood and clearance of carbon dioxide from blood. They also play a role in water and heat maintenance and in immunologic and detoxification processes. They have cilia which tend to move secretions up toward the throat where they can then be cleared.

The anesthetist must evaluate the airway and prepare to assure its patency throughout the anesthetic period. Under general endotracheal anesthesia, the anesthetist can deliver close to 100% oxygen to the airway and can usually achieve hyperventilation, thus clearing more carbon dioxide than the patient can clear for himself. The anesthetist can also increase end-expiratory pressure to try to get more oxygen across the alveolar membrane and counteract pulmonary edema. Normally, one breathes from zero pressure — to negative pressure — to zero pressure. During the negative pressure phase air enters into the lungs. Under general anesthesia if the anesthetist manages respiration by assisted (augmented depth) or controlled [both rate and depth] ventilation, either manually by squeezing the rebreathing bag or by the use of a ventilator, the cycle is zero or above pressure — to increased pressure forcing air into the lungs — back to zero or above pressure. This pressure reversal may prove deleterious to the cardiovascular system since the increased intrathoracic pressure tends to impede the return of blood to the heart. There are no functioning valves in the veins of the abdomen, head, neck and chest. There are valves only in the veins of the extremities. If the patient is hypovolemic or in shock, he may not be able to compensate for this pressure reversal. And, in fact, if the venous return is impaired, the exchange of gas in the lungs may also be impaired. If an anesthetist notes a blood gas with low oxygen and high carbon dioxide because of poor venous return, and reacts by increasing artificial ventilation, he will aggravate the problem. The solution is to increase circulating blood volume.

Hypovolemia (low blood volume) may be apparent or occult as in chronic shock. In the latter instance it may be unmasked by peripheral dilating drugs such as anesthetic agents. A rule of thumb in acute blood loss is that when the pulse rate is greater than the systolic pressure, at the point of crossing the patient is 20% behind in blood volume.

Blood pressure under anesthesia should usually be maintained near the patient's normal range. Excessively high blood pressure may result in pulmonary edema or stroke. Epinephrine could produce this result. Lower blood pressure, if accompanied by vasodilation and a normal blood volume, and the supine position, may not be hazardous. As a matter of fact, deliberate hypotension is sometimes induced by anesthetists. Properly performed, it can decrease blood loss and facilitate surgery.

Halothane (Fluothane) has been associated with liver failure and death. The actual cause is still unknown, but it may be a sensitivity reaction to a breakdown product. In any event, halothane should be avoided if jaundice followed a previous halogenated anesthetic. In modern anesthesia, it is best avoided altogether.

A patient on anticoagulants contraindicates deep-needling such as is necessary in nerve blocks and epidurals.

Serpasil at one time was discontinued two weeks before surgery but now is continued. (The pendulum swings.)

Inderal (propranolol HCL) was also once discontinued before anesthesia and surgery but is now continued because of reports of sudden death upon discontinuance.

The lawyer should check *PDR* for the year in question on a particular drug to learn what the recommendations were that year.

The anesthetist should remind the patient to remove all removable prostheses such as dentures, contact lenses, artificial eyes, etc. Many hospitals have a preoperative checklist listing such prostheses. The problem is usually well managed for elective surgery, but patients who need emergency surgery often come to the operating room with a prosthesis, especially dentures, in place. The anesthetist, especially when checking for the presence of a prosthesis, is responsible for a thorough preanesthetic examination. The anesthetist should also caution against coming into surgery with chewing gum or with other substances in the mouth. It does little good to stop smoking for a day or two, but if the patient can discontinue smoking for at least three months before elective surgery, the likelihood of postoperative atelectasis or pneumonia will be decreased.

Elective procedures should be postponed under certain circumstances. A "cold" or fever should cause postponement of elective surgery as should any acute infectious process in the airways or lungs. An acute asthmatic attack should postpone elective surgery until the asthma can be controlled. In asthmatics, and whenever indicated, the anesthetist should listen to the heart and lungs immediately before inducing anesthesia. If immediately preoperatively a cardiac dysrhythmia is noted for the first time, postponement of elective surgery to permit diagnosis and treatment is wise.

Surgical procedures are often classified as major or minor. With respect to anesthesia, however, any anesthetic agent administered by any route may precipitate cardiovascular collapse, so all anesthetic procedures must be considered major. It is important to understand that cardiovascular collapse may not be due to negligence nor are there always premonitory signs. Prompt recognition and appropriate treatment should result in a successful resuscitation without untoward sequelae if in fact the collapse was due to a reversible process. Resuscitation of the heart with residual brain damage (which means the process was reversible), means that there were premonitory signs or that recognition and treatment of inadequate cardiac output were unduly delayed.

As part of the preanesthetic evaluation, the anesthetist should communicate with those doctors familiar with the patient's condition. The anesthetist may contact the pharmacist to learn what drugs or medications the patient has been taking. And he must communicate with the surgeon to learn the surgeon's needs, the anticipated blood loss and to inform him of the proposed anesthetic techniques and agents.

[4] Physical Status and Risk

At the conclusion of the preanesthetic evaluation the anesthetist often grades the patients' physical status (PS) and risk.

Physical Status 1 is someone with no significant disease about to undergo relatively minor surgery; for example, a perfectly healthy male in his fifties about to undergo inguinal herniorraphy. Physical Status 2 is someone with one significant disease under control such, as moderate obesity, diabetes, essential hypertension, etc. Physical Status 3 is someone with two significant diseases or one not under control, such as someone with chronic obstructive lung disease and diabetes under control. Physical Status 4 is simply worse than 3. If an "E" is added, then the procedure is an emergency. Physical Status 5 is moribund, and surgery is a desperate attempt to save the patients' life.

Risk is a more general term. It is classified as "Good," "Fair" or "Poor." In addition to physical status, risk takes into consideration the skills of all personnel: the anesthetist, the surgeon, the nurses, and the hospital. It also includes season and climate, etc. The true purpose of this classification is to alert the anesthetist and surgeon as to whether more preparation might convert the patient to a better physical status or decrease the risk.

While intuitively one can infer that there is an increased incidence of anesthetic-associated morbidity and mortality as one progresses from PS1 to PS5 (the latter is always an emergency), the fact is that many anesthetic catastrophes occur to patients classified PS1 or PS2. These are particularly tragic, and often produce high jury awards.

§ 8.04 Preanesthetic Check

Just as a pilot should thoroughly check his instruments before taking off, so should an anesthetist check his drugs and equipment. Everything should be at hand in a standardized arrangement.

The anesthesia machine should have adequate oxygen and the oxygen flow meters and oxygen flush valve should be in good order. "Fail safe" should be functioning. "Fail safe," however, is not truly fail safe since it is based on oxygen pressure in the line and not on oxygen flow or oxygen concentration being delivered to the patient. Fail safe only indicates that oxygen has become exhausted or has not been opened at the pressure gauge level. There are machines available, however, that will not deliver any other gas if no oxygen at all is flowing.

The delivery system from the machine to the patient should be intact, i.e., unidirectional valves should be competent and not have undue resistance. Face masks, the rebreathing bag, and circle tubes should be clean. The pressure release value (pop-off valve) should be functioning properly.

Fresh carbon dioxide absorbent should be in the canister and the entire system should have no significant leak so that adequate pressure can be delivered to the airway. Machines can only deliver up to 40 or 50 mm of mercury pressure. A healthy human can blow with 100 to 120 mm and can resist, as in asthma, with a similar pressure. The inference is that if more than 40 or 50 mm pressure is required the anesthetist can do mouth-to-mouth or mouth-to-endotracheal tube. Attempts have been made to design machines that incorporate state of the art space age technology, but so far economic factors have made these unmarketable.

The agents to be administered should be in the machine, and the vaporizers must be functioning properly. There should be assurances that the scavenging system is not misconnected. Anesthesia equipment needs to be checked and maintained regularly to insure proper functioning. These maintenance checks should be performed by trained technicians and a record should be kept.

Suction should be available and catheters at hand. The laryngoscope light should function, and airways must be available and appropriate. Endotracheal tubes of various sizes and stylets must be laid out. Intravenous drugs for induction, muscle relaxation, resuscitation, etc., and syringes and needles must be at hand. (Photographs of typical layouts can be found in many anesthesia texts.)

Whichever monitors are to be used should be attached and functioning. These usually include a means of taking blood pressure, a means of continuous auscultation of heart and lungs, and an electrocardioscope. Patient temperature may be monitored and often the percentage of oxygen being delivered to the patient is monitored. The most sophisticated monitors available today are electroencephalographs, capnographs and multiple gas on-line analyzers, all of which can be computer programmed, displayed, and the information stored. Also, the FDA has approved a noninvasive "brain oximeter" to measure the amount of oxygen reaching the brain. Since the brain is dependent on a continuous, moment-to-moment supply of oxygen (and also glucose) this may prove to be a most important monitor. It is also fashionable to use a ventilator during anesthesia. That device should be very carefully inspected. It should be connected to various monitors that warn of "disconnect," "no ventilation," "excessive pressure," etc. The ventilator is a frequent cause of anesthesia catastrophes.

Minor items such as eye protective ointment, adhesive tape, bite blocks, and tongue blades should also be at hand. If heating or cooling blankets are to be used, they must be checked. Excessive heat for prolonged periods may cause burns.

Before any anesthetic is administered, a secure intravenous route must be established. Plastic catheters are currently utilized. The purpose of the intravenous route is to rehydrate the patient who has been fasting, and to administer drugs, fluids, electrolytes, and blood or blood products, if necessary, during and after the surgery. On rare occasions, part of the plastic catheter is sheared and goes to the heart. Also, if it is left in place too long, infection develops. (Phlebitis of the wrist can result in reflex sympathetic dystrophy.)

Just as it is wise for a pilot to have a co-pilot, it is advisable for the anesthetist to have a second person, preferably a knowledgeable nurse, with him during the induction of anesthesia. The surgeon or obstetrician should stand by during induction, particularly if a non-physician is administering the anesthetic. Should an emergency arise, a second pair of knowledgeable hands is mandatory.

Also, before any agent is administered, the anesthetist should record the patient's vital signs[5] (blood pressure, pulse rate per minute, and respiratory rate per minute).

Equipment for cardiac arrest should be at hand: As a minimum, there should be:

1. A board to place under the back.
2. A defibrillator with external and internal paddles.
3. A means of opening the chest (thoracotomy) and chest retractors if closed cardiac massage does not prove efficacious.
4. Oxygen. (The anesthesia machine itself serves as a source of oxygen. In a physician's office there should be at least an "Ambu" bag or a similar device which incorporates a mask or non-rebreathing valve, and a self inflating bag.)
5. Appropriate drugs, especially epinephrine and sodium bicarbonate.

---

[5] The term "vital signs" goes back to the days before cardiopulmonary resuscitation. Today these signs should be termed "vegetative" rather than "vital," since the present criterion of death is brain death, and it is possible mechanically to maintain respiration and circulation in spite of brain death.

Among the ancillary drugs that must be available for use during anesthesia are vasopressors and anticholinesterase inhibitors.

Vasopressors: If the anesthetic technique might result in undesirable hypotension, such as with a spinal for caesarean birth, the anesthetist should be ready to administer intravenously or intramuscularly an appropriate vasopressor such as ephedrine or Wyamine sulfate (mephentermine sulfate). (If the attorney discovers that a vasopressor was utilized or should have been utilized, he should carefully check the literature for deviation from the standard of care.)

Anticholinesterase inhibitors: Regonal (pyridostigmine bromide) may be used to antagonize nondepolarizing muscle relaxants such as tubocurare or Pavulon. Neostigmine also antagonizes nondepolarizing muscle relaxants. Both of the above may have a duration of action significantly shorter than that of the agonists. Because they produce bradycardia, they are often preceded by atropine.

Lidocaine for dysrhythmias also should be available, as should a beta blocker such as Inderal (propranolol HCL), and an alpha blocker such as Regitine (phentolamine mesylate) should be available.

Drugs for cardiac resuscitation such as epinephrine (adrenaline), norepinephrine (levophed), calcium chloride, calcium gluconate, and sodium bicarbonate also must be in the anesthesia cart. Before use, and at least on a daily basis, all anesthesia machines and accessories must be inspected in compliance with a checklist. These checklists are provided by manufacturers in user manuals and have been approved by the FDA. A sample checklist is published by ECRI (5200 Butler Pike, Plymouth Meeting, Pa. 19462) in the anesthesia section of its manual on *Operating Room Risk Management.*

§ 8.05 The Anesthesia Record

[1] The Permanent Record

In the United States a permanent record of the administration of every anesthetic agent and of the patient's response thereto should be concurrently recorded on a time-scale. Significant information such as beginning and end of anesthesia, beginning and end of surgery, the patient's response to premedicant drugs, position of the patient, and airway maintenance and intubation should also be in the record.

The anesthetic record will be the physician's and attorney's principal guide to what happened to the patient during the administration of the anesthetic. While learning to read an anesthetic record is fairly simple (although some surgeons profess to be unable to do so), inferring from the record what caused a therapeutic misadventure requires the highest degree of knowledge, experience, intelligence, and logical thinking.

Anesthetic records are sometimes rewritten in the interest of neatness. Many are written through carbons, sometimes in triplicate. One copy stays in the hospital chart, one copy is for the anesthetist, and one copy is used for billing and statistical purposes.

If the person administering the anesthetic could have anticipated a catastrophe, and should have prevented it, there can be a cause of action. Failure on the part of the anesthetist to interpret warning signs is a deviation from the standard of care.

Interpretation of the pathophysiological process which eventuated in a catastrophe always requires close analysis of the post-catastrophe course. If death occurs, an autopsy should indicate whether the death was *not* preventable.

If a crisis arises, the anesthetist will not be able to keep the record and take care of the patient simultaneously. On deposition, one hears the statement "I treat the patient, not the chart." It is inevitable that much of the record regarding the crucial time period immediately surrounding the catastrophe will have been recorded later from memory, even if there is more than one person administering the anesthetic (e.g., student and supervisor).

The attorney should inspect the original of the anesthetic record since photocopies do not indicate different colored inks, erasures, scotch taped records, etc. If advisable, a color photograph of the original anesthesia record should be made. Very rarely will the original anesthesia record be destroyed and a new one substituted. Corrections on the record should line out an error so that it can still be read, the correction always should be dated, timed and initialed. (Anesthetists take coffee breaks, get lunch relief, and are sent home at the end of their shifts. Seldom are all these changes of personnel recorded.)

Anesthesia records are kept on preprinted forms which are for the most part self-explanatory. The back of the anesthetic records may be preprinted to permit the anesthetist to record preoperative evaluations and postoperative visits.

Should a misadventure occur, the anesthetist and/or the director will usually write a summary of the incident on the doctor's progress sheet.

The forms for records for anesthesia should be detailed whether they are at universities and teaching hospitals or at a small community hospital. On the forms, the grid should show vital signs and monitoring by one minute intervals. Grids of five minute intervals are usually not detailed enough to record the progress of catastrophic events, since as little as four minutes of deprivation of oxygen to the brain at normal temperature will produce profound irreversible brain damage. Brain damage begins within twenty seconds of deprivation of oxygen and continues to worsen the longer the brain is deprived of oxygen. The so-called 3-minute or 4-minute rule merely means that after four minutes of deprivation of oxygen the cortex is usually irreversibly destroyed and the patient remains in coma. Any period of deprivation of oxygen to the developed brain will produce some damage. Little is known regarding the tolerance to anoxia of the brain of neonates.

The anesthetist should always enter the concentration of inhalational anesthetic agent in the percent administered through a precision vaporizer. These records are necessary since very small differences in concentration can produce profound effects. At the same time, it is necessary to document and plot the systolic and diastolic blood pressures and pulse rates by time. The respiratory rate should also be documented and plotted carefully since monitoring the spontaneous respirations of patients is the most sensitive clinical sign available to the anesthetist. Fluid administered to the patients via intravenous route, such as Dextrose 5% in Ringer Lactate ("D5R"), should be documented at the time they are administered. If a "code" is called, the reason for the "code" should be recorded and the time should be noted on the anesthetic record. In June, 2000, an anesthesiologist was sued in medical malpractice for misplacing the endotracheal tube into the patient's esophagus. According to the anesthetic records, the misplacement of the endotracheal tube probably occurred before the "Code Blue." The patient was re-intubated and this permitted the heart to be restarted. Had the tube remained in the esophagus, the cardiac action would never have been restarted. The period of anoxia was long enough to produce severe brain damage. The patient, who had been relatively healthy, was pronounced dead that evening. The autopsy was negative. The medical malpractice lawsuit eventually resulted in a plaintiff's verdict of $2 million dollars. In another case, the record indicated that from 7:00 p.m. until the patient suffered cardiac arrest at 8:13 p.m., something seriously wrong was happening. Although, the anesthesia record seemed superficially adequate, in actuality it was incomplete. Many of the significant details had to be obtained by deposition by which time even the nurse anesthetist did not remember them. This was a case of malignant hyperthermia (malignant hyperpyrexia syndrome). The patient, after resuscitation, remained brain damaged and expired some nine months later. On deposition it was learned that the ventilator may have been used from time-to-time, that the respiratory rate of 20 was only an approximation, that respirations were spontaneous, assisted, or controlled from time-to-time. The concentration of Halothane varied between 0.5 and 1.5%, but was never recorded. The muscle relaxant used was nondepolarizer tubocurare. Temperature of the patient was never taken. Position of the patient was never recorded. Time and other details of intubation were never recorded. A verdict of $5 million dollars was rendered against the anesthetist.

It is pertinent to note some abbreviations that are seen in anesthesia records of patients. Examples of such abbreviations include:

1. "DTC" means d-tubocurare
2. "Esophageal 36-5" indicates an esophageal temperature taken in degrees centigrade
3. "M" means Manual and "AV" means Assisted Ventilation
4. "AB" means Arterial Blood Gases
5. "LTA" is a kit to apply local anesthesia to the larynx

[2] Other Records

Other reports or records that the attorney should be able to cross-check with the anesthesia record are:

1. Preanesthetic evaluation on the doctor's progress sheet, on a separate form, or on the back of the anesthesia record.
2. The surgeon's long-hand operative notes and dictated, typed operative report. (Always check date dictated and date transcribed.)
3. Post-catastrophe reports by consultants either on a separate sheet or in the doctor's progress notes. (These often contain significant history.)
4. Operating room log.
5. Recovery room log.
6. Doctor's order sheets.
7. Cardiac arrest record.
8. Laboratory request slips for studies requested from the operating room, particularly X-rays, blood gases, electrolytes and blood sugar.
9. X-rays taken in the operating room. (Check the X-ray itself instead of relying solely on the dictated interpretation.)
10. The pathology report.
11. It also has become customary for the anesthesiologist, after an anesthetic mishap, to write a narrative summary on the physician's progress sheet.

Among the records that are often privileged, but sometimes can be obtained, are:

1. Incident reports;
2. Morbidity and Mortality Committee minutes;
3. Risk Management Committee minutes;

4. Peer review audits;
5. Outside evaluations by physicians at the request of an insurance carrier.
6. Personnel files.

§ 8.06 General Anesthesia

[1] Induction

The induction period refers to the time interval from the beginning of the administration of any agents, even oxygen, until the surgeon is advised he can begin the operation.

Anesthesia records and circulating operating room nurse records have a space to indicate the time anesthesia was begun. Often there will be other times recorded such as the time the patient is in the operating room, the time surgeon arrived, etc. Sometimes these various times will differ on different records. The attorney should look into the reasons for the recording of different times. Anesthesia is usually billed partially on a time basis as is operating room time. Some anesthetists record the time they begin anesthesia as the time they first greet the patient just before surgery, others at the time the intravenous infusion is started, still others at the time they begin preoxygenation or when they administer intravenous pentothal or another intravenous amnesic.

Anesthesia usually begins with preoxygenation. A mask is fitted over the patient's face and only oxygen, at a relatively high flow, is administered. The purpose is to substitute oxygen for nitrogen in the alveoli of the lungs. This substitution should serve as insurance against hypoxemia during intubation. If ventilation is spontaneous and unassisted, carbon dioxide levels will remain in the normal range and will rise to some extent during the apnea while intubation is performed. If the anesthetist hyperventilates the patient, he may also decrease carbon dioxide levels in the alveoli and tend to prevent hypercarbia during intubation.

It is possible to administer anesthetics such as pentothal or avertin rectally. In the days before antithyroid drugs such as propylthiouracil became available, it was the practice to administer enemas to a patient with Graves disease (thyrotoxicosis) over several days. One day the anesthetist would put avertin in the enema, put the patient to sleep, and "steal" her to the operating room, thus perhaps avoiding a "thyroid storm." In children, rectal pentothal would be used for similar purposes. These techniques are probably obsolete today.

Next, a soporific or amnesic is usually administered intravenously. So called ultra short-acting barbiturates such as sodium thiopental, surital, or brevital, can produce unconsciousness in one circulation time (under 30 seconds). Other drugs to produce amnesia rapidly may be used, such as scopolamine, diazepam, lorazepam, droperidol, propanidid, etomidate, or ketamine. One of the newest induction agents is diisopropylphenol. Research is aggressively pursued, particularly in Europe, to develop more satisfactory intravenous agents for induction and for brief outpatient surgical procedures. (Etomidate has been found to suppress adrenocortial function in intensive care patients.)

Pentothal and Valium (diazepam) are alkaline. The body is on the alkaline side, i.e. pH 7:44 or so (7.0 is neutral). Alkaline substances are extremely irritating, and the body does not neutralize them rapidly, so they act over long periods of time and can produce progressive tissue damage, necrosis, and phlebitis.

Pentothal injected into an artery in the arm may cause gangrene of the hand. Valium given intravenously frequently causes phlebitis and if injected in the small veins of the dorsum of the hand may cause reflex sympathetic dystrophy. The product insert recommends that the small veins of the dorsum of the hand not be used.

Frequently, either before induction or during maintenance, the anesthetist is asked to administer medication by the surgeon or by an internist standing by. For example, antibiotics are often given intravenously just before orthopedic procedures. The anesthetist must familiarize himself with the side effects of any drug he administers. Some of these drugs are ototoxic or renotoxic, others summate with muscle relaxants, etc. At the very least, if unfamiliar with the side effects of the drug, the anesthetist should read the product insert before administering the drug.

It is likely that intubation may result in hypertension and dysrhythmia which are thought to be deleterious in susceptible patients. These reflex responses may be blocked by topical anesthesia of the pharynx and larynx or by appropriate dosage of various medications such as narcotics.

At this point the principal anesthetic agent may be begun. (Discussion of the various agents will be presented under maintenance of general anesthesia in § 8.06 [2].)

If an endotracheal tube is to be inserted, it is customary to administer a muscle relaxant intravenously to facilitate laryngoscopy, visualization of the glottis and passage of the tube. Many operations can be performed without muscle relaxants, using only a mask and an oropharyngeal airway. However, even for foot surgery, today endotracheal tubes are utilized. An endotracheal tube secures the airway and after its cuff is inflated, prevents aspiration into the lungs while the cuff is inflated.

Endotracheal tubes are available in the nasotracheal length as sterilized plastic disposables with a bonded cuff. A catheter adapter is included in the package. The tube should be shorter if introduced through the mouth (as it usually is).

Great care must be taken when passing an endotracheal tube into a patient who has cervical spine disorders or fractures. Inexpert intubation may cause quadriplegia by hyperextending the head or the neck in an attempt to visualize the vocal cords. The capsule of the temperomandibular joint also may be injured during intubation, resulting in chronic pain. Other types of tubes such as anode or wire guarded, endobronchial, and trachestomy tubes are also available.

There are two main classes of muscle relaxants. The nondepolarizers are characterized by tubocurare and pancuronium (Pavulon), and their effects can be antagonized by cholinesterase inhibitors such as neostigmine. The duration of action of the antagonist is generally shorter than that of the agonist. Tubocurare does produce histamine release. The depolarizers are typified by succinyldicholine hydrochloride. There are no pharmacologic antagonists to their paralysis. If overdosed, the patient's ventilation must be supported, sometimes for days, until the body clears the drug. Recently, two new muscle relaxants have been introduced; Norcuron (vecuronium bromide) and Tracrium (atracurium besylate). Both of these are nondepolarizers.

All these muscle relaxants differ in onset of action, duration of peak action, summation, side effects, etc. They all can cause in the patient absolute helplessness and inability to maintain the airway and to breathe. They do not have any direct central nervous system effects, so there is no impairment of memory provided there is no hypoxia. They do not cross the placenta in significant amounts. The latter is a valuable property in cesarean birth since they can paralyze the mother without affecting the fetus.

The nondepolarizing muscle relaxants have extraordinarily prolonged duration of action in myasthenia gravis. One in 300 individuals has atypical pseudocholinesterase and cannot metabolize succinyldicholine rapidly. Note that this is atypical, not lower levels of normal pseudocholinesterases. Ordinarily as much as 90% of an intravenously administered dose is destroyed before reaching the myoneural junction. The duration of action in the individuals with atypical pseudocholinesterase may be thirty times that of a normal person. The intensity and duration of action of muscle relaxants can be monitored by a blockade monitor. In patients with severe burns, trauma or recent transection of the spinal cord, succinylcholine may result in marked elevation of serum potassium causing cardiac arrest.

Succinylcholine may trigger an attack of malignant hyperpyrexia. A warning sign is spasm of the masseter (jaw) muscles making intubation difficult. If this occurs, the patient should be allowed to recover from the drug. If surgery was elective, a work-up for malignant hyperpyrexia should be done. If it is an emergency, surgery should be performed with all the malignant hyperpyrexia precautions, particularly avoiding succinylcholine, halothane, and ethrane. Also, dantrolene should be available intravenously.

Initially, succinylcholine may cause muscles to fasciculate, resulting in postoperative chest pain. Some anesthetists administer a small dose of curare before succinylcholine in the hope of preventing these pains. Succinylcholine also initially causes spasm of the extraocular muscles. If the globe is open from injury or during a cataract operation, and succinylcholine is administered, vitreous may be extruded with possible loss of vision.

The patient should never be paralyzed unless the anesthetist is absolutely certain he can maintain the airway and ventilate the patient in spite of the paralysis. It is a grievous error to administer relaxants if the airway cannot be established after paralysis. Such a problem may be anticipated if there are tumors or abscesses in the throat or if there is Ludwig's angina. Muscle relaxants are excellent for the management of laryngospasm. Before their introduction, tracheostomy was often necessary. However, since larynogospasm is a protective reflex, the pharynx should be suctioned out before paralysis is produced. Larynogospasm can also be broken by pulling the jaw forward and upward if one is strong enough to overcome the masseters.

After paralysis is achieved, an endotracheal tube is passed usually through the mouth. A laryngoscope is used to permit direct visualization of the larynx. Perhaps the most common injury produced by anesthetists is damage to natural teeth or artificial teeth either by the laryngoscope or by the oropharyngeal airway.

It is not unusual for the endotracheal tube to be passed into the esophagus rather than the trachea, even by the most experienced anesthetists. Esophageal intubation is not necessarily negligence. Leaving the tube in the esophagus in a paralyzed apneic patient long enough to produce brain damage from anoxia *is* clearly negligence. Although the relaxant effect may have worn off, an anoxic brain will not drive respiration.

Because of the quality control and monitoring devices that are now in use, the incidence of brain damage from endotracheal tubes inadvertently left in the esophagus in operating rooms has decreased. However, these tubes are often inserted by paramedics, emergency medical technicians, respiratory therapists, physicians, and nurse anesthetists in locations other than the operating room (i.e., scene of an accident, the home, intensive care units, hospital rooms, emergency rooms, etc.), where there are no monitoring devices.

The anesthetist usually checks and records "BBS," bilateral breath sounds as an assurance that the tube is in the trachea. Unfortunately, the tube may be in the esophagus and the anesthetist may honestly believe he has heard bilateral breath sounds. For safety's sake the epigastrium should also be listened to. If the tube is in the esophagus, gurgling will be heard.

After the endotracheal tube has been passed, the safest technique is to place a mask over the tube and to ventilate. Even if the tube is in the esophagus, some alveolar ventilation with oxygen will be achieved. Then the larynx should be revisualized and the position of the vocal cords alongside the tube observed. Students have been known to report seeing the cords along the tube when it was in the esophagus.

If the tube is too long, it may pass into the right main stem bronchus and obstruct ventilation to some 60% of the lungs. The tube can kink and become obstructed, so even if it is in the trachea there is no guarantee of patent airway.

Most surgeons utilize cautery or a Bovie to coagulate blood vessels and occasionally to cut tissue. These require a ground plate. The current at the ground plate is exactly the same as at the hot point, but the heat is dissipated because the ground is so large. Misapplication of the ground plate may result in burns and failure to ground may cause burns at EKG or EEG leads or points where the patient's body comes in contact with the metal of the operating room table.

Flammable or explosive anesthetic agents must not be used if cautery is used. The location of the ground plate should be recorded by the circulating nurse, but both the anesthetist and the surgeon should also check its proper positioning.

Using a laser in the tracheobronchial tree requires special precautions since a plastic endotracheal tube may ignite in a high oxygen-nitrous oxide environment.

Once the induction is complete, skin cleansing, draping, and incision can be performed. If the cleansing agent is a tincture, i.e., alcohol based, and cautery is used, a fire may result because of the vapor.

[2] Maintenance

Explosive and flammable agents such as diethylether, cyclopropane, and ethylene are no longer selected for anesthesia because insurance companies and risk management committees forbid their use. Vinethene, which also is flammable, is no longer marketed. Usually, there are signs posted at anesthetizing locations forbidding the use of flammable and explosive agents. The equipment will also have such warnings. Chloroform is not flammable, not explosive, and is inexpensive, but the high incidence of liver failure and of ventricular fibrillation (cardiac arrest) have made it obsolete. (The first recorded anesthetic death was in 1847, with chloroform, in a doctor's office where it was being administered to a teenager for ingrown toenail surgery.)

Trichlorethylene (Trilene) is also nonflammable and nonexplosive. It is not a 100% potent agent, however. Also, it produces toxic phosgene when in contact with carbon dioxide absorbent materials, and is not used much in the United States. It can be administered with a self inhaler. Penthrane (methoxyflurane) is not explosive and is not flammable, but it produces kidney failure on a dose-response basis and has largely been abandoned. There are other anesthetic agents which are no longer used in the United States. Ethyl chloride and fluroxene are examples.

Intravenous barbiturates may be used for short procedures but the fact that they actually lower the patient's pain threshold, and their unpredictable duration of action, have decreased their popularity. If used as the primary agent without support of ventilation and monitoring, overdose and death are to be expected. The intravenous barbiturate agents available are thiopental sodium (Pentothal) thiamylal (Surital) and methohexital (Brevital). Some thiopental is rapidly broken down and excreted in the back of the throat as hydrogen sulfide which produces an offensive taste and is explosive. Right after the patient tastes the hydrogen sulfide he becomes unconscious. Pentothal may produce laryngospasm and singultus (hiccups).

Ketamine, which is an LSD-type drug, can be administered intravenously or intramuscularly. It is especially useful for children and for short procedures. Blood pressure tends to be elevated or normal and respiration is not impaired. Its disadvantages are that there is twitching and movement, and there can be very unpleasant memories. (Valium will tend to suppress these memories.) Vomiting and aspiration may also occur. Research is in progress to develop a more satisfying arylcyclohexylamine of which Ketamine is the prototype drug.

Innovar, which is a fixed mixture of a very potent narcotic and a neuroleptic, can also be used intravenously. It has many disadvantages and probably its effects should be achieved by the separate administration of its two components.

Open cardiotomy and other procedures may be performed with morphine or fentanyl or sufentanil as the main anesthetic. If this technique is used, amnesics must also be administered.

Although narcotic antagonists such as Narcan (naloxone) are available, these as a rule have a shorter duration of action than the narcotics. Recently, allegedly nonaddicting narcotic agonist-antagonists such as Stadol (butorphanol tartrate) or Nubain (nalbuphine HCl) have become available. There are other intravenous short-acting agents such as Althesin, for a time in common use in Great Britain and Europe, which were never approved by the Food and Drug Administration for use in the United States except for experimental purposes. At one time steroids were administered for general anesthesia but have been abandoned, as has electrical anesthesia.

Hypnosis and acupuncture are not satisfactory means of producing anesthesia for operating conditions in the United States, and expose the practitioner to the risk of a lawsuit.

Nitrous oxide (laughing gas) is not a fully potent anesthetic agent because it cannot produce satisfactory operating conditions in the absence of significantly decreased inhaled oxygen concentration. Years ago it was very popular, particularly in dental offices, but it is unsafe (in fact, entire books have been written about its subtle deleterious effects). Nevertheless, nitrous oxide is often used as a supplemental carrier gas with oxygen for potent agents such as halothane, ethrane and forane. (These three drugs, incidentally, are never administered in combination.) Nitrous oxide's flammability and explosiveness is about the same as oxygen. It will support combustion just as oxygen does, and will even produce a bigger explosion.

[3] Stages, Planes and Depth

When diethylether was the principal anesthetic agent administered, it was possible by close observation of the patient to estimate the blood level of ether and the depth of anesthesia. Guedel, in the early 1920s, systematized these observations into stages and planes of anesthesia. Ether could satisfy all the necessary properties of a general anesthetic. Today these stages and planes are irrelevant because the various requirements of a general anesthetic are achieved by administration of a number of drugs. General anesthetics must at least (1) obtund pain; (2) produce amnesia; and (3) relax muscles. Furthermore, they must achieve these three necessary effects without significant compromise of ventilation and circulation, and be reversible without untoward sequelae.

The surgical procedures attempted under ether were simpler than today's and the patients subjected to surgery in those days were much better risks than today.

Today the various properties of a general anesthetic are never achieved with a single drug such as ether or cyclopropane. Specific drugs are administered to achieve specific effects resulting in a type of balanced anesthesia or "polypharmacy." The result is that the classical signs of stages and planes are not present in their described sequence, and anesthetists "fly by the seat of their pants."

The concept of "MAC," or "minimum alveolar concentration," has been developed as a substitute for stages and planes. Research has determined the concentration of various anesthetic agents will suppress certain responses to painful stimuli in 50% of rats and dogs. When these concentrations were studied in humans, they had the same validity in terms of the patient's tolerance of otherwise painful surgical stimuli. Accordingly, the MAC for various anesthetic agents has been published and is a rough guide to the concentration of anesthetic agents needed to produce adequate operating conditions in the usual patient. For example, the MAC for middle-aged humans for Ethrane is 1.68% in 100% oxygen and 0.5% in 70% nitrous oxide.

The MAC for Forane in man is as follows:

AGE	100% O_2	70% N_2O
26 + 4	1.28	0.56
44 + 7	1.15	0.50
64 + 5	1.05	0.37

For halothane, anesthesia is usually obtained with concentrations between 0.5 and 1.5%. For methoxyflurane, the concentrations are 0.3 to 0.8%. The anesthetic concentrations needed may be lower if narcotics are administered. If muscle relaxants are administered, then possibly only amnesic concentrations are required.

Pupil size does not correlate well with depth except, of course, that widely dilated pupils that do not respond to light may indicate excessive depth or serious difficulty. Eye position does correlate to some extent, but is seldom observed and less often recorded. In full consciousness the eyes are conjugate. As the central nervous system is depressed, the eyes become roving or dysconjugate and there is nystagmus. In coma and stage III anesthesia, the eyes are fixed and slightly deviated.

Oxygen lack can cause depression of the central nervous system as can excessive carbon dioxide levels. High oxygen tensions and very low carbon dioxide tensions can produce cerebrovascular spasm with resultant deprivation of oxygen to nerve cells, even if the blood tension of oxygen is high.

General anesthetic agents have little, if any, effect on the functioning of the sympathetic and parasympathetic (autonomic-involuntary) nervous systems. It is this system which regulates the heart, intestines, tone of blood vessels, and many other vital functions.

General anesthetics do have effects on the various endocrine glands. Ether caused compensatory epinephrine secretion which counteracted its depressant effects on the heart. Most produce an increase in antidiuretic hormones and suppress urine output.

It is the responsibility of the anesthetist, in consultation with the surgeon, to estimate the blood loss and decide whether and when blood or one of its substitutes should be administered.

Numerous and various monitoring devices can be utilized, but none are absolutely correlated with the patient's condition, and none can reliably predict in all instances that a catastrophe is about to occur. In other words, the vigilant human can do better than the best computer.

Most anesthetic maintenance is based on administration of a nonexplosive, nonflammable anesthetic such as halothane, methoxyflurane, Ethrane, or Forane. These are liquids that must be vaporized in precision vaporizers because small fractions of a percent change in the concentration delivered can produce profound results in the patient. Halothane is useful in asthma since it tends to produce bronchodilation without bronchorrhea. It does overly relax the gravid uterus, and may produce uncontrollable bleeding if used for delivery. Whether it is the cause of liver failure has been the subject of numerous lawsuits. While absolute proof of its connection to liver failure is lacking, the anesthetist would be well advised not to administer halothane if the post-anesthetic period of a previous halogenated anesthetic has been complicated by jaundice or if the patient is suffering from hepatitis, or if the patient has multiple allergies. Eosinophilia may correlate with untoward reaction to halothane. Administration of epinephrine during halothane anesthesia may result in ventricular fibrillation. Also, halothane may trigger bouts of malignant hyperpyrexia. Ethrane may cause seizures and also may trigger malignant hyperpyrexia.

All general anesthetic agents, with the possible exception of nitrous oxide, are metabolized to some extent by the body.

During maintenance, if muscle relaxation is required, it is achieved by further intravenous doses of muscle relaxants.

Adequate concentrations of oxygen must be administered throughout the general anesthetic, and some means of clearing carbon dioxide must be provided. The actual mechanisms by which the anesthetic agents produce general anesthesia is not known, so the search for new anesthetic agents is still by trial and error.

[4] Delivery Systems

General anesthesia is delivered through an anesthesia machine. The current methods are semi-closed circle absorber (SCCA) and closed circle. Even if the anesthetic is not general, a machine set up to deliver oxygen for resuscitation and/or to convert a failed or worn-off spinal or epidural anesthetic to general anesthesia should be at hand and ready to use.

Basically, a machine will deliver oxygen and nitrous oxide, and will vaporize a halogenated agent. This mixture will flow into a circle which contains two non-rebreathing valves (one from the machine to the patient and one from the patient to the machine), a carbon dioxide-absorbing cannister, a rebreathing bag, and a pop-off valve. If the circle is closed, all the carbon dioxide is absorbed in the system and only as much oxygen and other agents should be delivered as the patient can consume and take up. If the circle is semi-closed, higher flows are required and some of the carbon dioxide is exhausted into the atmosphere, as are the excess oxygen, nitrous oxide and halogenated agents. It is a grievous hazard to deliver high flows with a closed pop-off valve. Ventilators have built-in pop-off valves, so when a ventilator is used the pop-off valve in the circle must be closed, or else inadequate pressure and flow will be delivered to the patient. The simplest and best way to ascertain the proper functioning and potency of the anesthesia circle is for the anesthetist to place the mask on her or his own face at the beginning of the day and breathe. Any problem will immediately come to light. Then fresh tubing and mask should be substituted to anesthetize the first patient of the day.

There also must be an intravenous route available to administer supplemental agents such as narcotics and muscle relaxants.

The actual consumption of oxygen is in the order of 200 to 350 cc per minute and the carbon dioxide production is 80% of the oxygen burned. In the closed system, all of the agent delivered is absorbed into the body except for leaks in the system and losses from the skin and into the urine.

In the semi-closed system, excess gas is blown off. Much oxygen, nitrous oxide, and agent is not utilized, making the SCCA system obviously wasteful, but because it is easier to manage and monitor (and thus safer in the hands of most anesthetists), it is the most common system used by far.

It is believed that chronic exposure to nitrous oxide and other inhalation anesthetic agents may be harmful to operating room personnel. Therefore, most anesthetic machines have a scavenging system to deposit these gases to ducts which usually deliver them to the outside atmosphere. If the scavenging system is misconnected, the patient may not be able to inhale or exhale. It must be carefully checked.

Most machines today have a ventilator that substitutes, if switched in, for the rebreathing bag. Although a ventilator certainly makes the work of the anesthetist less onerous, it introduces many hazards which, if not vigilantly protected against, can seriously damage the patient. The most serious loss in the training and practice of anesthesiology is that the "educated hand" is no longer on the rebreathing bag.

Ventilators can be set to deliver a certain tidal volume (normal is 500 cc) so many times per minute (normal is 12 to 16); they can vary the pressure from zero or above to some maximum inspiratory pressure (normal is zero to minus 5 to 7 mm Hg but under anesthesia we have zero to plus 20 or so); they can deliver a certain oxygen concentration up to 100%; the inspiratory-expiratory ratio can be varied (common is 1:2); they can deliver a deep breath or sigh every so often to prevent atelectasis; and they have a built-in pop-off valve. In anesthesia, they are usually driven by gas pressure. (In intensive care units they may be driven by electric power.)

It is a fact that within twenty seconds of deprivation of oxygen to the medulla of the brain, the patient will stop breathing. Within twenty seconds of deprivation of oxygen to the cortex of the brain, the electroencephalogram will become flat. Surgery can be performed with the patient just barely breathing, and the anesthetist assisting or augmenting the depth of each breath to insure adequate oxygenation and carbon dioxide excretion. If, under these conditions, the patient were to stop breathing (apnea), the anesthetist would be immediately alerted to the problem. After intubation, if the patient did not resume respiratory efforts, again the anesthetist would be alerted to the possibility of an esophageal intubation which can be missed if the endotracheal tube is immediately connected to a ventilator.

With a hand on the rebreathing bag, accidents due to a disconnect, misconnect, or ventilator malfunction would be detected immediately, and would not produce damage to the patient.

Other types of delivery systems are open-drop which is obsolete, non-rebreathing which is even more wasteful than semi-closed circle, and insufflation, in which the anesthetist has no means of assuring the adequacy of ventilation.

There are special systems for use in infants weighing less than ten kilograms. These are all designed to obviate potential problems of valve-resistance and dead space that exist with the adult systems.

Dead space is that fraction of tidal volume that does not participate in gas exchange. It is the sum of the anatomic and physiological dead space, and is normally about one-third of each breath. All anesthesia machines increase dead space to some extent. Mask anesthesia increases it significantly. Endotracheal anesthesia tends to decrease it.

[5] Monitoring

Monitoring simply means observing the patient. Anesthesiologist A. P. Rubin of Charing Cross Hospital, London, in a letter to the editor of *Lancet* (June 8, 1985) regarding minimal monitoring requirements wrote, "A strong chain attaching the anaesthetist to the operating table would be much cheaper and very much more effective. Increasingly complex monitoring devices distract anaesthetists from close clinical observations of the patient and encourage him to be further and further away from the patient." Monitoring does not require any sophisticated instruments, although as time has progressed one or another instrument may have become required by the "standard of care."

Although the administration of ether, chloroform or nitrous oxide to produce anesthesia for surgical procedures began in the 1840s, records of the anesthetics were not kept until many years later. Harvey Cushing, perhaps, was the first to require some sort of anesthesia record in the early 1900s. Through the years, as the complexity of surgery has increased, and as the number of bodily functions that technological advances have permitted to be maintained has increased, the evolving standard of care has required that more and more be monitored and recorded (see § 8.05, above). Some surgeons even videotape their operations. In some advanced centers, anesthesia is monitored by computers which produce detailed printouts.

In any event, and no matter how performed, monitoring of anesthesia must be continuous and uninterrupted. The minimal standard of care for monitoring the cardiovascular system is a continuous electrocardioscope, blood pressure at least every five minutes, and continuous heart sounds listened to from a precordial or esophageal stethoscope ending in the anesthetist's ear piece. Breathing is monitored through the same precordial or esophageal stethoscope by listening to breath sounds. Transesophageal echocardiography (TEE) may be useful to monitor blood flow and heart valve function during anesthesia.

Unfortunately the anesthesia record only has space for blood pressure and pulse every five minutes. This five-minute interval goes back to the days of ether and before muscle relaxants, and was adequate then. Since ventilators have come into common use, and respirations have been controlled (i.e., both initiation of each breath and depth of each breath is dependent on the machine), very few anesthetists record respiratory rate. Some anesthetists may record the frequency of breathing at which the ventilator has been set, the maximum and minimum pressure, and the tidal volume. Ventilators may have alarms to indicate disconnect, bradypnea and prolonged excessive airway pressure.

The body has innumerable monitors that protect us, and with which anesthesia interferes. At the carotid bifurcation there are the carotid sinus and carotid body. In effect, the sinus monitors blood flow to the brain. Actually, it monitors tension on the vessel wall, so that if external pressure is applied to this organ (which is just under the angle of the mandible), the body interprets it as a very high flow and reflexively lowers the blood pressure. The carotid body in effect monitors the amount of oxygen going to the brain. It actually monitors oxygen tension, so that in anemia it may not initiate corrective reflexes because the oxygen tension is normal.

There are carbon dioxide tension monitors in the medulla, temperature and volume monitors in the brain, etc. Under anesthesia, even if the transducing function of these natural monitors is not impaired, the efferent or reflex function always is.

If the patient is not breathing, i.e., if breathing is controlled under anesthesia, the anesthetist should, if possible, monitor the color of the blood which correlates with oxygen content and the carotid pulse which correlates with blood flow to the brain. By monitoring these two parameters the anesthetist substitutes for the carotid body and carotid sinus.

Devices are available that are noninvasive, and exhibit on a screen a plethysmographic waveform which correlates with the blood pressure and the oxygen content of arterial blood, both instantaneously and over time, so that trends can be detected.

Esophageal temperature is often monitored and recorded, particularly in pediatric cases. It must be monitored in the cardiopulmonary bypass operation.

Most anesthesia machines today have oxygen monitors that indicate the percentage of oxygen being delivered to the patient. (Ambient atmosphere contains 20 to 21% oxygen and negligible amounts of carbon dioxide. Exhaled air contains about 17% oxygen and about 4.0% carbon dioxide.) Beyond recording that there is an oxygen monitor in use, nothing else is usually entered on the anesthesia record. Many monitors may have alarms, for example, an electrocardioscope could be set to warn if the heart rate is too rapid or too slow. The electrocardioscope enables the anesthetist to observe and diagnose cardiac rhythm. It is not possible to diagnose ischemic changes with just one or two leads, and the amplitude of the signal does not correlate with the cardiac output.

The magnitude of the heart sounds does correlate with the cardiac output, but no reliable instrumentation is available to monitor magnitude of heart sounds, and listening with the human ear is unreliable. (According to the Helmholtz principle, a human cannot distinguish gradual increases or decreases in sensory input.)

A common error made by anesthetists is to assume that profound slowing of the heart (bradycardia) is always due to a reflex and they treat it with atropine. The unfortunate fact is that anoxia eventually produces profound bradycardia, and atropine may briefly speed up the anoxic heart, giving the anesthetist a false sense of security because of this presumably positive therapeutic test. Ventricular dysrhythmias require prompt diagnosis and correct management to avoid ventricular tachycardia and ventricular fibrillation.

A normal heart can beat for as long as twenty minutes anaerobically (without oxygen). During this period of oxygen deprivation, severe irreversible brain damage will be occurring. About four minutes of anoxia will destroy the cortex and eight to twelve minutes will destroy the ability of the medulla to drive respiration.

[a]   Cyanosis

Cyanosis is a bluish or purplish discoloration of the skin usually caused by decreased oxygenation of blood and tissues. Cyanosis requires at least five grams percent of reduced hemoglobin in the blood in order to be detectable. Normal hemoglobin content is twelve to fifteen grams per hundred cubic centimeters or milliliters of blood.

There are four causes of cyanosis:

1. Stagnation. Often seen in the "shawl" area (the neck and upper chest), stagnation is easily cleared by rubbing the skin and stimulating blood flow. If the cyanosis is due to a central cause, then rubbing and warming would make the cyanosis worse.
2. Polycythemia or excess of red cells. This occurs in persons living at high altitudes and in certain disorders such as polycythemia vera.
3. Low oxygen in the alveoli. This is the dangerous one. It can be caused by delivery of inadequate oxygen concentration from the anesthesia machine, by a disconnection of the rebreathing tubes or ventilator, by a tube in the esophagus, by airway or tube obstruction, etc. It may also be due to alveolar capillary blocks such as pulmonary edema, pulmonary fibrosis, emphysema, etc. This condition and an overdose of the anesthetic agent are the most common causes of anesthetic catastrophies.
4. Shunting of unoxygenated blood. This is a bypassing of the ventilated alveoli.

In severe anemia, cyanosis is not observable even though there is hypoxemia. The skin surface observed, the number of blood vessels near the skin or mucous membrane, the lighting in the room, pigmentation of the patient, and the skill of the observer are all factors in whether cyanosis is observed. The best site to observe cyanosis in the intact human is the palpebral conjunctivae (the inner eyelid). Also, once a surgical incision is made, and blood vessels are under direct observation, the surgeon is in an excellent position to observe whether cyanosis is occurring. An alert anesthetist, if possible, also will observe the surgical field during an operation, and should therefore be in a position to detect cyanosis early on. Methemoglobinemia and sulfhemoglobinemia may produce cyanosis without hypoxemia. Carboxyhemoglobin (carbon monoxide) does not combine with oxygen, and there is no cyanosis, although there may be hypoxemia. Cyanosis can develop from breath-to-breath, and can be reversed just as quickly.

The anesthetist may also monitor the patient's central venous pressure which tends to give some inkling of circulating blood volume versus ability of the heart to pump. However, since the right atrium of the heart may dilate, this reading is not as reliable as that obtained through a Swan-Ganz catheter which monitors the pressure from the left atrium.

More sophisticated monitors such as chromatographs and mass spectrometers may come into common use as their cost decreases and their reliability increases. A monitor such as the Puritan-Bennett can indicate the concentration of halothane, enflurane, methoxyflurane, or isoflurane as these agents are being delivered to the patient. These monitors are valuable because the vaporizers seldom maintain their calibration and sometimes can grossly malfunction.

A carbon dioxide monitor (capnograph) is an extremely valuable monitor that could prevent most anesthetic accidents.

An electroencephalograph is also valuable, but it is subject to many artifacts and is difficult to interpret. The electrical impulses from the scalp can be computer processed, displayed on a screen, and can be most informative.

Blood gases can be determined in most modern hospitals in five minutes or so. These are readings of arterial oxygen tension, arterial carbon dioxide tension and acid-base balance. They provide information that is not clinically otherwise available. Under anesthesia, oxygen and carbon dioxide may vary independently of each other. Cutaneous oxygen or carbon dioxide monitors are still experimental and unreliable.

Intra-arterial monitoring of blood pressure is done in cardiopulmonary bypass operations, major neurosurgery and other procedures. Since a small artery to the hand, usually the radial, is cannulated, the anesthetist should determine that the ulnar artery can maintain blood supply to the hand if the radial becomes occluded. This indwelling plastic catheter can also be used to draw blood gas samples.

§ 8.07 Local Anesthesia

No local anesthetic is effective through intact skin or epidermis. The local anesthetic agents act directly on nerves to interrupt conduction, and thus produce lack of sensation, or in higher concentrations, paralysis. The action must, of course, be reversible without permanent sequelae. Given intravenously, local anesthestics can produce general anesthesia, a method which is used in some foreign countries, but seldom in the United States. (General anesthetics, if applied directly to a nerve, will interrupt conduction, but this method of anesthesia is not used in the United States because the concentration of general anesthesia necessary to block nerve conduction would be cardiotoxic.)

Cocaine, a natural product, was the first local anesthetic introduced in medicine (about 1885 by Sigmund Freud). It is still used in 4% and 10% concentrations for topical anesthesia of mucous membranes, particularly of the nose. It is the only local anesthetic that has clear-cut vasoconstrictor properties, although the vasoconstriction does not prevent systemic absorption. It is not administered by injection because it causes necrosis of tissues. It is psychologically addicting and is a controlled substance.

Procaine, as are all the other local anesthetics, is a synthetic, and was introduced in 1905. It is still very useful. While it is not effective topically on mucous membranes, it is the standard against which other local anesthetics are compared with respect to onset of action, duration, potency and toxicity.

Nesacaine (2-chloroprocaine) is a very short-acting local anesthetic. Nerve injury, cauda equina syndrome, and paraplegia have been associated with its use.

Tetracaine (pontocaine) is more potent than procaine, and more toxic. It is effective topically.

The above anesthetics are esters, and true allergic reactions have been reported, although there are few if any documented cases of anaphylactic shock resulting in death from administration of procaine, tetracaine, or 2-chloroprocaine.

Among the amide anesthetics are lidocaine, mepivicaine, prilocaine, bupivicaine and etidocaine. Allergic reactions to these agents, if they do occur, are extremely rare. Lidocaine (Xylocaine) has a spreading action that makes it most valuable for nerve blocks. Since these nerve blocks are blind procedures, merely depositing the lidocaine near the nerve may produce a block while another agent would require that the deposit be in or contiguous to the nerve. There are available today weak electrical probes that can be used by the anesthetist to determine when the needle is near enough to the nerve to achieve a block.

All local anesthetics have some depressant action on various properties of the heart. Lidocaine is often used intravenously to control ventricular dysrhythmias. Prilocaine (Citanest) produces methemoglobinemia on a dose response basis. Bupivicaine and etidocaine are the longest-lasting local anesthetics available. They are relatively more cardiotoxic than the other local anesthetics.

Sometimes for the control of intractable pain or muscle spasm, a permanent interruption of nerve conduction is prescribed. Permanent block can be achieved with phenol or absolute alcohol. The risk of necrosis of adjoining structures is great with these agents, however, so spinal cord injury is not rare. They are best used to assist in the management of the pain of terminal cancer.

The toxicity of local anesthetic agents is to the central nervous system and to the cardiovascular system. Overdose may produce nausea, vomiting, convulsions, respiratory arrest and coma. Overdose may also produce cardiovascular collapse. Maximum recommended doses of local anesthetic agents are outlined in the product insert and in the *Physician's Desk Reference*. Addition of epinephrine 1:100,000 or 1:200,000 usually increases the maximum permissible dose of local agents by about 50%. Most drug manufacturers market local anesthetics with epinephrine. When the doctor or nurse chooses to mix epinephrine with a local anesthetic, the risk of an overdose of the epinephrine with a local anesthetic, the risk of an overdose of the epinephrine (because of miscalculation) is very great.

Minimal doses of local anesthetics, if injected directly intravascularly in the head and neck, especially if they reach the brain, can produce profound effects. In general, however, if this is promptly recognized and properly treated, there should be no residual damage. Regardless of the drug or route of administration, careful monitoring must be done, and equipment for resuscitation must always be at hand. An intravenous route should also be established before administration of a local anesthetic.

Bupivicaine injected intravascularly may produce a cardiac arrest from which resuscitation is unduly prolonged or cannot be achieved successfully, regardless of prompt recognition and treatment. For epidural analgesia, it is recommended that epinephrine be used with a test dose of bupivicaine. The epinephrine should permit immediate recognition of an intravascular injection because it will produce a brief tachycardia and hypertension. Epinephrine has a duration of action of about three minutes.

Often a slow, incompetent surgeon will subject the anesthetist to enormous pressure to use bupivicaine (for a shoulder repair or even to make an AV shunt) despite the attendant risk of a cardiac arrest which is very difficult and sometimes impossible to reverse because the drug binds to the cardiac muscle fibers. These requests from the surgeon must be resisted — 2% mepivicaine is far safer and gives enough anesthesia to do most procedures and anesthetic. If cardiac arrest occurs after the performance of a block, the reviewer should strongly suspect that bupivicaine was used — even if it wasn't written down on the chart.

Although practically any surgical procedure, whether involving the head, chest, abdomen, or extremities, can be performed under local anesthesia, in the United States most patients prefer to be unconscious or, at least, amnesic while surgical procedures are being performed. Even when the primary anesthetic is local, as in a rhytidectomy (face lift) enough so-called basal anesthesia is administered to produce amnesia.

The rising popularity of outpatient surgical centers, "emergicenters," ambulatory care centers, etc. (many of which are for profit and located in shopping centers) will certainly result in greater use of local anesthesia as opposed to general. Many surgical procedures can be performed in an outpatient set-up.[6] These can be done under local, block, or general anesthesia. The outpatient facility must have an arrangement with a hospital so that if the patient develops a complication, there will be no delay in appropriate treatment.

Administration of local anesthetics can be administered by infiltration or field block. In a Bier block the local anesthetic is injected in the veins of an extremity to which two tourniquets have been applied proximally. The purpose of the tourniquet is to limit the local to that part of the extremity distal to the tourniquet, but intraosseous blood flow may permit the local to reach the general circulation and cause cardiovascular collapse even when the tourniquet's pressure is higher than the systolic blood pressure.

Paracervical block was very popular for vaginal delivery because it was easy to administer. Unfortunately, lethal doses of local may reach the fetus and produce a brain damaged or still-born infant. All the local anesthetics cross the placenta.

Specific nerves or nerve plexuses can be blocked.

An epidural anesthetic is the instillation of local anesthetic in the back in a potential space just outside the spinal cord or cauda equina. A caudal is a type of epidural. Recently it has been learned that narcotics may be administered epidurally to provide prolonged pain relief. If the epidural is continuous rather

---

[6] Although the list will vary from place to place, some of the procedures that can be performed in an outpatient facility are: *Gynecology* — First trimester abortion; minilap tubal ligation; perineal procedures such as hymenotomy: *General Surgery* — Breast biopsy; cervical node biopsy; inguinal herniorraphy; anal procedures. *Orthopedic Surgery* — Arthroscopy, arthrotomy; removal of screws, pins and wires; excision of superficial masses. *Otorhinolaryngology* — Myringotomy; insertion of polyethylene tubes; antral puncture; stapes/tympanoplasty; rhinoplasty; arch bars for fractured mandible; tonsillectomy and adenoidectomy. *Plastic Surgery* — Blepharoplasty; breast implants; dermabrasion; suction lipectomy; many hand surgery procedures. *Pediatric Surgery* — Bronchoscopy and esophagoscopy; hernia repair; circumcision. *Genitourinary Surgery* — Orchidopexy; vasovasostomy; cystoscopy; fiberoptic colonoscopy. Also, cataract surgery can be performed in an outpatient facility.

than a single shot, a catheter is used. A part of the catheter may be sheared and remain in the body; these catheters, however, are biologically inert.

In a spinal or subarachnoid block, the local anesthetic is injected into the fluid surrounding the cauda equina. The local anesthetics used for spinal should contain no preservatives or germicides.

The level of the epidural or spinal is checked by determining the presence or absence of touch or pinprick sensation on the skin. This is called checking the segmental level. Unfortunately, some texts illustrate segmental levels incorrectly. The muscle innervation does not correspond to the skin segmental levels.

Local, regional and conduction anesthesia require a certain measure of cooperation on the part of the patient, either to place the needle properly or to remain still during the surgery.

It is a fallacy that very bad risk patients are more safely managed under local anesthesia. These patients are usually involuntarily uncooperative, are more sensitive to the toxicity of local anesthetics, and are better managed with endotracheal tubes and supplemental inspired oxygen.

Local anesthetics are all weak bases combined with stronger acids, e.g., procaine hydrochloride. In the human body it is the dissociated base that is primarily responsible for the nerve block. If the local is in an area of high acidity, such as an abscess, no analgesia may be produced.

Epinephrine should not be injected with the local to block nerves associated with end arteries such as those of the digits.

Rarely local anesthetics may produce permanent nerve dysfunction in spite of proper administration. Of course, high concentrations of local anesthetics are neurolytic.

§ 8.08 The Recovery Phase

Since many of the problems that arise in a recovery room are similar to those in a critical care unit, particularly support of respiration and circulation, and prevention of damage to the unconscious patient, many anesthetists have become critical care physicians.

During recovery serious preventable surgical or anesthetic complications may result in brain damage, paralysis or death. The anesthetist must remain with the patient until his or her care can be safely entrusted to a qualified recovery room person. The anesthetist should communicate to such person enough information to enable that individual to observe the patient for the development of possible complications. Furthermore, before the anesthetist leaves the patient, the recovery room person should make his or her own observations regarding consciousness, airway, color, movement, respiration, pulse and blood pressure to assure that recovery is progressing in a normal fashion. Patients who have conducted analgesia, such as spinal or epidural, also should be monitored in a recovery room.

Recovery room personnel must be skilled in establishing the airway, breathing for the patient and instituting closed chest massage. They must know how to monitor the efficacy of resuscitation measures. Equipment must be at hand and preferably in sight. Records must be kept that are similar to anesthesia records, and the information also should be entered in the patient's chart.

Probably the most common postanesthetic recovery room complication is airway obstruction with subsequent brain damage. Vomiting and aspiration also occur in the recovery room with serious and sometimes deadly consequences unless properly managed.

Staffing of the recovery room is sometimes insufficient either as to the number of personnel or as to their qualifications. There must be sufficient qualified personnel present in a recovery area to ensure that all patients are properly observed and adequately cared for. Unless specially qualified, "private duty" nurses should not be given the sole responsibility for recovery room care.

Some hospitals do not maintain a recovery room around the clock seven days a week. When the recovery room is closed, patients should be taken to a critical care facility. If the hospital does not have a suitable facility staffed with qualified personnel and proper equipment, the anesthetist should recover the patient in the operating room.

§ 8.09 Special Problems

[1] Management of the Full Stomach

There is absolutely no way to *guarantee* that aspiration of gastric contents will not occur since debilitated patients will often have aspirated such material into their lungs before any medication or anesthetic is administered. If the surgical procedure can be performed under local, nerve block, or conduction analgesia, and if the patient has intact glottic protective reflexes, not diminished by medication, aspiration should not occur during the surgical procedure.

If general anesthesia is used, as it most often is, the airway must be securely separated from the pharynx so that aspiration cannot occur. A cuffed endotracheal tube is best for this separation. The anesthetist's problem is to pass the tube into the trachea and inflate the cuff before aspiration has occurred.

A so-called awake intubation is often used. Here, topical anesthesia may be applied to the tongue but not to the glottis, because if the vocal cords are paralyzed, aspiration can occur even with local anesthesia, since the protective reflex of laryngospasm is blocked.

The success of "crash" inductions to avoid aspiration, through the use of the Sellick maneuver, i.e., pressing the cricoid against a vertebral body so as to close off the esophagus, depends on the skill of the anesthetist and his assistant. The cricoid is the only complete ring cartilage in the tracheobronchial tree. The stomach cannot be completely emptied by a nasogastric tube or stomach pump. Induction of vomiting is a most unpleasant experience to the patient and may be hazardous.

It has been shown that if mask anesthesia is prolonged, at least 50% of patients will have aspirated to some extent.

The management of aspiration once it has occurred is not always successful. The head-down position, suction of aspirated material, saline instillation, antibiotics, and steroids may be of little value. Supportive therapy until the lung recovers is the principal mode of therapy. Death may occur within a short time or adult respiratory distress syndrome (ARDS) may develop. Factors that determine whether the patient will survive are the volume and nature of the aspirate, its acidity, and its distribution in the lungs. Chest X-rays, blood gases and observation of cyanosis, dyspnea and mottling may be diagnostic of the course of aspiration pneumonitis.

[2] Cardiac Arrest

Cardiac arrest is inadequate output of the heart sufficient to prevent brain damage. It can be cardiac standstill (asystole), ventricular fibrillation, electromechanical dissociation, failure of venous return, or obstruction of the outflow tract. Its causes are many. (Sooner or later everyone will suffer irreversible cardiac arrest, so a death certificate giving cardiac arrest as the cause of death is not informative.) The anesthetist must prevent cardiac arrest if possible, so as to avoid brain damage, and must promptly recognize and properly treat reversible cardiac arrest. Cardiac arrest may be the eventual result of physiologic insults which, if detected and reversed early, would not result in cardiac arrest. By the time cardiac arrest is noted, irreversible, significant brain damage may have already occurred. So it is the anesthetist's primary responsibility to insure that avoidable brain damage does not occur.

Cardiac arrest is always characterized by unconsciousness, immobility, apnea and absence of a carotid pulse. There are numerous potentially preventable causes of cardiac arrest:

1. Oxygen deprivation;
2. Carbon dioxide retention;
3. A combination of (1) and (2) above (asphyxia);
4. Absolute overdose of anesthetic;
5. Relative overdose of anesthetic;
6. High spinal or epidural anesthetic;
7. Intravascular injection of local anesthetic;
8. External blood loss;
9. Internal blood loss;
10. Pooling of blood and failure of venous return;
11. Fluid and electrolyte imbalance;
12. Incompatible blood administration;
13. Reflexes (particularly vagal);
14. Anaphylactic shock.

Other causes of cardiac arrest that are considered preventable include:

1. Excessive catecholamine levels (exogenous or endogenous);
2. High serum potassium (hyperkalemia);
3. Malignant hyperpyrexia;
4. Overdose of a medical drug (such as digitalis, inderal, etc.);
5. Air embolization. (If the surgical procedure is such that air embolization is likely, e.g., some neurosurgical procedures in the posterior upper cervical region, a catheter can be placed preoperatively in the right atrium of the heart to aspirate air, and a doppler can be placed over the chest to diagnose its presence.)
6. Electrocution from invasive monitoring.

Sudden, unexpected death before, during or immediately after an anesthetic may be due to one of the following:

1. Failure of the cardiovascular system which could be due to massive myocardial infarction, pulmonary embolus, major deficit of intravascular volume, etc.;
2. Uncal herniation of the brain or medullary hemorrhage. (Of course, if there is increased intracranial pressure preoperatively, appropriate precautions must be taken to prevent uncal herniation.);
3. Undiagnosed bilateral viral pneumonia. (A chest X-ray would have indicated its presence.)

The cause of an anesthetic catastrophe can often be reconstructed by analysis of the effect of resuscitative efforts on the course of the recovery, if any. Autopsies are very important in establishing an anatomical cause of death. Exhumation is sometimes advisable. However, death caused by pathophysiological processes usually is not accompanied by any anatomical findings. Over 90% of preventable deaths associated with anesthesia will have essentially negative autopsies.

Toxicologic studies should always be performed as part of the autopsy, but seldom are revealing. If cardiac resuscitation has been accomplished, and the patient survives for a day or so, practically all the agent will be metabolized or excreted even if an overdose caused the cardiac arrest.

[3] Pneumothorax

Pneumothorax (presence of air or gas in the pleural cavity) may occur suddenly and unexpectedly under anesthesia. Positive airway pressure quickly converts it to tension pneumothorax, resulting in failure of venous return, failure of cardiac output, failure of uptake of oxygen, failure of clearance of carbon dioxide, and eventual cardiac arrest. Brain damage does not necessarily begin until the cardiac arrest occurs. Early recognition and correct management will prevent brain damage from tension pneumothorax.

Pneumothorax may also be produced by supraclavicular brachial plexus block or by stellate ganglion block. Early recognition and appropriate treatment should prevent permanent damage.

[4] Complications of Spinal Analgesia

Spinal analgesia may result in paralysis. Electromyography reveals significant peripheral changes not less than eighteen days after spinal injury. Anesthetists should order sequential electromyography as soon as possible if the patient complains of paralysis or numbness after a spinal or any nerve block.

Adhesive arachnoiditis may follow a properly performed spinal or epidural analgesia. Its cause is unknown, although some speculate that it is due to germicide or contaminants. Its course is indolent and inexorable, and treatment, including surgery, is of little value.

Headache may follow spinal analgesia, but rarely occurs after an epidural anesthetic. These headaches may be severe and incapacitating. Some last as long as six months. Very small- bore spinal needles and adequate hydration or over-hydration may decrease the likelihood of developing a headache. If a headache develops, it may be treated by a homologous blood patch in the epidural space. About 10 cc of the patient's blood is injected in the epidural space over the area where the spinal had been performed. However, these will not stop the headache if there is an active spinal fluid leak.

Meningitis may occur after spinal or epidural procedures, particularly if steroids have been injected. While the occurrence of meningitis may not be due to negligence, failure to recognize the signs and symptoms of meningitis promptly, to diagnose the etiologic agent, and to treat it properly may well be negligence.

[5] Blindness

In the days when mask anesthesia was common, patients might wake up blind in one eye. Since the retinal artery is an end artery and the retina itself is an extension of the brain, pressure on the retina greater than the systolic blood pressure for as little as four minutes can cause blindness. The problem still occurs if the patient is face down or if there is a prolonged bout of hypovolemic hypotension.

If the eyelids remain separated during general anesthesia, the cornea will dry, and an ulcer will develop.

[6] Nerve Injury

During anesthesia, nerves may be injured by direct injection, by pressure or stretching, or by prolonged tourniquet time.

The nerves commonly injured by injection are the radial in the arm and the sciatic in the buttocks. The ones commonly injured by pressure are the ulnar at the elbow and the common peroneal as it crosses the head of the fibula. The most common nerve injured by stretching is the obturator by the "frog position." The brachial plexus can be injured by compression between the clavicle and the first rib or by stretching from placing the arm in an awkward position.

[7] Baldness

Alopecia (baldness) may occur from prolonged pressure on the scalp.

[8] Memory of the Operation

Because today most anesthetics consist of a number of drugs, and because it is difficult to determine the depth of anesthesia, some patients may remember part or all of their operation even though they were supposed to be under general anesthesia. Narcotics and muscle relaxants do not produce amnesia. Since pain relief is obtained before memory is lost, patients who claim to remember will hardly ever complain of remembering pain if any concentration of a potent anesthetic has been administered.

[9] Intubation Trauma

Orotracheal intubation may cause trauma such as laceration and perforation of the pharynx, esophagus or trachea. These complications may occur in the absence of negligence. Vocal cord paralysis and vocal cord granulomata may also develop. If the cuff is overinflated, and the tube is left in place too many days, tracheal necrosis may occur, particularly in neonates.

[10] Products Liability

Since we live in a highly competitive economic climate, manufacturers of anesthetic drugs and equipment are constantly conducting research to find presumably better agents, anesthetic machines, and monitors.

No matter how careful the FDA is in the approval of anesthetic drugs and equipment, it is virtually impossible to conduct sufficient premarketing studies to discover all of the possible hazards. Accordingly, one must consider the possibility that an anesthetic catastrophe could be due to a drug side effect or equipment failure the manufacturer knew or should have known was likely. In this regard, obtaining Freedom of Information Act material from the government is seldom of value. The attorney should obtain by discovery the *Drug Experience Reports* or *Equipment Failure Reports* that are required to be maintained on each product.

§ 8.10 Conclusion

If the anesthesiologist maintains his/her ethical and personal responsibilities to his/her patient and is diligent in the performance of his/her functions, he/she is maintaining the obligations established by law. His/her activities must be supported by a continuing concern for the welfare of the patient. In the event of a complication, honest disclosure is essential, and the records must be adequate. The patient has the right also to make decisions relating to his/her personal wishes on his/her religious convictions. The law offers adequate protection to the conscientious, competent physician.

§ 8.11 Selected Bibliography and References

Ideally, the attorney would like specific references relating to every theory and allegation of the case in question. However, since the alleged and hypothetical facts vary so from case to case, and since the probable explanation of the pathophysiological process that resulted in harm, whether due to negligence or not, can seldom be found clearly stated in the literature, the attorney must consult a competent expert to develop the negligence and causation of a therapeutic misadventure. Also, the literature usually cannot be admitted unless it was published at or before the time of the alleged negligence. However, testimony can be elicited that a later publication does not contain information not known at the time of the alleged negligence. Furthermore, nearly all medical literature is accompanied by a list of references. Many of these references will have been published before the incident in question and will often contain knowledge and conclusions that have bearing on the issues. Remember that often the defendant doctor does not know what he did or did not do at the time that may have caused the damage; had he foreseen the course of events leading to the damage, he would have prevented it if at all possible.

Albright, ANESTHESIA IN OBSTETRICS, 2d ed. (Addison-Wesley 1985).

Benumof, J.L. & Saidman, L.J., ANESTHESIA AND PERIOPERATIVE COMPLICATIONS (Mosby 1992).

Blitt, ed., MONITORING IN ANESTHESIA AND CRITICAL CARE MEDICINE (Churchill-Livingstone 1985).

Bromage, Epidural Analgesia (W. B. Saunders 1978). (The most complete work in print on this subject.)

Buxton-Hopkin, D.A., HAZARDS AND ERRORS IN ANAESTHESIA (Springer-Verlag 1980).

Campton, F.X., GRAND ROUNDS ON MEDICAL MALPRACTICE (American Medical Association 1990).

Cooper et al., *Critical Incidents Associated with Intraoperative Changes of Anesthesia Personnel,* 56 ANESTHESIOLOGY 456-61 (1982).

Del Guercio & Cohn, *Monitoring Operative Risk in the Elderly,* 243 JAMA 1350-1355 (April 4, 1980). (Thus far, the best article outlining objective criteria for determining the operative risk.)

DiFazio et al., "Anesthesia," in LAWYERS' MEDICAL CYCLOPEDIA, Vol. 3A (Michie 1983).

Dornette, W.H.L., LEGAL ISSUES IN ANESTHESIA PRACTICE (F.A. Davis 1991).

Dorsch & Dorsch, UNDERSTANDING ANESTHESIA EQUIPMENT: CONSTRUCTION, CARE AND COMPLICATIONS, 2d ed. (Williams & Wilkins 1984).

Eltringham, POST-ANESTHETIC RECOVERY (Springer-Verlag 1983).

Frost, CLINICAL ANESTHESIA IN NEUROSURGERY (Butterworth 1984).

Gravenstein, N., MANUAL OF COMPLICATIONS DURING ANESTHESIA (J.B. Lippincott 1991).

Gray et al., GENERAL ANESTHESIA, 5th ed. (Butterworth 1985).

Greene, PHYSIOLOGY OF SPINAL ANESTHESIA, 3d ed. (Williams & Wilkins 1981).

Grundy & Gravenstein, eds., THE QUALITY OF CARE IN ANESTHESIA (Charles C Thomas 1982).

Harney, MEDICAL MALPRACTICE, 2d ed. (Michie 1987). (Good discussion of anesthesia cases, with citations.)

James, OBSTETRIC ANESTHESIA: THE COMPLICATED PATIENT (F.A. Davis 1982).

Krechel, ed., ANESTHESIA AND THE GERIATRIC PATIENT (Grune & Stratton 1984).

Levy, J.H., ANAPHYLACTIC REACTIONS IN ANESTHESIA AND INTENSIVE CARE (Butterworths 1986).

Lew, E.A. & Gajewski, J., MEDICAL RISKS (Praeger 1990).

Louisell & Williams, MEDICAL MALPRACTICE (3 vols.) (Matthew Bender 1985). (Anesthesia at S 3.03 lists appellate decisions.)

Mackauf & Tessel, MEDICAL MALPRACTICE: FAILURES IN ANESTHESIA CARE (Law Journal Seminars Press 1985). (General introduction by attorneys for attorneys.)

Mannina, THE NURSE ANESTHETIST AND THE LAW (Grune & Stratton 1982). (Only book specifically addressed to this subject. Useful for variation in law and practice from state to state.)

Marinacci, A.A., APPLIED ELECTROMYOGRAPHY (Lea & Febinger 1968).

Martin, J.T., POSITIONING IN ANESTHESIA AND SURGERY, 2d ed. (W.B. Saunders 1987).

Miller, ed., ANESTHESIA, 2d ed. (Churchill-Livingstone 1985).

Moore, REGIONAL BLOCK, 4th ed. (Charles C Thomas 1981). (The bible of regional anesthesia for many years.)

Orkin & Cooperman, COMPLICATIONS IN ANESTHESIOLOGY (J. B. Lippincott 1983).

Paget, et al., *Factors Affecting an Anesthetist's Work: Some Findings on Vigilance and Performance*, 4 ANESTH. INTENS. CARE 359-65 (1981).

Patterson, ed., DRUGS IN LITIGATION: DAMAGE AWARDS INVOLVING PRESCRIPTION AND NONPRESCRIPTION DRUGS, 6th ed. (Michie 1989).

Peters, et al., ANESTHESIOLOGY AND THE LAW (Appleton-Century-Crofts 1972).

PHYSICIANS' DESK REFERENCE (Published annually).

Ryan, et al., A PRACTICE OF ANESTHESIA FOR INFANTS AND CHILDREN (Grune & Stratton 1985).

Stoelting, *Allergic Reactions During Anesthesia,* 62 ANESTH. ANALG. 341-356 (1983).

Vickers, et al., DRUGS IN ANESTHETIC PRACTICE, 6th ed. (Butterworth 1984).

Wasmuth, ed., LEGAL PROBLEMS IN THE PRACTICE OF ANESTHESIOLOGY (International Anesthesiology Clinics 1973).

CHAPTER 9

RADIOLOGY

Leonard Berlin, MD, FACR

SYNOPSIS

§ 9.01 Introduction

[1] Historical Perspective

In 1794, the United States' first medical malpractice lawsuit was adjudicated by a Connecticut court. The husband of a woman who had died as a result of surgery sued the physician for operating in "the most unskillful, ignorant, and cruel manner, contrary to all the well-known rules and principles of practice," and violating "his promise to the plaintiff to perform said operation skillfully and with safety to his wife."[1] The lawsuit, the primary allegation of which was breach of contract, was won by the plaintiff. The jury found the physician liable and awarded damages of 40 English pounds.

[2] Standard of Care for Physicians: Nineteenth Century Court Decisions

One of the earliest State Supreme Court decisions in the United States setting forth the standard of care for physicians was rendered in 1832, again in Connecticut. A physician was accused of negligence for "unskillfully and carelessly making an incision into the plaintiff's arm to insert [smallpox] vaccine, such that she suffered great pain and her arm was irreparably injured." The jury found in favor of the plaintiff, and the defendant-physician appealed. Although the Connecticut Supreme Court upheld the jury verdict, its eloquent commentary regarding physicians seems as relevant today as it was 176 years ago.[2]

> A physician and surgeon, in the performance of his professional duties, is liable for injuries resulting from the want of ordinary diligence, care and skill. Physicians never warrant their work. They make no promise, except to do as well as they can, and as well as they know how to do. "Ordinary" means usual, common. The difference between a want of ordinary or useful skill and gross negligence is essential and important. To say that a physician did not perform a certain operation with ordinary skill conveys a very different idea from the assertion that he performs it with gross negligence.

> The defendant-physician prayed the Court to charge the jury that, unless the plaintiff had proved the defendant guilty of great and

---

[1] Cross v. Guthrey, 2 Root 90, Conn. (1794). (Quoted in: Sandor AA. The history of professional liability suits in the United States. *JAMA* 1957;163:459-466.

[2] Landon v. Humphrey, 9 Conn. 209, 1832.

gross negligence in vaccinating the plaintiff, she could not recover. The Court told the jury on this point that if there was either *carelessness*, or a *want of ordinary diligence, care and skill*, then the plaintiff was entitled to recover. The principal laid down by the Court is entirely correct. If in the performance of the operation there was a want or ordinary diligence, care and skill, or if there was carelessness, then the defendant-physician was liable.

In 1860, the Supreme Court of Georgia set forth a physician's standard of care in terms that still prevail today:[3]

The profession of the physician is one of the learned professions; and in regard thereto, as in all professionals in the practice of which learning and skill are required, the rule of law is that every person who enters into a learned profession undertakes to bring to the exercise of his profession a reasonable degree of care and skill. He does not undertake to use the highest possible degree of skill, for there may be persons who, for having enjoyed a better education and greater advantages, are possessed of greater skill in their profession; but he undertakes that he will bring a fair, reasonable and competent degree of skill....The physician is called in for the very purpose that by his skill he may judge what is necessary to be done, and by his skill to do it; and he is not responsible for an error in judgment on such an occasion, if such error arises from the peculiar circumstances of the case, and not from the want of proper care or competent skill on his part.

[3] Radiology Is Introduced into the Courtroom

The vast majority of malpractice lawsuits in the United States filed during the second half of the nineteenth century and first part of the twentieth century were related to orthopedic treatments of fractures, dislocations and amputations.[4]

A new chapter in medical malpractice litigation began with Roentgen's discovery of the X-Ray in 1895. Early cases in which radiographs were submitted as evidence in personal injury trials in the United States have been chronicled previously.[5] Here, however, we focus on radiologists and non-

---

[3] Smith v. Overby, 30 Ga. 241, 1860.

[4] Buckner F. *Overview of the history of medical malpractice*. West Hartford, CT. The Graduate Group, 1999:31-54, 68-80, 94-96, 106-113, 152-154.

[5] Berlin L. The miasmatic expert witness. *AJR* 2003;181:29-35.

radiologic physicians as defendants in medical malpractice actions. Medical historian James Mohr [6] provides an introduction to this topic:

> Within 20 years of their introduction, radiographs had become one of the nation's most prolific sources of malpractice actions (too much radiation, failure to read the films properly, and so forth). Litigation concerning radiographs produced many of the highest damage awards (in excess of $5,000) in the decade prior to World War I and generated a whole new body of evidentiary disputes (for example, ownership of films, interpretation of faint images). Radiographic tests also opened to exposure other sorts of medical mistakes that were previously difficult to demonstrate in court.

One year after Roentgen's discovery a malpractice lawsuit was filed against a Colorado surgeon, a founder of the American College of Surgeons, claiming that the surgeon negligently treated a fractured femur of a young boy who had fallen from a ladder.[7] The plaintiff attempted to admit as evidence a "roentgen picture" of the fractured femur. The defense attorney argued against admitting such evidence, but in an historic decision the judge admitted into evidence the pioneer-era radiographs:

> We have been presented with a photograph taken by means of a new scientific discovery, the same being acknowledged in the arts and in science. It knocks for admission at the temple of learning; what shall we do or say? Close fast the doors or open the wide the furrows? These photographs show the present condition of the head and neck of the femur bone, which is entirely hidden from the eye of the surgeon. Nature has surrounded it with tissues for its protection and there it is hidden; it cannot by any possibility be removed nor exposed that it may be compared with a shadow that developed by means of this new scientific process... These exhibits are only pictures or maps to be used in explanation of a present condition,...and may be shown to the jury as illustrating or making clear the testimony of experts.

The law is the acme of learning throughout all ages. It is the essence of wisdom, reason, and experience....Let the courts throw open the

---

[6] Mohr JC. American medical malpractice litigation in historical perspective. *JAMA* 2000;283:1731-1737.

[7] Withers S. The story of the first roentgen evidence. *Radiology* 1931;17:99-103.

door to all well considered scientific discoveries. Modern science has made it possible to look beneath the tissues of the human body, and has aided surgery in telling of the hidden mysteries. We believe it to be our duty in this case to be the first, if you please, to so consider admitting in evidence a process known and acknowledged as a determinate science. The exhibits will be admitted in evidence.

[4] Radiological Malpractice: 1975 – Present

A review of malpractice litigation over a 20-year span from the mid 1970s to the mid 1990s in the greater Chicago area disclosed that radiology-related cases accounted for 12% of all medical malpractice cases filed against physicians.[8] Physical injuries sustained by patients in or being transported to or from a radiology department accounted for 5% of the total; radiation oncology complications, 8%; complications of radiologic procedures, 16%; failure to order radiologic studies, 22%; and radiographic misses, 42%. Miscellaneous causes accounted for the remaining 7%. A more realistic indication of the prevalence among diagnostic radiologists of lawsuits claiming radiologic misses is obtained by excluding those lawsuits alleging complications of radiation oncology, and failure-to-order categories. With this approach, allegations of missed radiologic diagnoses accounted for an average of 55% of diagnostic radiology-related lawsuits during the period from 1970 to 1974, but rose to 71% in the 5-year period between 1990 and 1994. Between 1975 and 1984 malpractice litigation related to missed bone abnormalities of all types accounted for the greatest percentage of radiologic misses, but the ranking changed considerably in the period between 1985 and 1994, when cancers became the most commonly missed radiographic disease.

[5] General Medical Malpractice Litigation: 1970s – 2008

In the two decades following World War II the frequency of malpractice lawsuits increased gradually as did financial recoveries.[9] It wasn't until the 1970s, however, that the number of medical malpractice lawsuits filed against all physicians, and the insurance premiums charged by malpractice carriers, began to skyrocket.[10] The degree to which the medical malpractice phenomenon spiraled dramatically upward is illustrated by the following statistics. As of year 1957, the largest sum awarded in a medical malpractice

---

[8] Berlin L, Berlin J. Malpractice and radiologists in Cook County, IL: trends in 20 years of litigation. *AJR* 1995;165:781-788.

[9] Rosenbaum S. Law and the public's health: medical errors, medical negligence, and professional medical liability reform. *Public Health Reports* 2003;118:272-274.

[10] *Supra* notes 8 and 9.

case by any trial court in the United States was $230,000. Median damages in malpractice litigation hovered in the $200,000 range in the early 1980s, rose to $300,000 in the late 1980s, and exceeded $400,000 in the 1990s.[11] Insurance payouts for radiology lawsuits in 1983 averaged $104,000, accounting for 6% of all medical malpractice claims paid.[12] In Illinois, the average payment per paid claim increased from just under $129,000 in the period 1980-1984 to almost $500,000 in the period 1995-1999.[13] Texas has experienced a 500% increase in the size of judgments awarded just in the last 10 years. Settlement payments have also steadily risen over the last two decades. The average settlement payment per paid claim increased from approximately $110,000 in 1987 to $250,000 in 1999.[14] By 2002, the median jury award in malpractice cases exceeded $1 million while the average was nearly $4 million.[15]

§ 9.02 Radiological Errors

[1] Early Research

Nearly 60 years ago a California radiologist names L. Henry Garland introduced the subject of accuracy of diagnostic procedures by summarizing investigations that revealed a "surprising" degree of inaccuracy in many non-radiologic clinical and laboratory tests.[16] Garland referenced studies that found a 34% error rate in the diagnosis of myocardial infarction, an only 15% agreement among eight experienced internists on the presence of "the most simple signs" of emphysema when examining the chests of patients affected with that disease, a marked disparity in clinical evaluation of 1000 school children of the indications for tonsillectomy, an agreement rate of only 7% among five experienced pediatricians determining clinically whether children were suffering from malnutrition, a 20% error rate in the interpretation of electrocardiograms, a 28% error rate among 59 different hospital clinical laboratories in reporting the results of chemical analyses, and a 28% error rate among clinical laboratories in measuring the erythrocyte count.[17]

---

[11] Woolsey C. ISMIE update: jury awards rise. *Ill Med* June 1993:9-10.

[12] Professional briefs: OB/GYN leads the malpractice hit list. *Med Econ* Aug 1994:12.

[13] *Addressing the new health care crisis: reforming the medical litigation system to improve the quality of health care*. U.S. Department of Health and Human Services, Office of the Assistant Secretary of Planning and Evaluation. March 3, 2003.

[14] *Id.*

[15] Saxton J. *Liability for medical malpractice: issues and evidence*. Joint Economic Committee Study, United States Congress, May 2003.

[16] Garland LH. On the scientific evaluation of diagnostic procedures. *Radiology* 1949;52:309-328.

[17] Garland LH. On the reliability of roentgen survey procedures. *AJR* 1950;64:32-41; Garland LH, Miller ER, Zwerling HB et al. Studies on the value of serial films in estimating the progress of pulmonary disease. *Radiology* 1952;58:161-177.

Garland found that experienced radiologists will miss about 30% of chest radiographs positive for radiologic evidence of disease, will overread about 2% of them that are actually negative for disease, and will disagree with themselves 20% of the time.[18] These figures are today readily acknowledged, but in 1959 they astonished if not shocked virtually all radiologists.

[2] Prevalence of Radiographic Errors

In the decades following Garland's classic articles, a number of investigators replicated Garland's findings relative to plain-film radiographic studies.[19] In a 1976 study at the University of Missouri, an error rate of 30% was reported among staff radiologists in their interpretation of chest radiographs, bone studies, gastrointestinal series, and special procedures.[20] Researchers found that as many as 20% of colonic tumors were missed on lower gastrointestinal examinations.[21] Other researchers[22] reported that a group of Harvard University radiologists disagreed on the interpretation of chest radiographs as much as 56% of the time. Additional studies conducted by researchers at major academic medical centers disclosed that from 26% to 90% of all lung carcinomas were missed by radiologists interpreting plain chest radiographs.[23]

---

[18] Garland LH. Studies on the accuracy of diagnostic procedures. *AJR* 1959;82:25-38.

[19] Smith MJ. *Error and variation in diagnostic radiology.* Springfield, IL:Thomas 1967;4, 71,73-74, 144-169; Stevenson CA. Accuracy of the x-ray report. *JAMA* 1969;207:1140-1141; Berlin L. Does the "missed" radiographic diagnosis constitute malpractice? *Radiology* 1977;123:523-527; Markus JB, Somers S, Franic SE, Moola C, Stevenson GW. Interobserver variation in the interpretation of abdominal radiographs. *Radiology* 1989;171:69-71; Berlin L. Reporting the "missed" radiologic diagnosis: medicolegal and ethical considerations. *Radiology* 1994;192:183-187; Berlin L, Hendrix RW. Perceptual errors and negligence. *AJR* 1998;170:863-867; Berlin L. Errors in judgment. *AJR* 1996;166:1259-1261; Berlin L. Perceptual errors. *AJR* 1996;167:587-590; Renfrew DL, Franken EA, Berbaum KS, Weigelt FH, Abu-Yousef MM, Error in radiology: classification and lessons in 182 cases presented at a problem case conference. *Radiology* 1992,183:145-150; Potchen EJ. Measuring observer performance in chest radiology: some experiences. *J Am Coll Radiol* 2006;3:423-432; Berlin L. Defending the "missed" radiographic diagnosis. *AJR* 2001;176:317-322.

[20] Lehr JL, Lodwick GS, Farrell C, et al. Direct measurement of the effect of film miniaturization on diagnostic accuracy. *Radiology* 1976;118:257-263.

[21] Renfrew DL, Franken EA, Berbaum KS, Weigelt FH, Abu-Yousef MM, Error in radiology: classification and lessons in 182 cases presented at a problem case conference. *Radiology* 1992;183:145-150.

[22] Herman PG, Gerson DE, Hessel SJ, et al. Disagreement in chest roentgen interpretation. *Chest* 1975;68:278-282.

[23] Forrest JV, Friedman PJ. Radiologic errors in patients with lung cancer. *West J Med* 1981;134:485-490; Muhm JR, Miller WE, Fontana RS, Sanderson DR, Uhlenhapp MA. Lung cancer detected during a screening program using four-month chest radiographs, *Radiology* 1983;148:609-615; Austin JHM, Romney BM, Goldsmith LS. Missed bronchogenic carcinoma:

Numerous reports have documented similarly high error and disagreement rates for myriad other techniques utilized in radiologic practice, including sonography,[24] angiography,[25] MR angiography,[26] MRI when evaluating lumbar disk herniation,[27] thallium radionuclide heart scans,[28] MR when evaluating rotator cuff injury[29] and MR when evaluating prostatic cancer.[30] More recent studies have confirmed a 35% error rate among radiologists interpreting radiologic studies obtained in patients who had undergone trauma.[31] Statistics disclosing inaccuracies in the interpretation of mammograms are startling.[32] A 1994 study at Yale

radiographic findings in 27 patients with a potentially respectable lesion evident in retrospect. *Radiology* 1992;182:115-122.

[24] James AE, Fleischer AC, Sacks GA, Greeson T. Ectopic pregnancy: a malpractice paradigm. *Radiology* 1986;160:411-413; Hertzberg BS, Kliewer MA, Paulson EK, et al. PACS in sonography: accuracy of interpretation using film compared with monitor display. *AJR* 1999;173:1175-1179.

[25] Manning WJ, Li W, Adelman RR. A preliminary report comparing magnetic resonance coronary angiography with conventional angiography. *N Engl J Med* 1993;328:828-832.

[26] Litt AW, Eidelman EM, Pinto RS, et al. Diagnosis of carotid artery stenosis: comparison of 2DFT time-of-flight MR angiography with contrast angiography in 50 patients. *AJNR* 1991;156:611-616.

[27] van Rijn JC, Klemetso N, Reitsma JB, et al. Observer variation in MRI evaluation of patients suspected of lumbar disk herniation. *AJR* 2005;184:299-303.

[28] Sigal SI, Soufer R, Fetterman RC, Mattera JA, Wackers FJT. Reproducibility of quantitative planar thallium-201 scintigraphy: quantitative criteria for reversibility of myocardial perfusion defects. *J Nucl Med* 1991;32:759-765.

[29] Robertson PL, Schweitzer ME, Mitchell DG, et al. Rotator cuff disorders: interobserver and intraobserver variation in diagnosis with MR imaging. *Radiology* 1995;194:831-835.

[30] Schiebler ML, Yankaskas BC, Tempany BC, et al. MR imaging in adenocarcinoma of the prostate; interobserver variation and efficacy for determining stage C disease. *AJR* 1992;158:559-562.

[31] Janjua KJ, Sugrue M, Deane SA. Prospective evaluation of early missed injuries and the role of tertiary trauma survey. *J Trauma* 1998;44:1000-1007; FitzGerald R. Error in radiology. *Clin Radiol* 2001;56:938-946; FitzGerald R. Radiological error: analysis, standard setting, targeted instruction and teamworking. *Eur Radiol* 2005;15:1760-1767.

[32] Sickles EA. Breast imaging: from 1965 to the present. *Radiology* 2000;215:1-16

Berlin L. The missed breast cancer: perceptions and realities. *AJR* 1999;173:1161-1167;

Berg WA, Campassi C, Langenberg P, Sexton MJ. Breast imaging reporting and data system: inter- and intraobserver variability in feature analysis and final assessment. *AJR* 2000;174:1769-1777; Baines CJ, McFarlane DV, Miller AB. Role of the reference radiologist: estimates of inter-observer agreement and potential delay in cancer detection in the National Breast Screening Study. *Invest Radiol* 1990;25:

Beam CA, Layde PM, Sullivan DC. Variability in the interpretation of screening mammograms by US radiologists. *Arch Intern Med* 1996;156:209-213; Kerlikowske K, Grady D, Rubin S, Sandrock C, Ernster V. Efficacy of screening mammography: a meta-analysis. *JAMA* 1995;273:149-154; Mushlin AI, Kouides ;RW, Shapiro DE. Estimating the accuracy of screening mammography: a meta-analysis. *Am J Prev Med* 1998;14:143-153; Kerlikowske K, Grady D, Barclay J, et al. Variability and accuracy of mammography interpretation using the American

University School of Medicine found upon retrospective review of mammograms originally interpreted by experienced radiologists as normal that from 15% to 63% of breast carcinomas had been overlooked at initial readings.[33] A University of Arizona study found that in 75% of mammograms initially interpreted as normal, breast carcinomas were seen on retrospective evaluation.[34]

[3] Errors in Clinical Medicine

Garland's 1959 revelations about the incidence of errors in clinical medicine have also been confirmed and expanded upon by subsequent researchers. Agreement among academic faculty physicians performing physical examination for spleen enlargement,[35] liver enlargement[36] abdominal ascites[37] acute otitis media,[38] and other assorted physical findings [39]has been shown to be poor. Large autopsy studies have also uncovered frequent clinical errors and misdiagnoses, with error rates as high as 47%.[40]

A recent *Wall Street Journal* article[41] reported errors ranging from 25% to 49% in pathologists' interpretations of biopsy specimens, and a recent article in a pathology journal reported a 24% error rate in laboratory results.[42]

College of Radiology Breast Imaging Reporting and Data System. *J Natl Cancer Inst* 1998;90:1801-1809.

[33] Elmore JG, Wells CK, Lee CH, Howard DH, Feinstein AR. Variability in radiologists' interpretations of mammograms. *N Engl J Med* 1994;331:1493-1499.

[34] Harvey JA, Fajardo LL, Innis CA. Previous mammograms in patients with impalpable breast carcinoma: retrospective vs blinded interpretation. *AJR* 1993;161:1167-1172.

[35] Grover SA, Barkun AN, Sackett DL. Does this patient have splenomegaly? *JAMA* 1993;270:2218-2221.

[36] Naylor CD. Physical examination of the liver. JAMA 1994;271:1859.

[37] Williams JW, Simel DL. Does this patient have ascites? *JAMA* 1992;267:2645-2648.

[38] Pichichero ME, Poole MD. Assessing Diagnostic Accuracy and Tympanocentesis Skills in the Management of Otitis Media. *Arch Pediatr Adolesc Med.* 2001;155:1137-1142.

[39] Eliot DL, Hickam DH. Evaluation of physical examination skills; reliability of faculty observers and patient instructors. *JAMA* 1987;258:3405-3408; Sackett DL. A primer on the precision and accuracy of the clinical examination. *JAMA* 1992;267:2638-2644; Gruver RH, Freis ED. Study of diagnostic errors. *Ann Intern Med* 1957;47:108-120.

[40] Anderson RE, Hill RB, Key CR. The sensitivity and specificity of clinical diagnostics during five decades: toward an understanding of necessary fallibility. *JAMA* 1989;261:1610-1617; Roosen J, Frans E, Wilmer A, Knockaert DC, Bobbaers H. Comparison of premortem clinical diagnoses in critically ill patients and subsequent autopsy findings. *May Clin Proc* 2000;75:562-567.

[41] Landro L. Hospitals move to cut dangerous lab errors. *Wall Street Journal,* June 14, 2006: D1, D11.

[42] Plebani M. Errors in clinical laboratories or errors in laboratory medicine? *Clin Chem Lab Med* 2006;44:750-759.

[4] Error Rate Defined

Garland explained in his 1959 article that the error rate can be calculated in two different ways, depending on the denominator used:[43]

> If a series of 100 roentgenograms contains 10 positive and 90 negative films, and a reader misses three of the positive films and overreads two of the negative films, he may regarded as having only a 5% error. On the other hand, since the series of 100 roentgenograms is being examined to detect patient with disease, the reader who misses three of the ten positive films has an error rate of 30%. Coupled with an overreading of two of the ninety negative films, the combined error rate in the example mentioned is about 32%.

In virtually all of the studies of error rates to which this Commentary has thus far referred, the denominator consists of a preselected number of abnormal radiologic studies. Thus, if a radiologist participating in a research project is given 100 radiographs known to be abnormal and misses 30 of them, the error rate is obviously 30%. This should not be construed as indicating that radiologists commit an average 30% error rate in their everyday practices. Several studies have measured error rates of radiologists by determining how many errors were committed among a large number of radiologic studies interpreted by the radiologist in a practice situation over a selected period of time — in other words, with a different denominator. Texas researchers[44] in 1998 reviewed imaging interpretations rendered in radiology departments of six community hospitals affiliated with the University of Texas and found a 4.4% mean rate of interpretation error. Other researchers[45] reviewed the performance of more than 250 radiologists who had interpreted more than 20,000 examinations as part of clinical testing of a performance improvement product, *Radpeer*. They found an all-case disagreement rate of 3% to 3.5%. Yet another group of researchers[46] reviewed the results of a quality improvement study conducted among 26 radiologists who read 6703 cases, and found an overall disagreement rate of 3.48%. In other words, if the

---

[43] Garland LH. Studies on the accuracy of diagnostic procedures. *AJR* 1959;82:25-38.

[44] Siegle RL, Baram EM, Reuter SR, Clarke EA, Lancaster JL, McMahan CA. Rates of disagreement in imaging interpretation in a group of community hospitals. *Acad Radiol* 1998;5:148-154.

[45] Borgstede JP, Lewis RS, Bhargavan M, Sunshine JH. RADPEER quality assurance program: a multifacility study of interpretive disagreement rates. *J Am Coll Radiol* 2004;1:59-65.

[46] Soffa DJ, Lewis RS, Sunshine JH, Bhargavan M. Disagreement in interpretation: a method for the development of benchmarks for quality assurance in imaging. *J Am Coll Radiol* 2004;1:212-217.

denominator consists only of radiology studies that harbor abnormalities, the error rate averages 30%; if the denominator consists of an "everyday" mixture of abnormal and normal cases as is usually found in daily practices, the error rate averages 3.5% to 4%.

[5] Errors and Their Impact on Patient Care

It should be emphasized here that none of the studies referred to in this chapter reflect the degree (if any) to which patient care is jeopardized because of reader misinterpretation. "Extrapolation of reader error to medical care is complex," stated Herman et al.[47] Although some radiologic errors may indeed result in serious injury and/or mismanagement of a patient, many others are either corrected quickly or, fortunately, not clinically important, and thus exert no adverse effect on the management of the patient.

[6] Computer-Assisted Detection (CAD)

Over the past decade innumerable articles reporting on and discussing the results of new technologies have appeared in the radiologic literature. A series of recent articles[48] extensively reviewed major developments in digital radiography and computer-aided detection (CAD). Several conclusions can be drawn from these articles and those referenced in their bibliographies. Clearly, CAD improves sensitivity and decreases variability of interpretation by raising the level of the radiologist's suspicion in examinations where a potential abnormality has been highlighted. CAD has been shown to be of value in assisting radiologists in reducing radiologic errors and improving radiologic interpretation, particularly in mammography.[49] However, whether digital radiography and CAD will once and for all substantially reduce

---

[47] Herman PG, Gerson DE, Hessel SJ, et al. Disagreement in chest roentgen interpretation. *Chest* 1975;68:278-282.

[48] Warren Burhenne LJ, Wood SA, D'Orsi, CJ et al. Potential contribution of computer-aided detection to the sensitivity of screening mammography. *Radiology* 2000;215:554-562; Freedman M, Osicka T. Reader variability: what we can learn from computer-aided detection experiments. *J Am Coll Radiol* 2006;3:446-455;Williams MB, Yaffe MJ, Maidment ADA, et al. Image quality in digital mammography: image acquisition. *J Am Coll Radiol* 2006;3:589-608; Siegel E, Krupinski E, Samei E, et al. Digital mammography image quality: image display. *J Am Coll Radiol* 2006;3:615-627;

Erickson BJ, Patriarche J, Khorasani R, et al. New opportunities in computer-aided Diagnosis: Change Detection and Characterization. *JACR* 2006;3:468-469.

[49] Morton MJ, Whaley DH, Brandt KR, Amrami KK. Screening mammograms: interpretation with computer-aided detection - prospective evaluation. *Radiology* 2006;239:375-383; Dean JC, Ilvento CC. Improved cancer detection using computer-aided detection with diagnostic and screening mammography: prospective study of 104 cancers. *AJR* 2006;187:20-28.

radiologic error, the rate of which has not changed in the nearly half-century since Garland's classical article appeared, is yet to be determined.

[7] Causes of Errors

Author Malcolm Gladwell writing recently in *The New Yorker*[50] made the following insightful observation regarding uncertainty, one of the causes of errors in radiologic interpretation:

> The reason a radiologist is required to assume that the overwhelming number of ambiguous things are normal is that the overwhelming number of ambiguous things really are normal. Radiologists are, in a sense, a lot like baggage screeners at airports. The chances are that the dark mass in the middle of the suitcase isn't a bomb, because you've seen a thousand dark masses like it in suitcases before, and none of those were bombs—and if you flag every suitcase with something ambiguous in it, no one would ever make his flight. But that doesn't mean, of course, that it isn't a bomb. All you have to go on is what it looks like on the X-ray screen —and the screen seldom gives you quite enough information.

[8] Errors versus Negligence

As has already been mentioned, approximately 4% of radiographic interpretations rendered by radiologists in their daily practice contain errors.[51] Fortunately, most of these errors are of such minor degree, or if serious are found and corrected with sufficient promptness, that they do not cause injury to patients. Nevertheless, many radiologic errors do harm patients and, as a result, medical malpractice lawsuits are generated. If it is determined by a judge or jury that the diagnostic error committed by a defendant-radiologist was the result of negligence, in other words, a breach of the standard of medical care, the radiologist will be held liable and compensation will be awarded to the plaintiff-patient. Should the defendant's radiologic error be found not to be due to negligence, litigation is terminated without compensation. It follows, then, that certain

---

[50] Gladwell M. The picture problem: mammography, air power, and the limits of looking. *The New Yorker* December 13, 2004.

[51] Borgstede JP, Lewis RS, Bhargavan M, Sunshine JH. RADPEER quality assurance program: a multifacility study of interpretive disagreement rates. *J Am Coll Radiol* 2004;1:59-65; Soffa DJ, Lewis RS, Sunshine JH, Bhargavan M. Disagreement in interpretation: a method for the development of benchmarks for quality assurance in imaging. *J Am Coll Radiol* 2004;1:212-217.

radiographic errors result from radiologists' negligent conduct, others do not. One may then logically ask whether these two kinds of radiographic errors, those that constitute negligence and those that do not, can be distinguished and if so, how?

[9] Malpractice Defined

In order for a radiologist or any other physician to be found liable for — i.e., "guilty" of — medical malpractice, four elements must be established. There must be a physician-patient relationship;[52] the radiologist must have committed a negligent act (a breach of the standard of the care); the negligent act must have caused injury to the plaintiff-patient (proximate cause),[53] and the patient must have sustained an injury. Except in unusual circumstances three of these four elements—the physician-patient relationship, proximate cause, and patient injury—are not contentious issues in a lawsuit. The remaining allegation that must be proven for a plaintiff to succeed in a malpractice lawsuit, the one claiming that the defendant's conduct has breached the standard of care, is the most frequently contested. Inasmuch as nearly 75% of all medical malpractice lawsuits lodged against diagnostic radiologists allege negligence related to errors in diagnosis,[54] our discussion here will be limited to the relationship between radiologic errors and malpractice.

Let us briefly review several state Supreme Court decisions that dealt with this relationship.

In 1992 the Delaware State Supreme Court pointed out:[55]

> It is not enough...for the plaintiff to show that some other physician would personally have acted any differently than the defendant...or that there is an approach which would be better than that utilized by the defendant, if nevertheless the approach utilized by the defendant is regarded...as an acceptable approach....No inference of malpractice arises from the mere fact that there was an undesirable result. Malpractice is never presumed. The law does not make a physician an insurer of the best result of his treatment.

---

[52] Meena v. Wilburn, 603 So2d 866 (Miss 1992); Berlin L. Are radiologists contracted by third parties to interpret radiographs liable for not communicating results directly to patients? *AJR* 2002;178:27-33.

[53] Berlin L. Proximate cause. *AJR* 2002;179:569-573.

[54] Berlin L, Berlin J. Malpractice and radiologists in Cook County, IL: trends in 20 years of litigation. *AJR* 1995;165:781-788.

[55] Riggins v. Mauriello, 603 A2d 827 (Del 1992).

The Michigan Supreme Court expressed similar sentiments and emphasized that not all mistakes constitute negligence:[56]

> One's treating physician is not a warrantor of cure or of accurate diagnosis. He is responsible in damages for unfortunate results when and only when it is shown...that he has departed from that standard of care which is known as customary medical practice... Utilizing the benefit of hindsight, [the defendant-physician] made one of those occasional mistakes which even the most skilled of professional men do make as they proceed with the trial-and-error work they have chosen. Such a mistake is not actionable in the medical field unless it is shown...that the acts or omissions of the accused doctor were contrary to customary medical practice.

Twelve years ago the Illinois Supreme Court refined its perspective on the subject:[57]

> The term "standard of care" in common law is generally understood to mean a measure or rule against which a defendant's conduct is to be measured. The established standard of care for all professionals is stated as use of the same degree of knowledge, skill, and ability as an ordinarily careful professional would exercise under similar circumstances.

[10] A More Liberal View of How Malpractice Is Defined: The Wisconsin Court

In none of the decisions excerpted above did the respective courts deal specifically with radiographic errors. A 1997 Wisconsin Appellate Court decision is unique in having done so, however. In that case a Wisconsin radiologist had been sued for malpractice twice, once for missing a fracture of the proximal tibia, again for missing a carcinoma of the colon on a lower gastrointestinal examination. Both lawsuits were settled with payment made to the plaintiff-patients. Soon thereafter, the Wisconsin Department of Regulation and Licensing instituted legal action to suspend or revoke the radiologist's medical license for conduct that it considered to be negligent. A lower court exonerated the radiologist of the charge of negligence and the Department appealed to the state's Appellate Court. The higher court upheld

---

[56] Skeffington v. Bradley, 115 NW2d 303 (Mich 1962).
[57] Advincula v. United Blood Services, 678 NE2d 1009 (Ill 1996).

the lower court's decision in favor of the radiologist in a written decision that included a detailed analysis of radiographic errors:[58]

> A radiologist may review an x-ray using the degree of care of a reasonable radiologist, but fail to detect an abnormality that, on average, would have been found. …Radiologists simply cannot detect all abnormalities on all x-rays…Errors in perception occur when a radiologist diligently reviews an x-ray, following all the proper procedures and using all the proper techniques, and fails to perceive an abnormality which in retrospect, is apparent.…Several reasons for errors in perception include: 1) Humans differ in the perceptions of a single item, 2) The finding of one object may cause a physician to overlook another abnormality, and 3) The patient's body structure may make an abnormality more difficult to detect.…

> Errors in perception by radiologists viewing x-rays occur in the absence of negligence. The medical literature…states that in controlled tests, radiologists miss a certain percentage of abnormalities despite using extraordinary efforts.…There is no evidence in the record…to establish that [the defendant-radiologist's] errors in having failed to detect those defects came as a result of his failure to conform to the accepted standard of care in the field of radiology…This record is devoid of any evidence or suggestion that [the defendant-radiologist] is anything but a fully competent careful and conscientious radiologist or that he was not competent, careful, and conscientious in his examination of the affected radiographs in this case.

Aside from this Wisconsin Court decision that made an effort to define the words "average, and "reasonable" (but not the word "ordinary"), clear-cut definitions of these words have never been spelled out by the courts. Radiologists who are trained and expected to pinpoint radiologic abnormalities with precision and then render interpretations in specific and meaningful terms will probably feel perplexed if not frustrated at the vagueness of the words "reasonable" and "ordinary" as used by the courts in defining the standard of medical care. Unfortunately, the courts have not been able to give us a more concrete definition of standard of care as it applies to radiologists or other physicians. All courts have been consistent, however, in holding that the physician's level of knowledge and skill must at least be that

---

[58] Department of Regulation and Licensing v. State of Wisconsin Medical Examining Board, 572 NW2d 508 (Wis App 1997).

which is minimally acceptable but need not be perfect.[59]   Nevertheless, a substantial chasm exists between the courts' perceptions of the meaning of the words, "average," "reasonable," and "ordinary," and Webster's definitions. It would seem incongruous if not self-defeating for a defendant-radiologist to argue before a jury that the radiologist met the standard of care even though the radiologist's radiographic interpretation was "mediocre, not above but rather below average, somewhat inferior level of quality."

It is clear from the above that the theoretical legal issue that must be determined by a jury in cases that focus on an alleged missed radiologic diagnosis is not whether the radiologist missed a lesion but, rather, whether missing the lesion is acceptable within the usual and customary standards of the radiology community. Considering that the standard of care is not absolute and the jury during a trial will have been exposed to conflicting testimony from expert medical witnesses and arguments presented by the attorneys representing the plaintiff and defendant respectively, this determination is far from simple. Often the standard of care becomes whatever a contest of experts can persuade a jury is the most appropriate standard of care for the specific case on trial.[60] Nevertheless, ultimately the jury will render a decision in a given case as to whether the defendant-radiologist did or did not breach the standard of care. Whatever the verdict, another jury, hearing the same evidence and pondering over the same arguments, could well render a different verdict.

Several researchers have made independent studies of the relationship between errors and negligence. Harvard Medical Practice Study investigators reported that adverse events occurred in 3.7% of hospitalizations in New York, and that 27% of these were due to negligence.[61] Researchers in Utah and Colorado determined that adverse events occurred in 2.9% of hospitalizations and that up to 33% were due to negligence.[62]

The presence of error is a necessary but not a sole requisite for the determination of negligence.[63] Negligence occurs not when there is merely an error, but when the degree of error exceeds an acceptable norm. What is an "acceptable norm?" How many of the radiographic interpretations in the

---

[59] Berlin L. Defending the "missed" radiographic diagnosis. *AJR* 2000;176:317-322.

[60] Potchen EJ, Bisesi MA. When is it malpractice to miss lung cancer on chest radiographs? *Radiology* 1990;175:29-32.

[61] Brennan TA, Leape LL, Laird NM, et al. Incidence of adverse events and negligence in hospitalized patients: results of the Harvard medical practice study 1. *N Engl J Med* 1991;324:370-376.

[62] Thomas EJ, Studdert; DM, Burstin HR, et al. Incidence and types of adverse events and negligent care in Utah and Colorado. *Med Care* 2000;38:261-271.

[63] Brennan TA, Hebert LE, Laird N, et al. Hospital characteristics associated with adverse events and substandard care. *JAMA* 1991;265:3265-3269.

90%-missed-lung-cancer-group[64] and the 75% –missed-breast-cancer-group[65] referred to in §7 were within the radiologic standard of care, and how many were the result of a breach of that standard? The answers to these questions elude us.

[11]   Defending Radiographic Misses: Hindsight and Outcome Biases

It is difficult to defend a radiologist who has failed to perceive a radiographic abnormality that in retrospect can be readily perceived by both medical and non-medical observers alike. This difficulty is in part the result of two kinds of biases: hindsight and outcome. Hindsight bias is the tendency for people with knowledge of the actual outcome of an event to believe falsely that they would have predicted the outcome.[66] Although most people are not consciously aware that they are being influenced by hindsight bias, physicians, the lay public, and obviously jurors, remain susceptible to such bias in their judgments. A study conducted by researchers at the University of Pennsylvania indicated that the determination of negligence is substantially influenced by whether the patient has sustained injury.[67] One legal observer has pointed out that although our legal system promises not to hold defendants liable if they have conducted themselves reasonably before an injury occurs, hindsight bias ensures that some reasonably acting defendants will be unfairly subjected to adverse liability judgments when after-injury evaluation has taken place.[68]

Closely related is outcome bias: the tendency for people to attribute blame more readily when the nature of the outcome is serious than they would if the outcome were comparatively minor. According to some researchers,[69] the attribution of blame satisfies a psychological need to find an object to punish, for by punishing another we annul the wrong and lessen the hurt.

Neither hindsight nor outcome bias should influence jurors sitting in a medical malpractice trial in their determination of whether medical

---

[64] Muhm JR, Miller WE, Fontana RS, Sanderson DR, Uhlenhapp MA. Lung cancer detected during a screening program using four-month chest radiographs, *Radiology* 1983;148:609-615.

[65] Harvey JA, Fajardo LL, Innis CA. Previous mammograms in patients with impalpable breast carcinoma: retrospective vs blinded interpretation. *AJR* 1993;161:1167-1172.

[66] Siegle RL, Baram EM, Reuter SR, Clarke EA, Lancaster JL, McMahan CA. Rates of disagreement in imaging interpretation in a group of community hospitals. *Acad Radiol* 1998;5:148-154.

[67] LaBine SJ, LaBine G. Determinations of negligence and the hindsight bias. *Law Hum Behav* 1996;20:501-516.

[68] Kamin KA, Rachlinski JJ. Determining liability in hindsight. *Law Hum Behav* 1995;19:89-104.

[69] Merry A, McCall Smith A. *Errors medicine and the law.* Cambridge, UK: Cambridge University Press 2003:162-164, 194-198.

negligence has occurred, and if so the extent of compensation that should be awarded to the plaintiff. The fact is, however, that knowledge of the nature and severity of the injury sustained by the patient has been shown to substantially influence juries' findings of both the defendant's liability and amount of the plaintiff's compensatory damages.[70] Indeed, researchers have shown that the severity of the patient's disability, not the occurrence of the actual negligence, was predictive of payment to the plaintiff.[71]

[12] Errors and Malpractice: Pubic Perceptions

The question of whether a missed radiographic diagnosis constitutes malpractice has confounded radiologists, patients, attorneys, judges, jurors and the general public for more than a century, and it is not likely that the question will be resolved to the satisfaction of any of these parties in the foreseeable future. Radiologists continue to be subjected to malpractice litigation more for missing radiographic diagnoses than for any other reason. Furthermore, radiologists who are sued for missing diagnoses are likely to have more indemnification paid on their behalf to satisfy a settlement or adverse jury verdict than for any other malpractice allegation. Obviously, if radiographic errors could be eliminated, the prevalence of medical malpractice lawsuits would be immediately curtailed. Indeed, one radiology observer for a brief period pondered whether improved training could minimize mistakes, but quickly concluded that mistakes are unlikely to be significantly reduced until we have "perfect diagnostic tests" and "perfect observers."[72] Such perfection is not likely to occur. Furthermore, surveys have disclosed that two-thirds of the public believe that a physician should be sued for malpractice if he or she commits a medical error that leads to a fatality or other serious injury.[73] In fact, more than half of physicians also believe that a physician should get sued for committing an error if the error leads to the death or other serious injury to the patient. Thus, neither a reduction in radiologists' error rates, nor a reduction in malpractice litigation alleging a missed diagnosis, is likely to occur.

Much of the medical community, including many radiologists as well as attorneys and lay people alike, believe that if a radiologist has missed an

---

[70] Berlin L. Outcome bias. *AJR* 2004;183:557-560.

[71] Brennan TA, Sox CM, Burstin HR. Relation between negligent adverse events and the outcomes of medical-malpractice litigation. *NEJM* 1996;335:1963-1967.

[72] Turner DA. Teaching editorial: observer variability: what to do until perfect diagnostic tests are invented. *J Nucl Med* 1978;19:435-437.

[73] Blendon RJ, DesRoches CM, Brodie M, et al. Views of practicing physicians and the public on medical errors. *N Engl J Med* 2002;347:1933-1940.

abnormal finding that can be seen retrospectively on radiographs, the miss cannot be considered anything but negligence. The blunt fact is that it is difficult to argue in the courtroom that a radiologist who is supposed to be well trained and well paid to detect all abnormalities should be excused for failing to perceive a radiographic abnormality that, many years later with the benefit of "20/20" hindsight, can be seen not only by the radiologist but by other observers as well. Nevertheless, presenting data that include statistics regarding the frequency of errors committed by radiologists during the course of ordinary everyday practice, explanations of why certain radiographic abnormalities appear inconspicuous, evidence that the conduct of the defendant-radiologist has been careful and prudent, and expert testimony that it is not possible for any radiologist or other professional to adhere to a standard of perfection, can at times be sufficiently persuasive so as to effect a jury verdict in favor of the defendant-radiologist.

[13] The Inescapable Realities of Radiologic Practice

There is yet another way by which the malpractice burden on radiologists might possibly be lessened. Recognizing that unique and inevitable errors of perception and judgment occur among even the most learned radiologists, two medical-legal researchers[74] have recently proposed that judges should instruct juries to consider during their deliberation the following "inescapable realities" of radiologic practice:

> There is an absolutely unavoidable "human factor" at work in the review of films; some abnormalities may be missed, even the obvious ones; the mere fact that a radiologist misses an abnormality on a radiograph does not mean that he or she has committed malpractice; and not all radiographic "misses" are excusable. Therefore, the focus of attention should be on issues such as proof of competence, habits of practice, and use of proper techniques.

Whether the judiciary will ever be disposed to adopt this proposal is unknown.

Thirty one years ago an article posed the following rhetorical question:[75]

---

[74] Caldwell C, Seamone ER. Excusable neglect in malpractice suits against radiologists: a proposed jury instruction to recognize the human condition. *Ann of Hlth Law*, Loyola University, Chicago 2007;16:43-77.

[75] Berlin L. Does the "missed" radiographic diagnosis constitute malpractice? *Radiology* 1977;123:523-527.

In spite of all that has been written, as well as the various legal opinions that have been rendered, is there still no practical answer to the question, "When is a radiographic error simply an error and when is it malpractice?"

Three decades later, the answer to this question still eludes us; the distinction between radiographic errors and malpractice remains as blurry as ever.

§ 9.03 Communication

[1] Comparing Current Radiological Exams with Those Obtained Previously: The Alliterative Error

Comparing previous radiologic examinations and reports with current studies is recommended. Indeed, two radiology researchers found that reading a previous report was useful in 60% of cases, and provided a significant amount of help in another 24% of cases.[76] Likewise, in his classic book on radiographic errors, Smith[77] emphasized that failure to compare a current film with a previous one is an important and common cause of radiographic error. However, Smith also drew the attention to another common type of radiographic error, one that he called the *alliterative error*. It is a phenomenon caused by the influence that one radiologist can exert on another. In other words, if one radiologist fails to detect and report a radiographic abnormality, the chance of a second or subsequent radiologist also missing the same abnormality is increased. Smith explained that alliterative errors more frequently occur when radiologists read the reports of previous examinations before looking at a new set of films, thereby concentrating their attention on areas of the radiographs that may not harbor a new abnormality. Smith also believed that an interpreting radiologist's perception of a radiographic abnormality is influenced by the reports rendered by radiologic colleagues who have interpreted previous studies of the same patient.

Circumstances may exist, such as when a radiologist may note that a lesion was missed on a previous study, when the radiologist may choose deliberately not to compare a new radiograph with previous radiographs. Radiologists who elect not to disclose a radiologic missed diagnosis by

---

[76] Hunter TB, Boyle RR. The value of reading the previous radiology report. *AJR* 1988;150:697-698.

[77] Smith MJ. *Error and variation in diagnostic radiology.* Springfield, IL: Thomas 1967;4, 71,73-74, 144-169.

omitting documentation of comparison with previous radiologic studies may succeed in escaping legal exposure or criticism. However, radiologists should be aware that omitting comparisons for this purpose violates the spirit, if not the letter, of ACR Practice Guidelines. The preponderance of legal opinion and ethical commentaries favors comparison with previous studies whenever possible, even if such comparison results in disclosure of errors committed by the interpreting radiologists themselves or their colleagues.[78]

Based on the preponderance of articles and commentaries published in the radiologic literature, the formal Practice Guidelines issued by the ACR, and an informal consensus among practicing radiologists, it is generally accepted by the radiologic community that when rendering radiographic interpretations, the standard of radiologic care requires that radiologists compare new radiographs with those obtained previously. Any delay in establishing the diagnosis of serious illness that can be attributed to a radiologist's failure to compare current with prior radiographs may generate a medical malpractice lawsuit, and can result in a finding of liability against the radiologist.

If the radiologist is unable to make a comparison because previous radiographs cannot be located or are otherwise unavailable, the interpreting radiologist should contemporaneously document that fact in the report. I suggest inserting into the report a simple phrase such as, "previous radiographs are unavailable for comparison."

The duty to retrieve previous mammograms that may not be readily available for comparison with current studies is less clear and remains controversial. Although the ACR Practice Guideline on screening mammography favors obtaining previous radiographs "when practical,"[79] radiology groups should adopt their own local policies regarding how to deal with previous mammograms. The policy should be one to which all members can adhere.

If previous radiographic studies are not available within an appropriate pre-determined time period, but are still in the process of being sought by the patient or by radiology personnel, I suggest issuing a radiology report that indicates the previous films are not yet available. If previous studies become available later, radiologists can consider issuing an addendum report that includes the comparison.

Radiologists should be aware that deliberately omitting the comparison of current with previous radiographic examinations because a radiologist

---

[78] Berlin L. Reporting the "missed" radiologic diagnosis: medicolegal and ethical considerations. *Radiology* 1994;192:183-187.

[79] American College of Radiology. *ACR standard for the performance of screening mammography.* Reston, VA: American College of Radiology, 1995.

does not want to call attention to a lesion that was missed on a previous study is fraught with a myriad of medicolegal, ethical, and professional concerns. Radiologists who choose to omit comparisons because of this reason do so at great risk.

[2] Direct Communication of Radiologic Findings to Referring Physicians: The Courts' Perspective

Long before the American College of Radiology adopted its communication practice guideline, the courts had taken the position that radiologists have a duty to directly communicate significant radiologic abnormalities to referring physicians. Nearly 30 years ago an Ohio Appeals Court stated:[80]

> The communication of a diagnosis so that it may be beneficially utilized may be altogether as important as the diagnosis itself. Severity of condition, urgency of treatment, potential for interim injury, suffering from delayed response, need for further analysis and consultation, and the patient's awareness of the extent of injury or the nature of the condition may all be relevant in ascertaining the necessary course of conduct in reporting a diagnosis. In certain situations direct contact with the treating physician is necessary beyond communication through administrative personnel. Certain medical emergencies may require the most direct and immediate response involving personal consultation and exchange.

A decade later the Arkansas Supreme Court added:[81]
> When a patient is peril of his life, it does him little good if the examining doctor has discovered his condition unless the physician takes measures and informs the patient, or those responsible for his care, of that fact.

[3] American College of Radiology Practice Guidelines and Standards

In an attempt to provide consistency, promote better medical practice, and improve medical quality, various medical organizations and specialty societies began in the late 1980s to publish written guidelines and

---

[80] Phillips v. Good Samaritan Hospital, 416 NE2d 646 (OH App 1979).
[81] Corteau v. Dodd, 773 SW2d 436 (Ark 1989).

standards.[82] By promulgating the best available scientific evidence on efficacy and safety these organizations hoped that the guidelines and standards would not only elevate the level of patient care but at the same time diminish the incidence of and costs related to malpractice litigation.

It was anticipated that the guidelines would be used in litigation by both the patient-plaintiff and the physician-defendant — by the plaintiff for blame-placing purposes (in other words, as a "sword") by claiming that the defendant failed to follow the applicable guideline, and by the defendant for blame-relieving (in other words as a "shield") by showing that defendant conformed to the applicable guideline.[83] In either case, the party asserting the guideline would be asking the court to accept it as proof that the defendant-physician complied with or deviated from the legal standard of care. The courts, however, have rarely used guidelines in this fashion, and have instead continued to rely on expert testimony as the basis on which the standard of care is established. Nevertheless, studies have disclosed that published guidelines and standards have been used more often to strengthen the position of plaintiffs than that of defendant-physicians.[84]

[4] Do ACR Practice Guidelines Dictate the Standard of Care?

A recent *John Marshall Law Review* article surveyed state, appellate, and supreme court decisions to determine how the judiciary has viewed American College of Radiology Standards and Practice Guidelines. Most of the decisions available thus far have focused on the Practice Guidelines that dealt with communication.[85] Courts have generally given the ACR Practice Guidelines considerable weight, and have ruled that while the ACR Practice Guidelines in and of themselves do not establish a standard of care, they are nevertheless useful in assisting the courts in determining the radiologic standard of care applicable in a given situation.[86]

In order to understand the relationship between ACR Practice Guidelines and the legal standard of care, it is necessary to delve into the history of these Guidelines. ACR Standards (as they were initially called) were first presented

---

[82] Bovbjerg RR. Medical malpractice: folklore, facts, and the future. *Ann Intern Med* 1992;117(9):788-791; Hyams AL, Brandenburg JA, Lipsitz SR, Brennan TA. *Report to Physician Payment Review Commission: practice guidelines and malpractice litigation*. Boston: Harvard School of Public Health, Department of Health Policy and Management, 1994.

[83] Rosoff AJ. Evidence-based medicine and the law: the courts confront clinical practice guidelines. 26 *J. Health Pol. Pol'y & L.* 327 (2001).

[84] Hyams AL, Brandenburg JA, Lipsitz SR, Shapiro DW, Brennan TA. Practice guidelines and malpractice litigation: a two-way street. *Ann Intern Med* 1995;122:450-455.

[85] Ginsberg MD. Beyond the viewbox: the radiologist's duty to communicate findings. The *John Marshall Law Review* 2002;35(3):359-380.

[86] Aldoroty v HCA Health Services of Kansas, 962 P2d 501 (Kan 1998).

to the College membership at its 1990 annual meeting. At that time the new standards were envisioned to reflect "the baseline quality of medical care." This vision was reaffirmed and expanded upon in 2002:

> Qualifications of personnel, indications, specifications of the examination, equipment specifications, and quality assurance issues are addressed in each standard with the aim of creating guidelines that represent a minimal level of technical and professional expertise to enable consistently safe, quality imaging.

According to one researcher,[87] framers of the standards and guidelines of all medical organizations not only considered the standards to reflect a minimal standard of care, but they intended them to be mandatory and applied rigidly and envisioned that any deviation from a standard would be difficult to justify.

Because it was perceived by many in the radiologic community that ACR practice policies entitled "Standards" would be confused with the legal standard of care in the minds of jurors, the ACR at its 2003 annual meeting voted to rename those policies dealing with conduct in specific areas of clinical practice "Practice Guidelines."[88] Those ACR Standards that consist of specific recommendations for patient management or equipment specifications or settings would be renamed "Technical Standards."[89] It is intuitive to believe the name change would have lessened the likelihood of jurors' concluding that any deviation from a recommended ACR policy, no matter how minor, was tantamount to a deviation from the legal standard of radiologic care. This intuitive belief has not as yet been transformed into reality.

[5] Practice Guidelines (PG): The Disclaimer

If ACR Practice Guidelines are believed to represent a minimal level of mandatory care, then failure to adhere to them would be tantamount to negligence. The matter is not that simple, however, for if we turn to the introduction to each ACR Guideline, we encounter a contradiction. The following qualifying language ("disclaimer") has been and continues to be inserted at the beginning of every ACR Guideline:[90]

---

[87] Mello MM. Of swords and shields: the role of clinical practice guidelines in medical malpractice litigation. 149 *U.Pa. L. Rev.* 645 (2001).

[88] Berlin L. Standards, guidelines, and roses. *AJR* 2003;xx.

[89] *Id.*

[90] *2007 Practice Guidelines and Technical Standards.* Reston VA. American College of Radiology, 2007.

The Practice Guidelines of the American College of Radiology (ACR) are not rules, but are guidelines that attempt to define principles of practice that should generally produce high-quality radiological care. The physician and medical physicist may modify an existing standard as determined by the individual patient and available resources... The guidelines should not be deemed inclusive of all proper methods of care or exclusive of other methods of care reasonably directed to obtaining the same results. The guidelines are not intended to establish a legal standard of care or conduct, and deviation from a standard does not, in and of itself, indicate or imply that such medical practice is below an acceptable level of care. The ultimate judgment regarding the propriety of any specific procedure or course of conduct must be made by the physician and medical physicist in light of all circumstances presented by the individual situation.

What the "disclaimer" is telling us is that the ACR Practice Guidelines are setting forth a level of practice that produces *high-quality* radiological care, a practice level that is far different from that which produces a *minimal quality* of care. From a legal viewpoint, radiologists are held to a level of care that is termed *reasonable*, a level that presumably lies somewhere between *high quality* and *minimal quality*. This sets the stage for potential confusion. At trial a plaintiff's expert might testify that although a defendant-radiologist's conduct may have adhered to that suggested by the ACR, it was still minimal and fell short of "reasonable." A defense expert, on the other hand, might counter that although a radiologist's conduct adhering to the dictates of an ACR may have fallen short of "high-quality," it certainly exceeded "minimal" and was therefore indeed "reasonable."

Notwithstanding the semantic debate about whether the legal standard of care to which radiologists are held is determined by whatever the ACR's principles of practice are called, the Courts have been disinclined to be influenced by these written principles. As one legal researcher has pointed out, courts have taken the position of "what usually is done may be evidence of what ought to be done, but what ought to be done is set by the standard of reasonable prudence ... not written guidelines."[91] The courts have also acknowledged, according to this researcher, that "Perfection is an aspiration but not a legal requirement; an honest effort in conformity with standards is all that can be demanded of physicians."

---

[91] Mello MM. Of swords and shields: the role of clinical practice guidelines in medical malpractice litigation. 149 *U.Pa. L. Rev.* 645 (2001).

One final commentary on the ACR Communication Standard is worth noting. In the recently published law review article already referred to,[92] attorney-author Mark Ginsberg traced the evolution of the Communication Standard and then reflected on its impact on radiological malpractice litigation. It is a reflection of which all radiologists should take heed:

Does an ACR Standard define or evidence the standard of care applicable to a radiologist in a given circumstance? If so, an ACR Standard may have medico-legal dignity that the ACR did not intend...

The purpose of the ACR Standards may be advisory, and may not include defining a legal standard of care; however, it would be naïve to believe that practice standards will not creep into medico-legal litigation as evidence of the applicable standard of care. It is difficult to predict an explosion of medical negligence actions against radiologists based on lack of urgent communication, but it is reasonable to suspect an increase in the incidence of this type of claim. The ACR Standards will likely be recognized as evidence of the standard of care, despite the disclaimer contained in the standard....A jury might consider the ACR Standards tantamount to the standard of care...This truly places radiologists in peril.

ACR Standards will continue to have legal implications for radiologists.... Radiologists must realize that the ACR Standard of Communication is a double-edged sword. The potential use of this standard by courts and the possibility of a relaxed requirement for expert testimony in communication cases will likely generate claims against radiologists for failure to timely communicate radiology diagnoses.

[6] Should Radiologists Communicate Results of Radiologic Studies Directly to the Patient?

Historical Perspective

For three-quarters of a century following Roentgen's discovery of the X-ray, radiologists traditionally undertook radiologic examinations only upon the request of referring physicians, rendered interpretations of those examinations, and transmitted those interpretations in writing to those same

---

[92] Ginsberg MD. Beyond the viewbox: the radiologist's duty to communicate findings. The *John Marshall Law Review* 2002;35(3):359-380.

physicians.[93] Little attention was given to the possibility that the written report might not be received by the referring physician.[94]

It seems to have been the advent of screening mammography that began bringing about a change in this practice pattern. Previously the referring physician would suspect an abnormality because of a patient's symptoms or clinical findings, order a radiologic examination, actively await its results, and likely contact the radiologist if a written interpretation was not received in timely fashion. With screening mammography, however, because patients were asymptomatic and both the referring physician and patient expected the results to be normal, physicians were not likely to seek out the report if it went astray. The fact was, however, radiologists' reports not only of mammograms, but of other radiologic examinations as well, were indeed going astray — and the ACR leadership took notice.

In 1985 the ACR published a leaflet entitled, "Policy Statement: Breast Cancer Screening Centers,"[95] that contained the following admonition:

> A positive finding should be reported promptly in writing to a physician....The radiologist must be certain that the result of a positive mammogram is acknowledged by the primary care physician....In all cases, appropriate acknowledgement of the notification should be sought.

In 1990, the ACR issued its first Standard focusing on communication of radiologic results, although the Standard dealt specifically with screening mammography:[96]

> All reports in the high probability category should be communicated to the referring physician or his designated representative by telephone, by certified mail, or communicated in such a manner that receipt of the report is assured and documented.

One year later, the ACR published its first Standard dealing exclusively with communication in all aspects of diagnostic radiology:[97]

---

[93] Berlin L. The radiologist: doctor's doctor or patient's doctor? *AJR* 1977;128:702.

[94] Robertson CL, Kopans DB. Communications problems after mammographic screening. *Radiology* 1989;172:443-444.

[95] *Policy statement: breast cancer screening centers.* Reston, VA: American College of Radiology, 1985.

[96] American College of Radiology. ACR standards for the performance of screening mammography. In: *Standards.* Reston, VA: American College of Radiology, 1990.

[97] American College of Radiology. ACR standard for communication: diagnostic radiology. In: *Standards.* Reston, VA: American College of Radiology, 1991.

Some circumstances…may require direct communication of unusual, unexpected, or urgent findings to the referring physician in advance of a formal written report.

Against the backdrop of this increasingly-recognized expansion of the radiologist's duty to directly communicate to the referring physician significant radiologic findings, there began to emerge a second trend, one that began with very little notice by most of the radiologic community: extension of the radiologist's duty to include communication of findings directly to patients. Direct patient communication was fueled by four sources: the judiciary, the radiologic community itself, the federal government, and the consumer movement. Let us examine each in greater detail, beginning with the courts.

[7] The Courts Extend the Radiologist's Duty to Communicate to the Referring Physician

That the radiologist's duty to communicate extends beyond simply dictating and sending out a written report has long been espoused by the judiciary. Early court decisions expanded the duty to communicate, in certain situations, directly to the referring physician. As far back as 1971, a Federal Court in Indiana ruled on a case involving a radiologist who on Christmas Day dictated a radiographic report that raised the question of a skull fracture. Although the radiologist knew that the report would not be transcribed until two days later because of the holiday, he made no effort to telephone the report to the referring physician. Ruling that the radiologist should have foreseen that the 2-day delay in transcription and posting of the written report would prevent the referring physician from instituting treatment promptly, the Court held that the radiologist:[98]

…was negligent in failing to immediately bring his report to the attention of the proper persons… Due care would have required that he telephone his report to the attending physician.

[8] The Courts Extend the Radiologist's Duty to Communicate to the Patient

The Court decisions discussed thus far held that radiologists had a duty to communicate significant and/or urgent radiologic findings directly to referring physicians. None raised the possibility of extending to patients

---

[98] Keene v. Methodist Hospital, 324 F Supp 233 (Ind 1971).

themselves the radiologist's duty to communicate. But then, in New Jersey in 1987 and in Arkansas in 1989, two state appeals courts alluded to direct communication between radiologist and patient.

In the New Jersey case, a routine chest radiograph obtained on a woman who had been admitted to a hospital for treatment of a fractured wrist was interpreted correctly by the radiologist as disclosing a probable carcinoma of the lung. However, the radiologist's written report never reached the ordering physician or the patient's hospital chart prior to her being discharged. Diagnosis of the tumor was thus delayed, the patient ultimately died of carcinoma, and her family sued the radiologist and her physician because of the delay in diagnosis. The radiologist denied liability but the Court disagreed, stating:[99]

> ...In some situations, indirect service may provide justification for the absence of *direct communication with the patient* (italics added), but that does not in any way justify failure of communication with the primary care physician.

The Supreme Court of Arkansas went a tad further. A breathing tube had been placed into the trachea of a 20 year-old male who had suffered a fracture of the cervical spine in a diving accident. A subsequent radiograph of the neck was interpreted by the defendant-radiologist as disclosing displacement of the tube. The radiologist dictated and later signed a written report to that effect, but there was no direct communication with the treating physicians. Receipt of the report by the treating physicians was thus delayed, aggravating the injury to the patient. Although the Court found the defendant-radiologist not liable due to the technical reason that no expert witness had testified against him, nevertheless the Court did state:[100]

> [The patient] was in a life-threatening situation and indeed almost died. He deserved more than routine care under these circumstances ... When a patient is in peril of his life, it does him very little good, if the examining doctor has discovered his condition, unless the physician takes measures *and informs the patient* (italics added), or those responsible for his care, of that fact.

Other state appeals courts were far more direct in declaring that at times radiologists indeed have a duty to communicate abnormalities directly to patients. A District of Columbia Federal Appeals Court turned its attention to

---

[99] Jenoff v. Gleason, 521 A2d 1323 (NJ Super Ct App Div 1987)).
[100] *Supra* at note 81.

a 20 year- old potential Armed Forces inductee who had undergone chest radiography. A radiologist under contract with the Selective Service System interpreted the radiographs as suggestive of lymphoma. The potential recruit was rejected for service without explanation and was never informed of the radiographic finding. He later was diagnosed as having Hodgkin's Disease and eventually died. The patient's family sued the Federal Government, claiming that the radiologist who had been retained to interpret the radiographs was negligent for failing to inform the recruit of the abnormal radiographic findings. The Court held that the radiologist had the duty to inform the patient of radiologic results: [101]

> The government physician was under a duty to act carefully, not merely in the conduct of the examination but also in subsequent communications to the examinee....It was the doctor's silence that misled the examinee... [The plaintiff] assumed that the silence of the examining physicians meant that the results of tests they had performed were negative... A physician undertaking a physical examination has a duty to disclose what he has found and to warn the examinee of any finding that would indicate that the patient is in danger and should seek further medical evaluation and treatment... [The radiologist] owed a duty of care to [the plaintiff] [and] breached this duty when he failed to notify him of his abnormal X-ray.

A Washington State Federal Appeals Court in 1991 dealt with a similar issue, this time specifically involving a radiologist. The radiologist had been employed by a Veteran's Administration Hospital to interpret a chest radiograph obtained on a man undergoing a pre-employment physical examination. The radiologist noted an abnormality that later proved to be sarcoidosis. However, the patient was never informed of the findings until 4 years later when the diagnosis was established. Alleging that the delay in diagnosis caused permanent injury to his health, the patient sued the radiologist for malpractice. The patient was awarded damages at the trial court level, but the case was appealed by the defense. The Federal Appeals Court, after pointing out that "most courts that have considered this question (e.g., Louisiana, Maryland, Ohio, New York, New Jersey, and Mississippi) had reached similar results," affirmed the jury award, ruling that the radiologist had breached a duty to communicate with the patient:[102]

---

[101] Betesh . United States of America, 400 F Supp 238 (US Dist DC 1974).
[102] Daly v. United States of America, 946 F2d 1467 (9th Cir 1991).

We have a little trouble holding that the VA radiologist owed [the plaintiff] a duty... At a minimum, the radiologist should have notified [the plaintiff] of the abnormality. This duty is hardly burdensome.

[9] The Arizona Court Decision — and Its Far-reaching Implications

The most recent State Supreme Court decision regarding a radiologist's duty to communicate abnormal radiologic findings directly to a patient was issued in Arizona in 2004. A radiologist had been contracted to interpret pre-employment chest radiographs and to report his findings to a potential employer, a nursing home. Upon observing a possible carcinoma on chest radiography of a prospective woman employee, the radiologist appropriately notified the potential employer of the finding. The employer, however, failed to inform the patient of the abnormality. Ten months later the patient was diagnosed with lung cancer, and subsequently died. A malpractice lawsuit was filed against both the employer and the radiologist, but the employer declared bankruptcy, leaving the radiologist as the sole defendant. The trial court dismissed the radiologist from the lawsuit on the grounds that he did not owe any legal duty to the plaintiff, inasmuch as he had been contracted to render interpretations by the third-party employer.

The plaintiff appealed the dismissal to the Arizona Appellate Court, which reinstated the litigation, ruling that notwithstanding the fact that he was under contract by a third party, the radiologist had a duty to communicate findings to every patient in whom he "detects a medical condition for which further inquiry or treatment is appropriate."[103] The Court acknowledged that ordinarily the patient's primary care physician obtains the radiologic results and advises the patient of their meaning, but then added a sentence that many in the radiologic community found astonishing: "If there is no referring physician, or the referring physician is unavailable, the duty to inform the patient shifts to the radiologist."

The defendant-radiologist then brought an appeal to the Arizona Supreme Court, which affirmed the Appellate decision in language that may well exert considerable influence on courts in many other states and therefore warrants the careful attention of all radiologists:[104]

[The radiologist] recognized the existence of abnormalities on the X-ray that may have evidenced an unreasonable risk of harm to [the patient] of which she was unaware. [The radiologist] should have anticipated that [the patient] would want to know of the potentially

---

[103] Stanley v. McCarver, 63 P3d 1076 (Ariz App 2003).

[104] Stanley v. McCarver, 92 P3d 849 (Ariz 2004).

life-threatening condition and that not knowing about it could cause her to forego timely treatment, and he should have acted with reasonable care in light of that knowledge... By virtue of his undertaking to review [the patient's] X-ray [the radiologist] placed himself in a unique position to prevent future harm to [the patient]... In such a circumstance, an examinee reasonably expects the physician to sound the alarm if any serious abnormality is discovered... The trend [among] courts in many jurisdictions now favors imposing a duty to, and we can envision no public benefit in encouraging a doctor who has specific individualized knowledge of an examinee's serious abnormalities to not, disclose such information.

The Appellate Court held that a radiologist had a duty to report abnormalities directly to the patient if "there is no referring physician or the referring physician is unavailable." We decline to find a duty to report directly to the patient...[but] we do agree that the duty imposed is to act as would a reasonably prudent health care provider in the circumstances. But whether this duty requires direct communication with the subject of the X-ray regarding any abnormality discovered may depend on factors such as whether there is a treating or referring physician involved in the transaction, whether the radiologist has means to identify and locate the patient, the scope of − including any contractual limitations on − the radiologist's undertaking, and other factors that may be present in a particular case... Whether [the radiologist] acted reasonably...is a matter of the standard of care to be resolved by the trier of fact.

In short, the Arizona Supreme Court declined to hold that as a matter of law radiologists *automatically* have the duty to communicate significant unexpected findings to the patient if the referring physician is unknown or unavailable, but instead ruled that a jury must decide whether such a duty exists on a case-by-case basis, depending on the specific facts presented at trial. Given the fact that juries are often sympathetic to patients who have been injured while under medical care and may have difficulty in understanding why a radiologist would not directly inform patients of significant abnormalities, it is reasonable to believe that juries may be disposed to more likely than not find radiologists negligent under such circumstances.

The degree to which the Arizona Supreme Court decision will impact courts in other states remains to be determined. What is noteworthy, however, is that the Arizona Court's written decision is far from superficial or flippant; on the contrary, it is one that goes into minute detail and uses numerous authoritative sources to justify its outright rejection of previous court decisions that had exempted radiologists from the duty of directly communicating radiologic abnormalities to patients. Because of its depth and analytic perspective, the Arizona Court decision may turn out to be a watershed that once and for all opens widely the judicial door to the radiologist's duty to communicate to patients. It will be interesting to see whether appeals courts in other states adopt a similar stance in future decisions.

Let us now turn to the US Government's involvement with radiologic communication.

[10] The Mammography Quality Standards Act (MQSA) and Its Impact on Malpractice Litigation and Referring Physicians

MQSA, signed into law on October 27, 1992, established national quality standards for mammography. One of the Act's provisions, which became effective April 28, 1999, stated:[105]

> Each facility shall send each patient a summary of the mammography report written in lay terms within 30 days of the mammographic examination. If assessments are "suspicious" or "highly suggestive of malignancy," the facility shall make reasonable attempts to ensure that the results are communicated to the patient as soon as possible.

A Physician Insurer's Association of America — ACR Survey published in 1997 disclosed that a substantial percentage of malpractice lawsuits filed against radiologists had been brought by women who alleged that they had not been informed that their mammograms had been interpreted as suspicious for carcinoma.[106] Implementation of MQSA, with its mandate that mammographic results be transmitted directly to patients, has virtually eliminated failure-of-radiologic-communication medical malpractice lawsuits involving mammography.

Many referring physicians who had historically held the paternalistic belief that it is only they who should give radiographic results to their patients reacted with displeasure when MQSA mandated that radiologists communicate mammographic results directly to patients. However, inasmuch as this communication had been instigated and imposed by the

---

[105] U.S. Department of Health and Human Services, Food and Drug   Administration. *Mammography Quality Standards Act* of 1992: Policy Guidance Help System (updated February 26, 2007): 900.12(c)(2)(i),(ii). Available at: http://www.fda.gov/CDRH/MAMMOGRAPHY /robohelp/START.HTM   Accessed June 12, 2007.

[106] Physician Insurers Association of America and American College of Radiology. *Practice standards claims survey.* Rockville, MD: Physician Insurers Association of America, 1997.

government rather than by any voluntary effort on the part of the radiologic community, referring physicians had no choice but to accept this new standard, and any displeasure they voiced seems to have quietly and quickly disappeared.

Patients exhibit great anxiety as they await results of radiologic studies. Hamilton Jordan, Chief of Staff in former U.S. President Jimmy Carter's Administration and a survivor of three different cancers, has written about this "anxiety bordering on panic":[107] "Waiting for doctors to read your X-rays is like waiting for the jury foreman in a capital punishment trial to read your verdict. All it takes is a little spot on the X-ray to indicate that you have cancer."

A recent *New York Times* article[108] describes the anxiety experienced by a woman who spent "two terrible days waiting by the phone" for her doctor to tell her about results of a CT scan she had undergone to investigate a suspicious mass in her chest: "All those clichés when someone is facing a terminal diagnosis are true; racing pulse, dry mouth, total self-preoccupations with what-ifs to the point that real life doesn't exist — willing the phone to ring."

Would this anxiety be alleviated if patients received reports of their radiologic studies directly from the radiologist? A 1993 survey disclosed that 75% of referring physicians and 90% of radiologists favored a radiologist's directly informing patients of results of their radiologic examinations.[109] A 1995 survey conducted in Texas found that 94% of patients felt that they are entitled to an explanation of the test results by the radiologist.[110] A subsequent survey reiterated support by both radiologists and non-radiology physicians for such direct communication by the radiologist.[111]

A 1994 survey of women's attitudes regarding mammographic results, conducted 5 years before the MQSA Policy on Communication was instituted, disclosed that over 90% agreed that the radiologist should send a report of the mammographic findings directly to them.[112]

---

[107] Jordan H. *No Such Thing As A Bad Day*. Atlanta: Longstreet Press, 2000:153.

[108] Kolata G. Sick and scared, and waiting, waiting, waiting. *New York Times* Aug 20, 2005.

[109] Levitsky DB, Frank MS, Richardson ML, Shneidman RJ. How should radiologists reply when patients ask about their diagnoses? A survey of radiologists' and clinicians' preferences. *AJR* 1993;161:433-436.

[110] Schreiber MH, Leonard M, Rieniets CY. Disclosure of imaging findings to patients directly by radiologists: survey of patients' preferences. *AJR* 1995;165:467-469.

[111] Schreiber MH. Direct disclosure by radiologists of imaging findings to patients: a survey of radiologists and medical staff members. *AJR* 1996;167:1091-1093.

[112] Liu S, Bassett LW, Sayre J. Women's attitudes about receiving mammographic results directly from radiologists. *Radiology* 1994;193:783-786.

It seems quite clear that the public is receptive to, if not desirous of, direct communication from radiologists regarding results of their radiologic examinations.

[11]   The Prevalence and Causes of Communication Problems

Inadequate communication between patients and their physicians is an enormous and still-growing problem throughout our nation. A study of plaintiffs' lawsuits filed during the 1980s revealed that failed communication was the leading cause in more than 25% of cases.[113] In another survey in which malpractice attorneys were asked to cite the primary reason patients pursued a medical malpractice lawsuit, more than 80% pointed to communication issues.[114] The author of the survey emphasized that patients are most satisfied when they feel fully informed about their medical condition and that patients are more likely to sue their physician if they feel that the physician didn't inform them adequately.

The current environment in both hospitals and physicians' offices is rife for failure of communication between radiologists and non-radiological physicians, between non-radiological physicians and patients, and between radiologists and patients. The typical primary care physician in the nation receives 800 chemistry reports, 40 radiology reports, and 12 pathology reports a week.[115] Eighty-three percent of these physicians report delays in receipt of test results, and only 41% indicated they are satisfied with how test results are managed. Communication problems related to diagnostic testing account for 47% of all errors made by typical primary care physicians in their medical practices.[116]

A recent study that looked at deficiencies in communication and information transfer at hospitals found that direct communication between hospital-based physicians and primary care physicians occurs only infrequently—3% to 20% of the time.[117] Discharge summaries lacked important diagnostic test results in up to 63% of patient charts reviewed. Outpatient

---

[113] Beckman HB, Markakis KM, Suchman AL, Frankel RM. The doctor-patient relationship and malpractice: lessons from plaintiff depositions. *Arch Intern Med* 1994;154:1365-1370.

[114] Levinson W. Physician-patient communication: a key to malpractice prevention. *JAMA* 1994; 272:1619-1620.

[115] Poon EG, Gandhi TK, Sequist TD, et al. I wish I had seen this test result earlier. *Arch Intern Med* 2004;164:2223-2228.

[116] Fernald DH, Pace WD, Harris DM, et al. Event reporting to a primary care patient safety reporting system: a report from the ASIPS collaborative. *Ann Fam Med* 2004;2:327-332.

[117] Kripalani S, LeFevre F, Phillips CO, Williams MV, Basaviah P, Baker DW. Deficits in Communication and Information Transfer Between Hospital-Based and Primary Care Physicians, Implications for Patient Safety and Continuity of Care. *JAMA* 2007;297:831-841.

physicians estimated that their follow-up management was adversely affected in 24% of cases due to delayed or incomplete discharge communications. Communication of diagnostic test results presented substantial patient safety concerns, with radiologic studies posing the greatest problem.

Adopting direct patient communication could possibly generate myriad problems affecting relationships with referring physicians. In addition, there is the possibility that radiologists could find themselves in the uncomfortable position of having to advise patients on treatment options or other aspects of clinical management for which radiologists have not previously been involved and adequately prepared, thus subjecting radiologists to potential malpractice litigation. This leads us to another important question: if there is to be communication of reports from radiologist to patient, how much information should a radiologist provide? Can the radiologist give too much information to the patient? Can the radiologist give too little information? This could pose a dilemma.

Well-known San Francisco radiologist Roy Filly addressed grave concerns about giving too much information to patients. Filly pointed out that in 10% of normal pregnancies, sonograms contain apparent "abnormalities" that can be interpreted as markers of Down Syndrome, but turn out to be clinically unimportant findings. He then asked rhetorically what the radiologist performing a routine sonogram who finds one of these markers should tell the mother-to-be, answering:[118]

> [Once the parents are informed of this "abnormality,"] enjoyment of the anticipation of the birth of their son or daughter is now replaced by anxiety. From my vantage point, the identification of these "abnormalities" in low-risk women has crossed the line of "more harm than good"... Think about it! For the tiny residual number of Down Syndrome fetuses that may potentially come to light by chasing down every last "marker," we intend to put at least 10% of all pregnant women with perfectly normal fetuses through a great deal of worry.

> So then what should I do tomorrow? Should I have the courage of my conviction to simply ignore these features? I wish I had that courage, but I don't. Even with my considerable clout in world of obstetrical sonography, I cannot unilaterally ignore the sonographic medical literature. That is not how American medicine works.

---

[118] Filly RA. Obstetrical sonography: the best way to terrify a pregnant woman (editorial). *J Ultrasound Med* 2000;19:1-5.

[12] The Trend toward Communication of Results from Radiologist Directly to Patient

Should radiologists routinely communicate findings of all radiologic examinations directly to patients? The Courts have for many years espoused such action, the Federal Government has mandated it for mammography, various professional organizations including but not limited to the ACR have encouraged it under certain circumstances, various radiologists have recommended it, and the public seems to demand it. Direct communication between radiologist and patient of all mammographic findings as mandated by MQSA has improved patient care and virtually eliminated radiologic malpractice lawsuits alleging delay in diagnosis of breast cancer. If radiologists were to communicate findings of all radiologic examinations directly to patients, overall patient care would improve and virtually all lawsuits filed against radiologists alleging delay in diagnosis due to failed communication would be similarly eliminated.

At present neither the courts nor the ACR consider radiologists' communication of findings of all radiologic examinations directly to patients to be the standard of care. Whether such a duty may eventually be imposed on radiologists is yet to be determined but nevertheless, as this chapter points out, there does seem to be a clear trend in that direction. In the meantime radiologists, with an eye on the goal of potentially eliminating failure-to-communicate litigation, may wish to ponder the question of whether they want to hasten the practice. I suggest that the time has come for radiologists to embrace the concept that it is indeed the patient whom they are obligated to serve and to whom they are ethically responsible for their diagnoses. Has therefore not the time come to communicate results of all radiologic examinations directly to patients? I suggest that this question should be answered in the affirmative.

§ 9.04 Mammography

[1] Breast Cancer, Mammography, and Malpractice

Statistical data compiled by professional liability insurance companies disclose that the number of medical malpractice lawsuits alleging injury due to missing, or delaying, the diagnosis of breast cancer has continued to increase rapidly over the past two decades. Radiologists have become the specialists most frequently sued in malpractice lawsuits involving breast cancer; likewise mammography has become the most prevalent procedure involved in medical malpractice lawsuits filed against radiologists.[119] Indeed, the allegation that an error in the diagnosis of breast cancer has occurred is now the most prevalent condition precipitating medical malpractice lawsuits against all physicians.[120] Furthermore, monetary awards in the multimillion dollar range made to women in whom the diagnosis of breast cancer has been delayed have now become commonplace. Let us explore some of the reasons behind this surge in breast cancer malpractice litigation.

[2] Perceptions and Misperceptions

At the end of *Damages*, a book that describes in fine detail and with great poignancy the natural history of a medical malpractice lawsuit, author Barry Werth[121] observes that almost all malpractice cases are decided "not on the basis of fact but on the *perception* of what a jury is likely to think is fact" (italics are mine). Perhaps nowhere else in the medical field today does *perception* — or *misperception* — play as great a role as it does in breast cancer litigation. The public's *perceptions* — or *misperceptions* — related to breast cancer fall into three categories: the perception that women are at extraordinarily high risk of developing and dying from breast cancer, the perception that mammography is 100% accurate in detecting breast cancer, and the perception that the capability of mammography to diagnose breast cancer in earlier stages guarantees a cure. Let us take a closer look at these perceptions — or misperceptions — by examining the bases for them and then attempt to determine to what extent the perceptions — or misperceptions — reflect reality.

[3] The Perception of High Risk of Developing and Dying from Breast Cancer

In 1995, researchers at Dartmouth Medical School published the results of a survey regarding women's perceptions of breast cancer.[122] The survey found that women overestimated their probability of dying of breast cancer by more than 20-fold and the value of screening mammography in reducing that risk by 100-fold. The researchers attributed these misperceptions to widespread efforts to promote screening mammography. The researchers acknowledged that these efforts have been successful in encouraging more

---

[119] Physician Insurers Association of America. *Breast cancer study*. Rockville, MD: Physician Insurers Association of America, 1995.

[120] Physician Insurers Association of America and American College of Radiology. *Practice standards claims survey*. Rockville, MD: Physician Insurers Association of America, 1997.

[121] Werth B. *Damages*. New York: Simon & Schuster, 1998: 370.

[122] Black WC, Nease RF Jr, Tosteson ANA. Perceptions of breast cancer risk and screening effectiveness in women younger than 50 years of age. *J Natl Cancer Inst* 1995;87:720-731.

and more women to undergo mammography, but at the same time the researchers expressed concern that this has been accomplished at the cost of creating unnecessary public anxiety through manipulation of data.

One of the more obvious examples of manipulation of data is the familiar "one in eight" statistic, which refers to the cumulative lifetime risk of developing breast cancer for women who live past the age of 85 years. According to a senior fellow at the Hudson Institute in Washington, D.C., the American Cancer Society "concocted" this figure and it "quickly became a staple of any story on breast cancer and of government advice."[123] As pointed out in a recent article in the *New England Journal of Medicine*, [124] it is true that breast cancer is the most common cancer among North American women and the incidence of breast cancer has been steadily rising; however, the risk of breast cancer occurring in a woman in any decade of her life never approaches one in eight. A woman entering her 30s has a 1-in-250 chance of developing breast cancer in the next 10 years, and a woman entering her 40s has a 1-in-77 chance of developing the disease in the following decade. Although breast cancer is more common in older women, the risk of breast cancer developing in any decade of life never exceeds 1 in 34. As far as mortality rates are concerned, the cause of death among women at any age is always more likely to be something other than breast cancer, and in fact, the proportion of deaths due to breast cancer never exceeds 20%. Furthermore, the great majority of women in whom breast cancer is diagnosed do not die of the disease, a fact that statistics that focus merely on the incidence of breast cancer do not convey.[125]

[4] The Perception of Perfection

The basis for the second misperception possessed by the public — that radiologists achieve 100% perfection and accuracy in their interpretation of mammography — is not difficult to identify. American newspapers and magazines regularly publish advertisements that extol the virtues of screening mammography and have been doing so for years. The ads, usually prepared by the American Cancer Society and printed as a public service for the purpose of encouraging women to undergo mammography, have been extraordinarily generous in their assessment of the accuracy of mammography. For example, one ad showed a small dot measuring 1mm in

---

[123] Fumento M. Happy acceptance of a horrific procedure: preventative mastectomy. *Chicago Tribune*. February 2, 1999: 11.

[124] Phillips KA, Glendon G, Knight JA. Putting the risk of breast cancer in perspective. *N Engl J Med* 1999; 340:141-144.

[125] *Id.*

diameter. Referring to the dot, the ad declared, "You've just missed the first sign of breast cancer if you didn't see that small dot... Even though you may have missed the first sign of breast cancer, a mammogram won't." A similar advertisement in a local magazine placed by a hospital in Atlanta, GA, showed a dot that is 2 mm in diameter alongside a message that stated, in part, "We're making a big deal out of something this small... Detecting breast cancer in its earliest stages can make a big difference... And chances are it's time for you to get a mammogram... [We have] radiologists specially trained in mammography."

There is little doubt that these advertisements succeeded in convincing many women who otherwise would not have done so to undergo screening mammography. There is also little doubt, however, that by implying that mammography is 100% accurate, these advertisements have at the same time succeeded in creating among the public the perception that mammography is perfect. Is the public perception of perfection realistic? Scientific literature suggests that the answer is no, for there are numerous studies that indicate that the level of accuracy achieved in mammography is considerably less than perfect.

Published articles that document the accuracy of mammography in revealing breast carcinoma generally fall into two groups: those articles that specifically deal with radiologists' missing lesions on mammograms that are apparent on retrospective review (errors), and those articles that document the numbers and types of breast cancers that are simply not seen on mammography, even in retrospect (false negatives). The distinction between the two is not always clearly delineated. A Canadian national breast screening study revealed that interpreters of screening mammograms missed 17% of breast cancers and 35% of interval cancers that occurred within 1 year of screening.[126] A study published in 1992 revealed that 24% of cancers were missed on mammography.[127] A 1993 study[128] from the University of Arizona disclosed that, for women who developed cancer, 75% of mammograms initially interpreted as normal were in retrospect found to show cancer by at least one of three radiologist-reviewers. A study published in 1994 by researchers at Yale University revealed a miss rate for breast carcinomas on mammography ranging from 15 to 63%.[129]

---

[126] Baines CJ, McFarlane DV, Miller AB. Role of the reference radiologist: estimates of inter-observer agreement and potential delay in cancer detection in the National Breast Screening Study. *Invest Radiology* 1990; 25:971-976.

[127] Bird RE, Wallace TW, Yankaskas BC. Analysis of cancers missed at screening mammography. *Radiology* 1992; 184:613-617.

[128] *Supra* note 34.

[129] *Supra* note 33.

Subsequent articles commenting on the Yale study listed reasons for the lack of accuracy. These included differences in visual perception ("I just didn't see it"), differences in diagnostic criteria (one interpreting radiologist saying, "Any calcification may be malignant"; another saying, "If punctate, calcifications may be benign"), and varying thresholds of concern (one interpreting radiologist saying, "I recommend biopsy whenever my suspicion of cancer is 2%"; another saying, "My threshold of concern is 6%").[130] Referring to the same Yale study in a *New York Times* article, Dr. Daniel B. Kopans pointed out that "mammography is not an accurate diagnostic test because there is considerable overlap in the appearances of benign and malignant lesions on mammograms," and he emphasized that "even the most expert doctor will occasionally overlook an important abnormality" on a mammogram.[131]

A 1996 study of a large group of patients revealed a 40% disparity among American radiologists regarding the rate with which they recommended biopsy on the basis of mammography of women in whom cancer was later proven. The study concluded that there is indeed a "wide variability in the accuracy of mammogram interpretation within the population of U.S. radiologists."[132] A similar review by researchers at the University of California, San Francisco, found differing sensitivities for screening mammography that depended on the age of patients: 70% for women 30 to 39 years old, 87% for women 40 to 49 years old, and more than 90% for all women older than 50 years.[133] An Australian study described an overall miss rate of 25%.[134] A later article published in the *American College of Radiology Bulletin* reiterated that 30% to 70% of breast cancers detected at follow-up mammography are visible in retrospect on initial mammograms that had been interpreted as normal.[135] A meta-analysis of published literature also found that from 5% to 17% of breast cancers are missed on mammography, and emphasized that there is much variability in mammographic interpretation by American radiologists.[136] The

---

[130] Randal T. Varied mammogram readings worry researchers. *JAMA* 1993; 269:2616.

[131] Brody JE. Mammogram interpretations are questioned in a report. *New York Times.* December 2, 1994: B1.

[132] Beam CA, Layde PM, Sullivan DC. Variability in the interpretation of screening mammograms by US radiologists. *Arch Intern Med* 1996;156:209-213.

[133] Kerlikowske K, Grady D, Rubin S, Sandrock C, Ernster V. Efficacy of screening mammography: a meta-analysis. *JAMA* 1995;273:149-154.

[134] Goergen SK, Evans J, Cohen, GBP, MacMillan JH. Characteristics of breast carcinomas missed by screening radiologists. *Radiology* 1997;204:131-135.

[135] Can false positives be reduced without endangering patients? *ACR Bulletin* 1998;54(6):15-17, 28.

[136] Mushlin AI, Kouides ;RW, Shapiro DE. Estimating the accuracy of screening mammography: a meta-analysis. *Am J Prev Med* 1998;14:143-153.

analysis concluded that diagnostic accuracy of mammography has not changed substantially over time.

[5] The Perception that Early Detection by Mammography Will Cure Breast Cancer

An advertisement that has appeared frequently in medical journals and magazines stated, "If all women over 50 had regular mammograms, their death rate from breast cancer would drop by a third. . . No matter what your specialty, the American Cancer Society needs you to recommend an annual mammogram for every woman over 50—it is her only true protection." Is this advertisement accurate? Is the statement that mammography reduces breast cancer deaths by one-third based on reality, or is it a misperception? The answers to these questions are far from clear.

A review of data to determine the efficacy of breast cancer screening that was published in 1989 did indeed corroborate a 30% reduction in breast cancer mortality over a 10-year period after screening mammography was begun.[137] A report of a Canadian national breast screening study published in 1990 reached similar conclusions and then added that when detection of breast cancer is delayed, "concern arises that the benefits of screening will suffer and there will be an increased likelihood of death from breast cancer."[138] Of more recent note, Feig[139] at least twice has confirmed that screening mammography has led to a "statistically significant" reduction in breast cancer mortality of 29%–45% for women 40-49 years old and 34% for women more than 50 years old.

Other researchers, however, have reached different conclusions, and thus a controversy has been created. Sox[140] reviewed a meta-analysis of 13 randomized clinical trials conducted on women 50 to 74 years old and agreed that, in this age group, mammography reduces the risk of dying of breast cancer by 26%. However, Sox concluded that it is "not possible to claim that screening premenopausal women alters mortality from breast cancer." Another group of researchers[141] also voiced skepticism about the efficacy of mammography in reducing breast cancer deaths. These researchers stated that

---

[137] Shapiro S. Determining the efficacy of breast cancer screening. *Cancer* 1989;63:1873-1880.

[138] *Supra* note 126.

[139] Feig SA. Strategies for improving sensitivity of screening mammography for women aged 40 to 49 years. *JAMA* 1996; 276:73-74; Feig SA. A perspective on false positive screening mammograms. *ACR Bulletin* 1998; 54(6):8,13

[140] Sox HC. Benefit and harm associated with screening for breast cancer. *N Engl J Med* 1998; 338:1145-1146.

[141] Chu KC, Tarone RE, Kessler LG, et al. Recent trends in U.S. breast cancer incidence, survival and mortality rates. *J Natl Cancer Inst* 1996; 88:1571-1579.

the recent drop in breast cancer mortality has been too rapid to be explained only by the increased use of mammography, and suggested that the apparent decrease in mortality is the result of both improved therapy and better early detection methods. Harris et al.[142] also acknowledged that screening mammography appears to reduce the overall mortality from breast cancer by approximately 25%, and that in patients who are 50 to 70 years old, reduction in breast mortality may approach 30-40%. However, these same researchers admonished that the ability to detect cancers at a very early stage does not ensure that mortality will be reduced. Harris et al. further emphasized that "there is no firm evidence that screening either reduces or increases mortality from breast cancer in women between the ages of 40 and 49."

Adding to the controversy, Black and Welch,[143] writing in the *New England Journal of Medicine*, have raised serious questions about the efficacy of mammography in reducing deaths from breast cancer in women of any age. These researchers argued that mammography has lowered the detection threshold for breast cancer, a phenomenon that can explain the increase in carcinomas found. The lower detection threshold has led to an increase in the number of carcinomas-in-situ, an entity that may never be life-threatening to many women. These researchers then pointed to studies that show that small foci of breast cancer are found at autopsy in 39% of women between 40 and 50 years old who died of other causes. Most of these cancers never become clinically apparent, much less fatal. These researchers proceeded to point out the difficulty in evaluating the validity of mortality data.

Statistics regarding mortality are distorted by *lead-time bias* (pushing back the date of first diagnosis, thereby increasing the interval between diagnosis and death, resulting in apparent lengthening of survival), *length bias* (the more aggressive fast-growing tumors tend not to be diagnosed mammographically; thus, the tumors that are discovered by mammograms are often less dangerous) and *selection bias* (women who participate in medical research are often not the general population — they may be more affluent, more worried about their health, and thus do not reflect the population at large). These three biases, added to the fact that the total number of carcinomas detected by mammography now include an increasing percentage of cases of ductal-carcinoma-in-situ (DCIS), a tumor that has an extremely good prognosis and for which there is no consensus regarding treatment [144] and that in many cases

---

[142] Harris JR, Lippman ME, Veronesi U, Willett W. Medical progress: breast cancer. *N Engl J Med* 1992; 327:319-328.

[143] Black WC, Welch HG. Advances in diagnostic imaging and overestimations of disease prevalence and the benefits of therapy. *N Engl J Med* 1993; 328:1237-1243.

[144] Ernster VL, Barclay J, Kerlikowske K, Grady D, Henderson IC. Incidence of and treatment for ductal carcinoma in situ of the breast. *JAMA* 1996; 275: 913-918.

may never become invasive,[145] along with certain carcinomas that otherwise would have remained silent throughout the woman's life, can create what Black and Welch called the "spurious effect—a conversion of an apparent effect into an active effect of zero or negative."

[6] Additional Controversies Surrounding Efficiency of Mammography

In a provocative article appearing in *The Atlantic Monthly*, Plotkin[146] voiced similar sentiments and added that many or most of in-situ cancers never grow big enough to be detected by palpation, let alone to pose a threat to life. Plotkin, too, believes that the efficacy of mammography in decreasing mortality from breast cancer can be more apparent than real. Mammography reveals smaller tumors, many of which are slow-growing and might otherwise never be discovered, concluded Plotkin. Detecting such tumors will thus manufacture an apparent excess of "cures."

The very premise that early diagnosis by any technique reduces breast cancer mortality remains clouded by uncertainty. It is generally claimed that long-term survival exceeds 95% in women whose breast cancer is found before it metastasizes. On the other hand, according to one *New York Times* article, the question of whether early diagnosis reduces mortality from breast cancer "remains one of the most disputed issues in preventive medicine" and, despite being "so intuitively obvious," remains "so remarkably resistant to scientific validation."[147] This article also pointed out that finding breast tumors a few months earlier "may make very little difference in their response to treatment," and "If tumors are aggressive enough to spread out of the breast, markedly reducing chances of survival, they are likely to have done so already. . . In fact, early detection of these tumors may only increase the length of time a woman has to live with a diagnosis of cancer without actually changing her prognosis." The director of health policy studies at Dartmouth College's Center for Evaluative Clinical Sciences agrees, and, in referring to the public's "incredible fear of cancer" and its belief that "early cancer detection will save your life," concludes that those "assumptions are not always true."[148]

---

[145] Kolata G. Ability to find a tiny tumor poses dilemma. *New York Times.* March 27, 1996: A1, B8.

[146] Plotkin D. Good news and bad news about breast cancer *The Atlantic Monthly.* June 1996: 53-82.

[147] Zuger A. Do breast self-exams save lives? Science still doesn't have answer. *New York Times.* January 6, 1998: B9, B15.

[148] *Supra* note 145.

[7] Defending Malpractice Lawsuits Alleging Delay in Diagnosis of Breast Cancer

An analysis by Zylstra et al.[149] of breast cancer malpractice lawsuits found that the major difficulty in defending physicians successfully against allegations of failure to diagnose breast cancer in a timely manner is the public's perception of the seriousness of the adverse consequences that arise from even a short delay in diagnosis. The American Cancer Society and other agencies tell the public that earlier detection increases the likelihood of a complete cure, wrote these researchers, but "medical evidence does not support this premise." These researchers reasoned that any alleged delay associated with a noncurative outcome leads to a disillusioned patient and a physician being sued, and a good likelihood that the physician will be held liable. Although the premise that early detection improves breast cancer outcome remains controversial from a scientific perspective, a delay in either detection or treatment will likely be viewed as inappropriate by the patient and the legal system, speculated Zylstra et al. This "loss of chance" permits compensation to the plaintiff if, in the court's opinion, the physician's negligence reduces the patient's life expectancy.

In an environment in which there is widespread public perception that we are in the midst of an epidemic of breast cancer that has a high likelihood of being fatal, that accuracy of mammography is 100% perfect, and that early diagnosis is the only and best key to survival, we can easily understand why it is so difficult to successfully defend before a jury any radiologist accused of delaying the diagnosis of breast cancer by having missed a lesion on mammography. Another national poll released in October 1998 indicated that 75% of Americans eligible to serve on a jury say that they would act on their own beliefs, regardless of legal instructions from a judge.[150]

The degree to which public perceptions influence the outcome of a malpractice lawsuit involving breast cancer is exemplified by a case in Chicago in which a radiologist was accused of missing a carcinoma on a mammogram, causing a 14-month delay in diagnosis. Once the tumor had been found, excisional biopsy was performed and lymph nodes were negative for tumor. It was now 4 years after the initial mammography, and the woman was free of detectable disease. Three weeks before the trial was scheduled to begin, the defense attorney wrote a letter to the radiologist's

---

[149] Zylstra S, Bors-Koefoed R, Mondor M, Anti D, Giordano K, Ressequie LJ. A statistical model for predicting the outcome in breast cancer malpractice lawsuits. *Obstet Gynecol* 1994; 84:392-398.

[150] Lester W. Jurors say they follow beliefs, not instructions. *Chicago Sun-Times* October 24, 1998: 37.

insurance company, stating, "Even though our consulting oncologist in this case is prepared to testify that the 14-month delay in diagnosis had no effect whatsoever in either the treatment or prognosis of the patient, I recommend that the case be settled because given the public perception that a woman can be cured of breast cancer only through early detection by screening mammography, I believe it will be very hard to convince a jury to rule in favor of the radiologist." The case was settled for $350,000.

[8] The Perception versus Reality Dilemma

There is no doubt that the public, and to a large degree a sizable portion of the medical community, harbor perceptions that the incidence of breast cancer has reached epidemic proportions, that mammography is 100% accurate, and that screening mammography markedly reduces mortality from breast cancer. To be sure, considerable scientific data support these perceptions. My purpose is not to contradict these impressions or to advocate an opposing view, but I have presented data culled from the scientific literature that call into question the validity of these perceptions. I would not hazard a guess as to which set of data is more correct, but I do believe that a legitimate controversy surrounding these perceptions exists. The radiologic community is virtually unanimous in its recognition that the accuracy of mammography is considerably less than 100% and, in fact, acknowledge that review of mammograms interpreted initially as normal in women who later develop breast cancer discloses that many of the cancers can be seen retrospectively. Breast cancer is a common and a deadly disease, but much of the radiologic community realizes that its prevalence is nowhere near the "one in eight" figure that the American Cancer Society and associated organizations lead us to believe. Furthermore, while the bulk of the radiologic community readily accepts the premise that early diagnosis of breast cancer by screening mammography reduces the mortality rate of the disease, nonetheless, a "respectable minority" remains unconvinced.

I have made a point in this chapter to differentiate between perceptions and realities with regard to breast cancer, but from a practical perspective, the distinction is murky. An adage well known in the marketing field states that "perception *is* reality." The patriarch of a prominent American political family is said to have advised his sons, "What is important is not *what* you are, but rather, what people *think* you are." In the courtrooms of America, what ultimately determines the outcome of malpractice litigation is what the public, in the form of a jury, *believes* to be true, not necessarily what *is* true. In pretrial settlement discussions among plaintiff attorneys, defense attorneys, and claims managers for professional liability companies, what determines the final resolution of lawsuits is what the parties *think — that is, perceive —* a jury will decide.

It is exactly because perceptions and realities blend that the number of medical malpractice lawsuits alleging a delay in the diagnosis of breast cancer due to a radiologist's misinterpretation of mammograms is increasing, as are indemnifications paid in these lawsuits.

[9] The Delay in Breast Cancer Diagnosis Dilemma

The widely divergent scientific opinion about the degree to which a delay in diagnosis influences the survival of patients with breast cancer is illustrated by two articles that were published in the same issue of *Lancet* in 1999. One group of researchers found that delays of even 3 to 6 months were associated with lower survival rates.[151] The second group of researchers disclosed that delays in the diagnosis of breast cancer of 3 months or more did not seem to be associated with decreased survival rates in patients with breast cancer.[152] The second group of researchers explained their findings:

> Many breast cancers detected at screening have been present for some time. These breast cancers lead to average or higher than average survival, which suggests long doubling times and a non-aggressive phenotype. On the other hand, some aggressive cancers undoubtedly metastasize early, for which early detection would probably contribute little to long-term survival. It is hardly surprising, therefore, that data on delay are confusing. A systematic overview of the literature commissioned by the National Health Service suggests that delays of longer than 3-6 months have an adverse influence.[153] Much of the data reviewed in the study are, however, old and the study may have a substantial publication bias... Our results suggest that delays of more than 90 days are unlikely to have an impact on survival.

With such wide divergence of opinion among researchers who are presumably well-intended, fair, and objective, it should be no surprise that there usually exists an even greater divergence of opinion among radiology expert witnesses in the courtroom who, because they are retained by respective legal counsel who are adversaries, may not always be so well-intended, fair, and objective.

---

[151] Richard MA, Westcombe AM, Love SB, Littlejohns P, Ramirez AJ. Influence of delay on survival in patients with breast cancer: a systematic review. *Lancet* 1999;353:1119-1126.

[152] Sainsbury R, Johnston C, Haward B. Effect on survival of delays in referral of patients with breast-cancer symptoms: a retrospective analysis. *Lancet* 1999;353:1132-1135.

[153] *Supra* note 151.

[10] Delay in Diagnosis of Breast Cancer versus Patient Injury

Generally, in order to show that a patient has sustained injury as a result of medical malpractice, the injury to the patient has to be objective — either so physical that it is visible to the eye, or so physical that it is documented in terms of the need for additional treatment or loss of chance for survival. Compensation for emotional injury or pain, or mental anguish, is awarded only if physical injury is proven. However, in breast cancer, general legal rules can change. What constitutes patient injury when breast cancer is involved seems to have been greatly liberalized in a recent decision of the Supreme Court of the state of Colorado. There, a 32-year-old woman sued a physician for emotional distress caused by his failure to diagnose her breast malignancy 3 months earlier. No testimony regarding additional treatment or decreased prognosis as a result of the 92-day delay was offered at trial. The jury awarded the patient $220,000 in compensatory damages, and the physician filed an appeal. The Appellate Court overturned the verdict, but the Colorado Supreme Court reinstated it, stating:[154]

> We note that [the patient] sought damages for "emotional distress, including fear of an increased risk of recurrence of cancer." Similarly, the [patient's] case at trial focused more on emotional distress brought on by the increased risk caused by [the doctor's] misdiagnosis than the risk itself... Although surgery removed [the patient's] cancerous mass as well as her lymph nodes, medical evidence suggests that a delay in treatment which leads to the growth of a cancerous tumor "invariably results in a more serious prognosis" for long-term survival... [It is true that] where the plaintiff demonstrates that her cancerous condition physically worsened as a result of the delayed diagnosis, the plaintiff has demonstrated a sufficient physical injury to permit the recovery of emotional distress damages. [But] the usual reservations courts have concerning speculation and conjecture in cases involving plaintiff's seeking purely emotional damages are inapplicable in a case such as this... The reasonableness of the plaintiff's fears are sufficient [to deserve compensation].

Whether the Colorado Supreme Court's expanded definition of damages applicable in missed breast cancer cases is adopted by other states remains to be seen.

---

[154] Boryla v. Pash, 960 P.2d 123 (Colo 1998).

[11] Has Mammography Been Overpromoted?

In the past decade, mammography has been promoted as constituting the best, if not the only, means of detecting breast cancer early and effecting an improved cure rate. Unquestionably, this kind of promotion has been in the public interest, for it has led to more women undergoing mammography than ever could have been achieved without such promotion. On the other hand, has the pendulum swung too far—that is, has mammography been overpromoted? Jurors, judges, attorneys, patients, and even doctors, as members of the public, are exposed to the same barrage of information regarding breast cancer and mammography as is the general public. Has possible overpromotion made it too difficult—disproportionately difficult—for a defendant-radiologist to prevail in a malpractice lawsuit in which he or she is accused of missing breast cancer on mammography? The answer may be affirmative, because according to Physician Insurers Association of America data, more than 40% of malpractice claims that allege errors in diagnosing breast cancer result in indemnification payments, a figure considerably higher than the 33% indemnification rate of malpractice claims involving all physician groups as a whole.

The news media seem to have backpedaled to a small degree in its message that mammography always reveals breast cancer in its earliest stages and therefore assures patients of increased survival. Here are examples. In one *New York Times* article, science writer Jane Brody[155] emphasized that "the diagnosis and treatment of a tiny cancer is not a guarantee of cure." An article in a Chicago newspaper stated that "Women have come to expect too much from their yearly mammogram…They now mistakenly believe the tests are infallible, failing only when people fail. The truth is that what's flawed are the tests themselves."[156] The article concluded, "Mammograms are lifesavers. All women older than 40 should be getting yearly breast x-rays…the tests are incredible success stories, but you'll benefit if you realize they are not perfect. They are simply the best we have."

While admittedly not overwhelming, nonetheless evidence does exist in the radiologic literature that provides sound bases to argue that *a delay in the diagnosis of breast cancer may not necessarily diminish the patient's chance of survival or reduce the patient's chance for cure.*

---

[155] Brody JE. How good can mammograms be? Suits seek to set a standard. *New York Times.* November 2, 1999:D7.

[156] Breen M. Mammograms, Pap tests aren't perfect. *Chicago Sun-Times.* November 21, 1999:48A.

[12] Continuing Controversies: Breast Cancer and Mammography

The two issues at stake in lawsuits alleging delay in the diagnosis of breast cancer are whether the radiologist has been negligent in his or her interpretation of mammography, and whether the alleged delay in diagnosis has adversely affected the patient's treatment or prognosis. At trial, these issues are decided by a jury; in settlement discussions, these issues are decided by attorneys representing the plaintiff and defendants, and by claims managers of professional liability insurance companies. In either event, the testimony of radiology expert witnesses who are radiologists retained by the various parties in the lawsuit heavily influences final resolution. Jurors, attorneys, insurance claims managers, patients, and doctors are all members of the public-at-large, and thus all are influenced by varying degrees with the voluminous medical information to which the public is exposed by the printed and visual news media. In this way perceptions — and misperceptions — are formed. It is likely that medical malpractice lawsuits alleging delay in the diagnosis of breast cancer are more frequent and result in disproportionately greater indemnification because the public continues to perceive mammography to be unrealistically accurate and effective in improving prognosis.

That it continues to be the public's perception that even a short delay in diagnosis of breast cancer causes harm is quite clear. Examples of such perceptions can be found in the following comments made in a recent Texas State Medical Society publication:[157] "Women now expect to survive breast cancer if they follow medical advice… We have pretty much been told that if we catch breast cancer early, we stand a good chance of living;" "I shouldn't die from breast cancer…[Isn't it true] that if you catch the cancer soon enough I'll live?;" and "It's very hard for a doctor to argue that any delay was either in the patient's interest or didn't harm the patient."

In September 2002, then United States Secretary of Agriculture Ann M. Veneman announced that she had developed DCIS.[158] Commenting on the fact that Veneman's cancer "could not have been detected without a mammogram," President George W. Bush said:[159]

I knew I picked an extraordinary person when I named her to run the Department of Agriculture. I didn't realize I was going to pick a heroic figure as well, an example for many people to understand the

---

[157] Jones TL. The worst list: breast cancer now leading source of medical malpractice claims. *Texas Med* 1996;92:34-36.

[158] Becker E. Cabinet member has cancer. *New York Times*, Sept. 19, 2002; A28.

[159] Agriculture secretary has breast cancer. *Chicago Tribune*, September 19, 2002;18.

need to get a mammogram, the need to take care of yourself, the need to screen early, the need to understand that we can stop cancer in its tracks if we all take wise moves.

Some hospitals and radiologists continue to exaggerate the capability of mammography to detect very tiny lesions. One hospital-sponsored newspaper advertisement states, "Unlike a breast self-exam or a physical examination performed in a doctor's office, mammograms can often detect tumors as small as the head of a pin." An advertising supplement entitled "early detection pays off" published by the *New York Times*[160] states that "Mammograms can detect breast cancers as small a 1/5 of an inch (5 mm)."

That even short delays in the diagnosis of breast cancer can substantially adversely affect the patient's prognosis continues to be reinforced. A front page article in a Toronto newspaper[161] that focused on some women experiencing 1-2 month delays in obtaining mammography stated that "Previous research has shown that delaying treatment by 3-6 months among women with symptomatic breast cancer is associated with poor survival". The newspaper did not mention a report published 18 months earlier in a surgical journal that reviewed 606 patients with breast cancer, 8% of whom had a delay in diagnosis ranging from 6 months to 6 years, averaging 11 months.[162] The average size of the diagnostically-delayed cancers was 2.3 cm compared to 1.8 cm for cancers that had been diagnosed without delay. However, nodal involvement was no more frequent in the delayed cases, and incidence of local recurrences and distant metastases were similar in both groups. Outcomes were not statistically different, findings that the authors acknowledged were counterintuitive, but in agreement with findings from other studies.

In yet another study of patients in whom diagnoses of breast cancers were delayed, it was found that delays were not associated with a higher incidence of lymph node involvement, greater likelihood of having a mastectomy, or eventual outcome.[163] These researchers noted, however, that 25% of the women in this group filed medical malpractice lawsuits.

---

[160] From cause to cure: early detection pays off. *New York Times Magazine,* (special advertising supplement), Oct. 14, 2001:52.

[161] Yelaja T. Breast cancer diagnosis delays "alarming." *Toronto Star*, Aug. 7, 2001:A1.

[162] Tartter TI, Pace, D. Frost M, Bernstein JL. Delay in diagnosis of breast cancer. *Ann Surg,* 1999:229:91-96.

[163] Goodson III WH, Moore II DH. Causes of physician delay in the diagnosis of breast cancer. *Arch Intern Med* 2002:162:1343-1348.

[13] The Public Must Be Better Educated about Breast Cancer and Mammography

Various experts have urged more, rather than less, disclosure and discussion about the controversies swirling around the efficacy of mammography. The editor of an internal medicine journal wrote recently:[164]

> The debate about the effects of screening young women goes on, and nothing ...will dampen it. The debate is worth following closely because women are deciding about breast cancer screening, and it's our role to keep them informed as best we can.

An editorial published in the *Chicago Tribune* in August 2002 echoed this opinion:[165]

> The debate over mammography will go on. [Recent] developments are further evidence that women who want to make informed choices about their health need to know more about how studies are conducted, and what they really say.

Some commentators have gone beyond simply urging more open discussion about the controversies regarding mammography and in fact, have been critical of those who would like to curtail disclosure. A female Ohio oncologist, Leslie Laufman, has stated:[166]

> We doctors need to do a better job of reminding ourselves and informing women about the limitations of [mammography]....I am insulted by the medical community's attempt to distill the issue to a single message; don't worry about the controversy, just get a mammogram. As a women it frustrates me. The attitude is that women are too stupid to sort it out, so they need a simple straightforward answer. I have a lot more faith in women than that.

Many advertisements and marketing campaigns sponsored by the American College of Radiology, the American Cancer Society, and other professional organizations dedicated to furthering the welfare of the public, have extolled the benefits only, excluding any mention of potential limitations, of mammography. It may well be that this "overselling" of mammography and the raising of the public's expectations of what

---

[164] Sox H. Screening mammography for younger women: Back to basics (editorial). *Ann Intern Med* 2002;137:361-362.

[165] Women and mammograms. *Chicago Tribune* (editorial), Aug. 6, 2002:14.

[166] Aschwanden C. Real life decisions about mammograms. *Health,* Oct. 2002:104-108.

mammography can achieve in reducing breast cancer mortality have contributed to the rise in breast cancer medical malpractice litigation. If this is true and the pendulum representing the public's expectation of mammography has swung too far to the benefit side, then perhaps the medical establishment and its allied professional organizations should take a more even-handed approach and make a concerted effort to shift the pendulum of public expectation back toward the center.

Acknowledging rather than denying the existence of controversies regarding the efficacy of mammography, disclosing rather than disregarding scientific studies that question the premise that screening mammography reduces mortality rates from breast cancer, and expanding rather than limiting public discussion and debate of viewpoints and opinions critical of screening mammography expressed by various researchers in the scientific community, will serve to assist the public-at-large in developing a realistic appraisal of mammography's role with regard to breast cancer.

In the meantime, the controversies swirling around mammography, as well as malpractice litigation alleging delays in diagnosis of breast cancer, will continue.

[14] Screening versus Diagnostic Mammography

A screening mammogram is performed to detect breast cancer in an early stage in asymptomatic patients. A diagnostic mammogram, which often involves additional views and supervision by a radiologist, is performed when the patient has symptoms or a suspicious physical abnormality in the breast.

Radiologists should have a system in place that ensures that every patient presenting for mammography provides the radiologist with information regarding the patient's medical history, possible symptoms, and clinical signs and that such information be provided either by the patient or the referring physician.

Radiologists should make every effort to apprise themselves of all pertinent clinical information relevant to the patient before rendering interpretation of a mammogram. Effective communication among the radiologist, the patient, and the referring physician is essential.[167]

All mammographic studies should be defined as screening or as diagnostic and problem-solving breast evaluation. Diagnostic studies require monitoring by a radiologist to effect proper tailoring of the examination. When such monitoring is not feasible and an incomplete evaluation has occurred, the patient should be recalled for additional evaluation with the radiologist present.

---

[167] Berlin L. Screening versus diagnostic mammography. *AJR* 1999;173:3-7.

Once a policy that determines whether a patient undergoes a diagnostic or a screening mammogram is in place, radiologists should not deviate from that policy. For example, if the radiology facility requires that radiologists review questionnaires completed by patients before interpreting a mammogram, the radiologist should not render such an interpretation without first reviewing such a questionnaire. If the questionnaire is missing, the radiologist should request that the patient complete another one.

§ 9.05 Guidelines and Standards

[1] The Expert Witness and Professional Practice Guidelines

It has been long established in American courtrooms that evidence identifying the applicable standard of medical care is offered by expert witnesses whose special knowledge, skill, experience, training or education permits them to testify to an opinion that will aid the judge or jury in resolving questions that are beyond the understanding or competence of lay persons.[168] Up until two decades ago, medical expert witnesses had few if any objective measures of medical standards on which they, or the courts, could rely. The situation changed, however, in the late 1980s when various medical organizations and specialty societies began creating and codifying practice guidelines or standards.[169]

It is of interest to briefly review how various state appeals courts have viewed written professional guidelines and standards and the degree to which these guidelines and standards have been used to help determine the standard of care.

The first instance in which a state supreme court specifically analyzed a standard promulgated by the American College of Radiology occurred in Kansas.[170] In that case, a patient sued a radiologist for failing to diagnose findings on chest radiographs that later proved to be non-Hodgkin's lymphoma. During the trial of the lawsuit, an expert radiology witness retained by the plaintiff's attorney testified that "Radiology standards promulgated by the American College of Radiology include the following sentence: 'Comparison with previous...examinations and reports when possible are a part of the radiologic consultation and report.'" The radiology expert went on to testify that the report rendered by the defendant-radiologist of the chest radiographs in question "did not show that comparison had been made" and that, therefore, "the report did not comply with the applicable

---

[168] Berlin L. On being an expert witness. *AJR* 1997;168:607-610.

[169] *Supra* at note 135.

[170] Aldoroty v. HCA Health Services of Kansas, 962 P2d 501 (Kan 1998).

standard of care." The plaintiff's radiology expert concluded his testimony by stating, "Reading the current film without comparing with previous films would be deviating below an acceptable standard of care." At the conclusion of the trial the jury decided in favor of the plaintiff. The defendant appealed and the case found its way to the State Supreme Court.

In its decision the Kansas Supreme Court did not specifically state that the ACR Standard was equivalent to the standard of medical care, but nevertheless the Court let stand the jury's hearing testimony about the ACR Standard as evidence of the standard of radiologic care. The Court for other technical reasons remanded the case for a new trial, but before that happened the defendant-radiologist settled the lawsuit for an undisclosed sum.

In another case, the Alabama Supreme Court allowed a plaintiff's expert radiology witness to testify that the American College of Radiology's Standard of Communication was evidence of the radiological standard of care.[171] In fact, the Alabama Court went further. The Court allowed the expert to offer the printed ACR Standard as an exhibit, meaning that the jurors would be allowed to take the written Standard with them into the jury room in which they were to conduct their deliberation. While the courts in general readily acknowledge that jurors recognize that many expert witnesses testify untruthfully as well as truthfully,[172] it seems highly unlikely that jurors would question the validity, credibility, or authoritativeness of published ACR Standards, especially if not instructed to do so by a judge.

The ACR Standards were again the focus of judicial attention in a recent case decided by New York State's highest court.[173] In that case a hospital was sued by a patient who had been sexually assaulted by a male technologist while she was undergoing a transvaginal sonogram. A radiology expert witness retained by the plaintiff-patient testified that the hospital had deviated from the appropriate standard of care by not requiring the presence of a female staff member when a male technologist was performing a transvaginal sonogram. The plaintiff's expert referred to the *ACR Standard for the Performance of an Ultrasound Examination of the Female Pelvis*, pointing specifically to a sentence it contained: "It is recommended that a woman be present in the examining room during a transvaginal sonogram, either as an examiner or a chaperone."[174]

The New York Supreme Court rejected the argument of the plaintiff's expert witness, holding that, "The materials from the American College of

---

[171] Vaughan v Oliver, 822 So2d 1163 (Ala 2001).

[172] Berlin L. Bearing false witness. *AJR* 2003;180:1515-1521.

[173] Diaz v New York Downtown Hospital, 784 NE2d 68 (NY 2002).

[174] American College of Radiology. ACR standard for the performance of an ultrasound examination of the female pelvis. In: *Standards 2002-2003*. Reston, VA: American College of Radiology 2002:603-605.

Radiology clearly state that its guidelines 'are not rules.'" The Court also added that, "The guidelines relied on by plaintiff's expert failed to establish an industry standard, and the expert proffered no evidence to support the existence of an actual practice or custom in the radiological community requiring the presence of a chaperone during vaginal ultrasounds."

The most recent appeals court decision centering on an ACR Standard was delivered by the Arizona Supreme Court and has already been discussed in §27 of this chapter. With regard to the importance of the ACR Practice Guidelines, the Court concluded:[175]

> We do not hold that the [ACR] Standards in and of themselves establish a standard of care, but published standards or guidelines of specialty medical organizations are useful in determining the duty owed or the standard of care applicable to a given situation.

§ 9.06 Harmful Effects of Exposure to X-Radiation

[1] Burns and Other Injuries Resulting from Exposure to X-Radiation

Almost immediately upon the announcement in 1895 of Roentgen's discovery of the X-ray beam, a number of manufacturers began producing X-ray "apparatuses" designed to diagnose medical conditions. Because the potential dangers of X-radiation were not well understood at that time and equipment used low-energy X-ray tubes without shielding, beam filtration and coning, it is no surprise that many patients sustained skin injuries as a result of undergoing diagnostic radiography. It is also no surprise that where there was medically-induced injury, there was malpractice litigation. In 1896, in what was apparently the first malpractice lawsuit in the United States to be brought for damages sustained by exposure to X-rays, a Chicago laborer sued a physician who specialized in using this new diagnostic modality, claiming that an ulcerating burn of the skin overlying his ankle had developed as a result of radiographic studies. The patient had fractured his ankle and radiographs that were obtained had necessitated exposure times of 35 to 40 minutes each. The skin injury eventually led to amputation, and the jury awarded the patient $10,000 in damages.[176]

It wasn't long thereafter that a medical malpractice lawsuit dealing with another case of complications of diagnostic radiography reached the United States Supreme Court. In 1905 in Washington, DC, a woman who had

---

[175] *Supra* at note 103.

[176] Lichtenstein JE. Forensic radiology. In: Gagliardi RA, ed. *A history of the radiological sciences*. Reston, VA: Radiology Centennial, Inc. 1996:586-587.

undergone seven radiographic examinations in order to diagnose a rib fracture sustained injury to her skin, and sued the physician who had operated the radiographic unit. At trial a jury exonerated the physician because the attorney for the plaintiff had been unable to find an expert who would testify that the defendant-physician had been negligent in operation of the equipment. The patient appealed, and the case finally reached the nation's Supreme Court. In its ruling, the Court acknowledged that as a result of the radiographic examination, the woman "felt bad effects," and the portion of her body that had been "exposed to the X-ray ...was red and irritated...and burned...and caused and continues to cause much suffering."[177] The Court took note of and was persuaded by experts testifying on behalf of the defendant-physician, a "specialist in the use of the X-ray for diagnostic purposes," who stated that it was "impossible, by the use of any degree of care, to prevent ...or guard absolutely against...occasional X-ray burns from use of the apparatus." The Supreme Court affirmed the jury's finding that the defendant-physician was not liable for malpractice.

For the next 80 years there was a dearth of reported cases of radiographically or fluoroscopically induced skin injuries. Indeed, of a reported total of 73 cases of skin injuries resulting from fluoroscopically-guided procedures, only two occurred before 1990.[178] The infrequency of fluoroscopic complications perhaps can be explained by the fact that radiation dose rates for screen fluoroscopy in common use until the late 1960s were in the range of.03 to .05 Gy (3 to 5 rads) per minute.[179] Inasmuch as fluoroscopy use was limited mainly to gastrointestinal examinations that rarely exceeded 15 minutes in length and the means of reducing radiation exposure through appropriate filtration and coning were well understood, the likelihood of skin injury was remote. The introduction into the radiologic community in the 1960s and 1970s of the X-ray image intensifier lowered the dose rate even further.

[2] The Advent of Interventional Radiology

The birth of interventional radiology with its requisite higher-dose radiographic equipment and procedures often necessitating long fluoroscopic times drastically increased the radiation exposure to which

---

[177] Sweeney v. Erving, 228 US 233 (1913).

[178] Koenig TR, Mettler FA, Wagner LK. Skin injuries from fluoroscopically guided procedures – part 2: review of 73 cases and recommendations for minimizing dose delivered to patient. *AJR* 2001;177:13-20.

[179] Whalen JP, Balter S. *Radiation risks in medical imaging.* Chicago: Year Book Medical Publishers, Inc., 1984:26-27.

patients were subjected. In 1991, radiologists were warned that high-level fluoroscopic boost options would allow equipment to reach dose rates of .93 Gy (93 rads) per minute.[180] In an article published in the *ACR Bulletin* in 1992, the chairman of the American College of Radiology (ACR) commission on physics and radiation safety admonished the radiologic community that newly-manufactured fluoroscopy equipment using a "high-level control mode" could generate radiation exposure rates of as high as 1.2 Gy (120 rads) per minute and that its use in interventional procedures that often involve prolonged fluoroscopic times could result in patient exposures exceeding 20 Gy (2000 rads), more than enough to cause serious radiation skin burns.[181]

Not long thereafter, radiation injuries drew the attention of the federal government. In September 1994, the United States Food and Drug Administration [FDA] issued public health advisories that dealt with serious skin injuries caused by radiation received during fluoroscopy.[182] The FDA voiced its concern that an increasing number of invasive procedures using fluoroscopic guidance were inducing skin injuries due to exposure to radiation because of prolonged fluoroscopy times. These procedures included angioplasties of coronary and other vessels, cardiac ablations, vascular embolizations, stent and filter placements, thyrombolyses, transhepatic cholangiographies, endoscopic retrograde cholangiopancreatographies, nephrostomies, biliary drainages, urinary or biliary stone removals, and transjugular intrahepatic portosystemic shunts. The FDA advisory warned physicians performing these procedures to be aware of the potential of incurring serious injury and advised physicians to observe certain safety principals. Safety principals enumerated included recommendations that physicians establish standard operating procedures and clinical protocols, know the radiation dose rates for specific fluoroscopic procedures, assess each procedure's protocol for the potential for radiation injury to the patient, modify the protocol as appropriate to limit radiation exposure, and enlist a qualified medical physicist for consultation. One year later, the FDA issued another advisory that addressed the issues of which patients should have

---

[180] Cagnon CH, Benedict SH, Mankovich NJ, Bushberg JT, Seibert JA, Whiting JS. Exposure rates in high-level-control fluoroscopy for image enhancement. *Radiology* 1991;178:643-646.

[181] Fluoroscopy alert: HLC mode may cause acute radiation injury. *ACR Bulletin* 1992;48(7):4.

[182] United States Food and Drug Administration. Public health advisory: *avoidance of serious x-ray-induced skin injuries to patients during fluoroscopically-guided procedures*. Rockville, MD: Center for Devices and Radiological Health, United Stated Food and Drug Administration, September 9, 1994;United States Food and Drug Administration. Public health advisory: *avoidance of serious x-ray-induced skin injuries to patients during fluoroscopically-guided procedures*. Rockville, MD: Center for Devices and Radiological Health, United States Food and Drug Administration, September 30, 1994.

information regarding radiation exposure recorded, as well as what kind of information should be included in that recording.[183]

As might be anticipated, the ACR has remained inextricably linked to radiation safety issues. In the past decade the ACR has addressed in four different Standards the fact that excessive fluoroscopy used during interventional radiologic procedures can cause severe skin injury. Radiation dose to patients is directly addressed in the *ACR Standard for Diagnostic Medical Physics Performance Monitoring of Radiographic and Fluoroscopic Equipment,* [184] originally passed in 1992 and most recently amended in 2006. The Standard states:

> Patient radiation dose shall be evaluated for radiographic and fluoroscopic equipment at least annually. Tables of patient radiation dose for representative examinations shall be prepared and supplied to the facility. These tables shall be prepared using measured radiation output data and imaging techniques provided by the facility. These results shall be compared with appropriate guidelines or recommendations when they are available. The medical physicist should assist facilities in developing policies and procedures to evaluate patient risk from studies and interventions requiring prolonged fluoroscopy.

Various other technical standards published by the ACR[185] contain similar language with respect to patient radiation exposure. They all mandate that the physician performing the specific procedure should have a "thorough understanding" of radiation safety considerations including the principles of radiation protection, the hazards of radiation exposure to both patients and radiologic personnel, and the monitoring requirements of the imaging methods. The standards go on to include statements that a medical physicist should have the responsibility for overseeing the equipment quality control and for monitoring fluoroscopy studies. They also add that when fluoroscopy is used, fluoroscopic time should be kept to a minimum and that "the operator will use only as much fluoroscopy as is necessary to complete" the procedure.

---

[183] United States Food and Drug Administration. Public health advisory: *recording information in the patient's medical record that identifies the potential for serious x-ray-induced skin injuries.* Rockville, MD: Center for Devices and Radiological Health, United States Food and Drug Administration, 1995.

[184] American College of Radiology. ACR technical standard for diagnostic medical physics performance monitoring of radiographic and fluoroscopic equipment. In: *Practice Guidelines and Technical Standards 2007.* Reston, VA: American College of Radiology, 2007:1069-1072.

[185] *Supra* at note 90.

In addition to these guidelines and standards, the ACR has also published a booklet entitled *Radiation Risk: A Primer.* [186] In it the ACR urges all radiologists to accomplish fluoroscopically-guided interventional studies in a way that minimizes patient radiation dose. The ACR again admonishes radiologists to be familiar with dose-reducing features available on fluoroscopic equipment and with the radiation safety issues identified by the FDA that carry the risk of radiation-induced skin injury. Specific suggestions are given as to how to reduce radiation exposure.

Patient injury can result from radiation received during many kinds of interventional procedures performed by radiologists. For example in 1994 in Virginia, a patient who had undergone an 8-hour thyroidal arteriogram in the radiology department of a university hospital and had developed, shortly thereafter, a radiation burn on her back that required skin grafts sued the interventional radiologist for using "excessive" fluoroscopy. During a trial in federal court, the plaintiff had retained an expert in radiation physics who testified that the amount of radiation received by the patient was indeed excessive and sufficient to cause severe skin injury. Nevertheless, the court ruled in favor of the defendant-radiologist because the plaintiff did not provide any expert testimony that the defendant-radiologist had been negligent.[187]

In another case, a patient sustained a 10 x 7 cm severe skin ulceration as a result of a transjugular intrahepatic portosystemic (TIPS) procedure.[188] In order to determine the level of radiation to which that and similar patients were being exposed, researchers reviewed 50 TIPS procedures. Although the researchers found that the procedures averaged 5 hours, the actual fluoroscopy times ranged from 60 to 90 minutes and the estimated skin doses ranged from 5 to 8 Gy (500-800 rads). However, maximum radiation dose in certain cases reached 12 Gy (1200 rads). The researchers discovered that skin injuries were more common in patients who underwent multiple interventional procedures and in patients with collagen diseases such as rheumatoid arthritis, systemic lupus erythematous, scleroderma or mixed connective tissue disease. Exaggerated and intense reactions after high-dose interventional procedures were also more frequent in diabetic patients and in patients receiving certain chemotherapeutic drugs.

As techniques in interventional radiology continue to advance and radiologic equipment becomes even more sophisticated, patients are likely to be exposed to higher doses of radiation, which in turn may well lead to more

---

[186]American College of Radiology. *Radiation risk: a primer.* Reston, VA: American College of Radiology, 1996:23-25.

[187] Peck v. Tegtmeyer, 834 F.Supp.903 (VA, 1992).

[188] Wagner LK, McNeese MD, Marx MV, Siegel EL. Severe skin reactions from interventional fluoroscopy: case report and review of the literature. *Radiology* 1999; 213:773-776.

frequent and severe injuries. Newer technology generates dose rates to the skin of patients of up to .01 Gy (1 rad) per second, rates that can easily achieve dose levels that are far in excess of those required to produce erythema.[189]

Researchers have discussed in detail the natural history of skin reactions to radiation, including threshold doses and times of onset.[190] Multiple technical factors contribute to radiation injury to patients from fluoroscopy and fluorography. These include long fluoroscopy times through thick body parts, lack of radiation dose monitoring, incomplete training of physicians, reticence of interventional physicians to seek more experienced help when faced with a difficult procedure, unnecessary direct radiation of certain body parts such as arms and breasts, overuse of high-dose-rate modes of operation, and failure to use to heavy beam filtration and remove the grid when appropriate.

Excessive fluoroscopy has been implicated as a cause of breast cancer but thus far there is no evidence to link fluoroscopy to lung cancer. Lung cancer has been found to be more common in miners who have worked with uranium or ore from which radium has been extracted, but a definite cause-and-effect relationship between occupational exposure to radiation and lung cancer remains nebulous.[191]

[3] Minimizing Radiation Exposure

Radiologists should remind themselves of the truism that any radiologic procedure that places a patient at risk for sustaining a complication more than likely will also subject the radiologist to malpractice litigation.

Radiologists should ensure that all equipment used in interventional or other fluoroscopic procedures is maintained in optimal working condition so that acceptable image quality is achieved with the lowest possible radiation dose, and that appropriate individuals conduct and document periodic inspections.

Radiologists performing interventional procedures should be familiar with, and make use of, any available dose-reducing features such as low-dose fluoroscopy mode, collimators, and image-hold capabilities. Fluoroscopy times should be kept to a minimum and if possible, beam entry site should be changed periodically during prolonged procedures.

Consideration should be given to including radiation injury as part of the discussion of risks and benefits of the procedure during the consent process

---

[189] Wagner LK. CT fluoroscopy: another advancement with additional challenges in radiation management. *Radiology* 2000; 216:9-10.

[190] Koenig TR, Wolff D, Mettler FA, Wagner LK. Skin injuries from fluoroscopically guided procedures - part 1: characteristics of radiation injury. *AJR* 2001;177:3-11.

[191] Hall EJ. *Radiobiology for the radiologist*, 4th ed. Philadelphia: Lippincott, 1994:323-350.

in patients who are at high risk for developing skin complications, such as patients with connective tissue collagen disease and diabetes. Radiologists should also consider examining the skin of patients on whom a fluoroscopically-guided interventional procedure is being repeated.

Dosimeters allowing for dose measurement during interventional procedures should be utilized if possible. If a procedure has been prolonged and the radiation dose to the skin is known to have been high, the patient should be advised to undergo an examination of the skin 2 to 4 weeks after completion of the procedure.

Radiologists whose practices involve fluoroscopy, especially those performing interventional procedures, should be familiar with the FDA advisories of 1994 and 1995, and appropriate standards of the American College of Radiology, that address skin injuries to patients during fluoroscopically-guided procedures.

[4] Radioactive Iodine and the Pregnant Patient

That radioactive iodine most commonly utilized in the treatment of hyperthyroidism administered orally to a mother will deleteriously affect the thyroid gland of the fetus is well established. The placental transfer of radioactive iodine occurs as early as 8 weeks post conception.[192] The fetal thyroid gland is developed sufficiently to concentrate iodine and synthesize hormone by 11 to 12 weeks gestation. Iodine-concentrating and iodine- and thyroid hormone-storing capacities of the fetal thyroid gland increase progressively until term.[193] The fetal thyroid has a much greater relative affinity for radioactive material than does the maternal thyroid.[194]

The radiation dose to the fetal thyroid gland at 15 weeks gestation delivered by 2 millicuries (74 MBq) of iodine-131 is estimated to range from 10,000 to 40,000 rads (100-400 Gy).[195] Radiation from iodine-131 in this dose range and delivered during this period of gestation can cause hypothyroidism in the newborn.[196]

---

[192] Wagner LK, Lester RG, Saldana LR. Exposure of the pregnant patient to diagnostic radiations: a guide to medical management. Philadelphia: Lippincott, 1985;17-19,55-57.

[193] Harbert JC. Radioiodine therapy of differentiated thyroid carcinoma. In: Harbert JC, Eckelman WC, Neuman RD, eds. *Nuclear medicine: diagnosis and therapy.* New York: Thieme Medical Publishers, 1996:1006-1008.

[194] Green HG, Gareis FJ, Shepard TH, Kelley VC. Cretinism associated with maternal sodium iodine I 131 therapy during pregnancy. *Amer J Dis Child* 1971;122:247-249.

[195] *Considerations regarding the unintended radiation exposure of the embryo, fetus or nursing child.* Bethesda, MD: National Council on Radiation Protection and Measurements, 1994 NCRP Commentary No. 9:7-8.

[196] Stoffer SS, Hamburger JI. Inadvertent ^{131}I therapy for hyperthyroidism in the first trimester of pregnancy. *J Nucl Med* 1976;17:146-149.

That iodine-131 is contraindicated during pregnancy is explicitly stated in both the radiologic literature and in ACR Practice Guidelines. The ACR booklet entitled *Radiation Risk: A Primer* admonishes that "radiation exposure of a pregnant female should be avoided unless the patient has an acute medical problem."[197] Other publications state that it is "prudent to avoid" using even small amounts of radioactive iodine during pregnancy except in extreme cases when there is no alternative, and   with regard to *treatment* of hyperthyroidism with iodine-131, pregnancy is, of course, an absolute contraindication.[198]

Radiologists have a duty to assure themselves that women are not pregnant before administering iodine-131, but whether radiologists must mandate that every woman of childbearing age undergo a pregnancy test before administration of iodine-131 diagnostic radioactive isotopes is unclear.

However, *The ACR Practice Guideline for the Performance of Therapy with Unsealed Radionuclide Sources*[199] states that female patients should not be pregnant and points out that at the time of isotope administration, "pregnancy should be ruled out by a negative beta human chorionic gonodotropin (hCG) test obtained within 72 hours prior to administration of the radiopharmaceutical."

[5] Minimizing Radiation Exposure from Radiopharmaceuticals in Pregnant Patients

Administering a radionuclide such as iodine-131 to a woman who may unknowingly be pregnant not only represents a clinical hazard to the mother and her fetus, but it represents a medical-legal hazard to the radiologist as well.

Although no governmental regulation or professional standard absolutely requires that radiologists determine definitively the pregnancy status of women of childbearing age for whom administration of iodine-131 or other radionuclides are being considered, it is nonetheless prudent for all radiologic facilities to have in place a policy that assists in making that determination. Commonly used methods for this purpose include having radiology requisition forms contain an inquiry about possible pregnancy; posting signs throughout the waiting and examining areas of the nuclear medicine department that alert patients to inform a technologist or physician

---

[197] American College of Radiology. *Radiation risk: a primer.* Reston, VA: American College of Radiology, 1996:5-10.

[198] Hall EJ. *Radiobiology for the radiologist,* 4th ed. Philadelphia: Lippincott, 1994: 445-448.

[199] American College of Radiology. ACR standard for the performance of therapy with unsealed radionuclide sources. In: *Practice* Guidelines and Technical *Standards 2007.* Reston, VA: American College of Radiology 2007:857-869.

if they think they are or could be pregnant;[200] having patients fill out a form that includes a question about possible pregnancy; and authorizing nuclear medicine technologists to ask patients whether they are or could be pregnant.

If patients are to complete a questionnaire that includes a question regarding the possibility of pregnancy, the patient should be asked to affix her signature to the form after completion.

If patients are asked verbally whether they are or could be pregnant, the name of the questioner and the patient's specific response should be documented in writing.

§ 9.07 Total Body CT Screening

[1] Potential Malpractice Pitfalls of Screening

The era of CT screening began to emerge the early 1990s,[201] when radio and newspaper advertisements began appearing that exhorted middle-aged men and women to undergo routine CT testing. An abrupt surge in the public's clamor for CT screening occurred on October 2, 2000, the day the test was publicized by television talk-show personality Oprah Winfrey.[202] On the day following the Winfrey show, scanning companies all over the country were besieged and in the words of an executive of a CT scanning company, "We had 500-600 phone calls the next day...it was insane. People went nuts."

As the CT screening movement continued throughout the United States, it became apparent that malpractice litigation alleging various acts of radiologic negligence would emerge as well. Let us examine potential malpractice pitfalls involved in CT screening.

[2] The False Negative

As already discussed in §6 and §7 of this chapter, the radiologic literature for more than 50 years has been replete with studies showing that errors committed by radiologists when interpreting radiographic examinations are not uncommon.

As many as 32% of colon cancers are missed on barium enema examinations.[203] One might speculate that the error rate in detecting colon

---

[200] Saenger EI, Kereiakes JG. Medical radiation exposure during pregnancy. *JAMA* 1979;242:15:1669.

[201] Chase M. Ads for heart scans prompt wider use of helpful screening. *The Wall Street Journal.* February 9, 1998:B1.

[202] Burton TM. Do CT scans help or hurt patients seeking to prevent heart attacks? *The Wall Street Journal.* January 7, 2002:A13, A16.

[203] Cooley RN, Agnew CH, Rios G. Diagnostic accuracy of the barium enema study in carcinoma of the colon and rectum. *AJR* 1960;84:316-331.

cancers on CT colonography is lower, but this may not be the case. While there are studies showing that the overall sensitivity of CT colonography for polyp detection hovers in the 90% range,[204] no reports measuring actual error rates committed by radiologists interpreting the modality have yet been published. There are, however, many published reports that address the frequency of errors committed in the interpretation of other kinds of CT examinations. One experienced thoracic radiologist, even knowing prospectively that each chest CT in a study group included a missed cancer, was able to identify the missed lesion in less than half the cases.[205] Other researchers[206] found that half of the lung cancers detected on helical CT were present in retrospect on a prior CT examination. Still others[207] have documented miss rates ranging from 13.5% to 37% among radiologists' interpretations of body CT scans. There is little reason to doubt that error rates in the interpretation of CT colonography and full-body scans will fall into the same range. How a medical malpractice lawsuit can be generated by the alleged missing of a significant abnormality in a screening CT scan was exemplified by the litigation involving actor John Ritter.

[3] The John Ritter Lawsuit

A radiologist's alleged failure to diagnose an aortic aneurysm on a routine screening CT examination was the primary focus of the recent well-publicized wrongful death medical malpractice trial of television and movie actor John Ritter that was held in early 2008 in a Glendale California courtroom. Ritter had died on September 11, 2003, at the age of 54, of an aortic dissection. Two years earlier Ritter had undergone a routine CT screening examination that had been interpreted as normal by California

---

[204] Yee J, Akerkar GA, Hung RK, Steinauer-Gebauer AM, Wall SD, McQuaid KR. Colorectal neoplasia: performance characteristics of CT colonography for detection in 300 patients. *Radiology* 2001;219:685-692.

[205] White CS, Romney BM, Mason AC, Austin JHM, Miller BH, Protopapas Z. Primary carcinoma of the lung overlooked at CT: analysis of findings in 14 patients. *Radiology* 1996;199:109-115.

[206] Kakinuma R, Ohmatsu H, Kaneko M, et al. Detection failures in spiral CT screening for lung cancer: analysis of CT findings. *Radiology* 1999;212:61-66.

[207] Wechsler RJ, Spettell CM, Kurtz AB, et al. Effects of training and experience in interpretation of emergency body CT scans. *Radiology* 1996;199:717-720; Gollub MJ, Panicek DM, Bach AM, Penalver A, Castellino RA. Clinical importance of reinterpretation of body CT scans obtained elsewhere in patients referred for care at a tertiary cancer center. *Radiology* 1999;210:109-112; Kalbhen CL, Yetter EM, Olson MC, Posniak HV, Aranha GV. Assessing the resectability of pancreatic carcinoma: the value of reinterpreting abdominal CT performed at other institutions. *AJR* 1998;171:1571-1576; Siegel CL, Fisher AJ, Bennett HF. Interobserver variability in determining enhancement of renal masses on helical CT. *AJR* 1999;172:1207-1212.

radiologist Matthew Lotysch. After settling for $14 million a malpractice lawsuit that Mr. Ritter's family had filed against a hospital and eight other medical personnel, the family proceeded to trial in a $67 million lawsuit filed against radiologist Lotysch and an emergency department physician.[208] The family claimed that the radiologist should have reported that Ritter's aorta was abnormally widened on the original screening CT; the defendant-radiologist asserted that the aorta appeared quite normal.

At the conclusion of a month-long trial, the jury on March 15 found both doctors innocent of all charges.[209]

[4] Overdiagnosis

The term "overdiagnosis" in the context of screening has been defined as the finding of a tumor or other disease that is not dangerous but nevertheless cannot be distinguished from one that may become lethal,[210] or a preclinical "pseudodisease" that would not have produced any signs or symptoms before the individual would have died from other causes.[211]

Among the adverse sequelae of overdiagnosis are complications that may result from diagnostic procedures designed to investigate an apparent abnormality on a CT scan that later turns out to be clinically unimportant. William J. Casarella, MD, at the time Chair of the Department of Radiology at Emory University School of Medicine in Atlanta, has written a firsthand experience of the "clinical drama" that can follow a screening test.[212] Dr. Casarella underwent a CT colonographic examination that was interpreted as normal, but the interpreting radiologists noted lesions in the kidney, liver, and lungs. Contrast material–enhanced CT scan of the abdomen demonstrated the renal mass to be a cyst, but in order to identify the nature of the liver lesion, a CT-guided liver biopsy was performed. It showed only necrotic tissue but the findings were not definitive. Finally a positron emission tomographic scan and a video-aided thoracoscopy were performed, the latter involving three wedge resections of the right lung. A definitive diagnosis of histoplasmosis was finally made. Dr. Casarella then relates that he awoke after the biopsy with a chest tube, a Foley catheter, a subclavian central venous catheter, a nasal oxygen catheter, an epidural catheter, and an

---

[208] $67 million trial opens on John Ritter's death. *Chicago Tribune,* February 2, 2008

Deutsch L. Ritter's widow testified about his death. *LA Times,* March 3, 2008.

[209] Spano J. Jury clears doctors of negligence in Ritter's death. *LA Times* March 15, 2008.

[210] Kolata G. Test proves fruitless, fueling new debate on cancer screening. *The New York Times.* April 9, 2002;D1, D4.

[211] Black WC, Welch HG. Screening for disease. *AJR* 1997;168:3-11.

[212] Casarella WJ. A patient's viewpoint on current controversy. Letter to the Editor. *Radiology* 2002;224:927.

arterial catheter, all in place. He was also given subcutaneously-administered heparin, a constant infusion of prophylactic antibiotics, and analgesia with intravenously-administered narcotics. Eventually, after 5 weeks of convalescence and $50,000 in medical expenses, Dr. Casarella recovered. Casarella reflected on this experience:

> High-spatial-resolution chest CT is a superb imaging tool. At the moment, it is very sensitive but not specific enough. The pursuit of false-positive findings in the lungs is at best costly, anxiety producing, and involves 2 years of repeated CT scans. At worst, it will lead to painful, costly, and potentially risky major surgical procedures. Routine screening of the lungs with CT will produce more surgery and certainly more CT scans to monitor change. We as radiologists must understand the consequences to the patient. It is not nihilistic to suggest that more research is needed, and we still need to prove that search for occult lesions will improve the length and quality of life.

Addressing the issue of overdiagnosis, the Website of the US Food and Drug Administration contains the following admonition:[213]

> If your CT screening result is interpreted as abnormal and there is really nothing significant wrong with you, then you may be subjected to still further tests or treatments, all of which have their own risks….The surprising fact about a CT interpretation of abnormality when there is nothing significant wrong is that it is far more likely to happen to you than the finding of any actual life-threatening disease, since the likelihood that you actually had any deadly disease is so small to begin with.

In its statement on whole-body CT, the American College of Radiology expresses similar sentiments:[214]

> The ACR is concerned that [CT screening] will lead to the discovery of numerous findings that will not ultimately affect patients' health but will result in increased patient anxiety, unnecessary follow-up examinations and treatments, and wasted expense.

---

[213] *Whole-body CT screening — should I or shouldn't I get one?* US Food and Drug Administration, Center for Devices and Radiologic Health. Available at: http://www.fda.gov./cdrh/ct/screening.html. Accessed 7/9/2002.

[214] Imaging modalities for screening. *ACR Bulletin* 2001;57(11):56-57.

Patients who sustain complications and injuries resulting from medical procedures that may not have been indicated to begin with because they were performed due to an "abnormality" seen on CT screening that later turned out to be insignificant, may well choose to pursue malpractice litigation.

[5] Radiation Exposure

Effects of radiation exposure from interventional procedures were discussed in §47 and §48. Nevertheless, concerns regarding the amount and effect of radiation exposure to CT cannot be ignored. CT scanning systems used in the early 1990s generated an average radiation dose for head scans of 40 to 60 mGy (4-6 rads) and for body scans 10 to 40 mGy (1-4 rads). Radiation doses to patients with multidetector CT are 30-50% greater than with older single-slice CT scanners.[215]

The question of whether radiation exposure from CT screening will increase the incidence of cancer in the general population is controversial. On a Website, the US Food and Drug Administration,[216] explains the matter this way:

A CT examination may be associated with an increase in the possibility of fatal cancer of approximately one chance in 2000. This increase in the possibility of a fatal cancer from radiation can be compared to the natural incidence of fatal cancer in the US population, about one chance in five. In other words, for any one person the risk of radiation-induced cancer is much smaller than the natural risk of cancer. Nevertheless, this small increase in radiation-associated cancer risk for an individual can become a public health concern if large numbers of the population undergo increased numbers of CT screening procedures of uncertain benefit.

The potential damage from CT radiation is greater in children because they are ten times more sensitive to radiation.[217] The best risk estimates suggest that pediatric CT will result in significantly increased lifetime radiation risk than adult CT.[218]

---

[215] Hall EJ. *Radiobiology for radiologist.* 5th ed. Philadelphia: Lippincott, Williams & Wilkins 2000; 204-212, 230-233.

[216] *Whole body scanning: what are the radiation risks from CT?* US Food and Drug Administration, Center for Devices and Radiologic Health. April 17, 2002. Available at: http://www.fda.gov./cdrh/ct/risks.html. Accessed 7/9/2002.

[217] Slovis TL. CT and computed radiography: the pictures are great, but is the radiation dose greater than required? *AJR* 2002;179:39-41.

[218] Brenner DJ, Elliston CD, Hall EJ, Berdon WE. Estimated risks of radiation-induced fatal cancer from pediatric CT. *AJR* 2001;178:289-296.

Certain researchers[219] downplay the potential association of carcinogenesis with radiation. They have claimed that objective authentication of the nation's "knowledge" that low doses of radiation cause cancer simply is not available at this time, and may never be.

With regard to a woman who is pregnant or who may think she is pregnant, it should be pointed out that radiation-induced teratogenesis is primarily a concern from the 10th to 17th week of gestation.[220] Radiation-induced central nervous system abnormalities and growth retardation most commonly occur in fetuses between 2 and 15 weeks gestation. The radiation dose below which no deleterious effects on the fetus occur even in the most sensitive developmental phase is not known with certainty, but it has been estimated to range from .05 to .15 Gy (5-15 rads).[221]

The medical malpractice risks arising from allegations of radiation injury due to CT screening are unknown. Could potential plaintiffs be successful in alleging in a malpractice lawsuit that they developed carcinoma from a screening CT? Could a potential female plaintiff successfully claim that she gave birth to a baby with congenital anomalies caused by the radiation exposure received when she had undergone CT screening at a time when, unbeknownst to her or the radiologist, she was pregnant? These questions cannot be answered at this time.

[6] Abandoning a Patient

Radiologists incur certain duties to self-referred patients. The *ACR Practice Guideline for Communication of Diagnostic Imaging Findings*, 2001 revision[222] includes the following provision:

> Diagnostic imagers should recognize that performing imaging studies on a self-referred patient establishes a doctor-patient relationship that includes responsibility for communicating the results of the imaging studies directly to the patient and arranging for appropriate follow-up.

Historically most radiologists have not thought of themselves as primary care physicians to patients, but the CT screening movement has markedly altered this dynamic. Radiologists who solicit patients to undergo screening

---

[219] Brandt-Zawadzki M, Silverman JM. Cancer risk 'knowledge' may be an assumption. *Diagnostic Imaging* May 2002;24(5):21,23,25.

[220] Kalbhen CL. Question and answer. *AJR* 2002;178:1285-1286.

[221] Berlin L. Radiation exposure and the pregnant patient. *AJR* 1996;167:1377-1379.

[222] American College of Radiology. ACR practice guidelines for communication of diagnostic imaging findings. In: *Practice Guidelines and Technical Standards 2007*. Reston, VA: American College of Radiology 2007:3-8.

radiologic examinations without being referred by a primary care physician will find themselves placed in the position of acting as primary care physician. Once a patient undergoes the screening radiologic examination, a physician-patient relationship between the radiologist and patient is thus established. The radiologist cannot unilaterally terminate this relationship until or unless the patient is formally notified and arrangements for alternative medical care are made. A radiologist's failure to carry out this duty (and to document it appropriately) could well expose the radiologist to a charge of patient abandonment.[223]

[7] The Duty to Disclose and Informed Consent in Screening

A physician's legal duty to inform patients of the nature and potential complications of any diagnostic or therapeutic medical procedure and obtain the patient's informed consent before they undertake it is longstanding.[224] Radiologists are well acquainted with the need to disclose to patients the benefits and risks of invasive procedures, alternative measures that might give similar results, and the risks of not performing the procedure.[225] However, in recent years the informed consent process has been inexorably expanded not only to encompass a growing number of diagnostic radiologic and non-radiologic procedures, but also to broaden the content of the disclosures. Courts have begun to impose duties on physicians to disclose to patients such information as physicians' experience, credentials, and personal habits that could affect professional performance.[226]

The advent of CT screening will likely further expand the ground rules for informed consent. By encouraging persons to undergo testing designed to detect early disease, radiologists may be required to assume the responsibility of explaining to these persons the myriad uncertainties that pertain to early detection. A recent editorial in the New York Times described the nature of these uncertainties:

> The ability of screening tests to detect very tiny tumors in the breast, prostate and other organs has far outstripped scientists' understanding of how to interpret and respond to the findings... For some decades now it has been an article of faith in the cancer

---

[223] Berlin L. Are radiologists contracted by third party to interpret radiographs liable for not communicating results directly to patients? *AJR* 2002;178:27-33.

[224] Schloendorff v The Society of New York Hosp., 105 NE 92 (NY 1914).

[225] Obergfell AM. Law & ethics in diagnostic imaging and therapeutic radiology. Philadelphia: Saunders, 1995:85-92.

[226] Berlin L. The duty to disclose. *AJR* 1998;171:1463-1467.

community that early detection is a sure-fire way to save lives. It seems intuitively obvious that if one detects a tumor very early, when it is tiny and least likely to have spread malignant cells to distant parts of the body, doctors will have the best chance of removing the cancer entirely. But in recent years that rationale has been challenged in screening for several types of cancer... A key issue is whether the tests are finding a lot of tumors that would never become dangerous but cannot be distinguished from tumors that could become deadly, thereby causing many patients to undergo the risk of surgery, radiation or chemotherapy for no good reason... Patients and their doctors will have to chart a course that feels comfortable to them... No expert has the answer to what is essentially a matter of individual choice.

Patients will have to be explained this by their doctors, and failure to do so could lead to medical malpractice litigation.

[8] The Ethics of Screening

In order to reach a decision about whether to undergo a screening CT, patients will have to be educated by their physicians, and in the case of screening CT the self-referred patient's physician will be the radiologist. Radiologists are obliged to shed themselves of their personal feelings about the value of CT screening and accept the legal requirement as well as the moral imperative to provide unbiased information to patients about the procedure. The American Medical Association's *Principals of Medical Ethics* affirm this responsibility:[227]

The patient has the right to receive information from physicians and to discuss the benefits, risks, and costs of appropriate treatment alternatives. Patients should receive guidance from their physicians as to the optimal course of action... The patient has the right to make decisions regarding the health care that is recommended by his or her physician. Accordingly, patients may accept or refuse any recommended medical treatment... A physician shall deal honestly with patients and colleagues.

---

[227] American Medical Association Council on Ethical and Judicial Affairs. Principles of medical ethics. Fundamental elements of the patient- physician relationship. Guide to use of annotations. In: *Code of medical ethics: current opinions with Annotations.* Chicago: American Medical Association 2000:xii,xiv,xv.

The *Principles of Ethics of the American College of Radiology*[228] likewise affirms that the rendering of a service by a radiologist should be "governed by what is in the best interest of the patient."

The U.S. Preventive Services Task Force, an independent panel of experts that reviews research in a wide range of preventive services, has issued a statement regarding annual mammography that includes the following directive:[229]

> Clinicians should inform women about the potential benefits (reduced chance from dying from breast cancer), potential harms (e.g., false-positive results, unnecessary biopsies), and limitations of the test that apply to women their age.

While not directly addressing CT screening, the New Jersey Supreme Court nevertheless echoed similar sentiments:[230]

> Physicians do not adequately discharge their responsibility by disclosing only treatment alternatives that they recommend... Physicians may [not] impose their values on their patients.

We do not yet know how courts will deal with informed consent and duty-to-divulge issues that may arise out of CT-screening lawsuits that may be filed in the future. We do not yet know how the courts would respond to a potential plaintiff-patient's lawsuit charging a radiologist with misrepresenting the value of a CT screening examination by overemphasizing its accuracy and efficacy, while ignoring its potential downside risks. We do not yet know the extent of which a radiologist has a duty to recommend follow-up screening examinations.

[9] Contrast Media and CT Screening

The incidence of fatal or serious but non-fatal adverse allergic reactions to iodinated contrast media has been well documented.[231] It is thus not surprising

---

[228] American College of Radiology. ACR bylaws 2000-2001, article XIII, section1, *principles of ethics*. Reston VA: American College of Radiology 2001.

[229] US preventive services task force (USPSTF). *Recommendations and rationale: screening for breast cancer.* February 2002 Available at http://www.ahrq.gov/clinic/3rduspst/breastcancer/. Accessed 2/22/2002.

[230] Matthies v. Mastromonaco, 733 A2d 456 (NJ 1999).

[231] Spring DB, Bettman MA, Barkan HE. Nonfatal adverse reactions to iodinated contrast media: spontaneous reporting to the U.S. Food and Drug Administration, 1978-1994. *Radiology* 1997;204:325-332;. Spring DB, Bettman MA, Barkan HE. Deaths related to iodinated contrast

that radiologists are reluctant to administer these potentially life-threatening agents to patients unless there are valid medical indications to do so.

The determination of whether contrast media should be utilized in a CT examination rests primarily with the radiologist,[232] especially in the case of a screening CT examination in which the patient has no referring physician. However, as yet there is no consensus in the radiologic community that addresses the issue of whether contrast media is or is not indicated in the performance of screening CT. Many radiologists are critical of screening CT performed without administration of contrast, claiming that while images obtained on whole-body CT without contrast agents may be characterized by excellent anatomic detail, but nevertheless, much of potentially discovered diseases are not discernible. Certainly many tumors could be missed in the absence of contrast infusion. Although most radiologists involved in CT screening elect not to administer contrast media, some do.[233]

If contrast media is not used and a small carcinoma of one of the abdominal or pelvic organs is missed, a plaintiff's attorney may well be able to retain a well-credentialed radiology expert who will testify that the standard of care requires the use of contrast media in CT screening. In cases where contrast media is used and a patient sustains death or other serious complication resulting from the contrast media, the plaintiff's attorney may well be able to retain a well-credentialed radiology expert who will testify that the standard of care requires that radiologists not administer contrast media when performing CT screening.

[10] CT Screening : Present Status and Future Directions

The CT screening "craze" that descended upon the radiologic community in the 1990s has diminished somewhat. Nevertheless, "screening centers" still populate many cities in the nation and radio, television, newspaper, and magazine advertisements continue to urge men and women who are asymptomatic to come in to a nearby radiologic facility and undergo CT screening in order to determine whether they are harboring a small cancer that, if left undetected, would result in the patient's death.

Unlike conventional radiologic practice in which patients are referred to radiologists by other physicians for radiologic examinations, CT screening

---

media reported spontaneously to the U.S. Food and Drug Administration, 1978-1994: effect of the availability of low-osmolarity contrast media. *Radiology* 1997;204:33-337.

[232] American College of Radiology. ACR practice guideline for performing and interpreting diagnostic computed tomography (CT). In: *Standards* 2001-2002. Reston, VA: American College of Radiology 2007:65-69.

[233] Fishman EK, Horton KM. Screening strategy joins contrast, noncontrast scans. *Diagnostic Imaging.* June 2002;24(6):45,47.

studies are usually conducted on patients who refer themselves to radiologists, specifically because of these newspaper and radio solicitations. Many of these solicitations are advertisements containing headlines and texts that explicitly or implicitly infer that the accuracy of the CT is perfect or near-perfect, and that the detection of early disease or cancer will assure cure of these maladies.

Solicitations for CT screening have been characterized as "scare tactics to promote a particular behavior"... "Get screened today!", or "You can't see it or feel it, but you may have cancer"... "These messages make it clear that no one is really healthy"... "These aggressive tactics may convey a false sense of the magnitude and certainty of the benefits of interventions, engendering unrealistic expectations."[234]

In order to reach a decision about whether to undergo a screening CT, patients will have to be educated by their physicians. As has already been pointed out, in the case of screening CT the self-referred patient's physician will be the radiologist. Therefore radiologists, whether they be proponents or opponents of CT screening, will have to divorce themselves from their personal feelings about screening and provide unbiased information to patients about the procedure.

Clearly, the physician's allegiance is toward the individual patient and must be directed to fostering and championing what is best for that patient.[235]

The public is demanding now more than ever before complete and accurate information regarding medical diagnostic testing, and they may seek assistance from the courts if they fail to receive that information.

Patients who come to expect that CT screening tests will without exception detect all diseases in their earliest stages that they may harbor, and that that disease will be cured, may well respond with a malpractice lawsuit if those expectations are not met.

No one can predict with any degree of certainty whether CT screening will survive over the next decade. However, what can be predicted with reasonable certainty is that if CT screening does continue to grow, the types of allegations of alleged wrongdoing will also grow.

---

[234] Schwartz LM, Woloshin S, Welch HG. Risk communication in clinical practice: putting cancer in context. *Monogr Natl Cancer Inst* 1999;25:124-133.

[235] Murphy EA, Butzow JJ, Suarez-Murias EL. *Underpinnings of medical ethics.* Baltimore: The Johns Hopkins University Press, 1997:374-375.

CHAPTER 10

PLASTIC SURGERY

William J. Mangold, Jr., MD, JD

SYNOPSIS

§ 10.01. Introduction

§ 10.02 Plastic Surgical Procedures
- [1] Blepharoplasty
- [2] Facelift
- [3] Facial Chemical Peels
- [4] Rhinoplasty
- [5] Cosmetic Lip Augmentation
- [6] Breast Reconstruction
- [7] Breast Reduction
- [8] Mastopexy
- [9] Breast Augmentation
- [10] Abdominoplasty
- [11] Suction Lipectomy
- [12] Autologous Fat Graft Injections
- [13] Otoplasty
- [14] Skin Grafts
- [15] Cultured Epithelial Autographs
- [16] Hair Transplants
- [17] Soft Tissue Augmentation
- [18] Treatment of Skin Cancer
- [19] Silicone Implants in Hand Surgery
- [20] Removal of Tattoos
- [21] Botulinum Toxin Injections

§ 10. 3 Related Topics
- [1] Pressure Ulcers
- [2] Blood Transfusions
- [3] Emergency Coverage, Services
- [4] Medical Spas

§ 10.01   Introduction

Plastic surgical procedures have been performed for thousands of years, the first reported procedures beginning with attempts to reconstruct the nose, which was frequently lost in ancient times either to disease, in warfare, or from criminal punishment. In the middle ages, the Italians dealt with the problem using arm flaps, rather than forehead flaps, which had previously been used. However, it took the trench warfare of World War I for plastic surgery to come into its own as a distinct specialty.

The word "plastic" is taken from the Greek "plastikos," meaning movable. Thus, the name of the specialty did not arise from the use of alloplastic or nonbiologic implants, as many suggest. Rather, the plastic surgeon became that surgical specialist most involved with the moving of tissue from one place to another, initially to attempt to reconstruct the ravages of disease or trauma and more recently for cosmetic purposes.

In this chapter, the traditional distinction between "reconstructive" and "cosmetic" will be maintained. That is, a "reconstructive" procedure is one that is designed to improve form or function that is, to the average observer, <u>outside</u> the limits of "normal." On the other hand, a cosmetic procedure is one intended to improve that which the nonbiased observer would consider to be <u>within</u> the range of "normal."

Although the distinction between the two types of procedures will be retained for the purposes of this discussion, virtually all procedures undertaken by the plastic surgeon have a cosmetic component to them. That is, even when functional return is the chief motivation for the surgery, there remains an inherent cosmetic component to all but the most limited of such procedures. On the other hand, procedures that are routinely considered "cosmetic" can, nevertheless, often contain functional components. Thus, the dividing line between the two is somewhat blurred. It is important, therefore, to keep in mind in evaluating any plastic surgical procedure that both cosmetic and reconstructive elements must be considered.

Plastic surgical training originally required, as a prerequisite, completion of a general surgery residency. In the past couple of decades this has evolved into a requirement of either three years of general surgery residency or completion of training in one of the following: otorhinolaryngology, urology, orthopedic surgery, or obstetrics and gynecology.

Board certification requires passing both a written and oral examination and these can be applied for only after a required period of time in practice.

Plastic surgeons have traditionally presented relatively good risks for their liability insurance carriers. Although complaints and case volume have been somewhat high, severity of injury has not been. However, with an increasing volume of cosmetic surgical procedures, coupled with increased patient demand, and increased advertising of cosmetic surgery, an increase in the number of claims filed and amounts recovered can be anticipated. The highest risk areas appear to involve breast surgery and facial scars.

Additional factors have entered the equation for potential Plastic Surgery risk and liability since this chapter was first penned several years ago. Noted above are the "classical" educational requirements for a plastic surgeon. Today, quite frequently — some would suggest as likely as not — cosmetic procedures are performed by practitioners who just a decade or two ago would not have been considered by either patients or the profession to be candidates for carrying out such operations. Perhaps some such procedures are being included in residency training, but the vast majority of those to which I refer — family physicians, emergency physicians, dermatologists…the list has become quite long — learn the cosmetic part of their practices from short courses presented widely across the country. Or, they simply visit a purported "expert" to learn his/her techniques over a period of a weekend to perhaps a week or two.

Generally, these procedures have not changed in this transition from being done by fully-trained plastic surgeons to becoming the province of those who have developed their expertise in a much more informal setting. However, it has become my impression that quite often what is missing is a fully-formed sense of ideal patient and procedure selection. Egregious examples might be cases where a patient has significant complications, even death, from undergoing too many procedures at the same sitting or having too much tissue removed in an overzealous liposuction procedure. It is this potential lack of appreciation of "the big picture" involving a surgical approach that warrants close scrutiny when you are examining the facts of an untoward result with an eye toward possible liability.

Also a factor to be considered is the emergence of the "Spa" approach to cosmetic procedures. We are seeing a blurring of the line between medical care and cosmetic procedures undertaken by nonmedical personnel, either with or without close medical supervision/collaboration. This can be clearly seen by a brief reference to the Yellow Pages or the four-color ads in many local attraction magazines available in most communities. This is not to say that such procedures as "cold" lasers or botulinum injections are not adequately performed in such settings, but it does raise issues which include training, licensure/certification, expertise and appropriate patient and procedure selection.

§ 10.02 Plastic Surgical Procedures

[1] Blepharoplasty

Blepharoplasty, or "eyelid lift," is a commonly performed cosmetic procedure.[1] In evaluating a problem following blepharoplasty, the first focus of attention should be on the preoperative patient evaluation. Patient age, either young or old, is not a contraindication to the procedure, so long as the patient is in acceptably good health. The procedure is most often done on patients from the thirties to the sixties, but may be appropriate in some much older or younger.

The preoperative assessment of visual acuity is of special importance if some visual disturbance is noted postoperatively. A formal ophthalmologic examination is not generally necessary; usually having the patient read from a magazine in the office, coupled with a reasonable visual history, is adequate, unless other problems are apparent. Since there are systemic diseases that can be detected by abnormal findings in tissues of the eye, if there is any question about the involvement of systemic disease, the plastic surgeon should either evaluate these or have the patient examined by his or her primary care physician, or, if circumstances warrant, an ophthalmologist.

The patient should also be evaluated for "dry eye." As humans age, many develop inadequate production or distribution of tears. This can be accentuated by eyelid surgery. If the condition exists preoperatively, it is only a *relative* contraindication to the procedure, but it must be recognized and appropriate management steps taken. Even without preexisting problems in this area, however, the phenomenon of "dry eye" can exist postoperatively for days and sometimes weeks in the absence of any surgical wrongdoing. The key at this juncture is to keep the eye well-lubricated with such products as "Artificial Tears" until this usually self-limiting condition has resolved.

Complications are usually of short duration and include hematomas under the eyelid-skin flaps that are elevated and undermined at the time of surgery. This is not uncommon and usually does not require re-operation; it is appropriate in most circumstances to allow these to resolve spontaneously, which may take days to weeks. Prolonged ecchymosis (bruising) can develop with or without the presence of a skin flap hematoma. Though distressing, this is transient. Excess tearing, or epiphora is also not uncommon. This

---

[1] Under some circumstances, upper lid blepharoplasty may be covered by private insurance or Medicare because of the visual field defects caused by the drooping of excess eyelid skin across the visual fields, especially laterally. Lower lid blepharoplasty is rarely covered by insurance, especially Medicare, as redundancy of the lower lids rarely causes functional impairment.

usually lasts no more than two to three days, but sometimes longer. Epiphora is usually caused by normal postoperative swelling and edema, but if it persists, an evaluation must be made to determine whether a compromise of the lacrimal, or tear duct mechanism, has taken place.

Ectropion is the eversion of the eyelid margins, and it usually is most pronounced on the lower lids. When long-lasting, it is likely the result of over-resection of eyelid skin, and is of most concern when it occurs in the lower lids. In helping to understand the difference in consequence of retraction of the upper lids as compared to the lower lids, one might keep in mind that humans have muscles that can forcefully lower the upper eyelid, which can "stretch" the lid components if any retraction has occurred from over-resection of skin at the time of surgery. On the other hand, there is no muscle to effectively elevate the lower lid margin, so recovery from over-resection of the lower lid is much more difficult.

Transient ectropion is most commonly the result of swelling and edema, combined with the firmness and contraction of the scar and lid tissues. It will, therefore, generally resolve, but the lid margin, especially of the lower eyelids, might require support with tape from the lateral corner of the eye for several days to (infrequently) a couple of weeks. In more severe cases, placement of a temporary suture to keep the eye closed (usually termed a "Frost suture") may be required for a few days.

Ectropion that results from true over-resection of skin will almost always require surgical revision, most commonly, skin grafting. If this complication has occurred, a careful assessment of the surgeon's preoperative evaluation and planning plus a review of the surgical procedure dictation (to ascertain the method used to determine the amount of eyelid skin to be removed) is mandatory.

Problems with wound healing, thickening, and hypertrophy of scars can occur, but usually are not associated with negligent treatment, and are quite unusual in the eyelids.

Blindness has been reported infrequently. In a series of cases of blindness observed in the early 1980s, it was apparent that the blindness was secondary to pressure on the optic nerve from retrobulbar (behind the eyeball) hemorrhage due to laceration of an arterial vessel by the needle through which the local anesthetic had been injected. This phenomenon is invariably accompanied by severe pain, so such pain warrants immediate examination by the surgeon. Blindness is a surgical emergency, and if this has occurred, it is important to determine how long the surgeon waited before intervening or calling in an ophthalmologist skilled in the treatment of such problems, as rapid decompression of the swelling in the enclosed retrobulbar space can avert permanent visual compromise.

As can be noted from the foregoing discussion, most of the problems associated with blepharoplasty can occur in the absence of negligence. Careful review of the record, including preoperative photographs, and the dictated surgical narrative are useful in determining the quality of surgical care.

Note: This comment on operative note review applies not only to this procedure, but too many "routine" surgical procedures, based on my review of such records over the past 30+ years. Due most likely to a combination of factors (the press of time as surgeons look to maximize their practice volume; electronic records, which can encourage the use of "canned" reports; procedure being done by less-experience, less completely-trained surgeons; or perhaps others), operative reports appear to have become in many surgeon's hands less illustrative of the actual procedure performed on "that patient" on "that day." When reviewing **any** operative report, be especially cognizant of language suggesting all or part of the narrative is "boilerplate" as opposed to having been created contemporaneously with the procedure.

The question of informed consent is, of course, of utmost importance. Patients must be told of all material potential complications, and most surgeons today recommend that the remote possibility of blindness be mentioned to patients unless there are compelling reasons to the contrary. One possible corollary to the "lack of time" issue mentioned above is the reality that many surgeons now use their nurse or Physician's Assistant (PA) to conduct much of the informed consent discussion. The surgeon **must** personally receive the patient's informed consent for any surgical procedure; much of the procedure description and discussion of those items the patient should expect to occur can well and more efficiently be handled by ancillary personnel, but the surgeon must be involved and must give the patient the opportunity to have any additional questions answered. If the records suggests otherwise, that is a cause for concern for anyone reviewing such a record.

[2]   Facelift

The term "facelift," or facial rhytidectomy, can include both the true facelift and a number of ancillary procedures. The procedure has evolved from attempts made as early as in the 1920s to achieve tightness of the skin by excising ellipses of skin from the pre-auricular areas of the cheek. These attempts did not demonstrate long-term effectiveness, so more extensive procedures were tried. Today's procedure has evolved to the point where most primary facelifts involve wide undermining of the skin of the cheeks and neck as well as treatment of the subcutaneous fascia of the cheeks and of the platysma muscle of the neck. This muscle is a broad sheet that roughly extends from the clavicles to the inferior mandibular borders and from the midline to the sternocleidomastoid muscles. Extending the scope of the tissue undermining and advancement part of the procedure are various permutations of the original facelift procedure. The "Subcutaneous musculoaponeurotic space" or "SMAS" dissection led the way in attempts to increase the durability of the procedure by incorporating deeper tissues than just the facial skin. Now in vogue is the "subperiosteal" plane dissection. True "blind" assessment of the results of these more aggressive methods as compared to the classic approach is difficult and, indeed, such results remain equivocal in most hands.

In evaluating these cases, review of preoperative photographs, patient complaints, and the surgeon's observations are necessary. The procedure may be done slightly differently, depending upon where the chief area of complaint lies (neck, jowls, cheeks or "all of the above"). The procedure involves an incision that extends from high in the temporal hair-bearing scalp area in a curved line to the top of the ear, then along the immediate pre-auricular line, curving up behind the lobule or inferior portion of the ear, and then extending posteriorly into the occipital hair-bearing scalp. In the classical facelift, the cheek and neck skin are undermined to within about one centimeter of the corner of the mouth, the nasolabial crease line in the cheeks, and perhaps to the midline in the neck.

Of critical importance is protection of the motor branches of the facial nerve, the main trunk of which exits the skull just behind the inferior portion of the ear and spreads across the face in a pattern roughly similar to that illustrated by holding the spread fingers of the hand with the base of the palm over the ear. As can be seen by this analogy, there are basically five branches to the facial nerve, and all are responsible for the action of the muscles of facial expression. Transection of major branches can leave a cosmetically devastating result, especially if it involves the mandibular (marginal mandibular branch) or frontal branch. The mandibular branch controls the ability to mobilize the corner of the mouth, especially the ability to depress the area of the oral commissure. The frontal branch allows elevation of the brow and forehead. Absence of function of either of these leads not only to weakness or paralysis of the involved muscles, but often an exaggeration of the same function of the muscles innervated by the opposite side, from an unconscious attempt by the patient to compensate for the loss of innervation.

Injury to one or more branches of the facial nerve during facelift is reported at a one- to three-percent incidence, but most plastic surgeons would maintain that permanent loss of function of any branch is not an acceptable complication. Even in situations involving complete loss of motor function of one or more branches during the early postoperative period, function will usually return within days to months, depending on the extent of nerve involvement. As long as one year can be required for complete return of function, which strongly suggests that the weakness was due to neuropraxia caused by bruising or traction on the nerve rather than complete transaction.

If profound weakness has occurred, there should be evidence in the record of a postoperative neurologic evaluation of the patient, including electromyography studies. These can usually give some prognostic indications and are especially useful in reassuring the patient who has a good chance of nerve return.

Where the loss of facial nerve branch function is permanent, subsequent management decisions are controversial. Where an area of large branch transection can be identified, either by surgical exploration or by electromyography testing, nerve grafting has been successful. In cases of loss of function of the frontal branch, some surgeons recommend surgical sectioning of the same branch on the opposite side to avoid the overcompensation described above. Some patients are able to voluntarily limit this "over functioning" of the contralateral undamaged nerve and, therefore, such a relatively drastic surgical procedure is not required. In any event, this injury can be disfiguring and usually results from a preventable incident. Many surgeons, though probably a minority, attempt to avoid motor nerve damage by utilizing a nerve stimulator during the procedure. The necessity for its use remains unproven, thus somewhat controversial.

The more common complications with long-term consequences involve problems with extensive or widened scarring. Such wound healing problems are quite frequent in smokers who do not suspend this habit until wound healing has progressed. One report has cited a 1,400% greater incidence of wound-healing problems in smokers when compared to nonsmokers. If the patient is a smoker, it is mandatory that the surgeon discuss this problem preoperatively and document either that the patient agreed to stop smoking during the perioperative time or that the patient agreed to accept the increased risk of wound-healing problems with its attendant probability of extensive permanent scarring. It should be remembered, however, that some skin wound-margin loss, if limited to the areas of most tension in the skin graft-wound closure (the areas immediately above and behind the ear), can occur in the absence of negligence. Nevertheless, there is ample evidence that the better course of action is to avoid facelift surgery for the patient who is unable or refuses to stop smoking for at least the two weeks prior to and two weeks or so following the procedure. Given patient demands and the exigencies of medical (surgical) practice, that is a course to which not all subscribe.

In the surgeon's attempt to remove as much redundant skin as possible, the precise end point of acceptable wound tension is difficult to assess, especially since it can be affected adversely by unpredictable events such as excessive postoperative swelling. One early postoperative problem that can lead to preventable skin flap loss is hematoma under the skin flaps. This is usually due to bleeding in the first eight to twelve hours postoperatively from one or more arterial vessels that were not adequately controlled during surgery, and which began bleeding once the patient's blood pressure became elevated either from vomiting or pain. This early postoperative bleeding comprises the only predictable postoperative "emergency." If significant bleeding with hematoma accumulation occurs, it is mandatory that any significant clot be removed as quickly as possible. This usually, but not always, requires a trip back to the operating room. If this is not done, the increased wound tension will frequently lead to tissue loss.

Another frequent area of postoperative complaint is residual (or early return of) sagging or wrinkling of the face or neck. This will occur in the absence of negligence in a small but irreducible minimum number of patients. The surgeon has generally dealt with this in advance by pointing out the possibility for need of revision or a "touch up" procedure. Most surgeons do not charge a surgical fee for this, though the patient will generally be required to pay the facility fee and that of any anesthesiology service. The key is whether the patient was informed of the possibility before surgery.

There are a number of procedures that go hand in hand with the straightforward facelift as described above. Brow or forehead lift involves extension of an incision across the frontal scalp from top of ear to top of ear. This can be done either in conjunction with the facelift or as a separate procedure. When done with the facelift, the procedure involves connection of the two superior extents of the facelift incisions as noted above. The entire forehead is then elevated or peeled away from the pericranium or lining that is intimately attached to the frontal skull bone. To create an adequate brow elevation and smoothing of forehead wrinkles, the dissection must be carried inferiorly to a point over the supraorbital rims. There are two sets of muscles, the corrugators and the procerus muscles, that contribute to the deep creases frequently seen in the glabellar or mid-inferior area of the forehead just superior to the upper extent of the nose. If these muscles are not divided or partially removed, recurrence of this creasing is more likely. At times, muscle function will return even after a section has been removed, so it is not a "one hundred percent" successful procedure in any surgical hands.

The deep layer of forehead skin (the galea) lying just superficial to the pericranium must also be incised in order to allow enhanced advancement of the forehead tissue, and many authorities recommend removal of a strip of this tissue in order to further enhance this advancement of the skin margin and to add to the smoothing effect of the forehead. In a complaint of residual wrinkling or creasing of the forehead, the record should be reviewed for evidence in the dictated operative note that these portions of the procedure were carried out.

Over-resection and subsequent over smoothing of the forehead skin can result in over elevation of the brows, leaving the patient with a "startled" expression. In a perfectly executed forehead and brow lift procedure, this condition exists for a few days to three weeks but then subsides. If the condition is permanent, it can represent a significant cosmetic defect and can require reoperation to attempt anterior advancement of the scalp to lower the incision of the forehead lift. This is not always successful.

The incision for the forehead lift is ideally placed in one of two locations: either along the anterior or frontal hairline or, more posteriorly, within the hair-bearing scalp. The advantage of the former is that it does not elevate the hairline, but it does cause a scar that is more or less visible, depending on resolution of the scar tissue and on the patient's hairstyle. The advantage of the more posterior incision location is that the scar is not visible under normal circumstances. This incision does, however, result in elevation of the frontal hairline. In someone with a receding or a "high" forehead, this may not be advantageous. In any event, the decision should be made preoperatively, and the records should include some discussion on this point. A third alternative for incision placement is to locate it within a transverse wrinkle line of the forehead. This is more frequently done in men than women, since the creases are usually deeper in males, and the male can frequently better tolerate a visible scar (though it frequently heals to the point of near-invisibility). Performed in this fashion, the procedure is slightly less technically difficult because of the limited amount of skin that must be elevated, and, of course, the incision does not affect the hairline. A fourth option, and one that is generally a less attractive option, is to excise a lenticular-shaped area of skin and soft tissue from immediately above the brows, placing the resulting scar at the superior edge of the brows. This can be used to elevate only the brows, leaving the rest of the forehead, as well as the hairline unaffected. But the resulting scars can be unsightly and can require many patients to wear makeup to disguise them — not an acceptable for most male brow lift patients.

Most surgeons now include some treatment of the platysma muscle during the routine facelift procedure. However, this depends on preoperative assessment and discussion. This is done to attempt to alleviate the sagging at the neck and jowl line, which is attributed to sagging of the platysma muscle, or platysma "banding." This is a partial cause of the "turkey gobbler" type of chin defect, although this problem also involves excess skin. There are a number of different platysma-tightening procedures described in the medical literature. As is so often the case in any surgical procedure, the reason for the existence of multiple methods is that no one method works perfectly in all cases for all surgeons. In the best of hands, some residual, or perhaps recurring, platysmal banding can occur, and if it was present preoperatively, this should have been explained during the informed consent discussion. It probably would not be acceptable in the 21st century to do a facelift on a patient with platysmal banding and not deal directly with the platysma in some fashion.

As mentioned earlier, some plastic surgeons advocate a deeper plane of dissection in the cheek portion of the facelift. This is termed the SMAS, an acronym for subcutaneous musculo aponeurotic space. Some say this procedure gives a longer-lasting beneficial effect, but many surgeons have tried it and then returned to the classical cheek dissection because of a failure to observe significant improvement coupled with increased operative time and increased risk of injury to facial nerve branches. The plane of dissection in this case is immediately superficial to the parotid gland.

A lesser number of surgeons have elected to utilize, in some cases, what they call a sub-periosteal facelift. In this procedure, the facial area is approached through an incision above the zygomatic arch or "cheekbone," and dissection is carried out deeply into the periosteum and, consequently, to the branches of the facial nerve. Thus far, there have been insufficient studies of this procedure for a clear determination as to its advisability.

In summary, "facelift" involves the elevation of neck and cheek skin, with the possible inclusion of the ancillary procedures discussed above. A careful preoperative evaluation of each patient, with tailoring of the specific procedure or procedures to that patient's needs, is critical. The procedure must be done with careful attention to avoiding complications. Complications, should they arise, must be managed in an appropriate manner to prevent long-term postoperative sequelae.

[3] Facial Chemical Peels

Facial chemical peels, using primarily a phenol-based peeling solution, have been used in this country for at least five decades; however, there now appears to be an increasing incidence of complaints surrounding this procedure. This increase may be due simply to increased marketing by the many practitioners who offer this procedure. This increase in complaints also coincides with the development of alternative peeling solutions, most of which are milder and are expected to have a corresponding lower incidence of complications, such as scarring and major pigmentation alterations., it appears that patient expectations have not been consistently fulfilled in this regard. Nevertheless, the frequency of performance of the numerous variations of "superficial" peels, many highly-advertised as "lunchtime" procedures, offering assurance that the patient can go back to work that afternoon, or certainly the next day, is booming. Many of these have also become a part of the armamentarium of the cosmetic procedure spas noted earlier.

When a patient complains about an unsatisfactory chemical peel, the issue of informed consent becomes paramount in evaluating the case. Altered pigmentation of treated areas is a virtually universal result. The patient should be made aware of this preoperatively and informed that either hyper- or hypo pigmentation can occur, and that this complication may be largely outside the control of the physician. There are, however, some predictive factors—such as type and color of the patient's skin preoperatively—so patient selection is important. (For example, phenol peels have generally been considered inappropriate in darker-skinned patients.)

The patient's medical record should contain: (1) the specific instructions or "program" prescribed to the patient; (2) the identity and strength of the peeling solution; and (3) documentation on follow-up care. Evidence in the records that patient compliance was monitored may be a key component in evaluating the care rendered. For example, in a complaint of hyperpigmentation, the patient's condition could have worsened from overexposure to the sun. The records should show whether instructions to limit sun exposure were given to the patient and whether there were periodic inquiries to see that the patient was following these instructions.

[4] Rhinoplasty

Rhinoplasty is usually a purely cosmetic procedure that involves alteration of the size and contour of the nose by treatment of the bony and cartilaginous skeleton of the nose and, in some cases, skin resection. The "final" result (*i.e.*, for the skin and soft tissue to completely settle over the revised framework) can take as much as a year or more. This procedure carries, even under the best of circumstances, an approximately ten percent rate of revision, or "touch up."

Evaluation of the medical records of a rhinoplasty begins with the review of the patient's complaints about his or her nose preoperatively and the surgeon's assessment of these complaints. Many surgeons use preoperative photographs to make a permanent record of the patient's condition and for discussions with the patient during preoperative planning. A number of surgeons now use (and many widely advertise that use) a video camera and computer software to graphically demonstrate proposed surgical change options to allow the patient to "see" the changes that the surgery anticipates; however, failure to use such technology does not call into question the surgeon's preoperative assessment. In fact, many still feel that their use represents an arguably unwise "guarantee" of results. Though this technology has become quite good at showing the effects of bony contour alteration, a surgeon who uses this technology should always inform the patient of the limitations of this method of visualizing anticipated results.

Preoperative discussion should include proposed treatment of the nasal dorsum, nasal tip, nasal base, columella, and (not strictly a component of "rhinoplasty") the septum.

If major alterations of the height or width of the bony dorsum are to be undertaken, it will require fracturing of the nasal bones. This is done intraoperatively, either by use of a chisel or saw. Most authorities recommend the chisel because the saw can add to stability difficulty postoperatively due to excess bone obliteration. Nevertheless, this is a personal decision on the part of the surgeon, and either approach is appropriate. The basic approach is to view the nasal dorsum as a pyramid, with the intent being made to take off the top of the pyramid and narrow the walls, thus creating a shorter pyramid. In doing this, some shortening of the cartilage of the nose is also required, both from (possibly) the nasal tip and (more likely) the lateral walls, as well as the septum. Leaving a redundant edge of this cartilage is a frequent cause of postoperative dissatisfaction with the rhinoplasty.

Treatment of the nasal tip can be complex, and there are numerous approaches to it. If the tip is too full, resection of redundant portions of the alar cartilages is undertaken. Where there is a lack of sufficient prominence of the tip, some type of grafting may be done, using cartilage from the alar resections, the septum, or the ear. A complete discussion of the proposed surgery should appear in the preoperative record, and the operative dictation should clearly outline the approach taken. However, since the margin of difference between an "excellent" and a "poor" rhinoplasty result is measured in terms of only a few millimeters at most, the dictation may not shed sufficient light to adequately assess the reason for a poor result. The better method of evaluation in these cases is to compare pre- and postoperative photographs and obtain the evaluation of another surgeon.

Most problems involve complaints about the patient's postoperative appearance rather than any clearly defined "complication." Commonly involved complaints are under-resection of nasal bones and dorsum, leaving some redundancy of the dorsal hump; inadequate narrowing of the dorsum, leaving a flattened apex of the dorsum or top of the "pyramid"; under-resection of alar cartilage, resulting in residual fullness or unacceptable bulbous quality of the nasal tip; over-resection of alar cartilage, resulting in inadequate support to the alar rims, which can be manifested by creation of a valve mechanism wherein the alar rim is "sucked" against the nasal columella, effectively blocking the air flow when the patient forcefully inhales.

Over-resection of the cartilaginous dorsum leads to what is characterized as a "saddle-nose deformity." Unless there is some dire complication, such as infection of the cartilage, this does not occur absent some inadequacy in the way the procedure was carried out. Reconstruction of this significant defect is difficult and not always successful.

The most common skin resection in a rhinoplasty involves resection of wedges of skin and subcutaneous tissue from the lateral bases of the nostrils where they attach to the cheeks. This has the effect of narrowing the base of the nose and usually leaves an insignificant scar. Under-resection requires only revision and removal of additional tissue. Over-resection, on the other hand, is difficult and sometimes impossible to correct. It usually necessitates composite grafting and leaves a second scar. For this reason, most such resections are not aggressively attempted.

Cartilage grafting is most commonly done to attempt enhanced definition of the nasal tip. Failure to achieve a complete success in this attempt should not be considered beneath the standard of care, except in exceptional circumstances. It is difficult, if not impossible, to adequately assess the amount of relaxation, contouring, or stretch of the nasal tip skin that will occur with the use of cartilage grafts. If the graft is too prominent postoperatively, it can easily be trimmed as a "touch-up" procedure. If its alignment is lost, it can be realigned. If it has under corrected the defect, it can be redone—although if septal or alar cartilage were used from tissues resected for therapeutic reasons at the time of the original surgery, such tissues are not likely to be available for a revision procedure, necessitating use of ear cartilage. This procedure, however, leaves an insignificant scar on the posterior surface of the ear, so it is not of great consequence. The combination of skin, soft tissue, and limited cartilage resection can be done in correcting a drooping columella (structure separating the two nostrils); however, this is less commonly done and must be justified by the existence of a significant preoperative cosmetic concern.

Treatment of the septum is entirely separate from the cosmetic rhinoplasty, although is frequently done in conjunction with it. The most frequently performed septal procedure, either septoplasty or limited septal resection, is the correction of an airway obstruction that has occurred from the protrusion of the septum into the airway on one side or the other (or sometimes both). Since this causes a functional breathing problem, its correction is covered under the terms of many insurance policies. In fact, data suggest that some surgeons will, in some cases, allege a functional airway obstruction, treat the septum in some way, and then carry out a cosmetic rhinoplasty and submit charges for the "functional" repair to the patient's insurance company. Some carriers claim this is a frequent occurrence.

It is difficult and not generally worthwhile to establish a septal deformity clearly and graphically reproducibly by most preoperative evaluations, since photographs of the area are difficult and outside of the scope of practice of most surgeons. Few would argue with the necessity for any other kind of study to evaluate a nasal airway breathing difficulty. Therefore, it is incumbent on the reviewer of the record to evaluate the patient's postoperative condition in light of the preoperative assessment and the operative report, bearing in mind that this is a "gray" area in terms of record documentation.

[5]   Cosmetic Lip Augmentation

Although injectable collagen has been used for treatment of depressed scars and wrinkle lines of the face, the use of commercially available injectable collagen for lip augmentation has decreased. When the entertainment media responded to stories of well-known actresses using this method to give them a "pouty lip" appearance, some physicians began using collagen injections for their general patient population. The Food and Drug Administration (FDA) acted promptly to remind the largest commercial supplier of this product that the procedure was a nonauthorized use of the product, and the company in turn notified practitioners that it would no longer market the product for that purpose (if in fact it had previously done so).

The collagen product was ill-suited for this purpose. It has been well-demonstrated that any beneficial effects are transient, and that the patient must be reinjected at intervals of a few months to perhaps as many as two years in order to maintain any of the benefits of the injections. With this background, many plastic surgeons began looking for other ways to achieve this enhanced appearance.

Autologous fat graft injections (see § 10.02 [12]) are now used with increasing frequency in attempting to achieve a fuller lip. This is desirable not only to enhance the appearance of the youthful face, but also for treatment of a thinning of the vermillion mucosa of the lip, a condition that accompanies aging.

In the last few years, other products designed for augmenting the projection of the lips have been developed and extensively marketed to cosmetic surgeons.   Some involve "weaving" of thread(s) of synthetic material such as Gore-tex®, others use injections. Results can be dramatically good, but can also be seen as leaving the patient with a rather unsightly and distinctly "abnormal" appearance. Beauty truly is in the eye of the beholder, however, and the use of these procedures continues to grow.

A surgical approach to the problem of thin lips that has been demonstrated to be of benefit is "augmentation cheiloplasty." In this procedure, the visible margin of the lip is enhanced by advancing the mucosa of the inner surface by use of a "W plasty" sliding-advancement flap. The results are generally less dramatic than with injection of autologous fat grafts, but early experience suggests that the outcome is more predictable and may well be longer-lasting on an overall basis.

[6] Breast Reconstruction

Breast reconstruction following mastectomy has become a common operation. As recently as the early 1980s, the goal of the surgery was simply to attempt to replace a breast "mound," rather than achieving a reconstructed breast bearing any close resemblance to the one that was lost. However, with an evolution of technique and experience, today, most patients can expect to achieve a reasonably "normal"-appearing breast. The reason for the quotations around "normal" is that there will always be scarring of the breast, either the original mastectomy scar or more extensive scarring if distant tissue flaps have been utilized. Also, in a mastectomy for cancer, the nipple and areola have always been surgically removed. Though the reconstructed nipple areola complex can often look quite realistic, it will have circumferential scarring and usually will be readily distinguishable from its normal preoperative appearance. Evaluation of a surgical result depends in large part on the preoperative expectations established by the surgeon and patient.

Reconstruction options begin with simple placement of a breast prosthesis, much as would be done in a cosmetic breast augmentation, although in virtually all circumstances, placement under the pectoralis muscle is mandatory to avoid compromise of vascular circulation to the skin flaps and for protection of the prosthesis against extrusion through the mastectomy scar. Nipple areola reconstruction can be done in these procedures, but is not mandatory. As the procedure methodology has improved, more women now elect to have nipple areola reconstruction than two to three decades ago. In virtually all situations today, it should at least be offered as an option to the patient.

Next in line of reconstructive procedures, in terms of invasiveness, is the use of tissue expanders. In this method, an inflatable breast prosthesis is inserted in a pocket beneath the chest. Skin and muscle are then expanded over a period of weeks with saline injected through the skin and through a valve mechanism in the implant. This is used in situations where inadequate soft tissue remains to allow placement of the correctly sized prosthesis as an initial procedure, but for which sufficient tissue exists to allow gradual stretching so that an appropriately sized implant can subsequently be placed. These prostheses can be designed to remain permanently in place. The decision as to whether to use this implant or one that must be replaced is made by the surgeon after consultation with the patient.

Obviously, choices available to the patient and her surgeon have become more varied with the FDA's removal of the moratorium on approval of silicone breast implants, which were taken off the market during the early 1990s in what most (all?) unbiased observers believed then and continue to believe was an unwise and unwarranted decision, based on spurious allegations at best.

The third and most complex method of breast reconstruction utilizes distant flaps. There are a number of such flaps, and a discussion of their selection is beyond the scope of this chapter. There are, however, some basic points in evaluating an unsuccessful result. With the availability of tissue expanders, the primary need for distant tissue flaps occurs when there is insufficient skin and soft tissue in the chest for an even gradual expansion sufficient to allow formation of a breast. Many surgeons would hold that the standard practice requires that if a flap is to be used, it should be of sufficient bulk to preclude the need for a breast prosthesis. During the 1990s and early 2000s the residual negative media coverage surrounding the use of silicone implants led many women to elect the flap approach to reconstruction even though it requires a more extensive surgical procedure. This trend may well reverse as silicone implants have once again become available. Probably the most widely used flap procedure now is the TRAM (transverse rectus abdominis myocutaneous) flap. Developed in the 1970s and well-described in the 1980s, it involves use of the lower abdominal skin, being based on an arterial pedicle contained within the vertically oriented rectus abdominis muscle. The skin taken for the breast reconstruction closely corresponds to that which normally would be removed in a "tummy tuck," or abdominoplasty procedure, which is tunneled under the remaining upper abdominal skin and inset into the chest wall defect left by the mastectomy. This and other myocutaneous flaps can also be transferred as "free" flaps where the vascular supply is completely transected in the transfer portion of the procedure, then reanastomosed by microvascular technique—a much more complex and time-consuming process. Due to the complexity of this procedure (either done with vascular supply remaining as an intact pedicle or with microvascular technique), adequate preoperative evaluation is more critical than with other methods. In any event, the patient should be psychologically equipped to deal with the stress of the procedure, as well as the postoperative recovery period, which may extend up to three months before the patient can return to unlimited activity. This surgery may also involve revision or "touch-up" procedures.

[7] Breast Reduction

Reduction mammoplasty (breast reduction) is designed to accomplish two primary goals, reduction in size and bulk of the breasts and elevation of the nipples/areolae to a non-ptotic (or non-sagging) position. The procedure has been done with increasing frequency over the past three decades. There are a number of different approaches to this surgery, each of which has advantages and disadvantages.

The patient's complaints usually involve symptoms related to the size and weight of her breasts. Back and neck pain, bra shoulder-strap pain, and frequent skin rashes of the upper abdomen and inferior breasts. A frequent secondary complaint is that the patient has difficulty finding clothing that fits. Because of the functional problems with overly large breasts, most third-party payers, private insurance companies as well as Medicare, will consider insurance reimbursement for the procedure. Each insurer has its own set of criteria that must be met in order to allow payment, which is generally made on a case-by-case basis.

Patient selection depends on her general health, her complaints, and the size of her breasts, especially relative to her body size. Thus, a breast that would not be appropriate for reduction on a large woman might be for a much smaller individual.

Selection of surgical technique generally depends on physician preference. As techniques have evolved, some surgeons have become more comfortable with one type of procedure over another, and most are appropriate in most circumstances, as long as the technique is correctly carried out.

The primary concern is survival of the nipple/areola complex, which must be transposed to a more superior position in correcting the large, ptotic (drooping) breast. This is generally done by transposing it on its own vascular pedicle, the location of which varies, depending on the procedure. Some surgeons elect to remove the nipple/areola at the beginning of the procedure and replace it as a full-thickness graft. The advantage of this approach is that survival odds are increased, but there are some disadvantages, such as hyper- or hypo pigmentation of the areola, which has the healing characteristics of a full-thickness graft. There is usually some decrease in contractibility and projection of the nipple, as well as significantly diminished sensation to the nipple/areola area as compared to the pedicle transfer method.

Whichever method is used for preservation of the nipple/areola complex, the next most critical parameter of success is the preoperative measurement and determination of incision lines, and point of placement of the nipple. If the incisions and skin flaps are poorly designed, the nipple placement will not be ideal, and, in fact, the nipple can ultimately point downward, upward, or even be more medially or laterally placed than normal. The record should demonstrate that measurements were taken with the patient in a sitting or standing position prior to being taken to the operating room, and that marks were made so that they would be preserved during the prepping and draping of the patient. If this has been carried out and inappropriate placement of the nipple has resulted postoperatively, the operative note should be meticulously examined to see if the surgeon departed from the preoperative plan during the course of the procedure. Such a departure, except in very specific instances, is distinctly beneath the standard of care and is criticized by virtually all authorities in the field. Despite this proscription, however, "second-guessing" of the surgeon's preoperative plan intraoperatively remains a common cause of malpositioning of the nipple.

Apart from misplacement of the nipple, the most common complications are hematoma and partial loss of skin flaps or wound margins. This can occur with skin flaps that are dissected too aggressively and left too thin for an adequate blood supply (given the tension attendant to the wound closure) and also can be caused by unexpected and largely unpreventable swelling postoperatively. If a significant hematoma occurs, it can compromise circulation, but one of this degree is generally recognized and should be appropriately dealt with prior to the compromise of skin margins.

It is important to understand the role of fluorescein dye still used by some plastic surgeons in evaluating the circulatory integrity of nipple areola, flaps, and wound margins intraoperatively. The use of this dye is based on the principle that, when injected intravenously and given sufficient time (8-10 minutes) to completely circulate through the body, it will fluoresce a chartreuse color on exposure to ultraviolet light if adequate capillary circulation is present. If capillary circulation is not present, the tissue will remain black. This examination is performed by turning off the operating room lights and exposing the skin to a hand-held ultraviolet or "black" light. If this examination demonstrates inadequacy of circulation, something *must* be done at that time if loss of the tissue in question is to be prevented. This intervention can consist of: (1) remove a portion of the sutures; (2) further resect the pedicle to the nipple if its bulk is felt to have resulted in unacceptable wound tension; or (3) in a worst-case scenario (if the nipple and areola appear entirely nonviable) remove the nipple and areola as a full-thickness graft and reapply them (since they would require, at this point, a less reliable blood supply to maintain viability than if they were maintained as a flap as originally attempted). In making this assessment, however, it is important to remember that the fluorescein test cannot be repeated, except that, occasionally, the removal of sutures will allow immediate improvement in the circulation and result in a subsequent fluorescence.

If the fluorescein dye is injected prior to closure of all wounds, no subsequent ultraviolet fluorescence result is of any worth, since the circulation was allowed to occur before wound tension was applied by the closure. The author recently reviewed a case in which the surgeon described using fluorescein, but had it injected before wound closure was complete, thus completely invalidating the result he subsequently obtained.

Early postoperative complications include loss of the tissues described above, and this can occur even with positive fluorescence at the time of surgery. This is usually due to adequate circulation being present at that time, but subsequently lost because of postoperative swelling and edema. If a hematoma has occurred and has not been relieved by surgical drainage or large-bore needle aspiration, and is allowed to remain, the surgeon can be criticized for subsequent wound-margin loss. Absent such a definitive postoperative complication, there is little valid criticism of the surgeon, as long as no demonstrable departure from acceptable technique can be demonstrated. Once such a result occurs, however, conservative management is almost always appropriate. Thus, the surgeon who quickly returns the patient to the operating room for debridement and attempted reclosure of the wound frequently meets with failure, and this is a practice to be avoided. One aspect of review of such wound-healing complications that is often overlooked is to carefully analyze the early postoperative nursing records, if available. There have been unusual circumstances where in retrospect it appeared that resulting tissue loss was at least closely related to such events as the patient (against the advice that all surgeons would have given) positioning herself in a supine position through a large part of the night of the surgery. Given the fact that many, if not most, of these procedures are now done on an outpatient basis, that review becomes more of a challenge. Nevertheless, it is an issue that should be at least considered in these circumstances.

If infection occurs, appropriate cultures should be obtained, appropriate antibiotic treatment started, and adequate drainage carried out. In the event of infection or tissue loss due to vascular insufficiency, generally the appropriate course is to allow healing to occur and then carry out revisions as needed as a delayed secondary procedure some weeks or even months postoperatively.

Early hypertrophy of breast reduction scars is as much the rule as the exception. Any surgical revision or other treatment of these should be delayed to allow adequate time for healing and softening of the wounds and skin flaps, and for maturation of the scars. The scars will, at that point, frequently resolve spontaneously to a degree acceptable by the patient. Alternative treatments following an appropriate delay include steroid injection of the scars or excision revision. If scars, either normal or abnormal, are the patient's primary area of concern, it is an inappropriate complaint unless the subject of scars was not addressed by the surgeon during the preoperative evaluation and informed consent discussion. As is so often the case with major procedures, the patient must be adequately informed as to the expected results (even given an acceptable result, although this is frequently at variance with the expectations that led the patient to consultation with her surgeon). It is interesting, however, that once an adequate preoperative explanation has been given to the breast reduction patient regarding the expected results in terms of contour and scarring, she is usually less critical of the scarring than is her surgeon.

[8] Mastopexy

Mastopexy is carried out in almost the same fashion as breast reduction. The primary difference is that with mastopexy, no breast volume is removed; instead, excess skin is resected and the nipple-areola complex is elevated to a more ideal level. Since the mastopexy is considered more of a cosmetic procedure, rather than one designed to correct the problems associated with large breasts, most surgeons would maintain that more discussion with the patient preoperatively is warranted. Since these patients are usually seeking improved appearance of their breasts, the normal scarring may be of more concern to them, and this problem should be more carefully discussed preoperatively. In women who undergo a mastopexy without augmentation, their frequent complaint is that their breasts are not large enough postoperatively. This is usually because after the ptotic breast is elevated to its normal position and its redundant skin resected, it appears smaller. For that reason, many surgeons recommend insertion of small- to medium-size silicone implants, in addition to the mastopexy, in virtually all mastopexy cases.

With this procedure, as well as with breast reduction, decreased nipple sensation is a factor to consider. The patient should be made aware of this possibility preoperatively, but she can be reassured that the erectile function of the nipple will be retained. Questions of appropriate nipple placement in evaluating the success of this procedure remain the same as in breast reduction.

[9] Breast Augmentation

Silicone breast implants, as originally developed by Dow Corning, have been in clinical use for breast augmentation since the early 1960s, though use was markedly reduced during the period of removal of FDA approval of the use of silicone gel implants during the 1990s and early 2000s. The best estimate reported by the industry and plastic surgeons are that over one and one-half million women in this country have undergone breast augmentation by the use of silicone gel implants either for cosmetic purposes or for reconstruction following mastectomy or, less frequently, as treatment of other causes of breast deformity or marked asymmetry.

Through the first twenty-five years of their use, there was no information available to plastic surgeons suggesting any clinical or experimental evidence of immunological response in the human body to silicone implants. There were, of course, other "complications" reported during these years, the most common being periprosthetic capsule contracture, the incidence of which has been reported to range from 25-50/% of all gel implant patients. This phenomenon caused breasts to be firmer than "normal," ranging from slightly firmer to literally "rock" hard and sometimes painful and immovable. This "capsule," which develops around all silicone objects implanted in the human body, has been observed since the early years of silicone breast implant use, and ranges in thickness from a filmy layer no thicker than cellophane wrap to as thick as one centimeter and, infrequently, even thicker.

Due to its makeup of collagen this capsule also demonstrates contractile qualities, allowing the tissue to contract as well as thicken. It is this contraction around the noncompressible silicone implant that causes the firmness described above. Plastic surgeons initially were frequently been able to release this firmness by simply grasping and squeezing the breast, literally tearing the capsule and releasing its compression of the underlying implant. In some cases this resulted in increased softness of the breast, sometimes returning it to its pre-contracture degree of softness. Ruptures of implants following this procedure were rarely reported, although the incidence was not documented because no controlled studies had been carried out (and probably are not possible). Estimates are that severe capsule contracture may have occurred in as many as 5% of the patients, although most surgeons believed it to be less frequent than that. Reports concerning the newer generation of implants now available under FDA approval and closer scrutiny appear to show significantly less contracture than before. Long-term follow-up of this will remain a critical factor.

Implant ruptures from blunt trauma to the breasts and chest have been a potential problem, and this phenomenon should be mentioned in any informed consent discussion with a prospective breast implant patient. As recently as the 1980s (and prior to the lawsuits and FDA action), it was believed that rupture of silicone gel implants, absent evidence of extravasation into surrounding soft tissues, did not necessarily warrant removal of the implant. The training and experience of many plastic surgeons was that the periprosthetic capsule kept the gel retained within the original breast pocket so it would pose no problem for the patient. Obviously, if a saline-filled implant were ruptured, however, the saline would be reabsorbed in the body, necessitating implant replacement. In today's medico legal climate, any implant in which rupture or leakage of gel is suspected must be removed.

The potential problems related to the soft tissue migration of silicone globules after implant rupture was initially anticipated on the basis of experience with patients who had undergone silicone *injections* for breast augmentation. This was done frequently in Japan in the 1950s and 1960s. Even though it has never been approved in the United States, a number of women also had the procedure in this country. The main problem with the injection approach was that the injected silicone globules never became surrounded by the capsular tissue seen around breast implants. Therefore, the globules tended to migrate, often coalesced, and led to lumpiness of the breasts. Infection also frequently occurred, with the silicone spreading virtually from skin surface to pleura. Although the Japanese literature suggest otherwise, autoimmune diseases in even these disastrous cases were not apparent.

In the last half of the 1980s, several studies in Japan suggested that there might be an immunological response in humans to implanted silicone. These studies were apparently carried out by Japanese researchers because of anecdotal reports on some of the many thousands of Oriental women who had undergone silicone gel breast *injections*.

In 1989, litigation in the United States directed against silicone implant manufacturers resulted in the first jury verdict. In the discovery process involved in this litigation, internal documentation suggesting the possibility of immune system responses to silicone was identified. At least two independent studies seemed to confirm the possibility of some such response, but further research has ultimately refuted that notion. A confounding factor remains that, based on current data, the incidence of autoimmune disease in the breast implant patient population is no greater than the predicted incidence in any otherwise matched population.

In evaluating any medical negligence claim for damages related to silicone breast implants, it is important to keep in mind that there are areas of potential surgeon liability other than, and independent of, the silicone gel immunogenicity problem. The medical record should clearly indicate the surgeon's decision that the patient was a "reasonable" surgical candidate, and that the procedure chosen was likewise reasonable. Depending on the complaints presented, the type and brand of implant are important. Implants that have been available and used in this country include: (1) standard silicone gel within a silicone shell; (2) a double- lumen implant that generally consists of silicone gel within an inner lumen encased by an outer separate lumen, which is filled at the time of surgery with a variable amount of saline; (3) the standard gel implant with a polyurethane foam layer bonded to its outer surface (more on this below); and (4) the only implants currently available for all breast augmentation purposes without requiring formal follow-up reporting — saline- filled implants still utilizing the silicone shell. Also, at least one manufacturer distributed for a limited time in the late 1980s a "saline/gel" implant in which saline (to provide volume increase) was injected directly into the inner core of gel.

The polyurethane foam-covered silicone gel implants gained a flurry of interest in the late 1970s and continued throughout the 1980s to be used by a minority of plastic surgeons because the incidence of capsule contracture appeared to be less than when using the smooth-surfaced standard implants. However, it was also recognized early that the polyurethane foam was "broken down" in the body, and after a period of time ranging from months to possibly three years, the foam covering was found to be virtually gone. Some reports suggested that the incidence of capsule contracture thereafter increased to almost that seen with the use of standard implants. Many surgeons chose not to use the polyurethane foam- covered implants because of this breakdown phenomenon and because they could not be certain as to the fate of this material. Studies reported in the early 1980s demonstrated that polyurethane material causes tumors in rats, although this phenomenon has not been demonstrated in humans. These implants were withdrawn from this market prior to the removal of standard gel implants.

Concerning possible carcinogenicity of silicone gel itself, several studies, including retrospective ones in this country and a large prospective Canadian study, have been uniform in their findings of no causal relationship between silicone gel and breast cancer.

Another currently open question, however, is whether the presence of the implants delays diagnosis of breast cancer. Given the current state of the art of mammography, such an examination of a breast containing a silicone implant is compromised because of the radio-opaque quality of the implant, either gel or saline-filled. However, no study has demonstrated as yet any consistent delay in the diagnosis of breast cancer that develops in breast implant patients.

However, it is **critically important** that the medical record document that the patient has undergone a breast exam by the plastic surgeon **and** a recent mammogram. If she has not received one prior to the plastic surgical consultation, the surgeon should insist that she have one performed prior to the augmentation procedure. Even though up-to-date mammogram technique includes positioning the patient and breasts and taking of multiple views so as to minimize the amount of non-visualized breast tissue, a "baseline" mammographic record will be of significant assistance in the event of the subsequent development of a breast mass or other abnormality.

An unexplained finding in studies seeking a connection between silicone implants and breast cancer is that the breast implant patient population has demonstrated fewer breast cancers than would have been predicted in the normal population. Since silicone would not be expected to provide a protective factor, there is apparently some selection variable in this group of patients that remains obscure.

Numerous studies on breast implants are now ongoing, and it is hoped that, over the next few years, many of these remaining questions will be answered, although it is clear that *no* medical device would ever be expected to be *completely* safe under all conditions of use.

Class-action related litigation involving silicone breast implants was ultimately resolved in favor of the surgeons, in both the federal class action and in state courts. In the cases that did go to trial, the major question was informed consent—whether the patient was informed of all the potential problems with the silicone gel of which the physician had or should have had knowledge. Though the controversy, FDA's misguided removal of the implants from the market and—many would argue—virtual mass hysteria resulted in the bankruptcy of at least one of the primary involved companies, it appears that the breast implant industry is now doing well and the number of women presenting for breast augmentation surgery is greater than ever.

[10] Abdominoplasty

The classical abdominoplasty (tummy tuck) is a major surgical procedure requiring appropriate preoperative assessment of the patient's general physical condition, as well as assessment of the appropriateness of the procedure. Sometimes a protracted period of recovery is required for the procedure (following, in most circumstances, two to three days of hospitalization with the patient at bed rest in a flexed body position). The most common complications involve delayed wound healing and/or hematoma/seroma.

Perhaps the long-term complication with the most notoriety involves the "misplaced belly button." In performing the standard abdominoplasty, the rectus muscle fascia is plicated, or tightened, in the midline to enhance the effect of tightening the abdominal wall and to correct the diastasis recti, or abnormally large separation between the left and right muscles, usually seen in patients who have had multiple childbirths. In carrying out this plication, the muscles must be tightened equally on both sides or the umbilicus will be carried more to one side than the other. In addition, the location of the umbilicus must be carefully marked on the abdominal flap at the time the procedure is begun, and meticulously measured once the opening is made for its reinsetting at the end of the procedure. If either of these measurements is off significantly, it will lead to malpositioning of the umbilicus and is quite disconcerting to the patient. The problem can be corrected later, but will leave additional scarring. Widening of the abdominoplasty scars is frequently seen, because of the tension on the wound edges and the subsequent scar, and cannot be prevented in the routine situation.

Prolonged numbness of areas of the abdominal skin flap is frequent, but sensation will almost always return to normal or near-normal. This problem can occur in the absence of any deficiency in the execution of the procedure.

Surgical drain tubes should be used for at least a day or two postoperatively, because of the significant amount of serous oozing from the large open wound created in elevating the abdominal skin that is advanced downward to replace the skin removed. If drains are in place and seroma or hematoma still occurs, the operative note should be reviewed to determine if the drains were placed correctly. At least a portion of each tube should be placed as far laterally as the section has been carried; otherwise they will not work effectively. In the best of circumstances, some accumulation can occur and must be aspirated or removed by incision and drainage. An accumulation of fluid is not an indication of negligent treatment, but if it is not removed, and subsequently causes problems associated with increasing wound tension, it is an inference of mismanagement.

As with the other major cosmetic procedures, patient selection is frequently the most important criterion in appropriate surgical management. Smoking, as seen in facelift patients, can severely compromise adequacy of capillary circulation to the flap under tension. These considerations have now assumed an even greater importance due to the marked increase in the number of potential surgical candidates—and their demand for the surgery—resulting from the burgeoning growth of the Bariatric Surgery field. With the incidence of obesity in this country and the rapidly developing number of devices and procedures aimed at treating it, this surgery has within the past several years become a major growth industry. Given the economic factors influencing this growth, it is likely that patient selection shortcomings will be identified as the almost-certain litigation related to complications or simply bad results evolves. As of now, there are few reported cases, but that is likely to change.

The necessity for 48 hours of bed rest following abdominoplasty has been associated with the development of thromboemboli of the deep venous system of the legs, which sometimes results in fatal pulmonary emboli. In addition to the judicious postoperative use of anticoagulation, such as provided by low-molecular weight heparin (LMWH) products, either early partial mobilization of the patient, wrapping, or the use of surgical stockings is generally indicated in these cases. Embolization can probably occur even with these precautions, but is quite unlikely. It should be remembered that a history of smoking also is associated with increased pulmonary complications postoperatively. The combination of the pulmonary effect of the surgery and the circulatory problems associated with smoking make it inappropriate to perform the procedure on a patient who has not discontinued smoking for a reasonable period of time preoperatively and agreed to continue to refrain until at least fully ambulatory postoperatively.

[11] Suction Lipectomy

Suction lipectomy (fat suction or suction-assisted lipoplasty) is now probably the most frequently performed cosmetic surgical procedure. It was pioneered in the late 1970s, and since that time, parameters concerning surgical indications, optimal sites of fat removal, and outer limits of volume to be removed have been established—although there are exceptions to these standards.

Suction lipectomy is most appropriately used to remove localized fat deposits. The procedure is not designed or appropriate for use as a means of weight loss. In evaluating unsuccessful cases, careful attention should be given to the preoperative assessment of the patient and his or her goals. The goals should be to enhance contour by removal of fat deposits or areas of "lipodystrophy," which distort "normal" body contours. The more appropriate uses are to treat a slightly to moderately protuberant abdomen or trochanteric lipodystrophy ("riding breeches" deformity). Similar types of contour defects of the knees, ankles, arms, buttocks, and thighs are also appropriate indications for the procedure. Suction lipectomy has also become an important ancillary procedure in facelifts.

The advent of the use of tumescent local anesthesia techniques has allowed this procedure to be done more safely, due to the fact that much less blood loss is experienced. Nevertheless, an assessment of the volume of fat to be removed must be made preoperatively, and if more than 2,000 to 2,500 grams of tissue are to be removed, careful preoperative evaluation and postoperative follow-up must be carried out. Due to the sometimes massive fluid-balance problems attendant to removal of this large amount of fat, even with the use of the improved anesthesia technique noted above, the procedure can sometimes become an inpatient rather than outpatient one. In the judgment of many experts, this point establishes the practical limit for fat removal; they suggest that the procedure be "staged," or performed in multiple smaller procedures rather than risking problems of blood transfusion. However, as competition increases for patients in this relatively technically "simple" procedure, and as patient demand continues to evolve for surgical procedures in a culture where they have become perceived more as commodities for purchase rather than major surgical procedures, corner-cutting will probably increase.

The plans for incisions and the precise areas of suction removal should always be documented in the patient's medical record.

A common complication is "cobble stoning," or a ripple surface deformity of the skin overlying the treated areas. If this problem persists for longer than three months, it is quite likely permanent. Most authorities agree that such a result is avoidable and usually is the result of either using an inappropriately large suction cannula or failing to adequately "tunnel" and "cross tunnel" in carrying out the procedure. With the development of the use of smaller and smaller cannulae over the past decade, this has become much less common. If the complication is marked depression of all or parts of the suctioned area, it is due to over-resection and suggests a departure from the accepted standard of care. The most profound deformity associated with poor technique occurs when over-resection of fat is combined with removal of the tissue in a too-superficial plane, which results in adhesion of the dermal surface of skin to underlying structures and causes depressed "dimpling" of the skin. This can be extensive in a poorly done suction procedure.

Reports in the lay press (and to a lesser degree in the surgical literature) to the contrary, infection — possibly even leading to sepsis — rarely occurs in this procedure and is almost always associated with the perforation of an abdominal viscus by the suction cannula on entering the abdominal cavity. It is beneath the standard of care to have this occur and, more importantly, to fail to recognize and deal appropriately with the problem. At least two deaths in the late 1980s resulted from this complication, but we have seen no similar reports in the past few years.

Because most plastic surgeons have not had residency training in this procedure, a number of seminars and training sessions have been presented across the country, beginning in 1983. In evaluating alleged negligence in a suction lipectomy case, an attorney should determine whether the surgeon attended one of these formal programs or received "hands-on" training from someone who has been adequately trained. Due to the relative technical simplicity of the suction procedure, it is probably performed by more different medical and surgical specialists than any other cosmetic procedure. Depending on the location and size of the city, it is done by plastic surgeons, otorhinolaryngologists, gynecologists, general surgeons, family physicians, general practitioners, and dermatologists, among others. For this reason, one should carefully evaluate the surgeon's training, not only in terms of specific suction lipectomy course work or preceptorship-type training, but also training in basic surgical concepts. Especially in cases of large suction removals, fluid and electrolyte management can be of critical importance to the patient's health and even survival. The technical ability to simply remove the fatty tissue must be accompanied by an appreciation for, and ability to care for, the patient as a whole, and it has been suggested that this is not the case with some practitioners now performing this procedure.

Evaluation of postoperative management is also important in determining the adequacy of treatment of suction lipectomy patients. Pressure garments are almost universally used. Although there is not universal agreement as to length of time for this, most would recommend at least one month. The incisions may or may not be sutured, and this does not appear to determine the acceptability of postoperative scars. However, it is appropriate to place the incisions in skin folds or other inconspicuous places. Hematoma or seroma formation does not indicate an inadequately performed procedure, but may suggest that the pressure garment was not used long enough postoperatively. These are usually self-limiting complications, but they may require needle aspiration.

The preoperative informed consent discussion should involve each of the potential problems discussed above. The patient must also be made aware of the potential for long-term numbness of suctioned areas, and in some cases, especially with suctioning of the lateral thighs, prolonged pain along the distribution of the lateral femoral cutaneous nerve. This can be especially uncomfortable in joggers. Prolonged bruising of the skin can also occur and, in fact, in a small percentage of cases can lead to permanent staining of the skin. This can occur absent any negligent management, but should be mentioned during the informed consent discussion.

In summary, suction lipectomy is relatively simple, although refinements in the "art" of the procedure require significant training, skill, and experience. Complications can range from minor up to, and including, death. Since this is a commonly done procedure, there is little traditional textbook literature on it, but much has been written in journal articles.

[12]   Autologous Fat Graft Injections

Some plastic surgeons are now reinjecting a patient's own fat in small quantities (after removal through the suction technique) to smooth wrinkles and fill out depressions. This has proven potentially useful in treating crease lines of the face, and has found application elsewhere. A few practitioners are attempting this method for breast augmentation. Most, however, would condemn the latter, based on current knowledge.

The most likely complaints following injection of autologous fat grafts involve infection (unlikely) or the reabsorption of the fat and the return of the treated defect (more likely). The issue in both of these complications is usually lack of informed consent. We know that, despite the approach used in preparing the fat for injection (which includes washing it with saline or reinjecting it "as is") as much as fifty percent or more of the injected bulk will disappear over the first few days to weeks. At six months, the majority of patients will retain less than fifty percent of initial improvement. Infection is rare, but is a recognized potential problem and should be discussed preoperatively with the patient. Each patient should be aware that residual contour deficits, either short-term or long-term, are more than just a possibility. Overfilling, or elevation of the injected contour, is less likely, but is possible, especially in the short term.

Autologous fat injections of breasts raise additional concerns. Survival of the injected fat is dependent upon a sufficient blood supply being established. This requires that only small amounts of fat be injected in any one location and that the fat be dispersed where large volumes are to be used. Only a few cubic centimeters are used in most facial injections, but large amounts are required for significant enlargement of the breast. This requires multiple injections, probably over several sittings, and the injections must be widely dispersed through the existing breast tissue. This increases the chance of infection as well as the chance of irregular enlargement (because of greater reabsorption in some areas of the breast than others).

The most serious concern of most practitioners, however, is the development of minute calcifications during the healing process. The problem is that in mammography, which is the most sensitive early breast cancer detection method available, much of its diagnostic capability is based on the fact that the most common detectable characteristic of developing carcinomas is the presence of calcific stippling. If these areas of calcification are the result of autologous fat graft injections, it is feared that early cancer detection will be jeopardized. Since the fat injection procedure is a relatively recent development, and is criticized by most practitioners and since most patients seeking such treatment are not yet at the age for a high incidence of breast cancer, longer-term follow-up will be required before a determination of the real risk can be made. Recent reports of an upsurge of interest in a variation on the original reports of this technique have emerged. Stay tuned.

[13] Otoplasty

Otoplasty is the procedure for the treatment of protruding ears. Commonly referred to as "ear pinning," the procedure is best done for children around age six, by which time their ear growth has achieved approximately eighty percent of adult size. The procedure involves cutting or weakening the cartilage framework of the ear and usually some skin resection. The incisions are made on the posterior aspect of the ears, so there should be no exposed scars except in unusual circumstances.

The incidence of recurrence of the protruding ear defect varies with the type of procedure used, but should be no greater than five to ten percent. The most devastating complication is obliteration of the cartilage framework, which is associated with overwhelming infection. Infection is a recognized complication and occurs in one to three percent of the cases. It can usually be managed by antibiotic treatment and wound drainage, but if the infection is particularly virulent, or if it is not recognized and treated in a timely fashion, the cartilage can literally "disappear," leaving the ear twisted and misshapen.

In evaluating an inadequate correction of the defect, recurrence of the protrusion, or a severe deformity resulting from infection (or, in less common instances, from a hematoma), the review of the preoperative record of the informed consent discussion, as well as meticulous review of the operative note, is critical. If infection is a part of the complaint, dressing, postoperative instructions, and follow-up must also be critically reviewed. In a case in which the author was involved some years ago, a young girl had undergone otoplasty at a teaching hospital late in June and, because of the changeover in residents at the beginning of the next school year, there was a 48-hour delay in follow-up care. What would have likely been an inconsequential infection turned into a devastating complication requiring extensive additional reconstructive surgical procedures.

In evaluating a bad result in which there was no infection, hematoma, or other unusual occurrence, one should compare the operative technique outlined in the surgical procedure dictation with the surgical literature which, in most cases, will reveal whether the appropriate procedure for that patient's defect was carried out. There are procedures still being done that have clearly been shown by the literature and decades of experience to have less than acceptable results when compared to newer methods.

[14] Skin Grafts

Skin grafts are basically of two types: partial (split) thickness and full thickness. In both types, the skin is transplanted by completely removing it from its connection to the body, thus from its blood supply, and insetting it onto the recipient site. Selection of the appropriate graft begins by deciding between split and full thickness. It is important to understand some of the differences between the two types, in order to evaluate the appropriateness of the graft selected.

Split-thickness grafts are thinner, and the wound on which they are placed will contract more than with a full-thickness graft. So, if avoidance of wound contraction is desirable, a thicker graft is usually selected. The split graft, however, can "take," or successfully develop a blood supply, in wounds offering less ideal conditions than those required for the thicker full-thickness graft.

The average split-thickness graft utilized in most practice situations today measures between 0.012 and 0.018 inches. It should be taken from a site that is as inconspicuous as possible. The donor site will heal spontaneously, but is usually permanently visible, appearing as a scarred, hyper pigmented or hypo pigmented area. Under most circumstances, therefore, these grafts should not be taken from areas that would be exposed in most social settings. In addition, unless circumstances require otherwise, the donor site should be in an area protected from pressure or abrasion from sitting or lying. It should be remembered that the donor site is frequently the most painful area involved in a split-thickness skin-graft procedure, so the surgeon should attempt to minimize the pain by carefully selecting the donor site. Under most circumstances, therefore, the lateral buttock is a better donor site than the lateral thigh: both are protected from irritation from sitting, but the thigh is more frequently publicly exposed.

Color matching of the graft is important. All other points being equal, the graft should be taken from an area as close as possible in color to the recipient site. A graft to the face, for instance, should not be taken from the lower extremity unless absolutely necessary. Rather, it should come from the supraclavicular area or scalp, or postauricular sulcus. The upper arm is a reasonable donor site for use on the hands and fingers. The forearm should not be used due to cosmetic considerations.

If grafts must be used in a trauma patient who has had areas of skin avulsed in the injury, this avulsed skin should be considered as the graft donor site at the time of initial surgical treatment. This opportunity does not often occur, but the possibility should not be overlooked.

Full-thickness grafts offer better long-term wear under most circumstances, and color, texture, and contour match are usually better. Whereas the split-thickness donor site can be quite painful, the full-thickness donor site is normally sutured just as any other full-thickness wound would be. Therefore, it is usually much less painful initially and usually heals much more quickly.

Both types of grafts must be effectively immobilized for some period of time — approximately five days under most circumstances. This requires that the graft be held firmly against its "bed," or recipient site, and that shear forces be neutralized. For most purposes, a "bolus" tie-over dressing is advisable. In a bedridden patient in whom the wound and graft are on a convex or rounded surface, such as the anterior leg, the graft may simply be laid on the wound and the wound otherwise left open. This is frequently advisable in a contaminated wound where close observation of the wound would not be possible if it were covered or wrapped. A critical point in evaluation of wound infection cases involving grafts is whether the grafts were placed on a contaminated wound and the wound was wrapped and not inspected carefully at periodic intervals. This occurs often in treating open fractures with skin loss, such as in motorcycle accidents.

Most split-thickness grafts will not have hair growth, whereas many full-thickness grafts will. (Hair follicles are located in the dermis, only a portion of which is transplanted in split-thickness grafts, but all of which is included in full-thickness grafts.) The surgeon must be aware of this fact and should not, under most circumstances, use a graft that will grow hair in undesirable locations. This is especially bothersome when using groin skin, which could ultimately demonstrate pubic hair growth. This problem is generally avoidable.

Most experts agree that fresh grafts should not be exposed to the sun to prevent permanent hyperpigmentation. If hyperpigmentation has occurred, the record should be examined to see if the surgeon warned the patient of this risk.

[15] Cultured Epithelial Autographs

In cases of tissue destruction or removal where the skin- graft donor site is insufficient to allow complete wound coverage, various treatment substances have been tried; none with complete success. Burns are the most typical example of such injuries. In recent years, cultured epithelial autographs (CEA) have become available. In this technique, epidermal cells from the patient are grown in tissue culture and then used as grafts. The technique was first described in the mid-1970s, but only recently have commercial facilities been established that will take the patient's epithelial cells and grow them under the required culture environment.

In some cases, CEA can represent the difference between life and death for a severely burned patient, but the method is quite expensive, and the grafts are unusually sensitive to infection. The technique will likely be improved, become more available clinically, and eventually become less expensive.

[16]   Hair Transplants

There have not been a large number of lawsuits involving baldness treatments. As we have seen with other areas of medical treatment, however, this may change.

For an initial evaluation of complaints about baldness treatment, the patients' history should be reviewed to ascertain the cause of the original baldness. Next, the precise means of treatment should be identified. The earliest commonly used method of surgical replacement of lost hair was transplanted plugs of hair-bearing scalp, usually taken from the sides of the head (temporoparietal area). These consisted of approximately 4 mm plugs, harvested with what was essentially a miniature "cookie-cutter," or punch. Similar-sized holes were created in the recipients' scalp and the plugs inserted. A later refinement of the procedure utilized strips of scalp taken from the donor sites and then cut into squares, which provided a slightly better volume of hair follicles per plug. A still later development, which can be used alone or in combination with plugs, is the use of hair-bearing flaps of scalp.

Whichever approach is used, informed consent is critical. When plugs are used, all the transplanted hairs initially fall out and then regrow at the same rate as normal scalp hair. However, not all the plugs always survive. Thus, the patient must be aware of the extended length of time required for regrowth, as well as the possibility of loss of some of the transplanted hairs. He also must understand that at least two or three separate procedures will be required to achieve the best possible result. This is because the plugs cannot be placed immediately adjacent to one another and still maintain an adequate blood supply to assure a successful "take." The flap approach, though a more involved procedure, requires less time to achieve its ultimate result, but also carries a risk of some loss, especially at the tip of the flap, where the blood supply is limited.

In evaluating results, one must look at the method utilized and the mechanics of carrying it out. Were the plugs of an appropriate size? (If they are too large, they cannot develop sufficient circulatory support soon enough to assure their survival.) Were they "defatted" (thinned) too much? (If so, the hair follicles can be irreparably injured.) Were they placed so as to result in the highest degree of survival and adequacy of coverage possible? (If too close, survival is in doubt; if too far apart, little cosmetic improvement can be expected.) Was the patient prepared for the fact that multiple procedures will be required?

Complications that the patient also should have been made aware of before treatment include bleeding and infection. Though unusual, both can occur and must be managed in a timely fashion. Infection, inadequately treated, can lead to loss of all or most of the plugs, but flaps can usually survive this complication. Most surgeons do not use prophylactic antibiotics, and data generally show that their use is not warranted or helpful.

Many surgeons today would advocate the use of flaps, supplemented by strategically placed plugs, for enhancement of hair margins and for "back-fill" between or behind the flaps.

The reviewing attorney must keep in mind the protracted length of time required for achieving a "good" result. The dissatisfied patient/client should be appropriately counseled if his complaint is premature.

[17] Soft Tissue Augmentation

In the past decade, injectable collagen has been used, primarily by dermatologists and plastic surgeons, for treatment of depressed scars and wrinkle lines, mostly of the face. The material is made of bovine collagen, so it has a potential for hypersensitivity response in some people. For this reason, a skin test, usually injected intradermally in the skin of the forearm, is required. Current guidelines for the use of this product require that a one-month wait elapse between the skin test and institution of therapeutic injections. Even with this precaution, however, a small chance of an allergic reaction remains. Some have recommended two test injections, one month apart, then waiting another month to begin injections. Most surgeons have rejected this option because they feel the delay and added expense are not warranted, given the relatively low risk of a hypersensitivity response. The author believes the better approach is to present the rationale for each approach to the patient, and let him or her make the ultimate decision.

In the use of collagen material, obtaining the patient's informed consent is of paramount concern. In the event of a hypersensitivity response to injections in the face, the patient will likely experience swelling, redness, pruritis (itching), and sometimes serous oozing. This phenomenon is time-limited, however, and can be expected to disappear after a few days or, in the worst case scenario, after a few weeks. Some physicians treat these patients with steroids, but others think this is not appropriate or necessary.

One of the shortcomings of this treatment modality is that the beneficial effects are virtually never permanent. Thus, during the informed consent discussion, the patient should be advised that the injections, even if successful, will have to be repeated at some future date, usually from three to twenty-four months. Most patients seem to require reinjection about every six months.

Patients should also be informed that the injections can be uncomfortable; no local anesthetic injections are used, since they would distort the anatomy of the area to be treated. The commercially available collagen material contains a small amount of lidocaine, a local anesthetic agent, so most patients gain some anesthetic effect as the injections are given. Others, however, have difficulty tolerating them.

There is some evidence to suggest that the use of collagen injections, in rare cases, can be associated with development of collagen vascular diseases, such as scleroderma with dermatomyositis. This evidence is not clear, however, and most physicians who have used the material will probably continue to do so. They should, of course, discuss the possibility of this disease with their patients.

There are physicians, especially plastic surgeons, who do not offer these injections to their patients. Most say that this is not because of the risk of causing disease, but because of the temporary nature of the treatments. The majority opinion at this time, however, which is certainly consistent with the accepted standard of care, is to offer collagen injections to patients as long as they understand all the risks and disadvantages involved.

An attempt to duplicate the smoothing effects on wrinkles and scars seen with collagen injections involves injections of autologous fat "grafts," using small amounts of fat removed from an area of excess elsewhere on the body. Though usually approximately 50% of the transplanted fat is reabsorbed, results can be quite good and cost and risk are minimal. Review of untoward results should focus on location of the grafts, amount transplanted in any one site at any one time and close follow-up in the event of infection or bleeding.

[18] Treatment of Skin Cancer

Skin cancers, primarily the basal cell and squamous cell varieties, are virtually at an epidemic proportion in today's society. Though there are numerous factors involved, the chief common denominator is exposure to the sun. Since it is believed that most patients who develop skin cancers today are doing so because of chronic exposure decades ago, failure to warn is not seen in complaints against physicians, although failure to recognize, diagnose, and refer or treat the cancer is frequently charged against primary care physicians. The focus of complaints against plastic surgeons is primarily in the area of adequate treatment and follow-up care.

The most common skin cancers, and those to which this discussion will be limited, are (in increasing order of severity) basal cell carcinoma, squamous cell carcinoma and malignant melanoma.

Basal cell carcinomas usually can be adequately treated by excision or by cauterization ("burning" them off). Each of these methods statistically carries an approximately 97-98% cure rate. Most plastic surgeons prefer excising small tumors whereas many dermatologists use cauterization. The primary advantage of excision is that a specimen is obtained, which can be examined by the pathologist to confirm the diagnosis and, more importantly, to establish that the margins of resection are clear of residual tumor. In treating by cauterization or electrodessication and curettage, the only notice that residual tumor remains will be its recurrence, months or years later.

Even with involved margins of resection, the incidence of recurrence of basal cell carcinomas is only about 33%. Therefore, even with small amounts of residual tumor retained in the surgical wound, two-thirds of these cancers are "cured" and only one-third recur. This is apparently due to the ability of the body's defense mechanism to deal with the debulked tumor mass. On the other hand, even with clinically and microscopically clear margins of resection, recurrences can occur. This is because basal cell carcinomas can be multicentric, or can spread in a tentacle-like fashion, thus making 100% assurance of clean margins of resection virtually impossible. The importance of making every effort to determine whether residual tumor is present is magnified when the tumor is located near a structure that could be easily deformed by repeated treatment, such as the nose, eyelids, or corner of the mouth.

Tumors located in critical areas as described above are often removed under "frozen-section control." This means that the physician removes the tumor and sends it immediately to the pathologist who examines a portion and freezes the remainder. Determination of surgical margins at this point is not infallible. In fact, given tumor size, type, and location, a false negative determination has occurred in as many as 10% of the cases, though it is usually much less. These false negatives are usually discovered, however, when the pathologist examines the "permanent" sections of the specimen some 24 to 48 hours later. Even then, the physician, in consultation with the patient, may decide to "wait and watch," relying upon the two-thirds chance of nonrecurrence.

Once the tumor has been removed, the question of surgical wound repair arises. If the tumor has been cauterized and curetted, only a small, open wound remains, which many dermatologists will simply allow to granulate and heal. Though this is not the treatment of choice of most plastic surgeons, in most circumstances the results are acceptable. Exceptions are made when the tumor is in areas such as the corner of an eye, an eyelid, the base of the nose, or the corners of the mouth, where small amounts of wound contraction can noticeably distort normal features. In these situations, flap or graft closure may be indicated (simple straight-line wound closure would have much the same result as allowing the open wound to heal on its own). There are usually several available options. Selection should be based on (1) the probability of a functionally and cosmetically acceptable result; (2) the cosmetic and functional result of the donor site (one would not want to create a worse donor site defect than was involved in the original wound, except in unusual circumstances); (3) cost, including patient recovery time. (Here, with other circumstances being equal, a patient might prefer the shorter "return-to-work" period often experienced with a flap as opposed to the frequently longer period experienced with a graft, even though the donor site scar might, ultimately, be more visible.)

Melanoma, generally the highest-risk of the cutaneous malignancies continues to increase in frequency. This is currently believed to be due to the propensity—especially in younger individuals—to get marked overexposure to sun, especially resulting in sunburn. That appears to be the most frequent item of a patient's history when, years later, they develop melanoma. Wide local resection of the tumor remains the most accepted treatment at this time. Dissection of regional lymph nodes remains controversial, even after decades of consideration. Thickness of the primary lesion gives the currently best-available prognosis, though depth of extension ("Clark" level) has also been used and continues to be a relatively good predictor of distant spread. The difficulty with relying totally on level of extension is that it is difficult to precisely ascertain the depth on histological examination.

Mohs surgery, is a method of removing cutaneous malignancies in which the surgeon (usually a dermatologist) acts as both surgeon and pathologist and which can result in a more precise lesion removal, allowing sparing of tissue by limiting the extent of dissection. The "cure" rate of Mohs for basal cell and squamous cell carcinomas is at least equal to—and some data suggest slightly superior to—standard surgical resection. It is also used by a number of Mohs surgeons for treating melanoma, though this remains controversial, owing to the fact that the frozen section technique used for determining the required extent of resection remains questionable in most hands for adequate management of melanoma margins of resection. In reviewing such cases, it is important to confirm the training and experience of the Mohs surgeon, as some have undergone formal fellowship training and others have not.

[19] Silicone Implants in Hand Surgery

Debate continues over the advisability of using silicone implants in hand and wrist surgery. The problem arises from the sloughing of silicone particles into synovial tissues surrounding the implants. This can cause a synovitis, which can lead in some cases to erosion of the bone adjacent to the implants. A 1989 review by the inventor of silicone implants for use in hand surgery reported that 52% of his patients had cystic changes on X-ray after an average of four years. It appears that the incidence of this complication began increasing in the mid 1980s after a new "improved" silicone product had been introduced.

If evaluating a complaint referable to such implants, one should look for the indications for surgery, the type of implant used and, as always, the completeness of the informed consent process, which will vary depending on the clinical information available to the surgeon at the time the procedure was performed.

[20] Removal of Tattoos

Any casual observer will agree that the incidence of tattooing has increased astronomically in the United States in the past decade, for both men and women. The increased interest of younger people in tattoos with the relatively new phenomenon of diminishing of social and workplace stigma attached to them will likely lead to continuation of this increase, at least for the next few years. Unfortunately, requests for *removal* of those tattoos consequently appear to also be on the increase. A number of modalities have been used in tattoo removal, all with varying degrees of success. Dermabrasion or simple excision has been the classic mainstays of tattoo removal, but both methods leave scars. Often, in the case of dermabrasion, these scars can be quite disfiguring. For a patient who desires a tattoo removed, but who is unconcerned with the resulting scarring, the process of dermabrasion can be carried out by the patient himself through "salabrasion," which is literally "rubbing salt into the wound." Surface skin over the tattoo is abraded down to the dermal depth. This reaches the superficially placed tattoo pigment, but also tends to leech out deeper imbedded pigment. I have had patients who have treated themselves in this fashion with relative success, but this technique is not for most patients.

The advent and evolution of laser surgery has added another dimension to tattoo removal. Most of the earlier lasers simply dispersed the pigments, leaving an obvious pigmented area, but one in which the shapes or letters involved in the tattoo were disrupted, thus making it perhaps more socially acceptable. Initial reports suggest that the Q-switched ruby laser and even later laser versions can lead to "almost perfect" results. Long-term follow-up of a large number of patients will be necessary to firmly establish the utility of this approach, but for now it appears to be the predominant method utilized.

In those who are not candidates for, or who cannot afford to pay for, laser therapy, quite large tattoos can be removed through staged excision, in which only a portion of the tattoo is removed initially. The wound is then sutured and several weeks are allowed for the skin tension to relax. The procedure is then repeated. This can be done three or four times without compromising the ultimate result. The same principle is involved in the use of tissue expanders. The expander is placed under normal skin adjacent to the tattoo and inflated over a period of time which stretches this skin. The tattoo is than removed, and the defect is closed. The advantage of the expander technique is that it can usually be done in only two stages. "Downtime" for the patient, total cost, and patient and surgeon preference are all weighed in deciding which, if any, of these techniques is best in an individual case.

[21]   Botulinum Toxin Injections

Botulinum toxin, derived from the bacterium *Clostridium botulinum*, acts as a neuromuscular blocking agent. It is used, with literature support for treating a number of conditions related to muscle spasticity. It is also appropriate for use in treating some cases of hyperhidrosis (excessive sweating). In addition, as of this writing, there are clinical trials in process for assessing its applicability in the treatment of migraine headaches. Obviously, however, quite likely its primary use in today's environment is in the treatment of facial wrinkles. With its action in blocking nerve action as the neuromuscular junction — temporary though it is — it has become the "treatment of choice" for many in reducing the impression of aging imparted by the facial wrinkles related to facial muscle activity. Small amounts of the toxin are injected into areas such as the glabellar area of the forehead, periorbital and perioral wrinkle lines primarily. As such, this area of utilization is strictly cosmetic. In the time since initial publication of this Chapter, the use of botulinum toxin has increased significantly and has spread from being a physician-only provided service to also being provided by other, sometimes non-medical personnel. As noted below, it is at least in some areas a mainstay of the services provided by the "Medical Spas." There are currently two major products on the market, Botulinum A (Botox®) and Botulinum B (Myobloc®). The preponderance of literature currently available concerns the use of Botulinum A, due primarily to the fact that it has been available for several years longer than Botulinum B. Nevertheless, most physicians consider that they are virtually interchangeable, but close scrutiny must be paid to literature support for the particular use that would be the subject of any review you might be involved in. Also, as one recent spate of well-publicized complications — with subsequent criminal prosecution activity — demonstrated, one must also ensure that the product being used is FDA-approved and that its purity and strength must be well established and documented. In that case, unlicensed botulinum product was apparently packaged and sold by a distributor as for human medical use, but was in fact a much stronger preparation of the active ingredient. With any complication arising from the use of botulinum products, invoices and (if possible) assay of the product utilized, in addition to medical records documentation of the volume injected will be important. At the time of this writing, reports are emerging of complications, up to and including death, occurring in a small number of patients, primarily in the pediatric age group who are being treated for the spasticity resulting from cerebral palsy. Further research and follow-up will obviously be required in order to fully assess the implications of these reports.

§ 10.03 Related Topics

[1] Pressure Ulcers

As our population ages, and as more elderly people are cared for at home and in nursing homes, the incidence of significant pressure ulcers (also called "decubitus," or bedsore, ulcers) increases. In addition, recent reports of substandard nursing care (and often, even acute hospital care), suggest this further adds to this increase. Severe pressure ulcers can make overall management of the patient much more difficult, and, if extensive enough, can result in sepsis or generalized infection, with or without infection of the underlying bone, which can ultimately lead to death.

In evaluating a patient with pressure ulcers, the initial investigation should focus on the cause of the problem. It is clear that, except in rare instances, these ulcers can be prevented by attentive nursing care. However, studies have shown that, especially in debilitated patients, as little as two hours of uninterrupted pressure on skin overlying a bony prominence, such as the sacrum or ischial prominences in the pelvis or heels and ankles in the lower legs, can lead to sufficient ischemia to result in skin breakdown. Once this has begun, it requires even more diligent nursing attention to stop and reverse the process. If the patient has been cared for in a nursing home, skilled nursing facility or, as frequently happens when patients have been treated for an acute injury or illness, in an acute care hospital, arguable liability can often be found.

Special air-fluidized beds, one of which is the Clinitron®, are effective in the non-surgical management of pressure ulcers. These beds, however, are quite expensive, and managed care entities often refuse to authorize their use. Such denial of service, if any, should be reviewed in any applicable case.

Nursing notes should be critically reviewed for the frequency with which a bedfast patient was turned. Also, it is important to know the number of individuals involved in turning the patient. A single nurse or attendant cannot turn most patients without exerting a great amount of pressure on the patient's skin. This can cause or worsen these ulcers. In fact, it is likely that this is the most common contributing cause in the development of pressure ulcers in institutionalized patients.

Since the mid 1970s, the treatment of choice for most pressure ulcers has been the use of myocutaneous (skin muscle) flaps. Prior to that time, we had not recognized the usefulness of incorporating underlying muscle with skin flaps, and in those days healing problems were more frequent. The use of muscle provides a better blood supply and a flap that is more resistant to infection, which can be common in these wounds, since they are usually close to the patient's perianal area. It is, therefore, probably beneath the acceptable standard of care to utilize a large skin flap alone when its underlying muscle is available for use. Conversely, an acceptable approach is often to use only the muscle, by skin grafting its surface. (This approach is often used in injuries around the knee, such as those seen in motorcycle accidents, which are also currently on the rise.)

In the face of an infection, the use of an isolated skin flap will almost always fail, at least partially. However, in many cases it may be appropriate to use a *skin-muscle* flap even in the face of infection, for example, in an area of bone in which osteomyelitis has been diagnosed. This is virtually never the case with an isolated skin flap, and it is even less appropriate to use skin grafts on such wounds.

During the 1980s, the use of "free" flaps was developed. These are flaps that are completely separated from their donor sites, with their vascular supply being reestablished at the recipient site through microvascular anastomoses. An advantage of this approach is the ability to use tissue from a distant location for reconstruction of the defect. Disadvantages include difficulty and length of the procedure, which often requires two surgical teams, one to "harvest" the flap and the other to re-anastomose it. In most circumstances, non-free flaps are available.

[2] Blood Transfusions

Blood transfusions are not usually needed in plastic surgical procedures, and when they are warranted, this fact is usually highly predictable. The awareness of both patients and physicians to the possibility of blood-borne disease transmission was heightened by the AIDS crisis that began in the early 1980s. However, the transmission of hepatitis remained then and now a higher risk than the HIV virus, and blood-bank testing technology has progressed significantly since AIDS became an issue, resulting in minimal risk of transmission of any communicable disease via blood transfusion. In any event, it is incumbent upon the surgeon to plan accordingly. If he or she is performing a procedure that has a high probability of blood transfusion (*i.e.,* breast reduction, abdominoplasty, or the use of large flaps, especially in a paraplegic or quadriplegic patient), it is may be advisable and appropriate to have the patient, some time before the operation, give one or two units of his or her own blood for use later as autologous transfusions. Most authorities maintain that, in view of the risk of blood-borne disease, single-unit transfusions are not indicated in any circumstance, but some controversy exists as to whether single-unit autologous transfusions are included under this proscription. Experts also maintain that, except for unusual circumstances, patients can tolerate a postoperative hemoglobin as low as eight grams percent, which is lower than the ten grams that surgeons have traditionally used as the low point at which a transfusion would at least be considered. However, many plastic surgeons continue to dispute this point, especially in flap procedures. If one is reviewing a case in which HIV virus or hepatitis was transmitted to a patient by blood transfusion, the questions to be asked are: (1) was the transfusion indicated; (2) should it have been predicted preoperatively; and (3), if so, why was autologous transfusion not utilized? In 1990, a $28 million jury verdict in an Arizona case involving AIDS infection of an infant gives eloquent testimony to the liability risk in this area.

[3] Emergency Coverage, Services

One area of growing concern among health care providers, government and the population at large is the issue of access to emergency services. The decrease in reimbursement, in conjunction with the perceived increased litigation risk of emergency facility treatment has led many individual physicians to limit or stop altogether their availability for emergency room calls. Also contributing to this decline in emergency room availability is the change in physicians' view of and dedication to a lifestyle less consistent with the uncertainties involved in emergency room call participation. State lawmakers are struggling with these issues as of this writing. They are being asked to consider, for example, increasing the burden of proof for plaintiffs complaining of treatment rendered in an emergency facility setting. The problem is compounded by the fact that a growing percentage of the population does not have an identified primary care physician, and many of these appear to seek their medical care routinely by going to an emergency room or urgent care facility. Consequently, the physician who does see these patients generally has no access to their medical history. Given the volume of patients seen in any given time frame, this becomes a formula for potential problems of misdiagnosis and/or mismanagement.

When dealing with a complaint of the physician's refusal to come to the emergency to see the patient, it is important to discover if they were on the call roster or had any other requirement to participate in the emergency care of the patient, such as a contractual agreement by virtue of participating in the patient's insurance coverage plan. If there is not that requirement, there appears to be little recourse for either the patient or the facility.

If, on the other hand, the physician, such as a plastic surgeon, does agree to see the patient in this circumstance, it has become a frequent and recurring problem that the plastic surgeon examines the patient and then determines that the presenting injury is one that the surgeon considers to be outside his/her training, practice and or experience, thus declining to participate further.

Assuming that the surgeon does agree to undertake treatment, the primary areas of complaint in today's environment appear to involve timing of treatment (tonight versus the next day or two) as well as type and quality of treatment rendered.

In past years, the parameters outlined here were much more clearly demarcated. Doctors previously almost uniformly participated on the emergency room on-call roster and generally agreed to come to the emergency room at any time of day or night. This left the main potential complaint being one of quality of care. The perceived change in patient attitude toward their medical care (and caregiver) has led to what many believe to be unreasonable demands for services in these conditions and for the "perfect" result they — and most of us — expect.

The convergence of all the factors noted above make for difficulty in assessing the care, complaints and acceptability of result of emergency treatment in America today. The medical record, hospital staff policy, state legislation and the myriad factors surrounding the treatment encounter are arguably more complex than ever before. Among the specialties of neurosurgery, orthopedic surgery and a few others where emergency coverage can be uncertain, Plastic surgery is also at issue. With the propensity of many plastic surgeons to now limit their practices to cosmetic surgery — and, even then, often to specific areas of cosmetic surgery — one could argue that they should not even be available for emergency room call. All of these issues must be taken into account and researched fully in assessing any question of professional liability in the emergency setting.

[4] Medical Spas

Medical spas as a phenomenon of the growth of health care delivery as a commodity in general and for cosmetic surgery specifically are becoming prevalent in most parts of the country. As of this writing, there are estimated to be more than 1000 of such facilities in the U.S. Regulation has been slow to be applied by either state governments or their regulatory authorities. Due primarily to "horror stories" of complications or death of patients involved in obtaining treatment in these facilities, numerous efforts are now underway to understand the problems presented by these sites of care and to propose and implement appropriate regulatory provisions.

The facilities offer numerous cosmetic surgery and surgery-related services, including, but certainly not limited to dermabrasion (more specifically "microdermabrasion), laser hair removal, laser treatment of areas of hyperpigmentation, injections of botulinum toxin, along with other goods and service more previously associated with resort spa settings.

Generally such facilities have one or more physicians associated in either an ownership or supervisory capacity, but the adequacy of their participation and oversight has been called into question in many instances. For evaluation of complaints concerning services provided by such Spas, the role played by the physician will be critical. Be sure to check the Medical Practice Act of the state in question as well as any regulations or guidelines promulgated by the state medical board. In addition, the licensure or certification, as well as training and documented scope of activities of the non-medical personnel must be closely scrutinized. It appears anecdotally that many such employees are receiving only "on-the-job" training. A number of states have established committees, workgroups or task forces to look at the phenomenon and apparent or probable problems and begin to suggest solutions. Massachusetts has established a currently active task force as an example of this activity. Their current web site is http://www.massmedboard.org/public/med_spa.shtm. By the time this is published, there will likely be numerous other examples.

CHAPTER 11

NEUROLOGY

James C. Johnston, MD, JD, FCLM, FACLM

SYNOPSIS

---

§ 11.01 Introduction

[1] Preface

Neurology is arguably the most difficult and exacting medical specialty, requiring a thorough understanding of fiendishly complex topics such as neuroanatomy, neurophysiology, neuropathology and neuropharmacology. There are ghastly diseases presenting with baffling symptoms. It is extraordinarily challenging for an outsider to understand the distinctive terminology, bewildering examination techniques and medieval-appearing diagnostic methods. Moreover, the unprecedented evolution of neurology is creating an ever-changing landscape of testing procedures and therapeutic options. The attorney trying to overcome these barriers faces two additional hurdles. First, there is a paucity of literature providing guidance through a neurological malpractice case. The many excellent textbooks, monographs and journals covering this specialty are written for practicing clinicians and are of limited value to the lawyer trying to ascertain whether a malpractice claim is meritorious. Second, neurologists, like most physicians, have limited understanding of the legal process and may not present clinical information in a useful manner, making it even more burdensome to review a case. The resulting dearth of information can make a neurology case seem forbiddingly complex. This chapter attempts to bridge the gap by providing an overview of neurology for the legal profession and other nonphysician readers. It is not a substitute for the extensive nosological approaches of conventional medical writings. Nor is it a treatise of neurological malpractice; indeed, an impossible feat for a single chapter or even a single volume. Rather, it is designed to provide the attorney with a rudimentary understanding of the specialty in order to more effectively evaluate neurological opinions, thereby determining the strength, and identifying the weak points, of a case at the earliest possible stage.

[2] Outline

Parts I, II, and III define neurology; summarize the education, training and certification of a neurologist; and outline the various types of practice. Hopefully this will help the lawyer assess experts' credentials. Part IV provides a list of reputable textbooks, journals and internet sites as a starting point for further research on specific neurological topics. Practice guidelines are discussed. Part V is an abbreviated synopsis of the structure and function of the nervous system, which is best read in conjunction with one of the recommended neuroanatomy texts. It is the most intimidating section of the chapter, akin to learning basic conversational terms of a new language. However, this background is a prerequisite to understanding the neurological examination, role of diagnostic testing, and mechanisms of disease. The neurological evaluation is outlined in Part VI. A solid understanding of this part will help the lawyer effectively review medical records and minimize the risk of overlooking a significant sign or symptom. Part VII reviews common neurodiagnostic testing procedures with an emphasis on the indications for and limitations of each procedure. Part VIII highlights the scope of neurology with descriptions of common disorders and diseases. The material to be reviewed is a *mer à boire*, which necessitates omitting many conditions, truncating differential diagnoses, and ignoring various diagnostic and therapeutic options. It focuses on the more frequently encountered malpractice issues. Part IX briefly discusses medical records and the expert witness role.

§ 11.02 Defining Neurology

[1] Definition

Neurology is the medical specialty providing for the diagnosis, treatment and management of diseases and disorders affecting the central, peripheral and autonomic nervous systems, muscles, and supporting structures including coverings and vascular supply.

[2] Scope of Neurology

The broad scope of neurological practice includes a host of diverse conditions that may be grouped into disease oriented categories: headache and facial pain, cerebrovascular diseases, seizures and epilepsy, craniocerebral trauma, spine disorders, peripheral neuropathy, brain and spinal cord tumors, demyelinating diseases, movement disorders, muscle diseases, neuromuscular junction diseases, motor neuron diseases, infections, dementias, sleep disorders and chronic pain.

[3] Relationship to Other Specialties

There is often confusion among lay persons and medical professionals alike regarding the role of a neurologist in any particular case. This may be attributed to several unique facets of the specialty. First, neurology is a consulting practice with significant overlap among other branches of medicine. For example, the patient with back pain may be treated by a family physician, evaluated by an orthopedic surgeon, and referred to the neurologist who performs an electromyogram, initiates physical therapy and advises the family physician to consult neurosurgery. The role of the neurologist in further care may not be clear to the primary doctor, other specialists or patient. Second, neurologists may not be particularly attentive to providing care for progressive incurable diseases. These patients are often referred back to the primary doctor without defined neurological follow-up. This is slowly changing as new diagnostic and therapeutic options are raising the standard of care for many of these conditions. Third, neurologists treat a number of conditions that may not appear neurological such as chronic pain, dizziness and sleep disorders. Fourth, there is often uncertainty about whether a particular case should be handled by a neurologist or neurosurgeon. It seems straightforward — neurologists perform diagnostic services and medical treatment; neurosurgeons perform surgery. However, the distinction becomes blurred as neurologists perform more invasive procedures (nerve blocks and other pain procedures, botulinum toxin injections) and manage postoperative conditions as well as head trauma, while neurosurgeons increasingly treat non-surgical disorders including headache, neck and back pain, and seizures. Both specialists provide ongoing care for some conditions. In any particular case, the attorney may need to inquire about these relationships to determine who was responsible for referrals, prescriptions, or follow-up care.

§ 11.03 Education, Training and Certification

[1] Premedical Education

There are specific course requirements for all medical school applicants unrelated to neurology or any other specialty. These include biology, chemistry, physics and calculus courses, with less emphasis on the humanities. The typical medical school applicant has an undergraduate degree majoring in one or more of the sciences. Medical schools consider a variety of factors in the admission formula, with particular attention to the applicant's grades and Medical College Admission Test scores.

[2] Medical Education

The four year medical school curriculum is divided into two distinct components. The first two years are devoted to basic science lectures and laboratory practice. Courses include gross anatomy, histology, physiology, microbiology, biochemistry, pharmacology, gross and microscopic pathology, internal medicine, obstetrics and gynecology, pediatrics and surgery. During the end of the second year, many schools have a course in physical diagnosis representing the first exposure to clinical medicine. The last two years focus on clinical training, where students are assigned to clerkships involving rotations in general practice and the core specialties: internal medicine, general surgery, pediatrics, obstetrics and gynecology, and psychiatry. These rotations last from a few weeks to several months, and the students are supervised by teams of interns, residents and attending physicians. Students may choose a limited number of elective rotations that vary according to the particular university but typically include specialties such as neurology, ophthalmology, radiology, orthopedics, and cardiology. Thus, it is not uncommon for a student to graduate without any significant clinical neurology training. Those electing to rotate on the neurology service have a limited exposure for a few weeks — not even enough time to learn how to competently perform a neurological examination. This limited training is the main reason that an adequate neurological examination is almost universally neglected among non-neurologists. A hasty appraisal of the pupillary light reflex, cursory evaluation of hand grip strength, and tap of the patellar tendons is all too often deemed sufficient. Shrinking from a proper neurological evaluation frequently results in the failure to recognize neurological disease, especially at an early and potentially treatable stage. A proper examination is admittedly complex, but essential for even an elementary understanding of neurological disease. Until the medical education system teaches all physicians how to examine the nervous system, many will remain uncomfortable diagnosing or treating neurology patients.

[3] Postgraduate Training

The medical school graduate interested in becoming a specialist must complete a postgraduate educational period called residency. Most prospective neurologists enter a residency program accredited by the

Accreditation Council for Graduate Medical Education (ACGME), a prerequisite for board-certification. The ACGME is a private organization made up of four representatives from each of five bodies (American Board of Medical Specialties, American Hospital Association, American Medical Association, Association of American Medical Colleges, and Council of Medical Specialty Societies), one representative from the federal government, two resident members and three public members. It accredits residency programs in 120 specialties and subspecialties. The organization has 28 Residency Review Committees (one for each of the 26 medical specialties, one for the transitional year program and one for institutional review) responsible for ensuing that an accredited program meets established standards. Each committee consists of 6 to 15 physicians appointed by the American Medical Association Council on Medical Education and the appropriate medical specialty board—in the case of neurology, the American Board of Psychiatry and Neurology.

The adult neurology residency requires four years and includes an internship year that is usually in internal medicine. Pediatric neurology requires an internship in general pediatrics followed by a year in adult neurology and two years in child neurology. The ACGME residency requirements for neurology and child neurology set forth standards for faculty qualifications, educational programs, outpatient care, hospital services, medical libraries, call coverage and a host of other details along with the broader requirements for basic neuroscience courses, clinical activities and administrative duties.[1] Residents, upon completion of training, may elect to pursue a fellowship program for one or two years to develop expertise in a particular subspecialty.

[4] Board Certification

The American Board of Medical Specialties (ABMS), established in 1933, is comprised of 24 medical specialty Member Boards, one being the American Board of Psychiatry and Neurology (ABPN).[2] The primary function of the ABMS is to assist Member Boards in developing and implementing professional standards to evaluate and certify physician specialists. The ABPN, founded in 1935, sets the standards for the knowledge and skills required for certification in neurology and psychiatry. There are sixteen voting members: eight neurologists nominated by the American Academy of Neurology and the American Neurological Association, and eight

---

[1] www.acgme.org accessed 12 October 2007.
[2] www.abms.org accessed 12 October 2007.

psychiatrists nominated by the American College of Psychiatrists, American Psychiatric Association and American Medical Association. Board certification requires successful completion of an ACGME accredited residency training program and passage of the two part ABPN examination. Part I is a lengthy written examination covering neurology and psychiatry which may be taken one year after completion of residency. Applicants successfully passing Part I have six years or three opportunities to pass the Part II oral examination. This part requires the neurologist to examine adult and pediatric patients in a hospital or clinic setting under observation and questioning by senior neurologists. The successful neurologist is then considered board certified and a Diplomate of the ABPN. The most recent AAN statistics indicate that 70% of adult neurologists are board certified.[3] Since 1935, the Board has issued a total of 12,667 certificates as of 1 December 2006. The certificates issued prior to 1 October 1994 are of lifetime validity; the later ones have a ten year limitation and require the neurologist to pass a re-certification process.

[5] Subspecialty Certification

The ABPN offers certificates for special qualifications in several subspecialties including clinical neurophysiology, geriatrics, neuro-developmental disabilities, pain medicine, neuromuscular medicine, sleep medicine and vascular neurology. The requirements vary, and there is typically a grace period of five years for practitioners to be grandfathered into a new certification.

[6] Professional Organizations

There are a plethora of neurological organizations and associations which generally do not have stringent membership requirements. Most simply require payment of annual dues. Others have different membership categories reflecting varying levels of qualifications or peer recognition, which might serve to distinguish one neurologist from another. However, membership in a professional organization is not a requirement for medical licensure. Several of the hundreds of organizations and societies are briefly mentioned.

The American Academy of Neurology (AAN), established in 1948, is perhaps the largest and most recognized professional organization. There are 17,872 worldwide members including over 9,000 adult and pediatric neurologists in the United States, as well as resident trainees, other

---

[3] www.aan.com. *AAN Member Demographic and Practice Characteristics* at 10. Accessed 8 October 2007.

neurological specialists (neurosurgeons, neuropathologists, physiatrists), non-clinical neuroscientists, and non-physician members.[4] Its mission is "to advance the art and science of neurology, and thereby promote the best possible care for patients with neurological disorders."[5] The AAN holds annual meetings, and publishes a reputable journal entitled *Neurology,* as well as various ethical assessments, practice guidelines and continuing education materials. It is also active in political matters that relate to the practice of neurology. Membership categories include *junior members* (medical graduates engaged in post-graduate studies directed towards certification in neurology), *affiliates* (non-physicians practicing in fields related to neurology), *associates* (physicians fully trained in clinical neurology but not board certified, and physicians in other specialties practicing in fields related to neurology), and *active members* (physicians board certified in neurology or child neurology). Active members may become *fellows* after seven years by attending five annual meetings and receiving sponsorship from two other fellows.

The American Neurological Association (ANA) is a smaller organization of "academic neurologists and neuroscientists devoted to advancing the goals of academic neurology; to training and educating neurologists . . . and to expanding both our understanding of diseases of the nervous system and our ability to treat them."[6] The ANA holds annual meetings and publishes a journal entitled *Annals of Neurology.* Membership categories of *active* (United States and Canada) and *corresponding* (other geographical locations) *members* require a doctorate degree, evidence of teaching and research activities, and publication of at least ten scientific papers.

The American Clinical Neurophysiology Society (ACNS), established in 1946 as the American EEG Society, describes its mission as "fostering excellence in clinical neurophysiology and furthering the understanding of central nervous system function in health and disease through education, research, and the provision of a forum for discussion and interaction."[7] There are over 1,200 members including neurologists, neurosurgeons, psychiatrists and other specialists. The ACNS holds annual meetings, and publishes educational materials including clinical guidelines for electrodiagnostic testing as well as a journal entitled *Journal of Clinical Neurophysiology.*

The American Society of Neurorehabilitation (ASNR), established in 1990, sets forth a mission to "promote medical and social wellbeing of persons with disabling neurological disorders, to advance training and research . . . and to

---

[4] www.aan.com accessed on 5 October 2007.

[5] *Id.*

[6] www.aneuroa.org accessed 6 October 2007.

[7] www.acns.org accessed 6 October 2007.

disseminate the knowledge of this research among professionals and the general public."[8] The members include physicians from a wide variety of specialties and nonphysicians. The ASNR holds annual meetings, affiliates with the American Congress of Rehabilitation Medicine, promotes educational activities, and publishes the journal *Neurorehabilitation and Neural Repair.* There are several member levels culminating in *certified* membership, which requires a one year training program in neurorehabilitation or one year of experience managing patients with chronic neurological diseases, as well as periodic continuing educational assessments and examinations.

The American Association of Neuromuscular and Electrodiagnostic Medicine (AANEM), established in 1953 as the American Association of Electromyography and Electrodiagnosis (renamed in 1989 the American Association of Electrodiagnostic Medicine, and again in 2004 to the current name), states its primary goal is to "serve physicians who diagnose and treat patients with disorders of muscle and nerve, extend the knowledge of electrodiagnostic medicine, and improve the quality of patient care."[9] There are over 5,000 members, predominantly neurologists and physiatrists. The AANEM holds annual meetings, and publishes a variety of educational materials and guidelines, as well as the journal *Muscle and Nerve.* Political advocacy seems to focus on qualifications and reimbursement issues. Membership categories include *junior* (trainees in residency or fellowship), *associate* (non-board certified physicians) and *active members* (physicians board certified by one of the ABMS member boards). *Fellow* membership requires passing an examination by the American Board of Electrodiagnostic Medicine, a non-ABMS board that is organized and approved by a committee of the AANEM itself.

§ 11.04 Types of Practice

[1] Academic Practice

Approximately one-quarter of neurologists are in university based groups.[10] There is often significant overlap between the academic and private sectors. In general, the term academic practice implies that the neurologist is employed by a university medical school with an affiliated residency training program. The university based neurologist may see private patients, and is usually responsible for supervising residents one or more months a year, as

---

[8] www.asnr.org accessed 8 December 2007.

[9] www.aanem.org accessed 6 October 2007.

[10] www.aan.com. *AAN Member Demographic and Practice Characteristics* at 10. Accessed 7 October 2007.

well as teaching medical students, neurology residents and residents from other specialties rotating on the neurology service. Additionally, there may be basic science or clinical research duties. University based neurologists typically devote slightly less than half of their time to clinical practice.[11] Some devote most of their time to research and perform very little clinical work. These individuals may be excellent researchers and teachers, but lacking in clinical judgment compared to the practicing neurologist. Inquiry into the percentage of time spent in various practice activities (patient care, teaching, research and administrative) may be worthwhile.

[2] Private Practice

Sixty five percent of neurologists are in solo, single specialty or multi-specialty groups.[12] These private practitioners devote most of their time to direct patient care, but may also be affiliated with a medical school on a voluntary basis (or for a nominal salary) and referred to as clinical faculty. Otherwise, private practitioners have no teaching responsibilities and research activities are usually limited to clinical drug trials sponsored by the pharmaceutical industry. The neurologist bills on a fee-for-service basis but may elect to participate with any number of health plans. This is unquestionably the most lucrative form of practice. Neurologists may choose to provide consultations, or give continuing care for primary or secondary neurological problems.

The clinical neurology practice predominantly focuses on outpatient care and is based in an office, which may be freestanding or associated with a hospital. The neurologist performs initial and follow-up consultations in the office, and may elect to see self-referred patients. Most neurologists perform neurodiagnostic procedures in their office; however, these tests may also be performed in the hospital setting. The generous reimbursement for neurodiagnostic testing often creates tension between the hospital and neurologist. These procedures are reimbursed for both "technical" and "professional" components. The technical component is about two-thirds the total payment and goes to whoever owns the machine; the professional component constitutes the remaining one-third and goes to the interpreting neurologist. Thus, the neurologist performing office based testing receives the global payment; however, the neurologist performing hospital based testing receives only the professional component while the hospital is paid for the technical component. Both parties have a deep financial interest in

---

[11] *Id.* at 13.
[12] *Id.* at 10.

utilizing on-site equipment. Other procedures commonly performed in the office include lumbar puncture, muscle and nerve biopsy, and pain management involving injections of corticosteroids and local anesthetics.

Neurologists may admit patients that require hospital care, and provide consultations for inpatients that are under the care of other physicians. Additionally, it is usually necessary to provide emergency room coverage for neurological cases. Many practitioners cover more than one hospital which increases the possibility of an unacceptable delay or lapse in attending patients. The neurologist typically has arrangements with associates or other staff neurologists to provide coverage; this may be unacceptable, especially if a resident or non-neurologist is providing coverage. If the neurologist in a particular case was unavailable or late in attending a patient, then it is prudent to inquire into other activities at that time including schedules at all hospitals where the neurologist practices.

The many potential conflicts of interest in private practice usually center on ownership of diagnostic testing equipment. For example, neurologists often hold financial interests in computerized tomography or magnetic resonance imaging centers; referring a patient to these facilities may present a conflict of interest that compromises patient care. Uncovering these relationships may strengthen a borderline malpractice case, and reveal violations of the federal *Stark* laws against self-referral as well as a number of ethical canons.

[3] Other Practice Types

The remaining ten percent of neurologists practice in government positions through the military branches, Veterans Administration hospitals, or Public Health Service facilities, and a very few are employed by health maintenance organizations. These positions offer a salary and benefits for specific employment services without all of the private practice demands.

§ 11.05 Literature

[1] Treatises

There are a number of highly regarded textbooks covering general neurology and the subspecialty areas, as well as many monographs on specific diseases, conditions and syndromes. Some of the more common and readily available textbooks are listed below. Additional references for specific conditions are denoted in the relevant section of the chapter.

- Aminoff MJ, Boller F, Swaab DF, series eds. succeeding Vinken PJ, Bruyn GW, eds. *Handbook of Clinical Neurology.* Amsterdam, The Netherlands: Elsevier (publication dates vary in this multi-volume collection numbering 82 as of December 2007).
- Brazis PW, Masdeu JC, Biller J. *Localization in Clinical Neurology,* 5th ed. Philadelphia: Lippincott Williams & Wilkin; 2006.
- Campbell W, ed. *DeJong's The Neurological Examination,* 6th ed. Philadelphia: Lippincott Williams & Wilkin; 2005.
- Chiappa KH. *Evoked Potentials in Clinical Medicine,* 3rd ed. New York: Lippincott Williams & Wilkins; 1997.
- Dobkin BH, ed. *The Clinical Science of Neurologic Rehabilitation,* 2nd ed. New York: Oxford University Press; 2003.
- Dyck PJ, Thomas PK, et al., eds. *Peripheral Neuropathy,* 4th ed. Philadelphia: Saunders; 2005.
- Evans RW, ed. *Neurology and Trauma,* 2nd ed. Philadelphia: Saunders; 2006.
- Jackler, RK, Brackmann DE, eds. *Neurotology,* 2nd ed. St. Louis: Mosby; 2005.
- Kimura J. *Electrodiagnosis in Diseases of Nerve and Muscle: Principles and Practice,* 3rd ed. New York: Oxford University Press; 2001.
- Mayo Clinic Department of Neurology. *Mayo Clinic Examination in Neurology,* 7th ed. Mosby; 1997.
- Mendez MF, Cummings JL. *Dementia: A Clinical Approach,* 3rd ed. Boston: Butterworth-Heinemann; 2003.
- Mesulam MM. *Principles of Behavioral and Cognitive Neurology,* 2nd ed. New York: Oxford University Press; 2000.
- Miller NR, Newman NJ, eds. *Walsh & Hoyt's Clinical Neuro-Ophthalmology,* 6th ed. Lippincott Williams & Wilkins; 2004.
- Netter FH. *The CIBA Collection of Medical Illustrations, Volumes I and II, Nervous System.* CIBA-Geigy; 1983.
- Niedermeyer E, da Silva FL, eds. *Electroencephalography: Basic Principles, Clinical Applications, and Related Fields,* 5th ed. Baltimore: Lippincott Williams & Wilkins; 2004.
- Posner JB, Saper CB, Schiff ND, Plum F. *Plum & Posner's Diagnosis of Stupor and Coma,* 4th ed. New York: Oxford University Press; 2007.
- Pourmand R, Harati Y, eds. *Neuromuscular Disorders.* Philadelphia: Lippincott Williams & Wilkins; 2002.
- Ropper AH, Brown RH. *Adam & Victor's Principles of Neurology,* 8th ed. New York: McGraw-Hill; 2005.
- Rowland LP, ed. *Merritt's Neurology,* 11th ed. Philadelphia: Lippincott Williams & Wilkins; 2005.

- Standring S. *Grays Anatomy: The Anatomical Basis of Clinical Practice,* 39th ed. Elsevier Churchill Livingstone; 2005.
- Watts RL, Koller WC, eds. *Movement Disorders: Neurologic Principles and Practice,* 2nd ed. New York: McGraw-Hill; 2004.

[2] Journals

Journals provide the most up-to-date information, which may take several years to be published in a textbook. There are hundreds of journals that publish articles pertaining to the neurological sciences, such as the *New England Journal of Medicine* and *Lancet,* as well as scores of neurology journals. The following abbreviated list of clinical neurology journals is in decreasing order of quality according to a recent survey of neurological experts.[13]

- *Neurology*
- *Brain*
- *Annals of Neurology*
- *Journal of Neurotrauma*
- *Stroke*
- *Archives of Neurology*
- *Neurocase*
- *Epilepsia*
- *Neurological Research*
- *Journal of the Neurological Sciences*
- *Journal of Neuropathology and Experimental Neurology*
- *Pain*
- *Seminars in Neurology*
- *Journal of Neurology, Neurosurgery and Psychiatry*
- *Sleep*
- *Epilepsy Research*
- *Clinical Neurophysiology*
- *Journal of Clinical Neuroscience*
- *European Journal of Neurology*
- *Headache*
- *Cerebrovascular Diseases*
- *Acta Neurologica Scandinavica*
- *Alzheimer Disease and Associated Disorders*
- *Neurologic Clinics*
- *Canadian Journal of Neurological Sciences*
- *Journal of Nervous and Mental Disease*

---

[13] Yue W, Wilson CS, Boller F. *Peer Assessment of Journal Quality in Clinical Neurology.* J Med Libr Assoc 2007; 95(1):70-76.

- *Amyotrophic Lateral Sclerosis and Other Motor Neuron Disorders*
- *Cephalalgia*
- *European Neurology*
- *Revue Neurologique*

[3]   Internet Resources

The following internet sites provide an excellent starting point to learn more about specific diseases, review practice guidelines, and locate some of the experts for various conditions.

- www.aan.com (American Academy of Neurology)
- www.abta.org (American Brain Tumor Association)
- www.achenet.org (American Headache Society Committee for Headache Education)
- www.alsa.org (Amyotrophic Lateral Sclerosis Association)
- www.americanheart.org (American Heart Association)
- www.asnr.org (American Society of Neurorehabilitation)
- www.ata.org (American Tinnitus Association)
- www.ataxia.org (National Ataxia Foundation)
- www.biausa.org (Brain Injury Association of America)
- www.epilepsyfoundation.org (Epilepsy Foundation)
- www.mdausa.org (Muscular Dystrophy Association)
- www.myasthenia.org (Myasthenia Gravis Foundation of America)
- www.nationalmssociety.org (National Multiple Sclerosis Society)
- www.neuropathy.org (The Neuropathy Association)
- www.nia.nih.gov/alzheimers (Alzheimers Disease Education and Referral Center)
- www.ninds.nih.gov (National Institute of Neurological Diseases and Stroke)
- www.pdf.org (Parkinsons Disease Foundation)
- www.spinalcord.org (The National Spinal Cord Injury Association)
- www.tsa-usa.org (Tourettes Syndrome Association)

[4]   Practice Guidelines

Evidence-based medicine refers to "practice guidelines," "practice parameters," or "protocols" designed to help the physician and patient make health care decisions based on the best available scientific evidence or expert consensus. The National Guideline Clearinghouse details 324 current neurology guidelines which were developed, reviewed or revised within the last five years.[14] The overall quality of guidelines varies, as some organizations have agendas that may influence their recommendations. However, the AAN is a leader in developing unbiased, predominantly evidence-based parameters which undergo a rigorous peer-review process — each guideline is reviewed by the Quality Standards Subcommittee or Therapeutics and Technology Assessment Subcommittee, by an extensive network of clinical experts, and by three to five reviewers for the journal *Neurology*.[15] The guidelines are not inflexible standards of care and, if fact, have a generic disclaimer: "This statement . . . is not intended to include all possible methods of care for a particular neurologic problem . . . The AAN recognizes that specific patient care decisions are the prerogative of the patient and the physician caring for the patient, based on all of the circumstances involved."[16] Physicians must be keenly aware of individual patient circumstances that warrant deviation from the recommended treatment protocols. However, these guidelines represent a powerful tool — they may be introduced by either the plaintiff or defendant to meet the burden of establishing the standard of care. Courts have ruled both ways on admission of practice guidelines, and the issue is far from settled.[17]

§ 11.06 Overview of the Nervous System

[1] The Building Blocks

The nerve cell or *neuron* is the primary anatomic and functional unit of the nervous system. There are an estimated one hundred billion neurons that produce electrochemical impulses to provide communication within the nervous system. A neuron consists of a cell body or *soma* containing a nucleus with the genetic material, a *dendritic tree* and an *axon*. Dendrites receive stimuli and conduct impulses generated by those stimuli to the cell body. These are termed *afferent* processes. The axon of a neuron is a single fiber that conducts impulses away from the cell body — an *efferent* process. Axons may be up to two meters long, and divide into a number of branches before connecting to other parts of the nervous system, or to a muscle or gland. Communication occurs at the *synapse*, where the axonal terminal of a *presynaptic* neuron abuts the dendrite, cell body or axon of a *postsynaptic* neuron. The axonal terminal contains presynaptic vesicles filled with

---

[14] www.guideline.gov accessed 7 October 2007.

[15] Franklin GM, Zahn CA. *AAN Clinical Practice Guidelines: Above the Fray.* Neurology 2002; 59:975-976.

[16] www.aan.com/practice/guidelines accessed 12 December 2007 (standard disclaimer).

[17] Sokol AJ, Molzen CJ. *The Changing Standard of Care in Medicine: E-health, Medical Errors, and Technology Add New Obstacles.* J Leg Med 2002; 23:449-490.

neurotransmitters (substances such as norepinephrine, acetylcholine, dopamine, serotonin and gamma-aminobutyric acid). Transmission of a nerve impulse creates a change in electrical potential (*action potential*) which propagates current down the axon causing neurotransmitter release into the *synaptic cleft*. The neurotransmitter traverses the synaptic cleft and either stimulates or inhibits the postsynaptic neuron. These synaptic potentials are graded responses called excitatory postsynaptic potentials, which lead to impulse propagation, or inhibitory postsynaptic potentials, which inhibit impulse generation. The many different synaptic inputs on a postsynaptic neuron are combined through the process of *synaptic integration* to result in the final response of either excitation or inhibition.

The brain and spinal cord neurons are supported by several types of *glial* cells: *oligodendrocytes* forming and maintaining myelin, *astrocytes* affecting neuronal chemical balance and playing a neurotransmitter regulatory role, and *microglia* immune cells dealing with inflammation and infection. Peripheral nerve fibers may have a *Schwann cell* myelin sheath insulating axons to permit rapid *saltatory conduction* of impulses between the Schwann cell gaps, or *nodes of Ranvier*.

The nerve cell bodies are usually located in groups termed *nuclei* in the brain and spinal cord, and *ganglia* outside the brain and spinal cord. Laminated sheets of nerve cell bodies on the cerebral surface make up the *cerebral cortex*. Aggregations of nerve cell bodies in the brain and spinal cord are called *gray matter*. The remaining areas of the brain and spinal cord consist of nerve fibers referred to as the *white matter*. Axon bundles in the brain and spinal cord that have a common origin and common termination constitute a *tract;* anatomically distinct bundles of pathways may be referred to as *fasciculus, brachium, peduncle* or *lemniscus*. Nerve fiber bundles outside the brain and spinal cord are called *nerves*.

[2] General Organization

The nervous system is divided into central, peripheral and autonomic portions. The *central nervous system* (CNS) includes the *brain* (*cerebral cortex, diencephalon, basal ganglia, brainstem,* and *cerebellum*) and *spinal cord*. It is also referred to as the *neuraxis*. The *peripheral nervous system* (PNS) includes the spinal nerve roots, ganglia, peripheral nerves, neuromuscular junctions and muscles. The *autonomic nervous system* includes both central and peripheral components, and provides involuntary regulation of respiratory, circulatory, gastrointestinal, metabolic and other functions through the sympathetic (derived from thoracic and upper lumbar spine) and parasympathetic (derived from brainstem nuclei and sacral spine) divisions.

[3] The Brain

The meninges. The *meninges* consist of three membranes — *dura mater, arachnoid mater,* and *pia mater* — covering the brain and spinal cord. The dura is thick, fibrous and adherent to the inside of the skull. It has folds separating the cranial cavity into compartments — the *falx cerebri* separates the two cerebral hemispheres, the *tentorium* separates the cortex from the posterior fossa, and the *falx cerebelli* separates the cerebellar hemispheres. The pia mater is a thin, delicate membrane closely adherent to the surface of the brain and spinal cord. Between the dura and pia is the arachnoid, which bridges over the sulci of the brain. The space between the arachnoid and pia is called the *subarachnoid space* and contains the cerebrospinal fluid (CSF).

The cerebrum. The right and left *cerebral hemispheres* are incompletely separated by the median longitudinal fissure; *gyri* (convolutions) and *sulci* or *fissures* cover the surface of each hemisphere. The *Sylvian (lateral) sulcus* begins on the basal surface of the brain, then traverses posterolaterally and upward. The *central sulcus of Rolando* runs from the approximate midpoint of the dorsal hemisphere border obliquely downward and forward, nearly abutting the lateral fissure. Each hemisphere is divided into four *lobes* and there are two other ill defined lobes. The *frontal lobe* is the largest, located anterior to the central sulcus and above the lateral sulcus. The *primary motor cortex* is located in the *precentral gyrus* immediately in front of the central sulcus; it controls movements. *Broca's area* for productive speech is in the language-dominant frontal lobe, usually the left. The *prefrontal cortex* or anterior portion of the frontal lobe is responsible for executive functions — insight, abstract thinking, motivation, initiative, judgment, problem solving and planning. The *parietal lobe* extends posterior to the central sulcus; immediately adjacent to the sulcus is the *postcentral gyrus* with *primary somatosensory cortex* receiving sensory input from the spinal cord about touch, pressure, pain, vibration and position on the opposite side of the body. Posterior to the postcentral sulcus is the inferior parietal lobule, which is concerned with language comprehension. The superior parietal lobule is involved in some visual and spatial functions as well as complex sensory integration allowing judgment of size, shape, weight and texture. The posteriorly located *occipital lobe* contains the primary visual cortex receiving input from the contralateral half of each visual field, and the association cortex allowing complex processing of visual information for shape and color recognition. The *temporal lobe* contains the primary auditory cortex *Wernicke's area* for processing and interpretation of sound, and plays an important role in learning and memory. A fifth lobe called the *limbic lobe* is a diffuse ring of cortical tissue incorporating the cingulate, paraterminal and parahippocampal gyri. It is associated with behavior and emotions. The *insular lobe (Island of Reil)* may be considered a sixth lobe made up of the cortical tissue forming the floor of the lateral fissure.

The diencephalon. The *diencephalon* includes the *thalamus, hypothalamus* and *epithalamus.* The thalamus acts as a relay and processing station for impulses passing from the periphery or brainstem to the cortex, and receives feedback from cortical projections. The hypothalamus controls many bodily activities that affect homeostasis — hunger, thirst, temperature, blood pressure, and water balance. It is the key neuroendocrine effector mechanism of the neuraxis, releasing regulatory factors that act on the *pituitary gland*, which in turn releases or blocks various hormones. The epithalamus includes the *pineal gland,* which is involved in sleep and wake cycles.

The basal ganglia. The *basal ganglia* are gray matter regions deep in the cerebrum and brainstem, including the *caudate, putamen, globus pallidus, substantia nigra,* and *subthalamic nucleus.* These structures have extensive interconnections, as well as reciprocal connections with the cortex, thalamus and brainstem, and are involved in control and modulation of movement.

The brainstem. The brainstem contains the *midbrain* (mesencephalon, between the cerebrum and pons), *pons* (metencephalon, between midbrain and medulla, in front of cerebellum), and *medulla oblongata* (myelencephalon, upward continuation of the spinal cord). The pons lies against the *clivus,* a slide-like region of bone that extends to the *foramen magnum,* an opening in the occipital bone where the spinal cord becomes the medulla. In the very serious condition of increased intracranial pressure (due to a mass lesion or edema), the brainstem may in fact "slide" down the clivus and herniate into the foramen magnum which usually causes a very rapid death. The brainstem controls vital functions including heart rate, blood pressure and respiratory activity. All of the ascending and descending pathways between the spinal cord and higher brain centers pass through the brainstem. There are twelve pairs of *cranial nerves* (CNs) which traverse the skull through specific foramen, and all but the first two arise in the brainstem. The anatomic pathway of each nerve may be assessed by clinical testing, thus allowing relatively precise localization of brainstem lesions. CN I is the *olfactory nerve* which provides the sense of smell. The *optic nerve* or CN II deals with vision. CNs III (*oculomotor*), IV (*trochlear*), and VI (*abducens*) are responsible for eye movement. CN V is the *trigeminal nerve* which conveys sensory information from the head, face and meninges back to the brain, and provides motor input to the mastication muscles. CN VII is the *facial nerve* that provides movement of the face muscles. CN VIII is composed of *vestibular* and *cochlear* divisions concerned with balance and hearing, respectively. CN IX or the *glossopharyngeal nerve* provides palatal movement as well as sensation in the posterior tongue and pharynx. CN X is the *vagus nerve* which controls autonomic function throughout the body including heart, lungs and gastrointestinal tract. CN XI, the *accessory nerve*, supplies the trapezius and sternocleidomastoid muscles. CN XII, the *hypoglossal nerve*, supplies the tongue muscles.

The cerebellum. The *cerebellum* is located posteriorly beneath the cerebral hemispheres and overlying the lower brainstem. It is composed of two hemispheres and a midline vermis, with extensive connections to the cerebrum, vestibular nuclei and spinal cord. The cerebellum controls complex motor functions such as walking, balance, posture and general coordination of activities. Cerebellar lesions produce *ataxia* — incoordination of posture and gait — as well as poor movement coordination with *dysmetria* and *dysdiadochokinesia* (impaired rapid alternating movements), and scanning speech composed of irregularly spaced sounds.

[4] The Spinal Cord

The spinal cord is a caudal continuation of the medulla, approximately 46 cm long, and cylindrical or oval in shape, with enlargement at the cervical and lumbar regions, where neurons innervating the upper and lower extremities, respectively, are located. The membranes covering the spinal cord — pia, arachnoid and dura mater — are contiguous with those of the brainstem and brain. The cord consists of central grey matter (cell bodies and synapses) and peripheral white matter, which contains the *ascending* and *descending* fiber pathways. The ascending pathways relay sensory information to the brain; the descending pathways relay motor commands from the brain. The spinal cord is somatotopically organized, with 31 segments, each containing an entering dorsal sensory root and exiting ventral motor root. At birth, the spinal cord and spinal column are approximately the same length. Thus, paired spinal nerve roots travel horizontally and exit the same level as their corresponding vertebrae. The spinal column grows more that the cord, which ultimately terminates in adults between the first and second lumbar vertebrae. However, the nerve roots still exit the canal through their original foramina by lengthening and traveling caudally. Below the *conus medullaris,* or lower end of the cord, the canal contains the *cauda equina,* a collection of nerve roots destined for the lower lumbar and sacral foramina. The cervical nerves C1-C7 exit *over* their corresponding vertebrae, but C8 and the remainder exit *below* their correspondingly numbered vertebral body. C8 is unique because there is no correspondingly numbered vertebra. The fifth through eighth cervical and the first thoracic nerve roots form the *brachial plexus* which sends nerves into the shoulder and arm. The main terminal branches include the *musculocutaneous, axillary, median, ulnar, and radial nerves.* The lumbar and sacral nerve roots form the *lumbosacral plexus* before entering the leg to terminate in the *femoral, obturator,* and *sciatic nerves,* the latter dividing into the *peroneal* and *posterior tibial nerves.*

Ascending pathways. Sensory receptors are specialized structures responding to certain stimuli. Exteroceptors in the skin respond to touch and pressure (mechanoreceptors), temperature (thermoreceptors), and pain (nociceptors). Proprioceptors are in deeper structures such as the muscles, joints, tendons and bones, and respond to movement and position. Enteroceptors respond to internal organ stimuli. These sensory receptors are the termination of sensory nerve fibers. Bundles of these fibers constitute peripheral nerves. The nerve fibers are classified according to size, myelin covering and conduction velocity. Different fiber types have specific functions (large myelinated axons include motor neurons and large fiber sensory nerves mediating position and vibration; small thinly myelinated and unmyelinated axons carry nociceptive and autonomic input) and various pathological vulnerabilities. Groups of sensory neuron cell bodies form the dorsal ganglia. The sensory fibers transmit impulses from the periphery through the dorsal root into the appropriate spinal cord pathway. The pathway (*spinothalamic tract*) for pain and temperature enters the spinal cord, almost immediately crosses to the opposite half of the cord (within one or two levels), ascends to the thalamus, then to the cerebral cortex (many fibers end in the brainstem). A lesion of this tract will result in a contralateral loss of pain and temperature sensation below the level of the lesion. The pathway (*posterior columns*) for position (proprioception), vibration and stereognosis remains on the same side of the spinal cord that is enters, then crosses over at the level of the brainstem, ascends to the thalamus, then to the cerebral cortex. Just prior to the crossing, the synaptic regions *nucleus gracilis* and *nucleus cuneatus* contain sensory input from the lower and upper parts of the body respectively. Their corresponding spinal pathways are termed *fasciculus gracilis* and *fasciculus cuneatus,* collectively referred to as the posterior columns. A posterior column lesion will result in an ipsilateral loss of proprioception, vibration and stereognosis below the level of the lesion. The pathway for light touch combines features of the spinothalamic tract and posterior columns — part of it crosses over at lower levels, and part remains uncrossed until it reaches the brainstem (explaining why light touch is often spared in unilateral cord lesions). Both the spinothalamic tract and posterior columns cross over, albeit at different levels, terminate in the thalamus, and are then relayed to the sensory cortex. Thus, cortical lesions may result in a contralateral (opposite side) deficit of pain, temperature, vibration and position. The pathway (*spinocerebellar tract*) for unconscious proprioception (allowing one to perform complex acts such as walking without thinking which joints to flex or extend) remains ipsilateral as it connects to the cerebellum. Cerebellar lesions, in contrast to cerebral insults, produce ipsilateral deficits.

Descending pathways. The motor system responds to sensory input with conscious and unconscious muscle contraction requiring the coordination of *pyramidal* and *extrapyramidal* systems. The frontal lobe motor cortex cells project axons through the *corticobulbar* and *corticospinal* (*pyramidal*) tracts which terminate on motor nuclei of cranial and spinal nerves, respectively. The bulk of corticospinal fibers cross at the lower medulla in the *pyramidal decussation*. Cerebral lesions will result in contralateral motor deficits. The corticospinal tract synapses in the anterior horn or gray matter of the spinal cord; the postsynaptic motor neuron innervates skeletal muscle. It is important to understand this synapse because motor neurons above it (connecting cortex with anterior horn) are called *upper motor neurons* (UMNs), and those below this level are *lower motor neurons* (LMNs). Upper and lower motor neuron insults both result in paralysis, although with different clinical signs. In UMN lesions, there is spastic paralysis without atrophy, hyperreflexia, and a Babinski reflex without fasciculations or fibrillations. LMN lesions produce flaccid paralysis with atrophy, fasciculations and fibrillations, hyporeflexia, and no Babinski reflex. The extrapyramidal system (basal ganglia, subthalamic nucleus) is deeply interconnected with the pyramidal system to regulate movement by modulating coordination, tone, posture and reflexes. The integration of input from higher brain centers through the two descending systems converges on the anterior horn motor neurons in the spinal cord. These neurons project axons through the ventral roots into peripheral nerves to the neuromuscular junction, and activate muscle contraction by releasing a neurotransmitter at the junction.

The stretch reflex. The interplay of these pathways may be demonstrated by a review of the basic stretch or deep tendon reflex. Striking the patellar tendon with a reflex hammer stretches the quadriceps tendon. This stimulates stretch sensory receptors, triggering an afferent impulse in the sensory fibers of the femoral nerve, which travels through the dorsal root into the lumbar spinal cord. The sensory neuron synapses directly on a motor neuron in the anterior horn gray matter. The motor neuron conducts an efferent impulse to the neuromuscular junction of the quadriceps femoris muscle, releasing acetylcholine, making it contract. This represents a *monosynaptic reflex arc* — the sensory nerve synapses directly on the motor neuron. There is also coordinated stimulation of an interneuron (*disynaptic reflex arc*) which inhibits the motor neuron to the antagonistic hamstring muscles. This results in the classic *"knee-jerk" reflex*, which is modulated by descending supraspinal (pyramidal and extrapyramidal) pathways. The reflex provides clinical information about the supraspinal or upper motor neuron pathways, spinal cord segments L2-L4, and the femoral nerve.

[5] The Vascular Supply

The brain. The brain derives its blood supply from the two internal carotid arteries and two vertebral arteries which supply roughly the anterior two thirds and posterior one third of the brain, respectively. Each internal carotid artery divides into the *anterior cerebral artery*, supplying the anterior and medial parts of the cerebral hemisphere, and the *middle cerebral artery*, which subdivides into several branches supplying the lateral parts of the cerebral hemisphere. The two *vertebral arteries* join within the skull to form the *basilar artery*, and this vertebrobasilar system supplies the posterior fossa structures including brainstem and cerebellum. The basilar artery divides into the *posterior cerebral arteries* supplying the occipital lobes. There is a connection or anastomosis of these anterior and posterior circulations at the *Circle of Willis*. The posterior cerebral arteries anastomose with the internal carotid system via the *posterior communicating arteries*, and the anterior cerebral arteries connect via the *anterior communicating artery*. The brain arteries are end arteries which supply a given territory, but do not anastomose with other arterial systems. Venous blood drains through the *superior sagittal, inferior sagittal* and *straight sinuses* into the *jugular vein*. In contrast to the arterial system, there are extensive anastomoses between the venous supply of the brain, meninges, skull, scalp and sinuses.

The spinal cord. The spinal cord is supplied by multiple radicular arteries, which form the *anterior spinal artery* and two *posterior spinal arteries*. The anterior spinal artery runs the entire length of the cord in the midline, with central and penetrating branches to supply the anterior two-thirds of the spinal cord. The paired posterior spinal arteries run along the posterior aspect of the cord, are discontinuous at times, and supply the posterior one-third of the spinal cord.

[6] The Cerebrospinal Fluid

There are four communicating cavities or *ventricles* within the substance of the brain. The walls of each ventricle contain the *choroid plexus* which secretes *cerebrospinal fluid* (CSF). CSF flows from the two lateral ventricles in the cerebral hemispheres through the two *intraventricular foramina* into a single midline *third ventricle* bounded by the thalami and hypothalamus, then through the single midline *aqueduct of Sylvius* into the single midline *fourth ventricle* between the brainstem and cerebellum, before passing outside the brain via three openings: a midline *foramen of Magendie* and two lateral *foramina of Luschka*. The CSF circulates in the *subarachnoid* space and then exits through *arachnoid villi* in the wall of the *superior sagittal sinus*. An obstruction anywhere along this pathway will lead to ventricular dilation, or *hydrocephalous*. The mean CSF volume in the brain is 100-150ml, and the average rate of production is 500ml/day. Thus, the CSF is completely renewed four to five times a day. Normally CSF does not circulate in the central spinal canal; however, it does flow freely throughout the subarachnoid space. Thus in a subarachnoid hemorrhage blood seeps into the spinal region and may cause a severe neckache or backache.

[7] Intracranial Pressure

This is a logical point to discuss intracranial pressure (ICP) because it requires a basic understanding of several anatomical features, and the issue of increased pressure pervades so many conditions that will be discussed later in the chapter—craniocerebral trauma, cerebral infarction, intracerebral hemorrhage, brain tumor, cerebral abscess, meningitis, encephalitis, and ischemic hypoxic states. The average intracranial volume is 1700ml which includes the approximate 1400ml brain, and 150ml each of blood and CSF. The cranium and vertebral canal together with the inelastic meninges form a rigid container, and any changes in the volume of the cranial contents— brain, blood and CSF—will affect intracranial pressure. The *Monroe-Kellie doctrine* explains that an increase in one component or a mass lesion will increase pressure and necessitate a decrease in the other components in order to maintain the fixed intracranial volume. Initially an expanding lesion can displace CSF and blood with little increase in the ICP; however, the accommodative pressure-volume relationship or *compliance* diminishes rapidly. Ultimately, a small change in the volume results in an exponential rise of the ICP. The increased ICP may lead to either cerebral ischemia or cerebral herniation, with permanent damage or death, unless aggressively monitored and treated. There are a number of diverse conditions that may be associated with increased ICP. Traumatic brain injury is the most common condition requiring ICP monitoring, and is indicated in any patient with a Glasgow Coma Score less than 8 and an abnormal CT or two of the following signs: age greater than 40, motor posturing, or systemic hypotension. Indications are less clear for the other conditions, and each case must be considered individually. ICP should be maintained below 20mm Hg, with cerebral perfusion pressure between 60-80mm Hg. Mass lesions including hematoma may warrant surgical intervention. Hyperventilation reduces ICP and should be used for brief periods pending initiation of other therapies;

then normocapnia is recommended for brain injury. Sedation, paralysis, head-up positioning, hypertonic saline, mannitol, and barbiturates are all therapeutic options. For refractory cases, hypothermia and drug induced coma are options. Decompressive craniotomy is an unproven treatment for increased ICP associated with head injury, but may be indicated in patients with a massive hemispheric infarction.

§ 11.07 The Neurological Evaluation

[1] The Neurological Method

The neurological evaluation is directed toward determining first what part of the neuraxis is causing the symptoms, or *where is the lesion?* Then, second, *what is the lesion?* Anatomical localization allows a focused differential diagnosis. Adhering to this approach avoids many of the pitfalls in diagnosis, safeguarding against tragic error. For example, the patient with diplopia, vertigo and nystagmus should not be labeled "multiple sclerosis" (etiology) but "pontine lesion" (localization); this precludes missing a diagnosis of brainstem tumor or vascular malformation.

[2] The History

The importance of the medical history in the diagnosis of neurological disease cannot be overemphasized. A thorough and accurate history is essential, and generally allows diagnosis of the patient's condition before undertaking physical, neurological and laboratory examinations. The proper examination is predicated upon an accurate history to define the anatomic area of interest. For example, optokinetic nystagmus may be important in a patient with dressing apraxia but is irrelevant to the examination of a patient with a lumbar radiculopathy. The neurological examination techniques depend, in part, on questions formulated by a proper history. Too often, the inexperienced, poorly trained or hurried neurologist distorts the history which leads to diagnostic confusion, inappropriate testing and unnecessary treatment. A history directed exclusively toward the nervous system is incomplete—neurological conditions are frequently the first manifestations of serious systemic diseases. Thus the history should inquire beyond neurological issues to include appropriate demographic questions, and specifically address past medical and surgical history, habits including recreational drugs, medications including non-prescription agents, allergies, family history, and social history including living arrangements, occupation, hobbies or other relevant issues such as potential exposure to toxins or infectious agents. The history should be clearly recorded in a logical, well organized manner. There are two additional points that frequently arise in the medical malpractice case. First, the medical story often begins with the trauma or event in question. It is imperative that events preceding that time are reviewed, especially if the injury involved is thought to have aggravated a pre-existing clinical condition. This scenario is common with neck and back injuries that are superimposed on underlying degenerative spine disease. Second, it is not uncommon for patients involved in litigation to magnify their symptoms. A careful evaluation is necessary to address discrepancies between the history and neurological findings. At the same time, it is important to recognize that many neurological conditions are not static—there may be progression or regression with time, the natural disease process accounting for any disparity between the patient's description of symptoms and findings on serial examinations.

[3] The Neurological Examination

The attorney should recognize the components of a neurological examination and have a general understanding of how it is performed. There are several internet sites providing an overview of the process.[18] In addition, the interested reader may refer to one of the recommended guides for more detail on the neurological evaluation. This section highlights the salient features that would be expected on any examination, and which should be documented in the medical records. There are several reasons for minor modifications of the examination from patient to patient. First, the case setting affects the type, order and completeness of the examination. For example, evaluation of a critically ill patient may be limited to a quick screening until the condition is stabilized. Likewise, an examination will have to be modified for an infant or comatose patient. Second, neurologists have several test options to evaluate certain functions, and these must be gauged to the patient's level of comprehension and ability. For example, certain tests may be more suitable in one individual than another for assessing sensation or coordination. Third, different cases call for different degrees of thoroughness. There is no substitute for a detailed examination, but a screening exam may suffice for the patient with minor symptoms. Further examination would depend on the findings of the screening. Despite these caveats, the standard neurological examination should incorporate testing of cognitive function or mental status, the cranial nerves, motor and sensory systems, reflexes and cerebellar function.

---

[18] www.emedicine.com/neuro/topic632.htm or www.neuroexam.com accessed 12 December 2007.

[4] Mental Status Examination

The astute neurologist can obtain a great deal of information about the cognitive status and other functions simply by observing the patient and taking a history. The patient's posture and gait, ability to dress, particular mannerisms, voice and speech patterns, and even handshake all provide valuable clues. Simply talking with the patient provides insight into language and comprehension, general affect, and overall intellectual functioning. Specific questions are designed to test orientation, attention, concentration, memory, calculations, insight, judgment, abstract thinking and fund of general knowledge. A variety of bedside tests are available. The following screening represents a traditional mental status examination. Orientation to time, place and person must be determined. Retentive memory and immediate recall can be assessed by repetition of a series of digits in forward and reverse sequence. Recent memory is tested by recall of three items of information after five minutes. Attention and concentration, as well as ability to calculate, may be evaluated through serial subtractions of 7s from 100, or other arithmetic problems that comport with educational background. General knowledge as well as memory can be tested by various means such as inquiring after the last four presidents or prime ministers, states or countries, important dates or outstanding points of current events. Abstract reasoning ability may be screened by assessing the interpretation of one or more proverbs. The patient's account of medical consultations, dates of hospitalization, medical procedures and related events as well as social activities represents an excellent test of more remote memory; the narration itself including vocabulary provides information about intelligence. The experienced neurologist will have a better idea about the patient's mental status by performing a thorough evaluation and using a few of these queries than by relying on formal mental screening test scores. However, some practitioners use the "mini-mental state" examination or similar instruments.[19] It is the author's experience that these tests are not particularly sensitive to cognitive dysfunction, especially early or mild impairment. Ideally, such testing should not supplant the bedside evaluation.

Specific higher cortical functions should be tested if the above screening suggests the presence of deficits. Evaluation of language function necessitates assessment of spontaneous speech, naming, repetition, reading, writing, spelling, and comprehension. Tests of visual-spatial function may require checking ability to draw a clock, floor plan of one's home, or copy figures. Calculations, identifying left from right, and praxias (dressing, brushing

---

[19] Folstein MF, Folstein SE, McHugh PR. *"Mini-Mental State." A Practical Method for Grading the Cognitive State of Patients for the Clinician.* J Psych Research 1975; 12:189-198.

teeth, combing hair) may be assessed. The extent of testing depends on the patient's deficits. It is recommended that patients with higher cognitive impairment be referred for formal neuropsychometric testing, which is far superior to bedside evaluation and provides objective data for follow-up.

[5] Cranial Nerve Examination

CN I: The patient is asked to smell and identify various odors such as clove, coffee or lemon oil in order to test the olfactory nerve. It is important to occlude each nostril sequentially during the test. Noxious stimuli such as ammonia probably activate CN V sensory fibers and should not be used. It may be preferable to have a quantitative assessment to precisely characterize any deficits, identify malingering and monitor changes over time. Additionally, objective documentation may support a disability rating. There are several commercially available tests including the University of Pennsylvania Smell Identification Test which can identify malingering. *CN II:* Optic nerve testing includes checking pupillary responses to light and accommodation, measuring visual fields by confrontation testing, and fundoscopic evaluation of the optic nerve head and retina. The presence of any deficits usually warrants formal testing which may include visual evoked potentials, mapping of visual fields or neuro-ophthalmology consultation. *CNs III, IV and VI:* These three nerves (oculomotor, trochlear, and abducens) supply the extraocular muscles, allowing the eyes to move together as a pair. Impairment of one or more nerves results in diplopia, and possibly other signs. The patient stabilizes the head and tracks the examiners finger to the right, left, up and down. Then vertical eye movements are checked in the far right and left lateral gaze positions. The common causes of unilateral CN III palsy are infarction (often with diabetes mellitus), aneurysm, tumor and trauma. CN VI lesions are seen with trauma, subarachnoid hemorrhage, demyelinating disease and tumor. It is unusual to have an isolated CN IV palsy which causes a pure vertical diplopia. Pupillary testing including the light reflex is also an important part of the assessment. *CN V:* The trigeminal nerve (ophthalmic, maxillary and mandibular branches) is a mixed nerve carrying sensory information from the face and meninges, and supplying motor fibers to the muscles of mastication, tensor tympani (dampening sound in the middle ear) and tensor veli palatine (involved in swallowing). Jaw muscle strength and bulk (temporalis and masseter) are tested with opening, protrusion and lateral excursion against resistance. Sensation over the entire face is tested with light touch and pinprick. The presence or absence of corneal reflexes must be determined by lightly touching the cornea with cotton (measuring trigeminal sensory function and CN VII motor activity). It is frequently necessary to test for psychogenic sensory loss in the face. The various examination techniques are based upon three key neuroanatomic features. First, sensory loss does not change abruptly at precisely the midline because the trigeminal sensory fields overlap. Second, vibration over the forehead of the affected side will not be impaired (it is appreciated by the single frontal skull bone even with complete sensory loss). The patient reporting that the tuning fork "splits the midline" and is not perceived on the symptomatic side is embellishing or has a non-organic sensory loss. Third, facial numbness extending to the ramus (angle) of the mandible cannot be attributed to the trigeminal nerve since that region is supplied by the cervical nerves. *CN VII:* The facial nerve is predominantly motor to the facial muscles, with the chorda tympani carrying taste sensation for the anterior two-thirds of the tongue to the brainstem. Facial nerve abnormalities are often noted on the history but must be confirmed on examination: testing eyebrow elevation, forehead wrinkling, eye closure, smiling, frowning, puffing of cheeks, whistling and chin muscle contraction. Taste is testing by applying sweet, sour, salty and bitter substances on the lateral margin of the protruded tongue halfway back from the tip. *CN VIII:* The vestibulocochlear nerve contains fibers supplying the cochlea for hearing, and those supplying the vestibular complex for balance. Weber's (lateralization of a tuning fork placed on forehead midline) and Rinne's (air versus mastoid bone conduction) tests distinguish conductive from neural hearing loss. Quantitative testing of hearing requires audiometry. Vestibular examination requires testing of gait and balance, including the ability to stand with eyes closed (Rhomberg test). Formal balance testing is available in most medical centers. *CN IX:* The glossopharyngeal nerve is mixed with autonomic fibers supplying the parotid gland, motor fibers to the stylopharyngeal muscle, and sensory input from the posterior one-third of the tongue, and parts of the external ear and tympanic membrane. It is extremely rare for CN IX to be affected in isolation. Testing is difficult and requires assessing sensation in the posterior pharynx and posterior third of the tongue. *CN X:* The vagus nerve is mixed with autonomic fibers throughout the thoracic and abdominal organs, motor fibers to muscles of the pharynx, larynx, tongue and vocal cords, and sensory input from a portion of the throat and ear. It is assessed at bedside by observing the palate and uvula at rest, and checking for symmetric elevation with phonation. The pharyngeal or gag reflex is tested by stimulating the posterior pharyngeal wall on each side with a blunt instrument. Autonomic function may be evaluated with a variety of neurodiagnostic tests. *CN XI:* The accessory nerve innervates the sternocleidomastoid and trapezius muscles which may be tested by having the patient rotate the head and shrug shoulders against resistance, respectively. *CN XII*: The hypoglossal nerve supplies the tongue muscles. It is tested by examining the bulk and power of the tongue, checking for atrophy, tremor or fasciculations, and deviation from midline upon protrusion (the tongue "points" to the affected side with a hypoglossal nerve lesion; and deviates contralateral to a supranuclear lesion).

[6] Motor Examination

Motor function includes evaluation of strength, bulk, tone, coordination and abnormal movements. Muscle size and shape are assessed by visual inspection and measurement. Atrophy may be secondary to loss of innervation or intrinsic muscle disease; hypertrophy may suggest deposition of abnormal substances in the muscle. Tone is checked by testing resistance to passive motion of a relaxed limb. Diminished tone is usually due to lower motor neuron, peripheral nerve or cerebellar dysfunction. Increased tone may be secondary to spasticity (upper motor neuron lesions), rigidity (extrapyramidal disease), or paratonia which is also known as Gegenhalten, meaning variable changes in resistance to repetitive passive movements (frontal lobe or thalamic disorders). Involuntary abnormal movements may be present at rest (tics, myoclonus, ballismus, chorea), during maintained posture (Parkinson's disease), or with action (cerebellar or familial tremor). Strength testing requires patient cooperation to move a body part or limb against resistance while individual muscles are evaluated. The strength of each muscle or muscle group should be recorded and rated on the following scale: 0 = no movement. 1 = trace of contraction. 2 = active movement without gravity. 3 = active movement against gravity. 4 = active movement against resistance. 5 = normal power. The ratings are further refined by adding a + or – to indicate intermediate levels of strength (for example, 4+ means movement against strong resistance as opposed to 4- movement against a minimal degree of resistance).

[7] Sensory Examination

Five primary sensory modalities—light touch, pinprick, temperature, vibration and position — are tested in each limb to detect areas of abnormal or absent sensation. Sensory deficits may be widespread or anatomically restricted, and involve one or more modalities. There are characteristic syndromes for lesions involving particular parts of the brain, spinal cord, plexus, root or peripheral nerve. Therefore, determining the location and type of sensory loss will usually lead to an accurate anatomic diagnosis. For example, a gradient of distal more that proximal loss may be present in a peripheral neuropathy. Likewise, vitamin B12 deficiency may present with impaired vibratory perception in the lower extremities due to posterior column dysfunction. Light touch is tested with a wisp of cotton, pinprick with a pin comparing sharp and dull ends, and temperature with cold and hot metal discs. For vibration a 128 Hz vibrating weighted tuning fork is applied to the terminal phalanx of the great toe or middle finger, allowing comparison with the neurologist's own threshold of perception. Passive movement testing for position involves grasping the terminal portion of a digit (great toe or finger) on the lateral surface and making small vertical movements, with the patient responding "up" or "down" in relation to each previous position. Patients with lesions above the level of the thalamus may have a loss of double simultaneous stimulation, impairment of two point discrimination, and difficulty judging texture and weights. Impaired stereognosis (identifying objects by touch) and graphesthesia (identifying numbers or letters written on skin surface) may be present.

[8] Deep Tendon Reflex Examination

The deep tendon reflexes most commonly tested include the biceps, brachioradialis, and triceps in the upper extremities, and the patellar and Achilles in the lower extremities. This permits a sampling of spinal cord levels C5 (biceps), C6 (brachioradialis), C7 (triceps), L3 (patellar) and S1 (Achilles). The reflexes are best elicited in a relaxed limb—it may be useful to distract the patient with conversation, or facilitate the reflex by encouraging voluntary contraction of distant muscles (Jendrassik maneuver). During the testing of each reflex, the right and left limbs should be similarly positioned and the two sides evaluated sequentially. It is most helpful to determine the smallest stimulus required to elicit a reflex, as opposed to seeking the maximal response. Grading is based on the following scale: 0 = absent. 1 = present but diminished. 2 = normal. 3 = exaggerated. 4 = clonus. Clonus refers to repetitive rhythmic contractions precipitated by a stretch stimulus. It is most commonly noted in the Achilles reflex, and indicative of an upper motor neuron disorder. Superficial cutaneous reflexes also provide important localizing information. The plantar response is elicited by stroking the lateral sole of the foot with a blunt object, beginning at the heel and moving toward the toes. The normal response is planter flexion of the toes. In upper motor neuron lesions above the spinal cord S1 level, a paradoxical extension of the great toe occurs with fanning and extension of the other toes (*Babinski* sign). There may be a prominent triple flexion response involving the ankle, knee and hip. Some patients withdraw from the uncomfortable stimulus leading to an inconclusive interpretation of the reflex; it may be necessary to pursue alternative testing that can elicit a Babinski sign such as applying pressure to the anterior tibia (*Oppenheim* sign), pinprick on dorsum of great toe (*Bing* sign) or pressure to the calf (*Gordon* sign). Superficial abdominal reflexes may be of diagnostic value in localizing lesions of the pyramidal tract. The upper abdominal reflex (spinal cord level T9) is elicited by stroking the lateral upper corner of abdomen towards umbilicus; the lower (spinal cord level T12) by beginning at lower lateral abdomen. The normal response is a diagonal deviation of the umbilicus toward the stimulus. These reflexes are absent in upper motor neuron diseases. There are also a number of primitive reflexes which are not normally present in the adult, but may be unmasked with dementia, frontal lobe dysfunction or hydrocephalous (*snout, grasp,* and *palmomental reflexes*).

[9] Cerebellar Examination

Observation of the patient during the history and activities such as walking, picking up objects and undressing provides invaluable clues regarding coordination. However, disturbances of movement simulating cerebellar incoordination may be caused by lesions of the frontal cortex, posterior columns, peripheral nerves, and muscles. Therefore it is important to specifically test for cerebellar dysfunction. The neurologists observes the accuracy, speed, direction, rhythm and force during the *nose-finger-nose test* (patient repeatedly touches index finger to nose then examiner's finger, repeating the sequence while examiner moves finger around), *knee pat test* (while sitting, the patient pats the knee alternately with palm and dorsum of hand), *toe-finger test* (while supine, the patient uses great toe to touch examiner's finger), and *heel-knee test* (patient slides heel of each foot from knee down the shin to dorsum of foot on the opposite leg). Rapid alternating movements should be tested in the hands (*finger wriggle* involves tapping of thumb with tip of index finger on same hand) and feet (*foot pat* involves patting the floor as rapidly as possible with ball of the foot while keeping heel on the ground). Finally, gait analysis is an essential part of any neurological examination. Normal walking requires that multiple systems (motor, sensory, coordination, and praxis) function is a coordinated fashion. Rising from a seated or lying position, walking and turning, heel-toe walking on a straight line and standing with eyes closed and feet together (*Rhomberg* test) are tested. There may be a stooped posture with *marche à petit pas* gait (Parkinson's syndrome), scissoring gait (corticospinal dysfunction), broad-based unstable gait (ataxia), high stepping foot slapping gait (peripheral neuropathy or posterior column impairment), or magnetic gait where the patient appears stuck (apraxia). Armswing range and symmetry should be observed (for example, unilateral diminished armswing may be the earliest sign of Parkinson's disease). Walking may uncover various movement disorders (for example, walking on toes may reveal dystonia of a hand).

§ 11.08 Neurodiagnostic Testing

[1] Basis for Testing

The experienced neurologist can usually make an anatomical diagnosis after completing the history and examination. Sometimes the etiological diagnosis is obvious; however, many times additional investigation is necessary to identify or confirm the pathology underlying the patient's signs and symptoms. The commonly used neurological tests include lumbar puncture, imaging procedures, neurophysiology studies, genetic testing, biopsies, and neuropsychological assessments.

[2] Negligence in Testing

Advances in neurodiagnostic testing will open the door for an increasing number of malpractice claims. Some tests are invasive and potentially harmful; others may cause psychological or economic harm. Most negligence claims related to testing, however, will fall into one of the following categories: (1) Negligent failure to perform a test. This is certainly the most common type of claim in neurology; it is epitomized by the failure to order an MRI on the patient with progressive headache symptoms, with later evaluation uncovering a treatable lesion. The rapid growth of available studies means that some neurologists are not aware of certain tests, the proper indications for performing the tests, or how to interpret the results. Or, they may respond to cost containment pressures by withholding tests that should be performed. The combination of these factors foreshadows an increasing number of claims for negligent failure to order medically necessary testing. (2) Negligent choice of test. The neurologist, rather than failing to order a test, may choose the wrong test. For example, an MRI of the cervical and thoracic spine would likely be ordered on a patient with weakness and spasticity in the legs and, with normal results, the neurologist may diagnose a degenerative disease. If the symptoms progress and subsequent evaluation demonstrates a parasagittal meningioma (brain tumor), there may be a claim for negligent misdiagnosis. (3) Negligent performance of testing. Most neurologists perform their own diagnostic testing and are vulnerable to a claim of physical injury due to a carelessly performed test. However, they may also be liable for a negligently performed study generating inaccurate data. For example, a poorly performed carotid ultrasound may result in missing a lesion otherwise amenable to endarterectomy. (4) Negligent interpretation. The neurologist may misinterpret data, such as reading an epileptiform spike on an electroencephalographic recording as normal, or misdiagnosing a brain tumor on computerized tomography as a stroke. In any negligence action, the preponderance of expert opinion must be that the defendant neurologist violated prevailing standards of care in ordering, performing or interpreting the test.

[3] Lumbar Puncture

It may be necessary to examine the cerebrospinal fluid (CSF) which surrounds the brain and spinal cord. This is particularly important with infective disease such as meningitis or encephalitis. CSF examination is a valuable diagnostic aid in subarachnoid hemorrhage (SAH), and may be useful in some forms of malignancy, demyelinating disease, vasculitis and certain neuropathies.

A lumbar puncture (LP) provides access to the CSF. This involves inserting a spinal needle between two lumbar vertebrae below the L2 level (in adults, the spinal cord normally terminates at or above the level of the second lumbar vertebrae). The needle is directed far enough to penetrate the dura mater. Measurement of the spinal fluid opening pressure may provide useful information, especially in the diagnosis of *pseudotumor cerebri*. The fluid is analyzed for cell count and differential; microorganisms including bacteriological cultures and viral isolation; glucose, protein, and other chemical measurements; immunoelectrophoresis for gamma globulin level, oligoclonal banding, and other biochemical tests; serologic and genetic tests; and cytology as well as a host of other studies depending on the clinical suspicions.

There are several absolute or relative contraindications to LP. First, it should not be performed in the presence of neurological signs of elevated intracranial pressure suggesting structural pathology in the brain or spinal cord. An LP in this setting increases the possibility of fatal herniation of the uncus through the tentorium or cerebellar tonsils through the foramen magnum. In such cases, CT or MRI should be performed to exclude mass lesion prior to LP. An isolated exception to this rule is in suspected meningitis where timely CSF examination is crucial. The LP should then be performed with a fine-gauge needle. If opening pressure is 400mm Hg or higher, the minimal required amount of CSF should be obtained, the needle removed and, if indicated, followed by administration of mannitol. Second, patients with coagulation disorders or thrombocytopenia should be approached with particular caution due to the risk of hemorrhage into the extradural or intradural space. The prudent course of action is to transfuse platelets, administer fresh frozen plasma, or reverse therapeutic anticoagulation prior to the LP. Third, LP should generally not be performed in the presence of local skin or soft tissue infection along the needle tract due to the risk of spreading infection to the meninges.

There are several potential complications. First, and most common, occurring in up to 40% of patients, is the post dural puncture headache (PDPH). The headache begins within 48 hours in the majority, and within 72 hours in 90% of patients, although onset can be delayed for up to two weeks.[20,21] The duration of the headache is less than five days in most patients, but can persist for up to a year.[22] The headache is bilateral, described as a frontal, occipital or generalized pressure or throbbing, maximal in the upright position and decreasing or resolving when supine. It is aggravated by movement, coughing, sneezing or straining. Associated symptoms may include neck stiffness, nausea, vomiting or cochlear symptoms. The pathophysiological basis is probably low CSF pressure due to leakage through a dural and arachnoid tear which exceeds the rate of CSF production. PDPH risk factors include the female gender, age 18-30 years, and a history of headaches. Additionally, the diameter of the needle and orientation of the bevel are exceedingly important—the incidence of PDPH decreases markedly with a smaller diameter needle, and orientation of the bevel parallel to the dural fibers.[23] Treatment ranges from bedrest, hydration and analgesics in mild cases, to an epidural blood patch in more severe cases. Second, LP may cause CN III, IV, V, VI, VII or VIII neuropathies which are usually transient and attributed to intracranial hypotension with resultant traction on the nerves. CN VI (abducens) palsy is the most common cause of diplopia; it may occur days after the procedure and take weeks to resolve. Hearing loss may occur in up to 8% of patients; it is usually reversible but may be permanent.[24] Third, back pain and nerve root irritation are not infrequent. The back pain may persist for months due to local trauma but usually resolves in a short time. Inserting the needle beyond the subarachnoid space may damage the annulus fibrosis resulting in disc herniation or, with the introduction of bacteria, discitis and vertebral collapse

---

[20] Kuntz KM, Kokmen E, Stevens JC, et al. *Post-Lumbar Puncture Headaches: Experience in 501 Consecutive Patients.* Neurology 42:1884-1887, 1992.

[21] Lybecker H, Djernes M, Schmidt JF. *Postdural Puncture Headache (PDPH): Onset, Duration, Severity, and Associated Symptoms.* Acta Anaesthesiol Scand 39:605-612, 1995.

[22] Lance JW, Branch GB. *Persistent Headache after Lumbar Puncture.* Lancet 343:414, 1994.

[23] Evans RW. *Complications of Lumbar Puncture.* Neurol Clin 16(1):83-105, 1998.

[24] Broome IJ. *Hearing Loss and Dural Puncture.* Lancet 341:667-668, 1993.

which has a latency of up to three months.[25] Nerve root irritation is another common complaint, and the patient may experience shocks or "pins and needles" when the spinal needle makes contact with a sensory root. Rarely permanent motor or sensory loss may occur. The spinal cord may be damaged if the procedure is performed at an improper level. Fourth, a variety of infectious complications besides discitis may occur including bacterial meningitis, lumbar epidural abscess, and spinal cord abscess. The source of infection is secondary to using a contaminated needle, inadequate disinfection of the skin, performing the LP when there is an infection in the area, and introducing blood in the subarachnoid space in the presence of an underlying bacteremia. Fifth, there are a multitude of potential bleeding complications with LP. Intracranial hemorrhage can occur in otherwise healthy patients without bleeding disorders. Subdural hematoma may occur after an interval of months, presumably due to intracranial hypotension resulting in traction on the meninges causing dural vessel tearing.[26] Post-spinal SAH may occur due to traction on the basal blood vessels causing rupture of a saccular aneurysm.[27] Rare LP complications include spinal subarachnoid hematoma and spinal epidural hematoma. Both present within days after the LP with severe back or radicular pain, progressive paraparesis, a sensory level, and sphincter disturbances. Treatment usually requires emergent decompressive laminectomy with hematoma evacuation. Risk factors for LP related hemorrhagic complications include bleeding disorders, thrombocytopenia, therapeutic anticoagulation, and a traumatic or "bloody tap" (usually due to puncture of the radicular vessels accompanying each nerve root). Management of these factors requires replacement therapy for bleeding disorders, ensuring platelet count is 50,000 or higher, and adequate reversal of heparin (protamine or vitamin K) or warfarin (fresh frozen plasma). Sixth, it should be kept in mind that other complications such as seizures can occur.

LP is also performed for myelography, which involves injecting a radio-opaque dye into the subarachnoid space around the spinal cord and then taking x-rays. MRI techniques have largely replaced this procedure, although there remains a role for myelograms (for example, implanted metal may preclude a patient from MRI). The potential complications include all of those for LP plus the risk of the dye injection. The modern contrast medias are water soluble, and have been linked to seizures. The older oil-based

---

[25] Bhatoe HS, Gill HS, Kumar N, et al. *Post Lumbar Puncture Discitis and Verbebral Collapse.* Postgrad Med J 70:882-882, 1994.

[26] Vos PE, de Boer WA, Wurzer JAL, et al. *Subdural Hematoma after Lumbar Puncture: Two Case Reports and Review of the Literature.* Clin Neurol Neurosurg 93:127-132, 1991.

[27] Hart IK, Bone I, Hadley DM. *Development of Neurological Problems after Lumbar Puncture.* BMJ 296:51-52, 1988.

agents had the potential to cause arachnoiditis, or inflammation in the tissue surrounding the spinal cord.

[4] Imaging Studies

X-ray. Plain radiographs of the skull and spine remain important despite availability of more sophisticated imaging modalities. X-rays delineate fractures more clearly than CT or MRI. Special views of the skull may be necessary to identify the foramina of exiting cranial nerves. Radiographs of the cervical spine are essential for measuring canal diameter and, with flexion and extension views, determining spinal stability. In addition, plain films are quite useful for demonstrating Paget's disease and destructive lesions of the vertebrae.

Computerized Tomography. Computerized tomography (CT) involves computerized analysis of x-ray attenuation coefficients in the skull, cerebral gray and white matter, CSF and blood vessels. The greater the x-ray attenuation, such as by bone, the higher the density. Differing densities of the skull, brain, CSF and blood are visualized in the resultant picture. The precise locations of the ventricles and midline structures are apparent, and it is relatively easy to distinguish edematous brain, extra-axial or intracranial hemorrhage, and focal structures such as a tumor or abscess. Intravenous contrast may be administered to identify vascular structures, and detect blood brain barrier defects associated with tumors, infarctions and infections. Newer techniques such as spiral CT permits rapid testing with improved images. CT is useful for imaging osseus detail of the skull base, temporal bones and spine. It is also sensitive for acute parenchymal and subarachnoid hemorrhage. In the spine, CT permits evaluation of osseus spinal stenosis and spondylosis, but cannot directly identify the spinal cord. If the cord needs to be imaged, contrast must be introduced by lumbar puncture before CT (CT myelography). CT related complications may occur with intravenous contrast agents, especially the inexpensive ionic types. These include pain, nausea and vomiting as well as more serious nephropathy and anaphylactic reactions. If there are risk factors such as a prior reaction, then non-ionic agents should be used in conjunction with steroid and antihistamine pretreatment. MRI has replaced CT for evaluation of most conditions affecting the brain and spine parenchyma.

Magnetic resonance imaging. Magnetic resonance imaging (MRI) is the preferred imaging modality for most neurological disease. It involves placing the patient in a powerful magnetic field, causing the brain and CSF protons to align themselves in the orientation of the magnetic field. A radiofrequency pulse introduced into the field causes the protons to resonate and change alignment; the protons return to their original alignment when the pulse is removed. The pulse energy that was absorbed and emitted is detected by electromagnetic devices and subject to computer analysis, and then converted to a picture. It is far superior to CT, especially for imaging of the temporal lobes, posterior fossa (brainstem and cerebellum), and cervicomedullary junction. Gray and white matters are easily distinguished, and lesions generally well demarcated. Infarctions are seen earlier that with CT; hemorrhages can be dated because the by-products of disintegrating red blood cells are easily recognized. Demyelinating lesions stand out quite clearly. In the spine, MRI provides excellent images of the vertebral bodies, intervertebral discs, spinal cord, nerve roots and cauda equina. It has essentially replaced myelography for most conditions including herniated discs, tumors, epidural or subdural hemorrhages, congenital anomalies and syringomyelia. The administration of intravenous gadolinium enhances proton relaxation and permits greater definition of lesions. Complications from the contrast material are exceedingly rare and generally limited to allergic reactions, as well as the more recently recognized nephrogenic systemic fibrosis. MRI is contraindicated in patients with metal clips on blood vessels, metal dental devices, and other ferromagnetic objects including metal fragments in the orbit (which may be unnoticed in machine workers). The metal may be torqued or dislodged; an aneurysm clip may result in vessel rupture, and dislocation of metal fragments in the eye may cause intraocular hemorrhage. If there is any question, then plain radiographs should be performed to ascertain the presence of metal before the patient enters the MRI facility. Ferromagnetic objects brought into the magnet room can be attracted to the magnet and act as a missile. Cardiac pacemakers are an absolute contraindication to MRI due to the risk of induced arrhythmias. Other contraindications include cochlear prostheses, spinal cord stimulators, electronic infusion devices, bone growth stimulators, and a variety of other implants, prostheses and certain catheters. Magnetic resonance angiography (MRA) uses MRI techniques to demonstrate the contrast between fixed and moving (blood flowing in vessels) tissues. It is noninvasive, and provides evaluation of vessel narrowing (stenosis) or obstruction, as well as detection of aneurysms and vascular malformations. It has not yet completely supplanted conventional angiography.

Angiography. Despite the advent of CT and MRI/MRA, there remains a role for angiography in the diagnosis of aneurysms, vascular malformations, narrowed vessels, dissections and angiitis. The most common technique is a transfemoral approach to the aortic arch, followed by selective catheterization with contrast injection into each carotid artery and into the basilar system, thus demonstrating the intracranial vasculature. However, angiography carries the greatest risk of all diagnostic imaging procedures.

Up to 5% of patients may suffer transient or permanent neurological deficits following cerebral angiography. A thrombus may form on the tip of the catheter, or plaque may be dislodged by the guide wire or catheter or by the force of injection, with distal embolization in the cerebral circulation resulting in a stroke. High concentrations of injected contrast may induce vasospasm, resulting in a stroke. A cervical myelopathy from progressive spinal cord ischemia may occur after vertebral artery injection. Thus, the decision to perform angiography requires a careful weighing of the diagnostic or therapeutic benefits and potential risks.

Ultrasound. Ultrasound (US) is predominantly limited to clinical study of the developing brain, and noninvasive assessment of the extracranial cerebral vasculature. A transducer converts electrical energy to ultrasound waves. These waves are transmitted to tissues which have variable acoustical impedance, and send back echoes that may be displayed as points of light with varying intensity. In the fetal and neonatal brain, US provides images of nuclear masses, ventricles, and choroid plexuses which allows visualization of intracerebral and subdural hemorrhages, mass lesions and congenital defects. In the adult, US is predominately used for estimating the degree of stenosis of the extracranial carotid vasculature. Vertebral artery and intracranial vessels are less reliably visualized.

Positron emission tomography. Positron emission tomography (PET) scanning measures cerebral blood flow, oxygen uptake and glucose utilization; it is a valuable procedure for grading primary brain tumors, localizing epileptic foci, and differentiating various types of dementia. However, it is not readily available for routine diagnosis. Single photon emission computed tomography (SPECT) evolved from PET scans, and is useful for studying cerebral blood flow and intense tissue metabolism in seizure discharge. The roles for these modalities will continue to evolve with advancement of imaging techniques.

[5] Neurophysiology Studies

Neurophysiology studies, also referred to as neurodiagnostic or electro-diagnostic testing, or electrophysiology, include electroencephalography; visual, auditory and somatosensory evoked potentials; and nerve conduction studies and electromyography. Additional specialized studies that play a role in the diagnosis of particular conditions are beyond the ambit of this chapter.

[6] Electroencephalography

The electroencephalogram (EEG) records spontaneous electrical activity originating in the cerebral cortex. This activity represents the summated effects of excitatory and inhibitory post-synaptic potentials from innumerable vertically oriented pyramidal cells in the cortex. Afferent impulses from subcortical structures are probably responsible for entraining these cortical neurons to produce the characteristic brain wave patterns. Electrodes are attached to the scalp to record this activity. The potential difference between pairs of scalp electrodes or between individual electrodes and an inactive reference point is amplified a million-fold, displayed on an oscilloscope, and recorded on paper or digitally. An EEG is usually sampled from 16 or more channels (areas) of the scalp simultaneously in selected montages (combinations). The montages are arranged to compare the activity in one region of the cortex to the corresponding region on the opposite side. The activity is characterized by frequency, amplitude, quantity, morphology, reactivity, variability, topography and phase relationships. Activation procedures such as hyperventilation, photic stimulation and sleep deprivation are utilized in an effort to provoke abnormalities. The proper interpretation of EEGs requires the recognition of normal and abnormal patterns and background rhythms, the detection of asymmetries as well as periodic rhythm changes, and the differentiation of artifacts from abnormal findings. It is imperative for the neurologist to fully understand the technical features and limitations of testing.

In many parts of the world the EEG is still used to identify focal structural abnormalities such as tumors, strokes or hematomas. The limitations are severe—EEG does not indicate the nature of the underlying pathology, and infratentorial or slowly expanding lesions may fail to produce any abnormality. In the developed countries, CT and MRI have supplanted EEG for the diagnosis of most neurological disorders. However, EEG remains essential in the evaluation of suspected epilepsy. The presence of electroencephalographic seizure activity—the sudden onset and termination of abnormal, repetitive, rhythmic activity—provides diagnostic certainty. The absence of such activity does *not* exclude a seizure disorder; there may be no change in the EEG during a simple or complex partial seizure. It may prove impossible to obtain an EEG during a clinical event suggesting seizures, especially if such events are infrequent. The development of portable equipment allows 24 hour or longer EEGs in ambulatory patients. Inpatient video EEGs may be beneficial in selected patients, especially those individuals with non-epileptic fits or pseudoseizures. Other uses in seizures: Interictal EEGs may show abnormalities supportive of a diagnosis of epilepsy. EEGs are helpful in classifying seizure disorders and selecting the proper anticonvulsants. They may also provide insight into the prognosis of a seizure disorder. Non-convulsive status epilepticus may not be recognized without an EEG.

The EEG may be useful in dementia, but cannot distinguish between different causes of cognitive decline except in a very few instances such as Creutzfeldt-Jakob disease or subacute sclerosis panencephalitis. There is a distinct role for EEG in evaluating the cerebral effects of systemic metabolic diseases, and assessing sleep disorders. Lastly, EEG plays a crucial role in evaluating coma, identifying locked-in syndrome, and as an adjunct to the brain death determination.

[7] Evoked Potentials

The stimulation of afferent sensory pathways evokes spinal or cerebral potentials that may be recorded from the scalp. These evoked potentials (EP) are so small that responses to numerous stimuli must be computer averaged in order to permit identification of the waveforms. Evoked potentials are an important means of assessing the functional integrity of certain neural pathways, although they do not indicate the pathologic basis of a disruptive lesion. Visual, auditory and somatosensory potentials are the most commonly tested EPs.

Visual evoked potentials (VEPs) evaluate portions of the visual pathways. The usual stimulus is monocular presentation of a reversing checkerboard pattern, with recording from the occipital region in the midline and on both sides. The major component of clinical relevance is a positive peak with latency at approximately 100ms, called the P100 response. The presence, latency and symmetry of the P100 are measured on each side of the scalp. An absent response or prolonged latency of P100 following stimulation of one eye indicates a lesion in the ipsilateral visual pathway anterior to the optic chiasm. In acute or severe optic neuritis the P100 may be absent; with clinical recovery the P100 is restored but with an increased latency that remains indefinitely. The VEPs may be used to identify subclinical or previous optic neuritis, which is helpful in evaluating demyelinating diseases such as multiple sclerosis.

Brainstem auditory evoked potentials (BAEPs) measure both peripheral and central auditory pathways. These EPs are elicited by monaural stimulation with repetitive clicks, and recorded between the mastoid process and vertex of the scalp. The series of potentials occurring in the first 10ms after stimulation represents sequential activation of structures from the auditory nerve (wave I) to the midbrain inferior colliculus (wave V). The presence, latency and interpeak latencies of the first five potentials recorded at the vertex are measured. BAEPs are particularly useful for detecting acoustic neuromas and screening for brainstem lesions. They are also helpful in evaluating the comatose patient—the potentials are normal in coma due to metabolic or toxic disorders or bihemispheric disease, but abnormal with brainstem pathology.

Somatosensory evoked potentials (SSEPs) evaluate proximal parts of the peripheral nervous system and assess the integrity of the central sensory pathways. These potentials are recorded over the scalp and spine in response to stimulation of a peripheral nerve; usually the median or ulnar in the arm, and tibial or peroneal in the leg. The presence, latency and interpeak latencies of the potentials track sensory pathways ascending the posterior columns, traversing the brainstem and terminating in the contralateral somatosensory cortex. SSEPs are predominantly used to evaluate myelopathy or spinal cord disease, and may be beneficial during intraoperative monitoring to warn the neurosurgeon on impending spinal cord injury. The SSEP testing should not be confused with *dermatomal somatosensory evoked potentials* (DSEPs) with are elicited by skin stimulation and serve no clinical purpose. These latter tests are often performed in independent laboratories or private offices, as well as by non-neurologists, solely as a means of generating revenue. The AAN set forth a final opinion on these knock-off tests by concluding "there is no evidence that DSEP findings provide any reliable information beyond the routine clinical examination."[28]

[8] Nerve Conduction Studies and Electromyography

Nerve conduction studies (NCS) and electromyography (EMG) are valuable tests for diagnosing neuromuscular diseases ranging from peripheral nerve compression (carpal tunnel syndrome) to motor neuron conditions (amyotrophic lateral sclerosis) and muscle disorders. They are an extension of the clinical examination, not simply diagnostic tests performed in isolation like a radiograph or electrocardiogram. The neurologist must interview and examine the patient, and design a testing protocol for that particular patient's clinical presentation. It requires a dynamic and flexible approach since unexpected findings during the test may necessitate alterations in the procedure.

EMG involves recording electrical activity from muscles by inserting a recording needle electrode directly into the muscle. The muscle electrical activity is displayed on an oscilloscope screen and broadcast over a loudspeaker for simultaneous visual and auditory interpretation. Many abnormalities are more accurately heard rather than visualized. The examination of insertional, spontaneous and voluntary activity patterns

---

[28] Therapeutics and Technology Assessment Subcommittee, *Assessment: Dermatomal Somatosensory Evoked Potentials.* Neurology (1997) 49:1127-1130.

allows the neurologist to distinguish between disorders at different levels of the motor unit (a motor unit consists of an anterior horn cell, its axon, neuromuscular junction and all the muscle fibers innervated by that axon). For example, the presence of abnormal spontaneous activity such a fibrillation potentials and positive sharp waves (acute denervation) in the S1 innervated muscles may be indicative of an L5S1 disc herniation. Similarly, polyphasic potentials suggest a myopathic process. Although EMG results allow disorders of the motor units to be characterized as neurogenic or myopathic, the findings do not provide an etiological diagnosis. Importantly, EMG should not be confused with *surface* EMG where electrical potentials are recorded from the skin overlying muscles.

NCS complement the EMG testing. These tests are performed by stimulating a motor or sensory nerve with electrical impulses and, at a distant site, recording the resultant compound muscle action potential or sensory nerve action potential, respectively. Measurements of the latency, size and velocity of a response allow determination of the presence and extent of peripheral nerve disease. NCS address whether sensory symptoms are arising from pathology proximal or distal to the dorsal root ganglia, and whether neuromuscular dysfunction is due to peripheral nerve disease. These tests are particularly valuable in patients with mononeuropathy, providing a means to localize a focal lesion, determine the extent and severity of pathology, provide prognostic expectations, and detect subclinical findings in other nerves. Additionally, NCS can distinguish a polyneuropathy from mononeuropathy multiplex, and determine whether a polyneuropathy is demyelinating or axonal in nature, an important distinction because of the etiological implications. There are specialized studies such as F-waves, H-reflexes, and repetitive stimulation that have a role in specific neurological disorders.

NCS and EMG are generally well tolerated and rarely associated with any significant side effects. However, needle EMG is invasive with the potential for expected complications including bleeding, infection, nerve or muscle injury and pneumothorax.[29] NCS may have leakage currents that carry a risk to patients with cardiac pacemakers or other electrical devices, although a recent study concluded routine testing is safe for implanted pacemakers with bipolar sensing configurations and defibrillators.[30]

---

[29] Al-Shekhlee A, Shapiro BE, Preston DC. *Iatrogenic complications and risks of nerve conduction studies and needle electromyography.* Muscle Nerve (2003) 27(5):517-526.

[30] Schoeck AP, Mellion ML, Gilchrist JM, Christian FV. *Safety of nerve conduction studies in patients with implanted cardiac devices.* Muscle Nerve 2007; 35(4):521-524.

[9] Biopsies

There are situations where noninvasive testing fails to yield a diagnosis, and it may be necessary to perform a nerve, muscle or brain biopsy. The nerve biopsy uses a sensory nerve, commonly the sural nerve, leaving an area of sensory loss but no weakness. It may be helpful to differentiate demyelinating from axonal neuropathies, or reveal evidence of inflammation or infiltration of the nerve with abnormal substances or cells. The muscle biopsy may be performed by a direct surgical approach or percutaneous method, and is used to evaluate weakness, abnormal tone, or other signs of muscle disease as well as inherited disorders. Brain biopsy may need to be performed to determine the nature of certain tumors, and rarely in selected cases of infection and genetic diseases.

[10] Neurogenetics

Genetic testing refers to "the analysis of human DNA, RNA, chromosomes, proteins, and certain metabolites in order to detect heritable disease-related genotypes, mutations, phenotypes, or karyotypes for clinical purposes."[31] A growing number of gene abnormalities have been linked to neurological diseases, and many of these are amenable to diagnostic testing.[32] Genetic testing can provide a specific and accurate diagnosis in a symptomatic patient, and avoid the need for many traditional tests. However, the neurologist must then be prepared to address prenatal, predictive, and carrier testing, as well as risk factor assessment. The legal, ethical and social implications of genomic medicine will generate a host of novel claims.

[11] Neuropsychological Testing

Brain injuries and diseases frequently produce cognitive and behavioural changes. These are evaluated on mental status testing, but in certain situations precise, detailed, formal testing is warranted. This is especially true when litigation concerns the patient's cognitive status, such as personal injury claims for traumatic brain injury or toxic exposure. Other indications for formal testing include the need to quantify deficits to follow a disorder; to provide information for constructing a rehabilitation plan; and for the preoperative assessment of epilepsy surgery. Neuropsychologists are able to

---

[31] U.S. Task Force on Genetic Testing available at www.genome.gov/10001733 accessed 2 December 2007.

[32] American Academy of Neurology, *Neurogenetics*. Continuum 2005;11(2):1-160.

use a standardized battery of tests to identify and measure cognitive deficits, outline the severity of injury on the patient's overall level of functioning, and correlate the results with what is known about the underlying pathology to determine if the test results are consistent with the diagnosis. Most of the tests have normative values with known rates of reliability and validity, and can address malingering, symptom magnification and poor motivation.

§ 11.09   Spectrum of Neurological Disease

[1] General Overview

The extraordinarily broad scope of neurological malpractice precludes a compendium of potential claims. Moreover, any such listing would be quickly outdated as emerging diagnostic and therapeutic options open the door for new claims. It is more instructive to familiarize the attorney with the most prevalent patient conditions generating suits against neurologists (in decreasing order of frequency): cerebrovascular accident, intervertebral disk displacement, back disorders, convulsions, headache, epilepsy, migraine, malignant neoplasm of the brain, subarachnoid hemorrhage, musculoskeletal disorders affecting the neck region, and occlusion and stenosis of cerebral arteries.[33] Lack of space precludes discussion of the myriad disparate claims involving these conditions. Therefore, several key topics are selected because they affect a large segment of the population, are frequently seen by neurologists, and generate recurring claims that have the potential for exceptionally high indemnity payments or judgments. The truncated discussion of spine disorders reflects the fact that claims in this category are generally related to simple diagnostic errors, and few result in an indemnity payment. Remaining neurological disease categories are briefly reviewed with particular attention to the most relevant forensic issues. In addition, some of the legally fashionable conditions are covered, including post-concussion syndrome, whiplash injuries, post-traumatic movement disorders, and statin myopathy.

[2] Diagnostic Error

The discussion of each disease category focuses on diagnostic error—it is the most prevalent medical misadventure in neurology, reported as the primary issue in one-third of all claims.[34] The most frequent incorrectly

---

[33] Physician Insurers Association of America, *Risk Management Review (Neurology) 2005* (20 year cumulative analysis of data 1985-2005).

[34] *Id.*

diagnosed neurological conditions are brain tumor, followed by abscess, subarachnoid hemorrhage, and other causes of headache.[35] These errors commonly stem from the failure to perform an adequate history and examination which is, in fact, the most prevalent procedure resulting in claims against neurologists.[36] Therefore, the discussion of each topic is written from the perspective of a neurologist, a style designed to provide the attorney with some insight into the key points that should be covered during evaluation of a particular symptom or disease. It is more beneficial for the legal practitioner to have a proper understanding of this clinical approach than to memorize arcane details of obscure diseases. Specific malpractice points are interspersed throughout the discussions. References are kept to a minimum and, as much as possible, selected to provide the reader with additional background material for specific conditions.

[3] Headache

Headaches are ubiquitous, arguably the most common disorder encountered by the practicing physician, and unquestionably the most common presenting complaint in malpractice claims against neurologists.[37] Headache symptoms may be of little clinical significance or, paradoxically, herald a catastrophic illness, such as subarachnoid hemorrhage or brain tumor. A complete and accurate diagnosis of the headache patient requires a detailed history, coupled with a general and neurological examination, as well as neuroimaging or other specialized testing in certain cases. It is imperative to classify the headache type and, *pari passu*, ascertain whether it is acute, chronic or with recent change. This practical approach allows the neurologist to determine the need for further testing and initiate a proper treatment plan, all with the appropriate degree of urgency. It is not uncommon for the neurologist to misinterpret a patient's history, resulting in an erroneous diagnosis and improper treatment. In fact, most malpractice suits stem from the failure to elicit an accurate history. The art of taking a history cannot be taught in this chapter or any other book; it includes an innate ability to establish a rapport, and instill a sense of confidence and trust. The author provides a suggested history-taking methodology, for the sole purpose of demonstrating several pitfalls that may lead to a misdiagnosis:[38]

[35] Id.

[36] Id.

[37] Id.

[38] American College of Legal Medicine, *The Medical Malpractice Survival Handbook.* Philadelphia: Mosby Elsevier; 2007 at 438-439.

- Allow ample time for the consultation. Introduce yourself and invite the patient to sit for the interview before changing into a gown. Advise the patient that you have read the referring physician's letter, but never accept either the patient's or referring doctor's diagnosis.
- Ask the patient: "Tell me about your headaches." Allow the patient to speak uninterruptedly before asking questions. Then begin taking a history with open-ended questions to determine the quality, severity, location, duration, and time course of the pain, as well as precipitating, exacerbating and relieving factors. It is often helpful to ask the patient to describe a typical attack. Be certain to determine whether the patient has more than one type of headache. It is essential to separately evaluate each type of headache, which may not be possible during the initial consultation due to time constraints.
- Communication skills are critical. Knowing which clues to follow and when to interrupt the patient are fundamental to an accurate history. Failure to understand the patient's terminology often leads to a misdiagnosis. For example, the word "throbbing" may be incorrectly translated into a migraine. It is not uncommon for a headache specialist to distort the history until it fits a preconceived diagnostic category.
- The scope of the history must be sufficiently broad to address systemic diseases that may be relevant to the headache. Past, family, and social histories provide valuable information about the patient's condition. Before concluding the history, always ask the patient's opinion about the cause of the headache. This is often the most enlightening part of the interview.

[a]   Systematic Approach

Headaches are classified as *primary* (no specific cause) or *secondary* (headache is symptomatic of an underlying disease) disorders. Evaluating the patient with HA requires a systematic approach to exclude more serious conditions, diagnose the primary HA, and formulate a treatment plan. The following overview is limited to non-traumatic HAs in the adult population, with particular attention to more common diagnostic and treatment errors.

Exclude secondary headaches. The first step is to exclude serious conditions causing secondary headaches. The neurologist should direct particular attention to the following "red flags" or warning signs: (1) *Sudden onset (thunderclap) headache.* Sudden onset of a severe HA mandates immediate and thorough evaluation for potential etiologies such as SAH, intracerebral hemorrhage, venous or sinus thrombosis, aneurysmal expansion, intracranial or extracranial arterial dissection, pituitary apoplexy, or less common conditions such as intermittent hydrocephalous. SAH warrants further discussion. It affects 30,000 persons annually in the United States, is among the most frequently missed serious causes of HA, and has a mortality rate of 50%. SAH refers to the extravasation of blood into the subarachnoid space. Non-traumatic SAH is usually due to a ruptured aneurysm, less commonly bleeding from an arteriovenous malformation (AVM), and rarely other causes such as arteriopathies, bleeding disorders and eclampsia. An aneurysm refers to weakening of the blood vessel wall, typically at an arterial bifurcation, with resultant ballooning that slowly increases in size until it leaks or ruptures. The *sine qua non* of SAH is a sudden HA, often associated with nausea and vomiting. It is classically described as the "first" or "worst HA of my life." In addition to cervical or occipital pain with meningismus, there may be focal deficits, cognitive impairment, or a history of premonitory symptoms suggestive of a sentinel bleed or aneurysmal expansion. It is important to recognize that even known migraneurs may suffer a SAH. Over one-half of patients presenting to the emergency room with a sentinel HA and SAH are misdiagnosed. The failure to diagnose SAH results in the highest average and highest total indemnity for all claims involving diagnostic error.[39] The patient with a thunderclap HA must have an immediate brain CT and, if negative, a lumbar puncture to include measurement of opening pressure and testing for xanthochromia. It may be necessary, based on the history, time course and sequence of events, as well as CT and CSF results, to proceed with MRA or angiography. The differential diagnosis of the patient admitted in coma should include SAH. Medical and surgical management of the patient with SAH is exceedingly complex due to associated electrolyte imbalances, cardiac and pulmonary complications, cerebral vasospasm and edema, possible development of hydrocephalous, and consequences of prolonged bedrest. The potential for a re-bleed must be considered, and if surgery is indicated then critical questions regarding the timing must be addressed. Surgical options including clipping of the aneurysm fall within the realm of neurosurgery. (2) *Escalating or worsening headache.* The patient's HA pattern must be interpreted in light of the overall history. The recent onset of HAs with progression may indicate a tumor, abscess, subdural hematoma, or other mass lesion, and there may be focal deficits. In contrast, a slow growing mass may not be associated with any neurological findings. Chronic primary HAs with progression may represent the development of a new superimposed primary or secondary HA, or transformation of the original primary HA (typically due to medication overuse). It is often impossible to distinguish a transformed HA from a new

---

[39] *Supra* note 33.

disorder; therefore, an escalating HA, whether acute or chronic, warrants investigation. (3) *HA with focal signs.* The HA associated with focal deficits other than a typical aura, whether transient (seizure, transient ischemic attack, collagen vascular disease) or permanent (mass lesions, cerebrovascular insults) requires further evaluation. (4) *HA triggered by cough or exertion.* A sudden, severe HA triggered by cough or exertion, as well as orgasmic or postcoital HAs, are "red flags" due to the possibility of SAH, mass lesions, or posterior fossa structural abnormalities such as tonsillar ectopia or Chiari malformation. Neuroimaging is necessary to provide a definitive diagnosis. MRI is the procedure of choice because it is far superior to CT in evaluating the posterior fossa. (5) *HA with systemic disease.* There are myriad systemic diseases that may present with acute HA including intracranial and systemic infections, neoplasms, vascular conditions, metabolic diseases, autoimmune disorders and toxic exposure. The clinical picture directs further diagnostic evaluation. For example, an older patient with HA and visual loss may need a temporal artery biopsy for the possibility of giant cell arteritis. The patient with cancer and HA requires appropriate imaging and CSF analysis for the possibility of metastases including leptomeningeal disease. HA secondary to exercise may be an anginal equivalent necessitating cardiology evaluation. (6) *HA during pregnancy or postpartum.* The new onset of HAs or progression of a known primary HA during pregnancy or postpartum is always concerning due to the possibility of sinus thrombosis, cerebral infarction, carotid dissection, pituitary apoplexy, and pre-eclampsia. These disorders usually occur in the third trimester or postpartum, and the HA may be associated with focal signs or seizures. MRI and MRA are generally indicated.

Diagnose the primary headache.   After excluding a secondary HA, the primary HA disorder should be diagnosed in accordance with International Headache Society criteria.[40] It is impossible to review the various HA presentations in this introductory chapter, and the interested attorney is encouraged to read symptomatic descriptions in one of the recommended texts. However, the importance of correctly diagnosing a patient's HA cannot be overstated. It is not uncommon for the neurologist to mislabel a patient with a particular HA type during the initial consultation and, despite a poor response to treatment, never consider revisiting the diagnosis. These patients are branded with the wrong diagnosis; resultant therapy is ineffective. This creates a breeding ground for malpractice claims.

Treat the primary headache. Once diagnosed, the primary HA should be treated with a comprehensive multi-modality approach incorporating

---

[40] Headache Classification Subcommittee of the International Headache Society, *The International Classification of Headache Disorders,* 2nd ed. Cephalgia 2004; 24(Supp 1):1-160.

pharmacological intervention predicated on evidence-based guidelines.[41] This approach is frequently ignored by the neurologist content with simply prescribing a medication. There are several general treatment principles that should be considered, remembering that the goal of therapy is to improve the patient's quality of life by reducing HA frequency, severity and disability. First, the diagnosis should be confirmed before initiating treatment. It the symptoms are atypical, or it is difficult to classify the HA, then the possibility of a secondary HA should be reconsidered. Second, patient education plays a significant role in successful HA management. The diagnosis and treatment options should be reviewed in a discussion commensurate with the patient's level of education and comprehension. The patient should be instructed to keep a HA diary, which the neurologist should review in follow-up visits. Dietary modifications, avoidance of trigger factors, and the impact of HAs on occupational, social and recreational activities must be addressed. Third, pharmacological treatment is empiric, using medications with the highest benefit to risk ratio, which are compatible with any coexistent diseases. The medical records should document that the patient was advised regarding the potential benefits, side effects and contraindications of any prescribed drugs. Medication error is a recurrent theme in many suits, usually because the neurologist neglected one or more of the following treatment principles:

> Acute therapy for moderate to severe migraines, or those unresponsive to routine medications, requires a migraine specific drug with the fewest side effects. The most common cause of treatment failure is medication overuse resulting in rebound phenomena. Acute therapy should be limited to two days per week. If HAs are more frequent or particularly disabling, then prophylactic therapy should be considered. Additionally, prophylactic medication may be warranted for complicated migraines such as hemiplegic or basilar migraine, or migraine with prolonged aura. The choice of medication should be determined by appropriate guidelines, with particular attention to potential side effects and coexistent diseases. A systematic approach is essential: initiate treatment with the lowest effective dose; titrate slowly until reaching a maximal response or side effects intervene; give an adequate trial of several months before changing drugs; and monitor efficacy using the patient's HA diary. A medication taper is reasonable after the HAs are well controlled for 6 or more months.

---

[41] American Academy of Neurology, *Report of the Quality Standards Subcommittee: Practice Parameter: Evidence-Based Guidelines for Migraine Headache* (2000).

Fourth, the neurologist must identify coexisting conditions such as hypertension, asthma, and Raynaud's phenomena as well as associated psychiatric disorders such as anxiety, depression and panic attacks. Drug selection should focus on treating both the HA and coexisting disorder, or at least using medications that are not contraindicated. For example, beta-blockers would be an excellent choice for migraine prophylaxis in the patient with hypertension, but absolutely contraindicated with asthma or Raynaud's phenomena. Likewise, valproic acid may effectively treat the patient with migraine and epilepsy, but is contraindicated with underlying liver disease. Fifth, non-pharmacological treatment modalities such as behaviour training, biofeedback, and physical therapy may help certain patients. It should be obvious there is no "standard" therapy for HAs—the treatment plan must be individualized for each patient and documented in the records.

[b]   The Unresponsive Patient

The majority of patients with refractory HA have been misdiagnosed or improperly treated, due to one of the following errors: (1) *Incomplete or incorrect diagnosis.* There may be an undiagnosed secondary HA, or misdiagnosed primary HA. The patient may have two or more HAs, with one or more unrecognized, or the number may not be clear.   If the diagnosis remains unclear, the neurologist should consider CSF analysis for the remote possibility of chronic granulomatous, vasculitic or inflammatory meningitides. (2) *Imaging studies failed to target pathology.* There may be imaging studies, interpreted as normal, which failed to target the site of neuropathology. For example, a patient with HA and a "normal" CT may be labeled with migraine but actually harbor a posterior fossa brain tumor, which would have been visualized on MRI. (3) *Exacerbating factors or triggers overlooked.* Neurologists and patients alike frequently overlook exacerbating factors as well as dietary, hormonal and lifestyle triggers. (4) *Rebound phenomena.* Overuse of prescription or over the counter medications may lead to persistent rebound HAs, which are often quite difficult to treat. (5) *Improper pharmacotherapeutics.* Refractory HAs may be secondary to improper dosing strategies such as an excessive initial dose, subtherapeutic final dose, or inadequate length of treatment. Drug interactions and absorption issues must be considered. An alternative drug or combination therapy may be needed.

[c]   Neuroimaging in the HA Patient

The role of neuroimaging in the HA patient with a normal neurological examination remains a controversial topic. The American Academy of

Neurology Practice Guidelines state "neuroimaging is not usually warranted in patients with migraine and a normal neurological examination," but should be considered in those with an abnormal examination or "patients with atypical headache features or headaches that do not fulfill the strict definition of migraine or other primary headache disorder."[42] These parameters presuppose an accurate diagnosis, which is frequently not the case. A classic example is when the neurologist diagnoses a HA without imaging studies, and subsequent evaluation uncovers a brain tumor. Ironically, the most common diagnostic error in neurology is failure to diagnose brain tumor. It requires a great deal of experience and clinical acumen to forgo imaging of the HA patient. For many neurologists, the most prudent course of action is simply to perform an imaging study on every HA patient early in the evaluation. There is no need to repeat a test if it was normal, the patient's condition is unchanged, and treatment is successful. There are no evidence-based recommendations in the United States regarding the relative sensitivity of MRI compared with CT in HA disorders.[43] However, every reasonable expert would agree that MRI is the superior choice in most cases due to its sensitivity and ability to visualize the temporal lobes and posterior fossa. Unfortunately, neurologists may be deterred from ordering these studies due to concerns over deselection or negative capitation, and failure to diagnose brain tumor will likely remain one of the most common malpractice claims.

[4] Cerebrovascular Disease

Cerebrovascular disease is the third leading cause of death in the United States — there are approximately 700,000 newly diagnosed cases and 200,000 fatalities annually.[44] Recent advances in stroke therapy including specific treatment options (thrombolysis) and prevention strategies (anticoagulation, carotid endarterectomy) create a heightened expectation of proper management and, combined with the catastrophic impact of stroke, portend increasing litigation in this area. For the purposes of this discussion, cerebrovascular disease can be divided into transient ischemic attacks (TIAs) and strokes. A TIA refers to an episode of neurological dysfunction caused by ischemia (insufficient blood flow) which lasts less than 24 hours without evidence of infarction. Strokes are predominantly due to cerebral infarction

---

[42] Id.

[43] Sandrini G, et al. *Neurophysiological tests and neuroimaging procedures in nonacute headache: guidelines and recommendations.* Eur J Neurol 2004; 11(4):217-224. A European Task Force recommended MRI in these circumstances.

[44] www.cdc.gov accessed 2 December 2007.

(brain cell death) from ischemia, hypoxia or hypoglycemia, although 15% are hemorrhagic and due to nontraumatic spontaneous intracerebral hemorrhage (ICH) or SAH. SAH is discussed under headache §11.09 [3].

[a]   Transient Ischemic Attack

TIA signs and symptoms depend on which brain region is deprived of blood flow. The majority occur in the anterior circulation when flow through the carotid artery or one of its branches is blocked. Approximately one-half of patients describe the abrupt onset of weakness or clumsiness in the upper or lower limb or face, or in various combinations on one side of the body. Sensory symptoms such as numbness, tingling or deadness occur in many patients. The patient may be dysphasic if language centers of the brain are involved. Common manifestations include visual field deficits, cognitive impairment, behavioural disorders, and amaurosis fugax or transient monocular blindness. A vertebrobasilar TIA usually causes simultaneous bilateral symptoms such as diplopia, vertigo, tinnitus, dysphagia, dysarthria, ataxia, visual field defects and drop attacks. TIAs are caused by the same mechanisms responsible for strokes, which may be simplistically thought of as failure of the heart (valvular disorders, arrhythmias, heart muscle disorders and related conditions predisposing to emboli), blood vessels (atheromatous disease, dissection, vasculitis), or blood (hyperviscosity, coagulation disorder). The diagnostic evaluation requires a thorough history and examination, brain imaging to rule out structural disease, chest X-ray and electrocardiogram screening for arrythmias, echocardiogram to evaluate for cardiac emboli, carotid ultrasound which may need to be followed with MRA or angiography, and hematologic studies including chemistries, blood and platelet counts, sedimentation rate, and coagulation studies. Children and younger adults require specialized testing for the many unusual causes of TIA. Importantly, other conditions can mimic TIAs including migraines, partial seizures, metabolic disturbances, subdural hematomas, and tumors. The mainstay of treatment entails effective control of risk factors (hypertension, hypercholesterolemia, hyperlipidemia, diabetes, tobacco and alcohol abuse) and antiplatelet therapy. Most neurologists recommend aspirin at 75-325mg per day. If the TIAs recur or there is a high risk factor, it is common to switch to an aspirin-dipyridamole combination or add either clopidogrel or ticlopidine. Ticlopidine, in particular, must be closely monitored because of several potentially serious side effects. Anticoagulation or carotid endarterectomy may be necessary in selected circumstances. TIAs are a warning sign of impending stroke; a significant percentage of patients develop a stroke within several weeks after a TIA, and many within the first twenty-four hours. It is crucial that the patient with a TIA be promptly evaluated in order to initiate appropriate preventative treatment. The failure to do so provides the legal practitioner with a straightforward claim.

[b] Cerebral Infarction

The majority of strokes are characterized by the sudden onset of neurological deficits or, if the stroke occurred during the night, the patient wakens in the morning aware that something is wrong. The clinical picture depends on the area of brain affected. Infarctions most commonly involve the anterior circulation. *Middle cerebral artery* infarcts result in contralateral weakness and sensory loss of the face, arm and leg, and visual field defects. Weakness is more pronounced in the arm than leg. If the left hemisphere is involved, there will be dysphasia; with the right hemisphere, visuospatial abnormalities and neglect will be evident. *Anterior cerebral artery* infarctions result in contralateral weakness greater in the leg than arm. Posterior circulation strokes involve the *posterior cerebral* or *vertebrobasilar* arteries resulting in occipital lobe damage with visual field deficits, or signs referable to the brainstem and cerebellum. *Lacunar infarctions* are usually due to hypertensive arteriosclerotic thrombosis of the deep penetrating arteries. Lacunar strokes may be missed on CT, but are readily visualized by MRI. These lesions occur in the deep white matter rather than cortex, and are therefore not associated with visual field defects or disturbances of higher intellectual function. There are various lacunar syndromes depending on the location of infarction: pure motor stroke (internal capsule), sensory motor (internal capsule and ventral thalamus), pure sensory (posteroventral thalamus), and dysarthria-clumsy hand syndrome (contralateral pons).

Stroke is a neurological emergency leaving only a few hours available for therapeutic intervention. The main goal of evaluation is to make a correct diagnosis of stroke (5% of classical stroke presentations are actually due to other causes such as subdural hematoma, tumor or abscess), establish the pathological type (infarct or hemorrhage), and delineate the underlying cause (cardiogenic embolism, thromboembolism, small vessel occlusion, vascular malformation). This entails an appropriate history, examination and diagnostic testing including MRI and possibly vascular imaging with angiography, MRA or US. General initial management includes proper maintenance of cardiovascular, pulmonary, fluid, electrolyte and nutritional status; recognition and treatment of systemic complications; recognition and treatment of early causes of neurological deterioration; initiation of secondary prevention; treatment of any coexisting disorders; and commencement of rehabilitation. Perhaps one of the most common errors during early initial care is the mismanagement of hypertension. The stroke itself disturbs cerebral autoregulation causing a degree of hypertension. Aggressive treatment will diminish cerebral blood flow which is likely to extend the infarction.[45] Specific management options for ischemic stroke include thrombolysis, anticoagulation and carotid endarterectomy.

Thrombolysis. Tissue plasminogen activator (tPA) thrombolysis represents the neurological standard of care for acute ischemic stroke. Administration of tPA within three hours of ischemic onset significantly improves functional outcome in selected patients.[46] The therapeutic window is narrow and mandates strict adherence to approved protocol inclusion and exclusion criteria. There should be a dedicated stroke team capable of responding to every acute ischemic stroke in a timely fashion and, if indicated, administering tPA. The hospital may incur liability for failing to provide appropriate facilities and personnel (for example, 24 hour CT and technician support). Alternatively, tPA eligible patients must be promptly transferred to another institution for definitive treatment. The failure to recommend or administer tPA to an eligible patient constitutes negligence, unless it can be proven that tPA would not have made a material difference in the patient's outcome. The neurologist deciding not to use tPA in an acute ischemic stroke should have the reasons for that decision clearly documented in the medical records. Modification of the 3 hour time constraint decreases the benefit of tPA and increases the risk of intracerebral hemorrhage. It is, therefore, crucial to determine the time of stroke onset. It is a common error to label the onset as the time symptoms were first observed rather than the last time the patient was known to be well. For example, if the patient awakens with deficits, the onset time must be considered the night before (when the patient was known to be well), not when symptoms were first noticed upon awakening. The same holds true for patients unable to communicate the onset time. Likewise, patients with stroke related neglect syndromes cannot reliably observe the onset time. Another common error is the administration of antiplatelet or anticoagulant agents in the first 24 hours after tPA, which greatly increases the risk of intracerebral hemorrhage. The protocol guidelines must be followed. However, there are cases where the neurologist considers all of the benefits and risks, and decides it is in the patient's best interest to deviate from the protocol. If so, this decision should be documented in the records along with a discussion with the patient or legal representative and family.

---

[45] Adams HP, Adams RJ, Brott T, et al. *Guidelines for the early management of patients with ischemic stroke: a scientific statement from the Stroke Council of the American Stroke Association.* Stroke 2003; 34:1056-1083.

[46] American Academy of Neurology, *Report of the Quality Standards Subcommittee: Practice Advisory: Thrombolytic Therapy for Acute Ischemic Stroke* (2003).

Anticoagulation. The use of heparin to prevent an impending stroke remains controversial, but evidence supports immediate anticoagulation for fluctuating basilar artery thrombosis and impending carotid artery occlusion, as well as in certain cases of cardioembolic cerebral infarction. Warfarin is probably beneficial in the first few months after an ischemic event, but there is no definitive evidence that the benefits of long term anticoagulation for thrombosis or embolism outweigh the potential risks except in patients with nonvalvular atrial fibrillation (AF), prosthetic heart valves, and acute myocardial infarction. AF increases the risk of stroke 4- to 6-fold across all age groups. There is a 5% annual ischemic stroke rate in untreated AF, which increases with high risk factors such as hypertension, left ventricular dysfunction, TIA or prior stroke. Anticoagulation with warfarin significantly reduces this risk of stroke, and represents the standard of care for stroke prevention in these patients.[47] If the patient is at low risk of stroke, or warfarin is contraindicated, then antiplatelet therapy is recommended. Neurologists may be reluctant to use warfarin because of the required follow-up and monitoring, or may inappropriately minimize the dosage out of undue concern about bleeding. This is a frequent subject of litigation, with the claim that a major stroke would have been prevented if the patient was properly anticoagulated. The attorney considering such an action may want to establish whether the patient's risk for stroke was properly identified; if there was an accurate diagnosis, with imaging to exclude hemorrhage before therapy was initiated; that the reasons for or against anticoagulation were documented in the records; the patient and family were properly educated regarding anticoagulation; and the neurologist followed written protocols for monitoring warfarin. Certain medications are contraindicated because they increase the risk of bleeding (i.e., aspirin, barbiturates, cephalosporins, sulfa drugs, high-dose penicillin).

Carotid endarterectomy. Over one-quarter of recently symptomatic patients with a high grade carotid stenosis (70-99% diameter reduction) will suffer an ipsilateral stroke with two years, despite appropriate risk factor management and antiplatelet therapy. Carotid endarterectomy (CEA) significantly reduces the risk of cerebral infarction in these patients, and represents the standard of care.[48] There must be careful patient selection, and skill of the surgical team is paramount. The most common malpractice claim is failure to diagnose TIA or minor stroke, or failure to perform a workup for carotid stenosis, allowing

---

[47] American Academy of Neurology, *Report of the Quality Standards Subcommittee: Practice Parameter: Stroke Prevention in Patients with Nonvalvular Atrial Fibrillation* (1998).

[48] American Academy of Neurology Clinical Practice Guidelines, *Assessment: Carotid Endarterectomy — An Evidence-Based Review: Report of the TTA Subcommittee of the AAN.* Neurology 2005; 65(6):794-801.

the patient to suffer a recurrent or massive stroke. There is no question that every TIA and stroke patient should have a carotid US or MRA unless surgery is plainly contraindicated. Patients with symptomatic carotid artery stenosis greater than 70% should be offered surgery. Delay in referring the TIA patient with high grade stenosis for definitive treatment constitutes negligence, since a high percentage of strokes occur within 48 hours of a TIA. Surgery should be offered as soon as possible after a TIA or nondisabling stroke, preferably within two weeks after the last symptomatic event. Premature surgical intervention after a moderate to severe stroke creates a liability risk for extension or hemorrhagic conversion of the infarction; however, there is insufficient evidence to support or refute delaying surgery for 4-6 weeks.

[c] Intracerebral Hemorrhage

Intracerebral hemorrhage is a devastating disease with a mortality rate approaching 50%, and significant morbidity in survivors. The majority of primary ICH cases are due to hypertensive vasculopathy (occurring in the basal ganglia, thalamus, brainstem and cerebellum) and cerebral amyloid angiopathy (associated with lobar hemorrhages). The initial evaluation of the stroke patient includes neuroimaging which will define the hemorrhage. Hematoma expansion is common in the first 24 hours after presentation and associated with a higher mortality and worse outcome; therefore, early intervention is crucial. Judicious management of hypoxia, hypertension, hyperglycemia, coagulopathy, pyrexia, intracranial pressure and seizure activity are the mainstays of medical treatment. There is one specific life-threatening hemorrhage that may be treated with dramatic results: the cerebellar hemorrhage. Emergent surgical evacuation of a cerebellar hemorrhage is warranted if the hematoma is greater than 3cm, or there is evidence of obstructive hydrocephalous or brainstem compression. Similarly, a cerebellar infarction with impending obstruction of the fourth ventricle or brainstem compression may require surgical decompression, ventriculostomy or both. Supratentorial hemorrhages are generally managed medically, although evacuation may be reasonable in certain cases of lobar ICH with deterioration.

[d] Other Vascular Conditions

Cerebral venous thrombosis. Thrombosis may develop in the venous sinuses, cortical veins and deep veins. These may be precipitated by local (head injury, intracranial surgery, nasopharyngeal sepsis) and systemic (dehydration, septicemia, pregnancy, systemic malignancy, autoimmune disease) conditions. The clinical features depend on location of the clot. These patients tend to present with a slowly developing encephalopathy over days to weeks, with headache, seizures, confusion, and sometimes focal neurological deficits such as hemiparesis. The diagnosis is often delayed, and made by exclusion. MRI and MRA are supplanting angiography for evaluating these conditions. Therapy must be directed towards the underlying disorder, with anticoagulation for the intracerebral clotting.

Giant cell arteritis. Giant cell or temporal arteritis most commonly occurs in patients over the age of 50, in isolation or associated with polymyalgia rheumatica. The clinical symptoms include new onset headache, scalp tenderness, jaw claudication, and most concerning, visual disturbance which may range from obscuration to complete blindness. The sedimentation rate is elevated in most patients. Treatment should begin as soon as possible with corticosteroids and, if the diagnosis is correct, there will be a dramatic response within 48 hours. Many neurologists would consider this response and a corresponding decrease in the sedimentation rate confirmatory. Others prefer a temporal artery biopsy to provide a definitive diagnosis. However, any delay in treatment pending the biopsy subjects the patient to an increasing risk of blindness. The crucial point is that steroid therapy must begin immediately. If the patient responds, steroids should be continued for 12-18 months before tapering; complications from long term treatment must be considered. Immunosuppressants may be used if steroids are ineffective.

[5] Seizures and Epilepsy

There are over 2 million epileptics in the United States.[49] Approximately 150,000 adults will present annually with a first seizure; almost half of these incident seizures will recur to be classified as epilepsy.[50] The lifetime cumulative risk of a seizure ranges from 8% to 10%, with an approximate 3% chance of developing epilepsy.[51] Intellectual impairment, cognitive dysfunction and psychiatric symptoms are common in epilepsy patients.[52]

A *seizure* reflects the transient occurrence of signs or symptoms due to a sudden, excessive, and ungoverned abnormal neuronal discharge in the brain. The clinical manifestations vary depending on whether the seizure is focal (beginning in a particular area of one hemisphere) or generalized (beginning simultaneously in bilateral cortical regions), how the discharge

---

[49] Browne TR, Holmes GL. *Epilepsy.* N Engl J Med 2001; 344:1145-1151.

[50] Annegers JF, *Epidemiology of epilepsy* In: Wyllie E, ed. *The Treatment of Epilepsy: Principles and Practice,* 2nd ed. Baltimore: Williams & Wilkins; 1997.

[51] *Id.*

[52] Bortz JJ. *Neuropsychiatric and memory issues in epilepsy.* Mayo Clin Proc 2003; 78:781-787.

spreads, and the function of the affected cortex. Seizures may range from the dramatic loss of consciousness with convulsive shaking, tongue biting and urinary incontinence to experiential phenomena without any overtly discernable signs. There can be any combination of changes in the level of consciousness, motor functions, sensation, behaviour and emotion. *Epilepsy* is characterized by recurrent (two or more), unprovoked seizures. Epilepsy refers to a clinical phenomena rather than a single disease entity, since there are numerous causes and forms of epilepsy. It may be due to genetic or unidentified causes (*primary epilepsy*) or an underlying neurological etiology such as trauma, brain tumor, cerebrovascular disease or degenerative conditions (*secondary epilepsy*). An *epilepsy syndrome* represents an epileptic disorder characterized by the constellation of similar features such as seizure type, age of onset, etiology, neurological abnormalities, and imaging and electroencephalographic findings which suggest a specific underlying etiology. Patients within the same syndrome have similar pathophysiological mechanisms, response to treatment, and prognosis.

[a] Diagnosis

The diagnosis of a seizure is almost entirely dependent upon the history. Patients are usually unable to describe their own seizure due to the associated amnesia. The neurologist must interview witnesses to the event, seeking a detailed description of seizure characteristics including the prodrome, initial manifestations, progression and postictal state. Understanding the typical seizure manifestations and pattern of spread may allow the neurologist to exclude non-epileptic events, and predict the ictal onset zone location. The history of past events and risk factors, as well as past medical history ranging from birth insults to head trauma, family history addressing neurological disease, and social history including drug and alcohol use may prove relevant to the diagnosis. Epilepsy is frequently misdiagnosed, often because the neurologist fails to take an adequate history. 20 – 30% of epileptics presenting to epilepsy centers for treatment failure are found to be misdiagnosed.[53] The most common misdiagnosis is psychogenic non-epileptic seizures (PNES), although syncope and a host of other conditions causing paroxysmal neurological dysfunction must be considered in the differential diagnosis.   There is a mean 7.2 year delay in the diagnosis of PNES, an unacceptable figure in light of the fact that epilepsy can be diagnosed with near certainty.[54] It suggests that neurologists do not have a

---

[53] Chadwick D, Smith D. *The misdiagnosis of epilepsy.* BMJ 2002; 324(7336):495-496.

[54] Reuber M, Fernandez G, et al.   *Diagnostic delay in psychogenic nonepileptic seizures.* Neurology 2002; 58:493-495.

high enough index of suspicion to question the diagnosis of epilepsy in patients refractory to treatment. Unfortunately, once a patient is labeled with epilepsy, that diagnosis, with all of the attendant medical, psychological, social and economic consequences, is generally accepted without question.

The physical and neurological examination remains the most important procedure for evaluating the new seizure patient. The general examination may reveal signs of infection, cancer, illicit drug use, or other findings accounting for the seizure. Neurological abnormalities, especially if asymmetric, suggest an intracranial etiology for the seizure. Hematologic studies and urinalysis may be helpful to demonstrate the presence of infection, metabolic or toxic disturbance, or other disorders as well as drug and alcohol abuse.

There is no question that evaluation of an unprovoked first seizure in the adult warrants neuroimaging of the brain and EEG testing.[55] MRI is preferable to CT because it shows much greater detail, and is more sensitive for tumors, vascular malformations, abscesses, and other epileptogenic intracranial abnormalities. The attorney should recognize that standard imaging scans are unacceptable in evaluating certain epileptic patients—they fail to identify more than half of potentially treatable structural lesions. The MRI must incorporate specialized epilepsy protocol scans.[56] Functional imaging with PET or SPECT may be beneficial in evaluating surgical candidates.

The EEG remains shrouded by mystique. There is a common misconception that it can diagnose epilepsy. This is not true, unless the patient has a seizure during the recording. Most inter-ictal EEGs will be normal. The test can detect abnormal electrical activity, which must be correlated with the clinical picture. A small percentage of normal individuals may have epileptiform discharges with no evidence of seizures. In contrast, the EEG may be normal in approximately one-half of patients with clinical evidence of seizures. Thus an abnormal EEG is not pathognomonic for epilepsy, and a normal EEG does *not* exclude a diagnosis of epilepsy. It is worth noting that about one-third of patients misdiagnosed with epilepsy have had prior EEGs misinterpreted as epileptiform, thus contributing to the misdiagnosis.[57] Most are normal variants that are overinterpreted. Unfortunately, once a patient has an "abnormal" EEG, no amount of

---

[55] Krumholz A, Wiebe S, et al. *Evaluating an apparent unprovoked first seizure in adults (an evidence-based review): Report of the Quality Standards Subcommittee of the American Academy of Neurology and the American Epilepsy Society.* Neurology 2007; 69:1996-2007.

[56] Von Oertzen J, Urbach H, et al. *Standardized magnetic resonance imaging is inadequate for patients with refractory focal epilepsy.* J Neurol, Neurosurg and Psychiatry 2002; 73:643-647.

[57] Bendabis SR, Tatum WO. *Overinterpretation of EEGs and misdiagnosis of epilepsy.* J Clin Neurophysio 2003; 20(1):42-44.

subsequent normal EEGs will "cancel" it. The only resolution is to review the actual recording that was interpreted as "epileptiform." This may be exceedingly difficult—it may not be available if it was a paper recording; if computerized, the digital systems may not be compatible. Moreover, the neurologist interpreting the original study will likely be reluctant for an epileptologist to review the record. If the patient has PNES, the question of epilepsy will languish and probably necessitate long term therapy. The recommended management for patients without a definitive diagnosis or with failure to respond to treatment is referral to an inpatient epilepsy center for prolonged EEG monitoring with simultaneous video recording.

[b] Classification

The proper classification of seizure types and epileptic syndromes is necessary to determine long term prognosis and make appropriate treatment recommendations. The two currently accepted schemes are the *International Classification of Epileptic Seizures* and the *International Classification of Epilepsies and Epileptic Syndromes*. The recently proposed *International League Against Epilepsy* diagnostic scheme remains controversial, but will probably be accepted after modification and revision.

The primary distinction is between partial or focal seizures and generalized seizures. *Partial* or *focal* seizures begin in one part of the brain. *Simple partial seizures* occur without loss or alteration of consciousness, and have motor, sensory, psychic or autonomic phenomena referable to the site of abnormal electrical discharge. Epileptiform discharges in the motor cortex can produce clonic movements; spreading of the discharge results in a corresponding spreading of the movement, known as a *Jacksonian seizure.* Inhibitory motor seizures and aphasic seizures may occur. Abnormal sensations can include visual, olfactory and gustatory hallucinations with no outward clinical manifestations. Déjà vu, jamais vu and other complex cognitive phenomena including depersonalization and derealization may occur. Hallucinations may be difficult to distinguish from psychiatric disorders, except that the ictal phenomena are very stereotyped from one seizure to another. Some temporal lobe seizures cause fear or panic that can lead to inappropriate psychiatric treatment for an anxiety disorder. Patients may have multiple symptoms occurring during the partial seizure. *Complex partial seizures* are associated with an impaired awareness or complete loss of consciousness. The abnormal electrical discharge usually arises in the temporal lobe, and causes patients to stare off into space, unable to respond appropriately, with *automatisms* or repetitive purposeless movements such as lip smacking, chewing, and hand wringing. A simple partial seizure may progress to a complex partial or secondarily generalized seizure; or it may progress sequentially from simple partial to complex partial to generalized seizure. Complex partial seizures may become secondarily generalized. Some patients may not recognize the partial seizure and present for medical care only after it generalizes. The secondarily generalized seizure follows a progression much like a primary generalized seizure, culminating in a postictal state with drowsiness, confusion and headache. The clinical presence of *Todd's paralysis* after a generalized seizure suggests a focal onset with secondary generalization.

Generalized seizures begin with the discharge spreading to all parts of the cortex coequally. Consciousness is usually impaired, and motor manifestations are bilateral and synchronus. Primary generalized seizures are more likely than partial seizures to have a genetic basis, and usually occur for the first time in children. There are several types. *Absence* or *petit mal seizures* are characterized by loss of awareness with brief staring spells, an abrupt onset and offset, without postictal confusion, and a characteristic EEG 3 per second spike and slow wave discharge. *Atypical absence seizures* have less abrupt changes in consciousness and may show postictal confusion. *Tonic-clonic* or *grand mal seizures* begin with an abrupt loss of consciousness, followed by stiffening, then clonic movements, usually lasting less than three minutes. Patients may bite their tongue or lose bowel or bladder control. The patient is usually stuperous or obtunded in the immediate postictal state, and may be confused for hours. *Myoclonic seizures* consist of sudden symmetric jerking movements of the extremities or trunk, and may occur without loss of consciousness. *Tonic seizures* demonstrate sustained contractions of axial or limb musculature lasting from 5 to 20 seconds. *Atonic seizures* or *drop attacks* consist of a sudden loss of muscle tone; the patient may actually fall.

[c] Status Epilepticus

Status epilepticus (SE) refers to a state of unremitting seizures. A prolonged seizure or a set of recurrent seizures is deemed to become SE when the duration of seizure activity exceeds 5 minutes. There are three subtypes. *Generalized convulsive status epilepticus* (GCSE) is the classic motor form; seizures may be overt, or there may be subtle motor manifestations, especially if activity is prolonged. It is a neurological emergency requiring immediate treatment. These seizures will most likely lead to cerebral injury if not promptly terminated. *Focal motor status epilepticus* (FMSE), or *epilepsia partialis continua,* most commonly presents with focal twitching of one limb or one side of the face. These seizures are very difficult to control with medications, and there is no definitive evidence that prolonged FMSE causes substantive brain injury. Thus, reasonable efforts to control the seizure are appropriate, but high risk therapies should not be used. *Nonconvulsive status epilepticus* (NCSE) is an umbrella term for a broad array of continuous nonmotor seizures including absence, simple partial and complex partial seizures. The neurological hallmark of NCSE is somnolence, but the patient may present anywhere along the spectrum from awake to comatose. An EEG is required for diagnosis. It is prudent to initiate treatment as rapidly as possible, but there is no consensus on how aggressive attempts should be to abolish the EEG paroxysms. The pathophysiology, etiology and therapeutic options for SE are beyond the remit of this chapter. The key point is that SE, and GCSE in particular, must be identified and treated promptly, as clear evidence demonstrates that persistent seizures cause potentially grave neurological injury. Aggressive treatment of seizures engenders unique risks pertaining to drug choice, side effects and the risk of toxicity.

[d] Non-Epileptic Paroxysmal Disorders

There are a host of non-epileptic events that may be classified as either physiologic or psychogenic non-epileptic paroxysmal disorders. The key to determining the etiology of a particular spell is an accurate history and examination, appropriate diagnostic testing, and a thorough understanding of epileptic seizures and the non-epileptic events that mimic seizures. Non-epileptic spells can mimic virtually any type of seizure. The co-existence of epileptic and non-epileptic spells in the same patient may complicate the picture.

Syncope is a common physiological non-epileptic paroxysmal disorder. It is frequently misdiagnosed as seizures because of the erroneous belief that syncopal episodes are motionless when, in fact, they are frequently associated with convulsive movements. Additionally, there is a misperception that seizures can cause a flaccid motionless loss of consciousness; no such seizure type exists. Management of syncope depends on the cause — it is frequently due to a benign vasovagal event, but clinical findings may dictate cardiac evaluation including monitoring for arrhythmias. A number of patients have persistent unexplained syncope which may represent psychogenic pseudosyncope. Other physiological conditions that may be misdiagnosed as seizures include hypoglycemia, panic attacks, transient ischemic attacks, complicated migraines, transient global amnesia, vertigo, movement disorders (acute dystonia, hemifacial spasm, non-epileptic myoclonus), and sleep disorders (cataplexy, hypnic jerks, parasomnias).

Psychogenic non-epileptic seizures (PNES) or *pseudoseizures* (a commonly used term although it fails to specifically denote the psychogenic aspect of these seizures) are the most common non-epileptic event, occurring in one-quarter to one-half of patients with intractable spells presenting to referral centers. Pseudoseizures may be exceedingly difficult to diagnosis on clinical grounds; there may be excellent mimicry of tonic-clonic jerking with injuries and even urinary incontinence. "Red flags" include resistance to anti-epileptic drugs, descriptions of characteristics that are inconsistent with epilepsy, absence of post-ictal confusion, occurrence in the presence of an audience (such as the physician's office), no occurrence during sleep, and a past history laden with psychogenic diagnoses such as chronic fatigue syndrome, chronic pain, or fibromyalgia. These patients are frequently hospitalized, mislabeled as epileptics and treated with anticonvulsants before neurological consultation. Video EEG remains the gold-standard for diagnosing pseudoseizures and, in fact, is recommended for all patients who have seizures despite anticonvulsant medication. Pseudoseizures represent a conversion or somatoform disorder, factitious disorder or simply malingering for manipulative and secondary gain. The common thread among these patients is an underlying psychiatric disturbance such as depression, anxiety, or dissociative or personality disorder, and often there is a history of trauma or sexual abuse. The diagnosis spells a poor prognosis—almost three-quarters of pseudoseizure patients continue to have spells years after diagnosis and more than half are unable to work.[58] Psychiatric consultation is essential, although continued neurological care may be necessary to wean the patient from anticonvulsant drugs and follow-up for the possibility of coexistent epilepsy.

[e] Treatment

There are many effective antiepileptic drugs (AEDs), subdivided into first generation (phenytoin, carbamazepine, phenobarbital, primidone, valproate, ethosuximide and benzodiazepines) and second generation (felbamate, gabapentin, lamotrigine, topiramate, tiagabine, oxcarbazepine, levetiracetam, zonisamide and pregabalin) medications. Neurologists must prescribe the proper medication based on individual patient characteristics and seizure type, with attention to potential side effects and drug interactions. More than half of patients can be effectively treated with monotherapy. Polytherapy increases the risk of adverse reactions and toxicity, often without any improved seizure control. All AEDs have potentially devastating side effects which can be acute or chronic, and dose related or idiosyncratic. Baseline evaluations must be performed before starting some medications. For example, dangerous and even fatal skin reactions (Stevens Johnson

---

[58] Reuber M, Pukrop R, et al. *Outcome in psychogenic nonepileptic seizures: 1 to 10 year followup in 164 patients.* Ann Neurol 2003; 53:305-311.

syndrome or toxic epidermal necrolysis) may occur with carbamazepine, and are much more likely in the patient with human leukocyte antigen (HLA) B1502. Screening is imperative for at-risk patients, and if positive for HLA B1502 then carbamazepine should not be used unless expected benefits clearly outweigh the potential risks. AEDs must be properly monitored during the course of therapy, some with drug levels and hematologic studies of blood cell counts or liver functions.

There are differing opinions on treatment of the patient who presents after a single unprovoked seizure, or the patient with long time intervals between seizures. The patient with a first seizure and normal EEG has a 24% risk of recurrence, which increases dramatically with a remote seizure or abnormal EEG.[59] Most neurologists would not initiate treatment unless there is an EEG abnormality, evidence of structural disease, or the patient has an epilepsy syndrome with a high risk of seizure recurrence. The decision is highly individualized, requiring case by case consideration of the medical picture as well as psychological, social, occupational and recreational factors. The patient with a single seizure that is not treated requires periodic follow-up with neuroimaging for the possibility of a brain tumor.

The withdrawal, or failure to timely withdraw, anticonvulsant medication may generate a negligence claim. The majority of patients who are seizure-free on AEDs for longer than two years can remain seizure-free after medication withdrawal.[60] It is impossible to definitively predict which patients will remain so, but favorable factors include: fewer seizures during treatment, a normal neurological exam with normal imaging studies, and being seizure-free over two years on monotherapy.[61] Almost all recurrences are in the first year after medication withdrawal.[62] The decision to wean a patient off AEDs requires a methodical but individualized assessment of the potential benefits and risks.[63]

Patients who have failed medication therapy (effective trials of two or three properly prescribed anticonvulsants) should be referred to an epilepsy center for consideration of surgical treatment. Those with focal or secondarily

---

[59] Berg AT, Shinnar S. *The risk of seizure recurrence following a first unprovoked seizure: a quantitative review.* Neurology 1991; 41:965-972.

[60] O'Dell C, Shinnar S. *Initiation and discontinuation of antiepileptic drugs.* Neurol Clin 2001; 19:289-311.

[61] Berg AT, Shinnar S. *Relapse following discontinuation of antiepileptic drugs. A meta-analysis.* Neurology 1994; 44:601-608.

[62] Brodie MJ, French JA. *Management of epilepsy in adolescents and adults.* Lancet 2000; 336:323-329.

[63] Quality Standards Subcommittee of the American Academy of Neurology. *Practice parameter: A guideline for discontinuing antiepileptic drugs in seizure free patients (summary statement).* Neurology 1996; 47:600-602.

generalized seizures are usually the best candidates for resective surgery. Seizure control may be anticipated in one-half or slightly more of patients undergoing focal resection. Temporal lobectomy has the best outcome for seizure control and quality of life improvement. The key to a successful outcome is multi-modality localization of the seizure focus. Evaluation includes video-EEG recording of seizures with scalp and possibly intracranial EEG. Imaging techniques including ictal SPECT scans, magnetic resonance spectroscopy, and PET scans can be used to guide placement of intracranial electrodes. If localization is not possible, or a seizure focus cannot be resected because of its proximity to essential brain tissue, the patient may be a candidate for callosotomy or subpial transection. Non-destructive options include vagus nerve and intracranial stimulation.

Management of the epileptic patient entails much more than simply prescribing medication. There remain major misconceptions and fears about this disease which necessitates detailed counseling to encourage avoidance of trigger factors, medication compliance, and lifestyle modifications. Employment is a major consideration, and seizures preclude some occupations (airline pilot, taxi driver). Recreational activities such as climbing or swimming may have to be modified or abandoned. Many patients are concerned about the chronic toxicity of anticonvulsants causing slowing of mentation, and impairment of memory and concentration. Two particular concerns warrant further discussion: driving a motor vehicle, and the effect of anticonvulsants on pregnancy.

[f] Driving

Every state restricts issuance of a driver's license to individuals who have suffered a seizure or loss of consciousness. The laws vary among different states, but generally require that an individual be seizure-free for some period of time (ranging from no fixed duration to one year) before obtaining a license. A physician's evaluation must be submitted to the state before a license will be issued. Six states—California, Delaware, Nevada, New Jersey, Oregon, and Pennsylvania—have express mandatory reporting statutes requiring physicians to report patients with epilepsy or other conditions associated with a loss of consciousness or impaired ability to drive. All other states have voluntary reporting statutes. The neurologist has a duty to advise patients of the legislation in their particular state; in those with self-reporting requirements, the neurologist should advise the patient in writing to comply and keep a copy of the letter in the records. If an epileptic continues to drive because the neurologist failed to report in a mandatory reporting jurisdiction or failed to instruct the patient in a voluntary reporting state, then a seizure related accident may be grounds for a malpractice suit by the patient or patient's estate. Neurologists may also be liable to third parties for failing to report a patient or certifying a patient to drive. This is an emerging area of liability, with most decisions turning on whether the neurologist owed a duty to the third party. Courts have ruled in both directions, and the issue is far from settled.

[g]   Teratogenesis

Neurologists must address a host of complex issues in the 1 million plus epileptic women of childbearing age in the United States.[64] Perhaps the most serious concern is that women taking AEDs have an up to 7% risk of bearing a child with congenital malformations (orofacial clefts, congenital heart disease, neural tube defects, skeletal deformities, and urogenital malformations), threefold higher than nonepileptic women. The higher risk is probably multifactorial with genetic and social components, but AEDs are clearly implicated as human teratogens. Prior to pregnancy, it is important to determine whether AEDs are necessary; for example, the patient taking an AED for migraine or depression may be able to discontinue the drug. Additionally, if the patient with a single type of seizure has been in remission for over two years, and has a normal neurological exam and EEG, then it may be reasonable to withdraw the drug. This withdrawal must be performed slowly over months, and completed at least six months prior to conception, since seizure recurrence is most likely during this time frame. When treatment is indicated, every effort should be made to prescribe the single most suitable first generation AED, excluding valproic acid which harbors a greater risk of major fetal malformations and should be avoided in women who may become pregnant.[65] The teratogenic potential of the newer AEDs remains unknown, and these drugs should be avoided during pregnancy. Monotherapy at the lowest effective dose, with frequent daily dosing to avoid high peak levels, may decrease the potential for teratogenesis. The administration of folic acid reduces the incidence of neural tube defects and should be given to all women of childbearing potential. Optimal dosage for epileptics is controversial, and data must be extrapolated from nonepileptic women. The author recommends 4.0mg/day combined with vitamin B12.

---

[64] American Academy of Neurology, *Report of the Quality Standards Subcommittee: Practice Parameter: Management Issues for Women with Epilepsy (Summary Statement)* (1998).

[65] Wyszynski DF, Nambisan M, et al. *Increased rate of major malformations in offspring exposed to valproate during pregnancy.* Neurology 2005; 64:961-965.

It is not uncommon for epileptic women on medication to present to the neurologist after becoming pregnant. In general, the risk of uncontrolled epilepsy is greater than the risk of AED-induced teratogenesis, and drug treatment must be continued throughout pregnancy. It is a serious albeit common error to change medications for the sole purpose of reducing teratogenic risk: there is a risk of precipitating seizures that may reduce placental blood flow and impair fetal oxygenation; exposing the fetus to a second agent during the cross-over period increases the teratogenic risk; and discontinuing an AED does not lower the risk of malformations since the critical phase of organogenesis has usually passed. Therefore, if an epileptic woman presents after conception on effective monotherapy, the AED should not be changed.

The free or non-protein-bound AED levels should be monitored at least preconception, at the beginning of each trimester, in the last month of pregnancy, and 2 months postpartum. Pregnancy screening should include serum alpha-fetoprotein at 16-18 weeks and a level II ultrasound at 18-20 weeks, at which time amniocentesis may be offered if indicated. The patient should be properly counseled if there is a serious malformation, and provided with the option to terminate the pregnancy.

[6] Craniocerebral Trauma

The terms "head injury" and "brain injury" are not synonymous. Head injury includes damage to the scalp, skull and face, and may occur with or without an associated brain injury. Brain injury may be caused by blunt or penetrating trauma, or nontraumatic events such as cerebrovascular disease or infection. Penetrating trauma generally falls within the scope of neurosurgery. This discussion is limited to brain injury from blunt trauma, hereinafter referred to as traumatic brain injury (TBI). TBI is exceedingly common in our society, primarily due to motor vehicle accidents, occupational injuries, recreational mishaps, assaults and simple falls. There are probably over 2 million cases annually in the United States. The consequences of TBI are enormous—only one-third of patients are able to return to their occupation within 2 years after injury.[66] The Center for Disease Control estimates that over 5 million Americans are unable to independently perform activities of daily living as a result of TBI.[67] The precise incidence of TBI is unknown because many patients with mild injury do not seek

---

[66] Dikmen SS, Temkin NR, et al. *Employment following traumatic head injuries.* Arch Neurol 1994; 52:244-248.

[67] www.cdc.gov accessed 28 November 2007 citing Thurman D, Alverson C, Dunn K, Guerro J, Sniezek J. *Traumatic brain injury in the United States: a public health perspective.* Journal of Head Trauma Rehab 1999; 14:602-615.

immediate care or, if the patient presents with serious bodily injury, the associated brain injury may be overlooked or simply not recorded in the emergency room or hospital discharge records. The reader may be surprised that such an injury, no matter how mild, could be neglected. However, non-neurological physicians generally do not assess cognitive function in an alert, conversant patient presenting with multi-system trauma. As a result, patients with prominent TBI sequellae may be evaluated and treated for systemic injuries, and released without any type of neurological assessment.

[a] Assessing Severity

The patient with a CHI frequently has associated systemic injuries that require evaluation and treatment before complete neurological examination is possible. The physician may be limited to a screening examination to determine the patient's level of consciousness. A standardized rating scale is preferable in order to avoid descriptive terminology (drowsy, stuperous, delirious) that is subject to varying interpretations. The Glasgow Coma Scale (GCS) is the most widely used rating system for measuring severity of coma.[68] This scale allows clinical assessment of the head trauma patient with minimal inter-observer variability among nurses, non-neurologists and neurologists. It requires standardized scoring of eye opening, verbal response and motor response. The range is from 3 to 15; 3 – 8 means severe, 9 – 12 moderate, and 13 – 15 mild coma. A GCS allows some degree of prognostic determination. However, the majority of patients with CHI are conscious on presentation with a GCS of 15. The rating is meaningless in this situation—a patient with a top score may harbor significant cognitive deficits or even serious focal brain injury. It may be helpful to determine the duration of post-traumatic amnesia (PTA)—the time after injury when a patient is alert but confused or disoriented, and incapable of forming new memories. There is no recollection of events during the amnestic period. The duration of PTA allows a prediction of outcome following TBI.[69] Retrograde amnesia refers to a loss of memory for events preceding the head injury. During recovery, this amnestic period contracts and approaches the time of injury. Most patients have a retrograde amnesia of a few minutes or less. Thus, the loss of personal identity and related information (birthplace, occupation, spouse's name) in the absence of significant brain damage suggests a dissociative disorder or malingering.

---

[68] Teasdale G, Jennet B. *Assessment of coma and impaired consciousness: A practical scale.* Lancet 1974; 2:81-84.

[69] Ellenberg JH, Levin HS, et al. *Posttraumatic amnesia as a predictor of outcome after severe CHI.* Arch Neurol 1996; 53:782-791.

[b]   Mechanism of Injury

Determining the mechanism of injury is quite helpful in evaluating the severity and clinical manifestations of a TBI. The pathophysiology may be categorized according to whether the injury is primary or secondary, direct or indirect, blunt or penetrating, focal or diffuse, and intracerebral or extracerebral. Of course, not all damage is apparent at the time of injury; many processes such as seizures and cognitive deficits may evolve over weeks, months or even years.

Primary damage occurs at the moment of injury. A *direct* injury refers to the actual impact, such as a baseball striking the head or the head hitting a windshield. This may result in scalp lacerations, skull fractures, contusions or intracerebral hemorrhage. *Coup* lesions are contusions at or beneath the point of impact; *contracoup* lesions are diametrically opposed contusions, and occur because the brain moves within a rigid closed skull. Regardless of the location of impact, there are certain brain regions that are especially prone to injury due to their proximity to the irregular bony skull base. These areas include the basal portion of the bifrontal lobes and tips of the temporal lobes. An *indirect* injury is due to rapid acceleration and deceleration of the head, often with an associated rotational component. The movement of the brain within the rigid confines of the skull results in *diffuse axonal injury* (DAI) — shearing or tearing of the long axons such as those traversing the cerebral hemispheres or connecting the cortex and brainstem. The varying severity of DAI explains the range of clinical deficits. Mild injuries may temporarily disrupt axonal function, probably accounting in part for simple concussions. More severe injuries cause permanent effects with evidence of small scattered hemorrhages especially in the corpus callosum and brainstem. This is a slowly developing process, possibly accounting for the progression of symptoms after injury.

Secondary brain damage may be due to extracerebral or intracerebral causes. The former commonly includes post-traumatic circulatory and respiratory insufficiency, which is more likely to occur with severe systemic injuries causing blood loss, airway obstruction or chest wall trauma. This may cause ischemia (inadequate blood flow) and hypoxemia (poor oxygenation) with concomitant metabolic changes severely compounding the brain injury. The resultant hypoxemic-ischemic brain damage produces a pattern incorporating diffuse neuronal loss, focal changes in susceptible regions and watershed infarctions (strokes at the terminal junction of two vascular territories). Intracerebral causes of secondary brain damage include edema and mass lesions such as contusions and hemorrhages, which increase the intracranial pressure and may result in potentially fatal brain herniation.

The proper management of head trauma requires prevention of secondary injury through aggressive treatment of hypotension, hypovolemia, hypoxemia and associated intracranial pressure changes.

[c] Complications of Traumatic Brain Injury

A CHI may cause *focal brain damage*, with varying clinical deficits depending on the location of injury. Regardless of the location of impact, the anterior and inferior bifrontal lobes and tips of the temporal lobes are commonly contused. These areas constitute part of the limbic system and are involved in the regulation and control of emotion, behaviour and personality. Damage produces apathetic behaviour, loss of self-motivation, difficulty with problem solving, poor judgment, easy frustration and impairment of independent functioning. Impulsive, explosive and disinhibited behaviour may result in violence. Memory impairment is common with temporal lobe injury. These emotional and behavioural changes often blend into pre-existing personality traits, masking the extent of brain injury. The attorney, perhaps more so than the patient or family members or even physician, may be the first to discern a neurological source for the patient's personality changes.

Seizures arising at the moment of impact are a nonspecific response to trauma or bleeding, and do not herald an increased risk of epilepsy. Post-traumatic epilepsy occurs in 3 – 5% of head injuries, and refers to recurrent seizures which can develop even years after injury. Approximately one-half of these patients will suffer the first seizure within one year after injury. Risk factors include depressed skull fractures, intracranial hemorrhage, penetrating head trauma, prolonged coma or post-traumatic amnesia, and seizures in the first week after CHI. The risk for developing seizures persists for greater than ten years following severe injury (brain contusion, subdural hematoma, coma or amnesia greater than 24 hours); the increased risk of seizures from mild and moderate injury disappears after 5 and 10 years, respectively.[70] Current anticonvulsant regimens are generally effective in controlling these seizures. Prophylactic treatment does not reduce the incidence of post-traumatic epilepsy.

The post-traumatic complications of *epidural hematoma* (EDH), *subdural hematoma* (SDH), and *intracerebral hemorrhage* may be missed because the patient appears lucid after injury, only to suffer delayed deterioration due to a late epidural clot, delayed hemorrhage or expansion of a SDH, or increasing brain edema. EDHs usually occur in association with a skull

---

[70] Annegers JF, Houser WA, et al. *A population based study of seizures after traumatic brain injuries.* N Engl J Med 1998; 338:20-24.

fracture, often tearing the middle meningeal artery. The hematoma arises between the inner skull and dura mater; it is more common in the young, and uncommon with age as the dura becomes adherent to the inner table of the skull. An EDH may expand rapidly with progressive neurological deterioration. Alternatively, there may be a lucid interval after injury followed by deterioration over hours or days. EDHs usually require emergent craniotomy with evacuation. SDHs are due to venous bleeding between the dura mater and brain. An *acute* hematoma often presents as a mass lesion. In the older patient, *chronic* SDHs can occur with minimal head trauma; the patient may have even forgotten the trivial injury. These chronic SDHs develop over weeks to months and may include a progression of symptoms such as personality changes, cognitive impairment, apathy and headaches. The patient may appear demented or depressed. Ultimately there is decompensation due to increased intracranial pressure with hemiparesis, coma and death if untreated. Risk factors for chronic SDHs include increasing age, bleeding tendencies or use of anticoagulants, and pre-existing brain atrophy. Craniotomy is generally warranted for an acute SDH; surgical outcomes are less certain for a chronic hematoma. There may be one or more *intracerebral hemorrhages* (ICH) immediately after injury, or they may be delayed by several days (*spätapoplexie*). These may occur in a subcortical lobar region, or in deeper structures including the thalamus or basal ganglia, and be clinically indistinguishable from a spontaneous or hypertensive hemorrhage. It may be impossible to tell whether a patient suffered a fall because of a spontaneous hemorrhage, or fell down sustaining a head injury with a post-traumatic hemorrhage. Surgical evacuation of an ICH depends on a number of factors including level of consciousness, associated damage, and time since injury.

Basilar skull fractures are particularly problematic because they are difficult to detect and give rise to a host of problems. The clinician must have a high index of suspicion which may be supported by examination findings of Battle's sign and raccoon eyes (delayed ecchymoses over the mastoid protruberances and periorbital regions, respectively). The fracture can tear the dura and arachnoid resulting in a CSF leak, thereby creating a high risk of meningitis. It is common for the meningitis to be remote from the injury. The leak itself may be exceedingly difficult to treat requiring repeated procedures including CSF shunting. Anosmia or loss of smell commonly occurs in head injury. It is due to damage of the olfactory nerve receptor fibers, and resolves spontaneously over months in roughly one-half of patients. Fractures through the skull base may involve certain foramina resulting in cranial nerve injuries. The facial nerve may be transected by a fracture through the petrous bone resulting in facial paralysis; surgical intervention is controversial. A second type of facial nerve injury results in delayed paralysis which often improves spontaneously. Deafness may occur from injury to the eighth nerve by petrous ridge fractures, which must be distinguished from hearing loss due to bleeding into the middle ear or disruption of the ossicular chain. Post-traumatic vertigo is especially disabling, but most cases resolve over months. Persistent symptoms warrant neuro-otologic evaluation. Trigeminal nerve injury may result in facial pain, and it is poorly responsive to medical and surgical treatment. The optic nerve may be lacerated by a sphenoid bone fracture with resultant blindness. Oculomotor, trochlear and abducens nerve injuries can result in various disorders of extraocular movement. Cranial nerves may also be injured in the absence of basilar skull fractures by other mechanisms including stretching from the impact itself, as well as traction due to herniation.

Hydrocephalous occurs when trauma disrupts the normal flow of CSF. An acute blockage produces headache, visual symptoms, nausea and vomiting, impairment of consciousness and, if untreated, herniation. The gradual onset results in a classic triad of dementia, ataxia and urinary incontinence. Shunting is performed to bypass the blockage.

Headache is the most common complaint after a TBI, and is paradoxically more likely to occur following mild rather than severe trauma. Physicians often diagnose "post-traumatic headache" without making any further effort to identify the source of pain. This approach fails to recognize that post-traumatic headache is not a diagnosis in and of itself, but symptomatic of an underlying disorder. The head pain is not from injured brain tissue, which is actually insensate. It may originate from a multitude of diverse pain generators including the dura, blood vessels, and cranial nerves (II, III, V, IX, and X), as well as most extracranial structures such as skin, muscles, nerves, vessels, bones, joint capsules, sinuses, sense organs (eyes, ears, and nose), oropharynx and cervical nerves. The predominant headaches following trauma include tension headache and related musculoskeletal pain, migraine and its variants, and neuralgic pain syndromes such as greater occipital neuralgia. The treatment of post-traumatic tension and migraine headaches generally comports with the recommended therapy for the same nontraumatic headaches. Rare conditions that must be excluded by appropriate diagnostic testing include extra-axial collections (subdural hygromas), communicating hydrocephalous, tension pneumocephalous, carotid-cavernous fistula, and abscess.

[d] Post-Concussion Syndrome

Mild TBI has dominated courtrooms for hundreds of years, and continues to generate more litigation than any other aspect of head trauma.[71] A mild injury or *concussion* (trauma induced alteration of mental status) may produce dramatic cognitive deficits (impaired information processing and executive functions, memory and learning deficits, difficulties with attention and concentration, slowed reaction time) without any apparent physical basis. The combination of cognitive changes along with behavioural (impulsivity, irritability, personality changes), emotional (depression, anxiety), or somatic (headaches, dizziness, diplopia, hearing loss, tinnitus, anosmia, fatigue, sleeping disturbances) complaints constitutes the *post-concussive syndrome* (PCS). There is usually slow improvement. Young patients who do not experience a loss of consciousness may recover within days to weeks. The older the patient, and more severe the injury, the longer the recovery time. Perhaps 85-90% of patients suffering a concussion recover within one year.[72] The remaining patients are labeled with chronic PCS. Risk factors include age over 40 years, prior CHI, lower educational and socioeconomic status, and alcohol abuse. Those with premorbid psychiatric illness or suffering marked stress at the time of injury are more likely to have chronic symptomatology. It remains unclear whether apolipoprotein E ε4 status is a factor in recovery from mild or any type of brain injury.[73] The medical community is sharply divided over the nature of chronic PCS. Many physicians believe symptomatic complaints lasting more than a few months with a normal examination and diagnostic testing constitute malingering or a somatization disorder. Likewise, the lay population is skeptical of complaints without evidence of damage. This view is perpetuated through popular television and cinema productions showing countless stereotyped concussions that bear no resemblance to reality—the hero is knocked out, gets up, shakes his head, and proceeds to catch the villain. However, this narrow view ignores the bulk of neuropathological, neurophysiological, neuroimaging and neuropsychological studies documenting a host of abnormalities in many cases of mild TBI. Litigation raises the issue of

---

[71] Evans RW, ed. *Neurology and Trauma.* Philadelphia: W.B. Saunders; 1996 at 94 citing de Morsier G. *Les encephalopathies traumatiques. Etude neurologique.* Schweiz Arch Neurol Neurochir Psychiat 1943; 50:161. (three physicians in 1694 opining for the court that postconcussive symptoms in a maid struck on the head with a stick "will leave its mark in the form of an impediment.").

[72] Alexander MP. *Mild traumatic brain injury: pathophysiology, natural history and clinical management.* Neurology 1995; 45:1253-1260.

[73] Ponsford J, Rudzki D, et al. *Impact of lipoprotein gene on cognitive impairment and recovery after traumatic brain injury.* Neurology 2007; 68:619-620.

secondary gain; however, many patients with PCS are not involved in legal matters. In those patients pursuing litigation, resolution of the suit does not consistently lead to resolution of symptoms. Therefore, patients with persistent PCS warrant a thorough neurological evaluation, including medical and psychiatric history, as well as analysis of injury mechanisms, and appropriate diagnostic testing to exclude unrecognized injuries or coexistent disorders. Formal neuropsychological testing may document the deficits and address concerns of symptom magnification or malingering. This comprehensive approach is more likely to lead to successful treatment than simply categorizing the patient as having organic or psychogenic symptoms. Neurologists must be equally cautious not to relate all cognitive symptoms directly to the CHI. Chronic pain, depression and other conditions may cause memory, concentration and attention impairment. It is imperative to pursue other potential sources of cognitive dysfunction before simply attributing it to trauma.

[7] Spine Disorders

Neck and low back are among the most common medical problems in the adult population, with enormous social, economic and psychological burdens. It is estimated that up to 80% of adults will experience back pain at least once in their lifetime. Risk factors for developing spine pain are multifactorial, with age, socioeconomic status, obesity, substance abuse, heavy labor, depression and anatomical spine variations all playing a role.[74]

[a] Anatomy of the Spine

A basic knowledge of spinal anatomy is essential to understanding diseases and disorders of the spine. The reader is referred to the most recent edition of *Gray's Anatomy* for details. The spinal cord and spinal column must be clearly distinguished when discussing a particular level; it is an obvious but often overlooked point that the cord segments are not contiguous with their corresponding vertebrae. Spinal cord anatomy is reviewed in §11.06 [4]. The bony spinal column is divided into four sections including seven cervical, twelve thoracic, five lumbar, and five fused sacral vertebrae. Coccygeal bones are at the lower segment of the sacrum. The vertebral bodies increase in size from the cervical to lumbar regions; the former region must be mobile, and the latter specialized for weight bearing. The individual cervical, thoracic and lumbar vertebrae are similar in structure except for the first (*atlas*) and second

---

[74] Levin KH, ed. *Neck and back pain.* Neurol Clin (2007) 25:331-575.

(*axis*) cervical vertebrae. The axis has an *odontoid* process around which the ring-like atlas rotates, allowing the head to turn. Each of the remaining vertebrae consists of a body, two *pedicles*, two *lamina*, four articular *facet joints* and a *spinous process*. The vertebral bodies are separated by *intervertebral discs*, which consist of a *nucleus pulposis* core surrounded by an elastic *annulus fibrosis* ring. These discs maintain the interspace width and bind together opposing vertebral surfaces to allow a degree of painless motion. The bony elements and discs along with various ligaments form the *spinal canal*, which contains the spinal cord. There are 31 pairs of spinal nerves, traversing the canal through *foramina* formed by the juxtaposition of paired vertebrae. The canal diameter varies but can be pathologically narrowed by degenerative disease or congenital abnormalities, resulting in *stenosis* with spinal cord compression and *myelopathy*. Foraminal narrowing from bony encroachment or disc *herniation* (extrusion of nucleus pulposus through the annulus) may cause *radiculopathy* or nerve root compression.

[b] Acute Neck and Back Pain

Most patients with acute neck or back pain present to primary care physicians. Neurologists are consulted if there are signs of spinal cord or nerve root dysfunction, or the pain becomes chronic. It is not uncommon for patients to present to the neurologist with permanent deficits because the primary care doctor failed to recognize a serious disorder, or delayed referral to comply with managed care regulations.

The history requires particular attention to the pain characteristics, which may be of diagnostic significance. For example, pain that awakens the patient or is aggravated by lying supine suggests spinal malignancy. Radicular pain radiating in a dermatomal distribution indicates nerve root compression. Leg pain that worsens with walking may be consistent with vascular or neurogenic claudication. The history should be followed by a thorough examination focusing on motor, sensory and reflex functions to determine whether there is spinal cord dysfunction (myelopathy), nerve root compression (radiculopathy), or both, or another process. Diagnostic testing, if warranted, usually commences with MRI of the relevant spinal levels.

Most cases of acute pain are due to nonspecific musculoskeletal injury (originating from muscles, tendons, ligaments, facet joints or related structures), and labeled as strain, sprain, myofascial pain or some similar diagnosis. Non-narcotic analgesics and non-steroidal anti-inflammatory agents as well as muscle relaxants are helpful. Physical therapy progressing to a self-directed exercise program is beneficial. Bed rest must be avoided or limited to a short time, because it leads to deconditioning with exacerbation of the pain.

There is little if any evidence to support the many other available treatment options.[75] The most reasonable approach is early mobilization with a return to normal activities, imposing restrictions to avoid aggravating the pain.

[c] Chronic Neck and Back Pain

Some patients with acute neck or back pain progress to a chronic state, arbitrarily defined as persistent pain for more than six months. The neurologist must ensure these patients are not suffering from an undiagnosed disease such as arachnoiditis, inflammatory arthropathy, metastatic cancer or spinal instability. The patient labeled with chronic pain is generally shuttled among various specialists and pain clinics without any chance of ever again receiving a thorough evaluation, barring frank deterioration with overt neurological signs. Unfortunately, there are many patients with chronic pain in the absence of any identifiable underlying pathology. These patients fail to respond to conventional therapy, and share common features such as depression, symptom magnification and overuse of medication. Maladaptive illness behaviours impede recovery. Deconditioning aggravates the clinical picture. The result is a crippling combination of cognitive, behavioural and psychological dysfunction that will not respond to any standard treatment regimens. The only reasonable option is a multi-modality interdisciplinary team approach focusing on a progressive exercise and work hardening program.[76] Successful participants are more likely to have improved functional capacity and return to occupational activities. Some patients fail to respond to any approach. These patients are at risk for two physician-driven sources of harm: overuse of narcotic medications, and progressively more invasive therapeutic intervention.

[d] Spondylosis

Spondylosis is a natural degenerative process affecting the vertebral facet joints, intervertebral discs, spinal ligaments and related column elements. The resultant structural abnormalities can cause spinal canal narrowing with spinal cord dysfunction (myelopathy) or foraminal encroachment compressing a nerve root (radiculopathy), or both may coexist, at one or multiple levels. Cervical spondylotic myelopathy develops when the canal becomes narrow enough to compress the cord. The symptoms include difficulty walking with aching in the legs that is aggravated by activity, diffuse paresthesias and

---

[75] Atlas SJ, Nardin RA. *Evaluation and treatment of low back pain: an evidence-based approach to clinical care.* Muscle Nerve 2003; 27:265-284.

[76] Levin KH, Covington EC, et. al. *Functional restoration of the patient with chronic spine pain.* Continuum 2001; 7:152-178.

bladder impairment. The normally slow progression may be aggravated by trauma or flexion-extension injuries. Cervical spondylotic radiculopathy caused by intervertebral disc herniation or bony foraminal narrowing is perhaps the most common degenerative spine presentation. Risk factors include aging, heavy lifting, vibratory forces and coughing. Clinical symptoms vary according to the level of foraminal narrowing or disc herniation and, if a disc, whether it is located centrally, paracentrally or laterally. Central herniations may compress the cord; paracentral herniations may give rise to a Brown-Sequard syndrome or hemicord compression; and lateral disc herniations compress the nerve root. Lumbar spondylosis may cause nerve root compression or spinal stenosis with *neurogenic claudication*. Symptoms of the latter include slowly progressive leg pain, aggravated by walking, with partial relief upon rest or hip flexion, which must be distinguished from vascular claudication. It is not uncommon to have chronic radicular symptoms with intermittent neurogenic claudication. Initial management for spondylosis, whether cervical or lumbar, involves a multi-modality approach incorporating pain management and physical therapy. Surgical decompression should be considered for progressive or recalcitrant symptoms, or neurological deficits.

[e] Disc Disease

Cervical disc herniation most commonly occurs posterolaterally at C5-C6 or C6-C7, affecting the C6 or C7 nerve roots, respectively. Neck pain and stiffness are followed by radiation of pain into the involved dermatome. There may be a dermatomal sensory impairment and motor weakness in the muscles supplied by the involved nerve root. Patients that fail to respond to conservative management, or develop motor, sensory or reflex deficits, may benefit from neurosurgical intervention. *Lumbar disc herniation* most commonly occurs posterolaterally at L4-L5 or L5-S1, affecting the L5 or S1 nerve roots, respectively. L1-L2, L2-L3 and L3-L4 disc disease accounts for less than 5% of all lumbar disc abnormalities. Back pain is usually followed by lower extremity pain and paresthesias. Rarely a central herniation can affect the cauda equina resulting in bowel and bladder dysfunction. Most patients respond to conservative management; however, intractable pain, motor weakness, or bowel or bladder involvement warrants neurosurgical consultation. Although disc herniations and spondylosis are the most common causes of radiculopathy, it is important to keep in mind the wide range of diseases causing noncompressive radiculopathy: infection (herpes zoster, Lyme disease, cytomegalovirus), inflammatory conditions (vasculitis, sarcoidosis, diabetic radiculopathy), neoplastic disease (lymphoma, metastatic tumor, carcinomatous meningitis), and spinal hematoma.

[f] Spinal Cord Injury

The most common cause of spinal cord injury is trauma and, like head injury, often due to motor vehicle accidents, recreational mishaps and accidental falls. Other causes of spinal cord injury including infection, tumors (primary and metastatic), vascular diseases, degenerative conditions, radiation myelopathy and syringomyelia are discussed in 11.09 [9], 11.09 [10], 11.09 [11], 11.09 [16]. The clinical picture depends on the location and severity of damage. A total absence of motor and sensory function below the level of injury is termed a *complete injury.*   An *incomplete injury* refers to the preservation of some function, and includes the *central cord syndrome* (cord compression causing bilateral upper extremity weakness and sensory impairment, less pronounced lower extremity weakness, and bowel and bladder dysfunction), *anterior cord syndrome* (weakness and loss of pain and temperature sensation below the compression, but preservation of posterior column vibration and proprioception), and the *Brown-Sequard syndrome* (injury to one side of the cord with ipsilateral paralysis and loss of posterior column function below the level of injury, and contralateral loss of pain and temperature sensation beginning several segments inferior to the injury). The patient with a suspected spinal cord injury must be properly immobilized and, after treatment of life-threatening medical and surgical problems, undergo emergent neurological evaluation. The window of opportunity for treating an acute spinal cord injury is very narrow and timing is crucial. The prognosis for recovery is best in patients with an incomplete lesion showing signs of recovery within 48 hours. The higher the level of the lesion, the greater the neurological impairment. The prognosis is poor if there is no functional recovery within 3 months after injury, although there may be continued recovery for 2 years and, in the rare case, perhaps longer. Rehabilitation requires a multi-disciplinary team approach focused on maximizing residual functions to facilitate the highest level of independence.

[g] Whiplash

Whiplash refers to a cervical strain or sprain due to hyperextension and flexion movements, and should not be diagnosed in the presence of fractures, disc herniations, spinal cord damage or nerve root injuries. It is most commonly caused by a rear-end motor vehicle collision. The interested reader may refer to the wealth of literature detailing injury mechanisms.[77]

---

[77] *See* Severy DM, Mathewson JH, Bechtol CO. *Controlled automobile rear-end collisions, an investigation of related engineering medical phenomena.* Can Services Med J 1955; 11:727-759 and its progeny.

Epidemiological data suggests there are more than one million whiplash injuries annually in the United States.[78]

Neck pain develops within 6 hours in 65% of patients, within 24 hours in 28% of patients, and within 72 hours in the remaining 7%.[79] The pain is usually associated with stiffness, tenderness and restricted movement of the neck. Initial treatment includes judicious use of pain medication, non-steroidal anti-inflammatory agents, and muscle relaxants in combination with early mobilization and physical therapy. The use of a soft cervical collar should be avoided, or limited to a few days, to avoid deconditioning. The sequellae of whiplash injuries are legion and include headaches (tension, migraine, and greater occipital neuralgia are common), neck and back injuries (facet joint syndrome, disc herniation, radiculopathy, spondylosis, spinal cord compression, and fractures and dislocations), dizziness, weakness, paresthesias, visual changes, and a host of cognitive and neuropsychological deficits (nervousness, irritability, sleep disturbances, fatigue, attention and concentration impairment). These nonspecific symptoms are common in the PCS; however, it remains unclear if the cognitive deficits following whiplash injury are indicative of mild brain injury.[80]

Most litigation surrounding whiplash seems to focus on two separate questions. First, is it possible for a whiplash injury to aggravate an underlying condition? Yes, these types of injuries may convert a pre-existing asymptomatic myelopathy or radiculopathy into a symptomatic condition with profound deficits. Additionally, whiplash seems to hasten the development of spondylosis and degenerative disc disease. Second, does the patient have a chronic whiplash? Most patients recover within six months. The etiology of chronic symptoms remains highly controversial. Medical opinions are divided over organic and non-organic causes of persistent symptomatology. The attorney will have no difficulty advancing arguments for either side. It is the author's experience that many whiplash patients have persistent symptoms because they were, in fact, injured and harbor neurological impairment which will not be cured by a settlement or verdict. There are, of course, a minority of patients that malinger or exaggerate complaints in order to bolster their legal case, and some develop a somatization disorder. Additionally, chronic pain can cause depression,

---

[78] Evans RW. *Whiplash injuries.* www.medlink.com accessed 14 November 2007.

[79] Deans GT, McGalliard JN, Kerr M, Rutherford WH. *Neck sprain – a major cause of disability following car accidents.* Injury 1987; 18:10-12.

[80] Taylor AE, Cox CA, Mailis A. *Persistent neuropsychological deficits following whiplash: evidence for chronic mild traumatic brain injury?* Arch Phys Med Rehabil 1996; 77:529-535.

leading to neuropsychological symptoms, and this does not equate to malingering.[81]

[8] Peripheral Neuropathy

Peripheral neuropathy refers to any disorder of the peripheral nerves, whether hereditary or acquired, generalized or focal, acute or chronic, or mild or severely disabling. These conditions are responsible for significant worldwide disability, with a prevalence that approaches 10% of the population.[82] There are over 200 recognized causes of peripheral neuropathy; thus, a methodical approach to evaluation is necessary to minimize the risk of an erroneous diagnosis or failure to recognize a treatable underlying condition.

[a] Clinical Manifestations

The clinical manifestations of a neuropathy depend on the degree of nerve or myelin damage, type and distribution of affected nerve modalities, and time course of disease. Motor nerve damage results in weakness and atrophy. The onset of symmetric distal lower extremity weakness suggests a generalized peripheral neuropathy, whereas weakness localized to the distribution of a single nerve implies damage to that particular nerve. Muscle wasting usually indicates a long-standing neuropathy. Sensory nerve damage can cause positive (paresthesias and dysesthesias, pain) or negative (loss of sensation or numbness, proprioceptive ataxia) symptoms, which may be generalized in a polyneuropathy or focal with isolated nerve damage. The classical feature of a generalized neuropathy is numbness starting at the toes and ascending to the upper calves, then beginning in the fingers and spreading up the arms, resulting in a *stocking glove* distribution. A less common presentation is the loss of proprioception, with inability to localize the feet and hands in space, resulting an unsteady gait and clumsiness of the hands. Autonomic involvement results in postural hypotension, gastrointestinal dysfunction, genitourinary impairment and a host of other symptoms.

[b] Classification

There are several different ways to classify peripheral neuropathies.[83] Neurologists rely on multiple schemes simultaneously in order to narrow the

---

[81] Alexander MP. *Whiplash: chronic pain and cognitive symptoms.* Neurology 2003; 60:733.

[82] Martyn CN, Hughes RA. *Epidemiology of peripheral neuropathy.* J Neurol, Neurosurg Psychiatry 1997; 62:310-318.

[83] Harati Y, ed. *Peripheral neuropathies.* Neurol Clin 2007; 25:1-329.

diagnostic field. First, neuropathies may be *inherited* or *acquired*. The most common *inherited* types are labeled *hereditary motor and sensory neuropathies (HMSN) types I and II* (formerly *Charcot-Marie-Tooth disease*) and due to genetic abnormalities impairing neuron or Schwann cell development or maintenance or folding of the myelin sheath. These conditions are present from birth although symptoms and diagnosis are often delayed; the classical finding is *pes cavus* due to intrinsic foot muscle weakness, and there may be subsequent development of weakness in the hands. Inheritance is predominantly autosomal dominant, but there is variability of expression due to the extent of gene defect. Genetic testing is available for some types. Management is symptomatic for these slowly progressive diseases. *Acquired* neuropathies are grouped into several broad etiological categories: metabolic and endocrine (diabetes, uremia, hypothyroidism), nutritional (thiamine, B6, B12, and E deficiencies), toxic (lead, arsenic, mercury, nitrous oxide, radiation), medications (chloramphenicol, cisplatin, amiodarone, isoniazid, phenytoin, vincristine), infections (hepatitis, cytomegalovirus, lyme disease, tuberculosis, HIV, leprosy), immune mediated diseases (Guillain-Barre disease, chronic inflammatory demyelinating polyneuropathy, rheumatoid arthritis, lupus, cryoglobulinemia, Sjogren syndrome), tumors and paraneoplastic syndromes (anti-Hu antibody associated sensory neuropathy, multiple myeloma, monoclonal gammopathies, lymphoma), trauma, and entrapment syndromes (carpal tunnel syndrome, median neuropathy at the elbow, anterior and posterior interosseus neuropathies, ulnar neuropathy at elbow or wrist, radial neuropathy, sciatic neuropathy, common peroneal and posterior tibial neuropathies, lateral cutaneous nerve of the thigh, spinal accessory nerve). The listed conditions under each acquired neuropathy category are merely representative examples and not inclusive of the many potential disorders in that category. This etiological classification is not particularly helpful for diagnostic purposes, unless the relationship between a specific cause and the neuropathy is unquestionable. Second, neuropathies may be classified according to their anatomical distribution. *Polyneuropathy* refers to a generalized or diffuse involvement of the peripheral nerves, usually beginning distally in the feet before ascending into the legs and affecting the hands. *Plexopathy* refers to involvement of the brachial or lumbosacral plexus. *Mononeuropathy* includes diseases that are confined to a single nerve, while *mononeuropathy multiplex* signifies disease of two or more nerves. Third, a physiological classification is helpful because different nerve fibers—motor, sensory or autonomic—are susceptible to different disease processes. Fourth, neurodiagnostic studies distinguish between *demyelinating* (predominantly affecting myelin sheath) and *axonal* (affecting peripheral nerve axons) neuropathies, a useful finding since each category suggests different causes. Fifth, a clinical time course labeling the onset as *acute* (Guillain-Barre syndrome, acute intermittent porphyria, thallium toxicity or infection), *subacute* (most toxic exposures, some metabolic disturbances, nutritional deficiencies and paraneoplastic syndromes) or *chronic* (inherited neuropathies, connective tissue disorders, some metabolic derangements) narrows the differential diagnosis. A systematic approach incorporating several of the above classification schemes increases the diagnostic yield while avoiding unnecessary testing. For example, an *acquired, subacute, distal, sensorimotor polyneuropathy* suggests diabetic peripheral neuropathy, especially if there is a chronic hyperglycemic exposure, and additional testing can be limited to exclude immune mediated neuropathies, vitamin B12 deficiency, amyloid neuropathy and hypothyroid or uremic neuropathy.

[c] Diagnosis

Symptoms of numbness, tingling, pain and weakness are frequently ignored or belittled, or, conversely, approached in a "shotgun" fashion with extensive testing before first categorizing the neuropathy. A careful history focuses on localizing the lesion within the peripheral nervous system (anterior horn cell, root, plexus, single or multiple nerves, neuromuscular junction and muscle), identifying the involved nerve fibers (motor, sensory, autonomic, or mixed), assessing the primary pathology (demyelinating, axonal, mixed), and documenting the time course of events. The medical history including past and current medications may uncover a number of neuropathies which are due to underlying diseases or treatment. Diabetes mellitus, for example, is the most common cause of neuropathy; in fact, peripheral neuropathy may be an early symptom of impaired glucose tolerance. Social, travel and occupational histories may alert the neurologist to systemic causes such as alcohol or toxic exposure. The family history may uncover a hereditary neuropathy. It is not uncommon for these diseases to be asymptomatic until adulthood. Inquiry about CMT disease may not elicit recognition; thus, direct questions about family members with difficulty running as a child, high arched feet or hammer toes are more probative. A review of systems may reveal signs suggestive of malignancy, collagen vascular disease, infection or other conditions. General physical examination should include an assessment for autonomic dysfunction, thorough inspection of the skin (coldness, dryness, scaling suggests small fiber and autonomic dysfunction), and fundoscopic evaluation (optic pallor suggests B12 deficiency). Detailed neurological examination is necessary to confirm the presence of a neuropathy, and to provide information regarding distribution, functional impairment and severity of disease. After demonstrating a peripheral neuropathy by history and examination, NCS and EMG testing can determine what type of fibers are involved (motor, sensory or a combination), whether the neuropathy is demyelinating or axonal, and the distribution and severity of disease. Neurodiagnostic studies predominantly evaluate the function of large diameter nerve fibers, which reduces the sensitivity of testing in small fiber and autonomic neuropathies. However, these latter conditions can be assessed with quantitative sensory or autonomic function testing as well as epidermal skin punch biopsy. SSEPs and nerve and muscle biopsy play a role in certain conditions. Hematologic and CSF studies aid in the evaluation of infectious, metabolic, endocrine, toxic, nutritional and a host of other conditions. If the etiology remains unclear, routine testing should include, as a minimum, complete chemistry profiles and blood count, sedimentation rate, serum protein electrophoresis, immunoelectrophoresis and vitamin B12 levels.

[d] Treatment

The management of neuropathies should be directed at the underlying cause, if possible, along with symptomatic therapy. Treatment for the causes may include improved glycemic control for diabetic neuropathies, antibiotics or antivirals for infectious neuropathies, immunomodulating agents for immune-mediated or paraneoplastic neuropathies, nutritional replacement for vitamin deficiency states, and surgery for entrapment syndromes. Symptomatic management includes medical therapy for painful paresthesias, physical therapy to improve mobility and function, and supportive measures for orthostatic hypotension and bowel or bladder dysfunction.

[e] Plexopathies

Brachial Plexus. The brachial plexus is formed by the fifth through eighth cervical and first thoracic spinal nerves, subject to anatomical variations. It is "prefixed" if there is a fourth cervical contribution, and "postfixed" if there is no fourth cervical contribution but a significant second thoracic root contribution. The spinal roots form three trunks above the clavicle (upper, middle and lower), each dividing into anterior and posterior divisions behind the clavicle, and uniting below the clavicle to form three cords (the three posterior divisions form the posterior cord, two upper anterior divisions form the lateral cord, and the lower anterior division becomes the medial cord). Thus, the posterior cord contains fibers from the fifth through eighth cervical spinal nerves, and divides into the radial and axillary nerves; the lateral cord contains fibers from the fifth, sixth and seventh spinal nerves, and divides into part of the median nerve and musculocutaneous nerve; and the medial cord contains fibers from the eighth cervical and first thoracic nerves, and terminates in the ulnar nerve and a contribution to the median nerve. Disorders of the plexus may be simplistically divided into those above the clavicle (supraclavicular) and those below the clavicle (infraclavicular). Upper plexus lesions (upper trunk) predominantly affect the shoulder girdle musculature. When severe, the upper arm hangs uselessly, rotated such that the palm is visible from the rear (waiter's tip position). Infraclavicular lesions are more common, predominantly involving the proximal portions of the median, ulnar and radial nerves, resulting in forearm or hand weakness. The brachial plexus is particularly subject to traction injury, primarily because of the distance between fixation points (vertebral column and axillary sheath). It is at risk from penetrating trauma as well as closed injuries with birth trauma, falls, shoulder dislocations, motor vehicle accidents, and improper positioning on the operating table. Surgical procedures in the supraclavicular fossa may cause a plexopathy. Radiation therapy is a well recognized cause of brachial plexopathy, as is neoplastic disease, particularly Pancoasts syndrome (secondary neoplasms from the lung). *Neuralgic amyotrophy (Parsonage-Turner syndrome)* is an idiopathic form of plexopathy characterized by the abrupt onset of severe shoulder pain. As the pain subsides over a few days, weakness and sensory loss are apparent. Recovery usually takes months. Precipitating factors include viral infections, vaccinations, and surgical procedures. There is also a rare familial form. It is probably an autoimmune disorder.

Lumbosacral plexus. The lumbar plexus derives from L1, L2 and L3 nerve roots with minor contribution from T12 and L4, giving rise to the femoral nerve. The sacral plexus derives from L4 through S3, giving rise to the sciatic nerve. Lumbosacral plexus insults affect the proximal muscles, are typically associated with pain, and should be suspected following abdominal pelvic surgery, pelvic fracture, hip dislocation, childbirth, diabetes or buttock injection. Bleeding disorders or anticoagulants may cause a retroperitoneal hematoma with compression of the plexus.

The proper diagnosis of a plexopathy requires skilled electrodiagnostic testing that may be beyond the capabilities of some neurologists. Treatment is directed towards any underlying disorder, and supportive management should include pain relief as well as physical and occupational therapy.

[f] Mononeuropathies

Peripheral nerves can be injured by compression, traction, or sharp or blunt trauma, and are usually the result of falls, motor vehicle accidents, occupational injuries and penetrating trauma such as lacerations. Upper limb injuries most commonly involve the median, ulnar or radial nerves, and are more common that lower limb injuries, which usually involve the sciatic or peroneal nerves. Nerve trauma may be classified as *neurapraxia* (mildest injury; myelin disruption without axonal damage; recovery is typical), *axonotmesis* (intermediate severity; myelin and axon affected; supporting tissue intact; regrowth and recovery possible), or *neurotmesis* (most severe injury; disruption of myelin, axons, supportive tissue; no spontaneous recover). In axonotmesis and neurotmesis injuries, *Wallerian degeneration* or axonal wasting occurs distal to the site of damage, with atrophy and weakness of the muscle supplied by that nerve. Axonal regrowth after Wallerian degeneration requires the intact layers of surrounding support tissue. The commonly injured nerves are reviewed with mention of select malpractice issues, as lack of space precludes discussion of the pathophysiology or treatment of entrapment neuropathies.[84]

Median nerve. The two heads of the inner and outer cords of the brachial plexus join to form this nerve. It supplies the forearm flexor muscles of the wrist and fingers. Injury results in grip weakness and sensory loss in the first through third digits, and radial half of the fourth digit. The median nerve may be compressed at the elbow by the pronator teres muscle. It is vulnerable to diagnostic or therapeutic needles punctures in the antecubital fossa. Entrapment at the wrist is due to carpal tunnel syndrome and may occur spontaneously, or due to acute trauma or occupational injury, or less likely thyroid disease, acromegaly and hypothyroidism.

Ulnar nerve. The ulnar nerve is derived from the eighth cervical and first thoracic spinal nerves. It lies behind the medial condyle of the humerus at the elbow, supplying muscles that flex the wrist on the ulnar side and most of the small hand muscles. Injury at the elbow causes grip weakness in the ulnar side of the hand and wasting of the first dorsal interosseus muscle. Sensory loss is in the fifth finger, ulnar side of the fourth finger, and the ulnar edge of the hand extending up to the wrist. It may be caused by minor trauma such as resting the elbow on a hard surface for a prolonged period, or by diabetes or other metabolic dysfunctions. Iatrogenic ulnar neuropathies occur peri-operatively, may be unilateral or bilateral, and are usually attributed to arm position at the time of surgery. Lacerations may injury the nerve at the level of the wrist. A deep palmar branch neuropathy can occur with prolonged or recurrent pressure on the outer palm.

Radial nerve. The radial nerve is a continuation of the posterior cord of the brachial plexus. It innervates the triceps, and extensor muscles of the

---

[84] Dawson DM, Hallett M, Wilbourn AJ. *Entrapment neuropathies*, 3rd ed. Lippincott, Williams & Wilkins; 1999.

wrist and fingers, and provides sensation to the lower half of the radial aspect of the arm as well as dorsum of hand. The nerve is most vulnerable to damage in the spiral groove of the humerus. Injury results in wrist and finger drop with sensory loss. Compression occurs when an intoxicated individual falls asleep with an arm draped over the back of a chair, resulting in *Saturday night palsy.* Less common injuries are due to malpositioning of a patient during surgery, and misplaced injections.

Sciatic nerve. The sciatic nerve is derived from the lumbosacral plexus, running through the pelvis, out the sciatic notch into the buttock, than descending into the posterior thigh. Near the popliteal fossa, it divides into the common peroneal and posterior tibial nerves. The nerve supplies the hamstring muscles in the thigh and, via the common peroneal and tibial nerves, all the muscles below the knee. A complete sciatic lesion results in weakness of knee flexors, and all leg and foot muscles. Foot drop occurs due to paralysis of the anterior tibial and peroneal groups; patients drag the toes of the affected foot, are unable to stand on toes, and have sensory loss over the outer and lower aspect of the leg and across dorsum of foot. The sciatic nerve may be damaged due to fractures of the pelvis or femur. The most common injury is a misplaced injection in the buttock.

Common peroneal nerve. The common peroneal nerve curves around the head of the fibula and is likely to be damaged at that site, especially with compression. It may be damaged in patients incorrectly strapped in the lithotomy position. Most common peroneal neuropathies resolve over months. It is sometimes misdiagnosed as an L5 radiculopathy.

[9] Central Nervous System Tumors

Primary tumors of the central nervous system (CNS) originate in the brain, spinal cord or adjacent tissues (meninges, cranial nerves, pituitary gland); *secondary* or metastatic tumors result from systemic cancer that spreads to the brain or spinal cord. There are 40,000 new primary tumors and over 150,000 new metastatic cases annually in the United States.[85]

[a] Primary Brain Tumors

The etiology of primary CNS tumors is largely unknown. Exposure to ionizing radiation is the only well documented environmental risk factor for developing brain tumors. Vinyl chloride exposure may predispose to the development of glioma. There are several heritable syndromes associated with an increased risk of brain tumors (von Hippel-Lindau syndrome, von

---

[85] Wen PY, Schiff D, eds. *Brain tumors in adults.* Neurol Clin 2007; 25:867-1258.

Recklinghausen's disease, tuberous sclerosis). Epstein-Barr virus infection is implicated in the development of primary CNS lymphoma. Current views on the pathogenesis of primary brain tumors suggest that viruses or toxins trigger an underlying gene mediated disorder.

[b] Clinical Presentation

Brain tumors cause symptoms by infiltrating normal tissue and destroying brain cells, increasing intracranial pressure through a mass effect, and producing cerebral edema. It must be emphasized from the outset that brain tumors may exist in the absence of symptoms, or with minimal findings such as mild intermittent confusion or decreased capacity for sustained mental activity. Those brain tumor patients harboring clinical symptoms usually present with (1) seizures, (2) subacute progression of a focal neurological deficit, or (3) a nonfocal neurological disorder such as headache, cognitive impairment, personality changes, or gait dysfunction. The presence of systemic symptoms such as fever, weight loss, anorexia or malaise suggests a metastatic as opposed to primary brain tumor.

Seizures, focal or generalized, are the presenting symptom in one-quarter to one-third of patients with brain tumors. There may be one seizure or many, which may precede other symptoms by weeks or months or, in the case of some tumors such as an astrocytoma or meningioma, several years. The majority of patients with parenchymal tumors and almost half of those with metastases will develop seizures at some time during the disease course. Most of these seizures respond to standard anticonvulsant medications. A new onset seizure in an adult is suggestive of a brain tumor and warrants an appropriate evaluation including neuroimaging. Focal signs and symptoms are secondary to tumor invasion, ischemia from vascular compression, or cerebral edema, and dependant upon the region of brain affected. For example, frontal lobe lesions may cause cognitive changes, behavioural disturbances, gait dysfunction, speech difficulties, anosmia and gaze impairment. Temporal, parietal and occipital lobe lesions cause deficits referable to the functions of those lobes. Brainstem tumors cause cranial nerve dysfunction and various patterns of motor and sensory impairment. Pituitary and hypothalamic tumors may present with endocrine disturbance. Third ventricular and pineal tumors often cause hydrocephalous, pupillary disturbances, and autonomic dysfunction. Cerebellar tumors cause headache, ataxia, and nystagmus, and may result in fourth ventricular obstruction with resultant hydrocephalous. Nonfocal signs due to increased intracranial pressure include altered mental functions, headache, nausea or vomiting and dizziness. These initial symptoms may be quite vague and present for considerable time before the onset of localizing deficits. The changes in mental function include emotional lability, excessive irritability, forgetfulness, limited insight, lack of initiative, and an overall reduced range of mental activity which is especially notable during conversation. These signs and symptoms gradually progress to more pronounced impairment with focal deficits and somnolence as intracranial pressure increases and the brain can no longer compensate. There are patients who become overtly confused and agitated. Headache warrants further discussion because it is an early symptom in one-third of brain tumor patients, and ultimately presents in a far larger number of patients. Additionally, it is one of the most prevalent conditions leading to claims against neurologists. There is no specific "brain tumor" headache — it is usually dull and steady like a tension headache, with minimal localizing value, and may or may not be worsened by bending, coughing, sneezing or physical exertion. It is the change in nature or intensity of the headaches, new onset headaches in middle age, headaches refractory to treatment, and any type of headache with focal or lateralizing signs that should serve as warning signs prompting further work-up with appropriate neuroimaging. The misdiagnosis of headache is at the root of the most common diagnostic error in neurology — failure to diagnose brain tumor.[86]

[c] Diagnostic Evaluation

Primary brain tumors do not produce hematologic abnormalities such as tumor specific antigens or an elevated sedimentation rate. Lumbar puncture may precipitate cerebral herniation in the presence of a mass lesion, and its indications are limited to evaluation for meningeal metastases or meningitis. CT and MRI play complementary roles in the diagnosis of CNS tumors. The availability and speed of CT is helpful for evaluating unstable patients, and it is excellent for detecting calcification, bony skull lesions, and hyperacute hemorrhage. MRI is far superior for soft tissue resolution, as well as detecting tumor enhancement, isodense lesions, infarction, edema and non-hyperacute hemorrhages. PET and SPECT scanning are primarily used post-therapy to distinguish tumor recurrence from radiation necrosis. EEG serves to evaluate patients with possible seizures.

[d] Treatment Principles

Treatment varies according to the tumor type, histologic grading, and individual patient factors. Hyperventilation, furosemide, corticosteroids, and mannitol are used to control the cerebral edema. Anticonvulsants are

---

[86] *Supra* § 11.09 [3].

essential for patients with seizures, and may be used prophylactically if indicated. Most tumors in most locations should be surgically resected or debulked as completely as possible within the constraints of preserving neurological function. Some deep-seated tumors such as brainstem gliomas are an exception to surgical removal, although it is preferable to have a stereotactic biopsy for definitive diagnosis. Radiation therapy for many tumor types can increase the cure rate or prolong survival. It may also be useful for treating recurrence in patients initially treated by surgery alone. Chemotherapy may increase survival in patients with certain tumor types, and is reported to lengthen disease free survival in patients with gliomas, medulloblastomas, and some germ cell tumors. Biological and immunological therapies are emerging. Patients with unresectable incurable tumors should be considered for clinical trials that evaluate hyperthermia, interstitial brachytherapy protocols, new drugs or biological response modifiers.

[e] Classification

The World Health Organization (WHO) classification of nervous system tumors incorporates morphology, cytogenetics, molecular genetics and immunological markers to construct a universally applicable system providing valid prognostic determinations based on histologic grading. The scale ranges from grade I (tumors that are frequently discrete, with low proliferative potential, and have the possibility of a cure) to grade IV (active necrosis-prone lesions associated with rapid evolution of disease). Treatment and prognosis depend upon accurate pathological analysis of the tumor sample obtained at surgery or biopsy. The following discussion is limited to key points of several common tumor types.

Gliomas. Gliomas are the most common primary brain tumor, arise from glial cells, and include *astrocytomas, oligodendrogliomas,* and *ependymomas.* Astrocytomas are the most common gliomas; they may develop in either the cerebrum or cerebellum, and occur in any age group. Low grade astrocytomas (grades I and II) have an average survival period after the first symptom of 5 years for cerebral tumors, and 7-8 years for cerebellar tumors. Unfortunately these low grade tumors may transform into the more malignant *anaplastic astrocytoma* (grade III) and *glioblastoma multiforme* (grade IV). These latter types account for 55% of all gliomas, and 20% of all intracranial tumors. The glioblastoma multiforme tends to occur in middle age, is located in the cerebrum, and has a dire prognosis—median survival after surgery and radiation is measured in months. Oligodendrogliomas are relatively benign, slow growing tumors occurring in the cerebral hemispheres of young adults. They often present with seizures, underscoring the necessity of perfoming imaging studies in every patient with new onset seizures. The conventional treatment of surgical resection followed by radiation creates a dilemma for some patients. If the only symptom is epilepsy, then given the slow growing nature of these infiltrative tumors, the risks of surgery may outweigh any potential benefits. The seizures can be controlled, delaying surgery until the appearance of further neurological deficits. If surgery is not offered, then a decision must be made regarding radiation or chemotherapy; some of these tumors are quite sensitive to certain chemotherapeutic agents. Ependymomas arise from the lining of the ventricles, occur mainly in children, and are amenable to surgery, with a prognosis dependent upon the degree of anaplasia. Postoperative radiation addresses the high rate of tumor seeding in the ventricles and spinal axis, and chemotherapy may be added for the more aggressive tumors.

Meningiomas. Meningiomas account for approximately 20% of all primary intracranial tumors. These are intracranial tumors arising from cells forming the arachnoid villi, and thus not brain tumors. However, they compress the brain (rather than invading it) resulting in neurological signs and symptoms. They are fairly common, more frequent in women, rarely malignant, and symptomatic in about 2 per 100,000 people. Meningiomas grow exceedingly slowly, compressing the brain, and may reach prodigious size before clinical presentation. The symptoms depend on tumor location; common locations are where arachnoid villi are adjacent to venous sinuses including the parasagittal region, cerebral convexity, sphenoid ridge, olfactory groove, suprasellar area and tentorium. Many meningiomas are asymptomatic and identified as an incidental finding during neuroimaging for other conditions. Surgical resection is the usual treatment; radiation may be warranted for incomplete removal (the relationship to venous sinuses may preclude complete removal) or recurrence.

Primary CNS lymphoma. This tumor occurs primarily in middle and older age, may be monofocal or multifocal, and arise in any part of the cerebrum, cerebellum or brainstem. The clinical course is similar to glioblastoma, with behavioural and personality changes as common presenting symptoms. Patients with acquired immunodeficiency syndrome and less common immunodeficiency states as well as those receiving immunosuppressive drugs are especially prone to develop this type of lymphoma. The tumors usually enhance on MRI but location and appearance are variable, and diagnosis should be confirmed with stereotactic needle biopsy. Corticosteroids may produce a transient resolution of the lesion. Surgical resection is ineffective due to the deep and often multicentric location of the tumors. Chemotherapy and radiation are the primary treatment modalities. The median survival time is under 5 years.

Acoustic neuroma. Also know as *vestibular schwannoma*, these are benign tumors arising from the Schwann cells of cranial nerve VIII (vestibulocochlear nerve). They are unilateral, spreading into the cerebellopontine angle, and produce symptoms by compressing CNs VIII, VII and V. The most common symptoms are headache, loss of hearing, imbalance or unsteady gait, dizziness, tinnitus and facial pain or weakness. Some patients do not recognize the unilateral hearing loss, and present with headaches. CT is likely to be interpreted as normal in the early stages, unless it includes high resolution contrast enhanced posterior fossa views. Enhanced MRI is the diagnostic procedure of choice. The treatment is surgical excision, and should be performed with intraoperative monitoring by facial nerve EMG and brainstem auditory evoked potentials. Gamma or proton radiation may be an option for smaller tumors, especially in older patients. Neuromas can also arise from other cranial nerves, particularly II or V. Bilateral acoustic neuromas are the hallmark of neurofibromatosis type 2.

Pituitary tumors. Pituitary tumors come to medical attention because of headache, visual disturbances and endocrine abnormalities (nonsecreting adenomas destroy normal pituitary tissue leading to endocrine deficiencies; secreting adenomas result in excessive hormone production). Serum measurement of pituitary hormones by radioimmunoassay makes it possible to detect these tumors at an early stage. Enhanced MRI is the imaging procedure of choice. Tumors less than one centimeter are referred to as microadenomas and initially confined to the sella turcica. With growth, a tumor will compress the pituitary gland, extend through the sella, distort the optic chiasm (producing visual field defects) and, with continued growth, may extend to the cavernous sinus, third ventricle, temporal lobes or posterior fossa. It is crucial to identify the adenoma while it is still confined to the sella, since total excision is possible at this stage. Depending on the patient's age and childbearing plans, type and size of tumor, and status of the visual and endocrine systems, it may be possible to use drug therapy (for example, bromocriptine in certain prolactinomas), or proton beam therapy or some other stereotactic radiosurgery.

[f] Metastatic Brain Tumors and Paraneoplastic Syndromes

Brain metastases probably arise through hematogenous spread by the arterial circulation. The most common primary cancers metastasizing to the brain include lung (primary lung cancer and cancer metastatic to the lung can metastasize), breast (propensity to metastasize to the cerebellum and pituitary gland), melanoma, colon and renal cancer. The clinical picture does not differ significantly from that of glioblastoma multiforme. Headache, cognitive and behavioural abnormalities, focal weakness, aphasia, ataxia, seizures, and signs of increased intracranial pressure progress over weeks to months. There are several unusual presentations that are more likely to lead to misdiagnosis: Some patients present with nervousness, confusion, depression and forgetfulness reminiscent of a dementing disease. Others with cerebellar metastases have ataxia that is only evident upon walking; this may be missed because so many physicians enter and leave the exam room without ever examining a patient's gait. A smaller group present with an apoplectic stroke-like picture, presumably due to hemorrhage into the tumor or tumor embolism causing cerebral infarction, and may be mismanaged as a stroke. Diagnostic evaluation with contrast enhanced CT and gadolinium enhanced MRI are quite sensitive in diagnosing metastatic disease. A very serious error is to assume that a lesion in the brain is a metastasis simply because the patient has systemic cancer—it may result in missing the opportunity to treat a curable tumor. A brain biopsy is usually necessary for the solitary lesion or any lesion if there is a questionable relationship with the primary tumor. Metastatic disease must also be distinguished from *paraneoplastic syndromes*—nervous system disorders that arise as remote effects of systemic tumors. These disorders, often the presenting feature of an undiscovered tumor, must be considered in every cancer patient that develops neurological dysfunction. The diagnosis of a paraneoplastic syndrome must trigger a search for the underlying tumor since earlier diagnosis means earlier treatment and often improved outcome. Paraneoplastic syndromes are caused by substances secreted by the tumor, or more commonly autoimmune diseases. The diagnostic importance cannot be overemphasized. For example, with paraneoplastic cerebellar degeneration the patient develops classical cerebellar symptoms that may be attributed to alcoholic or some other degenerative disease. However, the presence of anti-Purkinje cell antibody (anti-Yo) suggests an underlying breast or ovarian cancer, which may be asymptomatic and can be successfully resected. If antineuronal nucleoprotein antibody (anti-HU) is found, the patient probably has small cell carcinoma of the lung which may be small enough for successful removal. Other paraneoplastic syndromes include limbic encephalomyelitis, paraneoplastic sensory neuronopathy, opsoclonus-myoclonus-ataxia syndrome, necrotic myelopathy, motor neuronopathy, progressive multifocal leukoencephalopathy, and stiff man syndrome. The treatment and prognosis of brain metastases depends upon a host of factors including age, general medical condition, size and number of brain lesions, extent of systemic disease, and responsiveness of cancer to therapy. Treatment of secondary tumors is evolving; it utilizes various combinations of corticosteroids, surgical intervention, radiation and chemotherapy. A minority of patients (10-20%) with metastatic brain disease have a single metastasis, allowing combined modality treatment if there is minimal extracranial disease; usually surgical resection followed by whole-brain radiation therapy. Patients with multiple metastases are treated with whole-brain radiation therapy; surgery is only recommended for tissue biopsy with an unknown primary tumor, or possible resection of a large symptomatic lesion. There may be a role for chemotherapy or stereotactic radiosurgery in select cases. The average period of survival with therapy is about six months, although it may be longer with certain radiosensitive tumors.

[g] Spinal Cord Tumors

Spinal tumors may be extramedullary (epidural or intradural) or intramedullary. Intradural extramedullary mass lesions are usually benign meningiomas and neurofibromas. The former have a predilection for the thoracic cord and foramen magnum, the latter arise from nerve sheaths near the posterior root. Symptoms are referable to the tumor location, and treatment is surgical resection. Intramedullary tumors are rare, present with central or hemicord syndromes, often in the cervical region, with poorly localized burning pain in the extremities but sparing the sacral region. Most of these tumors are ependymomas, hemangioblastomas or low grade astrocytomas. Surgical resection including debulking of an astrocytoma is the treatment of choice, and the benefit of adjunctive radiation is unclear. The vast majority of neoplasms in adults are epidural, resulting from metastases to the adjacent vertebral body, pedicle, or spinous or transverse process. Almost any malignant tumor can metastasize to the spine, but breast, lung, prostate, and renal cancers as well as lymphoma are particularly frequent. The thoracic cord is most commonly involved, except for prostate and ovarian cancers which notably affect the sacral and lumbar vertebrae. The initial symptom is pain, which is worse with movement, and may awaken the patient at night. The pain often precedes cord compression by weeks or months; however, once compression begins, it is always progressive and may advance rapidly. Early diagnosis is essential to avoid permanent neurological impairment. Unfortunately, the diagnosis is frequently delayed for a host of reasons, during which time neurological function progressively deteriorates.[87] MRI is the imaging procedure of choice. A significant percentage of patients with symptomatic epidural disease at one level have asymptomatic disease at another level; therefore, the entire spine must be

---

[87] Levack P, Graham J, et al. *Don't wait for a sensory level — listen to the symptoms: a prospective audit of the delays in diagnosis of malignant cord compression.* Clin Oncol 2002; 14:472-480.

imaged. Management includes corticosteroids for the edema, radiotherapy to the symptomatic lesion, and specific treatment of the underlying neoplasm. Biopsy of the epidural mass is usually not necessary if the patient has a known primary cancer. Radiotherapy appears to be as effective as surgery, although recent data suggests that select patients with epidural metastases meeting certain eligibility criteria treated by surgery plus radiation regained the ability to walk more often and maintained it longer than patients treated by radiation alone. However, surgical intervention may be considered when signs of cord compression progress despite radiotherapy, when the maximum dose of radiotherapy was previously delivered to the site, or when a vertebral compression fracture contributes to cord compression. Neither radiotherapy nor surgery will provide any benefit for fixed motor deficits.

[h] Radiation Injury to the Brain and Spinal Cord

Cognitive dysfunction is a common side effect of radiation therapy to the brain. Complications of radiation are classified according to time course, and must be distinguished from progressive or recurrent tumor growth. PET scanning is the most reliable test. *Acute radiation encephalopathy* occurs within days of treatment, is associated with seizures, headache, drowsiness, and related signs of increased intracranial pressure, and attributed to cerebral edema although it is not usually visible on MRI. The symptoms usually subside in days to weeks. *Early delayed encephalopathy* develops within weeks of therapy, is associated with increase tumor symptoms including focal deficits, and MRI shows an enlarged tumor mass. The symptoms usually resolve in 6-8 weeks; corticosteroids may help. *Late delayed encephalopathy* or radiation necrosis begins months or years after radiation, with clinical symptoms that vary with the site of the lesion. Whole brain radiation can lead to multi-focal zones of necrosis with severe symptoms of progressive dementia, ataxia and urinary incontinence. The spinal cord may be damaged by radiation therapy. A transient *early delayed myelopathy* due to demyelination results in paresthesias with Lhermitte's sign, and gradually resolves over months. *Late delayed myelopathy* begins a year or more after radiation as a Brown-Sequard syndrome, progressing to a paraparesis or quadriparesis. It does not improve and there is no treatment. If the radiation damage is below the spinal cord there will be a lower motor neuron syndrome resulting in asymmetric leg weakness and atrophy. Radiation also damages the cranial and peripheral nerves, most commonly affecting the brachial plexus.

[10] Demyelinating Diseases

The demyelinating diseases encompass immune-mediated (multiple sclerosis, optic neuritis, transverse myelitis, acute disseminated encephalomyelitis), inherited (adrenoleukodystrophy, metachromatic leukodystrophy), metabolic (B12 deficiency, central pontine myelinolysis) and infectious (progressive multifocal leukoencephalopathy, subacute sclerosing panencephalitis) conditions characterized by destruction of normal myelin. Dysmyelinating diseases, rare childhood degenerative disorders with abnormal myelin formation, are not discussed.

[a] Multiple Sclerosis

Multiple sclerosis (MS) is characterized clinically by recurrent or chronically progressive neurological dysfunction due to multiple areas of demyelination affecting the brain, optic nerves and spinal cord.[88] It affects approximately 400,000 people in the United States, is more common in women and Caucasians, with a peak at 30 years of age, and geographical variation demonstrating a markedly higher prevalence in temperate climates.[89] The etiology is unknown, but a variety of studies suggest that several interacting genes influence susceptibility to MS. It is partly an autoimmune or immune related disease. MS is pathologically characterized by plaques, occurring throughout the CNS and consisting of demyelination with relative axonal sparing, loss of oligodendrocytes, and astrocyte proliferation with resultant gliosis.

The diagnosis is based on the clinical signs and symptoms; imaging and neurodiagnostic studies play an ancillary supporting role. There must be evidence of dissemination of lesions in time and space, with no other causes. There should be a history of more than one episode of neurological dysfunction, with evidence of white matter lesions in more than one CNS location. The diagnosis rests on careful clinical judgment, and should be made by an experienced neurologist. Specific diagnostic criteria are defined.[90] MS can cause virtually any neurological deficit, but there are several characteristic signs and symptoms suggesting the diagnosis: optic neuritis, internuclear ophthalmoplegia (INO), heat sensitivity (Uthoff's phenomena), and Lhermitte's sign. Optic neuritis is the initial symptom in almost one-quarter of patients with MS, and ultimately develops in more than one-half of all MS

---

[88] Wolinsky JS, ed. *Multiple sclerosis.* Neurol Clin 2005; 23:1-306.

[89] www.nmss.org accessed 2 December 2007.

[90] Polman CH, Reingold SC, Edan G, et al. *Diagnostic criteria for multiple sclerosis: 2005 revisions to the "McDonald Criteria."* Ann Neurol 2005; 58:840-846.

patients. It is usually restricted to one eye, with retro-orbital pain and a central scotoma. INO causes diplopia and is due to a lesion in the medial longitudinal fasciculus. Heat sensitivity is characteristic of MS, with the appearance of new symptoms or recurrence of old symptoms after exercise, fever, a hot bath or similar activities. It is caused by a temperature induced conduction block in partially demyelinated fibers. Lhermitte's sign, paresthesias radiating down the spine or extremities upon neck flexion, indicates a lesion in the cervical spine. The other common MS symptoms can occur in virtually any pattern, and are also present in many other diseases: cognitive disturbances, fatigue, weakness, sensory loss, ataxia, and bowel and bladder disturbances. Signs of prominent gray matter disease (dementia, aphasia, movement disorders and seizures) are suggestive of a different diagnosis.

MRI is the single most helpful diagnostic test for MS. It is extremely sensitive but non-specific for detecting white matter lesions. There are a number of diseases causing multiple white matter lesions, so MRI should never be used as the sole basis for diagnosing MS. CSF analysis can support a diagnosis of MS in equivocal cases by demonstrating abnormal intrathecal antibody production (oligoclonal bands, elevated IgG index and synthesis rate), and increased myelin basic protein during acute attacks. These nonspecific findings may be seen in other CNS infections or diseases. Evoked potentials, especially VEPs, may be helpful in detecting clinically silent lesions. The differential diagnosis is based on the clinical picture; there is simply no standard list of diagnoses that should be considered in every MS patient. The neurologist must consider the clinical features and diagnostic findings to guide further evaluation. In many cases, common considerations include structural disease, degenerative diseases, chronic infections (syphilis, Lyme disease), neurosarcoidosis, vasculitides, and vitamin B12 deficiency.

An early and accurate diagnosis is essential, especially since there are now treatment options that modify the course of disease. It is not uncommon for patients *without* MS to be diagnosed with the disease. One reason is the physician's desire to provide a disease label to persistent subjective complaints, which are actually due to depression, somatization or simply malingering. Another source of error is basing a diagnosis on MRI findings of nonspecific white matter lesions in the absence of clinical deficits. Conversely, the patient with MS may be misdiagnosed simply because the disease can mimic so many other conditions.

There are numerous conflicting reports regarding the relationship between head trauma and the development of multiple sclerosis. Many of the earlier studies finding an association were anecdotal reports of uncontrolled case series, or were seriously flawed due to small sample sizes or inadequate reporting of methods or results. The more recent literature, including a large population-based study, demonstrates no significant increase in risk of MS at either short or long term intervals following head injury.[91] Nor is there any definitive support for trauma precipitating new symptoms.

The clinical course is variable but characteristically has a relapsing-remitting pattern, with acute exacerbations followed by partial or complete resolution. Deficits develop over hours or days, remain stable for a few weeks, and then gradually subside. There are symptom free intervals of months to years between attacks. The frequency and severity of recurrence remains unpredictable. Repeated exacerbations leave permanent deficits. A minority of patients suffer progressive symptoms in the absence of clearly defined exacerbations. The prognosis varies from patient to patient, but large cohort studies allow some generalizations. MS does not significantly affect lifespan. Some patients have minimal or no disability 20 years after onset; in others, the median time from disease onset to disability requiring aids for ambulation is 15 years. The median relapse frequency is once every two years. There are several clinical variants of MS: Neuromyelitis optica or Devic's disease (simultaneous or sequential optic neuritis and transverse myelitis); Marburg or acute MS (fulminant monophasic disease course); Schilder disease or diffuse sclerosis (progressive variant with large cerebral lesions); and Balo disease (concentric cerebral lesions).

There is no cure for MS; treatment is directed towards managing acute exacerbations, modifying the disease course, and providing symptomatic relief for the fatigue, spasticity, bladder dysfunction and related symptoms. The currently approved treatments that can be used as disease-modifying therapy include glatiramer acetate, three forms of beta-interferon, mitoxantrone, and natalizumab.[92] Therapy should be initiated early in the course of disease. Patients with clinically isolated syndrome (CIS) (isolated demyelination affecting optic nerve, spinal cord or brainstem) are at a very high risk of developing clinically definite MS (CDMS), especially if there are multiple MRI lesions. Early intervention delays the conversion to CDMS. Once the diagnosis of CDMS is established, treatment should be initiated as soon as possible. It appears a delay in treatment at this stage can have consequences in terms of disease progression. There are no blinded, randomized, controlled studies comparing any of the approved agents. The treatment approach must be individualized based on the clinical picture, tolerance of side effects, and compliance issues. The most reasonable

---

[91] Goldacre MJ, Abisgold JD, et al. *Risk of multiple sclerosis after head injury: record linkage study.* J Neurol Neurosurg Psychiatry 2006; 77:351-353.

[92] American Academy of Neurology, *Multiple Sclerosis.* Continuum 2007; 13:144-180.

approach, based on the available data, is to treat CIS with multiple MRI lesions or relapsing MS with any one of the three beta-interferon preparations. Use of glatiramer acetate in CIS is under study, but may be used at this time if there are contraindications to the beta-interferons. Mitoxantrone or natalizumab are not recommended as first line therapy, but may be used for refractory relapsing disease despite previous treatment.

There are three other immune mediated demyelinating diseases. *Optic neuritis* is an acute inflammatory optic neuropathy with unilateral visual loss and retro-orbital pain. The differential diagnosis includes compressive lesions of the optic nerve (due to tumors of the nerve, orbit or sinuses), anterior ischemic optic neuropathy (painless and usually occurs over the age of 50), Leber's hereditary optic neuropathy (painless and develops rapidly), and toxic and nutritional optic neuropathies. There is considerable debate regarding treatment with corticosteroids—it may enhance recovery; however, the optic neuritis treatment trial revealed that steroids were associated with more recurrences. It remains controversial whether optic neuritis is a distinct entity or part of a continuum of MS. In patients with optic neuritis in the absence of any other neurological deficits, almost 40% have MRI lesions, and CDMS eventually develops in 60%. Patients with a normal MRI and CSF analysis rarely progress to MS. *Transverse myelitis* is a syndrome with rapid onset spinal cord dysfunction that may occur after infection or vaccination, or without any discernable precipitant. It may be the initial presentation of MS. Symptoms include flaccid paraparesis followed by spasticity, sensory loss with a truncal sensory level, and bowel and bladder dysfunction. The lesion is typically in the thoracic spinal cord. The differential diagnosis includes extradural structural lesions, spinal cord tumors, ischemia, and vasculitis. MRI serves to exclude structural disease and confirm the presence of an intramedullary lesion at the spinal cord level commensurate with the symptoms. Corticosteroids are often prescribed, but no treatment is definitively beneficial. The risk of developing MS is high if brain MRI also demonstrates white matter lesions. Prognosis is limited— one-third have a good outcome, another third a fair outcome, and the remaining third do not recover. *Acute disseminated encephalomyelitis* is a monophasic syndrome, typically in children and young adults, following a viral infection (measles, paramyxovirus, varicella, rubella, Epstein-Barr virus) or vaccination. There is rapid onset with headache, meningeal signs, seizures and cognitive impairment. Neurological deficits are variable and may include hemiplegia, paraplegia, visual loss, sensory loss or transverse myelitis. It may be caused by an autoimmune response against myelin antigens elicited by cross-reactive viral proteins. Corticosteroids and plasmapheresis are often used, although neither have been proven beneficial in clinical trials. Mortality reaches as high as 30%, and survivors are often left with residual deficits.[93]

[b] Other Demyelinating Diseases

Inherited demyelinating diseases include *adrenoleukodystrophy* (an inherited disorder with progressive demyelination and adrenal cortex dysfunction) and *metachromatic leukodystrophy* (an autosomal recessive disorder causing demyelination of central and peripheral nervous system axons). *Metabolic demyelinating diseases* include *central pontine myelinolysis* (neurological deficits occurring after hyponatremia is corrected too rapidly) and *vitamin B12 deficiency* (demyelination of central and peripheral nervous system axons). *Infectious demyelinating diseases* are represented by *progressive multifocal leukoencephalopathy* (lethal demyelinating disease secondary to Jacob-Creuzfeldt virus) and *subacute sclerosing panencephalitis* (rare late complication of measles virus).

[11] Spinal Cord Diseases

Spinal cord diseases are frequently devastating. They can produce profound impairment because, in a very small cross-sectional area, the spinal cord contains virtually the entire sensory input and motor output systems of the trunk and extremities. Insults may result in quadriplegia or paraplegia, with sensory and autonomic deficits. Many diseases can be treated if promptly recognized. These are true neurological emergencies requiring efficient use of diagnostic studies based on a working knowledge of the relevant anatomy and clinical features of spinal cord diseases. The first step in evaluating any patient with an acute myelopathy is to determine if there is a compressive or non-compressive lesion. Compressive lesions include spinal cord trauma, cervical spondylotic myelopathy, and spinal cord tumors which are discussed in §§11.09 [6], 11.09 [7], and 11.09 [9], respectively. These conditions may require emergent surgical decompression. If the lesion is non-compressive, the second step is to determine if there is an inflammatory cause and if so, the location within the nervous system. Transverse myelitis (TM) is reviewed with demyelinating diseases in §11.09 [10]; however, it may also be caused by post-infectious disorders and systemic inflammatory diseases (*systemic lupus erythematosus, Sjögren's syndrome, sarcoidosis,* and *Behçet's disease*). It is imperative to distinguish TM from noninflammatory myelopathies, and to segregate idiopathic TM from TM associated with multifocal CNS demyelinating disease and systemic inflammatory disorders.

---

[93] American Academy of Neurology, *Postinfectious syndromes.* Continuum 2002; 8:89-109.

This distinction seems to be neglected at times and, for example, the patient with a high risk for developing MS may not receive immunomodulatory treatment. It is not uncommon for an acute myelopathy to be misdiagnosed as Guillain-Barrè syndrome. The third step, if there is no evidence of inflammation, is to consider noninflammatory myelopathies: (1) Ischemic myelopathy is most often due to anterior spinal artery infarction secondary to artherosclerosis, vertebral artery dissection, or iatrogenic occlusion of intercostal arteries during aortic aneurysm surgery. Unusual causes include positional vessel occlusion, fibrocartilaginous embolism, and decompression sickness. Treatment is usually supportive and directed at the underlying cause. Arteriovenous malformations allow early detection due to a more progressive myelopathy, and are amenable to surgery. (2) Metabolic myelopathies must be promptly identified because the neurological deficit is only reversible if therapy is started before secondary axonal degeneration commences. The most common worldwide myelopathy is vitamin B12 deficiency; others include vitamin E, B-complex vitamins, and copper deficiencies. Importantly, the neurological deficits from vitamins B12 or E deficiencies may be the presenting feature of celiac or other gastrointestinal diseases. (3) Hereditary myelopathies include the clinically and genetically heterogenous group of hereditary spastic paraplegias. Genetic testing is available for some of the conditions, and treatment at this stage is supportive with a focus on rehabilitative efforts. (4) Structural abnormalities may cause an acute myelopathy by direct compression or affecting blood or CSF flow in a focal region of the spinal cord. Spondylosis and Chiari malformation have been discussed. Occasionally intervertebral disc herniations may cause a myelopathy by impairing venous return from the cord. Congenital defects such as a narrow spinal canal may predispose the patient to an ischemic myelopathy. (5) Radiation myelopathy is discussed in § 11.09[9][h]. In summary, there are effective means of treatment for many of the spinal cord diseases including extramedullary tumors, spondylosis, epidural abscess or hematoma, and several metabolic myelopathies. It is incumbent upon the neurologist to promptly determine whether the patient with spinal cord signs or symptoms has a treatable condition. The early signs can be subtle, and it is not uncommon to find a delayed diagnosis with devastating outcome.

[12] Movement Disorders

Movement disorders encompass a broad range of conditions that are characterized by abnormalities in the speed, quality, and fluency of volitional movements or by the presence of excessive involuntary movements. These disorders have traditionally been divided into two categories—hypokinetic and hyperkinetic disorders. The hypokinetic disorders (*parkinsonisms*) feature slow, delayed, and low amplitude voluntary movements with rigidity, and impairment of posture and gait. The hyperkinetic disorders (*chorea, hemiballismus, tremor, dystonia, ataxia, myoclonus, tics*) feature involuntary movements that are either superimposed on volitional movements, or occur spontaneously. These disorders are collectively attributed to dysfunction of the basal ganglia, a region of gray matter that lies deep in the cerebrum and upper brainstem incorporating the *caudate nucleus, putamen, globus pallidus, substantia nigra,* and *subthalamic nucleus.* These nuclei have connections with each other, as well as afferent and efferent connections to multiple other brain areas. This simple classification scheme remains clinically useful, but there is no question that many movement disorders contain both hypokinetic and hyperkinetic features—Parkinson's disease may present with dystonia; or spinocerebellar ataxia may exhibit parkinsonian signs. The pathophysiology of these movement disorders reflects a complex interaction of neuronal activity, with changes in pattern, frequency, and synchronization of extensive feedback loops between and among the basal ganglia structures, and between the basal ganglia and other central nervous system regions.

[a] Hypokinetic (Akinetic Rigid) Syndromes

Parkinson's disease (PD) is the prototypical hypokinetic syndrome. It is one of the most common neurodegenerative disorders, affecting approximately 500,000 people in the United States, and usually presenting between the ages of fifty and sixty with a prevalence that increases with age, generally estimated at 200-300 per 100,000 population. The neuropathological characteristic is a loss of dopaminergic neurons in the substantia nigra pars compacta and accumulation of Lewy bodies in the same area; the concomitant reduction of dopamine decreases excitatory activity from the thalamus to the cortex, resulting in the bradykinetic features. Caffeine consumption and smoking are inversely associated with the risk for developing PD; pesticide exposure, rural living, drinking well-water, and head injury are consistently associated with an increased risk for developing PD. Several genetic mutations resulting in PD have been discovered. The etiology of PD is probably a combination of genetic and environmental factors.

In a majority of patients, there is an insidious onset of tremor, stiffness and clumsiness affecting one upper limb. The voice becomes hypophonic, speech dysphasic, and walking more difficult. The disease may remain confined to one side of the body for several years before spreading to affect both sides. Further progression leads to a mask-like facies, slow small steps (*marche à petit pas*), and diminished armswing. Cognitive slowing is common, with dementia and often depression. The greatest difficulty is with initiating movement, such as getting out of a chair or trying to walk. There is "freezing" when attempting to maneuver or pivot. Most patients develop a resting tremor, described as "pill-rolling" which comports with its characteristic appearance. The tremor is neither uniform nor consistent; unfortunately, it is not uncommon for non-neurologists to mislabel a benign essential tremor as PD. There seems to be a misconception that all patients with tremor have PD.

Diagnosis in the early stages depends on the presence of at least two out of three cardinal signs (bradykinesia, rigidity, and tremor) in the absence of other features (dementia, postural instability, peripheral neuropathy, autonomic dysfunction, myoclonus, and oculomotor impairment). The diagnosis of PD is entirely clinical; there are no pathognomonic tests or diagnostic aids. It is, therefore, imperative to exclude parkinsonism plus syndromes or neurodegenerative disorders (progressive supranuclear palsy, diffuse Lewy body disease, multiple system atrophy, spinocerebellar ataxias), and secondary causes of parkinsonism including structural disease (tumor, subdural hematoma, hydrocephalous, trauma), vascular insults, metabolic disorders (hypoxia, hypocalcemia), toxic exposure (carbon monoxide, manganese, MPTP), infectious agents (postencephalitic, subacute sclerosis panencephalitis, AIDS), and drug induced parkinsonism (neuroleptics, metoclopramide, reserpine, lithium, calcium channel blockers). A response to levodopa provides helpful diagnostic confirmation, as it improves PD with very little effect on the neurodegenerative disorders. Neuroimaging and laboratory studies are directed towards excluding secondary causes. As in other diseases where the diagnosis is clinical, and the differential is lengthy, there is considerable diagnostic variability. One prospective study found that up to one-quarter of patients diagnosed with PD actually suffered from other conditions.[94]

Treatment is symptomatic and should be initiated based on quality of life issues.[95] No neuroprotective agents are available.[96] There are a number of medications for mild symptoms, but ultimately it will be necessary to start levodopa or a dopamine agonist. Many neurologists prefer to initiate treatment with a dopamine agonist, delaying the onset of dyskinesias, and keeping levodopa in reserve for the time when symptoms no longer respond

---

[94] Rajput AH, Rozdilsky B, et al. *Accuracy of clinical diagnosis in parkinsonism — a prospective study.* Can J Neurol Sci 1991; 18:275-278.

[95] Hauser RA, Pahwah R, eds. *Current treatment challenges and emerging therapies in Parkinson's disease.* Neurol Clin 2004; 22:S1-S148.

[96] Suchowersky O, Gronseth G, et al. *Practice parameter: neuroprotective strategies and alternative therapies for Parkinson's disease. Report of the Quality Standards Subcommittee of the American Academy of Neurology.* Neurol 2006; 66:976-982.

to agonists.[97] Others favor starting with levodopa.[98] Regardless, the longer levodopa is continued, the more drug induced side effects will surface. Within five years of treatment, up to one-half of patients will experience reduced effectiveness with motor fluctuations. The loss of benefit requires an increased dose; then each dose begins to wear off quicker with a return of symptoms. Up to three-quarters of patients suffer drug related dyskinesias or involuntary choreoathetotic movements within five years of treatment; any body part may be affected but legs and cervical areas are most common. It requires an extraordinary amount of experience to properly modify the drug regimen (increasing doses, decreasing dose intervals, adding combination therapy) to maintain near constant therapeutic levodopa levels, treat associated side effects, and manage the diverse complications that come with advanced disease. Stereotactic surgery may be a useful adjunct treatment in select patients with advanced PD. A multi-disciplinary approach is essential, with careful screening of candidates, and depending on the particular patient, either pallidal surgery (modest improvement but a marked reduction of dyskinesias) or subthalamic nucleus surgery (significant improvement in motor symptoms, allowing reduction in dopaminergic medications). Fetal cell transplantation is not recommended at this time.

The *atypical parkinsonian disorders*, also known as *parkinson plus syndromes*, are characterized by rapidly evolving parkinsonism often with postural instability, a poor response to dopaminergic therapy, and a host of signs including motor (early instability, pyramidal or cerebellar impairment), oculomotor (supranuclear gaze palsy, saccadic dysfunction), cognitive and behavioural (dementia, apraxia, neglect), and autonomic dysfunction. The clinical characteristics of these features allow the proper diagnosis of each disorder — *progressive supranuclear palsy, corticobasal degeneration, multiple system atrophy, dementia with Lewy bodies,* and *frontotemporal dementia* — and, more importantly, help differentiate these disorders from idiopathic PD. This is a crucial distinction from a legal and medical standpoint, because the treatment and prognosis of PD is markedly different from the atypical parkinsonism disorders.

[b] Hyperkinetic (Dyskinesias) Disorders

Chorea.   Chorea is defined as flowing, irregular, rapid, purposeless, unpredictable and brief jerking movements that appear to randomly flit from

---

[97] Miyasaki JM, Martin W, et al. *Practice parameter: initiation of treatment for Parkinson's disease: An evidence-based review. Report of the Quality Standards Subcommitte of the American Academy of Neurology.* Neurology 2002 58:11-17 (re-affirmed 2005).

[98] Wooten GF. *Agonists vs. levodopa in PD.* Neurology 2003; 60:360-362.

one part of the body to another. A mild presentation simply appears as restlessness, and may be missed by the clinician. Moderate or severe movements are generally symptomatic although certain patients may neither feel the movements nor see them when gazing into a mirror. The choreic movements often blend into volitional movements. There may be motor impersistence with difficulty holding the tongue out (darting tongue) or maintaining a continuous handgrip (milkmaid's grip). *Choreoathetosis* refers to chorea coexisting with dystonia or athetosis. *Ballism* describes chorea with large amplitude proximal movements. The hemidistribution of movements (*hemichorea, hemiballismus*) suggests focal pathology in the contralateral deep brain. The differential diagnosis of chorea is extremely broad including benign variants, degenerative conditions, structural lesions, vascular insults, metabolic disorders, and toxic and drug induced states. *Huntington's disease* (HD) is a progressive, autosomal dominant disorder featuring chorea, a subcortical dementia, and various psychiatric and behavioural problems. Genetic testing is available. Presymptomatic testing raises serious ethical issues since identification of gene carriers may lead to social, occupational, and insurance discrimination as well as emotional disturbances. There is no treatment beyond symptomatic management. *Sydenham's chorea* is an autoimmune reaction triggered by rheumatic fever, and appears months after the index streptococcal infection. It usually presents with the insidious development of chorea in a girl during childhood or adolescence, evolves over weeks, and recedes in six months. There is recurrence in a significant number of cases, and it is thought to be the source of chorea during pregnancy (*chorea gravidarum*).

Dystonia. Dystonias are involuntary sustained muscle contractions that produce twisting and repetitive movements, or abnormal postures, in the absence of weakness, spasticity, ataxia or any other findings. These are dynamic disorders that change in severity depending on activity and posture. For example, writer's cramp is a dystonia present while writing but not with any other activity. Likewise, leg and foot dystonia may by present when walking forward and disappear upon walking backwards. Another characteristic is that touch or sensory input may reduce or eliminate the dystonia (*geste antagoniste*). Dystonia may be focal (single body region), segmental or multifocal (contiguous or non-contiguous body regions, respectively), or generalized (both legs and at least one other body part). It is classified as primary (idiopathic) or secondary, the latter arising from underlying conditions including dystonia-plus syndromes, inherited degenerative disorders, dystonia associated with parkinsonian features, and acquired or exogenous causes (vascular insults, structural disease, perinatal cerebral injury, encephalitis, cervical cord or peripheral nerve injuries, head trauma, and drug and toxin exposure). The diagnosis rests on clinical assessment; there are no diagnostic tests for primary dystonia, and evaluation of secondary dystonia must be guided by the historical features. The bizarre appearance of dystonia and fluctuations in symptoms are frequently mislabeled as a psychiatric disturbance. Psychogenic movement disorders are not uncommon, and can mimic any type of movement. It is difficult and sometimes impossible to sort the organic from psychogenic cases, especially since both may occur in the same patient. Children and younger adults that develop dystonia without a definitive etiology should receive a trial of levodopa which is dramatically beneficial in the rare condition of dopa responsive dystonia. Genetic testing is currently available for some of the early onset dystonias. Treatment is symptomatic and includes oral medications, chemodenervation, and, in the presence of intractable symptoms, surgical intervention. Misdiagnosis is frequent given the broad differential of secondary dystonia as well as the psychogenic disorders, and there are also several syndromes presenting with dystonia-like symptoms (*stiff person syndrome, Hallervorden-Spatz disease, Wilson's disease, hemifacial spasm*).

Tremor. Tremor is defined as an involuntary rhythmic, oscillatory movement of part of the body. It is the most common movement disorder, and may range from inconsequential to profoundly disabling. Tremor may be the only manifestation of a clinical entity (*physiologic tremor, essential tremor*), or simply one of many symptoms constituting a particular disease (*PD, Wilson's disease*). There may be tremor at rest or with action, the latter including postural, kinetic, task specific and isometric tremors. *Essential tremor* (ET) is predominantly a postural or kinetic tremor involving the hands and sometimes head, less commonly the legs, jaw, tongue and voice, in the absence of any other neurological signs. It is the most common tremor, affecting nearly 2% of individuals over sixty, and is slowly progressive but without an increased mortality. However, patients may have considerable difficulty writing or signing checks, performing chores and eating or drinking. The diagnosis, like most movement disorders, is by clinical examination, and there are no specific laboratory tests, biomarkers, or neuroimaging studies to confirm the disorder. Thus it is commonly misdiagnosed, and frequently mislabeled as PD. ET responds best to primidone and propranolol, although alcohol and other drugs may be helpful in some circumstances.[99] Surgical options for severe tremor include unilateral ablation or deep brain stimulation of the thalamic ventral

---

[99] Zesiewicz TA, Elble R, et al. *Practice parameter: therapies for essential tremor. Report of the Quality Standards Subcommittee of the American Academy of Neurology.* Neurol 2005; 64:2008-2020.

intermediate nucleus. Other tremor types include physiologic, orthostatic, dystonic, parkinsonian, cerebellar, palatal, neuropathic, drug and toxin induced, and psychogenic.

Tics. Motor tics are irregular, stereotyped, repetitive, nonrhythmic jerk-like movements that may be simple (eye blink, facial grimace, shoulder shrug) or complex (touching, gesturing, bending). Vocal tics are repetitive stereotypic vocalizations emerging from silence or interrupting speech that may be simple (throat-clearing, coughing, sniffing) or complex (words or phrases out of context). Tics can occur as a primary disorder, or they may be secondary to an identifiable etiology such as infections (encephalitis, neurosyphilis, Lyme disease), drugs (amphetamines, levodopa, antipsychotics, anticonvulsants), toxins (carbon monoxide), degenerative diseases (HD, dystonia, neuroacanthocytosis, Hallervorden-Spatz disease, Wilson's disease, tuberous sclerosis), a host of developmental problems and chromosomal abnormalities, and trauma.[100] *Gilles de la Tourette's syndrome* (GTS) begins before age 21, and includes multiple motor tics and one or more vocal tics occurring frequently over at least one year without a period of three months or more in which the tics are absent, in the absence of any other identifiable etiology.[101] Additionally, GTS is associated with a spectrum of behavioural abnormalities including attention deficit disorder and obsessive compulsive disorder. The pathophysiology is thought to reflect dopaminergic system dysfunction in the basal ganglia. Treatment is directed towards control of the motor and vocal tics, and management of the behavioural and psychiatric manifestations. Typical neuroleptics may be helpful but cause sedation, drug induced parkinsonism, dystonic reactions and a variety of other side effects including tardive dyskinesia. Atypical neuroleptics reduce motor and vocal tics, and adverse effects are less frequent.

Myoclonus. Myoclonus is defined as rapid, brief, involuntary shock-like movements which are frequently repetitive and sometimes rhythmical. It may be classified by distribution—focal, segmental or multifocal, or generalized—and anatomic origin—cortical, brainstem, spinal or peripheral nerve. Cortical myoclonus presents with both negative and positive jerks; brainstem myoclonus includes various disorders such as periodic myoclonus, essential myoclonus, startle syndromes, and palatal tremor; spinal myoclonus, if segmental, implies an underlying structural disease; and peripheral myoclonus is usually idiopathic. It is important to ascertain the

---

[100] Faridi K, Suchowersky O. *Gilles de la Tourette's syndrome.* Can J Neurol Sci 2003; 30:S64-S71.
[101] Comella CL. *Gilles de la Tourette's syndrome and other tic disorders.* Continuum 2004; 10:128-141.

anatomic origin because it ultimately guides diagnostic intervention and determines the appropriate treatment strategy. For example, palatal myoclonus may occur in brainstem structural disease such as tumor or MS. The etiological classification of myoclonus includes physiologic (occurs in otherwise normal individuals such as hiccups or sleep myoclonus), essential (inherited, benign, multifocal, originating in subcortical region), epileptic (focal or generalized, characterized by the presence of seizures), and symptomatic (due to a large number of underlying causes) categories. Diagnostic evaluation can include routine hematologic studies, imaging of the brain or spine if indicated, and appropriate electrodiagnostic testing. The recommended treatment is directed in part by the neurological origin of the myoclonus. For example, valproic acid or clonazepam are the recommended medications for brainstem myoclonus.

[c] Posttraumatic Movement Disorders

The legal cases involving movement disorders present a wide array of issues, but one recurring question continues to surface: Can trauma cause PD or other movement disorders? Direct trauma to the basal ganglia and related structures can cause abnormal movements; however, these cases are extremely rare and best substantiated when the movement disorder occurs in temporal relationship to the trauma, with concussion or other clinical signs of trauma, in the absence of a prior history of the movement disorder, and with evidence of CNS lesions on imaging studies. There is the theoretical possibility, along with anecdotal reports, that peripheral nervous system trauma may alter sensory input to the spinal cord resulting in central dysfunction of the motor pathways. In regard to PD, the current evidence including several case-controlled and prospective studies does not support the conclusion that trauma can cause PD. However, there is unequivocal evidence that trauma can cause post-traumatic parkinsonism. *Parkinson pugilistica* is a syndrome of parkinsonian features, dementia and emotional changes occurring in boxers. In addition, parkinsonian features have been reported in cases of isolated CNS trauma and subdural hematoma. There is further debate surrounding the question of whether trauma can aggravate an existing movement disorder. Both retrospective and prospective studies demonstrate that minor trauma can temporarily exacerbate PD, although the cause is unclear. However, the underlying basis (emotional distress or brain damage) is irrelevant from a legal standpoint as long as the worsening is related to trauma. There are conflicting reports regarding the permanence of worsening after trauma. The neurologist can be particularly helpful in defining PD and post-traumatic parkinsonism, securing a detailed history of whether subtle movement disorder signs were present before the trauma or may have even contributed to the injury, and providing a differential diagnosis to address other causes of parkinsonism including drug-induced and psychogenic movement disorders.

[13] Muscle Diseases

Myopathies encompass a heterogeneous group of disorders that affect muscle structure or function.[102] The staggering number and diversity of complex diseases precludes any type of systematic review in a single chapter and, for the practicing attorney, is probably not relevant to determining the merits of a case likely based on diagnostic error. It is more helpful to outline a diagnostic approach to the patient with presumed muscle disease.

[a] Systematic Approach

The first step in approaching a patient with a suspected muscle disease is to determine the correct site of the lesion (distinguish myopathies from motor neuron disorder, peripheral neuropathy, and neuromuscular junction disease) and identify whether the myopathy is due to a defect in the muscle structure or channels, or dysfunction of muscle metabolism. This requires a thorough history with particular attention to the relevant negative (weakness, fatigue, atrophy) and positive (myalgias, cramps, myotonia, contractures) signs and symptoms, the temporal evolution of disease, the family history of any muscle disease, any precipitating factors that trigger weakness, associated systemic signs or symptoms (cardiac disease, respiratory failure, hepatomegaly, dysmorphic features), and the distribution of weakness. This should allow the neurologist to make a preliminary diagnosis of either an acquired (*inflammatory myopathies, endocrine myopathies, drug-induced or toxic myopathies,* and *myopathies associated with systemic disease*) or hereditary (*muscular dystrophies, myotonias, channelopathies, congenital myopathies, metabolic myopathies,* and *mitochondrial myopathies*) myopathy.

The second step is a detailed examination incorporating manual or functional testing to determine the distribution of muscle weakness. This allows a pattern-recognition approach which narrows down the differential diagnosis, thus guiding laboratory and neurodiagnostic testing. The most common myopathy pattern is symmetrical weakness predominantly affecting the proximal leg and arm muscles, a *limb-girdle* distribution which is characteristic of inherited and acquired conditions. A distal weakness pattern affecting distal muscles in upper or lower extremities, or a *scapuloperoneal*

---

[102] American Academy of Neurology, *Muscle diseases.* Continuum 2006; 12:1-261.

pattern involving the proximal arm with distal leg weakness, can occur with various *distal myopathies* (from childhood to late adult onset types), *myotonic dystrophy, facioscapulohumeral dystrophy, inflammatory myopathies, metabolic myopathies*, and *congenital disorders*. Peripheral neuropathies may mimic the distal weakness and atrophy. A distal arm (wrist and finger flexors) and proximal leg (quadriceps) weakness pattern may be asymmetrical, and is virtually pathognomonic for *inclusion body myositis*. Myopathy patterns presenting with ocular and pharyngeal dysfunction represents a limited group of disorders. The combination of ptosis and ophthalmoplegia is a hallmark of the *mitochondrial myopathies*, and the additional symptom of dysphagia suggests *oculopharyngeal dystrophy*. Ptosis and facial weakness without ophthalmoplegia is a common feature of *myotonic dystrophy*. A pattern of prominent neck extensor weakness may be seen in *polymyositis, dermatomyositis, carnitine deficiency, myotonic dystrophy, hyperparathyroidism*, as well as the distinct *isolated neck extensor myopathy*. There are two neuromuscular disorders that commonly have prominent neck extensor weakness — *amyotrophic lateral sclerosis* and *myasthenia gravis*.

The third step, after narrowing the differential by history and examination, requires judicious use of laboratory and molecular genetic testing, neurodiagnostic studies, and muscle biopsy. The single most helpful screening test is a creatinine kinase (CK) level. The CK is elevated in the vast majority of patients with muscle disease, although it may be normal with a slowly progressive myopathy. Importantly, an elevated CK does not necessarily indicate a primary muscle disease; it can be elevated by trauma (including injections and EMG procedures), strenuous exercise, viral illness, hypothyroidism, and medications (including the commonly prescribed statins), as well as motor neuron diseases and neuropathies. NCV/EMG testing can exclude these latter diseases (motor neuron and neuropathies) and neuromuscular junction disorders. The EMG, however, can be normal in a patient with myopathy and must be interpreted in conjunction with the history, examination and laboratory findings. Muscle biopsy confirms the diagnosis. Molecular genetic studies are now available for a large number of hereditary myopathies (including the common *Duchenne muscular dystrophy*), which may eliminate the need for biopsy in every patient.

[b] Treatment

Treatment options for the inherited myopathies are limited to supportive care, although steroids appear to slow progression of Duchenne muscular dystrophy. Certain channelopathies may require dietary adjustments and medications, such as limited carbohydrate intake, potassium supplementation and acetazolamide (*hypokalemic periodic paralysis*) or avoidance of potassium rich foods and ingestion of simple carbohydrates along with a thiazide diuretic (*hyperkalemic periodic paralysis*). Mexiletene is preferred for bothersome *myotonia congenital*. Successful treatment for the diverse array of acquired myopathies is wholly dependent upon an accurate diagnosis. Treatment of the *endocrine myopathies* must be directed at the thyroid, parathyroid or adrenal dysfunction. Myopathies associated with *systemic illness* require treatment of the underlying disease. *Toxic* or *drug induced* myopathies may respond to removal of the offending agent. The inflammatory myopathies—*polymyositis, dermatomyositis,* and *inclusion body myositis*—must be treated with steroids or immunosuppressive agents, although inclusion body myositis will generally not respond. Long term treatment is necessary, which raises the spectre of steroid myopathy and other complications.

[c] Statin Myopathies

An evolving area of legal interest surrounds the *statin myopathies*—muscle disease secondary to the commonly prescribed lipid-lowering agents such as lipitor, mevacor, and pravachol. These drugs cause a syndrome of acute rhabdomyolysis with recovery after discontinuation, and apparently a separate condition with a chronic inflammatory myopathy that begins within weeks of initiating therapy but requires long term dependence on immunosuppressive medication. The mechanism of statin myopathy is unknown. These drugs will probably be increasingly prescribed in the future to reduce the risk of cardiovascular and cerebrovascular disease, resulting in a higher number of adverse drug reactions.

[14] Neuromuscular Junction Disorders

There are two conditions that need to be considered: *Myasthenia gravis* (MG) and *Lambert Eaton myasthenic syndrome* (LEMS). These disorders must be properly diagnosed. MG is eminently treatable, and the failure to initiate therapy in a timely fashion may lead to grave complications. LEMS suggests the presence of an underlying malignancy which requires a prompt and thorough evaluation followed by appropriate therapeutic intervention.

[a] Myasthenia Gravis

MG is a chronic autoimmune neuromuscular disease characterized by weakness and premature fatigue, variably affecting the ocular, bulbar and peripheral muscles. The hallmark is muscle weakness that increases during activity and improves after a period of rest. The age of onset has a bimodal distribution affecting young adult women in their late teens and early twenties, and older men in their fifties to sixties, but it can occur at any age. The typical patient complains of intermittent ptosis or drooping of the eyelids which may or may not be associated with fatiguable diplopia (double vision). Indeed, some patients are unaware they have a neurological disorder and seek cosmetic eyelid surgery. In 10-15% of patients there will be no progression beyond the isolated palpebral and extraocular muscle weakness (*ocular myasthenia*). However, the remaining patients will develop generalized myasthenia within two years of onset. The disease progresses to involve the oropharynx resulting in difficulty with chewing, swallowing and speaking, symptoms that worsen later in the day. It then spreads to the limbs, and repetitive movements quickly fatigue the extremity to the point of being useless. Respiratory weakness may progress to hypoventilation and respiratory failure in a matter of hours. Pulmonary function must be carefully assessed and closely monitored in newly diagnosed patients or myasthenics suffering an exacerbation, often requiring hospitalization with serial vital capacities. Controlled intubation should be considered before respiratory failure develops.

MG is caused by auto-antibodies directed against the postsynaptic muscle acetylcholine receptors. The thymus gland is involved in the trigger for this immune reaction. Normally, the presynaptic nerve releases the neurotransmitter acetylcholine which traverses the neuromuscular junction and binds to acetylcholine receptors resulting in a muscle contraction. In MG, the acetylcholine receptor antibodies block, alter or destroy the acetylcholine receptors impairing the muscles ability to contract.

The diagnosis of MG requires a high index of suspicion for the disorder because many patients are asymptomatic during the examination. For example, a patient may present to the clinic with complaints of double vision but, by the time they have rested while waiting to be seen, the examination is normal. This explains why it is not uncommon to have a one or two year delay in diagnosis. The neurologist should specifically ask about the presence of fluctuating weakness or abnormal fatigability, and elicit a history of any factors provoking an unusual weakness. Elevated temperature, stress, viral infections, anesthesia and various medications (antibiotics, thyroid medications, cardiac antiarrhythmics) have the potential to unmask MG. Routine examination may be normal, requiring the neurologist to repetitively test strength in suspected muscles in order to demonstrate fatigability. Additional tests to confirm the diagnosis include (1) serum acetylcholine receptor antibodies which are found in almost all patients with generalized MG, but may not be detected in ocular myasthenia; (2) administration of edrophonium which produces a brief but dramatic improvement of strength; (3) repetitive nerve stimulation studies; and (4) single fiber EMG, which is highly sensitive and has the greatest diagnostic value in cases of ocular, mild generalized or seronegative MG.

MG is eminently treatable. Cholinesterase inhibitors improve symptoms in many patients. Prednisone and immunosuppressive agents such as cyclosporine and azathioprine suppress production of abnormal antibodies and may improve strength, but have the potential for serious side effects. Plasmapheresis improves strength by removing circulating antibodies but is usually reserved for a *myasthenic crisis* (exacerbation with respiratory distress) or situations where strength must be improved such as impending surgery. Thymectomy improves symptoms in the vast majority of patients, including those without thymoma. There is considerable evidence that the sooner thymectomy is performed, the quicker the remission and more complete the recovery. A practice parameter concluded that methodological flaws in the studies "prevent definitive conclusions regarding the benefits of thymectomy."[103]

[b] Lambert Eaton Myasthenic Syndrome

LEMS is the presynaptic counterpart of MG, with impaired release of acetylcholine from the presynaptic nerve terminal. The reduced amount of acetylcholine available to the postsynaptic muscle receptors results in fatigability. Conversely, patients improve their function with repetitive exercise. This feature is difficult to appreciate clinically, but clearly evident on repetitive nerve stimulation. Patients present with proximal muscle weakness manifest by difficulty climbing stairs, walking, holding up arms and lifting objects. Autonomic dysfunction (postural hypotension, dry mouth) is common. About one-half of patients harbor an underlying malignancy, usually small cell cancer of the lung. The etiology is unclear in the remaining patients. Treatment is based on whether the patient has cancer. If so, successful treatment of the malignancy often leads to improved strength. In those patients without malignancy 3-4 di-amino pyridine improves symptoms, and there may be a role for plasmapheresis or immunosuppressant agents.

[15] Motor Neuron Disease

Motor neuron disease (MND) refers to a group of sporadic and inherited disorders characterized by progressive degeneration of motor neurons in the

---

[103] Gronseth GS, Barohn RJ. *Practice parameter: Thymectomy for autoimmune myasthenia gravis (an evidence based review). Report of the Quality Standards Subcommittee of the American Academy of Neurology.* Neurology 2000; 55:7-15.

spinal cord, brainstem and cortex resulting in varying combinations of lower motor neuron (LMN) and upper motor neuron (UMN) signs.[104] The *inherited* MNDs include rare disorders such as the *spinal muscular atrophies*, characterized by progressive muscle atrophy and weakness due to degeneration of the anterior horn motor cells. The most frequent *sporadic* MND is *amyotrophic lateral sclerosis* (ALS), also known as *Lou Gehrig's disease.*

[a] Amyotrophic Lateral Sclerosis

ALS is an incurable disease of unknown etiology that generally occurs in middle life with an incidence of 1 in 100,000. It presents as progressive weakness with signs of both upper (weakness, spasticity, hyperreflexia) and lower (weakness, atrophy, fasciculations) motor neuron dysfunction, and relatively preserved sensory functions. Brainstem dysfunction results in dysarthria, dysphagia, sialorrhea and pseudobulbar emotional lability. As the disease progresses, atrophy and fasciculations become more prominent. Some upper motor neuron signs disappear because overwhelming muscle weakness precludes a contraction to create reflex movements. Extraocular muscles and bowel and bladder functions are rarely affected. Progressive frontal or frontotemporal dementia occurs in a minority of patients. Autonomic functions are generally spared. The important point is that ALS may have many different presentations. The disease can begin in any part of the nervous system, and patients may have variations in terms of the region of onset, degree of upper and lower motor neuron dysfunction, and time course of progression. *Progressive spinal muscular atrophy* refers to lower motor neuron picture with weakness and atrophy in the absence of corticospinal tract dysfunction. In *progressive bulbar palsy* upper and lower motor neuron signs are restricted to the bulbar muscles. Isolated upper motor neuron disease characterizes *primary lateral sclerosis.* The extent and distribution of the upper and lower motor neuron involvement in these disorders increases over time until they eventually merge into an ALS picture. There are specific diagnostic criteria for ALS.[105] Accurate diagnosis is essential—patients with suspected ALS must undergo diagnostic evaluation to exclude any other disorder that might account for their symptoms, with an emphasis on identifying treatable conditions. The

---

[104] Eisen AA, Shaw PJ, eds. *Motor neuron disorders and related diseases.* In: Aminoff MJ, Boller F, Swaab DF, eds. *Handbook of clinical neurology,* 3rd series, vol. 82. Amsterdam, Netherlands: Elsevier; 2007.

[105] World Federation of Neurology Research Group on Neuromuscular Diseases. *El Escorial World Federation of Neurology criteria for the diagnosis of amyotrophic lateral sclerosis.* J Neurol Sci 1994; 124:96-107.

exhaustive differential must be tailored to the individual patient's presentation although several conditions seem to be more commonly misdiagnosed. *Cervical spondylosis* produces spinal cord compression with upper and lower motor neuron signs that may be difficult to distinguish from ALS. Similar features occur with other structural diseases of the cervical region including *syringomyelia, Chiari malformation, arteriovenous malformations,* and *spinal cord* and *foramen magnum tumors.* MRI of the brain and spine is essential. *Myasthenia gravis* without ocular motor weakness may mimic ALS. NCV and EMG studies can distinguish this disorder and exclude other mimicking conditions such as peripheral neuropathies, plexopathies, and radiculopathies. *Post-polio syndrome* must be considered in the differential. Hematologic studies will exclude metabolic, toxic and endocrine abnormalities that may have some ALS-like symptoms (hyperthyroidism, neurosyphilis, lead or mercury intoxication, B12 deficiency). After completing the evaluation and confirming the diagnosis, the neurologist must appropriately counsel the patient. The author recommends a straightforward approach, providing ample informational resources, explaining that ALS complications and discomfort can be managed, and offering a second opinion. Treatment is supportive with multidisciplinary care. Percutaneous gastrostomy is performed as indicated for dysphagia. Riluzone appears to extend survival by a few months. There is, however, an inexorable progression to death in a matter of 2 to 5 years, perhaps longer in exceptional cases.

[16] Infections

[a] Overview

Meningitis — inflammation of the subarachnoid space and meninges — is the most common form of central nervous system infection. It is usually viral or bacterial, but may be due to other infections such as fungi, parasites, and rickettsia as well as a host of noninfectious causes including vasculitides, connective tissue disorders, leptomeningeal metastases, subarachnoid hemorrhage and chemical or drug-induced syndromes. Meningitis may be acute or chronic, the latter defined as fever and related symptoms for greater than four weeks with associated CSF pleocytosis. Acute bacterial meningitis is a true neurological emergency, and early diagnosis is essential since antibiotic therapy drastically reduces the morbidity and mortality. Viral meningitis may infect the brain tissue itself or the meninges and brain simultaneously, causing *encephalitis* or *meningoencephalitis*, respectively. It is equally imperative to promptly diagnose encephalitis because effective antiviral therapy is available for one of the common causes, herpes simplex virus. *Abscesses* or localized infections often arise from the spread of systemic infection (especially sinuses and ear) or trauma, present with headache, fever and focal deficits, and require surgery or antibiotics or both. CNS infections in solid organ and hematopoietic cell transplant patients entail special considerations. Patients infected with HIV may present with a daunting array of CNS pathogens. In this age of globalization and international travel, neurologists must be cognizant of the common world-wide nervous system infections: *dengue, Japanese encephalitis, malaria, neurocysticercosis,* and *rabies.*[106]

[b] Acute Meningitis

Acute meningitis, most commonly caused by bacteria or viruses, is a syndrome of fever, headache and meningismus with CSF pleocytosis due to infection and inflammation in the subarachnoid space. Patients may also have nausea, vomiting and lethargy. In bacterial meningitis, the level of consciousness progressively deteriorates and there may be seizure activity or focal neurological deficits. These latter features do not occur with viral infections, except for possible febrile seizures in children. The classical signs of meningeal irritation are nuchal rigidity, *Brudzinski's sign* (passive neck flexion results in flexion of hips and knees), and *Kernig's sign* (pain when attempting to extend the knee with hip flexed). The presence of a rash may be diagnostically helpful (for example, erythematous maculopapular lesions on the trunk and lower extremities becoming purpuric or petechial suggests meningococcemia). At least half of patients with acute bacterial meningitis develop neurological complications such as cerebral edema, hydrocephalous, venous sinus thrombosis, cranial nerve palsies, or seizures as well as systemic deterioration including disseminated intravascular coagulation, septic shock, or renal failure. The differential diagnosis of the classical triad (headache, fever, stiff neck) is very broad, but when altered consciousness, seizures or focal deficits are added, it usually narrows down to encephalitis, fungal or rickettsial infections, abscess, subdural empyema or venous sinus thrombosis. The first step upon suspecting bacterial meningitis is to obtain blood cultures and initiate empiric antimicrobial and adjunctive therapy before performing a CT and LP. CT should be performed before LP if there is altered consciousness, seizure activity, focal deficits or any other signs of increased intracranial pressure or the patient is immunocompromised. Empiric treatment is based on the most likely causative organisms, predicted

---

[106] www.who.org and www.cdc.gov provide information resources from the World Health Organization and Centers for Disease Control, respectively.

by the patient's age, underlying health, and predisposing factors including travel history. CSF analysis including an increasing number of polymerase chain reaction assays and latex particle agglutination tests provides diagnostic confirmation of the meningeal pathogens. Antimicrobial therapy is modified after the bacterial pathogen is isolated and antibiotic sensitivity confirmed by in vitro testing.   The results of a prospective, randomized, multi-center, double-blind trial demonstrated that dexamethasone improves the outcome and reduces mortality in adults with acute bacterial meningitis.[107] It is beyond the scope of this chapter to review the many causes of acute and chronic meningitis, or discuss specific pathogens, diagnostic tests or antibiotic regimens. Moreover, it is probably not relevant for the practicing attorney as most malpractice claims related to infection stem from a delay in diagnosis or failure to diagnose and properly treat acute meningitis.

[17] Dementias

Dementia is a clinical syndrome rather than a discrete pathological entity.[108] It generally refers to an acquired, persistent loss of cognitive function severe enough to interfere with occupational, social, recreational or daily activities. The term dementia does not suggest a specific etiology; indeed, there are dozens of causes of dementia. *Primary* dementia refers to a degenerative process arising in the brain, whereas *secondary* dementia describes nondegenerative conditions producing cognitive impairment (vitamin B12 deficiency, subdural hematoma, hypothyroidism, normal pressure hydrocephalous). The distinction is critical because many secondary dementias, if promptly identified, are treatable. The neurologist must perform a thorough evaluation to exclude any treatable causes of the cognitive decline, identify and treat any associated conditions, and properly classify the dementia, providing a specific diagnosis if possible (terms such as senility or old-age dementia are unacceptable). This will entail a detailed history from the patient and family or others familiar with the patient, mental status testing, neurological examination, hematologic studies (comprehensive serum chemistry, complete blood count, thyroid functions, vitamin B12 and folate levels, sedimentation rate, heavy metal screen), urinalysis, neuroimaging with MRI (tumors, subdural hematoma, hydrocephalous), and other tests such as EEG (partial or nonconvulsive seizures) or CSF analysis (fungal infections, tuberculosis, carcinomatosis)

---

[107] de Gans J, van de Beek D. *European dexamethasone in adulthood bacterial meningitis study investigators. Dexamethasone in adults with bacterial meningitis.* N Engl J Med 2002; 347:1549-1556.

[108] Graff-Radford NR, ed. *Dementia.* Neurol Clin 2007; 25:577-865.

based on the clinical picture.[109] It is not uncommon for two or more dementing conditions to coexist in the same patient, such as Alzheimer's disease and vascular dementia.

[a] Mild Cognitive Impairment

The construct of *mild cognitive impairment* (MCI) represents an incipient stage of dementia — a transitional state along the continuum between normal cognitive changes of aging and the earliest clinical features of dementia. It is the prodromal stage of a dementing condition, fundamentally different from the extremes of normal aging. This is an important distinction because it allows an earlier diagnosis of a degenerative process, which opens the door to treatment strategies that may delay the onset or progression of dementia. The first criterion to diagnose MCI is a cognitive complaint by the patient or an informant. The neurologist must then determine whether the cognitive status is normal or compatible with dementia. If the patient is neither normal nor demented, but has a cognitive decline with preservation of daily activities, then the appropriate diagnosis is MCI. After the diagnosis of MCI, the neurologist determines whether memory impairment is part of the picture, and then identifies the etiology of the symptoms. By combining the clinical syndrome with the presumed etiology, it is possible to make a reliable prediction about the outcome of the MCI syndrome. MCI with memory impairment of a presumed degenerative etiology progresses to dementia, usually Alzheimer's disease, at a rate of 10-15% per year. The risk factors for progression to dementia include hippocampal atrophy (documented by MRI volumetric studies), the presence of the apolipoprotein ε4 allele, and those patients with more severe memory impairment. Additionally, CSF tau and Aβ biomarkers, FDG-PET scan patterns, and molecular imaging involving amyloid deposition may be predictive for progression to Alzheimer's disease. MCI allows early identification of patients with a high probability of progressing to dementia, and allows for potential intervention at an earlier point in the disease process. Additionally, it allows patients the opportunity to make life planning decisions while still competent. Several randomized clinical trials have been completed recently with one suggesting that donepezil might be effective in treating MCI for a limited time.[110]

---

[109] Knopman DS, DeKosky ST, et al. *Practice parameter: Diagnosis of dementia (an evidence-based review). Report of the Quality Standards Subcommittee of the American Academy of Neurology.* Neurology 2001; 56:1143-1166.

[110] Peterson RC, Thomas RG, et al. *Vitamin E and donepezil in the treatment of mild cognitive impairment.* N Engl J Med 2005; 352:2379-2388.

[b]   Alzheimer's Disease

Alzheimer's disease (AD) is the most common type of dementia in the United States, afflicting as many as 4.5 million adults. The major risk factors for AD are aging and family history. Apolipoprotein E genotyping in a patient with dementia improves diagnostic specificity, but it remains unclear if the accuracy is improved enough to be useful in the clinical setting. In patients with MCI, the APOE ε4 genotype is associated with a greater risk of progression to AD. The metabolic syndrome and vascular risk factors appear to increase the risk for AD. Higher education and physical exercise may be associated with a reduced risk for AD. Nonsteroidal anti-inflammatory agents do not appear to prevent or delay progress of dementia, despite earlier reports to the contrary. The issue of head trauma as a risk factor remains unclear.

There are two sets of diagnostic criteria for AD—the *Diagnostic and Statistical Manual of Mental Disorders, Fourth Edition (DSM-IV)*[111] and consensus criteria developed by the *National Institute of Neurological and Communicative Disorders and Stroke* and the *Alzheimer's Disease and Related Disorders Association (NINCDS-ADRDA)*.[112] The history must be obtained from family, friends or caregivers. These patients typically present with memory impairment, although language difficulties, apraxia or other cognitive disturbances may be early signs. A history describing the insidious onset of short term memory impairment is essential to the diagnosis of AD. The patients are typically repetitive in conversation, frequently mislay objects, and forget day to day matters or what they were told. Some become frustrated and irritable when the difficulties are pointed out; others lose insight and deny any problem. Remote memories are typically retained until late in the disease. AD progresses slowly, with impairment of more and more cognitive functions. Visuospatial impairment develops, with the patient getting lost on familiar routes from one point to another, initially outside the house but later within the house. Calculations become difficult, and financial affairs cannot be managed. Dyspraxia makes it impossible to dress or operate home appliances. Behavioural disturbances include apathy, depression, and anxiety; as the disease progresses it is common to have paranoia and delusions. Misidentification and visual hallucinations occur. Agitation, disinhibition and aggressive behaviour may develop. Seizures occur in 10-20% of patients late in the disease.

---

[111] American Psychiatric Association. *Diagnostic and Statistical Manual of Mental Disorders, DSM-IV-TR*, 4th ed., Washington D.C. 2000.

[112] McKhann G, Drachmann D, et al. *Clinical diagnosis of Alzheimer's disease: report of the NINCDS-ADRDA Work Group under the auspices of Department of Health and Human Services Task Force on Alzheimer's Disease.* Neurology 1984; 34:939-944.

The neurological examination is essentially normal apart from the higher intellectual dysfunction. Prominent motor features or gait abnormalities at the onset suggests one of the dementia-parkinsonian complexes or cerebrovascular disease. An abrupt onset or stepwise deterioration may indicate vascular dementia. Early personality or behavioural changes without memory impairment suggests frontotemporal dementia. In the later stages of AD, primitive reflexes return (palmomental, snout).

The cholinesterase inhibitors donepezil, rivastigmine, and galantamine have the potential to mildly improve cognition, function in activities of daily living, and behaviour in mild to moderate stage AD for periods of up to 18 months. Donepezil appears effective in moderate to severe stage dementia. The benefits occur in a minority of patients, may be quite subtle, and should be weighed against any adverse effects of the drug. The N-methyl-D-aspartate (NMDA) receptor blocking agent memantine may be beneficial in moderate to severe disease and can be used in combination with the cholinesterase inhibitor drugs. No therapy is proven to delay AD progression, but current research focuses primarily on antiamyloid drugs and vaccination to stabilize or reverse the symptoms of AD. Median survival with AD is approximately eight years.

[c] Dementia with Lewy Bodies

Dementia with Lewy Bodies (DLB) is the second most common degenerative dementia in the aging population. The name acknowledges an association of dementia with the microscopic abnormality, but does not imply causality. Indeed, Lewy bodies are common in both AD and Parkinson's patients. Isolated DLB is characterized by dementia with prominent visuospatial and subcortical impairment, fluctuating levels of alertness, parkinsonism, formed visual hallucinations, autonomic dysfunction, and a REM sleep disorder in which patients appear to act out their dreams.[113] These patients are frequently misdiagnosed as AD, in part because Alzheimer's pathology frequently coexists with DLB. Parkinson's disease with dementia may be clinically indistinguishable from DLB. Treatment remains symptomatic with manipulation of a combination of medications in an effort to improve cognition, behavioural and motor symptoms while minimizing side effects. A levodopa trial is recommended although the response is often limited, and it may have to be discontinued due to aggravation of the behavioural symptoms. Dopamine agonists have a high risk of provoking behavioural disturbances, and anticholinergics may worsen

[113] McKeith IG, Dickson DW, et al. and Consortium on DLB. *Diagnosis and management of dementia with Lewy bodies; third report of the DLB Consortium.* Neurology 2005; 65:1863-1872.

cognitive performance. It is reasonable to undertake a trial of the anticholinesterase inhibitors. Atypical antipsychotics are preferred for psychosis. Clonazepam is a first line choice for the sleep disorder. Autonomic impairment may require medication. The DLB patient is very challenging to manage and best results are obtained when interested caregivers are enlisted to help maintain cognitive and social stimulation, attend to the medication schedule, and work with therapists to help the patient improve muscle strength and mobility.

[d] Frontotemporal Dementia

Frontotemporal lobar degeneration (FTLD), or *Pick's disease*, is a progressive neurodegenerative disorder affecting the frontal and anterior temporal lobes. It typically presents between 45 and 65 years of age, and almost half of cases have a positive family history. FTLD has three subtypes—*frontotemporal dementia* (FTD), *semantic dementia* (SD), and *nonfluent aphasia* (NFA)—which differ in prevalence, age of onset, sex distributions, genetic susceptibilities, coassociations with other degenerative diseases, and pathological features. FTD is the prototypical FTLD syndrome. Behavioural and personality changes predominate, with deficits in executive function, and relatively intact episodic memory. Alterations in social decorum with inappropriate disinhibited behaviour and impaired judgment and insight are common. A psychiatric misdiagnosis is not uncommon. Temporal lobe involvement results in problems with language output progressing to decreased fluency and mutism. Symmetric atrophy of the frontal lobes indicates FTD, while asymmetric atrophy of the frontal or temporal lobes suggests NA or SD, respectively. There is no effective treatment. Anticholinesterase inhibitors are not helpful and in fact may cause agitation. Selective serotonin reuptake inhibitors or atypical antipsychotics may be useful for some of the psychiatric disturbances.

[e] Vascular Cognitive Impairment

Vascular cognitive impairment (VCI) is a heterogeneous syndrome caused by cerebrovascular disease with the phenotype affected by a variety of risk factors, vascular pathologies, types of brain injury, regional distribution of infarctions or hemorrhages, profiles of cognitive impairment, and behavioural symptoms. Vascular dementia, formerly multi-infarct dementia, is a subset where cognitive impairment is severe enough to interfere with social and occupational functions. Executive dysfunction is common and verbal memory less affected than in AD. The rate of cognitive decline is slower than in AD. MRI white matter hyperintensities are associated with cognitive impairment and increased risk for stroke. VCI is potentially preventable by vigilant identification and treatment of risk factors, especially hypertension, diabetes, hyperlipidemia, heart disease and smoking.

[f] Normal Pressure Hydrocephalous

The classical features of normal pressure hydrocephalous (NPH)— cognitive decline, gait impairment and urinary incontinence—are not pathognomonic for the disease. These features are quite common in the elderly, and may stem from a variety of causes which must be considered in the differential diagnosis: PD and parkinsonian syndromes, cerebrovascular disease, frontotemporal dementia, cervical spondylosis, and multifactorial gait impairment (diabetics with peripheral neuropathy and visual dysfunction). The lack of cardinal features means the diagnosis is not uncommonly delayed until the patient deteriorates past the point of being a surgical candidate. The history, neurological examination, and diagnostic testing including MRI should focus on those issues that are relevant to the diagnosis and have a bearing on the surgical prognosis. Several factors are associated with a lack of improvement after surgery: moderate to severe cognitive impairment; dementia present for 2 or more years; cognitive impairment preceding gait disturbance; the presence of aphasia; and imaging studies with significant white matter disease or diffuse cerebral atrophy. It is necessary to perform one or more lumbar punctures removing 30-50cc of CSF; if the gait improves then the patient should be a good candidate for shunting. The general health may need to be treated before considering surgery. For example, congestive heart failure or lung disease may increase jugular venous pressure and decrease CSF flow into the venous sinuses. The potential complications of shunting include all the usual risks of surgery, as well as acute intracerebral hemorrhage, subdural hematoma, subdural hygroma, seizures, headache, hearing loss, tinnitus, oculomotor palsies and shunt malfunction. It is important to recognize that NPH and AD or other dementias may coexist in the same patient.

[g] Legal Issues

In recent past, the absence of meaningful diagnostic and therapeutic options for dementia effectively precluded any standard of care—physicians could not help patients with dementia or their families, and there were no legal remedies. Today, there are diagnostic techniques available to make an accurate and timely assessment and, if dementia is present, there are well defined therapeutic options: specific medications are beneficial for AD and possibly other dementias, shunting is crucial in the early stages of NPH, and risk factors for vascular dementia must be identified and treated. Moreover, the absence of a cure does not absolve neurologists from identifying and treating comorbid conditions, providing relief of accompanying symptoms and behavioural disturbances such as depression and agitation, educating caregivers in an effort to delay institutionalization, and allowing the patient an opportunity to participate in medical decisions, as well as timely financial and legal planning. All of these changes have created a paradigm shift to a higher standard of care, with neurologists increasingly liable for a delay or failure to diagnose and treat dementia.[114] Additionally, using *Tarasoff* reasoning, and extrapolating from cases involving seizures, neurologists may be liable to third party victims for failing to advise a patient with dementia to cease driving.

[18]   Pediatric Neurology

The above discussions are generally limited to adult cases; pediatric neurology is a separate and distinct specialty beyond the remit of this chapter.[115] It is, however, worth reviewing a few of the common childhood presentations that commonly generate lawsuits. Many of the cases seem to involve adult neurologists treating an occasional pediatric patient in the outpatient setting, or covering for pediatric colleagues in the emergency room. This situation raises questions regarding the applicable standard of care. The adult neurologist treating a pediatric patient may be held to the standards of a pediatric neurologist, and required to exercise the degree of skill, learning and care normally possessed by physicians in that specialty.

Infections. CNS infections in children require timely recognition and appropriate intervention to avoid immediate complications, long term morbidity or death. Diagnosis is challenging because infants and children present with nonspecific signs and symptoms. CSF analysis is essential, but treatment must be initiated presumptively pending final laboratory results. Neuroimaging is warranted prior to LP if there are signs of increased intracranial pressure. Supportive care must address seizures, which frequently occur with meningitis, and the syndrome of inappropriate antidiuretic hormone secretion. The decision to use steroids must be on a case by case basis. Children with meningitis who are on oral antibiotics (commonplace due to widespread use of antibiotics) present differently from children who have not received antibiotics. These children may harbor a partially treated meningitis and are more likely to have a longer duration of symptoms, lower temperature, and more vomiting; they are less likely to have

---

[114] Kapp MB. *Legal standards for the medical diagnosis and treatment of dementia.* J Legal Med 2002; 23:359-402.

[115] Swaiman KF, Ashwal S, Ferriero DM, eds. *Pediatric neurology principles & practice*, 4th ed. Philadelphia: Mosby Elsevier; 2006.

an altered mental status. Thus, the threshold for performing an LP must be considerably lower in children on antibiotics presenting with an apparent minor illness. CSF parameters are also affected by antibiotics, and it may be difficult to distinguish between viral and partially treated bacterial meningitis.

Cerebrovascular disease. Stroke can occur from fetal life through adolescence; the causes and manifestations differ according to age group. Congenital heart disease is a common source of stroke; other predisposing conditions include infections (causing vasculitis), systemic illnesses, vascular dysplasia, hematologic disorders, and hypercoagulable states. Stroke can occur in seemingly healthy children with certain conditions such as an arteriovenous malformation. Medical and surgical therapy may be beneficial for many of these conditions. Thrombolytic therapy is not used to treat ischemic stroke in children. Conditions that can mimic stroke include migraine, epilepsy, hypoglycemia and alternating hemiplegia of childhood. Sinus thrombosis may be misdiagnosed as bacterial meningitis.

Seizures. Seizures are perhaps the most common neurological emergency seen in children. The underlying etiologies, need for diagnostic intervention, prognosis and treatment options vary according to the seizure type, which in turn varies according to the age of the patient. Status epilepticus must be aggressively treated according to a timetable based on a clear understanding of antiepileptic drug pharmacokinetics. Neonatal seizures, infantile spasms, and febrile seizures present specific issues unique to the pediatric population. Anticonvulsant medication requires special considerations differing from the adult population. The differential diagnosis includes breath holding spells, benign paroxysmal vertigo, shuddering attacks, sleep related behaviours and pseudoseizures.

[19] Sleep Disorders

Sleep disorders generally fall into one of six major categories: insomnia, excessive somnolence, sleep related breathing difficulties, circadian dysrhythmia, parasomnias or sleep related behaviours, or sleep related movement disorders.[116] These disorders, as a group, are exceedingly common, especially among the elderly and patients with degenerative diseases. There are also links between sleep disorders and a variety of neurological conditions such as multiple sclerosis, myotonic dystrophy and certain types of epilepsy. The diagnosis rests on clinical history, exclusion of underlying disorders, and specialized testing such as the polysomnogram, multiple sleep latency test, and maintenance of wakefulness test. Pathophysiology, prognosis and treatment depend on the particular disorder. There is a growing recognition of

---

[116] Fayle RW, ed. *Sleep disorders.* Neurol Clin 2005; 23:945-1253.

and interest in sleep disorders by neurologists and other specialists, as well as by employers, transportation authorities and select government agencies.[117] Sleep related forensic issues will become increasingly commonplace, especially sleep related violence and sleep induced motor, rail and air disasters. From a malpractice standpoint, the neurologist may be increasingly liable for failing to diagnose a sleep disorder, and for sleep related motor vehicle and industrial accidents. Additionally, analogous to epilepsy, the neurologist may incur liability for neglecting to report a patient with sleep disorders to the transportation authorities.

[20] Iatrogenic Disorders

Iatrogenic disorders refer to conditions that arise from medical care. These include adverse drug reactions, diagnostic procedural mishaps, and medical and surgical treatment complications. For example, a carotid endarterectomy to prevent stroke may be complicated by an infarction, or anticoagulation for atrial fibrillation may cause an intracerebral hemorrhage. Likewise, radiation therapy may cause encephalopathy, myelopathy or plexopathy. A diagnostic LP may be complicated by an iatrogenic infection. However, drug induced neurological disorders are the most common iatrogenic disorders and may be due to either direct toxicity or a drug induced systemic dysfunction that harms the nervous system. *Encephalopathies* or neuropsychiatric effects are exceedingly common and may be secondary to dopa preparations, anti-epileptic drugs, acyclovir, anticholinergic drugs, benzodiazepines, and certain antibiotics. The elderly and those patients with pre-existing brain dysfunction are at high risk for cognitive side effects. *Seizures* may be induced by anti-depressants, certain anesthetics, theophylline, chemotherapy agents, and particular anti-microbial drugs. Radiological contrast agents and certain vaccines are associated with seizures. Many of the pain medications paradoxically induce *headache* by a rebound phenomena; anti-depressants and oral contraceptives frequently induce various headache syndromes. *Peripheral neuropathies* may be secondary to chemotherapy agents, some antibiotics and cardiac drugs such as amiodarone. There are drugs that frequently interfere with neuromuscular transmission and produce a *myasthenic syndrome*. This may be due to presynaptic anesthetic like actions (propranolol) or postsynaptic receptor blockage (D-penicillamine). Aminoglycoside and flouroquinolone antibiotics may cause this type of picture. Drug induced *myopathies* are not uncommon

---

[117] Kryger MH, Roth T, Dement WC. *Principles and Practice of Sleep Medicine*, 4th ed. Saunders; 2005.

and often involve corticosteroids or the newer cholesterol lowering statin medications. Steroid myopathy may develop acutely, but it is usually a chronic slowly evolving picture. Discontinuing steroids may or may not result in improvement of the myopathy. *Neuroleptic malignant syndrome* (NMS) is a rare but potentially fatal idiosyncratic reaction to neuroleptic medications which requires rapid, aggressive intervention. These patients develop severe muscle rigidity, altered consciousness, fever, autonomic dysfunction (rapid pulse and respirations, blood pressure fluctuations) and a massively elevated creatinine kinase indicative of muscle damage. The neuroleptic must be discontinued, and supportive care requires cooling the patient; restoring electrolyte imbalances; attending cardiac, pulmonary and renal complications; and providing dantrolene, although bromocriptine and benzodiazepines have also been used. *Movement disorders* are perhaps the most common adverse drug reactions, and typically due to antipsychotic medications. These may be hyperkinetic or hypokinetic, and may occur promptly after administration or only after prolonged treatment. Acute dystonic reactions may occur within hours or days after neuroleptics or even antinausea medications such as metoclopramide, and require prompt treatment with antihistamines due to painful muscle spasms and impaired breathing. Akathisia, or the inability to remain still, commonly occurs with neuroleptics or serotonin reuptake inhibitors and may require treatment including discontinuation of the offending agent and use of anticholinergics or benzodiazepines. The most disconcerting movement disorder is *tardive dyskinesia* (TD), a disorder of the face, especially lips and tongue, with choreic or rhythmic chewing and pouting movements. It is caused by exposure to neuroleptics or dopamine-blocking drugs, and can be permanent and irreversible. Currently, metoclopramide is the most common cause of TD.[118] Treatment is limited to withdrawing the drug which may not have any affect on the condition. Attention should be directed to preventive measures—avoiding high potency neuroleptics, or using the lowest possible doses for the shortest time, and if TD develops, then the drug should be immediately discontinued. Malpractice actions for TD may claim inappropriate drug use or misdiagnosis, inadequate monitoring of the patient, or lack of informed consent. These are just a very few examples of the many drug induced neurological disorders which may mimic virtually any neurological condition. It is usually an area ripe for malpractice claims.

---

[118] Pasricha PJ, Pehlivanov N, et at. *Drug insight: from disturbed motility to disordered movement — a review of the clinical benefits and medicolegal risks of metoclopramide.* Nat Clin Pract Gastroenterol Hepatol 2006; 3(3):138-148.

§ 11.10 The Expert Witness

[1] Securing the Records

Once the attorney elects to pursue a medical malpractice case, the medical records must be collected and assembled. This includes all physician reports, test results and hospital records as well as medical bills, prescriptions, and insurance records. In addition to paper records, counsel must demand true and complete electronic records of all relevant databases, which often have more detail than the paper chart. The records must then be thoroughly analyzed, but it is important the attorney, not an expert, decides whether there was malpractice. Otherwise, there is a risk of being seriously misled—some physicians believe only gross incompetence is malpractice; most believe a reported complication cannot be due to malpractice. Attention should be directed towards any alterations in the records. In the author's experience, whenever an attorney requests records, the hospital or clinic summons the attending physician to "review the request." This gives the physician ample opportunity to "correct" any deficiencies or otherwise amend the record. It is usually difficult to prove spoliation; however, if found, and if it has a material affect on the case, the court may impose drastic remedies.

[2] Securing the Expert Witness

If counsel, after reviewing the records, ascertains that a medical malpractice claim exists, it is necessary to secure expert witness testimony, barring certain exceptions (common knowledge, gross negligence, *res ipsa loquitur*), to establish the applicable standard of care, that the defendant's conduct departed from that standard, and that such conduct was the proximate cause of the injury in question. The elements of a claim are detailed in this text and numerous other sources, and will not be reiterated in this chapter.[119] It is imperative to locate a reputable expert—a well trained, board certified, practicing neurologist with an unrestricted license, belonging to appropriate professional organizations and, if possible, with teaching experience or peer reviewed publication in the area of interest. This may be difficult as it is "alarmingly common for accomplished neurologists to hire themselves out for [one-sided testimony]."[120] These partisan experts have

---

[119] Shandell RE, Smith P. *The Preparation and Trial of Medical Malpractice Cases.* New York: Law Journal Press; 2007 (update).

[120] S Holtz. *The Neurologist as an Expert Witness.* AAN Educational Program Syllabus 7DS.003 (2002).

flourished behind the common law expert witness immunity shield and lack of professional oversight. However, the pendulum is swinging back toward accountability with increased expert witness liability. The traditional immunity is not absolute, and the majority of states have carved out exceptions to hold the expert liable for professional negligence. Friendly expert lawsuits (suits against experts by the party that retained them) are increasing. Courts have also upheld suits against opposing and independent experts. Some jurisdictions continue to favor immunity for testimony, but that does not necessarily extend to nontestimonial expert activity (discovery of facts, literature search). More importantly, expert testimony and related activities are subject to increasing scrutiny by professional organizations and state licensing boards. The American Medical Association considers testimony to be the practice of medicine and subject to peer review, and supports state licensing boards in disciplining physicians who provide fraudulent testimony or false credentials. Some boards have expanded the definition of medical practice to include expert testimony, allowing disciplinary action if warranted.[121] The AAN adopted *Qualifications and Guidelines for the Physician Expert Witness*,[122] promulgated a code of professional conduct for legal expert testimony,[123] and established a formal disciplinary procedure for errant neurologists with potential sanctions ranging from censure to expulsion.[124] AAN disciplinary actions may trigger the ABPN to revoke certification. A Seventh Circuit Court of Appeals' decision validated these types of disciplinary policies and stated in dicta that the American Academy of Neurological Surgeons had a duty to discipline a neurosurgeon for irresponsible testimony.[125] The attorney should be aware of these trends to ensure that the expert complies with all relevant guidelines and policies, and is not likely to be impeached for any hidden bias. Some medical (American Association of Neurological Surgeons) and legal (Association of Trial Lawyers of America) organizations maintain repositories of deposition and trial testimony which may provide counsel with an excellent preview of the retained or opposing expert.

---

[121] F.L. Cohen. *The Expert Medical Witness in Legal Perspective.* J Legal Med 2004; 25:185-209.

[122] American Academy of Neurology. *Qualifications and Guidelines for the Physician Expert Witness.* (1998).

[123] §6(4) American Academy of Neurology, *Code of Professional Conduct* (2002) (readopted 2006).

[124] American Academy of Neurology, *Disciplinary Action Policy* (2004) (readopted 2006).

[125] *Austin v. American Association of Neurological Surgeons,* 253 F.3d 967 (7th Cir 2001).

CHAPTER 12

NEUROSURGERY

Bruce L. Wilder, MD, MPH, JD

SYNOPSIS

---

§ 12.01   In General

[1]   Introduction

Recognizing that, in neurosurgery, as in other fields of specialization, there is no absolute yardstick by which one can determine whether a case is meritorious, I hope this chapter will help lawyers evaluate the strong and weak points in their cases in the very early stages. It has long been the claim of some that far too many malpractice suits are filed, and that most are frivolous. On the other hand, no one can deny that malpractice occurs, and that compensation for the resulting injuries should be available.

It has been suggested that the frequency of injury due to substandard or negligent care and treatment is several times that of the frequency of such cases that actually result in claims or lawsuits.[1] There are, perhaps, several reasons for this: the patients or their families may not be aware that there has been negligent treatment, or the "value" of the case to an attorney is not enough to justify the amount of time and effort required to pursue it.

The goal of the attorney should be to identify and objectively evaluate each case by getting as much information as possible into the hands of a well qualified, thoroughly objective neurosurgeon as early as possible, so that she may quickly dispose of those cases that cannot be won. On-the-record expert opinion is the bedrock of any case where expert testimony is required for filing or at trial (law varies from state to state as to when, or if, or in what form, expert opinion is required). Too often, attorneys become convinced there has been wrongdoing, based upon an informal conversation with a neurosurgeon who, under the particular circumstances, may too readily provide an off-the-record opinion based upon inadequate or inaccurate information. Often, it is usually that same neurosurgeon who, for various reasons, will not make himself available to testify. This kind of informal, gratuitous opinion by a neurosurgeon does a great disservice, not only to a neurosurgical colleague, who may find himself faced with a frivolous lawsuit, but to the client's attorney who may find himself led down a costly and embarrassing road to defeat.

This chapter is not meant to educate lawyers sufficiently to evaluate a neurosurgical case and then find a witness to testify. There are several excellent textbooks and journals in the field of neurosurgery which provide far greater detail if answers to specific questions about treatment are needed. Rather, this chapter should be thought of as an overview of some fundamental principles of neurosurgical care that should help lawyers evaluate the strong and weak points of neurosurgical expert opinion, whether it is put forth for the client or for the opponent. The most reliable analysis of a case will come from a neurosurgeon who performs the procedure, or takes care of patients with the condition in question, and who has committed to providing an on-the-record opinion.

[2] Definitions

The definitions that follow are for the purposes of this chapter. Some have a general applicability, but may not be valid in all situations. It is left to the reader to compare them with other definitions and descriptions.

---

[1] Sack, K, *Thousands of Medical Errors, but Few Law Suits Study Says*, N.Y. TIMES, Jan. 29, 1990. Hiatt, H.H., et al, *A Study of Medical Injury and Medical Malpractice: An Overview*, N.ENG. J. MED. 1989;32:480-4.

Neurological surgery, or *neurosurgery* Is a discipline of medicine and the specialty of surgery that provides the operative and non-operative management (i.e. prevention, diagnosis, evaluation, treatment, critical care, and rehabilitation) of disorders of the central, peripheral, and autonomic nervous systems, including their supporting structures and vascular supply; the evaluation and treatment of pathological processes that modify the function or activity of the nervous system, including the hypophysis; and the operative and non-operative management of pain. As such, Neurological Surgery encompasses the surgical, non-surgical, and stereotactic radiosurgical treatment of adult and pediatric patients with disorders of the nervous system: disorders of the brain, meninges, skull, and skull base, and their blood supply, including the surgical and endovascular treatment disorders of the intracranial and extracranial vasculature supplying the brain and spinal cord; disorders of the pituitary gland; disorders of the spinal cord and meninges, and vertebral column, including those that may require treatment by fusion, instrumentation, or endovascular techniques; and disorders of the cranial, peripheral, and spinal nerves throughout their distribution.[2]

Nervous system: Brain and cranial nerves, spinal cord and spinal nerves, and peripheral nerves, including the sympathetic and parasympathetic nerves and ganglia.

Neurological surgeon, or *neurosurgeon*: A physician who holds himself out as such by virtue of some formal training and/or experience in the discipline or specialty of neurological surgery or neurosurgery. As a practical matter, few today will be able to succeed as specialists in neurological surgery without having completed all or most of an approved residency in neurological surgery; however, there are still a few neurosurgeons who practice without board eligibility or certification.

Board-certified neurosurgeon. Diplomate of the American Board of Neurological Surgery (ABNS) refers to certification by that board, one of twenty-four specialty boards that are members of the American Board of Medical Specialties (ABMS). Although the M.D. degree is not explicitly required for certification, the applicant must be "a graduate of a medical school acceptable to the Board."[3] The American Osteopathic Board of Surgery (AOBS) certifies D.O. neurosurgeons and imposes similar requirements for certification. Neurological surgeons not certified by the ABNS or by the AOBS may be certified by other boards with similar sounding names, which do not have the extensive training and examination requirements of the ABNS of AOBS.

---

[2] ABNS NEWSLETTER 2007;25:1.

[3] http://www.abns.org/content/primary_certification_process.asp (last access 6/1/08).

Board-eligible neurosurgeon: A neurosurgeon who has completed a training program approved by the ABNS, and who has passed the written Primary Examination. Rule 5.2 of the ABNS Rules and Regulations requires successful completion of the Primary Examination in order to complete training.[4] A board-eligible neurological surgeon may not have completed the twelve-month practice requirement, and is prepared to take the oral examination when otherwise eligible to do so. A candidate who does not take the Oral Examination within five years of completing an approved training program is no longer considered board-eligible. A candidate who fails the Oral Examination must re-take and pass it within three years. The AOBS has specific requirements for the designation of board eligibility.[5]

Accepted standards of neurosurgical care: Those levels of care, skill, diligence and knowledge on the part of the neurological surgeon, which, given the validity of the school of thought employed would be viewed as acceptable by most neurological surgeons in the recommendation and carrying out of treatment in a similar situation, with similar resources available. To some extent, such a definition needs to be adapted to conform to particular state law.

Reasonable medical certainty: That degree of certainty necessary to properly recommend and/or carry out a particular course of treatment, given the risks involved with that treatment, and considering all risks of making a decision that may ultimately be found to be incorrect (the fact that a decision is later found to have been incorrect does not necessarily mean that there has been a deviation from accepted standards of neurosurgical care).

§ 12.02 Education, Certification, and Professional Organizations

[1] Premedical Education

There are no required premedical courses for neurosurgeons, other than those that a particular medical school may require for all applicants. Usually, courses in biology, mathematics, physics, and chemistry are required for the medical school to assess a particular candidate's interest and aptitude for the study of medicine. Medical schools place varying degrees of emphasis on the

---

[4] 19 ABNS Newsletter 1 (2000).

[5] "The designation "Board Eligibility" is defined as that status granted by the AOA, registered through this Board, to candidates who:

1. Have documented program complete status by the ACOS.

2. Have met all the requirements for this designation as established by this Board.

3. Have made application and have been accepted as a candidate by this Board.

4. Are and remain a member in good standing of the AOA or the Canadian Osteopathic Association."

- *See* http://www.aobs.org/aobs-protocol.htm#eligibility (last access 6/1/08).

humanities, because of concern as to how compassionate and ethical the future physician will be.

[2] Medical Education

The medical school curriculum leading to the M.D. degree traditionally involves a two-year period with concentration on the basic sciences, i.e. gross and microscopic anatomy, physiology, biochemistry, gross and microscopic pathology, microbiology, genetics, usually a neuroscience curriculum, psychology, and often ethics and legal aspects of medicine, as well as history of medicine.

The last two years of medical school are largely clinically oriented in the form of clerkships, where students work closely with interns, residents, and faculty, and also continue didactic studies in medicine, surgery, and the various subspecialties. In recent years, the trend has been away from required rotations in clinical neurosurgery, perhaps because of the need for greater emphasis on general principles of surgery and medicine, or because neurosurgery has become specialized to a degree because neurosurgery has become specialized beyond the sophistication or interest of the average student.[6]

The Doctor of osteopathy (D.O.) curriculum is today, for all practical purposes, identical, except that training in manipulative skills is required.

[3] Postgraduate Training

Virtually all neurosurgeons completing training today have done so in accredited residency programs. There were eight hundred and ninety four residents in ninety seven accredited neurosurgical residency training programs in the United States in the 2006/2007 academic year.[7] The accreditation of neurosurgical residency programs is the function of the Residency Review Committee (RRC) for neurological surgery. The RRC for neurological surgery was reorganized in 1971, and consists of six neurosurgeons: two from the American Board of Neurological Surgery (ABNS), two from the American College of Surgeons (ACS), and two from the Council of Medical Education of the American Medical Association (AMA).[8]

The format of the accreditation process is implemented by the Accreditation Council for Graduate Medical Education (ACGME), which is made up of representatives from each of its parent bodies: the AMA, The

---

[6] Stern, WE, *A statement concerning neurosurgery in the undergraduate medical curriculum*, SURG. NEUROL. 1990;33:5-6.

[7] ABNS NEWSLETTER 2007;25:1.

[8] http://www.abns.org/content/primary_certification_process.asp (last access 6/1/08).

American Board of Medical Specialties (ABMS), the Council of Medical Specialty Societies (CMSS), The American Hospital Association (AHA), and the Association of American Medical Colleges (AAMC). Additionally, there is one representative from the federal government, one from the public, and one representing residents. The ACGME delegates to the RRC for neurosurgery accreditation authority for neurosurgical residency programs. This delegation of authority is reviewed every three or four years.

A neurosurgical training program is reviewed for accreditation based upon information supplied by the program director, by results of surveys by field representatives of the ACGME and, occasionally, by specialist site-visitors (normally, prominent neurosurgeons).

Presently, ACGME-accredited residency programs in neurological surgery require at least six months of training in surgical disciplines other than neurological surgery.[9] The residency program itself must be sixty months in duration, thirty-six months of which are in clinical neurosurgery, including twelve months as senior-most resident. Three months in clinical neurology are required. The additional twenty-one months should be devoted to related areas of neuroscience, such as basic research, neuroradiology, or neuropathology.

The ACGME has mandated that resident competency in six areas be assessed before graduation from a residency program: (1) patient care; (2) medical knowledge; (3) practice-based learning and improvement; (4) interpersonal and communication skills; (5) professionalism; and (6) systems-based practice. Each residency program is to develop its own training program and assessment tools to address each competency.[10]

[4] Board Certification

The American Board of Neurological Surgery (ABNS)[11] was established in 1940. There are fourteen directors of the Board, each of whom serves a six-year term. The "broad aim" of the ABNS is "to encourage the study, improve the practice, elevate the standards, and advance the science of neurological surgery, and thereby serve the cause of the public health."[12] As of August, 2007, approximately 3,368 board-certified neurological surgeons were in active practice. Board certification requires successful completion of an accredited residency training program (*see* §12.02 [3] *supra*), review of the applicant's professional practice over a twelve month period, including opinions reflected

[9] http://www.abns.org/content/primary_certification_process.asp (last access 6/1/08)

[10] AANS Neurosurgeon 2008;17:20.

[11] J.T. Hoff, *American Board of Neurological Surgery*, NEUROSURGERY 1988;22 (Supp.):175.

[12] ABNS NEWSLETTER 2007;25:1.

in statements of colleagues, and successful completion of an oral examination. The pass rate for the November, 2006 Oral Examination was 89%. For the May, 2007 Oral Examination, the pass rate was 85%. During the previous twelve months, six Certificates were revoked, and three were suspended.[13]

The written Primary Exam is given yearly in Houston, TX. It may be taken for self-assessment or credit by anyone in a neurosurgical residency program, or by anyone who has finished training. The current pass rate for the exam is about 85%. After completion of the accredited training program, the candidate is considered board-eligible. If a period of five years elapses after passing the primary written examination without passing the oral exam, the primary written exam must be taken again to maintain board-eligibility.

It has been estimated that there are 109 "self-designated" boards, some of which have certification designations suggesting special expertise in neurological surgery, but which do not have the rigorous requirements of training, practice review, and examination required by the ABNS or the AOBS. In other words, the "board-certified" qualifications of a neurological surgeon do not necessarily mean board-certified by the American Board of Neurological Surgery, or of the American Osteopathic Board of Surgery.

[5] Recertification/Maintenance of Certification

In 1999, the ABNS began issuing time-limited certificates valid for ten years. Prior to that time the ABNS had no recertification process, and recertification was not required.

In 1932 the Association of American Medical Colleges (AAMC) recommended requirements for continuing medical education. In 1940, the year the ABNS was formed, the ABMS recommended so-called time-limited certificates (TLC). In 1973, the ABMS unanimously adopted a policy calling for voluntary recertification.

An important concept that has not been widely appreciated is the idea that certification should be differentiated from recertification, i.e., certification should reflect satisfactory completion of a period of formal supervised training, and recertification should reflect satisfactory performance in practice. The thinking behind this view is that the recertification process should be primarily an assessment of the neurosurgeon's *performance* in practice; in other words, it should be a quality-assurance program, rather than primarily a testing of cognitive skills, which is more appropriate as a certifying process.[14]

---

[13] ABNS NEWSLETTER 2007;25:1.

[14] R.B. King, *Challenges in recertification*, SURG. NEUROL. 1989;32:403-7; W.E. McAuliff, *Measuring the Quality of care; process vs. outcome*, MILBANK MEM. QRTLY./HEALTH AND SOCIETY 1979;57:1.

The Maintenance of Certification process for neurological surgery combines aspects of cognitive skill testing and of quality assurance (including requirements of Continuing Medical Education and review of practice data). A requirement of Lifelong Learning and Self-Assessment is 150 Continuing Medical Education (CME) credits per three-year mini-cycle.[15] A Cognitive Knowledge Examination, consisting of 200 questions in 13 categories (anatomy, anesthesia, congenital, degenerative, functional, general clinical, infection, neurology, pain, trauma, tumor, vascular, and other (safety, ethics, compliance, and evidence-based medicine)) must be passed in each ten-year cycle. The first examination was given in March 2007.[16]

[6] Subspecialty Certification

Presently, the ABNS does not issue certificates for special qualifications. The ABNS endorses fellowships accredited by the ACGME, and recognizes Focused Practice through the MOC process.

[7] Professional Societies

The American Association of Neurological Surgeons (AANS), founded in 1931 as the Harvey Cushing Society, has grown in number to over 2,400. Board certification by the ABNS is a prerequisite for membership, and attendance at the national annual scientific meeting is required at least once every three years. Several committees of the board of directors of the AANS are involved in a multitude of activities, ranging from socioeconomic aspects of neurosurgical practice and research to the scientific aspects, and from ethics in the practice of neurosurgery to professional liability issues. The AANS, together with the Congress of Neurological Surgeons maintains the Joint Council of State and Neurosurgical Societies, which is active in political affairs as they relate to the practice of neurological surgery.

The Congress of Neurological Surgeons (CNS) was founded in 1951, primarily to give the younger neurosurgeon an opportunity to be active in organized neurosurgery. Its present membership numbers approximately 4,000. It encourages board-certification of all its members, recognizing of course, that many new board-eligible members may not have had the opportunity to complete all requirements of certification for at least two years after completing residency training. The activities of the organization are similar to those of the AANS, and a national meeting is held annually.

---

[15] ABNS NEWSLETTER 2007;25:3.
[16] ABNS NEWSLETTER 2007;25:5.

The American College of Surgeons (ACS) is composed of surgeons in all specialties. Neurosurgeons must be board-certified by the ABNS in order to be accepted for membership in the ACS.

Other organizations for neurosurgeons exist, with varied purposes and activities, including the Society of Neurological Surgeons, the Neurosurgical Society of America, and the American Academy of Neurological Surgeons, along with numerous State and regional neurosurgical organizations.

§ 12.03 Types of Neurosurgical Practice

[1] Academic Practice

Often there is no clear line between so-called academic practice and private practice. Generally, the term academic practice implies a significant degree of control of the neurosurgeon's practice by an institution, usually an accredited medical school that has a major affiliation with a teaching hospital, i.e., a hospital that has internship and residency programs. There may be varying degrees of control of finances and practice income, with portions being pooled for research and other institutional expenses, and there may be certain salary and benefit guarantees by the institution in return for teaching and research commitments. The academic neurosurgeon is not necessarily involved in teaching neurosurgical residents in a residency training program, but may simply participate in the teaching of medical students and general surgical or other residents who rotate through a neurosurgical service.

Neurosurgeons who are self-supporting as private practitioners often practice in institutions with neurosurgical or other residents, with or without affiliation with a medical school (virtually all neurosurgical residency programs today are affiliated with accredited medical schools), on a "voluntary" (without compensation) basis, or for a nominal salary. These practitioners provide valuable experience for trainees by allowing them to participate in the care of patients.

The "full-time" academic neurosurgeon usually has a private practice, but may have responsibility for "service" or "house" patients, i.e., those that are primarily cared for by residents who are supervised by the attending staff. Often, part-time or voluntary faculty (also referred to as "clinical faculty)" may have a similar relationship to house staff, residents, and patients.

The financial strains on academic medical institutions created by lowered reimbursement from private and government insurers, has created a trend toward largely incentive-based salary structures for practitioners in academic medicine in general.

Increasingly, academic neurosurgeons, like academic practitioners in other specialties, obtain significant remuneration from work as consultants to medical equipment manufacturers and pharmacological companies. Some inquiry into what these other sources of income are may reveal information that is highly relevant to the issues in malpractice case, particularly where there are informed consent issues (*See* §12.07[9] *infra*).

[2] Private Practice

Neurosurgeons in private practice are generally practitioners with little or no research or teaching responsibilities, except perhaps as described above. Up until recently, this form of practice was usually the most lucrative. Billing is still largely on a fee-for-service basis; however in areas with large managed care penetration neurosurgeons are facing declining reimbursements and being pressured to agree to capitation methods of payment. Largely because of changes in reimbursement methods, "private practice" neurosurgeons are tending to align with individual hospitals or health care systems.

The neurosurgeon may work as a solo practitioner, employee of a professional corporation, or member of a partnership. The number of solo practitioners is declining, except in rural areas. The solo practitioner is more vulnerable to liability situations where there are allegations of inadequate coverage, particularly where he is on the staff of multiple institutions separated by significant distances. While accepted standards of neurosurgical care are generally held to be national, as opposed to local, it is well to remember that the standard of care in a given set of circumstances is determined by the finder of fact, and the defense attorney may be able to create a good deal of sympathy for his client in a jury that can be made to understand how difficult practice conditions may be in a rural or underserved urban area, and to recognize that next year there could be *no* neurosurgeon in that area.

Additionally, the neurosurgeon in solo practice may find himself involved as a defendant where he was cross-covering for another solo practitioner, even when his own actions were faultless.

Group practices of neurosurgeons may be multi-specialty, i.e., a neurosurgeon may constitute a relatively small part of a large multi-specialty clinic or of a group practice, which may consist of neurologists and neurosurgeons, or may be solely neurosurgeons.

[3] Research

Some neurosurgeons, usually in academic positions, spend most of their time doing research, and may do very little clinical work. These individuals may have excellent reputations as researchers, teachers, and academicians, but their clinical and technical skills, clinical judgments, and general practical experience may not be as good as those of a neurosurgeon whose primary activity is that of practitioner. It is not suggested that academicians as a group are lacking in practical skills, but it is suggested that some inquiry into the way a neurosurgeon's week-to-week practice activity (vis-à-vis teaching, patient care, research, and other activities) is allocated may be revealing.

[4] Government Positions

Although not as lucrative as private practice, government positions for neurosurgeons offer certain advantages. Some highly competent individuals are attracted to military or other government positions, such as the Public Health Service or the Veterans Administration. These positions tend to offer a wide clinical experience without many of the pressures of private practice.

[5] Hospital-based Practice

There is an increasing trend toward practice within a single institution. Integration of the neurosurgeon's practice with a health care system is viewed by this author as beneficial with regard to maintaining sounds systems of patient safety and regulatory compliance.

§ 12.04 Scope of Neurosurgical Practice

[1] In General

There are many types of care, and in particular many procedures, that neurosurgeons do as part of their practice that are done by other practitioners who are not neurosurgeons. For example, in the area of carpal tunnel surgery, the same procedure may be done by a general surgeon, an orthopedic surgeon with or without hand subspecialization, a plastic surgeon, or by a neurosurgeon. Carotid endarterectomy may be done by a vascular or general surgeon, or by a neurosurgeon. Spinal surgery is done by orthopedic surgeons, occasionally by general surgeons, and by neurosurgeons. Endovascular procedures are done by invasive radiologists, as well as by specially trained neurosurgeons. There are many other examples. Where such areas of overlap occur, there may be differences among the members of the various specialties as to the respective accepted standards of care.

[2] Office or Clinic Practice

Part of every clinical neurosurgical practice is an outpatient practice in an office, either freestanding or in a professional building associated with, or contiguous with, a hospital, or in an office or outpatient facility integral to a hospital. It is here that many referrals are first seen, and follow-up evaluations are conducted. Occasionally, unreferred patients may be seen in this setting as well, although most neurosurgeons prefer to see patients that have been evaluated by another physician to determine of neurosurgical evaluation or treatment is necessary.

Records of the details of the patient's history and examination findings are kept either as handwritten notes or dictated for transcription to typewritten copy or for storage on a retrievable form of electronic media. These records are usually kept with copies of correspondence from other physicians, copies of test reports, and copies of certain portions of the patient's hospital records, such as the admission history and physical, discharge summary, operative notes, and other test results that might be pertinent.

Many offices, particularly those of large group practices, may have X-ray facilities and other diagnostic capabilities, including computed tomography (CT) units or magnetic resonance imaging (MRI) units. Many neurosurgeons or neurosurgical practices hold equity interest (usually as silent partners in a limited partnership) in such facilities located at other sites, to which they refer patients. Occasionally, ownership of a facility may present a conflict of interest that could compromise the level of care. At some facilities, such as MRI or CT scanners, interpretations of studies might be performed by "moonlighting" residents in radiology, but the reports might be signed only by the neurosurgeon who operates the facility, who might not have actually performed the interpretation.

Office treatment of patients, other than diagnostic procedures, is usually limited to removal of sutures and other minor wound care, local injections of corticosteroids and local anesthetics, lumbar puncture, aspiration of cerebrospinal fluid from an implanted reservoir or part of a CSF shunt, and occasionally very minor operative procedures such as sural nerve biopsy or administration of antibiotics or chemotherapeutic agents via subcutaneous reservoir, or administration of narcotics or other drugs into implanted pump reservoirs used in the treatment of certain types of pain and/or spasticity problems.

[3] Hospital Practice

Virtually all major neurosurgical procedures take place within a hospital. Here the neurosurgeon admits patients for surgery or other intensive treatment, either as an emergency or on an elective basis, seeks consultations (referrals of inpatients under the care of other physicians), and performs surgery. It is not uncommon for neurosurgeons to perform operative procedures at more than one hospital. A practice situation where a surgeon regularly performs surgery at several hospitals leaves open the potential for a lapse in patient care, which is usually minimized by arrangements with associates or other neurosurgeons with staff privileges at the respective hospitals. In many cases, the situation is less than ideal, especially if the coverage is by a resident.

Another potentially undesirable situation is when a busy neurosurgeon books simultaneous cases in different operating rooms within the same operating suite, and depends upon a resident to do significant portions of a procedure while the neurosurgeon is in the midst of another operation. If an unexpected, intra-operative complication occurs in one of the rooms, it may not be adequately handled if the attending neurosurgeon is not immediately available.

In cases where it appears that some unexplained lapse in availability of a neurosurgeon has occurred, it is well to inquire into his or her other activities at that time, and in particular to

Obtain operating room records and schedules for that day at *all* hospitals where the neurosurgeon practices.

[4] Outpatient Surgery and Ambulatory Surgical Centers

During the last thirty years, much surgery previously performed on inpatients is now performed on outpatients. Unquestionably, the major impetus for this shift has been the cost considerations engendered by the way in which hospitals charge and are reimbursed, as well as by pressure by insurers to minimize costs. It is debatable whether any real lowering in the actual cost of medical care has occurred as a result of this trend, but it is clear that hospital use has been reduced. Also, it is doubtful that any significant increase in risk to patients has resulted, as long as the approach by physicians has been prudent and adheres to common sense.

The kinds of procedures commonly performed as "outpatient" procedures are those for peripheral nerve problems, such as entrapment syndromes (carpal tunnel syndrome, ulnar tunnel syndrome, cubital tunnel syndrome, tarsal tunnel syndrome, and others), sural nerve biopsy, temporal artery biopsy, biopsy of skull lesions, and automated percutaneous (lumbar) discectomy. Occasionally, revision of CSF shunts, implanted pumps, or implanted electrical stimulators may be performed as outpatient procedures. More recently, minimally-invasive spine procedures are being performed on an out-patient basis.

Outpatient procedures may be done under local, regional, or general anesthesia. They may be done at hospitals or at so called freestanding or ambulatory surgical centers. Not uncommonly, the operating surgeon may have an equity or other financial interest in a freestanding surgical center, and there is a possibility that a conflict of interest could lead to a deviation from accepted standards of care.

[5] Independent Medical Examinations and "Second Surgical Opinions"

Neurosurgeons perform examinations and consultations in which it is understood ahead of time that the neurosurgeon is not a treating physician, but is to perform an examination for the purpose of evaluating a degree of impairment as a result of a condition that neurosurgeons ordinarily treat, or for the purpose of determining the cause of such a condition. These evaluations are usually to obtain medical evidence in an action for personal injury, and are often referred to as "independent medical examinations." In this context, "independent" refers to the fact that the neurosurgeon's involvement is not for the purpose of treatment, but as an expert chosen by a party to provide certain facts and opinions. Treating physicians are often reluctant to provide opinion evidence that they believe to be unfavorable to a patient's legal claim, because they risk alienating the patient.

Another purpose of the independent medical examination is to obtain a second opinion regarding surgery. Many insurance companies, as well as Medicare and Medicaid, require such an opinion in cases where certain elective procedures have been recommended by the treating neurosurgeon. Although not termed "independent medical examination," the so-called mandatory second surgical opinion is usually done with the understanding that the examining physician will not assume a treatment role.

Even though the physician performing an independent medical examination is explicitly not assuming a role in treatment, in the eyes of the law, a physician-patient relationship is created in the context of an independent medical examination. While the examining physician has some ethical and often legal obligation to advise an examinee of certain findings, if the physician gratuitously provides advice or recommendations to the patient, there could be some added liability on the part of the physician.[17]

[6] Medical-legal Consultations and Expert Opinion Evidence

Neurosurgeons find themselves asked to provide opinions regarding whether there has been a deviation from accepted standards of care. Some forthrightly decline to provide any such opinions in any case, because they

---

[17] Ken Baum, MD, JD, *Independent Medical Examinations: An Expanding Source of Physcian Liability*, ANN INTERN MED. 2005;142:974-978. *See also*, Laurie Barclay, MD and Charles Vega, MD, FAAFP, *Medicolegal Aspects of Independent Medical Examinations*, http://www.medscape.com/viewarticle/506896 (2005) (last access 6/1/08).

"do not want to become involved." Because of a perceived "crisis" in medical malpractice suits, it has even been asserted in the neurosurgical literature that by refusing to provide on-the-record expert opinion for plaintiff's attorneys, neurosurgeons can help solve the problem of too many lawsuits.[18]

Some neurosurgeons, perhaps unwittingly, demonstrate their own biases in dealing with their roles as experts in medical malpractice litigation, while striking out at what they perceive to be biases of others. Some reveal bias by indicating their willingness to testify on behalf of defendants, but not on behalf of plaintiffs. Others appear to be peculiarly sensitive about the fact that a fee is charged for their professional time.[19]

§ 12.05 The Spectrum of Clinical Practice

[1] In General

One can subdivide the practice of neurological surgery by examining the subspecialties that have evolved within the field (even though the American Board of Neurological Surgery (ABNS) does not officially certify neurosurgeons in subspecialties):

1. Cerebrovascular surgery
2. Functional and stereotactic surgery
3. Pediatric neurological surgery
4. Spine surgery
5. Peripheral nerve surgery
6. Neurotrauma and critical care
7. Neuro-oncology and tumor surgery
8. Endoscopic and minimally-invasive surgery

As in any other field where scientific and technological advances occur at a rapid pace and increasingly highly technical skills are required to maintain accepted standards of care, there is a natural tendency for the practitioner to concentrate to some degree on areas where he or she feels most proficient. It is well to remember, however, that new is not always better. When a neurosurgeon has invested much of his career in the development of a procedure, she may consciously or unconsciously express the belief that more traditional procedures for a condition are inadequate or ineffective. In neurosurgery, as in other fields of medicine, we have seen over the years that

---

[18] Friedburg SR, *A simple solution to the medical malpractice crisis*, SURG. NEUROL. 1987;28:320-321

[19] Alexander, Jr. EB, Editorial, *The expert witness- to serve or not to serve (and if so, for how much)*, SURG. NEUROL. 1987;27:505.

certain procedures come and go, and sometimes return years later in new technological clothes. It is usually not the human body or the disease that have changed, but, for various reasons, the attitudes and expectations of both patient and physician, some realistic and some not.

[2] Cerebrovascular Surgery

Cerebrovascular surgery refers to surgical treatment of intracranial or extracranial vessels which provide circulation to the brain. Disease, injury, congenital, or other abnormality of vessels *outside* the cranial cavity, and which supply intracranial structures may produce insult to the brain, either by intracranial hemorrhage, or by ischemia. Disorders of blood vessels within the cranial cavity (e.g. dural arteriovenoius malformation), whether or not they supply the brain itself, can also produce hemorrhagic or ischemic injury to the brain.

Perhaps the distinction of extracranial and intracranial vessels should be broken down further, since the internal carotid arteries penetrate and run a course in the skull base before they enter the cranial cavity itself. For years, the portion of the carotid artery that enters the base of the skull in the petrous portion of the temporal bone and winds through the cavernous (venous) sinus to emerge into the subarachnoid space has been considered a surgical "no-man's land." However, this segment of the carotid artery within the skull can now be reached by the neurosurgeon skilled in the technique of skull base surgery, which could be considered another area of sub-specialization in neurosurgery, overlapping considerably with corresponding areas of sub-specialization in the fields of otolaryngology, plastic surgery, and head-and-neck surgery. Moreover, the development of endovascular techniques employed by an invasive radiologist or neurological surgeon trained in such techniques has greatly expanded the armamentarium for treatment of both intra- and extracranial vascular disease. As the procedures become more sophisticated and rely on more refined medical devices, the number of parties potentially liable for harm increases.

The common carotid arteries arise from the arch of the aorta in the chest (on the right side, the common carotid arises as the innominate artery, which, after giving off the right subclavian artery, becomes the common carotid) and travel in the anterior part of the neck to near the angle of the jaw, where each bifurcates into the internal carotid (which travels to the base of the skull and to the intracranial cavity without giving off any branches) and the external carotid (which supplies the face and portions of the scalp). Some branches of the external carotid artery may form anastomoses with branches of the intracranial vessels (such as the ophthalmic artery) and, in some cases, provide essential blood supply to the brain, if vessels normally supplying the brain have been occluded by disease. The cavernous sinus, referred to above, is actually a collection of veins in a cavity or sinus in the dura mater (the tough membrane lining the inner aspect of the skull) at the base of the skull toward the center, through which the internal carotid artery passes on each side, along with cranial nerves subserving eye movements (the third, fourth, and sixth) and the ophthalmic division of the fifth cranial nerve supplying sensation to the cornea and upper third of the face.

The other vessels supplying the brain are the vertebral arteries, which travel from the subclavian arteries in the chest and ascend through bony openings in each side of the sixth through second cervical vertebrae and enter the base of the skull through the foramen magnum (through which opening travels the spinal cord) and join on the anterior surface of the pons-medulla junction to from the basilar artery. The basilar artery branches to form the posterior cerebral arteries, which join the carotid circulation via the posterior communicating arteries. After the carotid arteries have given off the posterior communicating arteries, they branch into the middle and anterior cerebral arteries, and the anterior cerebral arteries then join in the midline by a short vessel called the anterior communicating artery. The circle of vessels thus formed at the base of the brain is called the Circle of Willis, and provides some protection in situations where one or more vessels have been occluded.

The kinds of problems the cerebrovascular surgeon treats include those related to occlusive disease (largely, but not entirely, due to atherosclerotic disease), or to anatomical derangement of vessels usually congenitally determined, such as aneurysms and arteriovenous malformations. Arteriovenous malformations of the dura occur in both the intracranial and intraspinal cavities. Arteriovenous malformations of the spinal cord or spinal dura can be difficult to detect and to treat. Ischemic injury to the spinal cord is an inherent and dreaded risk of the treatment of such lesions.

Traumatic lesions of the cerebral vasculature include traumatic aneurysms, arterio-venous fistulas, and occlusions, and may be treated with direct intracranial surgery or an endovascular approach, as the individual case may require.

A not-uncommon injury of the extracranial circulation is traumatic dissection, usually caused by blunt-force or stretch injury to the vessel. Of course, direct injury to extra- or intracranial vessels from penetrating injury occurs. In both of these kinds of injuries, ischemic infarction of the brain (or spinal cord) can occur.

Ischemic infarction of the spinal cord can result from trauma to its supplying vessels, including the aorta, which gives off branches to the spinal cord.

[a] Cerebral Aneurysms

Aneurysm refers to an abnormal dilatation or enlargement of a blood vessel, and in the scope of this discussion refers to those found in the intracranial arterial circulation. The term "aneurysm" derives from an old concept that the walls of a vessel dilated because there were no nerves to supply the muscle layer of the vessel, and it therefore was weak and gradually expanded over time. In fact, the common so-called "berry" (because they resemble a berry on a plant) aneurysm probably develops over time as a result of some defect in the muscle layer, usually where a vessel branches or divides. Other aneurysms may occur as a result of degenerative or atherosclerotic changes in the vessel wall, as a result of infection (mycotic aneurysm) or some inflammatory process within the vessel wall, or as a result of trauma, such as a penetrating head injury or shearing action due to a fracture of the adjacent skull. These types of aneurysms may not occur immediately, but may develop over weeks or months following the insult.

A particular form of traumatic aneurysm is that which arises in, and may rupture within, the cavernous sinus. The result is a fistula or short circuit of blood from the internal carotid artery to the veins in the cavernous sinus, called a carotid-cavernous fistula. This often produces an audible sound to the patient which can be quite disturbing. It also produces a rapid-flow state in the artery below the fistula, and may even produce reversal of flow above the fistula to channel more blood through the fistula, thus producing an effect of decreased circulation to parts of the brain. Another effect may be to elevate venous pressure to a degree that may cause glaucoma of one or both eyes resulting in visual loss, and may produce hemorrhage within the brain, or even a fatal nosebleed.

The congenital or "berry" aneurysm may be present in up to two percent of adults. Aneurysms cause morbidity by spontaneous hemorrhage, usually occurring suddenly and without any warning signs. The diagnosis of ruptured aneurysms or aneurysms with the rare, but suspicious, symptoms of impending rupture (unilateral dilated pupil, new onset of severe retro-orbital or supraorbital pain) is extremely important, because of the high morbidity associated with rupture, the high risk of re-rupture in the immediate days and weeks following rupture, and the relatively good results that can often be obtained in repairing an aneurysm before rupture, when a rupture results in minimal neurological deficit.

Localized pain above or behind an eye may occur a few days to weeks before rupture occurs. Another early and more specific and objective sign of impending rupture is painless dilation of a pupil, produced as result of expansion of an aneurysm adjacent to the third (ophthalmic) cranial nerve.

Aneurysms may produce other problems other than those relating to rupture. They may produce a mass effect by slowly enlarging, much like a growth or neoplasm, and cause gradual loss of vision, interference with eye movements, or gradual weakness in an arm or leg, depending upon their location in relation to nervous structures within the cranial cavity.

When rupture of an aneurysm occurs, the person may experience symptoms ranging from a mild headache to sudden severe headache, nausea, vomiting, and loss of consciousness. When the symptoms are mild it is not unusual for both patient and physician, if the patient sees a physician, to overlook the seriousness of the symptoms. Bleeding most commonly occurs in the subarachnoid space, or the space surrounding the brain and ordinarily containing cerebrospinal fluid (CSF). Bleeding may occur directly into the brain, with or without subarachnoid bleeding. In such a case, there may be a development of weakness in an arm or leg, and progressive decrease in level of consciousness. Commonly, there will be a history of sudden physical or emotional stress, straining on defecation, or sexual orgasm concomitantly, or just prior to the rupture or hemorrhage from an aneurysm. The key point to remember about intracerebral aneurysms is that, if rupture occurs, there is a high risk of re-rupture, which gradually decreases over three to six weeks. Thus, in the patient with little or no neurological impairment following rupture of an aneurysm, the rationale for surgery is prevention of re-rupture, which has an attendant morbidity of 40 to 50%. If there is a significant brain hemorrhage, the rationale for surgery includes prevention of further brain injury and neurological deterioration. In that event the case for immediate surgery becomes stronger, depending upon the clinical condition of the patient.

Another complication of rupture of an aneurysm is ischemia, i.e., inadequate circulation to part of the brain. Ischemia is usually the result of vasospasm, a poorly understood phenomenon characterized by spasm of smooth muscle in the walls of brain arteries and arterioles. Recent work has identified abnormalities in the calcium metabolism of smooth muscle as a mechanism, and a drug that blocks calcium "channels" in smooth muscle cell membranes. Nimodipine and maintenance of adequate blood volume are believed to be effective in reducing the risk of this complication. More recently, endovascular techniques (*see* §12.05 [8] *infra*) have been successfully employed as a treatment modality in certain situations.

Although a CT scan will detect the presence of subarachnoid hemorrhage in the vast majority if cases, a lumbar puncture may be needed to confirm the presence of subarachnoid hemorrhage in the presence of a negative CT brain scan, depending upon the history and clinical examination. Large aneurysms may be seen on CT scan, MRI, or MRI angiography, but cerebral angiography is the definitive test for diagnosis and for assessing the feasibility of surgical treatment.[20]

There has been considerable debate about the timing of aneurysm surgery once rupture has occurred. In general, if the patient is doing well, or if a patient is deteriorating due to expanding brain hematoma, early operation is favored. If a patient is doing poorly as a result of ischemia and brain swelling, then operation is at high risk to increase morbidity, and it may be better to accept the risk of re-bleeding and defer surgery, because operation is much more difficult and risky if there is swollen and marginally perfused brain. Even in these cases, there has been a clear trend toward early intervention to prevent re-rupture, especially where endovascular treatment is feasible.

Another complication of subarachnoid hemorrhage is interference with cerebrospinal fluid (CSF) circulation and absorption. Ordinarily, CSF is formed in the cerebral ventricles (cavities within the brain) and circulates from the ventricles into the subarachnoid space surrounding the brain through openings in the fourth ventricle. Some of the CSF goes down and up the spinal column, around the spinal cord and nerve roots, and is absorbed into the bloodstream through small organs in the arachnoid layer, called arachnoid villi. When extensive hemorrhage occurs in the subarachnoid space, as when an aneurysm ruptures, there may be enough blood to interfere with the absorption process, to the extent that CSF pressure builds up significantly. Some fluid is actually absorbed into the brain tissue, causing increased water content of the brain (edema), which in turn causes brain swelling and neurological worsening due to increased intracranial pressure. Such a situation is generally easily treated temporarily by external ventricular drainage (EVD), utilizing placement of a small catheter into a lateral ventricle. The procedure can be done under local anesthesia, using a one- to two-centimeter incision in the scalp, a one-fourth-inch hole in the skull made with a drill, and a few special instruments. The catheter is then connected to a closed system for controlled drainage and monitoring of intracranial pressure. If the problem is longstanding, a shunt operation will be required. The hydrocephalus associated with subarachnoid hemorrhage is usually, but not always, "communicating" (*see* § 12.05 [8][b] *infra*).

The history of the surgical treatment of aneurysms is a story of many varied and unusual approaches. The present-day standard treatment of aneurysms considered amenable to such treatment is craniotomy and ligation (usually by a specially designed metal clip, but simply tying the neck of the aneurysm is an option) or wrapping or coating of the aneurysm to prevent

---

[20] Edlow JA, Caplan LR. *Avoiding Pitfalls in the diagnosis of subarachnoid hemorrhage.* N ENGL J MED 2000;342:29-36.

rupture. More recently, the endovascular approach, with placement of detachable coils to occlude the aneurysm sac is becoming more prevalent, and indeed is probably the first line of treatment if considered feasible, given the characteristics of the particular aneurysm. Occasionally, stenting is employed in conjunction with coiling if there are concerns about whether the lumen of parent of daughter vessels.

When craniotomy and clipping of the aneurysm is selected, the operating microscope and micro-instruments are virtual necessities for the surgeon who wishes to adhere to currently accepted technical standards. The use of micro-techniques has dramatically reduced surgical morbidity of aneurysm repair. The monitoring of brain function during surgery with the use of evoked cortical responses has added to our understanding of why and when morbid events occur as a result of surgery, and shows promise as a method for further reducing significant morbidity (*See* §12.06 [7], *infra*).

[b] Arteriovenous Malformations

Arteriovenous malformations (AVM) are less common than aneurysms, but they also produce subarachnoid hemorrhage and/or brain hemorrhage. These lesions do not have the high risk of rebleeding seen immediately after aneurismal rupture. Arteriovenous malformations are the result of shunting of blood through abnormal connections between the arterial and venous systems. They appear to the eye as tangles of blood vessels, and can occur in all parts of the brain or spinal cord. In addition to hemorrhage, they can present with seizures only, or they may present as a step-wise series of strokes, producing increasing neurological deficit. They may initially present as a migraine-like syndrome. They can usually be diagnosed by CT scan or magnetic resonance imaging (MRI), but generally require angiography for definitive diagnosis and the planning of treatment. The so-called "occult" AVM may be discovered only after microscopic examination of the tissue and is not identifiable in vivo by cerebral angiography.

A multitude of treatments has been proposed for AVM's, including microsurgical craniotomy and excision, coagulation with laser, proton-beam or focused-beam gamma irradiation (techniques designed to deliver very high doses of radiation to deep, discrete areas in the brain with relatively little damage to surrounding structures), and endovascular techniques, including embolization, sometimes used adjunctively or in concert with other treatments.

[c] Extracranial Cerebrovascular Disease

Another major area of cerebrovascular surgery is treatment of occlusive (usually atherosclerotic) disease. Extracranial procedures, which involve the opening of vessels in the neck, and removing of atheromatous plaques or other obstructive lesions (the source of small emboli) have been in existence for thirty to forty years. The most common such operation is carotid endarterectomy. Many neurosurgeons continue to perform carotid endarterectomies, but probably the vast majority of these procedures has been performed by vascular surgeons or general surgeons with expertise in vascular surgery. What was not appreciated in the early years of this operation, is that although atheromatous carotid lesions are present in many patients who present with transient ischemic attacks (transient neurological deficits of less than 24 hours' duration), there may be other causes of the symptoms, which too often are not discovered unless the intracranial and extracranial vessels are thoroughly studied with angiography.

[d] Other Cerebrovascular Disease

A more exclusive domain of the cerebrovascular neurosurgeon involves extracranial-intracranial reconstructive procedures. This surgery involves the use of vein or other bypass grafts from neck vessels to intracranial vessels and is often done in conjunction with vascular surgeons, using a team approach. This surgery is similar in concept and rationale to that of coronary artery bypass surgery, and involves bypassing occluded or partially occluded vessels to improve brain circulation or eliminate symptoms of brain ischemia. The much-popularized superficial temporal artery-to-middle cerebral artery (STA-MCA) bypass, which was widely performed in the early 1980s, has all but disappeared as a result of a cooperative study published in 1985.[21] Almost immediately after the results of that study appeared in print, insurers would not pay for the procedure, and the frequency of the STA-MCA bypasses dropped dramatically.

There continues to be a place for extracranial-intracranial reconstructive procedures, but they are limited to special types of problems. In most cases, such procedures probably should be limited to centers where advanced diagnostic capabilities and multidisciplinary care are available.

There are a number of conditions characterized by inflammatory or other processes that produce occlusion of intra- or extracranial vessels, predisposing to

---

[21] The EC-IC Bypass Study Group, *Failure of Extracranial-Intracranial Arterial Bypass to Reduce the Risk of Ischemic Stroke*, 313 N. ENG. J. MED. 1191-1200 (1985). *See also* Ausman, J.I. et al., *Critique of the Extracranial-Intracranial Bypass Study*, 26 SURG. NEUROL. 218-221 (1986).

either hemorrhage or multiple infarcts. Treatment is usually directed toward the underlying cause. In the case of Moya-moya disease, various re-vascularization procedures, including STA-MCA by-pass, have shown some benefit.

[3] Functional Neurosurgery

[a] In General

The term "functional," as used here, refers to a *strategy*, i.e., treating disease indirectly by affecting *function* and not necessarily directly attacking the disease itself. Stereotactic neurosurgery refers to a *technique* of surgery commonly used in functional neurosurgery. The two terms are often linked together, however, not because they are two like things, but because many of the activities of the one overlap with those of the other.

Functional neurosurgery, then, is a strategy concerned with altering nervous system function in some way in order to alleviate symptoms and improve quality of life in a person with some disease, but not necessarily a neurological disease. Subsequently, techniques have been developed for alleviation of pain, the abolition or reduction of tremors, involuntary movements, and spasticity, and the treatment of epilepsy, among others. Functional neurosurgery usually involves the ablation or removal of a normal structure (or some part or product of a normal structure) to achieve a therapeutic result, or it involves augmentation of a function or product of some normal structure or organ to achieve a beneficial result. Perhaps the most widely used technique of functional neurosurgery is electrical stimulation.[22] Or, it may simply involve a surgical procedure for delivering a drug to the nervous system, such as an indwelling pump to deliver drugs like morphine or baclofen into the nervous system in a way more effective and with fewer side effects than if given by mouth or injection.

Ablative procedures include frontal lobotomy, cutting, heating, or damaging in some other way certain areas in the brain, spinal cord, or peripheral nerves for the purpose of relieving pain, spasticity, or for some other reason. Just as the advent of Thorazine (chlorpromazine) dramatically reduced the incidence of lobotomies and similar procedures, the advent of L-dopa dramatically reduced the use of various lesions made to treat Parkinson's disease.

Augmentative procedures are those designed to enhance or increase function of an organ or structure and thereby produce alleviation of symptoms or improvement in function. Such procedures involve electrodes

---

[22] Racine, E, et al, *"Currents of hope": neurostimulation techniques in U.S. and U.K. print media*, CAMB Q HEALTHC ETHICS 2007;16:312-16.

to stimulate areas in the brain thought to be responsible for producing endorphins, which enhance the brain's normal process of relieving pain. Electrical stimulation of nerves and the spinal cord has been thought to alleviate certain types of pain. The administration of dopamine into certain areas of the brain has been believed to be beneficial in controlling the symptoms of Parkinson's disease. Also, the experimental procedure of transplanting adrenal medulla or fetal brain tissue cells into basal ganglia in the brain is believed to be effective in alleviating the symptoms of Parkinson's disease.

Although stereotactic surgery is often employed in functional neurosurgery, and owes its early development to its application in functional neurosurgery, it really has a much wider application today. Before the advent of computerized tomography (CT) scanning and computer technology linking CT imaging to stereotactic instruments, and after psychosurgery and surgery for Parkinson's disease declined as a result of pharmacological advances, stereotactic surgery was almost a lost art. With the introduction of CT and MRI imaging, it became almost immediately obvious that the combined technology of C and MRI imaging and the stereotactic technique would enable surgeons to pinpoint, with a high degree of accuracy, small areas anywhere in the brain. Prior to the advent of CT and MRI technology, small, deep lesions in the brain could not be detected. The stereotactic technique was needed, however, to gain access to the lesion or treat it, once it was identified. Other imaging techniques, such as angiography have further enhanced the capacity for stereotaxy to assist the surgeon in the treatment of disease, not just in functional neurosurgery, but in the areas of tumor biopsy, semi-robotic laser surgery, radiosurgery (the use of high-dose discrete dosages of radiation to targets in the brain), placement of electrodes, and transplantation.

The stereotactic technique is quite simple in concept. A target in the brain is selected (it could be a particular neural structure, a tumor, an arteriovenous malformation, an abscess, or other locus of disease or planned site of implantation) and its three-dimensional relationship to externally fixed coordinates or reference points is identified. This is done by attaching a specially designed frame outside the head, usually fixed to the skull by pins (this can be done under local anesthesia). The patient then undergoes CT or MRI scan, and the exact relationship of the coordinates on the external frame to the target are established and stored in the computer. Using the external frame as a reference, biopsy instruments, radiosurgical apparatus, or a laser beam may then be directed to the target with high precision. The operator may or may not work under direct vision. If not, he or she will be working much like the pilot "flying on instruments," with the ability to reach small targets deep within the brain through a small opening in the skull the size of a dime) or, in the case of radiosurgery, through *no* opening).

Within the last few years, with rapid advances in imaging technology, so-called frameless stereotaxy and other image-guided navigational systems have become widespread. It is now feasible for the operator to perform surgery outside of the operative field with the use of robotic instruments and navigational systems. While such surgery is not commonly used in neurosurgery practice settings, its use is likely to expand as more and more neurosurgeons become skilled in the techniques.

[b] Movement Disorders and Spasticity

With advances in technique and increased knowledge of nervous system function, the general approach to the treatment of movement disorders has trended toward augmentative procedures, and away from ablative techniques. Intracranial procedures have largely been deep brain stimulation, with implanted electrodes connected to a subcutaneous stimulator that can be controlled by an external transmitter. Controlled injection of neurotransmitters (chemicals with specific effects on neural transmission), and implantation of embryonic or adrenal tissue are less common, and more in the realm of experimental procedures.

Perhaps the most common movement disorder is Parkinson's disease, but the movement disorder in Parkinson's disease is only one component of this condition, which has other debilitating features. There is a number of other movement disorders, and the details of treatment depend upon the specific disorder.

The use of implanted spinal cord stimulators and intrathecal pumps can relieve spasticity. The management of these devices requires close attention, as increased neurological deficit can result from a malpositioned catheter.[23] Pump malfunction can result in adverse drug effects.[24]

[c] Psychiatric Disorders

Perhaps the earliest functional neurosurgery carried out by neurosurgeons was the frontal lobotomy, the rationale for which was that it made some

---

[23] Levin, GZ, and Tabor, DR, *Paraplegia secondary to progressive necrotic myelopathy in a patient with an implanted morphine pump*, AM J PHYS MED REABIL 2005 Mar;84(3):193-6. *See also*, Shell, M, et al, *Conversion disorder presenting in a patient with an implantable morphine pump and an epidural abscess resulting in paraplegia*, ARCHIVES OF PHYSICAL MEDICINE AND REHABILITATION , 1997;78:226 - 229.

[24] Shirley, KW, et al, *Intrathecal baclofen overdose and withdrawal*, PEDIATR EMERG CARE 2006 Apr;22(4):258-61.

patients easier to care for in the institutional setting or permitted them to be discharged to home care. Frontal lobotomies evolved into procedures designed to destroy specific areas of the brain. The procedures were though to produce the desired therapeutic effect but cause fewer undesirable side effects. Research into the area of surgical treatment of mental illness continues to be highly controversial.

In the late 1940s and early 1950s, the desire to destroy more discrete brain structures led to the introduction of stereotactic techniques for the destruction of targets in the brain, the instillation of psychoactive chemicals directly into certain areas of the brain, and the use of electrodes for stimulation of certain brain structures, all for the purpose of altering behavior or alleviating symptoms.

As in other areas of functional neurosurgery, the trend has been toward augmentative procedures, principally deep brain stimulation, and toward narrower and more specific indications.

[d] Seizure Disorders

Resection of damaged cerebral cortex remains a mainstay of the treatment of seizure disorders refractory to medical treatment. Cerebral hemispherectomy performed in children can be very successful and result in surprisingly little long-term deficit. Deep brain stimulation and vagal nerve stimulation using implanted electrodes and stimulators are also employed.

[e] Pain

Deep brain stimulation, spinal cord stimulation, and implanted pumps that deliver intrathecal morphine remain in common use. *See* §12.05 [1] *supra.*

[4] Pediatric Neurological Surgery

[a] In General

The practice of pediatric neurological surgery differs mainly in the spectrum of the diseased treated. With a few exceptions, the underlying principles and techniques employed in adult surgery are the same. Of course, the maxim that children, particularly infants, "are not just small adults" holds true; the neurosurgeon has to deal through the patient's parents and is presented with a different set of ethical problems and difficult issues of informed consent. Also, in pediatric neurological surgery, there is a larger patient population with congenital defects and anomalies, and many of these problems need immediate treatment when discovered.

[b] Spina Bifida

Spina bifida refers to a whole range of congenital birth defects that involve the incomplete fusion of the posterior or dorsal aspect of the nervous system, its covering, and its supporting structures in embryological development. Such embryological failure may occur on the head or at some portion of the spine. It may involve only some of the bone structures of the spine, producing *spina bifida occulta,* or it may involve failure of closure of the neural canal, where the child is born with an open spine with portions of an abnormally developed and poorly functional spinal cord and nerve roots herniated into a sac, the so-called myelomeningocele. Failure of skin closure, or rupture of the myelomeningocele may occur, causing neural elements to be exposed to the outside and thus vulnerable to infection of the entire central nervous system. Such children often have spinal deformities and partial or complete paralysis below the level of the defect. In addition, there may be similar abnormalities involving the brain.

The most common concurrent problem with spina bifida is hydrocephalus (enlargement of cerebral ventricles because of obstruction of the flow of cerebrospinal fluid from the ventricles to the point where it is absorbed into the bloodstream, *see* §12.05 [4][c] and §12.05 [8][c], *infra*).

The goal of surgical treatment in spina bifida cases is to minimize contamination and provide closure to prevent infection, thereby preserving as much function as possible. Management of hydrocephalus in spina bifida patients with myelomeningocele is difficult because of the high risks of infection and the need to maintain optimal decompression of the cerebral ventricular system. Overly aggressive intervention with shunting runs an increased risk of infection, since the presence of shunt tubing (a foreign body) makes it virtually impossible for the body to clear contaminating organisms. This is particularly true in newborns, who are immunologically immature. On the other hand, avoidance of shunting or drainage procedures runs the risk of impaired brain function and development.

Difficult decisions often must be made regarding treatment of children severely affected by spina bifida. It is critical for parents to be fully informed of the expectations with neurosurgical treatment, particularly in situations where decisions need to be made within hours, since such decisions can profoundly affect the outcome years later. Not uncommonly, the parents of these children, already traumatized by the shock of their child having been born with a severe neurological defect, simply do not recall what they were told by the neurosurgeon and may claim that they were told nothing, or that they were told something completely different from what was actually said. It is well to examine all available records before relying too strongly on the family's account of conversations with the treating physicians.

The discovery that folic acid deficiency in pregnancy causes spina bifida, and the administration of folic acid in a dose of 400 mcg (micrograms) a day to women of child-bearing age has resulted in a dramatic reduction in the incidence of this condition.[25]

[c] Hydrocephalus

The treatment of hydrocephalus is rather simple in concept, but often very difficult in practice. The basic approach is to decompress the ventricular system by bypassing obstructive fluid pathways. The term hydrocephalus (literally, *water head*) means that the cerebrospinal fluid (CSF)- containing spaces in the head are enlarged for some reason. This can occur as a result of absent or atrophied brain tissue, with CSF simply filling up the space that remains (hydrocephalus *ex vacuo*). The condition can be external (outside the brain), or internal (inside the brain or consisting of ventricular enlargement). For practical purposes, the term hydrocephalus today refers to internal hydrocephalus, i.e., enlarged ventricles, with or without enlargement of the head itself. In children, the bones making up the skull are separated by spaces called sutures, which fuse in the late teens, and the primary determinant of an increase in head size in the normal situation is growth of the brain. If, in addition, if there is enlargement of the ventricles due to backup of CSF, the gross volume of the brain increases abnormally in size, causing the skull to increase abnormally in size. In extreme cases of untreated hydrocephalus, nowadays a rarity, the head size can increase to be as much as two feet in diameter. Even small abnormal increases in head size are a relatively late sign of hydrocephalus, but do not necessarily mean that significant irreversible brain damage has occurred.

After the skull bones fuse together in the late teens (or earlier, in the so-called shunt-dependency syndrome seen in children who have had shunts placed at an early age) the head does not enlarge further, but in the presence of hydrocephalus the ventricles will continue to enlarge and produce increases in intracranial pressure with progressive visual loss and secondary brain injury to an even more rapidly progressive and advanced degree. Particularly in the case of shunt dependency, neurological deterioration can be precipitous and lack of immediate attention may result in fatality or severe neurological deficit.

Although all hydrocephalus is in a sense obstructive, the disorder is commonly subdivided into "obstructive" or "noncommunicating" and "nonobstructive" or "communicating." This distinction simply refers to whether there is a free connection or communication between the CSF in the

---

[25] http://www.cdc.gov/ncbddd/folicacid/overview.htm (last access 6/1/08).

ventricular system and that in the spinal subarachnoid space, or perhaps, in a broader sense, whether there is some blockage of circulation of CSF, or whether for some reason the mechanism of absorption of CSF into the bloodstream via the arachnoid villi is impaired. It is an important distinction, because in the case of communicating hydrocephalus, a lumbar puncture can temporarily relieve the increased pressure of hydrocephalus, and fluid can be shunted from the spinal subarachnoid space into the peritoneal cavity, effectively treating the hydrocephalus. In obstructive or non-communicating hydrocephalus, a lumbar puncture could produce a *catastrophic deterioration*. What happens is that, following removal of CSF from the lumbar subarachnoid space, the CSF may flow out of the cisterns or spaces around the brain and brain stem, causing brain structures to herniate into the space vacated by the CSF and producing pressure on respiratory centers in the brain stem, resulting in a vicious cycle of inadequate respiration, brain swelling, and death.

[d] Shunt Procedures and Complications

Treatment of hydrocephalus needs to be tailored to the individual situation, so that CSF is not allowed to build up under pressure in one part of the brain, while fluid is being withdrawn from another part of the head, a situation that could produce shifting and compression of brain structures (herniation). Obstructive hydrocephalus can result from a cyst or tumor that blocks one or more of the channels through which CSF flows within the brain. While shunting is an option if the obstruction cannot be relieved (such as occlusion of the aqueduct of Sylvius, a narrow passage that connects the third to the fourth ventricle), treatment is ideally directed toward correcting the underlying abnormality.

Endoscopic third ventriculostomy is a treatment option for some types of hydrocephalus, and avoids the need for shunting. A rare, but often fatal complication of this procedure is injury to the basilar artery.[26]

Communicating hydrocephalus is usually characterized by failure of CSF absorption at the level of the arachnoid villi, i.e. where it normally enters the bloodstream. Common causes are meningitis and subarachnoid hemorrhage.

Shunting procedures for hydrocephalus utilize the establishment of a free passageway between spaces where CSF is producing abnormal pressures, to allow fluid to be diverted to an area or space where it can be absorbed into the bloodstream. This may be accomplished simply by surgically creating an opening between the pool of backed-up CSF (for example, endoscopic third

---

[26] Abtin, K, et al, *Case Report: Basilar Artery Perforation as a Complication of Endoscopic Third Ventriculostomy*, PEDIATRIC NEUROSURGERY 1998;28:35-4.

ventriculostomy as described above), and the absorbing spaces, but more commonly requires implantation of a tube to drain CSF from the ventricule directly into the bloodstream (ventriculoatrial shunt) or from the ventricle or subarachnoid space into the peritoneal cavity (ventriculoperitoneal shunt).

There is a wide range of devices on the market designed for shunting CSF.

Not uncommonly, shunts occlude or malfunction and often require revisions, sometimes many times over the life of the patient. Special problems are presented in cases of shunt malfunction. Malfunction usually results from occlusion of some part of the shunt system, sometimes the result of otherwise unrecognized infection. Shunt occlusion can produce rapid neurological deterioration. In other instances, a chronic shunt obstruction can result in visual loss. Over-drainage of CSF can result in collection of fluid or blood between the brain and the dura, potentially requiring surgical evacuation of a subdural hematoma.

[e] Other Congenital Abnormalities

Another difficult problem in neurosurgery is in the area of craniofacial abnormalities. These conditions usually do not require emergency treatment, and present primarily because of severe cosmetic defects; however, correction of the deformities involved may also allow for improved brain development and prevention of seizures and retardation. The procedures performed are often extensive and involve lengthy operations requiring a team of neurosurgeons, plastic surgeons and possibly ENT surgeons.

An important point to remember about congenital craniofacial abnormalities is that congenital malformations and other structural defects of the brain can occur concomitantly and may not be affected by the surgical procedures performed primarily for cosmetic reasons.

[f] Neoplasms

The use of whole-brain irradiation and neuraxis irradiation (irradiation of the whole brain and spine) in children has a place in the treatment of certain types of neoplasms, but in children it also has the potential for long-term effects. For that reason, in pediatric neurosurgery, there is a greater tendency to attempt surgical cure of certain neoplasms, combined with close follow-up for recurrence. Understandably, then, the desire to avoid radiation in favor of a more radical and therefore risky procedure is a justifiable course of management. Most neurosurgeons recognize the need in these cases to explain and document the reasons for their recommendations to the patient's family.

[g] Spine Surgery in Children

Because there are many factors affecting normal growth of the spine, surgical procedures performed on the spine in children may have significant effects on the growth and development of the spine as the child matures. Extensive laminectomy for removal of tumors, non-neoplastic cystic lesions, or traumatic lesions, may have a devastating effect on development and produce severe scoliosis or other spinal deformity. Primarily for that reason, there has been an attempt in children to preserve, as much as possible, the integrity of the spine, by replacing the spinal laminae and posterior spinous processes after a laminectomy.

Another problem in pediatric neurosurgery is the spinal injury that produces instability and requires some form of external fixation. The usual "halo device," which is applied by screwing pins through the outer table of the skull, involves risk of penetrating the skull in small children, and external fixation in casts and Minerva jackets have been more often employed.

[5] Spine Surgery

Although most lay persons equate neurosurgery with brain surgery, most procedures in neurosurgery performed by the average practitioner involve surgery of the spine. Most of the procedures in the spine are for some form of degenerative disease or disc herniation.

The human spine can be divided into the cervical, thoracic, and lumbar spine, plus the sacrum. Each of these areas, while generally susceptible to the same disease processes, has its own peculiarities, which require different strategies and approaches to surgical treatment.

[a] Cervical Spine

The cervical spine consists of seven vertebrae, C1 through C7, which descend from the base of the skull to the thoracic region. The first cervical vertebra has a peculiar relationship to C2 (the axis), in that the odontoid process of C2 projects into the ring of C1 (the atlas) anterior to the spinal cord. The articulations between the base of the skull, C1, and C2 form a segment that is responsible for most of the rotational movement of the skull on the rest of the body. The C1-C2 segment is most often affected by either trauma or rheumatoid disease, and instability at this level can produce acute or chronic compromise of cord function. If severe enough, such instability can acutely compromise respiratory function and cause death.

The C2 through C7 vertebrae articulate with each other by means of discs, anterior to the spinal cord, and the paired facet joints, one on each side, situated posterolaterally to the cord. Eight pairs of cervical nerve roots, C1 through C8, emerge , one on each side, through the neural foramen, between the base of the skull and the C1 vertebra (C1 root), and so on, with the C8 root emerging between the C7 vertebra and the first thoracic vertebra. These cervical nerve roots carry nerve impulses to and from the diaphragm, the upper extremities, and the neck and posterior scalp.

In the lower cervical spine, the anterior approach is much easier than in the lumbar or thoracic region, since the anterior surface of the spine is easily reached by separating neck structures. This is the approach preferred by most neurological surgeons for the management of herniated cervical discs. However, the laminectomy, or posterior approach, is still widely used for disc problems, and appears to have comparably good results with those of the anterior approach. Most cervical disc herniations are at the lower two levels (C5-6 and C6-7).

Anterior approach to the spine above C3 becomes difficult because of the jaw and pharyngeal structures, and it is not needed very often. At the level of C2, C1, and the skull base, direct approach by incising the posterior wall of the pharynx is employed when necessary. If the posterior approach is needed, laminectomy at any level of the cervical spine can provide adequate exposure.

Misdiagnosis of cervical spine injuries continues to be problematic,[27] and provides a strong incentive for defensive medicine, which, in turn, tends to establish a false standard of care. That is, studies done "medical-legal" reasons may not have sound indications as evidence-based medicine.

[b] Thoracic Spine

The thoracic vertebrae, T1 through T12, differ in that they articulate with and support twelve pairs of ribs, one on each side. As in the neck, the vertebrae are irregularly shaped bony rings, with three points of articulation with the vertebrae above and below (i.e., the intervertebral disc and two facet joints, as in the cervical spine). In addition, as in the neck, several supporting ligaments give added strength and stability to the spine and provide protection for the spinal cord, which descends in the canal thus formed. One feature of the thoracic spine is that the rib cage appears to provide an added measure of stability and protection to the thoracic spine, not enjoyed by the cervical and lumbar spines, which bear most of the stresses of movement of

---

[27] Lekovic GP, Harrington TR, *Litigation of missed cervical spine injuries in patients presenting with blunt traumatic injury* NEUROSURGERY 2007 Mar;60(3):516-22; discussion 522-3.

the spine. Twelve pairs of thoracic nerves, T1 through T12, emerge from between the T1 and T2 vertebrae to between T12 and the first lumbar vertebrae, and, by and large, provide motor and sensory function to muscles of the trunk, as well as to the viscera and skin of the trunk.

Because of the presence of the spinal cord in the thoracic spine, disc surgery is quite different in the thoracic region and upper one or two levels in the lumbar spine, than in the lower lumbar spine (90 to 95% of herniated discs in the lumbar spine are at L4-5 or at L5-S1). One cannot safely use the same technique of retraction on the dural sac in the thoracic region, because the spinal cord is less vulnerable to manipulation than a single nerve root, which is much more mobile. In addition, the usual indication for thoracic disc surgery is spinal cord encroachment, or compression, rather than single nerve root compression. As a result, the disc, situated anterior to the spinal cord, must be approached in such a way as to avoid the need for any retraction or pressure on the spinal cord. The various approaches used may require removal of part of a rib or ribs, or may entail an approach through the chest cavity. The above also applies to operations for conditions other than herniated discs. Of course, when the problem (cyst or tumor, for example) is posterior to the spinal cord, a laminectomy (removal of the posterior bony arches of the vertebrae), for instance, is quite appropriate and is the easier procedure.

[c] Lumbosacral Spine

In the embryo and the newborn, the spinal cord may be present through most of the lumbar spine; however, as the infant grows during the first two years of life, the relationship of the spinal cord to the spine changes, and usually by the age of two, the end of the spinal cord is at about the L1-L2 vertebral level. That is, at the L2 level and below, in an adult, there are only nerve roots in the lower lumbar spinal canal, and no spinal cord. Occasionally, surgeons will describe seeing the "cord" at a lower lumbar level when preparing an operative report, and this usually represents an erroneous reference to the *dural sac*, which is a tough, thin membrane lining the inside of the spinal canal and enclosing the bundle of nerve roots as they travel within the canal to the neural foramina (from which they exit). The L1 through L5 nerve roots carry motor and sensory impulses to and from muscles and sense organs of the lower extremities and exit between the L1 and L2 vertebrae (L1 root) to between L5 and the sacrum (L5 nerve roots). In addition, all of the nerve roots from the sacral segments of the cord (located at the T12 and L1 bony vertebral level of the spine) travel in the lumbar spinal canal into the sacral canal, where they exit through five pairs of foramina (S1 through S5) and supply motor and sensory function to the perineum, and control bowel and bladder function. The sacrum is a single bone and makes up part of the pelvis.

Occasionally, there may be six lumbar vertebrae, or four or five lumbar vertebrae and a so-called "transitional vertebra," which may look partly like an articulated upper sacral segment and partly like a typical lumber vertebra. One physician might refer to a transitional vertebra as L5 or L6 (depending upon the anatomical configuration), another as S1, and still another as a transitional vertebra. *Where there is mention of four or six lumbar vertebrae, and/or the presence of a transitional vertebra, it is very important to be aware of the possibility of confusion relating to nomenclature, which in turn, raises the risk of wrong-level surgery.* In cases where surgery may have been performed at the wrong level, it is critical to determine from operative reports and postoperative studies just what level was operated upon, rather than relying solely on reports of imaging studies. With six lumbar vertebrae, such determination can be confusing, just as it may be to an operating surgeon, and there may be apparent contradictions (or apparent correlations) that are erroneous, in multiple radiological reports and in operative notes. For example, a surgeon may describe doing surgery at L4-5, and mean by this that it was between the first and second vertebrae above the sacrum, but the radiologist may have described a disc herniation at being between L5 and L6, with L6 being the first of six typical lumbar vertebrae above the sacrum, yet both may be referring to the same level. Of course, it can work the other way, i.e., each may designate a different level by the same numbers, inadvertently numbering the vertebrae differently.

[i] Lumbar disc disease

Perhaps one of the greatest misconceptions on the part of lay persons is the belief that most back pain is the result of a surgically treatable herniated lumbar disc. Undeniably, the surgical treatment of a herniated disc can often result in significant improvement in back pain, as well as pain occurring as a result of nerve root compression; however, most back pain is the result of a combination of factors that may involve degenerative disc disease, facet arthropathy, or other degenerative changes in the spine that may or may not be caused by severe or repeated undue stress on the spine that affects the individual's perception of pain and its relationship to perceived disability. Most back pain is an extremely complex phenomenon related to many factors, is poorly understood, and usually is not susceptible to an easy cure. Because of the tremendous economic significance of back pain in the United States, and perhaps because of the way in which insurance coverage for back pain is structured (often through worker's compensation), and because of the sheer volume of people who seek treatment for back pain, many segments of the medical and chiropractic communities readily offer treatment of one form or another for such pain. Neurosurgeons, like any group with certain areas of expertise, tend to look for those cases that can be treated successfully with the form of treatment they know best.

Lumbar disc excision is probably the most common operation performed by neurosurgeons. There are many approaches and techniques, and the operator generally uses the techniques he or she is most familiar with. The indications for surgery in lumbar disc disease are varied, but the most common is pain caused by compression of a nerve root by displaced (herniated) disc material as it exits the spine. The basic approach is exposure of the herniation at the point where it impinges upon the nerve root, and removal of the herniated disc material, as well as other disc material considered a risk for further herniation. Perhaps the most common complaint after disc surgery is failure of the pain to be relieved. Unfortunately, the reasons for persistent pain following lumbar disc surgery are not always clear.

Recently, procedures designed to accomplish the objectives of disc surgery without doing an open operation have been used. Chymopapain or other enzymes, injected via a long needle placed within the disc space to dissolve the disc material and thus cause its retraction back into the disc space, had a brief period of popularity in the United States in the early 1980s, but this procedure is used far less often at the time of this writing. Undesirable complications, including brain and/or subarachnoid hemorrhage, chemical discitis, and severe lumbar spasms may have been part of the reason. In addition, other procedures have been developed, whereby a large needle-like instrument can be placed into the disc space under local anesthesia, and disc material sonicated (disintegrated with the use of ultrasound) and aspirated automatically. This is the so-called automated percutaneous discectomy.

More recently, minimally-invasive techniques of lumbar discectomy have come into wide sue. The principles underlying the management of disc disease are by and large the same.

Occasionally, large disc herniations can compromise multiple nerve roots within the lumbar spinal canal and cause loss of bowel, bladder, and sexual functions. When this occurs, it is ordinarily a matter of surgical urgency, and delays in treatment, sometimes only a few hours, can greatly affect the prognosis for recovery of function.

[ii] Other degenerative conditions of the lumbar spine

Degenerative processes working in concert with lumbar disc degeneration may produce single or multiple nerve root compression by (1) thickened ligaments and bony excrescenses or spurs in the foramen (bony opening) where the nerve root exits the spine, or (2) narrowing the lumbar spinal canal, thus compressing *all* the nerve roots passing through the canal and affecting strength or sensation in both legs, as well as bowel and bladder function.

[iii] Nontraumatic instability of the lumbar spine

This condition may occur from congenital problems, the most common being spondylolysis (defects in the posterior bony element of a vertebra), which may or may not produce spondylolisthesis (a manifestation of instability such that one vertebra slips forward over the one below it, occasionally compressing nerve roots or causing pain not due to nerve root compression). This may occasionally need some form of stabilization, ranging from a brace to operative fusion to prevent progressive slippage and to restore stability. Fusion is usually accomplished by placing bone between the vertebrae to be fused. In addition, some surgeons employ internal fixation with specially designed metal devices. Frequently, such procedures are carried out in conjunction with orthopedic surgeons, depending upon the expertise and experience of the neurosurgeon.

Instability also commonly occurs as a result of degenerative disease and can be a complication of inflammation, infections, or malignancy. The principles of treatment are the same, taking into consideration the particular disease process responsible.

[d] Spine Infections

Spine infections that may require surgical treatment are abscesses within the spinal canal and osteomyelitis. Abscesses within the spinal canal compress the spinal cord or nerve roots and produce progressive loss of neurological function. In the face of neurological deficit, antibiotic treatment alone probably will be ineffective, and operative drainage of the abscess is almost always required to avoid further compromise of neurological function. Often improvement can be dramatic, but the longer neurological deficit progresses, the worse the prognosis for full recovery. Most abscesses requiring surgical treatment are epidural, i.e., within the spinal canal, but outside the dura mater. Fever, local spine pain and tenderness, focal neurological deficit, and radiographic and/or magnetic resonance imaging (MRI) evidence of a mass are virtually diagnostic in most cases.

Osteomyelitis is infection involving the bone of the vertebra itself, and, like epidural abscess, may occur spontaneously or postoperatively. It may be concurrent with epidural abscess. If there is not severe bone destruction and deformity, and if there is no neurological deficit, osteomyelitis may be treated with antibiotics, but if the disease is refractory to antibiotic treatment or if severe deformity or neurological problems develop in the face of treatment, it may be necessary to remove the infected bone and replace it with a bone graft in conjunction with internal fixation.

[e] Neoplastic Diseases

Benign or malignant neoplasms can occur in the spine, epidural space, dura mater, spinal cord, or nerve roots within the spine. Metastatic tumors of the spine can destroy bone and affect stability. They most commonly arise in the epidural space and produce spinal cord or cauda equina compression. Most metastatic tumors respond (more or less) to radiation treatment, and if detected before neurological deficit occurs, operation may be avoided. Sometimes, epidural metastasis with spinal cord compression is the first sign of a malignant tumor elsewhere in the body. All too commonly, localized spine pain has been present for weeks or months, and the patient is first seen by the neurosurgeon only after rapidly progressing paralysis has developed and an emergency operation is required. The ready availability of MRI scanning has greatly reduced the frequency with which this scenario occurs.

Benign tumors within the spinal canal, but not in the spinal cord itself, usually respond well to surgical treatment. If the tumor is within the substance of the cord, operation becomes much more risky. However, with present-day techniques, the trend is for neurosurgeons to be more aggressive with this type of tumor, especially in younger people, because the long-term side effects of radiation therapy can often include some neurological deficit as well as well as alteration of growth and development of the spine, producing delayed deformity. In other words, current thinking tends to favor a more aggressive procedure with increased chance of cure, rather than a more conservative operation with the hope that radiation therapy will delay or eliminate further manifestations of tumor growth. An accurate assessment of the type of tumor involved is an extremely important factor in determining the extent to which a radical surgical approach is employed.

[f] Vascular Lesions

Arteriovenous malformations (AVM) of the spinal cord, like those in the brain, may bleed, or they may produce a gradual, step-wise neurological worsening that often has been confused with multiple sclerosis. These lesions usually can be readily diagnosed with the imaging techniques available today, i.e., myelogram with CT scan, magnetic resonance imaging (MRI), and spinal cord angiography. Surgical treatment of a spinal cord AVM involves great risk, as does even the necessary diagnostic procedure of spinal cord angiography. With the use of microsurgical techniques and evoked potential monitoring (*see* §12.06 [7], *infra*), the risks of surgical treatment have been reduced, but remain substantial.

[g] Trauma

The management of spine injuries is a veritable mine field for the neurosurgeon. Nowhere in neurosurgery is the practitioner faced with so many decisions in which it is extremely difficult to weigh the high risks of options. Recent work appears to show that if mega-doses of methylprednisolone (a synthetic glucocorticoid) are given within eight hours of injury, the chance of a significantly better outcome is increased. Nonetheless, one must recognize that many severe and complete spinal cord injuries will still have no improvement even under optimal treatment circumstances, because the original trauma produced complete and irreparable cord injury. For the most part, it will be the *partial* spinal cord injury that will improve, given the opportunity afforded by proper treatment of the accompanying spinal column injury (so that secondary cord injury does not occur).

When a spinal cord is injured, some damage is sustained at the time of impact, i.e., disruption of nerve fibers, and also as a result of changes that occur in the cord tissue itself, initiated by the impact. In the first few hours following a blunt spinal cord injury, microhemorrhages and leakage of fluid into the interstitial spaces occur, causing swelling of the spinal cord tissue, and there may be progression of neurological deficit from a mild paralysis to a severe paralysis, even in the absence of any ongoing spinal cord compression. It is these changes that megadose methylprednisolone appears to ameliorate.

Although there is much controversy about what should be done (and when) in the management of spinal injury, the underlying concepts are simple: The goal of treatment is to prevent secondary injury or insult to the cord. Sometimes the only suspicion of a spinal cord injury is the known mechanism of an injury, particularly if the patient is unconscious. The first line of management is to stabilize the spine; in general, this is done, where practical, as soon as injury to the spine or spinal cord is suspected. The next tactic is to determine if any encroachment or distraction of the cord exists, such as might produce further neurological deficit. Herniated disc, epidural bleeding, or compromise by mobile dislocated vertebrae or bone fragments are examples of conditions that can compromise the spinal cord further, and if these are recognized and treated appropriately, the chance of recovery can be improved, and the chance of worsening as a result of secondary spinal cord injury can be reduced. How vigorously a practitioner carries out diagnostic studies is often a judgment call, depending upon how strongly spine and spinal cord injury is suspected, and how feasible it is to carry out studies in the presence of other more certain and possible life-threatening injuries. If compression of the cord or spine instability exists, measures should be undertaken to correct the problems identified. Again, the timing depends upon many factors, including the presence of neurological deficit, whether the deficit is getting better or worse, the priority of treatment for other injuries, and how well stability can be achieved by external fixation measures.

The concepts are simple in these injuries: recognition, medical treatment and decompression of the injured cord, and stabilization of the spine. But it is tremendously difficult to manage spinal cord injuries in practice.

[h] Disc Disease

Disc disease (*Also see* §12.05 [5] [c][*i*]-[*iii*], *supra*), is a poorly understood condition that is multi-factorial in its etiologies. While trauma may often have a significant role in its cause or evolution, the relationship to trauma may be overblown because of the not-uncommon situation where there may be insurance coverage for injury (i.e., workers compensation, or accident), but not for non-compensable injury, particularly where surgery or prolonged disability are factors.

Undoubtedly, there are important genetic factors at play in a large percentage of cases. The role of long-standing tobacco use, and other co-morbidities is less well-defined, but likely to be significant.

[i] Complications of Spine Surgery

Neurological complications of spine surgery may be due to direct injury to neural elements, i.e., spinal cord or nerve, or to delayed injury as a result of various complications such as hemorrhage, infection, compression due to instability, or dislodgement of a bone graft. Infection may produce its results by mass effect, i.e., abscess, or by meningitis that can occur as a result of contamination from cerebrospinal fluid leak.

The risk of direct injury to neural structures has been reduced as a result of microsurgical techniques, bipolar coagulation, and neurophysiological monitoring techniques (*See* §12.06 [8], *infra*). Another important factor in reducing direct neural injury is the recognition that conditions need to be approached as directly as possible with minimal manipulation of neural tissue: i.e., a mass anterior to the spinal cord should generally be approached by the anterior, or lateral, and not the posterior, approach.

Although surgeons differ widely in their preference of techniques, some techniques entail, in a particular situation, significantly more risk of serious injury than others with which the surgeon should be familiar. In other words, a technique generally accepted by surgeons in most situations may involve unnecessary risk in particular situations, where there may be equally suitable alternative techniques that do not involve significant risk of injury to neural structures.

Delayed injury to neural structures that are secondary to problems related to surgery can often be avoided or minimized by vigilant postoperative care and recognition of the potentially serious nature of those problems. In these cases, neurological worsening is usually a gradual process, and the patient who has not been seen by the surgeon for several days at a time, or whose seemingly minor complaints are ignored, may develop serious and permanent neurological deficit as a result of negligence.

Probably the most feared complication of spine surgery is paralysis that is not readily explained by any particular untoward circumstance or event. At least one study suggests that the neurosurgeon confronted with such a situation is most reluctant to go to court to defend a spinal cord injury that results from surgery, even when there is no apparent deviation from accepted standards of care.[28] This is probably true because of the dramatic and devastating effect on the patient, the defense's perceived unpredictability of juries, and the high damages at stake.

[i] Surgery with the patient in the sitting position

There have been a few reports of spinal cord infarction and paralysis occurring in connection with spine or intracranial surgery done with the patient anesthetized in the sitting position. A sitting position makes many operations technically easier, and, arguably, improves overall results. On the other hand, there appear to be added risks, in addition to the rare quadriplegia already mentioned. General anesthesia in the sitting position is stressful on the cardiovascular-respiratory system. The risk of air embolus has been reduced significantly by the use of Doppler monitoring for intracardiac air, but even if detected, swift removal of air must be accomplished, and the presence of a catheter in the heart atrium may not

---

[28] Fager, C.A., *Professional Liability and Potential Liability*, 16 NEUROSURGERY 866-872 (1985).

always be sufficient to evacuate all embolized air before significant hemodynamic effects occur. Air embolus can occur anytime there is a negative pressure in an open vein, and such a situation can arise with only minimal elevation of the head or other body part in relation to the heart. Although the use of the sitting position with appropriate monitoring techniques is an accepted practice, though not risk-free, there appears to be a trend toward using the sitting position more selectively and there is an overall decline in the frequency with which it is used.

[6] Peripheral Nerve Surgery

Peripheral nerves are nerves between the point where they emerge from the spine (or, in the case of cranial nerves, from the skull base) to the point where they innervate a muscle or sense organ. Included are the peripheral nerves of the autonomic nervous system.

The nerve fibers of peripheral nerves differ from those of the central nervous system in that they have the capacity to *regenerate*, which is probably due more to the nature of their supporting tissues than to any difference in the nerve fibers themselves. Peripheral nerves are made up of motor and sensory fibers, with the motor fibers carrying impulses from the brain or spinal cord to muscles or secretary organs. The cell bodies of these nerves are in the brain or spinal cord (or, in the case of autonomic nerves, may be in ganglia, which are specialized aggregations of cell bodies outside the skull or spine) and the nerve fiber is actually a process of a single nerve cell which may extend three feet or more from the cell body. In the case of sensory nerve fibers, the cell body is located in the dorsal root ganglion, separate from the spinal cord, but near the foramen or bony opening of the spine where the nerve emerges.

[a] Entrapment Syndromes

The most common type of peripheral nerve surgery performed by neurosurgeons is for various forms of non-traumatic nerve entrapment, such as carpal tunnel syndrome, ulnar tunnel syndrome, cubital tunnel syndrome, thoracic outlet syndrome, tarsal tunnel syndrome, and others. In these conditions, a nerve exhibits signs of gradual progressive deterioration of function due to constriction by thickened structures undergoing degenerative change, which may be the result of chronic inflammatory disease or occupational activity. Symptoms of numbness and tingling may be intermittent at first. Constant numbness and weakness may eventually occur. Once the diagnosis is made, a decompression operation is relatively easy and usually has a high rate of success. Generally, the surgery has a relatively low risk of complications, however, serious complications have occurred, particularly in cases where there has been a re-operation in the face of extensive scarring.

These procedures are also commonly performed by surgeons in other specialties, such as general surgery, plastic surgery, or orthopedic surgery. Thoracic outlet syndrome presenting with vascular-related symptoms may also be treated by vascular surgeons

[b] Surgery of Nerve Injury

When a nerve fiber is cut, if the proper conditions for regrowth are provided (nerve repair) the nerve fiber or nerve cell process (axon) will grow back into the same or similar supporting structure it had before. The rate of growth is about an inch a month, or one millimeter a day. Pure motor or sensory nerves have a much better result following nerve repair, because motor nerves tend to grow to muscle, and sensory nerves tend to grow to sense organs. Mixed nerves do not have as good a result, because some motor nerves grow to sense organs and some sensory nerves grow to muscle, and these connections are of no use.

Peripheral nerves have the capacity to regenerate following timely and skillful repair. Generally, the prognosis for nerve repair, in terms of regaining function, depends upon several factors. The greater the distance between the point of injury and the end organ innervated (muscle, sensory organ, or other structure), the lesser the chance of full recovery. Since nerves regenerate at the rate of approximately one inch per month or one millimeter per day, distal muscles may have atrophied and fibrosed to the point where they function poorly, even if satisfactory re-innervation occurs. "Pure" motor nerves, for example, the radial nerve, tend to have a better prognosis for recovery of muscular function than "mixed" nerves, which contain both motor and sensory fibers (*see* § 12.05 [6][b] *supra*). A sharp, clean cut of the nerve at the time of injury, as opposed to an extensive blunt injury and maceration of the nerve that often requires resection of a length of damaged nerve and insertion of a nerve graft, favors a good prognosis. Ideally, the cut nerve ends should exactly appose, so that nerve fibers in one portion of the nerve grow into the nerve sheaths of their respective fibers from which they were severed, and the apposition should not be under any tension at the time of repair. Either epineural repair (suturing of the outer layer of the nerve circumferentially), or interfascicular repair (suturing each nerve fascicle, or smaller fiber bundle, together) are acceptable methods of nerve repair.

Nerve repair need not be done immediately after an injury. In fact, in some cases, when there is a question as to how much nerve may have been damaged through concomitantly sustained blunt forces it may be better to delay definitive nerve repair for a few weeks, particularly where the nerve may have been only partially severed. If the injury has been a clean severance of the nerve by a sharp object, such as a shard of glass or a knife, early repair at the time of initial treatment for the laceration is probably more favorable, because a delay would increase certain technical difficulties associated with surgery, including scarring and identifying normal anatomy.

Where there has been loss of nerve function related to blunt trauma or a traction injury to a nerve, the patient is usually followed for signs of recovery; if recovery does not occur, and an area of damaged nerve can be identified, at some point resection of the damaged nerve and replacement with a nerve graft may be indicated.

In addition to nerve injuries from gunshot wounds, stabbings, or other traumas, including long-bone fractures, a number of iatrogenic (treatment-caused) nerve injuries are frequently encountered by the neurosurgeon. These include injuries from intramuscular injection of medication (which usually involve injuries to the radial nerve from injections in the deltoid muscle, or injuries to the sciatic nerve from injections into the buttock), injuries due to pressure that occurs while a patient is under general anesthesia for a prolonged procedure, injuries due to extravasion of intravenous medication (which may often cause other tissue damage in addition to nerve injury), and injuries to nerves that occur inadvertently in the course of an unrelated procedure. One example of this last instance is injury to the spinal accessory nerve during biopsy of a lymph node in the posterior triangle of the neck, which can result in significant shoulder dysfunction and pain.

The average neurosurgeon does not perform reconstructive (reparative) nerve surgery on a frequent basis, but some maintain a high volume practice in peripheral nerve, and referrals from other neurosurgeons are common. Orthopedic surgeons do a fair amount of peripheral nerve surgery, as do plastic surgeons.

[c]   Surgery of Nerve Tumors

Perhaps the most common tumor of peripheral nerve is the neurilemmoma, or Schwannoma, a (usually) benign tumor arising from the nerve sheath, or Schwann cells that, along with the nerve fibers themselves, make up peripheral nerve.

[d]   Surgery of Autonomic Nerves

The autonomic nervous system consists of sympathetic and parasympathetic nerves. Autonomic nerves arise from cell bodies in the brain stem and sacral segments of the spinal cord, and emerge with cranial or peripheral nerves and synapse with cell bodies in ganglia, which in turn send nerve fibers to various organs containing smooth (involuntary) muscle or to special sense organs. The autonomic nervous system affects certain "vegetative" functions, such as pupillary constriction and dilation, salivation, sweating, secretion of enzymes in the digestive system, sexual function, bowel and bladder function, heart rate, blood pressure, intestinal motility, and others. Some procedures have been performed by neurosurgeons on the sympathetic nervous system, e.g., to control hyperhidrosis (excessive sweating). Abdominal surgeons have performed vagotomies for years to control gastric acid secretion, but this operation is generally not a procedure done by neurosurgeons.

[7] Infections

[a] In General

The first line of treatment of infections, either those that present to the neurosurgeon *de novo*, or as a complication of surgical treatment, is antibiotics, after reasonable attempts have been made to obtain cultures. Occasionally this will require image-guided aspiration of a known site of infection. If antibiotic treatment does not produce a satisfactory response, a search for loculated infection (abscess) must be undertaken, and adequate drainage established.

The prevention of post-operative infection requires full attention to sterilization of the skin in preparation for surgery (a process that is too often not given the attention that it deserves); careful surgical technique that preserves as much as possible tissue viability, including meticulous wound closure; strict sterile technique intraoperatively; and maintenance of normal body temperature. While the use of pre-operative antibiotics and become standard, it is no substitute for these measures.

The increase in frequency and virulence of some hospital-acquired infections (such as C. difficile), while not established as causally related, has nonetheless paralleled the increased use of pre-operative antibiotic administration over the past two decades.

The detection and early management of post-operative infections may be critical to minimizing morbidity and mortality, depending upon the structures affected. The same is true of infections presenting *de novo*, and heightened vigilance is appropriate in either case, especially in patients that are immuno-compromised by disease, such as diabetes, or medication, such as corticosteroids.

[b] Intracranial Infections

Infections can occur as a result of direct contamination, either from an injury (*See* § 12.05[9], *supra*), or following surgery, and may affect the skull bone (osteomyelitis), or the epidural, subdural, subarachnoid (meningitis), or intracerebral spaces (cerebritis and/or brain abscess).

Following surgery for any of these infections, it is usually necessary to remove any non-vascularized bone (such as a free bone flap, in the case of a post-operative infection) that has been contaminated, even when the bone itself is not clearly infected at the time of surgery.

Brain abscess may be complicated by rupture into the subarachnoid space, producing a full-blown meningitis. A more devastating complication is rupture into a ventricle, which is too often fatal. Obviously, early detection and treatment helps to avoid these problems.

[c] Intraspinal Infections

Likewise, the spine and its contents may be the site of infection in the bone (vertebrae), or epidural, or subdural spaces. Epidural abscess is often overlooked in the early stages. It can produce spinal cord and/or compression, with permanent neurological deficit if not detected timely. If treated promptly and adequately, the results can be gratifying, even if there has been neurological deficit.

A delay in treatment of epidural abscess can result in extension of the infection to the subdural and subarachnoid spaces.

Infection within the spinal cord is exceedingly rare, and when it occurs, it is most always in the setting of immuno-compromise, or overly delayed detection and treatment of infection elsewhere in the spine.

[d] Meningitis

Meningitis as an isolated condition usually does not require surgical drainage, but may complicate injuries or surgical procedures. A not uncommon late complication of successfully treated meningitis may be communicating hydrocephalus, often requiring a shunt procedure (*See* § 12.05 [8][b], *infra*).

Meningitis that occurs as a result of spinal fluid leak is only rarely of a type that is highly contagious, such *N. meningitidis*. In almost all cases, it is due to contamination by an organism via the communication of the subarachnoid space with the outside. This even more true when the meningitis occurs as a result of contamination at the time of surgery.

Another cause of meningitis and/or ventriculitis (*see also* the discussion of ventriculitis complicating external ventricular drainage under §12.05[9][c], *infra*) is shunt infection, which virtually always requires removal of the shunt, a period of temporary external drainage until the infection is eradicated, and then placement of a new shunt. The use of antibiotic-impregnated shunt tubing is believed to reduce the incidence of infectious complications of shunt.

[e] Disc Space Infection

Disc space infection, or discitis, can occur *de novo*, but is perhaps more often seen by the neurosurgeon in the post-operative setting. It is rare in the cervical spine, relatively rare in the thoracic spine, and most common (in relation to other levels of the spine) in the lumbar spine, although still rare.

In the post-operative setting, discitis may present within days of lumbar disc surgery, usually with severe back and bilateral leg pain, which should be a red flag in a patient who otherwise would be expected to have done well after an otherwise uncomplicated operation.

Cultures of the disc space are usually negative, even before the institution of antibiotic treatment, which is usually prescribed empirically, and a period of six or more weeks of parenteral antibiotic administration is necessary. Pain may be severe for several weeks and require long-term narcotic administration.

Disc space infection usually arises as blood-borne contamination of the disc space, and this may be true is a substantial portion of post-operatively occurring disc space infections, although direct contamination at the time of surgery always has to be considered. The relatively poor vascularity of even the normal intervertebral disc is believed to account for the vulnerability of this structure to blood-borne infection.

[f] Osteomyelitis

As in the case of any bone in the body, the skull and spine are susceptible to infection. Infection may occur either through direct extension (middle ear, or sinus infection), blood-borne, or from direct contamination due to injury or surgical wound infection. Parenteral antibiotic treatment for a period of at least six weeks is required, and surgical excision and/or drainage is necessary where the response to antibiotic treatment fails to eradicate infection.

Unrecognized or inadequately treated osteomyelitis in the skull or spine can progress to involve epidural, subdural, or cerebral abscess, as well as meningitis. Temporal lobe abscess can arise from chronic middle ear infection or mastoiditis involving temporal bone, and present as a cerebral abscess.

The need for excision of viable bone in the skull is rare, and usually arises in the setting of sinus or middle ear infection. Wound infection following craniotomy (i.e., where a bone flap has been removed for exposure of the intracranial contents) almost always requires permanent removal of the bone flap.

Vertebral body infection can produce neurological deficit by direct impingement on neural structures, or indirectly, by producing instability. In such cases, it can usually be successfully treated with antibiotics, but occasionally, resection of an entire vertebral body with replacement by a bone graft and instrumentation to maintain stability. The latter situation seems to fly in the face of the traditional view that presence of non-viable bone (the bone graft) or foreign bodies (metal instrumentation) make healing of infection impossible. The successful treatment of post-operative infection in cases of spinal fusion with instrumentation with antibiotics with or without a surgical drainage procedure, but without removal of the graft or instrumentation, is also usually possible.

[8] Disorders of Cerebrospinal Fluid Circulation and Absorption

[a] In General

Hydrocephalus means literally "water [in the] head." As a practical matter, it refers to enlargement of cerebral ventricles due to obstruction of CSF, either by a block in the pathways through which CSF flows, or by insufficient absorption of CSF into the bloodstream (*See also* § 12.05 [4], et. seq., *supra*)

[b] Communicating Hydrocephalus

(*See also* § 12.05 [4][c], *supra*). In adults, a condition known as normal-pressure hydrocephalus (NPH), also referred to as "low-pressure hydrocephalus" may present with the classical triad of dementia, gait disturbance, and urinary incontinence. Sometimes a more vague clinical picture will emerge, with similar symptoms, and enlarged ventricles due to loss of brain substance from atrophy, where a shunt procedure produces little or no improvement. Particularly in these latter cases, but in any case where a shunt is performed, the procedure can be complicated by subdural hematoma. The use of programmable shunts may reduce the risk of this complication, and sometimes reverse it by re-programming the shunt to a lower flow rate, or to a higher pressure at which CSF will flow through the shunt.

Communicating hydrocephalus may also occur as a late complication of head trauma, or meningitis. Often, the response to treatment can be gratifying.

[c] Obstructive Hydrocephalus

Obstruction of the pathways through which CSF flows can be produced by bleeding within the ventricle, or by a tumor or other mass. It can produce a picture of increased intracranial pressure, with headache, visual loss, and decreased level of consciousness, occasionally progressing rapidly to the point of causing death.

[d] Benign Intracranial Hypertension (Pseudotumor Cerebri)

So-called benign intracranial hypertension is a poorly-understood condition in which CSF seems to accumulate in the brain itself, rather than enlarging the ventricular system. In fact, the ventricular system is usually reduced in size. This condition tends to occur in obese younger women for no obvious reason, but also in the setting of thrombosis of cerebral venous sinuses, vitamin A toxicity, and as a side-effect of certain drugs, among other things. It usually presents with headaches and may later produce an insidious visual loss. The optic nerve heads are usually swollen (papilledema) in the absence of any brain tumor of other mass (hence the term pseudotumor). It can often be treated by serial lumbar punctures and medication, but may require shunting, and usually responds well to lumbar-peritoneal shunt.

[e] Shunt Procedures and Complications

(See § 12.05 [4][d], supra).

[9] Neurotrauma

[a] In General

From the standpoint of neurosurgical practice, major trauma patients can be divided into those with (1) peripheral nerve injury, (2) craniocerebral trauma (skull and brain), and (3) trauma of the spine and spinal cord (See §12.05 [5][g] supra).

[b] Peripheral Nerve Injury

General principles of management of peripheral nerve injury are covered in § 12.05 [6][b] supra.

[c] Craniocerebral Trauma

Craniocerebral trauma is a major cause of death and disability, and most such trauma in the United States is the result of motor vehicular accidents. The concepts and treatment of head trauma, like those in management of spinal trauma, are simple: the goal of treatment is to prevent secondary brain injury.

For purposes of this discussion, head trauma has been divided into simple head trauma and head trauma occurring in association with multiple-system trauma. Also, in a discussion of head trauma, it is important to consider the *mechanism* of head trauma and to think of trauma to the brain, both blunt and penetrating, separately from trauma to the scalp, skull, and dura (membrane covering the brain).

[i]   Scalp injuries

Scalp lacerations and contusions commonly accompany blunt or penetrating head injuries. Generally, scalp injuries often heal without infection, if properly debrided and repaired, but, of course, if there is extensive maceration and crush injury of tissue, significant amounts of scalp may be lost, and skin grafting may be required. In such situations, the plastic surgeon is usually called upon to assist. The scalp is extremely vascular, and for that reason, bleeding from scalp lacerations can be extensive, even to the point of producing shock. With a few exceptions, definitive treatment of scalp lacerations can be delayed several hours (assuming bleeding has been controlled) without greatly increasing the risk of infection, as long as measures are taken to minimize contamination. Such delays are often necessary when other injuries require more urgent attention.

[ii]   Injuries to skull and dura

While the presence of skull fracture is an important *indicator* of head trauma, the presence or absence of fracture, at least in milder forms of head trauma, is probably not an important consideration in treatment. It is now generally accepted that far too many skull X-rays are taken in emergency departments in the routine evaluation of head trauma.[29] The evidence seems to indicate that presence or absence of skull fracture does not affect the management of head trauma, at least not often enough to justify the large number of otherwise unnecessary skull X-rays being taken. Linear fractures in the skull vault generally do not present any special problems, even if the overlying skin has been broken. If a fracture is comminuted (multiple bone fragments) or depressed significantly, and there has been a deep overlying laceration, operative debridement needs to be considered, because the risk of

---

[29] Harwood-Nash D, et al., *The Significance of Skull fracture in Children: A Study of 1,187 patients*, 101 RADIOL. 151-155 (1971). *See also* Thornbury, et al., *Skull Fractures and the Low Risk of Intracranial Sequelae in Minor Head Injury Trauma*, 5 AM. J. NEURORADIOL. 459 (1984).

bacterial or other micro-organism contamination and infection is high. Fracture of the vault, in addition to injuring dura and arachnoid, producing loss of cerebrospinal fluid (CSF), can lacerate vessels to cause hemorrhage, or cause the development of traumatic aneurysms, which can bleed dangerously days or weeks after an injury.

A rare complication of linear skull fracture is the "growing skull fracture," in which, rather than healing, the fracture line actually *widens* over a period of months. This phenomenon is caused by a tear in the arachnoid and dural layers, so that CSF leaks into the fracture, and transmitted pulsations gradually erode the edges and enlarge the bony defect.

Fracture of the skull base presents particular problems. While fracture of any part of the skull can tear the dura and arachnoid, causing leakage of spinal fluid, this is usually easily detected and repaired in a fracture of the vault. However, when fractures occur in the skull base, there is no laceration of the scalp at the site (since the scalp does not cover the skull base), and the fracture may not be detected unless special diagnostic studies are performed. If there is leakage of spinal fluid from an ear or from the nose, the likelihood of fracture is high, and the skull base needs to be studied to detect the site of CSF leakage, since, if the leak does not stop spontaneously (it may stop and recur days, weeks, or even months later), risk of meningitis is high. If blood is seen behind the eardrum, or if *delayed* ecchymosis appears over the mastoid eminence (Battle's sign), or periorbitally ("raccoon" eyes), the presence of a fracture of the skull base can be presumed. Fractures of the skull base can rarely produce significant trauma to the carotid artery (where it passes through the skull base) sufficient to produce an aneurysm or arteriovenous fistula (*see* §12.05 [1]-[2], *supra*).

Persistent CSF leak can be extremely troublesome to treat, and not uncommonly, repeated procedures are performed to repair the dural defect responsible. Often, some form of CSF diversion, temporary (external ventricular drainage) or permanent (shunt), is needed until the repair seals off. Since the cranial nerves arise near the skull base and exit the skull through holes or foramina, skull-base fractures through these foramina may cause injury to the nerves. In the case of the optic nerves, complete or partial blindness may occur. Because these optic "nerves" are really brain nerve tracts and not peripheral nerves, they do not regenerate and cannot be repaired. Other mechanisms by which cranial nerves are injured are by movement of the brain structures (sufficient to stretch or even tear the nerves), or by herniation, causing traction or compression of the nerves and temporary or permanent injury.

Determining the mechanism of injury is most helpful in assessing the degree of brain injury caused by trauma. When there is rapid deceleration, which often occurs in motor vehicle accidents, the brain may suffer diffuse axonal injury, or there may be extensive laceration and/or contusion of brain tissue, and bleeding may occur within the brain. Extensive blood loss with hypotension and shock may greatly compound brain injury and account for impaired brain perfusion. Also, there has been some interference with normal respiration, with significant hypoxia (decrease in oxygen) or hypercapnia (increase in carbon dioxide), the brain injury may be compounded severely, and a vicious cycle of increased intracranial pressure with impaired microcirculation, poor oxygenation, and further brain swelling may occur. In these circumstances, the prognosis becomes poor. Unquestionably, over the past few years, recognition of this phenomenon, plus the availability of helicopter emergency transport services and the training and sophistication of paramedics, has considerably reduced the morbidity of brain injury in multiple-system trauma.

Penetrating head trauma, on the other hand, tends to produce injury only to the areas actually affected or reached by the penetrating instrument. In the case of high-velocity missile wounds, however, shock waves transmitted by the bullet may injure remote areas of brain, in addition to those in the path of the bullet. Of course, if extensive hemorrhage is produced, or if there is extensive swelling in a lengthy missile tract, other parts of the brain are put at risk, and it is in these situations that emergency surgery may be needed. Penetrating head trauma is accompanied by significant risk of infection; however, gunshot wounds and other missile wounds from explosions tend to carry a relatively low risk of infection, perhaps because the missiles themselves are sterilized by the explosion that propels them into the brain. For this reason, a gunshot wound to the head that does not produce significant hemorrhage or mass effect from edema, may not need operative treatment.

The goal in the management of head trauma, therefore, is prevention of secondary injury to the brain, which can include injury caused by infection, increased intracranial pressure, generalized brain swelling or edema, or brain herniation due to mass effect (hemorrhage, localized edema, or contusion).

In head injury, it is critical to preserve adequate respiratory and ventilator function. If blood pCO_2 (partial pressure of CO_2) is allowed to exceed the normal range (approximately 40 mm Hg, or 40 Torr), the brain blood vessels dilate and intracranial pressure increases. This is so even in the normal brain. The injured brain, already compromised, is more susceptible to small increases in intracranial pressure for any reason. In fact, an emergency treatment for increased intracranial pressure is hyperventilation to produce hypocapnia (i.e., pCO_2 decreased to the range of 25-30 Torr). Although hyperventilation to bring the pCO_2 in this range has been widely used to control intracranial pressure for several hours or days, recent research has questioned whether or not this practice may be harmful in certain cases, because the injured brain may not tolerate the resulting decrease in blood flow.

Brain oxygenation is also critical in head injury. Cells not receiving enough oxygen, whether due to impaired blood circulation or low levels of oxygenation in otherwise adequately circulating blood, may swell, and leakage of fluid across cell membranes may occur, aggravating brain swelling and edema. Such a situation may arise because respiration is inadequate or there is significant lung injury with poor oxygenation of blood, or it may arise due to shock, with significant blood loss and resulting hypotension and hypovolemia. The complicating factors of hypercapnia, hypotension, and hypoxemia, then can convert a moderately severe closed head injury with a reasonably good capacity for recovery into a catastrophe. Thus, the team approach to multiple-system trauma, with well-trained paramedics in the field and early attention to *all* facets of injury, with assignment of priorities in the early hospital phase of treatment, is critical to optimal management of head injury.

[iii] Glasgow Coma Scale

The Glasgow Coma Scale (GCS),[30] perhaps the most widely used formula for following clinical change in the patient with head trauma. Its primary advantage is that there appears to be very little variability between observers, including paramedics, non-neurosurgeon physicians, neurosurgeons, and nurses. It grades the level of severity in three areas: best motor response (1-6), best verbal response (1-5), and eye opening (1-4), with the lowest score being 3 (no motor response to pain, no eye opening, and no verbal response), and the highest being 15 (obey commands, open eyes spontaneously, and good orientation (not confused), as manifested by the ability to answer questions appropriately).

[iv] Intracranial pressure monitoring

Various devices are available to monitor intracranial pressure, and each has disadvantages and advantages. Basically, monitoring can be accomplished either by placement of a catheter into a lateral ventricle, enabling continuous monitoring of intracranial pressure transmitted to the ventricular CSF, or by placement of a small pressure transducer directly into the brain parenchyma. The ventricular catheter permits withdrawal of small amounts of fluid for emergency reduction of intracranial pressure, or

---

[30] Teasdale G, Jennett B. *Assessment of coma and impaired consciousness. A practical scale.* LANCET 1974,2:81-84).

drainage if there is obstruction of CSF pathways, say, by blood in the posterior third ventricle. The disadvantages of using this method are difficulty of placement when there is brain swelling, obstruction of the catheter by blood or debris, or infection (ventriculitis). The risk of infection can be minimized by strict aseptic technique in sampling CSF, and in managing the wound, by using an antibiotic-impregnated catheter, and by empirically removing the catheter and placing another at a different site at intervals, usually 7-10 days. Using an intraparenchymal transducer has the advantage of easy placement, and low risk of infection, but it cannot be used for drainage of CSF. More recently, devices that permit both drainage of CSF and measurement of physiological parameters such as brain oxygen tension have come into use.

Generally, the indications for intracranial pressure monitoring in head injury are a Glasgow Coma Scale score of 8 or less, or "tight" or small cisterns or CSF-containing spaces at the base of the brain, as seen on CT scan, associated with a significant decrease in the level of consciousness. The rationale for monitoring intracranial pressure in head injuries is that an increase in intracranial pressure may be harmful in itself, but it may also be the earliest sign of development of bleeding or massive brain swelling, coupled with the fact that treatment of increased intracranial pressure (either by hyperventilation, osmotic diuretics, barbiturate coma, or surgery to remove a localized area of badly contused and swollen brain or hemorrhage), prevents secondary brain injury and improves outcome. Virtually every medical center treating a significant volume of head trauma cases employs one or more methods for intracranial pressure monitoring.

[v] Intracranial complications of head trauma

Traumatic *epidural* hematoma usually occurs in association with a skull fracture. With such a fracture, a tear in an artery of the dura mater is usually the source of the bleeding. Hemorrhage occurs between the skull and the dura, and can produce a rapid deterioration in brain function by causing brain displacement and herniation. Epidural hematoma is relatively common in young people, and relatively rare in older people, primarily because the dura tends to be quite adherent to the inner surface of the skull in older people. In children, particularly, bleeding can strip the dura off the inner surface of the skull (which produces more bleeding and further expansion of the mass). Often this occurs in the absence of severe direct brain injury, and early detection and operation can result in complete recovery. One the other hand, delays of only an hour or two can mean the difference between complete recovery and severe, permanent brain injury or even death.

The acute *subdural* hematoma accompanying head injury is usually due to brain laceration and bleeding and is almost always accompanied by severe brain injury, so that results of operative treatment are often disappointing, even though the hematoma has been removed in a timely fashion. Subdural hematoma may occur as a result of relatively minor head trauma, especially in older people, with little or no direct brain injury, but secondary brain injury can occur with nearly the same degree of rapidity as that seen in epidural hematoma. Sometimes, subdural hematoma can be a more delayed process, and may not be present on CT scan a day or two after injury, but gradually enlarges over several weeks following mild head trauma. It may then appear with a rapidly deteriorating course. More rarely, delayed hemorrhage *within the brain* can occur from head trauma. Here, the prognosis with operative treatment depends upon the location and size of the hemorrhage and severity of preoperative neurological deficit.

[d] Spine and Spinal Cord Injury

(*See* §12.05 [5][g], *supra*)

[10] Neuro-oncology and Tumor Surgery

[a] In General

The term neuro-oncology usually refers to the multidisciplinary treatment of brain and spinal cord tumors, which can vary from benign and slow-growing to highly malignant. Also included in the following discussion are metastatic tumors (tumors spread from primary malignant disease elsewhere in the body), and benign extra-axial tumors affecting the nervous system, i.e., those arising outside the brain and spinal cord, e.g., from the pituitary gland or from nerves or supporting structures of the central nervous system.

[b] Intrinsic Brain Tumors

Gliomas are tumors arising from non-neural cells in the brain and spinal cord. They range from benign (astrocytoma) to highly malignant (glioblastoma multiforme). There is no general agreement on the advisability of radiation treatment of the benign astrocytomas, but most agree that radiation provides some benefit and treatment of the malignant tumors. Surgery continues to be performed to remove these tumors, but it probably is of benefit by virtue of its "debulking" or palliative quality, rather than as a means of arresting the disease process. It is widely believed that decreasing the volume of viable tumor cells probably improves the result with radiation and chemotherapy.

[c] Pituitary Tumors

Tumors arising from the pituitary gland often secrete excesses of one or more hormones secreted by the normal pituitary gland. As a result, they can often be detected because of the manifestations of hormonal excess, rather than due to the presence of a mass. Also, large tumors may interfere with normal pituitary function, and the patient may present with evidence of too little secretion of normal pituitary hormones. These patients are usually seen first by the endocrinologist, who may consult a neurosurgeon if surgical treatment is considered. Another way for these tumors to present is with headaches. Commonly, however, progressive visual loss is the only sign of a pituitary tumor, and this occurs because the tumor causes upward pressure on the optic chiasm (optic nerve fibers crossing from one side to the other in the midline, just above the location of the pituitary gland). Occasionally, these tumors can become quite large before detection. One of the very early surgical approaches to this type of tumor, a sublabial incision just above the upper front teeth and an approach in the submucous plane through the nose and sphenoid sinus at the base of the skull, reappeared in the 1960s after the advent of the operating microscope, the development of microtechniques, and the availability of antibiotics. Prior to that time, craniotomy was almost the exclusive approach to these tumors. With the use of the trans-sphenoidal technique, the morbidity of surgery for pituitary tumors has been decreased considerably, chiefly through preservation of normal pituitary function after tumor removal.

Two kinds of tumors, usually benign, which commonly occur in the cranial cavity or spinal canal are meningiomas (which appear to arise from the arachnoid layer of the meninges, or brain covering) and neurilemmomas (which arise from nerve sheaths of cranial or spinal nerves). Sometimes these tumors can grow to a large size before detection. The size and location of these tumors can make a tremendous difference in the risks of surgery, and in the chance of achieving a surgical cure.

[d] Metastatic Tumors

For a discussion of metastases to the spine, *see* §12.05 [5][e] *supra.*

Metastatic tumors to the brain are most commonly spread from malignancy of the breast or lung; however, almost any malignant tumor can produce metastases to the brain. If multiple metastatic tumors are present in the brain, surgery is generally not going to be of benefit, except that stereotactic needle biopsy may be helpful if the primary lesion cannot be identified. The term "single metastasis," when referring to a brain metastasis, means that there is only one metastatic lesion *in the brain*, but there may or may not be an additional metastatic lesion somewhere else in the body. The term "solitary metastasis" means that there is only one metastatic lesion in the brain *and* none elsewhere in the body.

Surgical treatment, i.e., excision of the metastatic lesion, is often an option where there is a single or solitary metastasis, but the decision of surgery is usually based on many factors, including the overall prognosis and condition of the patient as it relates to the primary malignant disease, the location and feasibility of removal of the metastatic lesion, and the extent to which the lesion is producing neurological deficit. In some cases, dramatic improvement in the quality of life can be achieved by gross excision of the lesion, followed by radiation treatment, and the patient may never have recurrence of the intracranial problem.

[e] Tumors Arising from Skull, Meninges, Nerves

The growth pattern of benign, extra-axial (not arising within the brain) tumors can be unpredictable, but if it can be established that a small tumor should have been detected years before it produced a serious deficit (either from the direct effect of the tumor or because of indicated surgery, otherwise performed in accordance with accepted standards of care), it is difficult for anyone to refute a direct causal relationship between the early misdiagnosis and the resultant injury. It is well to remember that sometimes these tumors are best managed by watchful waiting and the use of serial CT or MRI studies. The availability of these highly accurate diagnostic modalities has probably increased the group of tumor patients who are simply followed without treatment because the risks of definitive surgery may exceed the risks of close observation and follow-up.

[f] Other Considerations

A delay in diagnosis of neoplasms affecting the nervous system is not *per se* significant in adversely affecting prognosis. The extent to which a delay does adversely affect prognosis depends upon the tumor type, the degree of irreversible neurological deficit that can be attributed to the delay, and the extent to which the increase in tumor size or involvement in adjacent structures may have added to surgical morbidity.

The availability and range of imaging studies that have developed over the past two or three decades has enabled the physician and patient to more often choose a non-surgical approach, for example, in patients of advanced age, or with co-morbidities that might increase the risk of surgery to a level unacceptable to one or both parties.

[11] Endoscopic and Minimally-invasive Surgery

The development of image-guided surgical techniques, primarily related to the coupling of sophisticated imaging methods with robotic and/or endoscopic techniques has laid the foundation for rapid advances in minimally-invasive surgery. As these techniques develop, the surgeon's skills require an increasing dependence upon proper function of the devices employed, and the interaction between these two factors is often difficult to analyze.

[12] The Surgical Treatment of Pain

As alluded to in § 12.05 [3][e], *infra*, a general trend has been for the surgical management of pain to involve augmentative procedures, rather than ablative (e.g., nerve section or methods of destroying normal structures that are believed to subserve pain sensation). The range of devices, including those used for deep brain stimulation, spinal cord or nerve stimulation, and instillation of morphine or other analgesics into the central nervous system, continues to expand, as does the potential for product defects and malfunction. As in § 12.05 [11], *supra*, the relationship between operator skill and proper device function is often a difficult one to parse.

[13] Complications in Neurosurgery

The range of complications that can occur in neurosurgical procedures is similar to that in other fields of surgery, i.e., infection; bleeding (both intra-operative and post-operative); unintended injury due to errors of technique or of judgment; anesthesia issues; and equipment malfunction among them. Because neurosurgical procedures often deal with small structures, but injury to which may cause devastating effects on the patient, the exact relationship between an adverse event and a particular complication is sometimes difficult to pin down. In other words, causation is not always easy to establish when there has been a complication plus a bad outcome.

§ 12.06 Diagnostic Studies

[1] Roentgenography (X-ray Studies)

The use of X-ray as a technique for imaging body structures is the most widely known and earliest such diagnostic tool to be used in medicine. Exposing film to an X-ray beam passed through the body tissues results in a picture that reveals bones and other bodily structures not seen by the naked eye. Depending upon the energy of the beam and technique of exposure, certain details can be emphasized, but standard x-ray techniques cannot distinguish well between tissues having X-ray densities that are very close.

One technique of roentgenography that has been helpful is *tomography*. The principle of this technique is to employ movement of the X-ray beam or target (or both) so as to blur out some structures while retaining a focused exposure of a plane through tissue (the plane being selected by making it relatively motion-free in relation to the beam and film). In this way, X-ray images simulating "slices" at different depths through the structure being studied can be created.

[2] Computed Tomography (CT)

CT scanning is another technique of obtaining axial tomograms (the procedure was originally called computerized axial tomography, or CAT scanning). It is a technique where image "slices" or tomograms are produced by passing an X-ray beam in the plane of the "slice" selected for imaging at many different angles, and then using a computer program to construct an image resembling a "slice" or cross-section of the body part being studied. It is important to remember that, with some routine X-rays or tomograms, the entire information obtained is stored on the X-ray film. More recently, most X-ray images are directly recorded and stored on digital media, but may be "printed out" on standard film. In the case of CT or magnetic resonance imaging (MRI) (*see* §12.06[6], *infra*), the entire information obtained is acquired and archived on some electronic medium. A specific portion of the entire information available may be "printed out" on non-electronic media and used in that form by the clinician to make medical decisions. Or, used by a reviewing physician for various purposes at a later time. For example, pictures showing primarily bony detail may be made from a brain CT, or pictures showing primarily brain or other soft tissue detail may be made. The attorney, therefore, should remember that, if the CT scan pictures available in a case do not provide the information needed for an adequate review, it may be necessary to obtain the complete archived data to perform an adequate review. Copies of the archived data can be requested for review, and additional pictures can be made that demonstrate the details that may not have been evident on a previous "print-out." More and more, however, imaging studies are provided to the patient and treating physician on CD-ROM, complete with the viewing application, rather than on an standard X-ray film.

Sometimes, the imaging of certain brain structures or lesions (such as tumors) can be improved upon by the use of contrast enhancement, i.e., injecting contrast material into the patient intravenously and performing a

CT scan shortly thereafter. In this way, some information can be obtained about the vascularity and pattern of vascularization of a tumor, arteriovenous malformation, or other lesion that can be most helpful in establishing an accurate diagnosis.

[3] Angiography

Angiography refers to imaging of the vascular system by injection of contrast material so as to fill the vessels one desires to study. (For a discussion of magnetic resonance imaging of vessels, *see* § 12.06 [6], *infra*.) It is usually a dynamic study, i.e., a series of rapid (often three-per-second) X-ray exposures are used to record the circulation of contrast through the brain, spinal cord, or other structure under study. In this way, arterial, capillary, and venous phases of the circulation can be studied. While intravenous injection of contrast with CT imaging can be used to image the arterial system, direct injection into the arteries to be studied and imaging with rapid-sequence X-ray remains the "gold standard."

Usually, it is necessary to inject contrast directly into the artery (or into a larger artery of which it is a branch, depending upon technical considerations) supplying the area under study. The use of enhanced imaging techniques, such as digital subtraction (which employs disk storage of the X-ray exposure and further computerized processing of the image data to improve detail), can further improve the diagnostic value of these studies.

The injection of contrast intra-arterially utilizes sophisticated techniques of vascular radiology to pass a catheter within the arterial system, usually from the common femoral artery in the groin, to the area to be studied. For brain angiography, this means advancing the catheter into the internal carotid or vertebral artery to be studied, and an automatic, controlled injection of contrast is then carried out while films are obtained in rapid sequence.

The techniques of intra-arterial catheterization developed in the 1960s and early 1970s gave rise to a whole new field of endovascular surgery, i.e., the practice of altering vessels and circulation using tiny catheters that enter the body at a remote site from the area being treated, inflating balloons to occlude or enlarge vessels, injecting glue or other materials designed to embolize vessels, and injecting chemotherapeutic agents.

Spinal angiography requires catheterization of individual segmental spinal branches at multiple levels, and because these vessels are small, there is significant risk of injury and occlusion of these vessels, which can produce serious spinal cord ischemia and infarction, with resultant paralysis. Similar problems can occur, of course, with the manipulation of any vessel by means of catheterization, and major stroke can occur as a result of iatrogenic injury to brain vessels as well, even when proper skill, care, and diligence are exercised, especially if the vessels are diseased to begin with.

[4] Spinal and Ventricular Puncture

Lumbar puncture (LP) is a technique used primarily to obtain cerebrospinal fluid (CSF) for diagnostic studies, for the injection of various drugs for therapeutic reasons, or for injection of contrast material in conjunction with myelography.

Normally, the subarachnoid space in the spine is large enough that a needle introduced at or near the midline in the back can be positioned easily. The lower lumbar region is used, because there is no risk of spinal cord injury (the spinal cord ends at approximately the second lumbar vertebra or above in almost every patient). With the use of sterile technique (skin sterilization with antiseptic, use of a sterile field with sterile drapes, and sterile gloves), the risk of infection is practically nil. Since the lumbar subarachnoid space normally communicates with the subarachnoid spaces in the brain (including the cisterns, or enlarged CSF spaces around the brain stem and at the base of the brain) and with the ventricular system, fluid withdrawn by lumbar puncture drains from, and decreases pressure in, either ventricles or cisterns. If there is a block within the ventricular system interfering with outflow from the ventricles and causing increased pressure in the ventricular system, the removal of CSF from the cisterns may allow the brain to expand into spaces normally filled by CSF to the extent that herniation occurs, causing compression or ischema of brain stem structures. This could lead to a decreased level of consciousness, impaired respiration, and a vicious cycle of more brain swelling and respiratory arrest. Or if there is some process causing diffuse brain swelling, or a mass within the brain, without necessarily an obstruction of CSF flow, removal of CSF from the lumbar area may precipitate herniation already impending. For the above reasons, and depending upon the clinical picture, it is *usually* advisable to obtain a CT brain scan prior to a lumbar puncture to rule out the presence of a potentially dangerous problem in the patient's head.

Lumbar puncture, even when performed properly, has been known to cause intracerebral hemorrhage, sixth cranial nerve paralysis (virtually always temporary, and probably due to traction on these nerves due to slight shift in brainstem position), and sometimes severe postural headaches. The latter complication, known as spinal headache, can sometimes be dramatically relieved by the use of a "blood patch," (i.e., injection of the patient's own blood over the site of the needle hole of the original puncture site in the dura).

When lumbar puncture is not feasible, CSF can be obtained via insertion of a needle at the level of the cisterna magna (at the cranio-cervical junction), or by a lateral approach at the C1-2 level. Ventricular fluid can be obtained via a trans-cerebral route, but this approach is rarely used solely for one-time sampling of CSF. If repeated samples are needed or there are other indications, a small catheter is placed in the ventricle. If samples are needed for only a few days, it is usually brought through the scalp and accessed as needed. If samples are required over a longer period of time, it can be connected to a small reservoir that is placed subcutaneously.

[5] Myelography

Historically, myelography is thought of as involving the injection of contrast into the spinal subarachnoid space for imaging with X-ray. Today, in practice, CT is the imaging modality of choice in myelography. Standard X-ray imaging is used less and less, as the quality of CT imaging has improved.

The technique of myelography employs the imaging of contrast material injected into the subarachnoid space, so as to provide, in effect, a shadow of the spinal cord and spinal nerves and nerve roots within the subarachnoid space. The contrast can freely flow around the spinal cord and nerve roots within the spinal subarachnoid space and allow for visualization of the structures. Virtually all myelographic studies today are done with a water-soluble contrast, which is absorbed by the body and excreted within twenty-four hours. The use of CT to image cross-sections of the spine after intrathecal (subarachnoid) injection of contrast has greatly increased the capability of imaging the intraspinal structures. Advances in computer technology and imaging software have enabled the reconstruction of sagittal and coronal slices that greatly enhance the diagnostic value of these studies. Myelography is most commonly used to evaluate disc disease and other spine abnormalities that impinge on the spinal cord or nerve roots. It also can provide important information about intraspinal tumors. For the most part, MRI has replaced myelography as an imaging modality for spinal conditions, but there remains a use for myelography in patients who are unable to undergo MRI imaging (for example, due to the presence of a pacemaker, or other device sensitive to a strong magnetic field), or in conditions where a relationship of certain structures to bony detail may be desired.

[6] Magnetic Resonance Imaging (MRI)

The technique of magnetic resonance imaging exploits the principle that different tissues emit different levels of energy as a result of a rapid shift in the direction of an imposed magnetic field. These differences in energy are detected and measured in the same way X-ray energy is detected and measured after an X-ray beam has been passed through tissue. (The energy of the beam will depend upon the thickness and particular X-ray density of the tissue.) In the case of MRI, the level of energy emitted depends upon the chemical composition of the tissue (or cerebrospinal fluid) and its particular response to a controlled shift in the vector of a magnetic field. The energy thus detected and measured from many detection points is converted by use of a computer program into images of the body area under study, in much the same way as CT pictures are imaged from detecting energy emitted outside the body and passed through tissue. CT employs the difference in X-ray's absorption characteristics of different tissues; MRI uses the differences in nuclear magnetic resonance of different tissues with different chemical composition.

In many respects, the imaging capabilities of MRI are superior to those of CT; however, there are certain advantages to CT if bone detail is needed. Also, the logistics of MRI scanning make it difficult to use with critically injured or critically ill patients, because the patient cannot be monitored as well in the MRI unit. Certain details relating to vascularity of tissue can be high-lighted with the use of a contrast material called gadolinium, which is used in conjunction with MRI scanning in much the same way that iodinated contrast material is used in conjunction with CT scanning. Magnetic resonance angiography (MRA) and magnetic resonance venography (MRV) use the ability of MRI to demonstrate the contrast between stationary (brain and other intracranial structures) and moving (blood flowing in the vessels of the brain) tissue. MRA/MRV requires sophisticated image-acquisition techniques and is employed as a matter of standard practice in most centers. Its major clinical value at this time is that it is noninvasive and can be done relatively rapidly; however, cerebral angiography (see § 12.06 [3], supra) continues to be a superior method of imaging intracranial blood vessels.

[7] Electrophysiology

[a] Electromyography

Electromyography is the detection, amplification, and recording of electrical activity of muscle. This is usually carried out by putting needle electrodes into the muscle to be studied and using special equipment to display the electrical pattern on an oscilloscope. Certain muscle diseases show characteristic abnormalities on EMG. In addition, and more commonly of interest to the neurosurgeon, certain EMG abnormalities allow the examiner to indirectly diagnose certain disorders of nerves, because certain diseases or injuries of nerves affect the electrical activity of the muscles innervated by that nerve.

In the case of acute injury to a nerve or acute compression of a nerve, as with a ruptured disc, it takes two to three weeks for the abnormal EMG findings to develop. Thus, EMG may not be of help in the first two to three weeks after an acute nerve injury.

[b]   Nerve Conduction Studies

The normal conduction of nerve impulses depends upon the integrity of the nerve fiber or process (axon) of the nerve cell, as well as of the myelin sheath, which surrounds the axon. Nerve fibers conduct impulses at varying speeds, ranging approximately from 0.5 to 60 meters per second (m/sec.), depending upon the thickness of the myelin sheath and the distance between nodes or gaps in the myelin. The heavier myelinated nerve, with longer distances between gaps or nodes, conducts impulses more rapidly, and the unmyelinated or small fibers conduct impulses more slowly.

If a peripheral nerve is stimulated at one point, an action potential can be recorded from the muscle, or a compound nerve action potential can be recorded at another point along the nerve. The compound nerve action potential is the sum of all the nerve action potentials that occur when a nerve has been stimulated electrically. For the standard stimulus, the amplitude and latency (time between stimulation and recording of an impulse) are measured, and the nerve conduction velocity is then calculated, using the distance between the recording and the stimulating sites. If there is an acute compression of a nerve, the amplitude may be decreased, depending upon the severity of the compression. Obviously, if a nerve is cut, there will be no response to attempted conduction across the nerve; however, if a nerve has been cut, and the end going to muscle (distal to the cut) is stimulated, one may still record a normal muscle-action potential for several hours after the injury.

Nerve compression produces loss of the myelin sheath of the nerve, and the conduction speed of myelinated nerve is thus slowed, depending upon how much myelin loss occurs. If there is localized compression to a nerve, such as commonly occurs at the elbow, nerve conduction velocity across the area of compression will be slowed, but conduction in other parts of the nerve will be normal.

[c] Electroencephalography (EEG)

Electroencephalography is a technique by which brain electrical activity is detected, amplified, and recorded by means of electrodes placed on the scalp. This procedure has no risk, and it provides information helpful in the diagnosis and management of seizures and of some metabolic processes that interfere with normal brain function (such as liver failure leading to a hepatic coma). It also serves as an indicator of complete loss of brain function, which is generally required by accepted medical practice to fulfill the legal definition of death due to complete and irreversible cessation of function of the entire brain.

The EEG is also sensitive to reductions in cerebral blood flow, below a certain point. For this reason, it is widely used as a monitoring technique for carotid artery surgery.

[d] Evoked Potentials

A more recent innovation, both as a diagnostic modality and as a technique for electrophysiological monitoring during surgery, is the use of *evoked potentials*. The term is derived from the fact that if some area of the nervous system is stimulated by a flash of light, audible click, or electrical shock, depending upon the system being studied, one can record the response by means of electrodes on the scalp, just as an EEG, or by electrodes on peripheral nerve, spinal cord or muscle (again, depending upon which system of nerves is being tested).

The usual technique of recording evoked potentials employs the use of a computer to average the response of several stimuli, in order to average out "background" electrical activity or produce a "pure" response. The use of evoked potentials in spinal and intracranial surgery may significantly decrease the risks of severe harm that occurs as a result of the manipulation of nerve structures sometimes necessary to completely excise tumors, or to gain exposure of an aneurysm at the base of the brain for clipping. If, during the course of a surgical procedure, the evoked potentials indicate some adverse change in neurophysiological functioning, it is possible for the surgeon to reassess or alter his or her technique and perhaps institute a change that will allow the evoked potentials to return to normal. Sometimes, change in evoked potentials may reflect and irreversible change, and it is not possible to make a timely adjustment in the procedure to preserve function. In such cases, however, it is at least possible for the surgeon to determine at what point the neurological changes occurred. A change in evoked potentials during surgery may be due to a drop in blood pressure, the effect of some drug given during the procedure, or the positioning of the patient (for instance, too much neck flexion and extension).

Although the efficacy of evoked potential monitoring in reducing surgical morbidity has not been established, the trend in current thinking is that it probably is effective, and its use in a wide range of neurosurgical procedures is commonly employed, and is preferred in certain procedures that carry a relatively high risk of neurological injury. It is important to remember, however, that, in addition to sophisticated electronic equipment, accurate and reliable neurophysiological monitoring requires adequately supervised and highly skilled technicians.

[8] Other Diagnostic Modalities

A number of other diagnostic procedures are in use, ranging from the relatively common and standardized use of ultrasound for non-invasive assessment of extracranial and intracranial vessels, to surface EMG studies and thermography, that may have relatively little clinical value, but tend to provide data that is objective, but not necessarily reliable or reproducible.

Certain techniques that exploit physiological changes may be used, i.e. blood-flow studies, and methods of assessing brain uptake of oxygen.

§ 12.07 Medical-legal Problem Areas

[1] In General

This section presents selected topics of particular interest, and that present novel legal questions in the determination of liability.

[2] Experimental and Innovative Surgery

This area of surgery is problematic for several reasons. Often the neurosurgeon performing the procedure may be the only one, or one of a small number, sufficiently versed in the procedure and in the indications for the procedure. There may be no consensus as to the efficacy of the procedure itself, so that it may be difficult to obtain expert opinion about the propriety and the technical standards of the procedure. In addition, the problem of informed consent becomes more troublesome for the same reasons. If a procedure has been officially declared experimental (some third-party payors make this designation for their own purposes) and, in particular, if implementation of the procedure has been discussed by an institutional review board (IRB), then the problem becomes simpler, because it is easier to apply higher standards of informed consent. Also, there may be a lengthy and detailed documentation associated with the informed consent process and signed by the patient. (If a procedure has been subjected to review by an IRB, any minutes of meeting or documents used in the deliberations of the IRB may be helpful in preparation of the case.)

The more difficult area is where there has been a procedure that is not widely accepted as standard and efficacious, but innovative and of unproved efficacy. It is well known that, with a few exceptions, new surgical procedures, or new indications for accepted procedures, are not usually subjected to the kind of rigorous testing required in the case of a new drug.

Ethical considerations may inform cases involving implants.[31]

[3] Marketing and Advertising

With the increased use by the medical profession and hospitals of media advertising, especially with regard to certain procedures and technical equipment, there is bound to be some effect on the expectations of the patient, as well as a strong influence on the patient's choice of physician or hospital as a result of such advertisement. In those situations, it is wise to obtain any tapes, pamphlets, or brochures the patient may have been given either directly or through his or her family physician, dealing with such procedures or treatments, especially when there are issues of lack of informed consent.

[4] Self-referrals and Referral among Co-investors

The *Statements of Principles of the American College of Surgeons* declare, "Any form of inducement to refer a patient to another physician, other than the superior care to be secured, is unethical," and a "violation of this tenet is a cause for expulsion from Fellowship." As more and more physicians become investors in facilities to which they refer patients, the referral patterns and motivations of physicians become more and more subject to scrutiny.

[5] Care Standards, Guidelines, and Practice Parameters

The setting of standards of care by professional societies has been a controversial issue for many years, and an issue that organized medicine has generally tried to avoid, perhaps primarily because of a fear that once a clear

---

[31] Ford PJ, *Neurosurgical implants: clinical protocol considerations*. CAMB Q HEALTHC ETHICS 2007;16(3):308-11.

standard of care is enunciated, any deviation from that standard will be tantamount to negligence and liability in a malpractice suit. The publication of standards is problematic because scientific progress may outpace the development of standards, and occasionally unique features of a particular case may require some deviation from accepted standards. In addition, there have been concerns that the setting of clinical practice guidelines parameters will foster a trend toward "cookbook" medicine.

It is the position of the American Medical Association that using practice parameters will not increase exposure to malpractice suits or create new liabilities and, in fact, may actually help the physician control liability risks. On the other hand, such practice parameters will become another source of evidence for what the standard of care should be, and physicians may be expected to explain why specific parameters were not adhered to.

The Agency for Healthcare Quality and Research (AHQR), of the Department of Health and Human Services (HHS), has developed clinical practice guidelines and issues requests for public comments in the Federal Register as each new guideline panel begins its work.[32]

[6] Misdiagnosis

Misdiagnosis, in itself, does not constitute a deviation from accepted standards of care, any more than a poor outcome does. The attorney preparing a case should not assume that because a diagnosis was ultimately found to be missed or incorrect, that negligence occurred. It is necessary to investigate the care and treatment, i.e., the process by which a diagnosis was arrived at, to establish a misdiagnosis as a deviation from accepted standards of care.

Early symptoms of conditions that may cause spinal cord compression can appear harmless and are often overlooked until a relatively rapid deterioration occurs. This is commonly the situation where malignant disease is responsible for the spinal cord compression, but may occur rarely with ruptured discs and with spinal, epidural, or brain abscesses. In these cases, the neurosurgeon often is not involved in the patient's care until after the worsening has occurred.

[7] Reviewing Diagnostic Studies

Virtually all imaging studies are reviewed and reported by a radiologist, who, usually but not always, is the same person who performed or supervised performance of the procedure. Often, neurosurgeons are required

---

[32] www.hpqr.gov (last access 6/9/08).

to interpret and make decisions based upon imaging studies before the radiologist has reviewed the study or rendered a written report. Recognizing that there can be honest differences of opinion in the interpretation of imaging studies, the fact that one interpretation differs from another is not, in itself, a deviation from accepted standards of care on the part of one observer or the other. In face, *some* degree of intra-observer variability is acceptable (i.e., the same neurosurgeon may have a different interpretation on review of the same films several months later). The radiologist, particularly where CT or MRI studies are concerned, has some advantage, because of the opportunity to review the data on the video display and highlight pertinent details before making films copies. Often a practitioner, only having access to filmed copy months later, does not have the ability to examine the data in as much detail. On the other hand, the neurosurgeon who requested the study often has specific ideas as to what to look for in a study, but ordinarily should communicate in some way that information to the radiologist performing and interpreting the procedure.

[8] Errors of Judgment

One of the most difficult questions to be answered in a case of misdiagnosis or an ill-fated course of treatment is whether the decision was an error of judgment within accepted standards of care or whether it was a *negligent* error of judgment. There is no question that neurosurgeons are daily faced with the need to make decisions based upon less information than they would like, and clinical decisions are sometimes a constant game of educated guessing. Often, all options are fraught with serious risk, and it is the task of the neurosurgeon to consider the risks of doing something against the risks of not doing it, or of doing something else. Judgment cases are necessarily highly individualized, and experts can vary widely in their views of just what is acceptable management, a fact that considerably weakens any one expert's opinion, unless it is formulated in terms of ignorance or misapplication of some fundamental principle of neurosurgical treatment.

[9] Informed Consent

A neurosurgeon's opinion of the risks of a particular procedure or decision might very well change after a serious complication has occurred. Obviously, any written material or audiovisual materials designed to explain a procedure, as well as any records of conversations between the physician and the patient or patient's family need to be reviewed. Surreptitious taping of such conversations by one of the parties sometimes occurs, even before any injuries or acts of alleged malpractice have occurred. Attorneys should be aware of being misled by their client's use of such tapes, and should be prepared to deal with ethical problems that may result from participating in such taping.

State laws vary as to the requirements for lawful recording of conversations. Informed consent cases need to be considered in at least three separate parts: (1) issues of fact as to what (and how) the patient was actually told by the doctor of the procedure, risks, and alternatives; (2) whether the risks and alternatives are ones generally accepted as being associated with the procedure, in a given patient with a given condition; and (3) whether the patient (as a reasonable person, or as the particular patient) would need the information to make a decision. It is suggested that the attorney determine early in the case in which one or more of these areas the dispute lies. If the defendant doctor is not in disagreement with the plaintiff's expert about the material risks, the possible complications, and what the patient should be told, the rest is for the jury. It may just be an issue of credibility, or it may mean that the plaintiff must convince a jury that an omitted disclosure would have materially affected his or her decision. If there is no issue requiring expert opinion, the lawyer may wish to consider, as a tactical decision, whether involvement of expert witnesses in issues that must be decided by the trier of fact will add anything of value to the ease or simply confuse matters, possibly to his or her detriment.

[10] Evidence of Technical Errors

Perhaps the most difficult area in discovering and proving negligence is where intra-operative technical errors may have occurred. Although the doctrine of *res ipsa loquitur* may help to prove negligence in certain kinds of cases, it may be extremely difficult to determine if negligence in technique occurred in the course of a surgical operation. While instances have occurred in which it was immediately obvious to everyone present in the operating room that a mistake had been made (usually because of some dramatic event, such as an explosion, massive hemorrhage, or a spontaneous comment by a member of the operating team), there are those cases where only the operating surgeon was aware of an error in technique (or maybe even the surgeon himself was unaware). Or, some misadventure on the part of the anesthesiologist may have occurred and was not communicated to the surgeon.

The surgeon's operative notes might be helpful in determining whether a surgical technical error occurred, either by directly describing in detail the error or indirectly glossing over certain parts of the narrative description so as to suggest a lack of awareness of a potential problem. Another indication is by determining the date of the dictation of the operative report to see if there had been an excessive delay in the dictation. Occasionally, sometimes for valid reasons and sometimes not, a delay of several months occurs. Whatever the reason for the delay, it is unlikely that minor details of an operative procedure are going to be recalled months after a procedure was performed, unless it was an eventful and memorable operation; however, one reason for a vivid recollection of a procedure would be if some major intra-operative error occurred.

Inquiry should be made as to the existence of any video recording that may have been produced at the time of the operation or procedure.

Some institutions have established protocols for the routine destruction of video recordings after they have been used for teaching purposes, and it may be important to inquire into whether or not such protocols exist, and whether or not they are routinely followed. Reviewing the description of an operation in light of other key documents created at the time of surgery (to be discussed in detail below) can be revealing. For instance, a description of an uneventful lumbar disc operation becomes suspect if other records in the chart indicate that four units of blood were transfused and the operation lasted three or four hours.

Samples of hospital records created at or around the time of a surgical operation are included here. Typically, as the reader will determine from these samples, much of what is written is illegible, and even when legible, it can be extremely difficult to decipher because of extensive use of medical shorthand. Yet, these parts of the medical record contain a wealth of information that may make or break a malpractice case, and taking the time and trouble to glean all the data possible from these few key pages in the hospital chart is a valuable investment. Not all hospitals use the same forms, of course, but similar forms are usually found in every hospital chart.

Although more and more hospitals are replacing the handwritten chart with the electronic health record (EHR), a substantial number of hospitals continue to use handwritten records. The EHR, while legible, presents other situations where precise determination of circumstances and details of adverse events may be difficult. (*See* §12.08 [6], *infra*).

[11] Telemedicine and the Internet

The outsourcing of interpretation of imaging studies to physicians half-way around the world is commonplace. Where issues of the interpretation of imaging studies exist, it is well to inquire into the details of the relationship between the interpreting physician and the clinician and/or hospital.

[12] Hospital Medical Staff Credentialing

The 2007 Joint Commission Credentialing and Privileging Standards have been "informed throughout by the six areas of General Competencies" developed by the ACGME and ABMS (*See* § 12.02 [3] *supra*) by simply changing the word "resident" to "practitioner."[33]

§ 12.08 Medical Records

[1] In General

Typical samples of hospital records created at or around the time of a surgical operation are included here. Typically, as the reader will determine from these samples, much of what is written is illegible, and even when legible, it can be extremely difficult to decipher because of extensive use of medical shorthand.

Moreover, the potential expert witness may receive copies of records with portions illegible due to the copying process. [Please see portions of the Post Anesthesia Recovery Record illustrated on pages 785 and 786.] In such cases, it may be crucial to examine the original records, or to insist on receiving legible copies.

These parts of the medical record contain a wealth of information that may make or break a malpractice case, and taking the time and trouble to glean all the data possible from these few key pages in the hospital chart is a valuable investment. Not all hospitals use the same forms, of course, but similar forms are usually found in every hospital chart. Additionally, as is evident in the examples provided, these records are usually a mixture of handwritten records and printouts of electronically stored data, and the date and time of printing are ordinarily shown on the printout.

---

[33] www.jointcommission.org/NR/rdonlyres/8AB389E2-412D-49F0-BAC9-996D7EF098B1/0/audio_conference_043007.pdf (last access 6/6/08).

MRN:　　　Visit:　　　DocType: OR Procedures

HEALTH SYSTEM

POST ANESTHESIA RECOVERY RECORD

Assessment/Signature

Time:

CODES:
UE = Upper Extremities
LE = Lower Extremities
U = Unable to Assess

Pulse:
0 = Absent
1 = Feeble
2 = Weak & Thready
3 = Normal Quality
4 = Strong & Bounding

= NL

Skin Temp:
W = Warm
C = Cool
Cd = Cold
Cl = Clammy

Strength:
S = Strong
N = Moderate
W = Weak
A = Absent

Color:
F = Flushed
N = Normal
P = Pale
C = Cyanotic

Capillary Refill:
N = Normal < 3 Sec.
S = Sluggish > 3 Sec.
A = Absent

Sensation:
N = Normal
Nu = Numb
T = Tingling
A = Absent

VENT SETTINGS

Time	FiO₂	TV	Rate	PEEP/CPAP	Mode

PLACE Scale

Time	Lab	Value

GLASGOW COMA SCALE

PHYSICIANS' ORDERS

No EKG ☐ Needed
No BP ☐ Needed
No SaO₂ ☐ Needed

POST ANESTHESIA AND PACU DISCHARGE NOTE

Transferred to: _____ Time Transferred: _____

PACU Nurse: _____

Page 18

MRN: Visit: DocType: OR Procedures

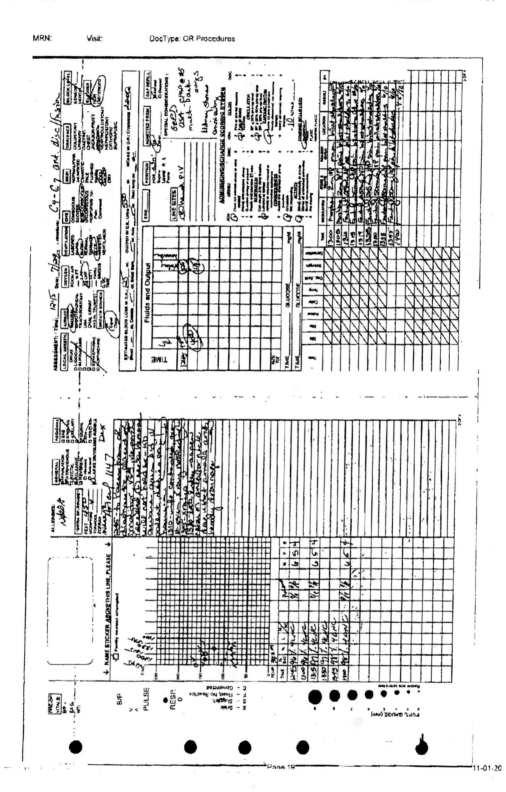

[2] The Anesthesia Pre-operative Evaluation

[Please see the Department of Anesthesiology Adult Health Assessment Questionnaire, illustrated on pages 788 and 789.]

This document is a brief medical history and record of physical findings that are most pertinent for the anesthesiologist. It is a document distinct from the attending physician's admission history and physical, and may contain important discrepancies when compared to that part of the hospital record.

HEALTH SYSTEM

Department of Anesthesiology
ADULT HEALTH ASSESSMENT QUESTIONNAIRE

PLANNED PROCEDURE:

PHYSICAL EXAM:

Airway:

Jaw:

Neck:

Lungs:

Heart:

ASSESSMENT:

ASA PHYSICAL STATUS:

ANESTHETIC PLAN:

Reviewed by:

Reader's CRNA | Date | Attending

How much can you walk before you need to stop? (Check one that fits you)
- ☐ Cannot walk up one flight of stairs
- ☐ Can walk up one flight of stairs
- ☐ Can walk up 3 flights of stairs without stopping
- ☐ Can walk uphill

Why do you need to stop? (Check all that apply)
- ☐ Short of breath
- ☐ Weakness, fatigue or dizziness
- ☐ Joint/ back pains
- ☐ Chest pain or pressure
- ☐ Muscle cramps
- ☐ Overweight

Is there anything else about your health that you think we should know to help us to care for you?

☐ NO ☐ YES If yes, please explain:

Patient's Signature _____ Date _____

Who is your family doctor? _____

Where can we phone you the afternoon before your surgery? _____ May we contact them? ☐ NO ☐ YES

Home Location _____ Home Phone ( )

_____ Work Phone ( )

May we leave a message? ☐ NO ☐ YES
Do you have call interrupt? ☐ NO ☐ YES
If you will be staying in a hotel, where? _____

If you are going home the same day of your surgery, who will take you?

Name Location _____ Home Phone ( )

_____ Work Phone ( )

Reviewed by: _____

Preanesthesia Evaluator
Center Clinician or CRNA

MRN: Visit: DocType: PETC/PACU

List all allergies (bad reaction) to the following: What happens:

Medicine: _None_

Food: _None_

Latex (rubber, elastic, balloons, tape, bandaids or similar product): _None_

List all the medicines that you now take (including over the counter medicines, vitamins, herbal products and nutritional supplements): _____

List any other medications that you have taken within the last year:
Tylenol   Topical   Ibuprofen   Sleep _____

List all of the operations that you have ever had:
Operation: _____   Type of anesthesia: _GA_   Any problems with anesthesia:
_9/14_

Has any blood relative ever had problems with anesthesia/ sleep medicine?   NO   YES

If yes, please explain: _____

DO YOU NOW HAVE: Comments:

A cough or cold	NO	YES
Contact lenses	NO	YES
Gill Lenses	NO	YES
Any chipped or loose teeth	NO	YES
Dentures, caps, crowns or bridgework, metal or plastic parts (e.g. hip replacement, metal rods, heart valves)	NO	YES
Do you use tobacco now?	NO	YES
Have you used tobacco in the past?	NO	YES
Chewing tobacco?	NO	YES
Cigars or pipe?	NO	YES
Cigarettes? _____ Packs per day for _____ years	NO	YES

If you no longer smoke, how long ago did you quit? _6 years_

Do you use alcohol (wine, beer and hard liquor)?   NO   YES   What kind? _____

Do you ever get high on alcohol?   NO   YES   What kind? _____

Do you use, daily, weekly, or rarely? (circle one)

Have you ever used drugs in the past?   NO   YES   How much? _____

HAVE YOU EVER HAD: (Circle correct answer)   Comments:

Stroke	NO	YES
Epilepsy or seizures	NO	YES
Weakness of an arm or leg	NO	YES
Numbness in the hands, legs or feet	NO	YES
Fainting spells	NO	YES
Muscle disease	NO	YES
High or low blood pressure	NO	YES
Heart murmur	NO	YES
Chest pain or pressure or angina	NO	YES
Heart attack	NO	YES
An irregular heart beat	NO	YES
Abnormal electrocardiogram (ECG)	NO	YES
Shortness of breath that wakes you up	NO	YES
Can you lie flat	NO	YES
Any abnormal chest x-ray	NO	YES
Pneumonia	NO	YES
Chronic or frequent cough	NO	YES
Asthma or wheezing	NO	YES
Sleep Apnea/ snoring	NO	YES
Rheumatoid arthritis	NO	YES
Excessive or easy bleeding	NO	YES
Anemia (low blood count)	NO	YES
Blood transfusion	NO	YES
Sickle cell disease	NO	YES
Heartburn or hiatal hernia	NO	YES
Yellow jaundice or hepatitis	NO	YES
Exposure to tuberculosis, hepatitis or AIDS	NO	YES
A "high" from drugs in the last week	NO	YES
Thyroid problems	NO	YES
Diabetes or high sugar	NO	YES
Recent kidney stones or infection	NO	YES
Kidney failure	NO	YES
Cancer	NO	YES
Fatty member with nerve or muscle disease	NO	YES
Parent, brother or sister who had a heart attack before age 50	NO	YES
Has your weight changed more than 10 pounds in the past year?	NO	YES

Women: Could you be or are you pregnant?   NO   YES

If your period is late, would you like a pregnancy test?   NO   YES

[3] Operating Room Nursing Record

[Please see the Perioperative Record, Intraoperative Section, illustrated on page 791 through 795].

This form is completed by the circulating operating room nurse and lists all personnel present—in this case, including the fact that a representative of the manufacturer of certain devices used in the operation was present, and the time period during which each person was present. It lists medications given. (Other medications, especially under anesthetic agents, will be found in the anesthesia record).

MRN: Visit: DocType: OR Procedures

'ERIOPERATIVE RECORD
INTRAOPERATIVE SECTION

PATIENT INFORMATION

Patient Name:	Account Num:	Gender:	M
Medical Record Num:	DOB:	OR Room	
Patient Status: INPT PREAD	Case Type: ELECTIVE	Sched Num:	
Attending:	Date: 7/7	Logged Num:	
Preop Diagnosis:	c4-5, c5-6, c6-c7 stenosis		

SKIN INTEGRITY

Temperature: WNL   Moisture: WNL   Color: WNL

Skin Integrity: Clear

Hair Removal Method / Location: NO HAIR REMOVAL NECESSARY

Prep Completed By:

Prep Solution: SCRUB, ALCOHOL & PREP

POSITIONING

Procedure	Position	Positioning Aids
CLOWARD (CERVICAL ANTERIOR DECO	SUPINE	ARM, BILATERAL, TUCKED AT SIDES
		ARM, OTHER POSITION, SEE COMMENTS/NURSES NOTES
		EGGCRATE
		GEL PAD
		HEAD REST HORSESHOE
		OTHER, SEE COMMENTS/NURSES NOTES
		PILLOW UNDER KNEES
		ROLL SHOULDER
		SAFETY STRAP OVER THIGHS
		SLED ARM

Comments: arms padded at side w/ sleds and kerlex to wrists. 10 lbs traction to head/neck w/ chin strap.

TEMPERATURE

Temperature Control Aids: FORCED AIR UNIT; HYDROTHERMIA UNIT; WARM BLANKETS; WARM IRRIGATION SOLUTIONS

Heating / Cooling Device	Site	Setting/Comments
FORCED AIR UNIT, BAIR HUGGER #44350	LOWER BODY	PER ANESTHESIA
HYDROTHERMIA UNIT, BLANKETROL #931-10962	UNDER GEL PAD/MATTRESS	40C

ELECTROSURGICAL

Unit Type #	Ground Pad Site	Prep Pad Site Condition	Hair Removal	Polarity	Cut Setting	Coag Setting
ESU VALLEYLAB #FOJ15167A	THIGH RIGHT ANTERIO		Hairless	Mono	30	30
BIPOLAR CODMAN #103117	N/A-NONE		Hairless	Bi	0	50

DEVICES / OTHER EQUIPMENT

Unit Type	Setting
OTHER DEVICE (SEE COMMENTS)	35-45MMHG

Comments: scd kendall #81686

Logged Num:

MRN: V   DocType: OR Procedures

PERIOPERATIVE RECORD
INTRAOPERATIVE SECTION

LASERS

Unit Type
N/A-NONE USED

ANESTHESIA

Anesthesia Type	ASA Code
GENERAL	2

PERSONNEL

Personnel	Role	Procedure	Time In	Time Out
	PCT	CLOWARD (CERVICAL ANTERIOR DE	07:26	12:40
	SCRUB 1	CLOWARD (CERVICAL ANTERIOR DE	01:50	12:40
		CLOWARD (CERVICAL ANTERIOR DE	07:26	11:17
	RN FIRST ASST	CLOWARD (CERVICAL ANTERIOR DE	07:26	12:40
	CRNA	CLOWARD (CERVICAL ANTERIOR DE	01:05	11:35
	PCT	CLOWARD (CERVICAL ANTERIOR DE	07:26	12:40
	SCRUB RELIEF	CLOWARD (CERVICAL ANTERIOR DE	01:17	11:50
	CIRC 1	CLOWARD (CERVICAL ANTERIOR DE	07:26	12:26
	SURG ATTENDING	CLOWARD (CERVICAL ANTERIOR DE	07:26	12:40
	ANES ATTENDING	CLOWARD (CERVICAL ANTERIOR DE	07:26	12:40
	SURG RESIDENT	CLOWARD (CERVICAL ANTERIOR DE	07:26	12:40
	ANES RESIDENT	CLOWARD (CERVICAL ANTERIOR DE	07:26	11:05
		CLOWARD (CERVICAL ANTERIOR DE	01:35	12:40
	CIRC RELIEF	CLOWARD (CERVICAL ANTERIOR DE	02:27	12:40

Comments: N   Danck rep in room.

IRRIGATIONS / SOLUTIONS

Type	Quantity
BACITRACIN 50,000UNITS/NACL 1L	1
STERILE WATER 1L (INSTRUMENT CARE)	1

MEDICATIONS

Type	Quantity	Route	Dosage	Comment / Site
EPINEPHRINE 1:1000 AMP	1	INJ. LOC./SUBQ	0.1CC	IN 20CC ROPIVACAINE
ROPIVACAINE 0.2% VIAL 20 ML	1	INJ. LOC./SUBQ	30CC	W/ 0.1CC EPI 1:1000
SURGIFOAM NO. 100	1	TOPICAL		

PROCEDURES

Procedure Name	Comment	Wound Class	CPT4 Code

Logged Num:

PERIOPERATIVE RECORD
INTRAOPERATIVE SECTION

CLOWARD (CERVICAL ANTERIOR DECOMPRESSION AND FUSI05,C5-6,C6-7	CLEAN	63075
		63076
		63076
		22554
		22845
		22585
		22585
		20931

Attending:
Dictating Physician:

CATHETERS

Type	Size	Inserted By	Return Color
FOLEY LATEX	16FR		CLEAR YELLOW

DRAINS / TUBES / PACKING

Type	Size	Quantity	Site
DRAIN HEMOVAC MEDIUM		1	NECK LEFT ANTERIOR

SPECIMEN / CULTURES

Specimen Type	Destination	Source
N/A		

Culture Type	Destination	Source
N/A		

IMPLANTS

Stocked Implants

Item Number	ID601628	CSS Load #	
Device Description	BONE DOWEL 12MM CLOWARD LNET+	Implanted	1.00
Manufacturer	LIFENET TISSUE SERVICE LIFENET	Used but not implanted	0.00
Catalog Number	CL12	Body Site	C-SPINE
Serial Number		Device Type	Implant
Lot #		Multi-Use	No

Item Number	ID603693	CSS Load #	
Device Description	FLOSEAL	Implanted	4.00
Manufacturer	Baxter BAXTER	Used but not implanted	0.00
Catalog Number	934057	Body Site	C-SPINE
Serial Number		Device Type	Implant
Lot #		Multi-Use	No

Item Number	ID601628	CSS Load #	
Device Description	BONE DOWEL 12MM CLOWARD LNET+	Implanted	1.00
Manufacturer	LIFENET TISSUE SERVICE LIFENET	Used but not implanted	0.00
Catalog Number	CL12	Body Site	C-SPINE
Serial Number		Device Type	Implant
Lot #		Multi-Use	No

Logged Num:

NO

MRN: Visit: DocType: OR Procedures

PERIOPERATIVE RECORD
INTRAOPERATIVE SECTION

Item Number	ID446862	CSS Load #	1994 29JUL05
Device Description	DANEK ATLANTIS SCREW 14MM SELFDRILL	Implanted	6.00
Manufacturer	Medtronic MEDTRONIC	Used but not implanted	0.00
Catalog Number	876614	Body Site	C SPINE
Serial Number		Device Type	Implant
Lot #		Multi-Use	No

Item Number	ID601628	CSS Load #	
Device Description	BONE DOWEL 12MM CLOWARD LNET+	Implanted	1.00
Manufacturer	LIFENET TISSUE SERVICE LIFENET	Used but not implanted	0.00
Catalog Number	CL12	Body Site	C-SPINE
Serial Number		Device Type	Implant
Lot #		Multi-Use	No

Item Number	ID485581	CSS Load #	1994 29JUL05
Device Description	DANEK ATLANTIS VISION PLATE 60MM	Implanted	1.00
Manufacturer	Medtronic MEDTRONIC	Used but not implanted	0.00
Catalog Number	976160	Body Site	C SPINE
Serial Number		Device Type	Implant
Lot #		Multi-Use	No

CHECKLIST

All generic standards, unit guidelines and procedures followed except as noted? Education Record and Plan of Care updated?   YES

Was documentation completed on Preoperative/Preprocedure Site Verification Checklist section three?   YES

Was primary procedure trauma related?   YES

Was Pathology specimen sent?   NO

Final Count Status: CORRECT

If an xray was taken, was it due to: XRAY TAKEN AS PART OF THE SURGICAL PROCEDURE

Was Fluoroscopy used in the OR?   NO

Was a flexible scope used during this case?   NO

Was Cardiopulmonary Bypass used in the OR?   NO

Were blood products given in the OR? RETURN UNUSED TO BLOOD BANK IMMEDIATELY!   NO

Were implants used in the OR?   YES, SEE IMPLANT SCREEN IN ORMIS

Was patient ID band present and verified using both name and MRN before transfer to postop destination?   YES

COUNTS

Procedure: CLOWARD (CERVICAL ANTERIOR DECOMPRESSION AND FUSION)

Class	Type	Status	Circulator	Scrub
FINAL	SPONGE, SHARPS	Correct		
FIRST	OTHER	Correct		
FIRST	SPONGE, SHARPS	Correct		
PRELIMINARY	OTHER	Correct		

Logged Num:

PERIOPERATIVE RECORD
INTRAOPERATIVE SECTION

PRELIMINARY   SPONGE, SHARPS   Correct

Actions Taken: NO ACTION TAKEN
FINAL CIRCULATING NURSE FOR COUNTS: , RN

TIMES

SETUP	Begin:	07:00	ROOM	In:	07:26	Out/OR Care Ended:	12.40
ANESTHESIA INDUCTION / PREP	Completed:	07:45	SURGERY	Start:	08:03	End:	12.30
PREP	Begin:	07:51					
TIME OUT PROCESS	Completed:	08:03					

POST OP

Discharge Information

Phone Report called at: 12:13   To: PACU   Date: 07/29

Skin Temperature: WNL   Moisture: WNL   Color: WNL
Skin Integrity: SAME AS PREOPERATIVELY
Postop Pad Site: Clear
Foley Removed: No
Postop Destination: PACU
Accompanied By: ANESTHESIA RESIDENT, SURGICAL RESIDENT
Blood Transport: N/A

NOTES
CIRCULATING NURSE COMPLETING CASE: , RN

Logged Num:

11-01-2006 09:50:28

[4] Anesthesia Record

[Please see the Anesthesia Record illustrated on pages 797 and 798.]

On these two pages are recorded the patient's vital signs every five minutes the patient is in the operating room. The administration of anesthesia appears to have been uneventful in the case shown. Medications given, inspired oxygen and oxygen saturation are recorded. End-tidal CO_2 is recorded, and abnormal or absent values may have some significance in intracranial surgery. Much other information is available, including the anesthetic agents used, other drugs administered, and the stop and start times of surgery.

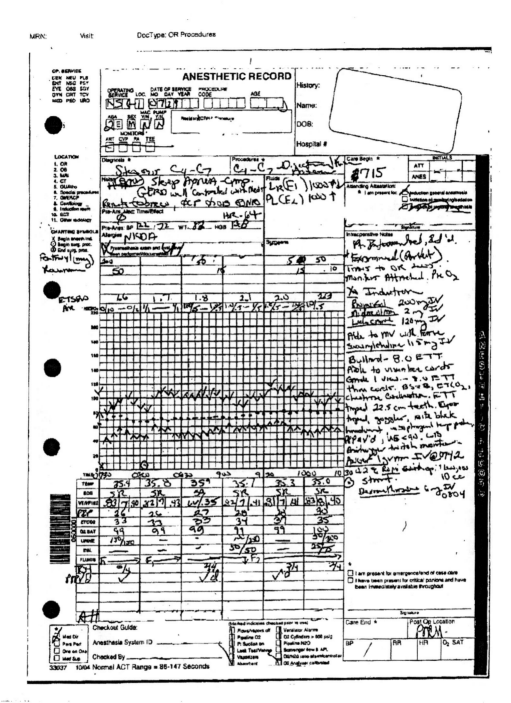

MRN: Visit: DocType: OR Procedures

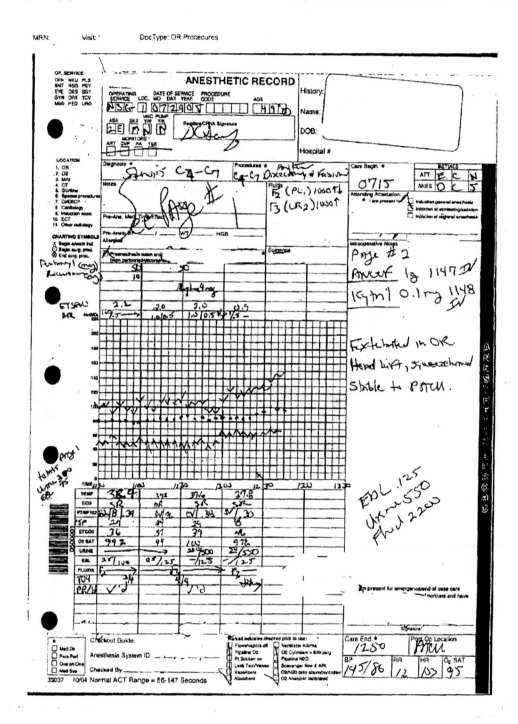

[5] Post-Anesthesia Recovery Room Record

[Please refer to the Post Anesthesia Recovery Record illustrated on pages 785 and 786.]

When postoperative neurological complications have occurred, an important question is often whether or not an adverse event is immediately present upon the patient's wakening from anesthesia, or is not initially present but evolves over a course of several hours, say. In the latter situation, such adverse changes are more likely to be treatable or susceptible to appropriate intervention. Often, close review of the recovery room record is essential to answering this question.

[6] The Electronic Medical Record (EMR)

The increasing use of electronic records poses many challenges to traditional methods of discovery, and even before discovery procedures are appropriate.[34]

There is an increasing number of health care entities (including hospitals, physician offices, and long term care facilities) that have gone "paperless," i.e. for all intents and purposes (except, say, for the production and retention of a signed informed consent form, and a few other selected documents) have entirely eliminated the paper record. The EMR contains a wealth of information not generally available in the traditional paper record, generally, in the form of metadata. Metadata is, simply put, data about data, i.e., a note generated in the form of text, may also contain information about who generated it, when it was generated, when it was altered, and by whom, etc. Different health care entities use a wide range of proprietary EMR products, so that exactly what metadata is obtained, what is retained and what is deleted may vary, depending upon the architecture of the particular EMR system and the policies of the particular institution.

Authentication of information entered into the EMR is usually by user name and password, and there is a presumption that the person with a unique user name and password in fact entered the information. Exactly how the law would treat such a presumption (i.e., whether it is rebuttable, and under what circumstances) remains to be seen.

The paperless hospital chart is still in its infancy, and a number of other potential problems of proof exist. Some systems provide for the input of information when the author is not physically present within the hospital. A

---

[34] Keris, M, New Legal Issues for Electronic Medical Records: Claims, Discovery & Compliance, Presented March 29, 2007, National Constitution Center, www.constitution conferences.com/main.asp?G=1&E=866&I=1 (last accessed 12/16/07).

physician might enter what looks like a progress note generated almost contemporaneous to being at the beside, when in fact the note could be worded such as to create an ambiguity, and include recent data about the patient, from a remote location, say, China, and a reader several months later may completely miss that fact. Presumably, a close look at metadata would at least raise a question about where the author of the note was at the time (whether actually in the presence of the patient or not).

Contemporaneous access to the EMR may emerge as an issue. A hospital has forbidden access to the EMR by a patient or family member with the patient's permission, under circumstances where it was quite clear that the paper chart would clearly be available as a matter of right under the law.

The generation of text as part of the EMR is fraught with the potential for the propagation of misinformation within the patient's chart.[35]

In 2006 the Federal Rules of Civil Procedure were amended, and in effect, created a new category of discoverable matter.[36] States are in various stages of amending their civil rules, and many adopting in concept the changes incorporated into the F.R.C.P.

Exactly what constitutes the "legal" health record is a concept in evolution. The "legal" health record has been defined as "[That which is] generated at or for a healthcare organization as its business record and is the record that would be released upon request. *It does not affect the discoverability of other information held by the organization* [italics added]."[37]

[7] Office Records

Physician and group practice offices are also moving toward a paperless EMR. Many offices, however, may have archived volumes of written information printed on paper, but stored electronically in non-authenticated form. Records printed out from information stored electronically may be difficult or impossible to properly authenticate.

---

[35] *See, for example,* Hirschtick, RE, Copy-and-Paste, N.ENGJMED 2006;295:2335. *See also,* Kush, RD, et al., Electronic Health Records, Medical Research and the Tower of Babel, N.ENGJMED 2008:358:16.

[36] Federal Rules of Civil Procedure (Dec. 1, 2006), www.judiciary.house.gov/media/pdfs/printers/109th/31308.pdf. *See also,* Paul, GL, and Nearon, BH, THE DISCOVERY REVOLUTION: E-DISCOVERY AMENDMENTS TO THE FEDERAL RULES OF CIVIL PROCEDURE, American Bar Association, Chicago, 2006.

[37] AHIMA. *Update: Guidelines for Defining the Health Record for Disclosure Purposes,* JOURNAL OF AHIMA 2005;76(8).

§ 12.09 Related Topics

[1] Peer Review Procedures

The peer review committee in a hospital studies medical records to evaluate patient care generally and the individual performances of the physicians on the staff. The committee looks for such things as how often a physician's admitting diagnosis is the same as the final diagnosis, whether appropriate treatment was rendered, whether a particular physician's treatment outcomes and other statistics are significantly different from other members of staff in the same specialty.

Much of the information generated by peer review activities is unavailable to, or extremely difficult to obtain by, a lawyer representing plaintiffs in medical malpractice cases. The idea is that, if such information is not protected, its generation will be suppressed in some way so that it is not available to the agencies for which it was originally intended and thus may interfere with the quality assurance functions of those agencies. If minor reductions in a physician's hospital privileges are to become a matter of public record, it will be harder for hospitals to place limits on a physician's privileges, and any disciplinary action may be more difficult and time-consuming if there are to be wide-ranging reverberations adversely affecting the physician. Many state legislatures have, therefore, taken the position that free peer review, narrowly privileged, is better for the public good than to allow too much disclosure of the discussion in the proceedings and in disciplinary actions.

Congress has also recognized the need for protection of peer review activities from antitrust liability of physicians engaged in peer review activities, and this recognition is explicit in the Health Care Quality Improvement Act;[38] however, that protection is circumscribed by the requirement of good faith, and more specifically by adherence to detailed procedural requirements in carrying out peer review activities.

Most of the information desired about a practitioner can be obtained by knowing what information to seek in the process of discovery. Information about individual cases can often be obtained with a greater degree of thoroughness than can be obtained from records of peer review proceedings, if the proper witnesses are identified and questioned. Information about other similar cases and patterns of complications may be difficult to obtain for reasons of patient confidentiality and relevancy.

---

[38] Health Care Quality Improvement of 1996.

Related causes of action, such as negligence on the part of the hospital in credentialing or litigation relating to disciplinary actions, may provide leads to obtaining important information.

[a] Protection of Peer Review

There is wide variation of state statutory and case law with regard to what information is discoverable, and this variation reflects continued struggle with the policy issues of the purpose of peer review (maintaining quality of care), and the need for open and candid discussion among peers to accomplish that purpose, balanced against the need for information about an individual case where an adverse event has occurred.

[2] The Neurosurgeon as Expert Witness

The American Association of Neurological Surgeons has published rules for members who provide expert opinions:

Impartial Testimony

■ The neurosurgical expert witness shall be an impartial educator for attorneys, jurors and the court on the subject of neurosurgical practice.

■ The neurosurgical expert witness shall represent and testify as to the practice behavior of a prudent neurological surgeon giving different viewpoints if such there are.

■ The neurosurgical expert witness shall identify as such any personal opinions that vary significantly from generally accepted neurosurgical practice.

■ The neurosurgical expert witness shall recognize and correctly represent the full standard of neurosurgical care and shall with reasonable accuracy state whether a particular action was clearly within, clearly outside of, or close to the margins of the standard of neurosurgical care.

■ The neurosurgical expert witness shall not be evasive for the purpose of favoring one litigant over another. The neurosurgical expert shall answer all properly framed questions pertaining to his or her opinions on the subject matter thereof.

Subject Matter Knowledge

■ The neurosurgical expert witness shall have sufficient knowledge of and experience in the specific subject(s) of his or her written expert opinion or sworn oral testimony to warrant designation as an expert.

■ The neurosurgical expert witness shall review all pertinent available medical information about a particular patient prior to rendering an opinion about the appropriateness of medical or surgical management of that patient.

Compensation

■ The neurosurgical expert witness shall not accept a contingency fee for providing expert medical opinion services.

■ Charges for medical expert opinion services shall be reasonable and commensurate with the time and effort given to preparing and providing those services.[39]

The Professional Conduct Committee of the AANS has sanctioned members for improper expert testimony. Sanctions have included censure, suspension, and expulsion, and are reported to the licensing authorities of the state in which the practitioner is licensed. It is the contention of the AANS Professional Conduct Committee that suspension or expulsion "must be reported" to the National Practitioner Data Bank.[40]

In at least one state, the fact that a member has been expelled for improper testimony has been held inadmissible to impeach the expelled member.[41]

The AANS maintains an electronic library of expert witness testimony to assist members and their attorneys in litigation. The database is searchable by witness name, but not by type of case or expertise.[42]

[a] Expert Witness Fees

Virtually all professional societies that have spoken on the subject abjure any kind of contingency fee paid to an expert witness. Perhaps the most

---

[39] A ANS BULLETIN 2004(Spring);13(1):33.

[40] Blackett WB, *Lessons from recent Professional Conduct Committee hearings*, AANS BULLETIN 1996(Winter);5(1):12. *Note:* It is not clear that the rules of the NPDB require a report, and no authority is cited.

[41] Haney v. Pagnanelli, 830 A.2d 978 (Pa. Super. 2003).

[42] A ANS BULLETIN 2000;9:33.

reasonable approach is for the expert witness to charge and be paid based upon the actual time spent on a case. The hourly rate should probably represent some kind of average that neurosurgeon is paid for his other professional practice activities. It is also reasonable for a neurosurgeon to charge a higher rate for deposition and trial appearance, because those activities involve dedicated time, usually during weekdays, and thus require more interference with the neurosurgeon's usual work schedule. Chart review and reports can often be done off hours and on a flexible schedule. When neurosurgeons discuss fees charged for expert testimony and how they answer questions about those fees in court, the existence of some unusual ideas and practices emerges.[43] Some feel that is impossible for anyone to render an opinion uninfluenced by the fact that he or she is being paid to render an opinion. Others feel the need to deceive the court. The paid expert witness who disagrees with another paid expert witness is sometimes characterized as biased and a "whore," and the feeling is usually mutual.

[b] Bias

Effective cross-examination continues to be the most effective way to demonstrate bias of expert witnesses.

Neurosurgeons may unwittingly reveal extreme bias by class of litigant, i.e., by consistently refusing to involve themselves if the litigant is a patient-plaintiff, but not if the litigant is a doctor-defendant. Why does a neurosurgeon, supposedly qualified to make critical clinical decisions sometimes without the benefit of consultation, need to have the agreement of three other colleagues in call cases before being able to state that a deviation from accepted standards of care has occurred? Or why does a neurosurgeon providing an opinion for a plaintiff insist that there be an agreement ahead of time that the opinion be provided in writing to the defendant in all cases? On the other hand, the defendant physician has an extensive network of colleagues on whom she may call, and can pick and choose from a wide range of opinions favorable to his case. And, of course, she will be under no obligation to divulge those opinions she obtains and chooses not to put on the record. At least one writer seems to imply that such a disclosure requirement is a good way for neurosurgeons to discourage plaintiff's attorneys from requesting an opinion about whether a deviation from accepted standards of care has occurred.[44] Would it not be easier to "Just say no!"?

---

[43] Alexander, EB, Jr., SURG NEUROL 1987;27:505.   *See also* Portnoy HD, SURG NEUROL 1987;28:473.

[44] Portnoy HD SURG NEUROL 1987:28:473.

Just as reasonable minds may differ, reasonable neurosurgeons' minds differ also. Naturally, parties will often evaluate opinions from more than one expert, and will then select the expert with the opinions believed to be most favorable to the case, given that other witness qualities are roughly the same. The bias of selection might be termed *objective* bias; it is not undesirable, and it is a natural result of the adversary system, which allows parties to select whom they will call as witnesses.

[c] Expert Witness Agencies

Defendant doctors decry the physicians who associate themselves with expert witness agencies, or who advertise their availability as expert witnesses. To some extent, these factors probably reflect negatively on a witness; however, the large expert witness "industry" would probably not exist if all neurosurgeons would agree to testify if they believed negligence existed. It is often extremely difficult for attorneys to locate neurosurgeons who are willing to review cases and provide on-the-record opinion. This is especially so when a neurosurgeon is in the same community as the defendant.

If all practicing neurosurgeons occasionally provided their opinions in medical malpractice cases, without regard to class of litigant, it is this writer's believe that there would be fewer lawsuits, and the system of medical negligence law would be a far more effective vehicle of peer review and tool of quality assurance.

[d] Liability as an Expert Witness

Potentially, an expert retained by a party could have civil liability for inadequate review of records, inaccurate testimony, or late expert reports.

[e] Disciplinary Action for Expert Testimony

The American Association of Neurological Surgeons (AANS) provides for discipline of its members who testify unprofessionally, through its Professional Conduct Program, established in 1983.[45] This Program has withstood legal challenge,[46] and has provided a model for other professional societies

More recently, state licensing boards have brought disciplinary action against licensees for alleged improper testimony.[47] Some state boards , and

---

[45] AANS NEUROSURGEOn 2007;16:37.

[46] Austin v. American Association of Neurological Surgeons, 253 F.3d 957 (2001); *cert. denied*, 534 U.S. 1078 (2002).

[47] In Re: Lustgarten, M.D., 629 S.E.2d 886 (N.C. Ct. App. 2006). *See* Rebecca Ridick, *Fla. Doctor Prevails in License Fight over Expert Testimony*, LAW.COM, 6/28/06,

the Federation of State Medical Boards have taken the position the expert witness testimony, at least in medical professional liability cases, constitutes the practice of medicine, a position that has not, to date, been upheld in any court case or legislation.

[3] Effect of Tort Reform

Efforts to change tort law are a high priority of medical specialty societies,[48] and illustrate the tension between the need to compensate victims of medical negligence and the economic and emotional costs to the practitioner.

The possible effects of such reform include (1) reduced access to compensation for injuries due to negligence, (2) a realization that the current tort system is uneven, with a perception that many such injuries do not result in lawsuits and that many lawsuits are without merit, (3) a realization that the current system, as a method of quality control, is extremely inefficient, (4) a greater realization that much can and needs to be done to prevent medical errors through a systems approach, (5) where caps on non-economic damages have been in place, there is a tendency to look to defendants other than the physician, such as product manufacturers, and hospitals, with novel theories of liability, and (6) a movement to resolve or prevent potential claims through more transparency and communication between practitioner and patient, or patient's family (several states have enacted statutes that provide for inadmissibility of expressions of apology, and even a few making admissions of fault inadmissible under certain circumstances).

[4] Health Care Quality Improvement Act of 1986 and the National Practitioner Data Bank

On the heels of Patrick v. Burget, Congress passed the Health Care Quality Improvement Act of 1986 (HCQIA), which established the National Practitioner Data Bank (NPDB).[49] The original intent of the legislation was to protect physicians engaging in peer review. In Patrick, a group practice that comprised most of the medical staff of a small hospital in Astoria, Oregon, suspended staff privileges (purportedly for substandard care) of a doctor who had left the group and wished to continue practicing at the hospital. The U.S. Supreme Court held those staff members who sanctioned

---

http://www.law.com/jsp/law/LawArticleFriendly.jsp?id=900005550036, for a summary and discussion (last access 6/10/08).

[48] *See for example,* http://aans.org/medical/ (last access 6/11/08).

[49] NATIONAL HEALTH CARE QUALITY IMPROVEMENT ACT OF 1986, as amended, 42 U.S.C. 11101 *et seq.*

the doctor, to be in violation of anti-trust law and liable for treble damages. The judgment bankrupted the group practice, and sent shock waves through medical staffs all over the country. In response to this decision and the reaction that followed, Congress passed HCQIA, which provided protection for good-faith peer review. HCQIA also established the NPDB to aid hospitals and other credentialing entities in identifying those physicians who moved from state to state with a hard-to-trace trail of medical malpractice judgments against them.

[5] Patient Safety and Quality Improvement Act of 2005 (PSQIA)

In response to the Institute of Medicine's 1999 report, *To Err is Human: Building a Safer health System*,[50] Congress passed the PSQIA of 2005.[51] On February 12, 2008, the Department of Health and Human Services published proposed regulations[52] to implement portions of the PSQIA. The comment period expired on April 12, 2008. The proposed regulations provide for voluntary reporting to Patient Safety Organizations (PSOs) for monitoring and analysis of patient safety events, including confidentiality protections, and penalties for impermissible disclosure of protected information. Presumably, information provided under the protection of the final regulations would not be protected if discoverable by other means.

[6] Neurosurgeon-industry Conflicts of Interest

In response to recent disclosures of kickbacks paid to physicians by medical equipment manufacturers,[53] both the American Association of Neurological Surgeons (AANS) and the Congress of Neurological Surgeons (CNS), recognizing the potential adverse effect on patient care, recently issued a joint statement promulgating guidelines for dealing with conflicts of interest.[54]

---

[50] Available at http://www.nap.edu/catalog.php?record_id=9728 (last access 6/1/08).

[51] PATIENT SAFETY AND QUALITY IMPROVEMENT ACT OF 2005, PUB. L. NO. 109-41; 42 U.S.C. 299 *et seq.* (2005).

[52] 73 FED. REG. 8112 (February 12, 2008).

[53] *For example, see* Evelyn Pringle, *Feds Crack Down on Medical Device Implant For Profit Industry - Part I*, http://www.lawyersandsettlements.com/articles/01570/device-maker-kickbacks.html (last accessed 6/1/08), and *Feds Crack Down on Medical Device Implant For Profit Industry - Part II* (Nov. 14, 2007), http://www.lawyersandsettlements.com/articles/01571/device-makers-agreement.html (last access 6/1/08).

[54] *Guidelines on Neurosurgeon-Industry Conflicts of Interest*, http://www.cns.org/about/pdf/NeurosurgeonsIndustryJointStatement.pdf (last access 6/1/08), or http://www. aans. org/about/membership/Neurosurgeon-Industry_Conflicts-of-Interest5-08.pdf (last access 6/1/08).

[7] Attorney Sanctions

Physicians who believe they are the victim of meritless or frivolous lawsuits are beginning to have some success in actions against the plaintiff's attorney.[55]

---

[55] Amy Lynn Sorrel, *Physicians challenge lawyers' meritless liability suits – and win*, AANS NEUROSURGEON 2007;16:45-47. *See, for example,* Sarah N. Ratliff and Charles Gibson III v. Lawrence E. Stewart, elder (5th U.S. Ct. App.); Gisele Ponder v. Robert W. Kamienski, MD, et al (Ohio Court of Appeals, 9th Judicial Circuit); Brenda Callahan v. Akron General Medical Center, Mark T. Jaroch, MD (Court of Common Pleas, Summit County, OH); Marie Sigmon v. Southwest General Health Center et al., (Ohio Court of Appeals, 8th Appellate District).

CHAPTER 13

OTOLARYNGOLOGY

Matthew L. Howard, MD, FACS

SYNOPSIS

§ 13.01 Training and Certification of Otolaryngologists

[1] Medical School

All otolaryngologists begin their education in medical school. Some medical schools allow a few students to begin after three years of undergraduate education; most require a Bachelor's degree. Medical school is normally a four-year program. Special programs exist requiring an additional two or three years and resulting in award of a PhD or JD degree along with the MD or DO degree.

[2] First Post-graduate Year

Specialty training begins after medical school. The first post-graduate year has traditionally been called an "internship" but in 1969 a study sponsored by the American Medical Association recommended abandoning the internship in favor of beginning residency specialty training immediately. Although the name was officially abandoned in 1975, many training programs still have their first post-graduate year trainees spend several weeks in multiple areas of medical specialization, thus duplicating the traditional rotating internship under another name.

[3] Residency Training

Residency training thus begins immediately after graduation from medical school, with the trainee either devoting his or her entire time to the specialty area, or spending the first year being exposed in addition to several other specialties that are closely related to otolaryngology, such as pediatrics or neurosurgery. All programs include a year in general surgery, intended to more fully acquaint the trainee with management of acute medical and surgical conditions. A minimum of three years is devoted to the specialty of otolaryngology itself, learning patient care, and gaining experience in performing surgical procedures included in the specialty. The first post-graduate year, the year of general surgery, and the specialty specific training years total five years. In some programs, an extra year devoted to full-time clinical or basic research is part of the program.

As this is written, there are 125 accredited otolaryngology or otolaryngology subspecialty training programs in the United States and Canada, with 1398 positions filled.

The majority of training programs require their residents to take the annual otolaryngology examination administered by the American Board of Otolaryngology. The results provide evidence of progress in learning the basic factual material needed, and may allow program directors to detect areas of weakness in their programs.

[4] Subspecialty Training

Specialties arose as a matter of necessity as the range of medical knowledge expanded beyond the abilities of a single person to master. Continuation of the same process has led to subspecialty training and certification. An extra year of training, called a "fellowship," leading to eligibility to undertake a separate examination for subspecialty certification, is available in neurotology and sleep medicine. Informal certification without a formal examination is available in pediatric otolaryngology, facial plastic and reconstructive surgery, major head and neck and reconstructive surgery, and otology.

[5] The American Board of Otolaryngology—Head and Neck Surgery

The American Board of Otolaryngology was founded in 1924, the second such organization founded to supervise the training, and to provide examinations, of persons wishing to be recognized as specialists in the field. The name has been changed twice, with the current name intended to convey the great range of responsibility assumed by its diplomates, extending far beyond traditional "ears, nose, and throat." A physician who has satisfactorily completed an approved training program is considered eligible to take the Board's examination. The examination consists of both a written and oral examination. The written examination must be passed in order for the second, oral examination to be scored. A passing score on the written examination provides the candidate with three opportunities to pass the oral examination, following which the written examination must be retaken.

Those who pass both examinations are immediately issued a document certifying their status as "Board certified" specialists.

Persons certified prior to 2002 received certificates valid for life, although procedures for revocation exist if concerns about ethics or competence arise. Persons certified after 2002 must be re-certified by demonstrating they have completed a minimum number of hours of continuing education, and by examination, every ten years.

The Board has expressed its intent to evaluate diplomates in the clinical settings in which they work, but has acknowledged that at present methods for such evaluation do not exist.

§ 13.02 Types of Practice

[1] Private Practice

"Private practice" encompasses a variety of practice settings that are neither academic nor governmental. Traditionally, this meant establishing an autonomous business, either alone, or with one to three partners or employed physicians, and necessary auxiliary staff. In this setting, the physicians combine fee-for-service, reimbursement through third-party contracts, and reimbursement from government programs such as Medicare or Medicaid. Many such practitioners maintain a relationship, usually as volunteers, with a nearby medical school or other academic institution, teaching students and helping train the next generation of specialists.

Private practitioners can also be part of large single- or multi-specialty groups such as HMOs.

[2] Academic Practice

Medical schools and their affiliated hospitals provide training for new physicians and specialists, carry out the largest part of clinical research, and provide patient care of the highest caliber, described as "tertiary care" because they deal with the difficult problems that family doctors and community based specialists find too difficult or unusual to deal with. The specialists who work in this setting, usually with an academic title such as "Professor," are in academic practice. As funding for teaching has become more difficult to obtain, many academic practice physicians are being required to devote part of their time to private practice in the academic setting, so that the fees generated can help support either their salary, personally, or the needs of the department.

[3] Governmental Practice

Otolaryngologists may work as salaried employees of state institutions, of the Armed Forces, Veterans affairs hospitals and clinics, or Public Health Service facilities. In such settings, their duties are identical to those described above. It is their employee status which differentiates them. In many instances, academic practice is also governmental practice.

[4] Research

Research activities are part of the academic physician's practice, and this is often true of private practitioners also. A small number of otolaryngologists will be involved only in research, without responsibility for patient care.

§ 13.03 Specialty Scope-of-Practice by Practice Area

[1] Disclosure of Risks and Informed Consent

We generally assume in the United States that competent adults have a right to determine for themselves the medical treatment they will accept. A surgeon may well conclude that a particular procedure is in his or her patient's best interests, but may not proceed on that basis alone. It is always necessary to obtain consent to any procedure planned, and for more than a hundred years, the courts have assumed that such consent must be "informed." Beginning in 1975, the courts have constructed a framework outlining the elements of the informed consent. Basically, the requirement is for disclosure of all material risks. Material risks are those risks a reasonable person would want to know before agreeing to a procedure. If the risk is common, or although uncommon, is severe, it should be disclosed. A fully informed consent requires the patient to know any alternatives available, and the consequences of not following the advice given.

The courts apply these requirements with common sense. If a patient's condition is life-threatening, or will cause significant functional or cosmetic impairment, and the patient is unable to consent, the courts will generally not second guess a surgeon's decision to proceed even where complications occur. If the procedure is purely cosmetic, disclosure must be painstaking, covering all eventualities. In the field of otolaryngology, where mutilation, severe functional impairment, and death are always possible due to the proximity of major vessels and nerves to areas requiring surgical attention, obtaining informed consent is a critical issue.

[2] Otology

Otology is the branch of otolaryngology dealing with medical and surgical treatment of diseases of the ear. Neurotology includes otology, but adds to it, "advanced diagnostic expertise and advanced medical and surgical management skills for the care of diseases and disorders of the petrous apex, infratemporal fossa, internal auditory canals, cranial nerves and lateral skull base (including the occipital bone, sphenoid bone, temporal bone, mesial aspect of the dura and intradural management), in conjunction with neurological surgery."

[3] Anatomy

The ear is divided into three adjacent but distinct areas. The auricle, or outer ear, is the visible structure. It consists of a cartilaginous framework covered with skin. Extending inward is the ear canal, with a skin lining covering cartilage laterally and bone medially, and terminating with the tympanic membrane or "ear drum." The tympanic membrane divides the ear canal from the middle ear.

In the middle ear, which lies "behind" or medial to, the ear drum are three small bones, or "ossicles." The first is attached to the ear drum, and is called the malleus, or "hammer." Attached to the malleus by a joint is the incus, or "anvil." The other end of the incus attaches through yet another joint to the stapes, or "stirrup." The malleus is held in position by its attachment to the ear drum and by suspensory ligaments and one muscle tendon. The stapes is held in position by the ligament securing it in the oval window, which is the opening into the inner ear, and also by the tendon of the stapedius muscle. The middle bone, the incus, is held in position by the joints at either end and by a group of suspensory ligaments. When sound waves reach the ear drum, causing it to vibrate, the vibrations are transmitted through the three bones to the inner ear, where the hearing portion of the inner ear, or cochlea, acts a transducer, converting the mechanical motion of a vibration into the electrochemical signal that travels up the hearing nerve to the brain.

The facial nerve, primary source of motion signals to the facial muscles, passes through the middle ear from its origin in the brain stem and exits the middle ear from the base of the skull behind a structure called the mastoid tip, a bony prominence one can feel behind and below the auricle. As the facial nerve passes through the middle ear it is joined by the fibers of the chorda tympani, carrying taste sensation from the tongue.

At the anterior and inferior margin of the middle ear is the opening of the Eustachian tube. The other end of the tube is in the nasopharynx, behind the nose. The tube remains closed at all times, except when a person yawns or swallows. During that moment of patency, air flows either in to or out from the middle ear to assure that air pressure on either side of the ear drum is equal, with the air pressures equal, the ear is most able to detect quiet sounds.

Behind the middle ear, and connected to it through a narrow opening at the upper end of the middle ear, is the mastoid sinus. This consists of a large number of connected air pockets in small bony cavities or "air cells." The facial nerve passes through it usually completely encased in bone. Except when it is involved with chronic infection, the mastoid is of no consequence.

The third component of the ear is the inner ear, itself comprised of two structures. These are the cochlea, which is the hearing portion, and the vestibule, which contains sensing organs responsible for measuring spatial orientation, and the degree and direction of movement. Signals from these two structures pass to the brain through the two segments of the 8th cranial nerve.

[4] Trauma to the External Ear

The external ear, also called the auricle and pinna, is composed of a layer of skin covering a flexible cartilage framework. It is vulnerable to trauma.

Wrestlers, and occasionally athletes in other sports, are subject to the formation of "auricular hematoma." This occurs when shearing forces are applied to the auricle, causing slight separation of the skin from the cartilage. Bleeding ensues. A blood-filled pocket is called a hematoma. Treatment is surgical drainage of the blood. If this is not done, or if not done properly, the ear heals by cartilage growth into the hematoma, resulting in a permanent thickening of the auricle. Such injuries can accumulate, leading to the deformity called "cauliflower ear." This may also occur in some cases despite adequate treatment.

The ear is also vulnerable to lacerations and avulsions, usually in motor vehicle accidents. These are treated by removal of devitalized skin and cartilage, and careful approximation of the wound edges by suturing the remaining undamaged skin. When the auricle is detached, or avulsed, repair is successful so long as adequate blood supply remains through the uninvolved remaining attachment. Up to one third of the ear can be removed and reattached with success. If fifty percent or more is missing, large portions of the reattached ear are likely to necrose, or die, resulting in a need for plastic surgery at a future time to refashion a cosmetically acceptable ear.

[5] Cerumen Impaction of the External Ear Canal

Lining the cartilaginous portion of the external ear canal are glands that secrete an oily substance which combines with skin cells shed from the canal lining to form cerumen, or ear wax. Normally the cerumen migrates from the deeper portion of the canal to the opening. In some people, the quantity of cerumen produced, or its consistency, or a combination of the two leads to accumulations that fill the ear canal. The use of cotton-tipped applicators and other objects to clean the ears frequently results in pushing the cerumen deeper into the ear canal. Persons with ear canals blocked by cerumen may experience a sensation of blockage and/or decreased hearing.

Cerumen removal is a common procedure. The ear canal can be irrigated with a stream of water. If care is taken to direct the stream of water along the edge of the canal, it will flow into and out of the ear canal, carrying the cerumen with it, and without risk of damaging the ear drum with the stream of water. The cerumen can be removed by suction, usually under direct vision. The third technique for removing cerumen is to use a variety of small metal hooks and loops to manipulate the cerumen from the canal.

In addition to ear drum damage from irrigation, injury can occur if the noise of suctioning, or discomfort caused by touching suction instruments to the ear canal or ear drum, or movement of the cerumen during suctioning, cause sudden patient movement. The likelihood of damage is also increased by anatomic abnormalities of the ear canal, such as stenosis or the presence of exostoses. Abnormalities of the ear drum may also contribute, such as an atrophic area of the tympanic membrane that could tear under the pressure of a stream of water that would not injure a normal ear drum.

[6] Infection of the External Ear Canal (Otitis Externa)

Infections of the external ear canal occur fairly commonly. When such infections result from water exposure, most frequently due to swimming, they are characterized as "swimmer's ear." Swimming, showering and hair washing can leave small amounts of residual water in the ear canal. It may be more easily trapped when the ear contains partially obstructing cerumen. The resulting warm, moist environment encourages bacterial proliferation of normal skin bacteria or of pathogenic bacteria incidentally present. Public swimming pools may be contaminated with enteric organisms, including Pseudomonas aeruginosa, often associated with ear canal infection.

Treatment consists of debridement of the ear canal to remove cerumen and purulent material debris obstructing the ear canal. This provides reduction of moisture, aeration, and allows ear drops to contact the infected skin. Topical antibiotic drops, dehydrating and acidifying drops, and/or antifungal drops may be used depending on the characteristics of the individual case. Few such infections are serious. However, a form of external otitis that spreads to underlying bone and cartilage, almost always in immunocompromised persons such as elderly diabetics, is known as malignant otitis externa. The term does not imply neoplasm; instead, it refers to the severity of the disease. Untreated, usually for failure to recognize its presence, malignant external otitis may lead to meningitis, brain abscess or uncontrollable bleeding and death.

[7] Trauma to the Ear Drum and Ossicles

Trauma to the tympanic membrane and middle ear ossicles occurs by several mechanisms. First, in the process of removing cerumen, whether by water irrigation or insrumentation, carelessness of the operator or movement by the patient may lead to injury. This may also result from patients' attempts to remove cerumen, including use of cotton tipped applicators and hairpins. Severe pain, some bleeding, and hearing loss are common symptoms.

Second, atmospheric overpressure from explosions can rupture the ear drum. The ossicles can be dislocated. At least one case has been reported where such an injury led to profuse CSF otorrhea through perforation of the round window membrane. A related injury occurs when a water skier or personal watercraft rider falls, striking the ear against the water surface. Because of the water entering the middle ear, such injuries have a higher risk of infection. A blow to the external ear may compress a column of air in the ear canal leading to ear drum perforation similar to that created by explosive overpressure.

Traumatic perforations are initially managed by observation. Even perforations involving more than 50% of the tympanic membrane will heal spontaneously, especially in persons with no prior history of ear infection. Antibiotic ear drops may be used when the injury included water entry into the middle ear. Healing may take several weeks, with full return of hearing if the tympanic membrane was the only injury. If a significant conductive hearing loss persists after healing of the tympanic membrane, exploration of the middle ear for replacement or repositioning of involved dislocated or disarticulated ossicles may be required.

[8] Trauma to the Inner Ear

Traumatic injury to the inner ear results from acoustic trauma, from penetrating injuries of the tympanic membrane, and from head injury.

Exposure of the ear to loud sound, especially from an explosion, leads to transmission of excess sound energy to the inner ear. The cochlea and vestibular labyrinth may be damaged with impairment of hearing and balance. If the injury is sufficiently severe, the hearing impairment may be permanent. Unless a fistula of the round or oval window has been created, balance impairment is usually self-limited. The vestibular system may heal, or central mechanisms may compensate even for severe injury, to eventually eliminate symptoms.

Blows to the head may lead to concussion without fracture. Sufficient energy can be transmitted to the inner ear to create hearing and balance impairment. The balance impairment typically resolves but the hearing loss can be permanent. Loss of consciousness is not needed for hearing impairment to be present.

Where fractures of the temporal bone occur, they may be either fractures parallel to the long axis of the temporal bone (running roughly medio-lateral) or transverse to the long axis (running roughly anterior-posterior). Those parallel to the long process of the temporal bone are more likely to involve injury to the middle ear ossicles and tympanic membrane. Immediate symptoms may include bleeding from the ear canal, disruption of the tympanic membrane, and dislocation of middle ear ossicles with resulting conductive hearing loss. Typically head trauma sufficient to cause temporal bone fracture leads to loss of consciousness, so that the hearing loss is not appreciated until later. Tympanic membrane tears usually heal spontaneously. Ossicular discontinuity will require later repair.

Transverse fractures, running at right angles to the long axis of the temporal bone, can cause injury to the 8th cranial nerve in both its auditory and vestibular divisions, the 7th nerve controlling the facial muscles, the cochlea and the membranous labyrinth. In other words, such a fracture will tend to cause sensorineural hearing loss rather than conductive loss. The balance symptoms caused by such a fracture tend to improve with time through central compensation mechanisms. Surgical exploration to locate bone spicules pressing on the nerve and to decompress and/or repair of the 7th nerve is advocated by some.

[9] Secretory Otitis Media

A normal middle ear contains air. The normal air pressure in the middle ear is the same as the environment. A moment's reflection is all that is needed to readily appreciate the necessity for this. If the ear drum is to be sensitive to quiet sounds, it must be able to vibrate freely. If its motion tends to be restricted by air pressure differences, sensitivity will be reduced. Nature has provided a mechanism for maintaining this middle ear aeration and pressure in the form of the Eustachian tube, which opens momentarily during yawning and swallowing to permit pressure equalization. Children, due to immature anatomy and possibly to other factors, tend to have less efficient Eustachian tubes. This expresses itself as either a true anatomic or functional occlusion. The tube does not open to permit air pressure equalization. A negative pressure develops in the middle ear as the air is absorbed by the lining mucosa. In response the middle ear becomes filled with a substance, fluid in most instances, but viscous and "like glue" in others. The fluid is generated by the lining mucosa. Presence of such fluid is the essential finding in secretory otitis media. It may also form as a residual after acute suppurative otitis media.

Diagnosis is made by inspection of the ear drum. Retraction and a dull appearance may be noted, although these findings are easily misinterpreted. Reduced mobility of the ear drum is a reliable finding. The diagnosis is therefore best made using an otoscope equipped for applying air pressure to the ear drum. A hand-held tympanometer, an electronic device for measuring ear drum mobility and middle ear pressure is also useful. Treatment has traditionally included antibiotics, decongestants and antihistamines. The antibiotics may be indicated as some studies have demonstrated a high percentage of patients from whom viable bacteria can be recovered when the middle ear fluid is cultured. There is less good evidence for the use of decongestants and antihistamines. The same can be said for nasal steroid inhalers and oral steroids. Fortunately, the vast majority of cases of secretory otitis media will resolve within 90 days of diagnosis.

If medical treatment fails, and the condition does not resolve after a few months, surgical treatment by myringotomy and placement of pressure equalization tubes may be performed. Myringotomy is the making of a small cut in the ear drum through which fluid may be suctioned. A pressure equalization tube, also referred to as a ventilating tube, is a plastic or metal tube with a bore of a millimeter or so. It serves to allow air flow between the middle ear and the ear canal, thus maintaining ventilation of the middle ear and preventing occurrence of fluid. It is in other words a Eustachian tube substitute. Once the tube is inserted, it will remain in place for a year or so. It will then spontaneously extrude in most instances. Occasionally tubes remain in place for up to three years. If fluid reforms after extrusion, the procedure can be repeated.

Many otolaryngologists advise removal of the adenoids in conjunction with ventilation tube placement. The rationale for removal is the location of the adenoid tissue adjacent to the opening of the Eustachian tube in the nasopharynx. Inflammation of this tissue is presumed to interfere with the tubes function, and some evidence has accumulated to confirm that removal of the adenoids reduces the risk of recurrent middle ear fluid.

Myringotomy and placement of pressure equalization tubes, with or without adenoidectomy, is the most common surgical procedure performed on children in the United States. In adults, placement of the tubes is an office procedure done with local anesthesia. Children require general anesthetic. Risk of general anesthesia is minimal in the modern era. Occasional episodes of malignant hyperthermia are still possible, as are idiosyncratic reactions to medication. Risks of the procedure include risks of the anesthetic, failure of the hole in the eardrum to heal after tube extrusion, failure of the tube to extrude and injury to the facial nerve or ossicles during the surgery. Facial nerve or ossicular injury is extremely rare and usually connotes negligence by the surgeon. When the myringotomy site fails to heal, subsequent surgical or office procedures may be needed to close it.

[10] Acute Otitis Media

Acute otitis media is an inflammation of the middle ear caused by viruses and/or bacteria. The infecting organisms may reach the middle ear through the blood stream or by migration up the Eustachian tube from a locus in the nasopharynx, sinuses or even the tonsils. Infants may indicate the presence of an ear infection by pulling at their ears, by head shaking and crying. Older children will articulate ear pain, pressure and hearing loss. Fever is often present. The ear drum will be reddened and may bulge from the pressure of accumulating pus in the middle ear. If the pressure becomes severe, the ear drum may tear or "rupture" with resulting bloody drainage from the ear canal. Many children are brought to emergency departments with complaints of fever, malaise and crying. As is well known, a febrile, crying, child will have a flushed appearance to the face. Similar flushing occurs on the ear drum. It is incumbent on the examining practitioner to verify the presence of otitis media and not to treat with antibiotics based solely on the presence of a "flushed" ear drum.

Viral otitis media does not respond to antibiotics. This fact has led to a growing movement among pediatricians to delay treatment of otitis media with antibiotics at least during the first few days to allow for a self-limited viral illness to run its course. Prior to the advent of antibiotics, severe complications of bacterial otitis media were not uncommon. These included perforation of the drum, destruction of ossicles, spread of infection to the facial nerve leading to facial paralysis, involvement of the inner ear with suppurative labyrinthitis, meningitis, brain abscess and septic sinus thrombosis all possible. It remains to be seen whether these complications, currently quite rare, will be seen more frequently in the future as antibiotics are more frequently withheld.

Removal of the tonsils and adenoids has proven effective in preventing recurrent acute otitis media in many patients, as has control of chronic sinus infection. Unfortunately, tonsil and adenoid surgery has risk and no good means of identifying those who will benefit from such surgery other than by performing the surgery has been found.

[11] Chronic Otitis Media

A "chronic" condition is one which persists. "Chronic otitis media" refers to an ear infection in which the normal ear anatomy and physiology has not been recovered after an infection, or more often, a series of infections. Why ear disease has such a tendency to become chronic is not entirely clear, although damage to the ear drum and ossicles through repeated episodes of acute otitis media, and the long-term effects of chronic Eustachian tube dysfunction, are both contributing factors.

Chronic otitis media is not painful. Symptoms may include persistent drainage from the ear, frequently with a foul odor, and hearing loss. Physical findings may include perforations of the ear drum and damage to middle ear bones, while testing will often confirm hearing loss. Accumulations of desquamated skin and purulent exudates commonly occur. Treatment requires regular removal of such debris to permit topical antibiotic drops to contact the affected mucosa, and application of ear drops and other medications to reduce infection. Systemic antibiotics may be given.

Once active infection is controlled, surgical treatment may be offered. Repair of the ear drum and any damaged middle ear bones is the basic goal. No surgical repair nor effective medical treatment of the Eustachian tube is possible; therefore successful surgery results when the chronic ear disease represents a condition established during youth when the Eustachian tube was immature. If the Eustachian tube's function is normal at the time of surgery, chances of successful surgery are greatly enhanced. For this reason, cessation of smoking in the immediate perioperative period also increases success rates.

Complications of surgery include the same problems that are complications of the underlying disease: facial nerve paralysis, sensorineural hearing loss, balance disorders, meningitis, brain abscess and septic sinus thrombosis.

[12] Mastoiditis

The mastoid is a subdivision of the temporal bone defined by the location of an interconnected series of air containing chambers called air cells. A relatively constant anatomical feature is a bony prominence posterior and inferior to the external ear called the mastoid tip. The mastoid air cells are connected to the middle ear and thus through the Eustachian tube to the outside. Acute otitis media will involve the mastoid air cells by localized spread through the narrow opening that connects the middle ear space to the mastoid air cell system called the antrum. As the middle ear infection subsides, so will the process in the mastoid. X-rays of the temporal bone taken during an episode of otitis media may therefore show evidence of mastoid involvement such as opacification of the air cells. This opacification should not be mistaken for mastoiditis. The term "mastoiditis" implies a risk of complications, which include septic thrombosis of the intracranial sigmoid sinus, brain abscess and meningitis. These complications rarely follow otitis media. When the infection progresses to the point that decalcification of the bony septae of the mastoid occurs, referred to as "coalescent mastoiditis," then true mastoiditis is present. Similarly, it is common when reviewing radiographs of the temporal bones to find that the degree of aeration, or to put it another way, the extent of air cell development, is not symmetrical. When air cell development is minimal, the mastoid is described as "sclerotic." Such asymmetry is believed to be due to episodes of otitis media during childhood, although it may also represent a congenital and insignificant anatomic variation. Radiologists often report such sclerosis as "mastoiditis," thus arousing concerns in pediatricians and other physicians that are not warranted. A better description would be "asymmetric air cell development consistent with prior mastoid disease."

The symptoms and physical findings of mastoiditis are initially the same as those of otitis media. As the otitis progresses into mastoiditis, acute tenderness and edema over the mastoid tip may occur. Swelling may be sufficient to cause the ear to protrude. Infection may spread through the venous channels to the subcutaneous tissue overlying the mastoid with development of a "Bezold's abscess." Facial paralysis may occur. Spiking fever is frequently present. If intracranial complications occur, changes in level of consciousness, stiff neck, and headache may be noted.

Treatment depends on the severity of the infection. Initial treatment is with antibiotics, preferably given intravenously. Myringotomy should be performed. Failure to respond is an indication for surgical treatment by performance of a mastoidectomy. Any evidence of intracranial complication or facial paralysis is an indication for immediate surgery. One example of the effect of antibiotic treatment on medical care is the frequency of emergency mastoidectomy. In the 1930s, a busy ear specialist could expect to perform the operation frequently. The Los Angeles County General Hospital in 1939 recorded more than 400 urgent or emergent mastoidectomy procedures in a city with less than a fifth its current population. At present, only two or three such procedures are done each year.

[13] Cholesteatoma

A frequent complication of repeated otitis media, with or without mastoid involvement, is the development of cholesteatoma. The suffix, "-oma," implies a tumor and to many implies a malignant tumor. Cholesteatoma was named at a time when its nature was not understood and because of its destructive behavior was regarded as a malignant process. A cholesteatoma is a skin-lined sac or cyst located medial to the ear drum. Such cysts grow and frequently invade the mastoid sinus. As they grow, they destroy structures around them, including the ossicles of the middle ear. They may erode the bony covering of the semicircular canals and/or the facial nerve. Thus, hearing loss, balance disorder and facial paralysis may be complications of a cholesteatoma. More often than not, the cholesteatoma is connected to the ear canal through a small perforation of the ear drum. Chronic infection with persistent foul smelling drainage is therefore a frequent symptom of cholesteatoma.

The origin of cholesteatoma remains controversial. There seems little doubt that some are congenital, as they may be found behind a normal appearing ear drum in children with no history of ear infection. The majority appear to originate as a retraction of the ear drum, especially in its posterior, superior region where the drum lacks the reinforcing fibrous layer present elsewhere. Such retractions become pockets, which because they are lined with skin begin to enlarge as desquamated skin cells accumulate. The debris in the pocket is a good site for bacterial growth, making infection common. It is clear that there are other, as yet undefined, factors involved. For example, there is good evidence that cholesteatomas, once they exist, secrete enzymes that facilitate enlargement.

Although not all cholesteatomas are treated by surgery, surgery is the only treatment that can eradicate a cholesteatoma. The surgery is a mastoidectomy, often in conjunction with a tympanoplasty (ear drum reconstruction) and ossiculoplasty (ossicular chain reconstruction). In this procedure, an attempt is made to remove all of the abnormally placed skin – the cholesteatomatous debris and the skin sac surrounding it. If successful, reconstruction to restore hearing may also be successful.

[14] Hearing Loss

Hearing loss is divided into three categories. Pure sensorineural hearing loss, commonly called "nerve deafness," results from abnormalities in the cochlea , 8th cranial or auditory nerve, or the auditory centers of the brain. By far the most common of these is injury to the cochlea, which may be congenital or acquired.

The second category is conductive loss, which results from an abnormality of the ear drum or the ossicles.

The third category is a mixed loss, containing elements of both sensorineural and conductive loss.

Sensorineural loss is commonly considered as a single category. However, in the presence of a severe hearing loss, cochlear implantation may be considered. Cochlear implantation depends on a functioning auditory nerve, so where implantation is being considered, special tests are required to differentiate between cochlear and auditory nerve disease. Where the 8th nerve is defective, or surgically absent, implantation of the brain stem may be performed.

[15] Audiometry

Audiometry is the measurement of hearing loss. Audiologists are persons trained in such measurement. Audiometric tests may be conveniently divided into standard tests, which are performed routinely for most persons with a complaint of hearing loss, and special tests done when specific diagnostic or other concerns are present.

[16] Standard Tests

The most basic audiometric test, performed by physicians as part of their physical examination, is the tuning fork test. Tuning forks, designed to vibrate at the frequencies 512, 1024, and 2048 Hz, are applied in turn to either the center of the forehead, or better, to the central maxillary incisors. The patient is asked to report whether the sound is heard in one ear or both, which is usually reported as the sound being located in the center. In a conductive loss, the tuning fork will seem louder in the ear with the conductive loss. In a sensorineural hearing loss, the sound will seem louder in the ear without the loss. This "Weber test" is combined with a second examination, the "Rinne test." Here the vibrating tuning fork is applied to the mastoid tip and then held near the ear canal meatus. The patient is asked whether the sound is louder behind the ear or in front. In a conductive loss, the sound will be louder in back. This test is most sensitive with the 512 Hz fork. Because this test works only if the difference between nerve threshold and conduction threshold is substantial and because it does not provide a quantitative measure of hearing loss, it is a useful physical examination tool but is not a substitute for audiometry. However, where conductive loss found on audiometry is not confirmed by the tuning fork tests, many authorities recommend that any surgical treatment contemplated be postponed until the discrepancy is explained.

The first audiometric test performed by the audiologist will be air and bone threshold measurements. In this test, the subject is asked to respond to sounds presented first through earphones, and then, if this test is not normal, through a vibrator placed over the mastoid posterior to the external ear. The air test utilizes the normal sound pathway through the eardrum and ossicles to the cochlea. In the bone test, the vibrator stimulates the cochlea directly with minimal input from the ear drum and ossicles. Six to eight frequencies, between 250 and 8000 Hz are presented, and the minimal loudness required for subject detection is recorded. Figure 1 represents a standard audiogram.

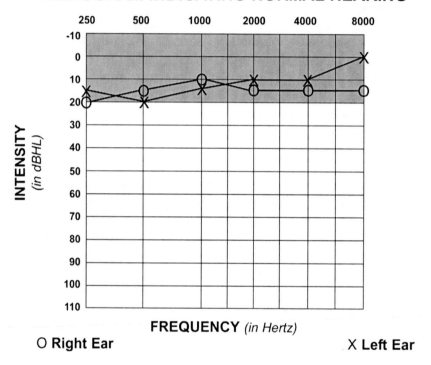

FIGURE 1

You will note that the frequencies (Hertz or cycles per second) are plotted on the abscissa, while the amplitude of the sound (decibels of loudness) is plotted on the ordinate. Although most human ears can hear frequencies as high as 20,000 Hertz, and below 125 Hertz, the sound energy for human speech is concentrated in the range from 500 to 3000 Hertz. Hence human testing only tests higher frequencies than 8000 in special circumstances. The main use of high frequency audiometers and testing is for monitoring the effect of ototoxic drugs. The toxic effects of such drugs on the cochlea are usually first manifested at the higher frequencies.

A decibel is a logarithmic function. That is, a progression from 10 decibels to 20 decibels to 30 decibels is not linear. A person with a twenty decibel hearing loss does not have twice as much hearing loss as a person with a 10 decibel loss. Instead, the ratio is such that an increase of 3 dB corresponds to an approximate doubling of power. (To be precise, the factor is $10^{3/10}$ which is 1.9953, an "error" of about 0.24%. Using the handy approximation, we can see that the difference between 10 dB hearing loss and 20 Db hearing loss, is that a person with a 20 db hearing loss needs an increase in sound level of about 10 times to hear what a person with a 10 db hearing loss would hear.

Persons whose air conduction threshold (earphones) shows a loss, but whose bone conduction tests are normal, are said to have a conductive loss. Where the hearing loss is low frequency for air, but normal for bone, the cause is likely to be middle ear fluid or abnormal bony fixation of the ossicles. Where the hearing loss is equal for both air and bone conduction, the person is said to have a sensorineural hearing loss. If the worst hearing is at the higher frequencies, this usually represents either cumulative noise damage, or presbycusis (age related hearing loss) or a combination of the two. When the sensorineural hearing loss is mainly low frequency, Meniere's disease is a likely cause. When the loss is present in the midfrequencies with normal hearing at both high and low ends, cochlear deterioration due to genetic predisposition is the most common cause.

Standard testing also includes obtaining threshold responses to the spoken word and determining the patient's ability to understand monosyllabic words at a sound level sufficiently louder than threshold to represent a comfortable listening level. Reductions in comprehension are guides to chance of success in wearing hearing aids and asymmetric reduction of comprehension can be a clue to presence of eighth nerve tumors (acoustic neuroma).

Most clinics include tympanometry in their basic test battery. Tympanometry permits several useful measurements. These include comparison of air pressure in the middle ear with that of the external environment. A reduced pressure is an indicator of Eustachian tube dysfunction. A flat response, in which no tympanic membrane motion can be detected in response to applied pressure, suggests middle ear fluid or other restricting abnormality. Acoustic reflex presence or absence can be determined by checking for the presence of ear drum movement in the presence of a suddenly applied loud sound. If the loud sound stimulates contraction of the stapedius and tensor tympani muscles, ear drum motion is affected. A normal ear will maintain contraction in the presence of loud noise for at least sixty seconds. If that is not true, tone decay is present and this may be another indicator of disease in the eighth cranial nerve.

[17] Advanced Tests

Evoked auditory brain stem test: This test is performed by stimulating the ear with thousands of sound pulses and recording by EEG the brain stem response to those sounds. The signal is small, and the difficulty of separating the response from background signal and other sources of electric signal is great, so that the test only became possible with the development of computers and appropriate software. Although still a useful test, its main use of screening for acoustic neuroma has been supplanted by low-cost MRI imaging of the eighth nerve.

Transient evoked otoacoustic emissions: In 1978 Kemp discovered that the normal human cochlea not only responds to sounds, but can produce them. This discovery has led to the development of rapid, non-invasive, objective and reproducible tests which can screen infants for hearing loss, confirm thresholds obtained on voluntary testing and screen for malingering.

[18] Vestibular System

The inner ear is divided into two sections: the cochlea is dedicated to hearing and the vestibular system to balance and equilibrium. The vestibular system has two divisions: the semicircular canals respond to angular acceleration and the utricle responds to position in space. Both vestibular components consist of a fluid-filled structure contained within narrow bony confines in the temporal bone with sensors embedded in the fluid containing structure. This convoluted structure is commonly referred to as the "vestibular labyrinth."

The portion of the labyrinth that responds to motion and angular acceleration is the semicircular canal. There are three on each side, each in a plane perpendicular to the other two. Inside the canal at the slightly broader end or "ampulla" is a collection of neural cells with hair-like appendages on each cell. These move in response to motion of the fluid, generating a signal to the brain. Head turn to one side leads to the lateral semicircular canal on one side moving forward, while that on the other side moves backward. The combination of equal but opposite signals contributes to the brain's understanding of head movement, while a damaged inner ear on one side leads to unequal stimuli and a sensation of dizziness or disequilibrium.

The ampullary ends of the semicircular canals at a common point join the second section of the balance system, the utricle and saccule. The sensory cells in the utricle and saccule contain a gelatinous matrix enveloping the "hairs" which contains small particles of calcium carbonate called "otoliths." These render the utricle and saccule sensitive to gravity and assist in determining position in space.

The vestibular system works in conjunction with vision and the somatosensory system, musculoskeletal sensors in the joints, skin, and muscles, to create an integrated system. If two of the three systems are permanently and significantly impaired, then chronic imbalance will result. Central nervous system compensation, especially in younger individuals, may lead to substantial, if incomplete, recovery.

[19] Vestibular Testing

Testing the vestibular system depends on the reflex connection between the vestibular system and the eye. Just as damage to the vestibular system will lead to the rhythmic to-and-fro motion of the eye called "nystagmus," stimulating the inner ear will stimulate the same response. Because the cornea carries a positive charge relative to the retina, eye motion can be recorded and measured utilizing electrodes applied to the face (electronystagmography). Eye motion can also be recorded by video cameras in goggles worn by the subject (videonystagmography). The subject's spontaneous eye motions are measured, and then recordings are made in different positions of head and body, and after stimulating the vestibular system with warm air or water through the ear canal. Such testing can help verify whether symptoms are due to the inner ear or the central nervous system, and can help differentiate between problems in one ear or the other.

Other testing may include having the patient stand on a balance platform, or measuring nystagmus after rotating the patient in a special chair.

[20] Tinnitus

Tinnitus is a subjective sound in the ear which may be described as roaring, ringing, hissing or similar descriptive terms. It may be a pulsatile sound synchronized with the pulse, which suggests vascular or central nervous system disease. Much more commonly it is a steady sound. Almost all ear diseases can produce tinnitus and it may be present in people with normal hearing and no evidence of ear disease on examination.

Because tinnitus is a subjective symptom, much like pain, measurement and quantification are problematic. Attempts have been made through matching frequencies and amplitudes on an audiometer. Such testing has confirmed that tinnitus of very small amplitude can cause major symptoms. Treatment is equally problematic. No reliable treatment exists, although some patients respond, at least temporarily, to intravenous lidocaine, to masking with external sounds, to gingko supplements and to various other substances. Lidocaine and gingko use is predicated on the theory that reduced circulation is an etiologic factor. As the Russian playwright Anton Chekhov, who began his career as a physician, once said, the existence of many treatments for a disease means that the disease has no cure. This is certainly true in the treatment of tinnitus.

Masking depends on a psychological phenomenon. A sufficiently loud external sound will cover up, or mask, the internal sound of tinnitus. Many people who are unable to ignore the internal sound are able to ignore an external one. Thus, the external sound relieves their distress. Success with masking is improved in a small percentage of users who experience "residual inhibition," the phenomenon of delayed return of the tinnitus when the external sound is removed. Behavioral modification, labeled tinnitus rehabilitation therapy or similar titles, also has had some benefit.

Aside from the reduced quality of life experienced by tinnitus sufferers, tinnitus has major implications in the workers' compensation context. Workers subjected to loud noise will suffer not only noise-induced hearing loss, but tinnitus as well. Compensation rates for the hearing loss can be established, and payment made based on reliable testing. Additional compensation for the tinnitus will be based on the subject's credibility as determined on other grounds.

[21] Varieties of Sensorineural Hearing Loss

Sensorineural hearing loss in children: Approximately 4000 children per year are born deaf in the United States. Hearing loss may also be acquired in early infancy. When congenital, it may be genetic or not. When genetic, sensorineural hearing loss in children may be syndromic or non-syndromic. Syndromic hearing loss includes Goldenhar, Waardenburg, Neurofibromatosis, Tietze, Hermann, Leopard, Kearns-Sayre, Crouzon, Forney, Achondroplasia, Duane, Marfan, and branchiootorenal syndromes, and many, many others. Congenital, non-genetic, losses may result from maternal rubella during pregnancy, which should be prevented by maternal vaccination, from infantile jaundice, which should be prevented by attention to Rh incompatibilities and treating with Rhogam. Maternal infection with toxoplasmosis is another possible cause. Acquired hearing loss in early infancy may be due to meningitis or viral illness.

Evidence is unequivocal that early attention to hearing loss is essential if children are to achieve their full potential. Whether treatment is by cochlear implantation or the use of hearing aids, early identification of deaf children is required. Delay in diagnosis until age 2 or more when many parents first realize that speech is not developing properly adds to the child's preexisting handicap. Many states have introduced infant screening programs to permit identification as newborns.

Children may also suffer a progressive sensorineural hearing loss resulting from a variety of congenital malformations of the inner ear. A normal screening audiogram, although strongly suggestive, does not permit assuming that hearing is normal. Suspicions brought to the physician's attention by concerned parents should therefore not be ignored, but additional testing done.

Presbycusis: "Presby" comes from the Greek word for "older." Presbyopia is visual impairment associated with age. Presbycusis is hearing loss associated with age. Although much sensorineural hearing loss among the elderly is associated with noise exposure, especially in men, some occurs naturally as a consequence of aging. One finds substantially more hearing aid use at the local senior center than at the high school for this reason. Presbycusis begins with reduced hearing at the higher frequencies. Most of the sound energy required for comprehension of human speech occurs in the range from 500 Hz to 2000 Hz. Reduced hearing at 6000 Hz and above therefore initially has a minimal effect on the ability to converse. As the hearing loss begins to extend into lower frequencies – 4000 Hz, then 3000, it becomes hard for the listener to distinguish consonants. "b" and "p" are easily confused, for example. Although context helps the listener distinguish between "baby" and "paper," ability to recognize words, especially in situations where there is background noise, deteriorates. Hearing aids provide only partial relief, as even modern advances in digital technology have failed to completely cure the problem of amplification of background noise by the hearing aid. Thus, in social situations such as restaurants and parties, where the hearing aid user has most need of assistance, hearing aids are of less use than at other times.

Sudden sensorineural hearing loss: Acute onset hearing loss occurs in persons of all ages, although more frequent in the aged. It is almost always in one ear, and may be present when the patient awakens in the morning. Others will describe the sudden onset of a feeling of pressure and tinnitus with rapid disappearance of hearing over a period of minutes to an hour. Specific etiology is difficult to determine in most cases. Antecedent URI symptoms suggests a viral cochleitis. Vigorous straining, as for example at stool, or doing heavy lifting, suggests rupture of Reissner's or round window membranes. Sudden pressure changes have also been implicated in hearing loss following sneezing and coughing, or when flying. Others, especially in the elderly, may be due to ischemia. Just as in the case of tinnitus, multiple treatments suggest absence of useful treatment. Spontaneous recovery, from even profound hearing loss, has been reported.

Progressive sensorineural hearing loss: Chronic bilateral progressive sensorineural hearing loss may result from presbycusis, from a congenitally determined atrophy of the cochlea, and from certain infections, including cytomegalic inclusion virus, syphilis, and HIV. It may also be associated with acoustic neuroma and Meniere's disease. While these latter two diagnoses usually cause unilateral loss, bilateral loss may occur.

Noise-induced hearing loss: Noise induced hearing loss has been known for centuries, first being identified in the 15th century among artillerymen. In the early 18th century, the first non-military occupational cause was recognized in coppersmiths, who produced copper utensils by hammering copper sheets into molds. In the 19th century, occupational hearing loss was labeled "boiler-maker's ear." Research in the 20th century determined that exposure to 85 db noise for eight hours would cause threshold shift in workers, and this level was set as the maximum occupational exposure permitted. However, some workers are more sensitive than others, so that they suffer damage even at permitted exposures. Many other persons are exposed recreationally, through shooting, power tools used in home shops, motorcycles and other power equipment.

Drug induced hearing loss: Ototoxicity is a characteristic of many useful drugs. Four categories are responsible.

First, aminoglycoside antibiotics such as neomycin, streptomycin, and gentamycin affect both the hearing and vestibular balance parts of the inner ear. These drugs are used systemically only in severe and potentially life-threatening infections by susceptible organisms. Harm is minimized by monitoring serum levels of the drugs, but some individuals have a greater sensitivity and lose hearing despite proper dosage and proper monitoring. This is more likely to occur if the treatment is prolonged. Failure to monitor serum levels or continuance of the drugs after culture and sensitivity tests show other less toxic alternatives could be used constitute negligence. Concomitant balance and equilibrium impairment may occur causing significant disability when walking or making sudden movements.

The second category of ototoxic drugs is diuretics, which are used to dehydrate the body by promoting excretion of sodium. Ethacrinic acid and furosemide are the two drugs that cause most of the trouble. When used at the same time as aminoglycoside antibiotics the potential for ear damage is increased.

Aspirin and quinine are associated with hearing loss. Quite high dosage of aspirin is needed to produce hearing loss and tinnitus and will usually be reversed when the aspirin is discontinued. Quinine can have the same effect in normal doses, and may cause permanent damage.

Chemotherapeutic agents for cancer, such as cisplatin, can cause severe hearing loss. Children's hearing is more susceptible to cisplatin than adults' hearing.

[22] Conductive Hearing Loss

Hearing loss caused by an abnormality of the cochlea in the inner ear, or the eighth cranial (acoustic) nerve connecting the cochlea to the brain, or an abnormality of the brain itself are all loosely termed sensorineural hearing losses. The other form of hearing loss is the conductive hearing loss caused by failure of sound to reach the inner ear.

Conductive hearing losses can be caused by blockage of the external ear canal. This can result from congenital absence of the ear and ear canal, blockage of the ear canal by cerumen or a foreign body, by swelling of the ear canal from infection and from blockage by tumors. The most common form of tumor blockage is "surfer's ear." The ear canal reacts to constant irritation by exposure to cold water by forming bony growths, or "exostoses." These can grow in extreme cases to the point of blocking the ear canal. Described in the 1950s in Australian surfers, it has since been found in people whose common denominator is not surfing, but frequent ocean swimming.

Abnormalities of the ear drum can prevent sound from reaching the inner ear. A large perforation will prevent the ear drum from responding to the sound pressure waves, so that hearing will be decreased. An ear drum can be heavily calcified, and it can be so atrophic that it retracts into the middle ear and becomes adherent to the middle ear bony wall. Hearing loss may be associated with each of these conditions.

The sound waves are transmitted from ear drum to inner ear through a chain of three bones, the malleus (embedded in the ear drum), the incus, and the stapes (that fits into a window or socket in the outer edge of the inner ear). Chronic infection may damage these bones, most commonly by causing part of the incus to deteriorate, leaving a gap in the chain. The malleus may become locked in place by calcification or new bony growth, preventing it from moving. The stapes bone may be prevented from moving in its socket by new bone formation. This condition is called otosclerosis, and is common among Caucasians, and more frequently seen in women than men.

[23] Dizziness and Vertigo

"Dizziness" is a common presenting complaint from patients seen in Otolaryngology offices. The term is commonly used to describe a variety of symptoms ranging from a general sense of giddiness or disequilibrium to severe vertigo associated with inability to rise from bed and with severe nausea and vomiting. A common and difficult chore for the ear specialist is to differentiate between the many possible systemic and neurologic causes of disequilibrium and true vertigo associated with vestibular inner ear disease. In § 13.03 [18], supra, the requirement of an integrated three-part system for maintaining balance was described. Elderly patients in particular are prone to a form of disequilibrium caused by a combination of reduced vision, reduced somatosensory input, reduced musculoskeletal strength, and deteriorated vestibular input. The only treatment for that form of "dizziness" is a walker or wheelchair. People suffering from drug-induced ototoxicity and from advanced syphilis may suffer from chronic disequilibrium as well, being able to walk during the day, but becoming markedly handicapped when deprived of visual clues at night. True vertigo, the sensation of spinning or tumbling motion, often associated with cold sweats, nausea and vomiting, requires an acute injury to the vestibular system.

In most cases of vertigo, a diagnosis can be reached through the patient's history. A complaint of dizziness associated with loss of consciousness is essentially never inner ear in origin. Among other possibilities, epilepsy needs to be considered. Dizziness to the point of vertigo associated with a sense of impending doom, and tingling around the mouth and in the hands, or cramps in the hands, suggests an anxiety attack with hyperventilation. Awakening at night with severe vertigo and nausea, with symptoms lasting up to 24 hours and then slowly improving, is associated with viral labyrinthitis and neuronitis. In such cases, hearing is often unaffected. Vertigo preceded by a feeling of pressure in the ear, hearing loss, and tinnitus, lasting several hours, suggests Meniere's disease. Vertigo lasting seconds, precipitated by head motion, as, for example, rolling over in bed, is the hallmark of benign paroxysmal positional vertigo. Vertigo associated with sensitivity to light or loud sound or with headache suggests migrainous vertigo. In the majority of cases, physical examination done at a time when the patient is without symptoms will be normal. Where the diagnosis is not clear, testing that includes audiometry, a general neurological examination, ENG or VNG, and imaging studies may all be done and can contribute to an accurate diagnosis.

[24] General Considerations in Ear Surgery

Prior to the advent of antibiotics, acute ear infection was the major indication for surgery on the ear. Episodes of otitis media would progress to acute mastoiditis. Septic thrombosis of the lateral (intracranial) sinus, epidural abscess, brain abscess and meningitis were seen with frequent lethal outcomes. The purpose of surgery was to drain infection from both the ear and any related purulent collections. Preservation of hearing was attempted, but was largely a forlorn hope. Introduction of sulfa drugs in the 1930s led to a gradual change in direction. Following World War II, two major advances opened the way to modern ear surgery. The first was the introduction to the civilian population of penicillin, and the subsequent antibiotic discoveries. The second was development by the post–war Zeiss company of the binocular operating microscope with coaxial light. Tuebingen, Germany ENT surgeon Horst Wullstein suggested that such an instrument was needed, and he is said to have commented when shown a prototype that this instrument was what otologists had been waiting all their lives to have. Development of modern ear surgery followed.

Most ear surgery today is elective, for the purpose of eliminating cholesteatoma, repairing ear drum perforations, or for improvement of hearing through stapedectomy, cochlear implant and other procedures.

All surgical procedures on the ear carry a risk of complications. A simple ear drum repair risks serious hearing loss in as many as 2% of cases. Therefore, a legal claim based on an ear operation raises the first issue—was the surgery indicated? If most ear procedures are elective, and they are, then risk must be balanced against possible gain for all procedures. Many perforations of the ear drum do not need repair, and even some cholesteatomas can be conservatively managed. If patients are elderly, or have significant other medical problems, the benefit of conservative management is greater. They should certainly be offered the opportunity to decide after being informed of the risks, side effects and benefits of the proposed procedure, and of the alternatives. The risks to be discussed should also include the risk of anesthesia, which may be heightened in cases that last several hours.

[25] Surgery of the External Ear Canal

Surgery of the ear canal may be indicated for congenital abnormalities, acquired conditions, and malignancies.

Congenital abnormalities consist of various degrees of hypoplasia and aplasia. Congenital atresia of the canal is often associated with maldevelopment of the external ear. Complete closure results in a 60 db hearing loss. Malformations of the middle ear are often associated. Techniques for creation of an ear canal, construction of an external ear and management of the middle ear ossicles have been developed. Procedures are limited to cosmetic ones if radiologic evaluation confirms that the middle ear is not present. Successful construction of an ear canal however may permit hearing aid use. Establishing a tubular structure like the ear canal can be very difficult as natural healing processes tend to cause narrowing of the cavity through scar contraction. As there is usually a bony plate between the middle ear and the outside, extensive drilling is required to create the new ear canal. The abnormalities of development often involve the route of the facial nerve also, with elimination of the normal surgical landmarks surgeons use to avoid injury to the nerve. Facial nerve paralysis risk is therefore much higher than in usual ear surgery, occurring as often as 1% of cases.

Acquired conditions include atresia of the ear canal due to repeated infection, or more rarely from burns. Closure of the canal can trap epithelium between the scar and the ear drum leading to the formation of ear canal cholesteatoma. "Surfer's ear" is a condition in which bony thickening in the form of exostoses or osteomas grow in the bony portion of the canal. Identified in Australian surfers after World War II, the condition has been found in divers and swimmers as well. Chronic exposure to the cold ocean water seems to be the precipitating cause; the specific activity leading to the exposure is not important. Removal of the excess bone removes the obstruction.

Tumors of the ear canal are uncommon. Both basal cell and squamous cell skin cancers can exist in the ear canal, as well as other rare tumors. Such tumors require extensive and often mutilating surgery to extirpate.

[26] Surgery of the Tympanic Membrane

The first question to ask when a patient with a perforation of the ear drum presents is whether any repair is needed. Perforations in the pars flaccida of the ear drum (that portion of the ear drum lacking a fibrous layer and mainly located superior to the supporting ligaments of the malleus head) and marginal perforations in general have a higher risk of complications, and therefore probably should be repaired. Unless cholesteatoma or chronic infection are present, however, the degree of hearing loss, age of the patient and risk of the procedure need to be considered when making the decision whether or not to operate.

For central perforations, with a low risk of complications, the decision requires even more consideration. Perforations involving less than 40% of the ear drum area are associated with fairly good hearing, while patients with larger perforations often have conductive hearing loss of significant degree. The degree of hearing loss, whether the patient swims frequently, whether the patient has frequent ear infections, with or without swimming, the patient's age and general medical condition, all influence the decision. In the absence of infections, and with almost normal hearing, the risk-benefit evaluation may mandate no treatment. In the absence of infection, even a significant conductive loss can be treated with a hearing aid, and patients should know of this alternative to surgery. For those patients for whom repair is indicated, in most instances office procedures should be attempted first. These include cauterizing and/or mechanically freshening the perforation margins, followed by application of paper or hyaluronic acid patches, fat plugs, or Derlacki aromatic oil therapy. If these fail, then surgical repair of the tympanic membrane may be attempted. Because office procedures have a vanishingly small risk of causing increased hearing loss, while formal tympanoplasty carries a 1% risk of sensorineural hearing loss and a small risk of facial nerve injury leading to facial paralysis, serious attention to the need for the procedure must be given.

Repair of the eardrum is accomplished by either surgically lifting the ear drum from its bed and placing a graft of fascia medial to it and in contact with it, or by removing the epithelial covering of the ear drum and placing the graft lateral to it. Experience has led to almost total abandonment of fat, vein and perichondrium as graft materials, and infrequent use of the lateral graft placement method. Success rates are in the range of 90% but recurrence of perforation may occur in up to 20%, another factor the patient should consider.

[27] Surgery of the Middle Ear and Mastoid

Middle ear surgery is performed to eradicate cholesteatoma or similar chronic disease, to repair discontinuity of the ossicular chain with resulting conductive hearing loss, and, rarely, for tumor. Surgery for tumor is rare because tumors of the middle ear are rare. Cholesteatoma (see § 13.03 [13]) and ossicular discontinuity are frequently associated with both tympanic membrane perforation and mastoid disease, so that a procedure called tympanomastoidectomy is typically performed to deal with all aspects of the chronic ear disease.

With the exception of an uncommonly used procedure called an atticotomy, mastoid surgery involves opening the mastoid area, which lies just behind the ear canal. Drills and curettes are used to remove diseased air cells contained within the bone under direct observation through an operating microscope. The cholesteatoma is removed along with infected mucous membrane. Even under the magnification of the operating microscope, removal of every epithelial cell cannot be guaranteed. Complete extirpation of the cholesteatoma may therefore be achieved in less than 90% of operations, while additional operations fail through the development of new cholesteatomas due to persistent Eustachian tube dysfunction.

Drilling is performed with irrigation to keep the healthy bone from overheating but the combination of mechanical vibration and heat, and the risk of actually entering into the inner ear labyrinth, mean that mastoid surgery carries a risk of causing additional hearing loss in up to 5% of cases, even to the point of total deafness. Because the facial nerve runs through the mastoid, it also is at risk. Temporary facial paralysis occurs in 1 to 2% of cases; permanent paralysis is rare.

Where cholesteatoma is present, many authorities recommend performing a "second look" procedure six to twelve months following the primary surgery, at which time any persistent cholesteatoma is removed. Reconstruction of disrupted ossicles is best delayed until this second look procedure. To reduce risk to the inner ear, delay is mandatory if surgery on the footplate of the stapes bone is required. In the absence of cholesteatoma, reconstruction of the ossicles can be performed at the time of primary surgery. Reconstruction can involve removing and repositioning ossicles or the insertion of prostheses. The use of homografts, ossicles taken from other patients or cadavers, has been largely abandoned.

Ossicular reconstruction very rarely results in normal hearing. Hearing sufficiently restored to avoid the use of a hearing aid is considered a success. Complete failure occurs in up to 30% of cases. As in all surgical procedures on the ear, ossicular reconstruction, even when performed as an isolated procedure, carries a risk of increased hearing loss and facial nerve injury.

The most common ear operation is much less dramatic than the above. The most common operation, principally performed on children in the United States, is myringotomy (incision into the ear drum) with placement of a trans-tympanic ventilating and pressure equalizing tube, as described at §13.03 [9] above.

[28] Surgery for Otosclerosis

Otosclerosis is a disease characterized by the formation of new bone surrounding the footplate of the stapes bone, the bone that fits into a socket, or "window," in the inner ear wall and transmits sound wave vibrations to the inner ear. If the flexible ligament that seals the window where the footplate rests is made rigid by new bone, a conductive hearing loss results. Development of this condition has a strong genetic component, as it tends to run in families, and is found in Caucasian women more frequently than any other racial group.

Surgery is reserved for those whose hearing loss is 30 to 40 decibels, and who have either expressed a preference for surgery over hearing aid use, or who have tried hearing aids and found them ineffective. At early stages of the disease, some authorities prescribe high doses of fluoride in attempt to arrest the disease progress. This is an "off-label" use of fluoride with side-effects possible. Its use was suggested by the observation that in areas with naturally high fluoride in the water, clinically significant otosclerosis is less frequent. Rapid progression of otosclerosis during pregnancy has also been observed leading some otolaryngologists to recommend pregnancy avoidance for those women whose disease is approaching clinically significant levels.

Surgery for this condition has evolved over the roughly 70 years it has been performed. Contemporary surgeons usually remove the superstructure of the stapes bone, make a hole in the footplate, and place a prosthesis connecting the incus to the newly created footplate window. The hole in the footplate may be created by a drill or a laser.

Surgery succeeds in closing the "air-bone gap" in 90% of patients. Even those with a significant sensorineural component are often helped by surgery, gaining much improved benefit from hearing aids. In 9% of cases, no improvement will be noted and in 1 to 2% of cases, hearing will be worse, even to the point of total hearing loss.

The direct trauma to the inner ear caused by the surgery causes not only the hearing loss mentioned, but also post-operative dizziness and vertigo. The majority of such patients' symptoms resolve within a day or two, but it can persist for months and in approximately 1% of patients permanent imbalance and disequilibrium symptoms persist. Patients whose occupations require good balance need to be warned of this possibility.

The ear drum is lifted out of the way to permit access to the middle ear. Access to the stapes often requires removal of some bone at the margin of the ear canal. In approximately 1% of patients, a perforation of the ear drum results from these manipulations, which may require secondary surgery or office procedures to close. Access to the stapes also frequently requires severing the chorda tympani nerve which is responsible for taste sensation in the tongue. Patients rarely find this loss of taste a significant problem so long as it is unilateral. Patients contemplating surgery on a second otosclerotic ear should be questioned about taste loss, probably tested as well, and the risks of bilateral taste loss discussed in detail prior to the second operation.

The facial nerve runs only millimeters away from the stapes footplate. Facial nerve injury is therefore possible, occurring in less than 1% of patients. This is most likely to occur when the bony canal through which the facial nerve runs is defective, leaving facial nerve exposed and at greater risk of injury.

[29] Surgery for Facial Nerve Paralysis

The facial nerve, the seventh cranial nerve, arises in the brain stem. It passes through the internal auditory canal along with the eighth cranial nerve. The eighth cranial nerve, or auditory nerve, contains two divisions, one for hearing and one for balance. It is a sensory nerve, with signals flowing from the inner ear sensing systems to the brain. The seventh nerve is primarily a motor nerve, providing nervous control for the muscles of the face and also for two small muscles in the middle ear. It continues past the inner ear to run through the mastoid bone, exiting through an opening at the base of the skull located about a fingers breadth medial to the mastoid bone palpable behind and below the ear, and passes through the parotid gland.

Paralysis of the face resulting from injury to the facial nerve has a variety of causes. Outside the scope of this chapter are such causes as external injury to the face from gunshot or other wounds, and from cancers of the parotid gland.

A common cause of facial paralysis is called Bell's palsy. Although the proof is not yet definitive, it appears likely that this condition is caused by a viral inflammation of the nerve as it passes through its bony tunnel. The most likely culprit is the herpes virus. Inflammation of the nerve causes swelling. But because the nerve is encased in bone, its swelling is limited by the confines of the bony tunnel. As it swells therefore, pressure increases on the nerve leading to obstruction of blood flow. Nerve death ensues. Approximately 85% of such cases heal completely with little or no residual impairment. The remainder result in some level of impairment.

Treatment is controversial. Administration of steroids is common and many physicians, accepting the likelihood that a herpesvirus infection is present, treat with antiviral drugs such as acyclovir. For many years, surgical decompression of the facial nerve was advocated and an elaborate series of tests was devised in an attempt to differentiate between those for whom recovery was likely and those for whom it was not, and who would therefore benefit from surgery. Eventually, the evidence led to realization that decompression generally needed to be extended into the skull base along the internal auditory canal to be effective. The resultant increased morbidity and risk, with additional questions about efficacy, led to a marked decrease in popularity of the procedure in the treatment of Bell's Palsy.

Decompression as a treatment for traumatic injury to temporal bone portion of the nerve from skull fracture and for treatment of paralysis resulting from infection still has its advocates.

Iatrogenic (caused by the physician) paralysis of the nerve during middle ear and mastoid surgery may be addressed by decompression and anastomosis of the cut ends. Where nerve tissue has been destroyed, rather than the nerve being simply cut, a nerve graft may be inserted, usually using part of the greater auricular nerve, a sensory nerve located behind and below the ear. Such repairs will very rarely lead to normal facial muscle function, but usually leads to a better result than no repair at all. The face will often look normal at rest after a year or so of healing, but will still exhibit asymmetry during voluntary motion such as smiling, lifting the eyebrow or closing the eye. A side-effect of errant regrowth of the healing nerve may be synkinesis. Synkinesis means that when the patient smiles, the eye may close or the forehead wrinkle, or similar erroneous motion.

[30] Treatment of Acoustic Nerve Tumors

Acoustic nerve tumors, which are most often benign tumors arising from the cells that surround the nerve fibers themselves, are slow-growing tumors that may never become clinically significant. When they are both causing symptoms, and growing, removal is best accomplished when they are small. Increased size of the acoustic neuroma is associated with injury to other nerves, including the facial and trigeminal, and with increased surgical risk. On the other hand, tumors causing minimal symptoms which are not growing, may be observed rather than treated. Treatment, when that is the course decided upon, may be either by surgery or radiation.

Surgical treatment of acoustic neuromas requires a craniotomy. The nerve is encased in the temporal bone medial to the inner ear, so an opening in the skull is required to approach it. Depending on the degree of hearing and balance impairment present, this may be done through an opening above the ear into the middle fossa, or behind the ear. The middle fossa approach permits direct observation of the facial nerve and the divisions of the acoustic nerve and increases the likelihood of facial nerve and hearing preservation. It is useful only for small tumors.

Retrosigmoid, suboccipital, and trans-labyrinthine approaches are all in use, depending on the preference of the surgeon and the size, specific location and inner ear function in the specific case. Total loss of hearing in the affected ear, facial nerve paralysis, and leakage of spinal fluid are all possible side-effects of neuroma surgery. Where testing shows the hearing to be largely absent, and the tumor is small, the trans-labyrinthine approach through the mastoid reduces the risk of intracranial complications and reduces morbidity.

Radiation treatment for neuromas is gaining popularity. Faced with the generally negative connotations of radiation treatment among the public, this technique has been given the misleading name of "gamma knife surgery." It entails stereotactic direction of radiation to the neuroma. Focusing the radiation beam on the lesion through multiple entry points concentrates the radiation injury on the target and reduces the likelihood of injury to surrounding structures.

Comparisons of the two techniques indicate similar control rates for the two procedures and reduced risk of hearing loss or other nerve injury with the radiation procedure. However, in younger patients with larger tumors, the reverse is true. Which method to choose, therefore, will require case specific analysis.

[31] Hearing Aid Use

Hearing aids are prosthetic devices intended to amplify sound to overcome hearing loss. They fall into roughly three categories. Standard hearing aids supply sound to the inner ear through a device worn in the ear canal or behind the ear, and usually rely on sound transmission through the ear drum and ossicles. In special cases, bone conduction aids are used. Many of these aids utilize digital technology, allowing more accurate programming to accommodate individual losses, and allowing creation of more than one algorithm, changeable by the patient through a remote control, to be used depending on the environment. The second category is that of implanted hearing aids, including bone anchored hearing aids (BAHA) and middle ear implanted aids. These are especially useful in patients with chronic ear infection, and loss of ear drum and middle ear structures from disease or surgery. The third category is the cochlear implant.

Cochlear implants are devices that provide electrical stimulation directly to the cochlea and hearing nerve by surgically implanting electrodes through the round window of the labyrinth and connecting these to the environment through an externally worn impedance device. Implantation of congenitally deaf children is demonstrating exciting benefits in speech development, although it is still resisted by some advocates of the hearing-disabled who find the prospect of elimination of their special culture an affront they have characterized as "cultural genocide."

§ 13.04 Bronchoesophagology

[1] Anatomy

Bronchoesophagology is the diagnosis and treatment of conditions of the upper aerodigestive tract, including the tracheo-bronchial tree and esophagus, using endoscopes to examine and treat. The tracheobronchial tree commences just below the larynx, at the level of the cricoid cartilage. The larynx is safely examined in the office with direct flexible laryngoscopes.

Extending below the cricoid cartilage is the trachea, comprised of horseshoe-shaped partial cartilaginous rings and lining mucosa. In the chest, the trachea divides into a main bronchus for each side, and each main bronchus divides, and divides again, leading to smaller and smaller airways until eventually the microscopic level is reached. On the right, there are ten main secondary segments; on the left, nine. Each of these segmental openings can be seen with the bronchoscope.

The esophagus commences at the level of the thyroid cartilage of the larynx and lies posterior to the larynx and trachea. It passes through the neck and chest to cross the diaphragm and join the stomach in the abdominal cavity.

[2] Endoscopy

Endoscopes were originally hollow metal tubes with electric light bulbs to illuminate the distal end. An adult-sized standard bronchoscope is roughly twenty inches in length. A set of bronchoscopes as would be found in the average endoscopy operating room would include multiple scopes with diameters from 2.5 to 10 mm, for use in children and adults of varying sizes. Esophagoscopes are approximately thirty inches long and with a wider bore than bronchoscopes because the wider and more flexible esophagus could accommodate the larger instrument. Extensive training is required to use such instruments safely. Perforation of the esophagus from rigid esophagoscopes is a life-threatening complication. Perforation of the hypopharynx by bronchoscopes, and the risk of hypoxia with the bronchoscope occupying the airway, are life threatening complications. Thus, until the late 1960s and early seventies the use of such instruments was entirely confined to otolaryngologists and some thoracic surgeons. Introduction of flexible fiberoptic endoscopes, with external lighting sources transmitted through the fiberoptic bundle, removed most of the difficulty in safely passing scopes. In addition, the illusion they permit that the examiner's eye is located at the distal end of the instrument provides a much clearer view. The difference is the same as looking at an automobile at the end of a long tunnel from the other end, versus walking through the tunnel to the distant end and looking at the automobile again. These two differences reduce the training and experience needed to pass the scope safely and to interpret what one is seeing to a period of months rather than years. The two improvements together resulted in widespread use of endoscopes by internal medicine subspecialists in pulmonary medicine and gastroenterology.

Endoscopy can be performed under either local or general anesthesia, but few patients who have undergone the procedure under local will accept that technique for a second procedure. Whether under local or general anesthesia, the appropriate scope is inserted into the mouth, passed through the pharynx and then through the vocal cords or into the esophagus as required. The structure is examined and the scope removed. The stomach can be entered with either type of scope. Inspection and biopsy of superior lung segments is more easily accomplished with the flexible scope.

[3] Uses of Endoscopy in Otolaryngology

Bronchoscopy for diagnosis, performed by otolaryngologists, is so uncommon at present that no discussion of it is required. Otolaryngologists still perform rigid bronchoscopy for removal of foreign bodies as flexible bronchoscopy is suitable only for removal of the smallest objects. Most foreign bodies are found in children, who, as every parent knows, put everything in their mouths. Objects can range from coins to buttons to peanuts to the six-pointed metal objects called jacks, used in an obsolete childhood game. With telescopes to overcome the looking-through-a-long-tunnel problem, and specialized forceps designed for the individual foreign body, objects can be removed from the trachea, bronchi and even in many cases the segmental secondary bronchi.

Similarly, the principal use of rigid esophagoscopy is the removal of foreign bodies from the esophagus. Children will swallow coins that lodge in the upper esophagus. Adults, especially those with dentures, will have large boluses of food lodge in the esophagus. Removal of these objects with flexible scopes is often not possible, requiring use of rigid scopes.

The soft flexible wall of the esophagus is susceptible to perforation by the rigid endoscope. This risk is increased by the manipulation required for foreign body removal. Because perforation will cause bleeding, the presence of bleeding during an esophagoscopy mandates post-surgical evaluation for perforation. Post-surgical esophagram, chest films, and observation for evidence of infection may all be required. An esophagram is an examination performed under fluoroscopy after the patient swallows water-soluble contrast material. If a perforation is present, leakage may be seen. The chest x-ray may show air that has passed into the soft tissues, leaked through the perforation.

Because children may swallow more than one foreign object, repeat bronchoscopy and repeat esophagoscopy are required after removal of a foreign body to verify the absence of a second, or even third, object.

Newly developed esophagoscopes capable of being passed through the nose are permitting esophagoscopy in the office setting with topical anesthesia and minimal or no sedation.

§ 13.05 Laryngology

[1] Anatomy and Physiology of the Larynx

Laryngology is the subsection of otolaryngology dealing with the larynx, or voice box. The larynx is located in the mid-neck. The prominent cartilage called the "Adam's apple" is the central v-shaped laryngeal structure known as the thyroid cartilage, and is the front wall of the larynx. The posterior wall is made up of smaller cartilages and soft tissue. Below the thyroid cartilage is the cricoid cartilage which is a complete ring and provides support for the trachea, which is itself comprised of partial rings anteriorly and a posterior soft tissue wall that blends into the anterior side of the esophagus. Lying within the wings of the thyroid cartilage are the vocal cords, consisting of bands of tissue anchored to the apex of the thyroid cartilage anteriorly and the arytenoids cartilages posteriorly. A complex arrangement of muscles is attached to the arytenoid cartilages. Contraction of these muscles provides for movement of the vocal cords. Superior to the vocal cords are two additional bands called the false vocal cords which contribute to airway protection. Superior to this is a cartilaginous structure resembling the tongue of a shoe called the epiglottis.

To produce a voice, air is forced through the larynx between the vocal cords, which move to the center and vibrate. Just as in a musical instrument, the bulk and length of the vocal cords, along with the tension applied to them, determine the pitch of the voice. Individual speech sounds are articulated by the mouth, tongue, teeth, lips and pharynx.

When breathing, the vocal cords separate to facilitate air flow. As the diaphragm and chest muscles expand the chest cavity, air flows downward through nose and pharynx through the larynx. When they contract the chest cavity, air flow reverses. The larynx plays no active role in this process.

During swallowing, however, the vocal cords and false cords close tightly to protect the airway from food and secretions. The epiglottis contributes to this by mechanically diverting the stream of swallowed material towards the esophagus, but its presence is not essential. Persons whose epiglottis has been removed, as a treatment for cancer, for example, swallow quite well after a period of adjustment. Contrary to public perception, the main function of the larynx is not speech, but this protective function.

[2] Examination of the Larynx

Commencing in the late 19th century, physicians began to examine the larynx by placing a coin sized mirror at the end of a handle into the pharynx, then looking at the reflection of the larynx in the mirror. This technique is described as "indirect laryngoscopy." Light was provided by a complex series of mirrors designed to bring in sunlight from the outside, and later by light reflected off a mirror worn on the physician's head. This "head mirror" is used by a majority of the 10,000 otolaryngologists in the United States, but by almost none of the other 715,000 physicians in the country. But, nevertheless, the head mirror is the recognized symbol of a physician in countless commercials, drawings and cartoons.

Easy use of the head mirror requires a year of practice, so increasingly electric head lights are being used for the same purpose.

Flexible fiberoptic direct laryngoscopy has several advantages over the mirror system. Because the scopes are passed through the nose, usually with topical anesthesia, the gag reflex that interferes with most indirect examinations is avoided. For the same reason, the examiner can devote more time to evaluation. Photographs can be taken. Even occasionally biopsy can be performed. The sole disadvantage is that current fiberoptic systems provide less resolution than mirror examination.

When the techniques above fail to explain voice change, magnified, slow-motion, videos of laryngeal structure and function can be obtained by means of videostroboscopy. This technique involves use of a hybrid instrument that permits view of the larynx through the mouth but using a rigid fiberoptic device. Changes in vocal cord vibratory pattern can be identified with this technique that may allow detection of vocal cord tumors and neurological diseases at a very early stage.

When the techniques described provide insufficient examination, or when larger specimens are required for biopsy, direct microlaryngoscopy can be performed. As usually performed, the operative laryngoscope is inserted into the mouth under general anesthesia. The larynx is exposed and an operating microscope is used to obtain a clear, magnified view of laryngeal structures. If a cancer is present, multiple biopsies can be obtained to determine type and extent. Small lesions can be removed, either mechanically or by laser.

[3] Tracheotomy

Tracheotomy is the operation of creating an airway directly through the neck into the trachea. Because the larynx provides a connection between the upper airway (including the nose, nasopharynx, oral cavity and lower pharynx) and the lower airway tracheo-bronchial tree, abnormalities of the larynx that reduce its size or function lead to airway obstruction. Trauma, infection, congenital deformities and tumors, both malignant and benign, can all block off the flow of air. Sleep apnea, disordered breathing caused by partial obstruction (especially at night), is caused by a partial obstruction. For each of these conditions, the obstruction can be bypassed by tracheotomy.

Tracheotomy can be performed in two ways. Percutaneous tracheotomy is performed by inserting a needle into the trachea through the neck skin, verifying accurate placement of the needle with a flexible fiberoptic bronchoscope in place. The needle is followed with a trochar, then a graduated series of dilators, and finally a tracheotomy tube. For patients whose anatomy or other problems make percutaneous tracheotomy unsatisfactory, standard surgical tracheotomy is performed. A skin incision is made, under either local or general anesthesia. The subcutaneous tissues are divided. The strap muscles of the neck are separated to expose the trachea. A small window is made into the trachea or a cruciate incision is made which is then dilated to permit insertion of the tracheotomy tube. With the tube in place, air passes directly into the trachea.

Tracheotomy is not performed, with rare exceptions, unless the patient's breathing is dependent on the presence of an artificial airway. Obstruction of the airway by mucous plugs, or displacement of the tube from the trachea can be fatal in minutes. Post operative care is therefore essential, and includes use of suction, frequent cleaning of the inner tube, and careful attention to the use of cloth ties around the neck or sutures, or both, to secure the tube in place. Humidification reduces the risk of mucous plug obstruction, as does suction. Adults can be taught to do this for themselves. Careful training of the parents of children with tracheotomy tubes is necessary. Infants may need to be hospitalized for prolonged periods until parents are capable of repositioning a dislodged tube, removing, cleaning and replacing the entire apparatus, suctioning, and operating humidification equipment.

Tracheotomy is frequently temporary, with the tube being removed and the opening allowed to heal, once the underlying disease is corrected. Removal of the larynx requires a permanent connection between the trachea and skin of the neck.

[4] Laryngeal Trauma

Injury by blunt or sharp trauma to the anterior neck can occur. Mild trauma may cause only swelling in the soft tissues surrounding and supporting the cartilaginous framework. Swelling of the inner laryngeal structures including the epiglottis and vocal cords, with or without hematoma, results from more severe trauma. Severe trauma can dislocate or fracture the cartilaginous structures. Marked distortion and obstruction of the airway can occur.

Any trauma to the neck mandates careful attention to the possibility of laryngeal trauma. Hoarseness, a crackling sensation in the neck ("crepitus") caused by air leaked into the soft tissues, stridor and air hunger are all clues to the level of trauma.

The larynx should be examined carefully. Distortion of the thyroid cartilage may be palpable. Direct or indirect laryngoscopy should be performed. Foreshortening of the vocal cords, vocal cord paralysis, and hematoma may be found. CT scan and/or MRI may demonstrate cartilage fracture and displacement.

Treatment depends on the degree of airway obstruction and the extent of the trauma. Mild to moderate injuries may result in swelling that can be managed by observation. Bilateral vocal cord hematomas can impair the airway, but may still be managed by observation in the majority of cases. If the airway is severely compromised, tracheotomy or endotracheal intubation may be needed. If displaced fracture is found, tracheotomy and open reduction and fixation of the fracture is required. The technique will depend on the injury. A common form of injury is fracture of the wings of the thyroid cartilage with posterior displacement of the anterior fragment. This can be reduced by traction, and the fractures bridged with suture. Stenting with an endotracheal tube or use of a laryngeal keel to prevent adhesions between the vocal cords may be required.

[5] Acute Infections of the Larynx

Laryngitis is a general term for any inflammatory process involving the larynx. The most common form is caused by a virus. Hoarseness and laryngeal pain are prominent. Treatment is generally supportive, with air humidification, pain medication, hydration with oral fluids, and voice rest, all until inflammation and swelling subside.

Croup is a form of viral inflammation involving the mucosa overlying the cricoid cartilage inferior to the glottis at the entrance to the trachea. The cricoid is a complete cartilaginous ring and is relatively bulky. The airway narrows due to the bulk of the cricoid, so inflammation in this subglottic region has a disproportionate effect on the airway. The result is a characteristically high-pitched "bark-y" cough and noisy inspiration or "stridor." Treatment consists of steroids to reduce inflammation and humidification. The airway obstruction may become life-threatening. In the past, many children with croup underwent tracheotomy; today the majority are treated with nasotracheal or endotracheal intubation and sedation for several days until the swelling subsides.

While croup is almost always viral, inflammation of the epiglottis and upper larynx is usually bacterial. Epiglottitis occurs in both children and adults. In children, it manifests as hoarseness, inspiratory stridor, painful and difficult swallowing leading to drooling, and a characteristic sitting position with the head forward and neck extended. Physical examination reveals a swollen erythematous epiglottis. Extreme care must be taken during examination. Use of a tongue depressor can precipitate sudden and complete airway obstruction, creating an airway emergency. Just as with croup, the traditional treatment was tracheotomy. This has been largely replaced by intubation.

However, the causative organism in children is usually Hemophilus influenza, type B. Children are now largely protected against hemophilus influenza through vaccination. As a result, epiglottitis is much less frequently seen today. In adults, immunocompromise, as in diabetics, may be associated with epiglottitis. Adult epiglottitis may lead to an epiglottis abscess requiring surgical drainage.

In both adults and children, aggressive antibiotic treatment, hydration and humidification are essential treatment and may obviate need for intubation or tracheotomy.

[6] Vocal Cord Paralysis

A diagnosis of vocal cord paralysis or paresis means that one or both true vocal cords is either immobile, or has reduced mobility. The vocal cords are innervated by a branch of the vagus, or 10th cranial nerve, known as the recurrent laryngeal nerve. The recurrent laryngeal nerve leaves the cranial cavity through an opening in the skull base, passes through the neck into the chest, and then makes a 180 degree turn to return to the larynx, entering the superior portion of the larynx to provide direct innervation of the muscles responsible for vocal cord movement. On the left, the nerve passes around the arch of the aorta. On the right, the turn occurs at the level of the thoracic inlet.

Vocal cord paralysis has many possible causes. Interruption of the signals transmitted through the vagus nerve can occur anywhere along its course. Abnormality in the brain, tumors or infections of the skull base, interruption of the nerve by trauma in the neck or tumors in the chest, can all lead to interruption of the nerve signal. Other causes of paralysis include arthritis of the cricoarytenoid joint and tumor involvement of the vocal cord or adjacent structures. Probably the most common diagnosis in cases of vocal cord paralysis is idiopathic vocal cord paralysis, most likely resulting from viral inflammation.

The primary symptom, especially when the paralysis involves one vocal cord, is hoarseness. Because a paralyzed vocal cord usually rests in a partially abducted, or open, position, breathing is satisfactory but the voice is breathy, hoarse, and weak. Coughing after swallowing may occur, especially early in the process before the patient adjusts, because closure of the larynx to protect the airway is defective. If both cords are paralyzed, they may rest in the midline and block breathing. Many such patients have little problem when they are sedentary, but activity leads to stridor and shortness of breath. This results from failure of the vocal cords to separate and allow greater air passage. Voice is usually close to normal. If the cords are resting in a separated position, airway will be good but the voice poor.

Unilateral vocal cord paralysis that is symptomatic is treated by surgical procedures to move the vocal cord to the midline so that the functioning cord can make contact with it during phonation. This can be accomplished by injection of the vocal cord with materials to add bulk, such as Teflon paste. A better method, because it is reversible, is to surgically insert silicone rubber or similar material between the thyroid cartilage and the vocal cord, thus pushing the vocal cord towards the midline. When the vocal cord paralysis is bilateral, and the airway compromised, surgical repositioning of one cord to open the airway is the treatment of choice. Tracheotomy may also be used to bypass the obstruction.

[7]   Cancer of the Larynx

Cancer of the larynx is associated with tobacco and alcohol use, and is found usually in adults over 50 years of age. Rare cases have been reported in teens and children. It is more common among men than women. Although cancer of the larynx is reported in persons with no alcohol abuse or smoking histories, many otolaryngologists go through their entire careers, treating many cancer patients, and never meet a patient without such a history.

Malignant tumors of the larynx are initially defined by location. Tumors of the epiglottis and supralarynx, tumors of the vocal cords, and tumors of the subglottis have different prognostic and treatment ramifications. Unless found early, however, tumors will grow and extend to two or even all three levels.

Hoarseness is an early symptom, especially of vocal cord lesions. The public is warned by cancer education campaigns to seek medical attention if hoarseness lasts longer than ten days. Another symptom is pain with swallowing and pain in the ear, with swallowing or persisting without. More than one person has been treated for a prolonged period for Eustachian tube dysfunction or ear infection when the pain of which they complain is due to a laryngeal cancer. As the tumor grows, airway blockage may develop.

Complaints of persistent ear pain, throat pain or irritation, pain with swallowing especially radiating to the ear, and persistent hoarseness require thorough evaluation of the larynx in every patient. The suspicion of malignancy is naturally heightened when the patient is over 50 years, and has a smoking and/or alcohol history. The first step is always to examine the larynx. This may be done either indirectly with a laryngeal mirror, or directly with a fiberoptic laryngoscope. Even early tumors can be seen. Of critical importance is examination of the laryngeal surface of the epiglottis, which may be obscured by epiglottic position.

Any suspicious area should be biopsied. Although this can sometimes be accomplished through a fiberoptic scope specially designed for the purpose, direct laryngoscopy in the operating room is generally needed. The direct laryngoscope is a lighted metal tube that serves to hold the mouth open and the tongue out of the way, while an operating microscope is used to examine the larynx and identify areas for biopsy. Special forceps are used to remove suspicious areas of the laryngeal mucosal lining for study, including both the visible lesion, and areas adjacent to permit delineation of tumor extent.

Radiologic evaluation by MRI and by CT scan are also useful. Positron emission tomography will allow identification of metastases.

Treatment depends on the tumor. The goal is removal of the tumor while preserving as much of the larynx's function as possible. For very early vocal cord tumors, complete curative removal may be accomplished by local excision of the tumor at direct laryngoscopy by laser or scalpel. Radiation treatment is effective in better than 90% of cases and permits maintenance of a normal voice. It has side effects of alterations in taste sensation and development of a dry mouth.

For larger tumors, a combination of either partial or total removal of the larynx, coupled with radiation therapy, is utilized. Total removal of the larynx means a lifetime of voice loss and breathing through a permanent tracheal opening in the neck. Restoration of the voice by insertion of a connecting valve between the esophagus and trachea, or use of an "electronic larynx," each provide a usable, if not normal, voice.

When total removal of the larynx is performed, surgical removal of the lymph nodes in the neck is frequently required. From the lymph nodes, tumors can spread widely. Modern use of PET scanning to identify distant metastasis has permitted avoidance of major surgeries in cases where cure is no longer possible. Chemotherapy is widely used but cure through chemotherapy is a goal not yet achievable.

§ 13.06 Pharynx

[1] Anatomy and Physiology

The pharynx is divided into three segments. The most superior is the nasopharynx, lying behind the nose and above the soft palate. Contiguous with the nasopharynx is the middle segment, or oropharynx, which is made up of the teeth, gums, floor of mouth, tongue and tonsils. Inferior to this is the hypopharynx or laryngopharynx.

The pharynx contains lymphoid tissue that contributes to the body's immune system. In the nasopharynx, this lymphoid tissue forms a mass called the adenoids. Enlargement of the adenoids can cause airway obstruction that can be significant in children. By age eleven years, the adenoids have regressed, or have become smaller in relation to the size of the nasopharynx, so that adenoid airway obstruction is much less common after that age. The nasopharynx is a passageway for air on its way to the lungs.

The oropharyngeal and laryngopharyngeal spaces are both air passages and passages for food and secretions. They also contribute to the formation of speech.

[2] Pharyngeal Disease

Acute pharyngitis, whether caused by virus or bacteria, is the most common infection of the pharynx. Inflammation and swelling may occur in any or all three of the pharyngeal regions, usually associated with sore throat and enlargement of the lymph nodes of the neck ("swollen glands"). Antibiotics are commonly prescribed for pharyngitis, but should not be unless testing confirms bacterial disease. Rapid screening tests for beta-hemolytic streptococcus infection that rely on the presence of bacterial DNA allow for almost immediate decisions about antibiotics in contrast to culture methods requiring a minimum of 24 hours for a result. Although other forms of bacterial pharyngitis occur, and should be treated with antibiotics when confirmed, strep infection is of most concern. Streptococcus infections can precipitate rheumatic fever (risking permanent damage to the heart) and Bright's disease (involving the kidneys with a risk of kidney failure). Streptococcus infections can also progress to the formation of abscesses around the pharyngeal tonsil requiring surgical drainage in addition to antibiotics.

Frequent tonsillitis, associated with pharyngitis, may lead to a decision to remove tonsils and adenoids in children. Enlargement, in both adults and children, can lead to nighttime airway obstruction manifested by snoring. Sleep apnea, a condition in which the airway obstruction leads to periodic pauses in breathing, can lead to problems of behavior, daytime sleepiness, heart failure and high blood pressure. Although enlarged tonsils and adenoids contribute to the condition, especially in children, it is more often associated with lax tissues with a tendency to collapse, and excess weight, especially in the middle-aged. An important part of treatment has been to shorten or stiffen the soft palate to reduce its tendency to collapse against the posterior pharynx.

Sleep apnea and snoring have been the subjects of extensive study and attempts at treatment in recent years. The adage that the existence of many treatments for a condition means that no cure for the condition exists is well illustrated here. Various modalities have been used to stiffen the soft palate, including implantation of plastic splints, encouragement of scar tissue by use of radio-frequency and other devices, and reduction in the length of the soft palate through laser assisted uvula and palate removal and through uvulopalatopharyngoplasty. The variable success of the different surgical treatments, plus the invariable risk of complications and side-effects, has encouraged reliance on breathing apparatus designed to prevent airway collapse. CPAP (continuous positive airway pressure) machines and their variations have a very good success rate in relieving the consequences of sleep apnea.

[3] Tonsillectomy and Adenoidectomy

In the 1950s, one might find in any community hospital in the United States, several children lined up to undergo tonsillectomy and adenoidectomy (T&A). These might include two or more children from the same family, scheduled because one child was advised to have the procedure done because of frequent infections and either the doctor or the parents suggesting doing the other children as well, as a preventive measure. As the risk of death from T&A was increasingly appreciated in the early 1960s, extensive research was carried out attempting to determine the factors that created the risks, so that surgery could be performed in a safer way. The conclusion reached was that bleeding is an inevitable consequence of T&A, occurring in 1% to 3% of patients. Bleeding may be immediate or late. Immediate bleeding results from failure to ligate or otherwise treat severed blood vessels. A cut vessel in spasm may be missed until it relaxes and bleeds an hour to twenty-four hours later. Late bleeding may occur seven to ten days post-surgery. This results from sloughing of eschar and ligatures from vessels that are not fully healed. Treatment includes a return to the operating room for cautery or ligation of the bleeding vessel or vessels with or without transfusion. In older children and adults, the bleeding can sometimes be controlled in the emergency department.

The only available means of reducing the number of deaths, it was concluded from years of research, is to reduce the number of operations performed. The indications for T&A changed in response. Operating on several children from one family because one child had clear indications became a thing of the past.

A frequent indication for adenoidectomy is the presence of intractable secretory otitis media. (See § 13.03 [9].) Although most surgeons do not recommend adenoid removal with a first instance of ventilation tube placement, repeat intubations do suggest the need for adenoid removal. Removal of tonsils and adenoids is recommended for treatment of frequent infections. Five infections in a twelve-month period, or four in two years, or three in several years, or peritonsillar abscess are considered indications. This is particularly true with laboratory evidence of repeated beta-hemolytic streptococcus infection. The gradual tightening of indications is demonstrated by a gradual shift in opinion to a requirement for two episodes of abscess formation before surgery is considered instead of one. Two episodes confirms the risk of recurrent abscess. Sleep apnea with right ventricular failure is another indication, although rarely encountered.

[4]   Fine Needle Aspiration Biopsy of Neck Masses

The presence of a hard neck mass an inch in diameter or more is strong indication of the presence of cancer. If careful examination of the head and neck does not provide an explanation for the mass, it must be biopsied. Biopsy by surgical removal significantly reduces the chance of curing the cancer. Instead, biopsy by fine needle aspiration (FNA) is recommended. A 20 gauge needle, identical to that used for simple blood draw, with a syringe is inserted into the mass. This requires substantial judgment on the part of the surgeon to assure that the needle has entered the mass. Suction is applied, drawing a small amount of cellular material into the needle. This material is then expelled onto glass slides and spread out. A trained pathologist can diagnose the tumor from inspection of the cells approximately 90% of the time. Fine needle aspiration biopsies have minimal risk.

[5]   Cancer of the Pharyngeal Region

Cancer of the pharynx can involve the nasopharyngeal cavity, the oropharynx and the hypopharynx.

Cancer of the nasopharynx is uncommon. It is not associated with alcohol and/or tobacco use. It is most common in Asians of Asian birth. Early tumors may present as middle ear fluid secondary to Eustachian tube involvement and as unilateral nosebleed and/or airway obstruction. The presence of unilateral middle ear fluid in a previously healthy adult with no other explanation such as a recent infection mandates careful examination of the nasopharynx to be sure there is no tumor. Such tumors spread to the neck lymph nodes early. The diagnosis of nasopharyngeal tumor is therefore frequently made when the typical nasopharyngeal cancer cell type is found at fine needle aspiration biopsy of the neck mass. Examination may be performed by indirect view of the nasopharynx with a mirror, or flexible or rigid endoscopy through the nose.

Treatment is by radiation to the nasopharynx coupled with either surgical removal of the lymph nodes an/or radiation to the neck. Cure rates are poor.

Cancers of the oropharynx and hypopharynx are typically associated with alcohol abuse and tobacco use and occur in the older age groups. Early symptoms include pain at the site of the tumor, intermittent at first. When the lateral wall and tongue are involved, pain radiating to the ear may be prominent. Tumors of the tongue and oral cavity in general should be visible by standard examination and are amenable to simple office biopsy. A tongue depressor and headlight will reveal almost all such lesions. Suspicious lesions should be biopsied. Areas to target include areas of leukoplakia and areas that stain darkly with o-toluidine blue dye.

Depending on the size and location of a tumor of the oral cavity or oropharynx, a combination of surgery and radiation may be used for treatment. Cure rates, especially for larger lesions, are poor.

§ 13.07 Sinuses

[1] Anatomy

The sinuses are air-containing cavities in the skull centered on the nasal passage. Normal sinuses are air-containing, lined by a thin mucous membrane. The normal lining is so thin that it will not be seen on x-rays. Each sinus has a drainage pathway leading into the nasal passage. In the forehead, the frontal sinuses lie superior to the eyes. Below the frontal sinuses and lying between the eyes, are the ethmoid sinuses. Posterior to the ethmoids are the sphenoid sinuses. Located below each eye are the maxillary sinuses. The drainage opening for the maxillary sinuses is located at the superior medial portion of the sinus. Mucous produced during the day can therefore not drain from the sinus by gravity, but must be moved out of the sinus against gravity by microscopic structures of the mucous membrane called cilia.

The sinuses are therefore located in close proximity to the eyes and brain. The frontal lobe of the brain and the sensory structures of the sense of smell are separated from the nasal cavity by a thin plate of bone called the cribriform plate. The structures of the orbit are separated from the ethmoid sinus by a thin plate of bone called the lamina papyracea, which is paper thin bone just as you would expect from the name. Its fragility is a major factor in surgical complications. Passing through the orbit from the cranial cavity to the nose are two blood vessels, the anterior and posterior ethmoid arteries. These vessels supply blood to the ethmoid sinus and nasal cavity. They are always cut during the process of sinus surgery, and occasionally can contribute to significant bleeding problems. The optic nerves pass through the skull in close proximity to the sphenoid sinuses. Although standard surgery of the sphenoid involves enlargement of the natural sinus opening, and rarely penetration of the sinus itself, the optic nerve can still be at risk.

[2] Sinus Infection

Sinus infection is simultaneously one of the most overdiagnosed and underdiagnosed infections. It is overdiagnosed because many upper respiratory infections with nasal airway obstruction or increased mucous production are assumed to be sinus infections and are treated as such without any objective supporting evidence. Similarly, chronic headache is assumed to be sinus infection. It is also underdiagnosed. While acute sinus infection may be associated with facial or dental pain, severe headache, fever and purulent discharge, chronic infection can be present with minimal symptoms.

Many sinus infections associated with upper respiratory illness are viral and are self-limited. Antibiotic use should therefore be instituted only when any symptoms have been present for ten days or more, and when physical examination confirms middle meatus purulent exudates or discharge. Positive radiologic findings may show clouding of the involved sinus. Tenderness of the sinus to percussion or pressure can be elucidated by percussion superior to the canine fossa. Diagnosing sinusitis because palpation of the infraorbital rim or face just below it causes pain can be misleading because pressure on the infraorbital nerve can elicit tenderness in the absence of sinus infection.

[3] General Surgical Principles

As noted in the section about middle ear and mastoid disease, the *sine qua non* of surgical treatment of infection is drainage. The need to "lance the boil" was recognized by Hippocrates and was certainly standard practice in pre-recorded history. The same principle applies to sinus infection. Modern research has demonstrated that failure of the natural sinus drainage pathways is a major contributing factor to sinus infection. Surgery is aimed at providing that drainage, removing diseased mucosa, and releasing infected material. The following paragraphs will describe sinus surgery in general. Specific surgical procedures will be described separately

Acute sinusitis is characterized by facial pain, "headache" and when the maxillary sinuses are involved, by pain in the teeth. When these symptoms are present, some of the pain is due to inflammation extending to the nerves, but most is secondary to pressure within the sinus. Relief of the pressure will provide relief of the pain. Examination of a patient's nose when such symptoms are present may reveal inflamed, edematous mucosa, and purulent discharge arising in the middle meatus region. Application of decongestants, such as a 4% solution of cocaine, may increase the amount of drainage sufficiently to provide some relief from pain. If so, medical therapy with antibiotics selected for their known activity against the bacteria commonly responsible for sinus infections along with decongestants and pain medication, will suffice for treatment. Although such an increase in drainage is rarely seen, few patients have pain of sufficient severity to require more than the same medical treatment. However, in a minority of cases, this is not true.

When a more aggressive approach to relieving the symptoms is required, sinus irrigation and drainage is instituted. In this procedure, under local anesthesia, a trochar is inserted into the maxillary sinus. This may be done through the canine fossa, lifting the upper lip out of the way and passing the instrument directly through the anterior face of the maxilla into the sinus. It may also be done by penetrating the inferior meatus of the nasal cavity entering the medial wall of the sinus. The former is more easily and quickly performed in most cases, but it carries a small risk of causing a permanently numb tooth through injury to the sensory nerve by the trochar. Once the trochar is in place, pus can be obtained, often flowing from the sinus through the trochar under its own pressure, following which gentle irrigation with warm saline can be carried out. The pus obtained can be submitted to the laboratory for culture and the procedure itself provides some pain relief. In a few patients, up to three such irrigations may be required. In the majority, one such treatment is sufficient.

Chronic sinus infection may cause headache. However, most headache is not caused by sinus infection. Many otolaryngologists report identifying objective evidence of sinus disease in fewer than 15% of patients seen for "sinus" or "sinus headaches" or "chronic sinusitis." Such headaches are often ultimately diagnosed as migraine or a variant thereof. Chronic sinus infection is often associated with nasal congestion. This congestion may be a consequence of mucosal edema, or it may represent septal or other abnormalities that are ultimately causative factors in the development of the sinus disease. A frequent cause of nasal congestion is the presence of nasal polyps.

Nasal polyps are growths, usually of the same size and shape as a grape attached to the sinus by a thin stalk. They result from inflammation and allergy, but it is often unclear whether they arise as a result of sinus disease, or themselves develop with sinus disease secondary to the stagnation and obstruction caused by the polyps. Contributing to this latter theory is the well-known association of aspirin sensitivity, asthma and nasal polyps, as well as the association between cystic fibrosis and nasal polyps. The answer probably lies in a combination of the two. Polyp removal as part of sinus surgery is routine.

[4] Formerly Conventional Surgical Approaches

For most of the 20th century, surgical treatment of the sinuses was divided between internal and external approaches. External approaches suffered the defect of leaving external scars, but were accompanied by fewer complications. Internal approaches reversed the balance. In skilled hands, creation of artificial openings into the maxillary sinus through the nose, and removal of the bony plates separating the ethmoid cells from each other and from the nose, could all be performed while looking at the operative site from outside through the nostril with the aid of light worn on the operator's forehead. Failure of such procedures to cure chronic infection, or to permanently cure polyps, led either primarily, or as follow-up surgery, to external approaches. The maxillary sinus could be entered through its anterior face via an incision superior to the canine tooth. The frontal sinus could be entered by an incision below the eyebrow. Where complete obliteration of the frontal sinus was required, an incision could be made from ear to ear over the top of the scalp, the skin flap created turned forward and the anterior frontal sinus plate removed. The mucosa of the sinus could then be obliterated with a drill under direct observation, and the sinus cavity filled with fat before restoring the anatomy.

[5] Endoscopic Sinus Surgery

Late in the 20th century, a realization that some of the conventional surgical procedures were counterproductive coincided with development of surgical telescopes. These devices provide a view through fiberoptics that creates the illusion that the eye is located in the nasal passage, or in the sinus, at the point of observation. The parallax and illumination problems created by "looking through a long tunnel towards its end" are eliminated. At the same time, research indicated that many surgical techniques, for example, creation of inferior meatus maxillary sinus "windows" were contrary to natural physiology. Instead of creating a situation which the body fights against, these researchers queried, why not use our surgery to enhance the body's natural mechanisms? The resulting surgical techniques were known as "functional endoscopic sinus surgery," and thirty years after their introduction, enhanced with new surgical instrumentation such as rotary suction-debriders, they are the standard for sinus surgery. The conventional approaches described above are reserved for special circumstances and are generally obsolete.

[6] Complications of Sinus Surgery

The complex anatomy of the paranasal sinuses, lying as they do in close proximity to many vital structures, means that complications when they occur may be catastrophic. A principle of medical malpractice law for the past 40 years has been that all risks must be disclosed that would be of concern, and would influence the decision whether to proceed with surgery, of a reasonable person. A correlate requirement is that common risks must be disclosed, and uncommon risks must be disclosed if they are serious. In the field of sinus surgery, everything must be disclosed to the prospective patient. A thoughtful review of the anatomy outlined in § 13.07 [1] will make the risks apparent.

The orbit is separated from the ethmoid sinus only by a thin plate of bone. That bone can be fractured during surgery, and the orbit entered by accident. Damage to the medical rectus muscle can result leading to double vision after surgery. There have been incidents of the medial rectus actually being removed. Injury to the orbital content can lead to bleeding into the orbit. Sufficient pressure can build up that damage to the eye causes blindness. Blindness can also result from direct injury to the optic nerve during surgery on the sphenoid sinus, where the nerve passes through the roof of the sinus, or during surgery on the very posteriorly placed ethmoid sinus cells. Blindness can be bilateral and total.

Injury to the thin plate of bone that separates the anterior cranial cavity from the nasal passage can lead to leakage of spinal fluid into the nose. The serious implication of such a leak is the risk of bacteria passing in the other direction, leading to meningitis and/or brain abscess. There are reports in the literature of surgeons failing to notice the inadvertent entry into the anterior cranial fossa. The continued removal of tissue after such an incident leads to pathological reports after surgery of "normal brain tissue" instead of nasal polyps or infection. As one can readily imagine, the consequences of such removal of brain tissue can be catastrophic, including death. Damage to the cribriform plate will also lead to loss of sense of smell. However, most chronic sinus infection patients have already lost their sense of smell, and this harm is less noticed than the others.

Any surgical procedure involves cutting multiple blood vessels in the normal course of surgery. Small "bleeders" are closed by cautery; larger or persistent bleeders are closed by suture. During sinus surgery, identification of a cut blood vessel end with sufficient precision to permit cautery is rare, and the chance to ligate non-existent. Bleeding control requires reliance on natural healing mechanisms, assisted in many cases by post-operative packing. Either during surgery, or in the days following surgery, bleeding from the nose can be substantial.

Secondary surgery may be required to deal with complications. In the case of persistent bleeding from the nose, it is possible to locate the anterior ethmoid artery in the orbit, and close it with a metal clip. The same thing can be done for the internal maxillary artery, either in the pterygomaxillary space behind the maxillary sinus, or endoscopically through the nose. Orbital hematoma that threatens vision can be treated by orbital decompression.

§ 13.08 Maxillofacial Trauma

[1] General Principles

A commonly heard explanation for the existence of sinuses is that they lighten the skull. That is, if the air filled spaces were instead solid bone, the head would be much heavier. The lighter skull presumably has evolutionary value. Another explanation for the existence of sinuses is that the resulting facial structure functions like a force-absorbing bumper and steering column in an automobile, cushioning the effects of a blow, thus protecting the brain. Whether either of these theories has any basis in fact is difficult to say. What is clear, however, is that the face consists of a series of buttresses connected often by extremely thin and fragile bone. Only a severe blow will fracture one or more of these buttresses.

When these bones are fractured, repair requires realigning them in their pre-trauma state, and then securing them in position to heal. As it is difficult to encase the head in a cast, more direct fixation is required. Otolaryngologists, oral surgeons, and plastic surgeons all have a role in repair of such injuries, sometimes in concert, and sometimes overlapping. Injury to the mandible, and occasionally injury to the maxilla, will disturb the occlusion, which is the fit between upper and lower teeth. Restoration of occlusion is of such importance to the patient's future well-being that in some countries, only physicians who also have dental degrees are permitted to perform such repairs.

[2] Treatment of Nasal Fractures

Injuries to the supporting structure of the nose may be the most common fracture.

It is without doubt the most frequent maxillofacial fracture. Whether due to walking into a door at night, disagreeing with a neighbor, or being subject to flying elbows under a basketball net, the nose is subject to trauma. The most anterior portion of the nasal skeleton is cartilaginous, and flexible. Substantial trauma can occur without the cartilage fracturing. When it is damaged, it frequently is dislocated from its bony connections leading to a deviated septum. The pyramidal nasal bones may also be broken, and when broken are easily displaced.

If displacement is moderate, and the fractured bones still mobile, closed nasal reduction can be carried out. Manipulation of the nasal bones from outside, coupled with placement of instruments inside the nasal passage to lift and reposition depressed bony fragments, is often sufficient. Internal nasal packing and external splints can then be applied to immobilize and protect the fractured bones, with removal of the packs and splints in approximately a week. This method provides a satisfactory result in 90% of patients. Where it fails, a later formal surgical procedure can be carried out.

In some people, the nasal distortion is severe and is coupled with an inability to move the bones through the simple means described. Repair may then be carried out in the operating room, making internal incisions to permit access to the fractured bones and cartilage. Many surgeons prefer to delay such repair until a later date when healing has occurred and swelling resolved. In each individual case, patient and surgeon will need to decide which approach is better. Packing and splinting are then carried out as described.

[3] Lower Jaw (Mandible) Fractures

The lower jaw, or mandible, forms an arch connected to the skull by joints at either end. Like all joints, the temporomandibular (TMJ) joints consist of two bones joined together by a complex web of ligaments with a cartilage plate between. When the jaw is struck, stress will be relieved by disruption of the joints, or a fracture in the arch, or both. Multiple fractures are common. Fractures are treated by either open or closed methods, depending on the stability of the jaw, the degree of disturbance in occlusion, the health and number of teeth, and the patient's general health.

The simplest fractures, such as a fracture at the upper end of the mandible where it is incorporated in the joint, if there is no disturbance of occlusion, can be treated with several weeks of soft diet. If bony displacement at any site is minimal, the teeth can be manipulated into occlusion and then the jaw can be immobilized by application of steel bands ("arch bars") to both upper and lower teeth with either wire or elastic bands holding upper and lower together. This is known colloquially as "wiring the jaw," and otherwise as intermaxillary fixation. This immobilization is maintained for six weeks, sometimes less in the very young. Failing to adequately immobilize the jaw will lead to failure of healing, as the forces applied to the jaw by mandibular motion inevitably distract the fracture edges

Open reduction is achieved by making incisions, either inside the mouth or external to it, permitting the fractured ends of bone to be realigned under direct observation. Repair is then effectuated by applying metal plates to the bone, secured with screws. There are two types of plates in common use. One secures the fractured bone. The other places the fractures under compression, drawing the edges together. Mandible repair can be made so secure by this means that, if the patient can be trusted to adhere to the prescribed liquid diet, no intermaxillary fixation is needed. Prior to the advent of plates, mandible repair in an edentulous person required manufacture of a complicated denture-splint which was then secured to both maxilla and mandible by stainless steel wires. Plating makes this unnecessary.

Complications of mandible repair include bleeding and infection. Healing in misalignment leading to malocclusion occurs. Often the error is minor and can be corrected by a dentist by "occlusal adjustment." Orthodontic treatment may be needed.

More significant malocclusions lead to pain in the temporomandibular joint and difficulty chewing. Re-fracture to make another attempt at proper alignment may be needed. Non-union, or failure of the bone to heal, occurs and will require secondary surgical procedures. When arch bars are secured to the teeth by circumdental wires, injury to the gums and even tooth loss can occur. All of these complications can occur in the face of properly performed procedures.

[4] Fractures of the Upper Jaw (Maxilla)

Trauma to the midface can fracture the bony buttresses that form its functional skeleton. If all are broken, the midface becomes mobile, and malocclusion results not from an incorrectly positioned lower jaw, but from the upper jaw. CT scans are invaluable in delineating the degree and number of fractures. Cosmetic and functional abnormalities are often obvious. Repair depends on the position and mobility of the maxilla. If the mandible is intact, and the deformity is minor, arch bars can be applied to both upper and lower, and elastic bands applied between them. Traction will gradually pull the maxilla into position. If the deformity is great, or if traction with elastic bands does not immediately correct the problem, external skeletal traction can be applied via a variety of steel frameworks affixed to the skull. When alignment is correct, plates and screws are applied in an open operation to secure position and immobility.

[5] Fractures of the Orbit and Supporting Structures

Fractures of the orbit can occur either in isolation, or in conjunction with, the other fractures discussed herein. Fracture of the cheekbone can cause both cosmetic and functional impairment by impinging on mandibular motion. Fracture of either the floor or medial wall of the orbit can result in herniation of orbital fat into the maxillary or ethmoid sinuses, respectively, causing the eye to be sunken in ("enophthalmos"). A marked cosmetic deformity can result, along with double vision. The majority of isolated orbital floor fractures with minimal herniation require no treatment. If there is evidence that orbital muscles have become entrapped in the fracture line, causing double vision, usually with upward gaze, then open reduction and repair is needed. Other fractures are treated for the cosmetic deformity that will result if they are not.

§ 13.09 Reconstructive and Cosmetic Surgery

[1] General Surgical Principles

Plastic surgery of the head and neck is divided into two broad categories. The first is repair and reconstruction of normal appearance and function after trauma, and removal of malignancies while minimizing the resulting cosmetic and functional impairments. The second is purely cosmetic surgery such as rhinoplasty, otoplasty, face lifts and similar procedures. Otolaryngology training programs provide extensive education in facial plastic surgery in the modern era, and it is no longer rare to find persons who have also completed training in plastic surgery programs, thus becoming dual qualified and "doubly boarded."

[2] Plastic Surgery of the External Ear

Children born without an ear, or with a partial ear, may undergo construction of an external ear. This may be done in conjunction with an operation to open a congenitally absent ear canal, or in isolation. Multiple procedures using the patient's own skin and either rib cartilage or plastic prostheses are required. A completely normal appearing external ear is very rarely seen, but significant improvement is common. It is important for parents to understand that the end result is not going to be a completely normal ear. Post-operative photographs of prior results are an important part of obtaining an informed consent.

The most common operation on the external ear is undoubtedly correction of "lop ears." The indication is the ridicule to which children with this deformity are subjected. Hair styles permit girls to obscure their ears, and there are probably fewer such procedures on girls as a result. The most common procedure involves placement of sutures to plicate the external ear, creating the fold in the cartilage that is congenitally absent. Complications include bleeding, failure due to sutures coming loose, and infection.

[3] Plastic Surgery of the Eyelids

Blepharoplasty, cosmetic surgery on the eyelids, is commonly performed in older individuals. Although the sagging upper eyelid can interfere with vision, most such procedures are performed for purely cosmetic reasons. Removal of the sags and bags can do much to restore a youthful appearance.

The surgical procedure involves removal of the excess skin and portions of the underlying fat. Once sutured, the lid is tightened and bulk and sagging reduced. Because the abnormality is a natural result of aging, surgical repair may not be permanent, with recurrence some years following the surgery. Excess scarring can occur causing permanent deformity of the eyelid with some risk to eyesight through corneal exposure if it is the lower lid that is pulled down. Infection also is possible.

[4] Plastic Surgery of the Nose

Cosmetic surgery of the nose can be divided into two groups. Some procedures are done to correct past traumatic deformities. These procedures are open reductions of nasal fractures. Others are done for purely cosmetic reasons, often in adolescent and young adults seeking to improve their appearance for social or vocational reasons. These procedures are rhinoplasties. Since the surgical techniques are identical, identification of the procedure as one procedure or the other depends on the cause of the deformity and the motivation of the patient in having it changed. The surgical approach involves correction of deformed cartilage and bone. The upper two-thirds of the nasal structure is bony. A large "dorsal hump" or displaced nasal bones require that this bony skeleton be treated. A deviated nasal tip or septum requires attention to the cartilaginous structures of the lower third of the nose. If a person's skin is thick, rhinoplasty will be less successful.

Whichever category is applicable, the procedure is carried out by making intranasal incisions that permit access to the cartilaginous and bony nasal skeleton. Bones may be loosened for repositioning with chisels or saws. In rare cases, incision across the base of the nose permitting the nasal skeleton to be "degloved" by upward traction on the skin will be needed.

Complications include failure to correct the deformity, overcorrection of the deformity, bleeding and infection. Overly enthusiastic removal of cartilage, especially of the nasal tip, led to a stereotypical deformity of a pinched nasal tip and "polly's beak" deformity. Greater attention to removing abnormality, rather than trying to match every nose to an "ideal," has made such problems much less frequent.

Infection, or loss of nasal cartilage through interruption of blood supply, can result in nasal collapse. Severe cosmetic deformity and nasal airway obstruction can result. Less severe nasal airway obstruction through intranasal adhesions, or just consequent to narrowing the nose during removal of a dorsal hump, are more common. All rhinoplasty patients must be warned that permanent changes in nasal breathing may occur.

[5] Plastic Surgery of the Face

Correction of the changes in the aging face can be approached in several ways. Frown lines and some other lines may be relaxed through injections of botulinum toxin. Wrinkles may be filled by augmentation with injectable materials, such as preparations of hyaluronic acid, a normal constituent of the body. Fine wrinkles and lines can be improved by such means. Where excess skin, perhaps in the form of large jowls, or sagging "wattle" under the neck are present, surgery to remove the excess skin and tighten the skin is required. Such "face lifts" have been performed for a little more than 100 years and are perennially among the most common cosmetic procedures.

The first stage of the operation involves making incisions anterior and inferior to the ear, and separating the skin from the underlying muscles. The deeper tissues are then separated from their attachments and drawn upwards and backwards by placement of permanent sutures. The excess skin is then removed and the incision closed. This is typically done in conjunction with blepharoplasty, and with a separate procedure on the neck. In some cases, face peeling is added.

Bleeding and infection are possible complications. Scars from the incisions will always occur. Sometimes these become prominent and become a cosmetic issue themselves. Injury to the facial muscles, or to branches of the facial nerve responsible for facial muscle movement, can lead to partial or total facial paralysis. Injury to the marginal mandibular branch of the facial nerve results in a permanently skewed smile, introducing a new cosmetic impairment that did not exist before.

[6] Face Peeling

The superficial layers of the skin can be removed by application of phenol or trichloracetic acid. The resulting burn causes loss of the superficial layers after about a week. The peeled skin has a pink, fresh appearance and is particularly susceptible to sunburn. The pink coloration gradually fades leaving a more youthful skin appearance. This procedure can result in uneven re-pigmentation leaving the skin with a blotchy appearance. If the burn purposely created with the chemical agents is too deep, scarring can result equivalent to that from fire.

[7] Liposuction

Removal of fat with suction has been in use for thirty years in the United States. As it is most often used to reduce abdominal and thigh fat, it will have little applicability in otolaryngology. However, some surgeons use liposuction of the upper neck as treatment for sagging neck. Usually under local anesthesia, a short incision is made through which a blunt cannula is inserted. The cannula is moved back and forth, side to side, while suction is applied. The fat is removed. Bleeding, infection, and facial nerve injury are the most common problems with liposuction. Healing after surgery may be uneven, leaving a mottled or wavy appearance afterward. This skin abnormality following what is meant to be a cosmetic procedure is a major concern.

§ 13.10 Endocrine and Salivary Gland Surgery

[1] Thyroid Gland

The thyroid gland is a structure in the anterior neck that produces thyroid hormone, a potent regulator of metabolism. Infections, autoimmune diseases, and tumors may all affect it. The most common reason for surgical treatment is the presence of malignancy. Patients presenting with a mass in the thyroid region should be presumed to have a thyroid malignancy. Diagnosis can be obtained by needle aspiration biopsy. If malignancy is confirmed, the most common treatment will be by complete removal of the thyroid gland. A large non-malignant tumor may be treated by hemilobectomy.

The major complication of thyroid surgery results from the location of the recurrent laryngeal nerves. These nerves exit from the vagus nerve, pass around the aortic arch (left) or subclavian artery (right), pass up the neck in the "groove" between esophagus and trachea, and enter the larynx through the cricothyroid membrane. They provide innervation, and therefore movement, to the vocal cords. Because they lie immediately posterior to the thyroid gland, and because their path is often intermixed with branches of the inferior thyroid artery, both nerves are at risk during thyroid surgery. The consequences of injury are discussed in § 13.05 [6], above. The *sine qua non* of thyroid surgery is locating and protecting these nerves. When the nerve can be seen, it is much less likely to be injured during the surgery. Despite the greatest care, injury to the nerve with resultant impairment can still occur. However, it is a truism that the surgeon most likely to say, "I couldn't have cut the recurrent nerve, I never even saw it," is indeed the surgeon most likely to have this complication.

[2] Parathyroid Glands

The parathyroid glands are small glands in the neck which produce a hormone responsible for regulating calcium metabolism. They are usually four in number and are located very close to the thyroid gland, and sometimes are incorporated into it. Inadvertent removal of the parathyroids or injury to them during thyroid surgery can result in hypocalcemia, a condition in which severe muscle spasms and coronary rhythm abnormalities can occur. When total thyroidectomy is being performed, every effort must be made to preserve as many of the parathyroid glands as possible. Even when removed, they can be located in the surgical specimen, sliced, and then reimplanted into a muscle bed where they may function. Permanent deficiency in parathyroid hormone requires a lifetime taking calcium and vitamin D to counteract the loss of the hormone.

Purposeful surgery on the parathyroids is carried out to treat parathyroid hyperplasia, adenomas and cancers. Adenomas are benign tumors that produce parathyroid hormone. The excess parathyroid hormone causes loss of calcium from the body with resulting kidney stones, osteoporosis, muscle weakness and fatigue. A large majority of patients with parathyroid tumors have only mild changes, discovered through routine blood tests or in followup after an episode of kidney stones, but otherwise without symptoms. Surgical treatment involves removing the affected glands. This process can be assisted by scanning with aid of an agent called sestamibi, and by use of ultrasound. In many cases, the surgery can be performed with minimally invasive techniques involving endoscopic removal. Risk of secondary hypoparathyroidism is minimized by focusing on specifically the gland that is diseased, leaving the others untouched. Confirmation of successful treatment can be had through new rapid assays for parathyroid hormone. A significant drop in the amount of this hormone after removal of the diseased gland is good evidence that the problem has been solved.

[3] Salivary Gland Surgery

Both the parotid glands, lying on each side of the face anterior to the ear, and the submandibular glands, lying just medial to the mandible on either side of the midline, are susceptible to chronic infection, chronic stone formation, and tumor formation. Tumors may be either benign or malignant. Diagnosis is facilitated by fine needle aspiration biopsy. Treatment is surgical removal of the affected gland.

The 7th cranial nerve, the facial nerve, exits the skull just below and posterior to the ear. It then splays out, with its many branches heading to their destinations in the face. All pass through the parotid gland on their course. Surgical removal of the parotid gland is thus in actuality, surgical separation of the gland from the facial nerve. The main risk of the surgery is injury to the facial nerve. Temporary, partial paralysis is quite common, occurring in as many as 10% of patients. Permanent paralysis is fortunately quite rare, especially if one excludes cases of cancer of the parotid gland where removal of the facial nerve can be a necessary part of the operation. Other side-effects and/or complications that should be disclosed prior to surgery include numbness of the external ear, cosmetic deformity due to the surgical scar and the defect created by removal of the gland, and gustatory sweating, a condition in which eating, or even thinking of food, causes the skin overlying the surgical site to sweat.

The submandibular glands lie in a muscle sling just medial to the body of the mandible. Access to them requires drawing the mandibular branch of the facial nerve aside, often without actually having it under direct observation. Injury to this nerve with resulting changes in facial expression has been described earlier. The lingual nerve, controlling tongue sensation, and the hypoglossal nerve, controlling tongue movement, are also at a lesser risk during submandibular gland removal.

Other complications of surgery on either gland include infection, bleeding and unsightly scar.

§ 13.11 References

Brachmann, OTOLOGIC SURGERY (W. B. Saunders 1994)
Goss, GRAY'S ANATOMY (Lea and Febiger 1969)
Rowe, MAXILLOFACIAL INJURIES (Churchill Livingstone 1985)
Scott-Brown, DISEASES OF THE EARS, NOSE AND THROAT, 6th ed
    (Butterworth-Heinemann 1997)

CHAPTER 14

GYNECOLOGY

Julius S. Piver, MD, JD

SYNOPSIS

§ 14.01 Introduction

Good record keeping is not only good medical practice but can serve as a solid defense against claims which may or may not have merit. The record, whether in the hospital or in the office, should be a contemporaneous representation of all information relevant to the particular patient. This includes the history of the patient, physical examination, laboratory data, nursing notes, progress notes, etc. The record should portray a complete and accurate notation of the necessary information for the plan of treatment and actions by the physician to support allegations of merit-less or unjustified claims by the defense. The chart (record) should NEVER, NEVER, NEVER, be altered! Corrections or additions should be signed, timed, and dated with explanations.

Frequently performed hospital procedures that may lead to a claim of malpractice include complications of hysterectomy, failed tubal ligation, and delay in surgery for breast cancer. The most frequently reported litigated cases filed against obstetricians/gynecologists include the following: alleged fetal distress with brain damaged infants and failure to properly and promptly respond to "non-reassuring" fetal monitor tracings; VBAC (vaginal birth after cesarean section) has been increasing in the 90s and has led to malpractice suits by those who chose VBAC and had a bad outcome such as rupture of the uterus with death of the fetus. There has been a decrease in the VBAC rate over the past decade, with an increase in the rate of cesarean sections. Breast cancer cases with delay in diagnosis and its relation to both the extent of surgery and the life expectancy of the patient are a frequent source of malpractice litigation, as are shoulder dystocia injuries with permanent long term damage from injury to the brachial plexus. Strategies must be developed for the defense as well as the avoidance of these complications. Professional liability claims are increasing for failure to diagnose. The most frequently claimed gynecologic issue is failure to diagnose breast cancer.

The gynecologist may be found negligent in the treatment of a breast mass. Any patient who complains of a breast abnormality must have diagnostic testing, including mammography, with or without sonography, and/or biopsy, or be referred to a general surgeon for evaluation and examination. Routine breast screening includes instructing the patient in BSE (breast self-examination) and recording the instructions in the patient's chart.

Guidelines for the use of mammograms have been established by the American Cancer Society and the American College of Radiologists. Failure to adhere to these widely publicized recommendations may be difficult to defend. While gynecologists are not liable for failure of the radiologist to correctly read a mammogram, the courts may find a physician responsible for failing to refer the patient for a biopsy if it was indicated. The physician must respond to the patient's complaints and comply with professional standards in the evaluation of such complaints.

Sterilization failures occur at a rate of about four per thousand sterilizations. A claim may be alleged against the surgeon for negligent performance of the surgery when a failure occurs. There is the risk that tubal ligation may fail without negligence on the part of the gynecologist. The patient, therefore, must be informed about the failure rate along with the risks of surgery and the risks and benefits of the alternatives to sterilization. The patient also should sign a consent form prior to surgery that clearly states that, although the procedure is intended to be permanent, failure may occur. A signed consent form is the best defense to an action based on lack of informed consent. Many professional liability risks are minimized by close attention to medical record documentation. Successful tubal occlusion is now being done in the office as a hysteroscopic procedure with local anesthesia without the need for sedation or general anesthesia, and with prompt recovery and return to daily activities.

Before a patient can give true informed consent to a surgical procedure, the physician must provide a full medical explanation, including a description of the procedure to be employed. There continues to be disagreement among jurisdictions as to what constitutes informed consent. There is the "professional standard," which focuses on what information a REASONABLE PHYSICIAN would impart to the patient and a "prudent-patient standard," which focuses on what the physician should disclose to allow a REASONABLE PATIENT to make an informed decision to consent or not.

Failure to obtain a patient's consent may lead to more than just a malpractice suit. In some states, the loss of a malpractice suit might be considered the practice of poor medicine and could result in a loss of license. Failure to disclose alternative treatment is an important basis for malpractice litigation. Disclosure of alternatives, including the alternative of no treatment and the risk of foregoing treatment, is an integral element of informed consent.

A physician should not merely make a recommendation and expect the patient to ask questions or come up with an alternative. The physician has the responsibility to explain exactly what the patient's options are, and to provide relevant information to help the patient evaluate these options. If the patient refuses to follow the gynecologist's recommendations for surgery or further diagnostic testing, this may be an area of potential litigation. The right of a competent adult to refuse treatment or testing has generally been upheld by the courts, even if the decision is unwise and is not the decision that most patients would make. However, the physician has an obligation to make certain that the patient fully understands the consequences of refusal. The physician who does not inform the patient of material risks in refusing to accept recommended treatment or testing may be liable, in part, for the consequences. If the patient refuses to follow the physician's recommendations for testing or treatment, the physician should write the patient a letter about the medical recommendation, send it by certified mail, and keep a copy in the patient's office record. The physician also may withdraw from the patient with proper notice until the patient has had a reasonable opportunity to find another doctor.

It is the physician's responsibility to obtain the patient's consent to gynecologic surgery. He/she must make every effort to anticipate the operative findings. The consent form should be broad enough to cover all anticipated findings at surgery. A paragraph in the consent form giving the surgeon permission to "perform whatever procedures found necessary or advisable" during surgery, may not give a truly informed consent by the patient. The patient may perceive this paragraph as giving permission to perform added surgery for an emergency situation only, not for non-emergent, extensive additional intervention, particularly where there may exist two schools of thought and serious questions as to its actual necessity. In an emergency situation, where there has been no consent for an indicated procedure, good-faith medical treatment will be protected or would constitute a substantial defense in mitigation of a claim for malpractice damage. If an unanticipated procedure is indicated, but it is not an emergency, it may be best to complete that part of the surgery which was consented to, awaken the patient, and then get consent to surgery at a later date. The patient is the master in this situation. The physician is the servant and has an obligation not to exceed the patient's decisions as noted in the consent form. Patients may express clear preferences about the surgery to which they consent. They may refuse certain aspects recommended, or request a second surgeon be present during surgery. The physician who does not comply with the patient's agreement to a particular procedure may be found liable for failing to do so.

The HIV virus has had an extraordinary impact on medical practice and the law. An immense volume of literature has been generated concerning this problem. Gynecologists today are required to consider aspects from infection control to issues of confidentiality. The Centers for Disease Control (CDC) have published recommendations for prevention of HIV transmission in health care settings. Since gynecologists are among the medical professionals routinely exposed to blood and body fluids, they should be particularly aware of the CDC precautionary recommendations for routine and invasive work. These recommendations include the wearing of gloves and surgical masks, as well as the use of protective eyewear or face shields for procedures that result in the generation of blood or other body fluids. Physicians with a private office also have a duty to provide a safe work environment. Employees in a gynecologist's office should be trained in appropriate procedures in handling blood, body fluids, and tissues. Gynecologists should also ensure that employees comply with the infection control recommendations published by the Occupational Safety and Health Administration (OSHA). OSHA rules apply to private offices as well as hospitals in an attempt to provide a safe work environment for employees. Confirmed cases of CDC-defined AIDS are reportable to the state health department in all fifty states. HIV positivity, without other symptoms, is reportable in only a few states.

There are legal considerations in testing patients for HIV antibodies. Although no law forbids the policy of testing ALL patients for HIV antibodies, testing should be done only with patient consent. Some state laws require evidence of consent. Where the law is silent, many hospitals and laboratories that run these tests require the physician to note that the patient's consent was obtained. Many authorities believe that, if routine testing is to be offered, patient counseling should be available to all patients, whatever the testing reveals. The gynecologist with a routine testing policy may have problems in trying to explain this insistence on testing, both to the patient as well as to the managed care person from whom one is trying to get "authorization." It is important to remember that patients cannot be forced to accept testing.

Hospital and medical offices have developed new programs of record-keeping, involving the use of computers in medical practice. This has been in response to the need for data organization with demands for case quality improvement and quality assurance review. The goal is to replace traditional paper records with an electronic patient record that is immediately available and legible. Important clinical information such as nursing notes, laboratory reports, and operative notes, as well as labor and monitoring data in obstetrics are thereby preserved.

Potential legal issues associated with computerization of records include erroneous information input with resulting improper analyses or inappropriate guidelines for patient management. Confidentiality of clinical data with the related issues of informed consent and right to privacy are other areas of potential legal danger.

§ 14.02   Contraception and Conception

[1]   Oral Contraceptives

[a]   Risks and Benefits

There is a considerable need for contraception, a most sensitive and intimate decision that a person or couple makes. In one study period (1987), of the 6.3 million pregnancies that occurred in the United States, about 57% were unintended. Adolescent pregnancy rates are decreasing. Teen pregnancies decreased 36% since 1990, declining in every state, reaching its lowest level in 30 years. In the 1990 census, for the first time there were more women aged 30-44 years than those aged 15-29 years. This demographic change will continue. Health care professionals need to meet the contraceptive needs of women with divergent social or economic circumstances. Oral contraceptives (OCs) were first introduced in 1960. It has been estimated that approximately 14 million women use this method of birth control in the United States. The first OC formulation contained 150 mcg of estrogen and almost 10 mgm of progestin. Estrogen dosage has been reduced to 20-30 mcg after studies showed that the risk of vascular disease in OC users increased with age, smoking, high cholesterol levels, and duration of OC use. Contraceptive efficacy of these formulations was equivalent to that of higher-dose preparations, while the risk of thromboembolic phenomena was markedly reduced. Along with the reduction of estrogen dosage, there has been a decrease in progestin from ten to one mgm.

The data with ovarian cancer are significant enough to recommend OC usage to women considered at higher risk by family history or BRCA gene status. BRCA1 and BRCA2 are two major breast cancer predisposition genes. Mutations in these two genes are associated with an elevated risk for breast cancer as well as ovarian cancer.

Major noncontraceptive advantages from use of OCs in the U.S. include approximately 50,000 hospitalizations averted annually for conditions that include benign breast disease, retention cysts of the ovaries, iron deficiency anemia and pelvic inflammatory disease. Studies in the U.S. and Great Britain show that OC users have almost complete protection against ectopic pregnancies, and use of oral contraceptives is estimated to prevent 10,000 hospitalizations for this life-threatening complication annually in the U.S. alone.

Studies also showed a relationship between progestin dosage and the incidence of hypertension in OC users. As the dosage of progestin was decreased, there was a noted reduced rate of ischemic heart disease and stroke as well as an associated reduction in the incidence of arterial disease. The progestin dosage has been further reduced with the introduction of multiphasic dosage regimen

[i] Cardiovascular disease

Early studies associated OC use with an increased risk of thromboembolic disease, stroke, myocardial infarction, and hypertension. An OC user may have the risk of a cardiovascular event two to four times the risk of a non-user. Independent risk factors for vascular disease include smoking, increased age (over 35 years), preexisting hypertension, diabetes mellitus, obesity, family history of premature cardiovascular disease (CVD), and abnormal serum lipid or lipoprotein levels. Studies have shown that as the dosage has been reduced, the low-dosage OCs used by healthy women are not associated with an increased risk of stroke or myocardial infarction. The progestin component has been implicated in OC-related susceptibility to CVD and associated OC-induced changes in lipoprotein concentration.

[ii] Effects on lipids

Estrogen and progestin have opposing effects on lipoprotein levels. Estrogen increases triglyceride levels in postmenopausal women, increases low-density lipoprotein (LDL) cholesterol levels, and cause increases in high-density lipoprotein (HDL) cholesterol levels in both pre- and postmenopausal women. The changes in LDL and HDL levels are associated with a decreased risk of CVD. Progestin increases in the presence of estrogen cause a corresponding decrease in total triglycerides and induce changes that can increase CVD risk by increasing LDL cholesterol and decreasing HDL cholesterol levels. With the advent of newer progestins and reduction in dosages, there has been a reduction in the magnitude of progestin-led changes in the lipid/lipoprotein profiles and CVD risks. This has been accomplished through the introduction of lower potency progestins, in relation to the estrogen component, with expected decreases in LDL and increased HDL levels. The changes in lipid levels are related to dosage as well as to the type of progestin. Newer progestins with less adverse effects on lipoproteins have been introduced in the United States from Europe. Whether the differences in OC formulation with regard to alteration in lipids and lipoproteins have a clinically significant effect on CVD risks remains to be seen. There are clear differences in the changes in lipids and lipoproteins among the various OC formulations. These changes are consistent with the biologic effects of the progestin in relation to the doses of estrogen and progestin in the formulation. The OC preparation chosen should have the least detrimental effect on lipids and, therefore, may have a negative impact on atherogenesis and later CVD.

[iii] Cancer

OC users have a significantly reduced risk of uterine cancer and ovarian cancers. The risk of uterine cancer is reduced by 50% and the risk of ovarian cancer by about 40%, compared with the risk for nonusers. Protection begins after one year of OC use; is greatest in nulliparous women; increases as duration of OC use increases; and persists for 10- 15 years after OCs are stopped, according to studies done by the Centers for Disease Control (CDC) and the National Institutes of Child Health and Human Development.

The use of OCs increases the risk of cervical cancer. One study found no increased risk for invasive cervical cancer in OC users, but an apparent increase in carcinoma-in-situ cases due to better disease detection. Studies that showed an increased risk of cervical cancer in OC users failed to consider other risk factors, such as family history, history of gynecologic infection (particularly human papilloma virus), number of sexual partners, age of onset of sexual activity, frequency of Pap smears, and use of barrier methods of contraception. Most studies suggest that OCs do not influence the overall risk of breast cancer.

[iv] Contraindications to use

Absolute contraindications to OC use include:

- women over age 35 who smoke over 15 cigarettes daily;
- pregnancy, known or suspected;
- congenital hyperlipaedemia;
- cancer of the breast, known or suspected;
- estrogen-dependent neoplasm, known or suspected;
- markedly impaired liver function; and
- thrombophlebitis, thromboembolic disorders, cerebral vascular disease, coronary occlusion, or conditions predisposing to these.

[v] Other side effects

The American College of Obstetricians and Gynecologists (ACOG) has issued guidelines stating that the healthy non-smoking women who do not have other cardiovascular risk factors may continue using low-dosage OCs into their forties. Women over 35 who smoke should not use OCs. The Food & Drug Administration (FDA) stated that the advantage of OC use outweighs possible risks of heart attack and stroke for healthy women over 40 who do not smoke.

The number of women 45 years and older is increasing by an estimated 32%, while the number of women between ages 15-44 is increasing by only 4%, according to a recent census. With a decline in the birth rate, the focus of women's health care will be changing. Primary health care providers must be prepared to meet the needs of this changing population. While there will be less demand for obstetric care, older mothers who require obstetric care will need more counseling, testing, and supervision than younger mothers. With new methods for controlling uterine bleeding, tumor growth, and treating infection, there will be less need for surgery, but there will be an increased demand for preventive screening, primary health care, social care, and counseling. Future emphasis will be placed on the prevalence and prevention of various health problems and conditions within the female population.

Currently, the leading causes of death among women are CVD (heart attack and stroke), lung cancer, and breast cancer. These and other major health problems affecting women (osteoporosis, diabetes, etc.), can be affected by a number of factors, such as heredity, age, environment, and life-style. Future medical practice should focus on prevention rather than treatment of these disorders. Providers of primary care to female patients should focus on preventing chronic disease and other medical conditions that cause significant morbidity and mortality.

[2] Intrauterine Devices

The intrauterine device (IUD) is made of plastic, metal, or a combination of these. It is placed in the uterus through the cervical canal. There are two types of IUDs now available in the United States. The hormonal IUD and the copper IUD. The hormonal IUD needs replacement every 5 years. The copper IUD has a lifespan of at least 8 –10 years. There are many IUDs that have been approved by the Food & Drug Administration, but because of liability concerns and costs their manufacturers have discontinued sales in the United States. The IUDs that are still available come with special consent forms for the patient. They are expensive and should be fitted only after extensive informed consent has been obtained and documented. The risks of pregnancy, uterine perforation, infection, and expulsion associated with use of an IUD must be thoroughly explained to the patient and the discussion written into the clinical record.

[a] Risks and Benefits

The manufacturer of the Progestasert emphasizes in its literature that the Progestasert system is unsuited to those who have not borne a child or are in multiple sexual relationships. The manufacturer of the Copper-T 380A warn that it should not be used by women who have never been pregnant, most women under twenty-five, those not in a stable monogamous relationship, and those who have had pelvic inflammatory disease (PID). Despite the curtailment of IUD manufacture in the United States, several recent studies indicate that IUD users are highly satisfied with this method of birth control. IUDs are still very popular in most countries, with an estimated use worldwide in more than fifty million women.

The FDA considers the IUD safe and effective when used as indicated. In the absence of complications, IUDs currently in situ need not be removed before the normal time for replacement. The IUD is effective, convenient, and a relatively safe method of contraception for both short- and long-term use. The advantage is that long-term effective contraception is achieved with minimal effort expended by the patient. Candidates for IUD use are women who cannot tolerate OCs or who are at high risk for complications with OCs—those over thirty-five who smoke, have a history of thrombophlebitis, or have other preexisting diseases. Women should be screened carefully for any contraindications to use of an IUD and closely monitored for adverse effects. If complications do arise, the IUD should be removed immediately and appropriate treatment instituted.

[i] Contraindications to use

Contraindications to the use of an IUD are:

(1) Previous major pelvic surgery;
(2) Confirmed or suspected pregnancy;
(3) Abnormalities of the uterus with distortion of the cavity;
(4) Known or suspected uterine or cervical cancer, including an abnormal Pap smear;
(5) Genital bleeding of unknown etiology;

(6) Acute cervicitis—until the infection is completely controlled and shown to be nongonococcal in origin;

(7) Presence of pelvic inflammatory or sexually transmitted disease (gonorrhea, syphilis, chlamydia), postpartum endometritis or infected abortion, or ectopic pregnancy.

The manufacturers' lists of relative contraindications to the use of an IUD are:

(1) Hypermenorrhea (prolonged and/or very heavy periods)—spontaneous or associated with anticoagulant therapy;

(2) Severe dysmenorrhea (painful periods)—IUD use may increase menstrual pain;

(3) Multiple sexual partners—increased risk for sexually transmitted disease (STD);

(4) Congenital or valvular heart disease—use of an IUD may represent a potential source of bacteremia (bacteria in the blood stream);

(5) Nulliparity (never delivered a baby)—due to mechanical difficulty of insertion, increased risk of side effects, and potentially adverse effects on future fertility.

[ii] Other side effects

The side effects and complications of each method of contraception should be communicated in detail to the patient. If she indicates a preference for an IUD after considering all factors, the physician should consider the contraindications and perform an appropriate examination, with such tests as would be indicated by the medical history. Fully informed consent must be obtained from the patient before an IUD is inserted. The consent should be in writing, signed, dated, and witnessed. The patient must be informed about side effects and symptoms that warrant an office visit, as well as the availability of medical care in the event of an emergency. The overall failure rate (pregnancy) of the IUD ranges from 1 to 5% depending on the patient's age, parity, type of IUD, and other factors. This information must be explained clearly to the patient. Those women desiring a higher rate of effectiveness can then be advised to use additional barrier methods at the time of presumed ovulation, particularly during the first few months of IUD use. The major side effects of the IUD include pregnancy, expulsion, bleeding or pain, and pelvic infection. If the patient becomes pregnant with an IUD in place, and the patient wishes to continue the pregnancy, gentle traction should be used on the plastic tail to remove the IUD. If removal is not done easily, the IUD should be left in place. The patient should be alerted to the approximately 50% incidence of spontaneous miscarriage with the IUD in place. There is no increased incidence of congenital abnormalities in those infants conceived with an IUD in the uterus. Expulsion of the IUD occurs most often in the first few months after insertion. If the patient cannot feel the tail and may not be aware she has expelled the IUD, she should see her doctor at once, using another form of birth control until the appointment. Common reasons for removal of an IUD include bleeding and/or pain. If the IUD conforms to the natural size and shape of the uterine cavity, there is less likelihood of pain or bleeding than if it distorts the cavity. Pelvic infections (PID) are associated with IUD use. The highest risk occurs at the time of insertion. There does not seem to be evidence of an increased risk for PID 3 to 4 months after insertion. Insertion of the IUD may be facilitated by premedication with analgesics or antiprostaglandins. The size, shape, and position of the uterus should be ascertained, and a speculum examination should be performed to exclude any obvious vaginal or cervical infection. If indicated, cultures should be taken from the endocervix for gonorrhea and chlamydia. A Pap smear is warranted if one has not been obtained recently. It is essential to use aseptic technique during insertion. Following insertion of the IUD, the patient should be instructed to check for the string. Insertion should be performed during the last two days of menstruation or as soon afterwards as possible (where pregnancy has been ruled out) because the cervix is partially dilated at this time. Requests for IUD insertion at any other time during the cycle should be discouraged. The patient should be encouraged to return at the time of her next menses to avoid the possibility of interrupting an early intrauterine pregnancy. With the continued care of a woman having an IUD, the patient should be informed of all minor side effects, such as uterine cramping, pain, intermenstrual bleeding, increased menstrual flow, and increased vaginal discharge. Antiprostaglandins taken for several days after insertion and during the menses may decrease the incidence and severity of these side effects. Reexamination must be performed one month after insertion of an IUD, preferably immediately after the first post-insertion period. Annual examinations thereafter should be carried out with appropriate medical and laboratory evaluations as indicated. The presence of the IUD string in the vagina should be documented at each visit. Examination should be performed to exclude vaginal or cervical infection and upper tract infection or abnormality.

If the IUD tail string cannot be felt by the patient or seen by the physician, a determination of whether pregnancy, expulsion, or perforation has occurred must be made. Pregnancy may occur with the IUD in situ, possibly resulting in the pulling of the IUD tail string as pregnancy progresses.

Several methods are available to determine the presence or absence of the IUD once pregnancy is ruled out:

- ultrasonography;
- AP and lateral pelvic X-rays, with the position of the uterine cavity indicated by a radio-opaque instrument or dye:
- hysteroscopy to visualize the intrauterine space;
- probing the endocervical canal and the intrauterine cavity for the retracted string: or
- palpating the IUD with a uterine sound.

Uterine perforation is a known risk with IUD insertion, occurring in one to three patients per 1,000 insertions. The perforation may be recognized immediately on insertion; however, usually the perforation is not recognized, because only a portion of the IUD has perforated the uterine wall. The device must be promptly removed when perforation is diagnosed because of predisposition to adhesions, inflammatory peritoneal conditions, or perforation of the bowel. Laparoscopy, hysteroscopy, or laparotomy may be used as indicated.

An increased risk of pelvic inflammatory disease (PID) associated with the use of IUDs has been reported. The risk of infection is highest in the first few months after insertion, possibly due to the introduction of pathogenic organisms from the cervix into the uterus during insertion. Minor infections should be treated with the IUD in place. More severe infections warrant appropriate bacteriologic studies, followed by antibiotic treatment and removal of the IUD. Use of the IUD is not recommended for the woman who has more than one sexual partner or whose partner has multiple consorts, since the risk of pelvic infection is greatly increased.

There is an increased risk of spontaneous abortion in the first trimester when there is an IUD in situ, and the risk of septic abortion associated with septicemia, septic shock, or even death, the IUD tail strings may be pulled into the intrauterine cavity as the pregnancy progresses, with the risk of resulting sepsis. The woman must be counseled on these matters promptly. If termination of the pregnancy is decided, the IUD can then be removed. If, however, the woman decides to carry the pregnancy to term, the IUD should be removed only if necessary. Removal is facilitated if the strings are visible, but the woman should be informed of the risk of spontaneous abortion if the attempt is made. The patient should be monitored closely during the pregnancy if the strings are not visible and any signs of infection or impending abortion must be treated as an emergency. Intravenous broad-spectrum antibiotic therapy must be started immediately and the uterine cavity evacuated of its contents. Pregnancies carried to term show no association between IUD use and increased risk of congenital abnormality, although cases of fetal deformity have been reported in women with IUDs in situ during a pregnancy. Although most IUDs do not promote ectopic pregnancy, the possibility must always be considered. The likelihood of ectopic pregnancy appears to significantly increase when using the Progestasert device, so users should be warned of this greater risk.

[iii] Removal

Removal of the IUD is easily accomplished by use of forceps applied traction on the strings, and may be facilitated by use of a paracervical block anesthesia with appropriate instrumentation. Removal may be either elective, or indicated, because of abnormal bleeding, pelvic pain, pregnancy, infection, or replacement. Antibiotic prophylactic treatment may be used as indicated. If attempts to remove the IUD are unsuccessful, hysteroscopy or ultrasonography should be performed to ensure that the device is still in the intrauterine cavity. Because of partial embedment, a device may occasionally have to be removed under general anesthesia.

Fertility after discontinuation of IUD use appears to be similar to that in women discontinuing the use of other types of contraception. Unrecognized pelvic inflammatory disease may interfere with resumption of fertility among former IUD users just as it does among non-IUD users. The outcome of a pregnancy conceived after IUD removal appears to be no different from that in women after discontinuance of other contraceptive methods.

[iv] Legal and other issues

Legal and economic as well as political and moral issues influence technological advances in human reproduction. The decision to develop and produce new contraceptive devices may be affected by the rising cost of liability insurance. Distribution of IUDs by U.S. companies was discontinued in 1986, with the exception of the Progestasert IUD. The small number of Progestaserts manufactured and distributed each year has deprived millions of women of a safe and effective contraceptive device. The CopperT 380A was introduced in the United States only in 1988, although it has been used extensively since 1982 in more than thirty countries. It is a very effective (but expensive) device, with a pregnancy rate of approximately 1 per 100 women.

The relationship between IUD use and PID with resultant tubal infertility is, however, a valid concern. Recent studies have adjusted the relative risk of tubal infertility by type of IUD use and number of sexual partners. Women in a mutually monogamous relationship had no significant increased risk of tubal infertility. The IUD is presently recommended only for those women in such a relationship who desire no further pregnancies. The significant cost for this device (caused in part by the liability insurance issue) may, however, restrict its use. Liability issues involving the IUD include failure to remove it at the time of tubal ligation, with subsequent injury to the patient. This has been held to constitute sufficient evidence of proximate cause to warrant submission of the case to a jury.[1] When serious questions about the general safety of an IUD are raised and acknowledged in the general medical community, the physician must warn the patient of the dangerous effects of the device at the time the physician obtains factual knowledge of the hazards. Failure to warn the patient may be tantamount to a negligent breach of duty by virtue of the confidential relationship between the physician and the patient.[2] Failure to warn the patient of facts disclosed by X-rays of the extrauterine location of the device or failure to treat the patient for injury or condition disclosed by such X-rays also may result in liability of the physician.[3]

[3] Injection/Implantation Contraception

Injection of steroid sex hormones may provide contraception by suppression of ovulation. Depending on the drug and formulation, contraception may be provided for 1 month, 6 months, or 1 year. The most widely used compound is Depo-Provera 150 mgm every 90 days by intramuscular injection. This may be associated with irregular or absent uterine bleeding for months.

Norplant is an implanted contraceptive that releases a hormone through six Silastic rods implanted under the skin of the upper arm. Contraceptive protection is provided for up to five years. Side effects with the implant are common, including bleeding irregularity, headaches, weight gain, and breast tenderness. These tend to decline in incidence after one year of use. The rods must be removed by a minor surgical procedure. There does not seem to be any significant delay in restoration of fertility. Norplant is no longer available in the United States due to side effects. Women who have the implants currently, may continue to use this form of birth control until their removal after five years. There may be a substantial time delay with injection Depo-Provera in restoration of fertility. Lunelle, a once-a-month injectable combination progestational/estrogen contraceptive was approved by the FDA in 2000. This combines control of the menstrual cycle with convenient

---

[1] Green v. Lilliewood, 249 S.E.2d 910 (S.C. 1978).

[2] Tresemer v. Barke, 86 Cal. App. 3d 656, 150 Cal.Rptr. 384 (1978).

[3] Godard v. Ridgeway, 445 P.2d 757 (Wyo. 1968).

and effective contraception. Side effects are comparable to those of low-dose oral contraceptives.

Three other new methods of contraception that have become available include: a transdermal patch (Ortho Evra); a vaginal ring (NuvaRing); and Implanon,a single rod implant system. The patch is applied once weekly for 3 weeks on and one week off. It has the disadvantage of decreased effectiveness in women at or above 198 lb. The ring is introduced vaginally for 3 weeks, and removed for 1 week. Both contain a progestational/estrogen combination. The rod contains a progestational agent only and has been shown to prevent ovulation for 3 years in most women. It has the advantage of faster and easier insertion (and removal) when compared with the six rod Norplant system.

[4] Sterilization

Surgical sterilization is the most frequently used method of contraception in the United States. It has been estimated that, in the United States during the 1980s, 800,000 to 1,000,000 sterilization operations were performed yearly. Prior to the introduction of laparoscopy, most operations for sterilization were vasectomies. With the introduction of tubal cautery, or banding by laparoscopy, the number of vasectomies declined sharply with a marked increase in the number of female sterilizations. The relationship between vasectomies and female sterilization operations has remained stable the past several years, almost evenly divided, but with a slight preponderance of female sterilization operations. This is due in part to the greater use of local anesthesia and more frequent performance of these operations in ambulatory surgical settings. Tubal ligation or severance is the most often used means of female sterilization. Sterilization may be accomplished by hysterectomy but this method is generally considered too radical as a primary procedure, and is more appropriately indicated for treatment of specific gynecological conditions.

[a] Indications

The indications for sterilization occur when pregnancy is hazardous to either mother or fetus, and contraceptive methods may be harmful or unsuccessful. If a therapeutic abortion is necessary, sterilization may be warranted. Most intractable disorders (i.e., extreme, inoperable congenital heart disease) that are serious enough to warrant an abortion will continue to threaten future pregnancies as well. Other indications for sterilization include:

- any neuropsychiatric condition that would make pregnancy dangerous or prevent proper care of children, such as severe schizophrenia or epilepsy;
- medical conditions that would make a pregnancy dangerous, such as chronic leukemia, severe diabetes mellitus, or marked heart or kidney disease;
- obstetrical conditions such as extreme anti-Rh sensitization in a woman whose husband is Rh positive, uncorrectable uterine abnormality, or habitual abortion; and
- surgical conditions such as breast cancer.

Sterilization may be performed immediately after labor, with an induced abortion, or at any time during the menstrual cycle. Consent must be obtained for sterilization to be done concurrently with a delivery or induced abortion. The only exception is an emergency requiring immediate surgery to save the life of the patient, and it is not possible to obtain the consent of the patient or someone authorized to assume such responsibility. In the absence of an emergency, no husband may grant permission to a physician for the sterilization of his spouse. Neither is it necessary that the spouse's consent be obtained for the other to undergo a sterilization procedure.

[b] Contraindications

Mini-laparotomies are contraindicated where the patient is obese, has an enlarged or immobile uterus, or when adnexal disease or endometriosis is suspected. Absolute contraindications to a laparoscopic procedure include a ruptured ectopic pregnancy with hemoperitoneum, extensive intra-abdominal carcinomatosis, bowel obstruction, and acute untreated pelvic tuberculosis. Relative contraindications include heart disease, pulmonary disease, previous abdominal or pelvic surgery, acute peritonitis, and an obvious large pelvic mass.

[c] Hazards

The principal hazards associated with tubal sterilization are anesthetic complications, pulmonary embolism (rare), and failure to produce sterility which may result in an unrecognized and improperly treated ectopic pregnancy. The administration of a general anesthetic without endotracheal intubation is the leading cause of death during tubal sterilization. Peritonitis and pelvic abscesses occur in some patients as with any intrabdominal procedure, although infection is more common with the vaginal approach than with abdominal sterilization procedures.

Hazards of laparoscopy include untoward anesthetic reactions, perforation of a viscus (bowel, bladder), laceration of blood vessels with resulting sepsis and hemorrhage, bowel burns, abdominal wall burns, and gas embolism or emphysema. Women who are considering tubal sterilization must have clear and understandable counseling. This should include information about possible medical as well as psychological complications. Regret and/or dissatisfaction are more common when the procedure is done immediately postpartum than at any other time; these women are more likely to feel that the counseling, if any, was inadequate. Pregnancy associated stress may influence a premature decision for sterilization in some women.

It is also important that women be informed of the effectiveness and the chances of reversibility of the operation for sterilization. Tubal sterilization is generally not reversible, with success being directly related to how much normal tube has been preserved. Where prospective controlled studies of the so-called posttubal ligation syndrome (pain and menstrual disturbances) have been carried out, it was shown that these problems were no more common than in women who were not sterilized. These complaints were much less frequent after the first postoperative year. Finally, there is the possibility of a failed procedure. Lawsuits have been brought against physicians for the physical and financial injury resulting from improperly or negligently performed sterilization procedures. The claimed injury is the birth of an unplanned child. Two issues persist in these cases: the first concerns the measure of damages, and the second is whether to consider the unwanted pregnancy after a failed sterilization as a wrongful conception or wrongful birth.

[d] Informed Consent

Informed consent is particularly significant in sterilization matters. The physician should inform the patient of the various methods available to her for tubal sterilization, the possibility of natural failure, and, if the operation is performed in conjunction with cesarean section, of the higher rate of failure, of any method of tubal ligation at that time. The present trend is to allow for recovery of some damages against the physician for doing, or failing to do, something to prevent pregnancy or birth.

[e] Nonelective Sterilization

Nonelective sterilization statutes provide for sterilization of the retarded, the insane, the feebleminded, and the criminal recidivist upon application of a parent, guardian, or other designated authority, such as the director of a mental health institution. Legislation permitting sterilization for certain types of criminally insane and feebleminded persons has generally been sustained by the courts.

Some courts, however, have found sterilization statutes unconstitutional because: sterilization is cruel and unusual punishment; such statutes amount to unconstitutional class legislation; such statutes deny due process by failing to provide for notice of hearing to the person whose sterilization is proposed; or such statutes violate the Equal Protection Clause of the Constitution. A valid order for the sterilization of a mental incompetent must comply with the procedural requirements of the statute. Although the decisions are not uniform, most courts will not authorize such sterilization without statutory authority, regardless of the facts before them. Procedural safeguards to which an incompetent person is entitled may include:

- psychological test results in the petition for sterilization;
- notice of the required court hearing must be given the incompetent and his/her guardian;
- right to appeal the decision and a right to counsel (provided by the state, if necessary); or
- clear and convincing evidence before a court order can be entered.[4]

The liability of a physician who performs a eugenic sterilization is also usually governed by statute. Most eugenic sterilization statutes contain provisions that render the physician and administrative officials who participate in the procedure immune to civil or criminal liability, provided they act in accordance with the law.

[5] Genetics

[a] Counseling

Genetic counseling is conducted with potential parents for the purpose of discovering the risks of producing a genetically impaired child, assessing the prognosis for the child, and explaining the options available for dealing with those risks. The counseling must include an accurate diagnosis of the disorder, its mode of transmission, the risk of recurrence, and insight into the variations of the disease and prognosis. The diagnosis may be obvious on physical examination or by certain biochemical tests. Where diagnosis may not be readily apparent, the services of a genetic counselor or counseling

---

[4] North Carolina Ass'n for Retarded Children v. North Carolina, 420 F. Supp. 451 (D. N.C. 1976).

center, where there is access to various medical disciplines, including pediatrics, neurology, ophthalmology, and cardiology, may be necessary.

When an accurate diagnosis can be found, determining the mode of inheritance for a condition due to a single-gene mutation ordinarily presents no problem. Some 2000 disorders due to autosomal dominant, autosomal recessive, and X-linked mutations have been described. A detailed family history should be taken through three generations in all cases, and is of particular use in rare disorders where the risk of recurrence is unknown. A couple's decision to take a risk depends to a great degree upon the physical, emotional, and financial burdens that an affected child will be to the family. It is important for the counselor to know the prognosis and convey it to the family, so they will be able to make an informed decision.

Indications for referring a patient to a genetic counselor may include:

- genetic or congenital anomaly in a family member;
- family history of an inherited disorder;
- abnormal somatic or behavioral development in a child;
- mental retardation of unknown etiology in a child;
- pregnancy in a woman over 35 years old;
- specific ethnic background suggestive of a high risk of genetic abnormality;
- drug use or long-term exposure to possible teratogens or mutagens;
- three or more spontaneous abortions or early infant death; and
- infertility.

Genetic counseling differs from the conventional physician-patient situation in several instances. Where the disorders involved can result in genetic abnormalities, the decisions to be made must focus on future children, and the family or couple, rather than an individual, is "the patient." The obstetrician does not have the duty of becoming a genetic counselor, but should assess his/her own qualifications for offering counseling. There may be a legal duty to refer the patient to a genetic counseling specialist in the absence of these special qualifications.

Genetic counseling not only predicts the risk of disease for a specific couple, but may also apply to relatives and future offspring of the couple seeking advice. Prognosis is determined through an extensive family history, diagnosis, and knowledge of genetic principles. The family history involves constructing a lineage and listing the patient's near relatives by sex, age, state of health, and occurrence of relevant disease in the family. After evaluating the risk of reoccurrence of a genetic disease, the genetic counselor should communicate the diagnosis and associated risks in a nondirective manner to the couple. Failure to exercise due care in counseling, such as providing erroneous information, may result in liability.

More than half the present infant mortality rate is attributed to congenital malformation. As new technologies are developed for the identification, treatment, and control of hereditary defects, the field of genetic counseling is experiencing a parallel growth and increasing public recognition of its potential.

[b] Genetic Screening

The basic standards of care of the American College of Obstetrics and Gynecology (ACOG) recognize that genetic screening may prevent genetic disease in cases where:

- the disease occurs predominantly in a defined population;
- carriers can be identified simply and accurately; and
- the disease can be detected in utero early in pregnancy.

Physician liability may be imposed for negligence, such as incorrect diagnosis, failure to obtain informed consent to the screening procedure, failure to disclose test results to the person screened, and unauthorized disclosure of the results to persons other than the person screened.

Amniocentesis or Chorionic Villus Sampling. Amniocentesis is usually done on an outpatient basis at fifteen to seventeen weeks' gestation to detect inherited disorders. It can also be done as early as twelve to fourteen weeks. Amniocentesis is indicated when the family history suggests that one parent is (or may be) a carrier of a chromosomal/biochemical disorder.

When one parent has a history of a severely handicapping autosomal recessive inherited disease, such as Tay Sachs, amniocentesis is always indicated. Tay Sachs is one of the more prevalent genetic anomalies and most commonly affects Ashkenazi (Eastern European) Jews. Sickle-cell anemia is another prevalent genetic anomaly and occurs most commonly within the black population. X-linked disorders, such as Duchenne's muscular dystrophy, also demand that the carrier state be identified. Chromosomal abnormalities occur once per 2,000 live births, and include Down's syndrome, Turner's syndrome, and Klinefelter's syndrome. In mothers up to the age of thirty, the risk of a live-born Down's syndrome infant is less than 1 in 1,000, but by age forty-five the risk increases to one in thirty-two. Phenylketonuria (PKU) is not population specific and can be identified in newborns early enough to treat the disease, thus saving them from the mental disorders that accompany it. While PKU can be treated, sickle-cell anemia cannot. It is a hereditary disorder that can be eliminated only if carriers remain childless. Screening programs for sickle-cell anemia are designed to identify and warn carriers of the risk of bearing children with an incurable disease.

Current standards dictate that all women be told that prenatal cytogenetic studies are available. While the obstetrician is not obligated to actually perform the amniocentesis, or terminate the pregnancy if the result is abnormal, there is an obligation to inform the patient about the procedure and its significance. Generally, a maternal age of thirty-five at delivery is the point at which the risk of chromosomal abnormalities is considered to outweigh the small (but definite) risk of amniocentesis and justifies use of the procedure. While maternal risk is negligible, the risk of fetal loss with amniocentesis is generally stated to be 1 in 200. It is thus necessary to counsel patients that amniocentesis carries a 0.5% risk for spontaneous abortion. There is little evidence that the risk is reduced by concurrent use of ultrasound. Chorionic villus sampling (CVS) is safe and effective for early diagnosis of cytogenetic abnormalities. However, CVS has a slightly higher risk of procedure failure, and a considerably higher risk of fetal loss when repeated attempts are made to place the CVS catheter. While CVS is accurate and can be done early in the first trimester, the high rate of fetal loss suggests it requires a skilled team if repeated attempts are required. With increasing experience, CVS may offer the possibility of safe first-trimester cytogenetic sampling studies. The diagnostic accuracy of the two methods—CVS and amniocentesis—is nearly equal. Genetic amniocentesis may be indicated when:

- one parent is a carrier of chromosomal translocation;
- a couple has already produced a trisomic child;
- the pregnant patient is over 35;
- the fetus is at risk of being born with X-linked disorders;
- there is a parental or family history of certain metabolic disease; or
- it is necessary to determine alpha-feta protein levels in pregnancies with potential for neural tube anomalies.

The American College of Obstetrics and Gynecology (ACOG) has identified conditions and prerequisites for amniocentesis for prenatal diagnosis of genetic disorders:

- an appropriate indication exists;
- the duration of pregnancy is appropriate;
- information obtained will assist the patient and her family in decision making;

- the technique for a particular disorder has been established; and
- the patient and her family have been counseled adequately with regard to the risk of the disorder, the risks of the procedure, and the nature of the information to be obtained.

[i] Other aspects

The medical literature describes cases of physical injuries resulting from amniocentesis. Maternal risks include uterine infection, perforation of the intestine, and Rh sensitization of the Rh-negative mother by blood from an Rh-positive fetus if the placental vessels are perforated during insertion of the amniocentesis needle. Fetal risks include death from infection of the amniotic fluid, infection of the amniotic membrane, and perforation of the fetal blood vessels in the umbilical cord or placenta. In spite of these hazards, amniocentesis is generally considered a low-risk procedure. The risk of injury can be reduced, however, when it is performed with real-time ultrasound guidance so the advancing needle can be seen and the fetus avoided. If it is performed at 15-17 weeks of pregnancy, there is a 50% greater volume of fluid than at 14 weeks. Cell-culture failure is then reduced because of the greater quantity of fetal cells in the amniotic fluid. A greater quantity of fluid and fetal cells reduces the probability that additional taps will be needed; multiple attempts at amniocentesis have been associated with a greater risk of fetal injury.

As with any procedure, informed consent must be obtained from the patient. Any misconceptions about the procedure and the information that can be provided must be corrected at the time. The physician should explain that a negative chromosomal analysis, while highly reliable, does not guarantee that the fetus will be born normal. Additionally, the consent form should include a disclaimer that there are no guarantees that: the procedure will not injure the mother or the fetus; the attempt to obtain amniotic fluid will always be successful; and the attempt to obtain usable cultures will always be successful. Amniocentesis should properly be performed only in a hospital setting by obstetricians or other practitioners with the required skill and with access to adequate equipment. The fluid analysis should be completed by qualified laboratory personnel experienced in culturing amniotic fluid cells and performing the particular diagnostic tests.

The current state of medical knowledge probably mandates that any patient known to be at risk of producing genetically defective offspring should be informed of the availability of amniocentesis. Also, while wrongful life suits have not been generally favored by the courts, they have recognized causes of action by parents seeking compensation for the wrongful birth of a genetically defective child because they were not informed of the availability of amniocentesis. Other test modalities include: X-ray study for diagnosing structural defects; ultrasonography for diagnosing defects of the cardiovascular, genitourinary, gastrointestinal, neuromuscular, and skeletal systems; and direct sampling of fetal blood from the umbilical vein under sonographic guidance for evaluation of genetic conditions.

[ii] Summary

Genetic screening is a public health endeavor seeking out asymptomatic individuals at risk for developing or transmitting genetic disorders. Such screening can be performed on several different groups with whom obstetrician-gynecologists have direct or indirect contact. Important factors in deciding who should be screened and what diseases should be screened for include:

- frequency and severity of the condition:
- availability of a therapy of proven efficacy;
- extent to which detection by screening improves outcome;
- validity and safety of the tests;
- adequacy of resources to assure effective screening and follow-up;
- costs; and
- acceptance of the screening program by the community, including patients and physicians in practice.

Information gleaned from an accurate family history is the single most important step in genetic screening. Minimum information should include the history of three generations. Complicated family histories require extensive pedigrees. All first degree relatives of the subject should be listed, and their state of health noted. The number, sex, and state of health of second-degree relatives should also be recorded. A history of the more common specific genetic diseases should be routinely sought, and a history of rare genetic disorders obtained when relevant.

[c] Mendelian Disorders

Mendelian disorders result from the transmission of a mutant gene at a single locus and occur in approximately 1% of all live births. There are four patterns of inheritance: (1) autosomal dominant; (2) autosomal recessive; (3) sex-linked dominant; or (4) sex-linked recessive. Genes are situated on chromosomes at a given locus. If the effects of an abnormal gene are evident when the gene is present in a single dose, the gene is said to be dominant. If the disorder occurs only when the abnormal gene is present in a double dose, the gene is said to be recessive. The inheritance is further described as autosomal when the mutant gene is located on the autosomal chromosomes, or sex-linked when the mutant gene is located on the sex chromosomes.

Pedigree analysis is important in determining the type of inheritance of a given Mendelian disorder. Each type of Mendelian inheritance shows characteristic pedigree patterns. The mode of inheritance is important when counseling for Mendelian disorders. Pedigree analysis, in differentiating these patterns, is important in determining the recurrence risk for other family members. From a clinical standpoint, carrier screening generally refers to identification of carriers for an autosomal or sex-linked recessive disorder.

In patients determined by pedigree analysis or carrier screening to be at risk for having an offspring with a Mendelian disorder, prenatal diagnosis is often available by CVS, amniocentesis, fetal skin or blood samples, or ultrasonography. Not every Mendelian disorder is detectable prenatally, but many of the more common disorders are.

Newborn screening for most Mendelian disorders is performed by collecting capillary blood from a heel puncture onto a filter paper. Specimens are then sent to a reference laboratory where they are assayed for the specified disease. Abnormal screening tests must be confirmed with additional sensitive diagnostic tests. Assays for multiple disorders can be performed on an individual specimen. This makes screening for some rare disorders worthwhile when it would not be cost-effective to screen for those disorders individually. Minimal genetic-screening guidelines include those for Mendelian disorders of donors for artificial insemination, embryo transfers, and use of donor oocytes.

The most common use of genetics in obstetrics is in prenatal counseling, screening and diagnosis. Screening includes testing for neural tube defects using AFP (serum alpha-fetoprotein) drawn at 16 to 18 weeks from the mother's blood. Other screening includes testing for trisomy 21 and trisomy 18, cystic fibrosis, sickle cell disease, and Huntington's disease. Inborn errors of metabolism and many other genetic disorders can now be identified in the prenatal period.

Most neural tube diseases (anencephaly, spina bifida, etc.) occur spontaneously without prior family occurrence. A significant percent (10%), however, are appropriate subjects for genetic counseling. Radioimmunoassay kits are available for maternal screening. ACOG has recommended that all mothers be informed that such screening is available.

[i] Sickle-cell anemia

This disease is the most common Mendelian disorder in people of color, occurring in about 1 in every 400 blacks in the United States. The disease is inherited as an autosomal recessive disorder, while the trait is inherited as an autosomal dominant. The genetic mutation leads to the formation of an abnormal hemoglobin molecule. The disease is characterized by a chronic, severe, hemolytic anemia. Red blood cells become distorted, or "sickle-shaped," under conditions of lowered oxygen tension, and the sickle cell crises result from increased blood viscosity, capillary stasis, vascular occlusion, and infarction of tissues such as bone, lungs, and spleen. Newborn screening for sickle-cell disease can decrease the incidence of infection, often an inciting event in the sickle crisis. Carrier screening by hemoglobin electrophoresis shows about 50% sickle hemoglobin in carriers. Prenatal diagnosis is available through the direct analysis of the DNA encoding for the abnormal sickle hemoglobin.

[ii] Tay-Sachs disease

This disorder occurs in approximately 1 in 3600 Ashkenazi Jewish parents, and is inherited as an autosomal recessive disorder. The biochemical abnormality in this disease is the absence of the enzyme hexosominidose A, which is involved in the metabolism of a class of nervous system lipids called gangliosides. Accumulation of gangliosides in the brain of an affected individual causes motor weakness, psychomotor retardation, generalized spasticity, deafness, blindness, and convulsions. Death from broncho-pneumonia generally occurs by age three. Accurate carrier detection is possible by demonstrating intermediate reduction of the enzyme activity in the serum. Prenatal diagnosis of serum hexosominidose A activity in cultured cells from amniotic fluid or chorionic villi is recommended to determine serum enzyme levels. These levels are decreased relative to total hexosominidose A. Leucocyte assays are not altered during pregnancy and are recommended, since many noncarriers have been found with reduced hexosominidose A levels on serum testing, which may lead to erroneous diagnoses.

[iii] Thalessemias

Thalessemias are a group of hereditary anemias with the common feature of diminished synthesis of hemoglobin. The disorder is most common in Southeast Asia, Mediterranean countries, the Middle East, and parts of India and Pakistan. The severity of the anemia varies with the genes affected in the synthesis of hemoglobin. Screening for carriers is possible by evaluation of the red cell indices. Prenatal diagnosis is possible by molecular techniques. Accurate characterization of the hemoglobin defect is essential.

[d] Legal Issues

A major issue in all types of genetic screening is whether the program should be voluntary or mandatory. Some organizations have recommended that participation in a genetic screening program should be mandated by law, but left to the discretion of the person tested, or to the parents or legal guardian, if a minor. Others have endorsed voluntary screening while noting that mandatory programs may be justified if voluntary testing would fail to prevent an avoidable, serious injury to children and persons who are unable to protect themselves. The vast majority of newborn genetic screening programs remain mandatory.

A second major issue is the confidentiality of the genetic screening results. The importance of confidentiality has led to recommendations that genetic information should not be given to unrelated third parties (i.e., employers) without explicit and informed consent of the person screened or his/her surrogate. Genetic-related information should be coded whenever compatible with the purpose of data banks used by private or governmental agencies. Screening programs should not be undertaken unless the results produced are routinely reliable, and a full range of prescreening and follow-up services are available for the screened population.

The law generally recognizes suits brought by persons who have been injured by failures in the process of genetic counseling. The development of sophisticated biochemical and cytogenetic tests has enhanced the efficacy of predictive counseling. Certain chromosomal disorders and about fifty inherited diseases associated with enzyme deficiencies can now be diagnosed prenatally. Amniocentesis can identify various defects and chromosomal anomalies, as well as the sex and blood type of the fetus. In this vein, the conduct of the genetic counselor is subject to the same legal scrutiny from the private sector as the rest of the medical profession, with special regards to standards of duty and care, as well as to informed consent. Abortion of a fetus found defective by amniocentesis will most likely take place in the second or third trimester, because the 16th week of gestation is believed to be the most fruitful time for amniocentesis, and amniotic fluid analysis requires an additional 3 to 5 weeks.

Physicians may face wrongful birth suits in connection with negligence in genetic counseling involving:

- failure to take a proper history, which would alert the physician to the possibility of birth defects;
- failure to advise the mother of the availability of amniocentesis or the risk of bearing a deformed child; or
- failure to recognize the presence of a genetic disorder.

§ 14.03 Diagnosis and Treatment

[1] History and Examination

The medical history is a brief story of the patient's life presented with special reference to her physical and mental ailments, and to factors concerning heredity, habits, and environment. The history is of great importance since it is usually the major source of information leading to a diagnosis of disease; and more importantly, it leads to an understanding of the patient's personality, which is necessary for appropriate treatment of the patient's body and mind.

From the physician's viewpoint, the accuracy of a diagnosis frequently depends on the adequacy of the history, which, in turn, depends largely on the skill used in eliciting information. From the patient's viewpoint, the telling of a life story is an intensely personal experience that may be filled with anxiety and excitement. It requires a sympathetic listener. The physician who listens attentively and sympathetically usually gains the patient's confidence and often is considered by the patient to be the most important doctor concerned with her case.

The specialty of gynecology has expanded to encompass the disciplines of surgery, medicine, endocrinology, and obstetrics. It is not sufficient for the gynecologist to limit his/her interest to surgery for pelvic disorders. There must be an interest in basic scientific principles of human reproduction, since surgery may seriously alter the reproductive capacity and physiology of the patient. Reproductive endocrinology and immunology, as well as steroid chemistry, have become an integral part of the gynecologist's sphere of interest. The gynecologist spends less time in the operating room today, and is seeing relatively healthy patients whose concerns include cancer prevention, conception control, hormonal replacement, and infertility. The intimate relationship between metabolic disorders, endocrine dysfunction, and the genital tract, must be understood. It is also important to recognize the significance of psychosomatic influences on women's behavior. The gynecologist must be aware of the personal nature of the problems that bring the patient to the physician. Sympathy and understanding must be combined with tact in eliciting details the patient may intentionally omit. The causes of symptoms should be explained, with the logical reasons for indicated tests or procedures, to assuage the fears and misconceptions of the patient. Frank and reassuring discussions can often dispel these fears and misconceptions. Good history taking is an art that demands a methodical approach to avoid important omissions. A printed form will serve this purpose in most instances.

[a] Present Illness

The present illness is merely an expansion of the chief complaint, and together they constitute the most important portion of the history. The chief complaint should be brief, should refer to the main complaint (usually only one), and may employ the patient's own words if they are significant. It is important to estimate in general terms how sick the patient feels she is: how much the illness has interfered with her work, exercise, relaxation, and sleep; whether she has been confined to bed or has been too ill to go to the bathroom. Particular signs and symptoms must be defined by describing such features as onset, duration, recurrence or periodicity, character of sensation, site, exposure to radiation, associated symptoms, response to therapy, and factors producing exacerbation, aggravation or relief.

There should be a chronology of events from the onset of the illness up to the time of the examination. The exact dates of the last menstrual period and the previous period should be elicited. Intermenstrual bleeding should be described by time of occurrence, duration, and the presence or absence of pain or clots. Endometrial breakdown at the time of ovulation is often associated with staining. Skips and delays in periods at the time of menopause may be on the basis of irregularities in ovulation. Postcoital bleeding or bleeding after a douche may be due to a cervical polyp or malignancy. Postmenopausal bleeding may be caused by genital tract malignancy or in association with hormonal replacement therapy. Therefore, the physician must obtain exacting detail in the description of the bleeding. While a diagnosis may be suggested by the chief complaint, a careful history and review of systems will avoid the risk of a snap diagnosis with subsequent surprise by an unnecessary operation. A combination of judgment, reason, skill, and humanity is desirable for the complete and successful treatment of the patient. An unnecessary operation by the most skilled surgical technician may still result in death from infection, pulmonary embolism, or unrecognized cardiac disease.

[b] Past History

Date and place of birth, with residences and approximate time in each place, should be obtained. Information concerning previous hospitalizations should be obtained.-It is especially important to find out if pelvic surgery was performed and whether radium or x-ray therapy was used. The location of the hospital, the name of the surgeon, and the date of surgery should be noted and a copy of the patient's chart obtained to make certain what, in fact, was done. The past history is important because it bears upon the choice of anesthesia and on the advisability of certain surgical procedures. A checklist should include inquiries into any serious infections, and pulmonary, cardiac, and renal diseases. Injuries should be inquired into, including the date and information on hospitalization, symptoms, treatment, and sequelae for each. Information about life insurance or other examinations, with results, also should be obtained.

[c] Family History

Information about the patient's family, including age and health of parents and siblings should be obtained. If deceased, the date, age, and cause of death of the family member should be elicited, in the patient's own words if possible. Familial diseases should be inquired into, including incidence of diabetes, endocrine disorders, arthritis, gout, heart disease, hypertension, kidney disease, allergy, obesity, anemia, hemophilia, jaundice, cancer (especially breast), migraine, nervous or muscular disorders, mental disorders, and alcoholism. A social history should also be taken, including the patient's birthplace, ethnic heritage, religion, occupation, and previous marriages, if any. The age, occupation, religion, and health of the patient's husband should also be obtained where applicable.

[d] Review of Systems

The systems review should include all pregnancies—listed in order by year—with the length of gestation, type of delivery, fetal weight, and complications, if any. Long periods of infertility, primary or secondary, suggest endometriosis or pelvic inflammatory disease. The dates and normality of the last and previous menstrual periods should be accurately recorded with consideration of any possible intrauterine pregnancy, tubal pregnancy, and threatened or incomplete abortion. A careful pelvic examination and visualization of the cervix will aid the examiner in recognizing the true clinical picture. Pain associated with the menstrual flow should be classified as to site, duration, intensity, and nature—to aid in differentiating dysmenorrhea (painful menstruation), endometriosis, and pelvic inflammation.

The systems review frequently helps to establish a gynecological diagnosis to eliminate bowel or urinary tract disease. The proximity of the bladder, uterus, and rectosigmoid, and the inability of most patients to pinpoint their symptoms, makes this survey worthwhile. The age of onset, interval, and duration of menstrual periods are important data in every gynecological history. The age of menarche (first period) will vary, depending on climate and genetic background. In the United States, the first period usually begins between ages eleven and sixteen, with the average about thirteen. An extensive endocrine survey is not indicated for primary amenorrhea (absence of menstruation without ever having had periods) before age eighteen.

An interval of between twenty-six and thirty-two days between periods is considered normal. The singular characteristic of menstrual bleeding associated with ovulation is its rhythmicity. Patients who have rhythmic cycles of twenty-one or thirty-five days should not be considered abnormal. The average duration of menstruation is between three and four days, with an average blood loss of 25-70cc. The presence of clots may mean the absence of fibrinolysin (found normally in menstrual discharge), suggesting anovular bleeding. It may, however, indicate that the vascular breakdown in the endometrium is so rapid that whatever fibrinolysin is present is unable to maintain the fluidity of the blood, so that clotting occurs.

Vaginal discharge may be due to infection, malignancy, foreign bodies, or trauma. Therefore, inquiries should be made about its color, consistency, and the presence of blood. Certain douche solutions may be irritating to the vaginal mucosa and be the cause of the discharge. Postmenopausal bloody mucoid discharge may be due to carcinoma of the endometrium or cervix, or it may be due to prolonged estrogen replacement therapy, cessation of which results in cure. A list of all medications the patient is taking, or has received in the recent past, should be noted. Broad-spectrum antibiotics frequently cause monilial vaginitis, vaginal discharge, and pruritus (itching).

The patient's general health should be investigated. Generalized symptoms, such as nausea, anorexia, fatigue, and low-grade temperature elevation may be due to pulmonary or genital tuberculosis. Weight loss, dizziness, and anemia, with crampy right lower-quadrant pain suggest cancer of the right colon or cecum. Generalized symptoms such as these, however, are not common with most gynecologic ailments. The cardiorespiratory, gastrointestinal, urinary, and neuromuscular systems should be carefully investigated. Particular attention should be given to diminished appetite, change in bowel habits, alternating diarrhea and constipation, blood in the stool, and pain with bowel movements. Attention to such symptoms may permit the correct diagnosis to be made before rather than during surgery. Sigmoid or rectal carcinoma is all too often encountered by the gynecologist during surgery for a suspected ovarian cyst or myoma.

Urinary tract symptoms should be discussed in detail, since there is frequently a correlation with the gynecologic complaint. Loss of urine while coughing, sneezing, or laughing (stress incontinence), should be differentiated from urge incontinence. The former may require surgical treatment, the latter may only need urinary antiseptics. If urinary frequency occurs, it is important to know whether there is associated polyuria (excessive voiding) and polydipsia (excessive thirst) since these may be the first symptoms of early diabetes. Allergies or sensitivities to drugs, antibiotics, and anesthetic agents as well as previous thromboembolic disorders should be noted.

[e] Physical Examination

A complete physical examination should be performed at the first visit. This includes inspection of the head and neck and palpation of the thyroid gland, suparclavicular areas, and superficial lymph nodes. A thorough examination of the breasts should be made at each visit. Inspection of the breasts should be done first with the patient sitting erect with her arms at her sides and then with the arms raised. This maneuver will frequently outline asymmetry or fixation of the nipple and fixed masses under an adjacent areola. The supraclavicular areas and the axillae are palpated with the patient erect. Particular attention should be given to the apex of the axilla and the undersurface of the pectoralis major muscle. A systematic examination of the breasts should then be performed in both the erect and supine positions.

About 65% of all breast cancers occur in the upper outer quadrant of the breast. This area should be given particular attention. If bloody secretion is obtained from the nipple, it should be sent for cytologic examination. Cloudy fluid from parous (those who have given birth) women is of no significance. The differential diagnosis of masses in the breasts may be aided by mammography and/or sonography, although the report of the radiologist should be tempered by clinical experience and judgment. All discrete masses or dominant lumps should be excised in the operating room, a frozen section made, and appropriate therapy performed. An attempt should be made to aspirate a cystic lump. If withdrawal of fluid collapses the cyst, nothing further need be done other than repeat the examination at six months. If the cyst refills within six weeks to three months, an excisional biopsy should be considered.

Examination of the abdomen is begun by noting the presence of scars, striae, distension, and umbilical eversion. Having the patient raise her head and cough will delineate hernias or diastases recti (separation of the rectus abdominus muscles). Systematic palpation is performed for abnormalities of the liver, gallbladder, spleen, and kidneys. The cecum, right colon, and sigmoid colon are also palpated. Tenderness deep in the left lower quadrant may be the first clue in the diagnosis of diverticulitis of the sigmoid. Symmetric midline tumors should bring to mind either an intrauterine pregnancy or a distended bladder. Appropriate steps need to be undertaken in differentiating these from other pelvic conditions. Early pregnancy, if coincident with other masses, such as fibroids or ovarian cysts, is often difficult to diagnose unless constantly kept in mind. The costovertebral angles and flanks should be carefully evaluated, since renal and urethral lesions frequently cause symptoms that the patient interprets as "female trouble." The groins are inspected and palpated for enlarged superficial inguinal nodes that may be associated with venereal disease. Cancer of the vulva or lower vagina, or superficial infections of the skin of the thigh, may also cause inguinal adenopathy. Hodgkin's Disease and systemic illnesses should also be considered. Careful examination should be performed for inguinal and femoral hernias by having the patient raise her head and cough.

The extremities are examined for edema, ulceration, scars of previous surgery, and varicose veins. Bilateral edema may be due to increased intrapelvic pressure from a pregnancy, old phlebitis, or excessive salt intake. It may, however, also be due to impaired nutrition, carcinoma of the ovary with ascites, cardiac failure, or chronic nephritis. Its cause bears investigation. Ulceration of the legs suggests peripheral vascular disease due to venous stasis or diabetes. Varicose veins or scars of previous vein ligation or stripping should be adequate warning to initiate prophylaxis against thromboembolic disease if surgery is contemplated.

If the history and physical examination suggest that the original complaint might arise from an organ system other than the genital tract, appropriate X-rays, endoscopy, and laboratory procedures should be performed. This will avoid the embarrassment of operating on patients with unsuspected colonic or bladder carcinoma, diverticulitis, renal tumors, pelvic kidneys, or ulcerative colitis.

The pelvic examination is the most important part of the gynecologic examination, because of the ability to see, to palpate, and, especially, to interpret abnormal findings of the female genitalia. Frequently, these findings will explain the patient's symptoms. Often, however, they will bear no relationship. Occasionally, the pelvic examination will be normal, but laboratory procedures such as cytologic examination will aid in the diagnosis. A clean lower bowel is especially important if the examiner wishes to palpate the rectovaginal septum and uterosacral ligaments. Since fecal particles may simulate masses and modularity, an enema may have to be taken and the patient reexamined. In describing pelvic findings, it is important to bear in mind that all observers will not interpret the palpatory findings in the same way. Thus, it is better that the examiner give accurate or estimated measurements in centimeters rather than use such terms as the size of an apple, egg, or balls of various sizes. Abnormal masses should be described as to size, shape, consistency, position, mobility, and if they are tender.

Following the pelvic examination, a thorough digital examination should be performed of the anus and rectum, since about 50% of malignancies of the rectosigmoid may be palpated by careful digital exploration. A test for blood in the stool should be routine in every rectal examination, taking care to change gloves before performing the rectal examination if blood was noted in the examination of the vagina.

[2] Dilation and Curettage (D&C)

[a] Indications

A D&C is used for diagnostic as well as therapeutic purposes. The most common gynecologic and obstetrics indications include:

- menstrual disturbances;
- intermenstrual or postcoital bleeding or discharge;
- postmenopausal bleeding or discharge;
- dysmenorrhea;
- abnormal cytologic smear;
- infertility evaluation;
- abortion — voluntary or incomplete; and
- retained products of conception after pregnancy.

A D&C should be performed if profuse and prolonged vaginal bleeding occurs. This affords an opportunity for careful pelvic examination under anesthesia and may rule out ectopic pregnancy if placental tissue is obtained from the uterine cavity. If the curettings grossly resemble those from a normal endometrium, further investigation is indicated. A D&C should always be performed prior to hysterectomy, even when obvious indications, such as uterine myomas or adnexal masses are present. This could be done as an office procedure, such as endometrial biopsy or VABRA aspiration; or, prior to hysterectomy, by a diagnostic D&C with a frozen section to determine whether there is any abnormality of the endometrium. There is often a tendency to avoid a D&C in the absence of abnormal bleeding if there is an obvious indication for hysterectomy. This may be an erroneous concept, since the few minutes necessary to rule out the presence of endometrial disease may avoid the problem of unexpected pathology.

[b] Complications

The most common complications of a D&C are perforation of the uterus, laceration of the cervix, infection, and excessive postoperative uterine bleeding. In younger, nulliparous women, a D&C may result in later cervical incompetence. Excessive D&Cs on a patient may result in Asherman's Syndrome, with the development of intrauterine adhesions and subsequent infertility. A physician may be held liable for the negligent performance of a D&C in which there is a perforation of the uterus or failure to complete the procedure; however, perforation of the uterus can occur during a D&C in spite of the exercise of the proper degree of skill and care.

Uterine perforation may occur at the time of curettage for a variety of reasons. In the postmenopausal patient, the uterus has become atrophic and the wall more friable. If a malignancy is present in the uterine wall, the risk of perforation is even greater. Marked degrees of unrecognized fundal anteversion or retroversion allow perforation to occur more readily by misdirection of the uterine sound or curette. Thus, it is imperative that the position of the uterus be determined by bimanual examination before any instrument is introduced into the uterine cavity. Also, care must be taken to avoid the use of undue force when instruments are inserted into the uterine cavity. Upon recognition of a uterine perforation, subsequent management involves two phases; (a) treatment of the perforation; and (b) establishment of the histologic diagnosis. Most perforations during a diagnostic D&C in postmenopausal patients cause no harm clinically and may be managed by observation over several days for signs of bleeding, infection, and adjacent organ injury. A culdocentesis may confirm significant intraperitoneal bleeding. If there is a serous concern regarding adjacent organ injury, a laparoscopy is advisable to evaluate the necessity for laparotomy. In the event of severe bleeding or trauma, laparotomy or laparoscopy is indicated to control the bleeding or repair the injury. If infection has occurred, antibiotics are indicated and a colpotomy should be performed later to drain any abscess formed in the cul-de-sac.

Perforations occurring in the presence of cervical carcinoma are managed the same as any other type of uterine perforation at curettage. It is prudent, however, to make no further attempts at endometrial sampling, since the primary diagnosis is already established and the histologic evaluation of the endometrial cavity will have little or no influence on the determination of treatment of the primary disease. The question of dissemination of endometrial carcinoma to an intraperitoneal location is often considered in the discussions of uterine wall perforation at the tumor site. The initiation of therapy in the form of external radiation or surgery is usually undertaken promptly once the primary diagnosis of malignancy is established. The principles of management, therefore, would be similar to those for the nonmalignant state.

In younger patients undergoing a D&C for a pregnancy situation (i.e., incomplete or therapeutic abortion[5] or a hydatidform mole), the anatomic location of the perforation is of greater significance. Midline perforations could be treated conservatively with observation for complications. Lateral perforations are more likely to injure the uterine vessels dilated in the gravid state, and laparoscopy is indicated for any sense of broad ligament hematoma or significant intraperitoneal hemorrhage.

Complications may occur if the patient is not placed in the correct lithotomy position. This includes discomfort from strain to the sacroiliac, lumbosacral, and other intervertebral joints, especially in the elderly. Also, morbid placental adherence may occur to an area of perforation and result in a complication of a future pregnancy. Incomplete D&Cs for a miscarriage have led to complaints that the physician negligently failed to complete the procedure, leaving retained placental fragments in the uterus. This complication generally can be avoided by thoroughly curetting the uterine cavity and following up with a pelvic sonogram (if there is doubt as to the completeness of the procedure) prior to releasing the patient from the hospital. This is especially important because of the short hospital stays for D&Cs. Any doubt must be resolved prior to the patient's discharge, since retained placental fragments can be a source of infection, bleeding, and the potential for serious illness.

[3] Legal Aspects of Voluntary Abortion

In 1973, the United States Supreme Court ruled that a woman could not be denied an abortion in the first 3 months of pregnancy. The Court ruled that after 3 months, the state could regulate the procedure "in ways that are reasonably related to maternal health." The states may refuse the right to pregnancy termination after the fetus reaches the stage of viability (24 weeks +/-) unless indicated to preserve the life or health of the mother. Informed

---

[5] Surgical abortion can be performed by dilating the cervix and evacuating the products of conception by curettage, vacuum aspiration, or by a combination of both procedures. The cervix also may be dilated by insertion of a natural agent, laminaria digitata, into the cervical canal. The laminaria are a seaweed and are extremely moisture-absorbing. They slowly swell and gently dilate the cervix. The laminaria are removed after eight to twenty-four hours, and the uterus is carefully examined to determine its size and the status of the internal os (opening). Suction curettage is then used to aspirate the products of pregnancy. Mechanical curettage may then by performed to ensure that any remaining tissue fragments are removed.

consent must be provided the patient as to the nature of the procedure, the risks of possible infertility, as well as other risks. State laws regarding residence, stage of pregnancy, indications, consent and consultations must be adhered to.

The risk of death from a voluntary abortion is lowest when done at 8 weeks from the last menstrual period or sooner, the death rate being 0.7/100,000 procedures in that time frame. A synthetic steroid, RU486 (has recently been approved for use in this country for bringing about a first-trimester abortion in a non-invasive manner.)

[4] Hysteroscopy

[a] Indications

The hysteroscope is a rigid instrument similar in design to a laparoscope. It consists of an outer sleeve and two channels. There is a fiberoptic light source in the outer sleeve. The two channels are used to introduce a distending medium through one (saline, water, dextran, etc.), and probes, forceps, etc. to be introduced under direct vision into the uterine cavity. The indications for hysteroscopy include:

- diagnosis and treatment for abnormal uterine bleeding and
- diagnosis and treatment for infertility.
- in office tubal occlusion using the Essure device

With a negative D&C, hysteroscopy may be useful in a case of perimenopausal bleeding to establish a diagnosis. Other causes of abnormal bleeding that may be diagnosed with the hysteroscope include uterine polyps and submucous fibroids. These can often be removed through use of hysteroscopic resection. In cases of habitual abortion (three or more abortions), hysteroscopy may assist in treatment. Other conditions associated with infertility that may be dealt with via hysteroscopy include: foreign body (IUD embedded), uterine septum, cornual occlusion, intracavitary adhesions, and congenital anomaly. Hysteroscopy can also be used in treating infertility by use for intrauterine insemination or embryo transfer in selected patients.

Contraindications for hysteroscopy include PID, uterine perforation, sensitivity to the distention medium, and inexperience of the operator. Relative contraindications include heavy bleeding which would limit the visual field, and known gynecologic cancer with the theoretic risk of flushing cancer cells into the pelvic cavity.

[b] Complications

Hysteroscopy is generally safe when performed by an experienced physician. Uterine perforation can usually be prevented with use of laparoscopic assistance while performing the hysteroscopy. Hemorrhage from resection of a polyp, fibroid, or a septum can be managed by use of a probe through the laparoscope to slow the blood flow until a plan of management can be formulated. A Foley catheter can be placed into the uterus and inflated to tamponade heavy bleeding. Infection is an unusual complication of hysteroscopy, and many surgeons prescribe prophylactic antibiotics following the procedure. Complications with the distending media are unusual and can be prevented usually by not using excessive amounts of the medium.

[5] Hysterectomy

[a] Indications

Hysterectomy is the second most common major surgical procedure in the United States; approximately 600,000 hysterectomies are performed annually. The frequency appears to be decreasing as more women wish to avoid major surgery if equally effective alternatives are presented to them. Hysterectomy is still the procedure of choice in general in treating conditions unresponsive to other conservative treatment. There are elective indications as prophylaxis for uterine cancer, sterilization, and control of menstrual difficulties.

Indications for hysterectomy can be broadly divided into three categories: (1) cancer of the uterus; (2) less serious gynecologic disorders; and (3) obstetric complications. The last category (hysterectomy for excessive bleeding in an obstetric patient), and molar pregnancy are becoming less common. The most common benign diseases for which hysterectomy may be indicated are: myomas and endometriosis; diseases of the adnexae such as chronic PID; trauma to the uterus, including obstetric rupture; uncontrollable postpartum hemorrhage; abruptio placentae; septic abortion; abnormal uterine bleeding unresponsive to conservative measures; and uterine prolapse with pelvic relaxation.

Hysterectomy is a safe operation when performed by the well-trained specialist. Mortality rates vary from 0.1 to 0.9 percent. Most of the serious complications result from inadequate hemostasis, trauma to the urinary or rectal organs, and pulmonary disease. While the mortality rate from hysterectomies is less than 1%, complications may occur in as many as 25% of women undergoing vaginal hysterectomy and 50% of those undergoing abdominal hysterectomy.

There are two important basic surgical principles in performing an abdominal hysterectomy. First, good visualization is absolutely necessary. Second, adequate hemostasis is crucial. Good visualization is provided by proper positioning of the patient, well-chosen incisions, and relaxing anesthesia. Adequate hemostasis is obtained by good surgical technique-- careful dissection, meticulous ligature of major vessels, and elimination of unnecessary steps. The operative field must be free of adhesions and the specimen immobilized before beginning the actual procedure. Development of good cleavage planes facilitates the dissection.

Before recommending hysterectomy, the physician must:

- evaluate the medical indications for surgery;
- consider nonsurgical alternatives;
- determine which treatment will best address the medical indication;
- determine the type of hysterectomy—abdominal, vaginal, or LAVH (laparoscopically assisted vaginal hysterectomy, a relatively recent procedure);
- consider the inherent risks of each alternative; and
- consider the extent of surgical complications.

When myomas form in the uterus and cause excessive bleeding or pain, and enlarge rapidly with pressure on nearby structures, hysterectomy may be the only treatment the physician can offer the patient. The pain of endometriosis or adenomyosis, unresponsive to conservative measures such as hormonal or laser therapy, may require hysterectomy for relief. Premalignant conditions of the cervix, such as severe dysplasia or carcinoma- in-situ, may be best treated by hysterectomy. Adnexal disease, such as carcinoma of the ovaries or tubes, may require hysterectomy as part of the therapy. Trauma to the uterus from obstetrical complications may require a hysterectomy. These complications include rupture of the uterus with severe hemorrhage, uncontrollable postpartum hemorrhage, and abruptio placentae (premature separation of the placenta) unresponsive to conservative management. Menstrual irregularities unresponsive to curettage or hormonal therapy will be eliminated by hysterectomy, as will uterine prolapse. Hysterectomy may not be indicated where the diagnosis is uncertain, or as treatment for cancer where the evaluation is incomplete. Also, the operation should be avoided in patients who desire a larger family, or who are subject to extreme fears or depression. These patients are not good candidates for hysterectomy unless there is no alternative.

[b] Abdominal versus Vaginal Approach

Hysterectomy may be performed abdominally or vaginally. Each procedure has its own indications and advantages. There is less blood loss with a vaginal hysterectomy, and it may be performed more rapidly than an abdominal hysterectomy. The need for lengthy anesthesia is thus lessened. Also, there is less handling of the bowels in a vaginal hysterectomy. The possibility of paralytic ileus, omental and intestinal adhesions, and peritonitis is thus decreased.

With the vaginal approach, the patient is not left with an abdominal scar, she ambulates sooner, and she has a shorter recovery period. Vaginal hysterectomy is indicated for treatment of uterine prolapse with cystocoele, rectocoele, or enterocoele. It may also be appropriate for carcinoma-in-situ of the cervix, or if the patient is obese, elderly, or a poor operative risk. Abdominal hysterectomy is preferred over the vaginal approach if there is any suggestion of invasive malignant disease or if there is any pathology in the patient's pelvis or abdomen that requires further assessment at the time of surgery. Endometriosis and chronic pelvic inflammatory disease (PID) should be treated abdominally, particularly in the presence of a fixed, immobile uterus. The abdominal approach generally provides a better view of adjacent pelvic and abdominal structures and allows for more radical procedures than does the vaginal approach. Vaginal hysterectomy may be contraindicated if the uterus is too large to be removed easily. Vaginal hysterectomy is also contraindicated for prior surgery associated with ileus, peritonitis, or intestinal obstruction. The abdominal approach is generally favored for the treatment of malignancies in the reproductive organs, large myomas, ovarian lesions, and conditions in which the uterus is fixed in the pelvis.

The American College of Obstetrics and Gynecology has not identified specific standards for hysterectomy. Thus, a physician's decision to recommend hysterectomy becomes a matter of discretion and medical judgment. The physician must fully inform the patient of the reasons for the recommendation prior to the surgery. Risks, benefits, and alternatives should be included in the discussion. Spouse or significant other should be present to assure full understanding by both persons.

Once the physician concludes that the patient has the appropriate indications for surgery, the options must be explained to her. The history and findings of the workup should be reviewed. If the Pap smear and the endometrial biopsy are positive, abdominal hysterectomy with concurrent cancer surgery is the treatment of choice. If the endometrial biopsy was not positive, and the patient is of child-bearing age and wishes to preserve her child-bearing potential, cervical conization with careful follow-up is recommended. If she does not wish to preserve this option, abdominal hysterectomy may be indicated. If the Pap smear is negative, but the physician suspects malignancy of the ovary, tube or other intrapelvic or abdominal organ, abdominal hysterectomy with concurrent cancer surgery is the procedure of choice.

If the patient is a candidate for oophorectomy (excising an ovary), has had previous abdominal surgery, or has a history of endometriosis, PID, or pelvic irradiation that would render the vaginal approach untenable, abdominal hysterectomy is the indicated approach.

The patient may be given the option to choose between vaginal or abdominal hysterectomy. If she elects the former, the physician must explain that if uterine descensus (descent of the uterus) fails to occur when she is under anesthesia, the surgeon will have to do an abdominal procedure. Controversy exists over whether to remove the ovaries in conjunction with abdominal hysterectomy for benign disease in a woman in the fifth decade of life. Retention of the ovaries makes possible subsequent ovarian cancer, but removal may precipitate an abrupt surgical menopause. It is generally considered preferable to remove the ovaries and give replacement hormonal therapy when warranted. An argument can be made however for ovarian preservation. There is evidence that needed hormonal support makes the transition to menopause more comfortable for the patient, in the absence of family history of ovarian cancer in a first-degree relative (mother, sister, daughter). This is a matter for extensive discussion preoperatively between the physician and the patient. Removal of the ovaries is not a routine feature of vaginal hysterectomy, regardless of the age of the patient. Vaginal hysterectomy is specifically indicated for prolapse and outlet relaxation, with the reparative procedures combined with the hysterectomy. Cases of recurrent bleeding, symptomatic retroversion, and small myomas may also be treated with vaginal hysterectomy. The abdominal approach is generally used for endometrial cancer, although the vaginal approach may be just as satisfactory in selected cases.

[i] LAVH/LH

With the increasing use of laparoscopy in gynecologic surgery, there has been an increase in performing hysterectomies in a so-called "minimally-invasive" manner. Vaginal hysterectomy is performed by freeing the uterine supports intraabdominally by use of the laparoscope, then completing the procedure with removal through the vagina. This is known as LAVH (laparoscopic–assisted vaginal hysterectomy), or LH (laparoscopic hysterectomy). Advantages include shorter hospital stays, less need for postoperative pain management, and quicker convalescence time. Disadvantages are longer operating time, the need for increased training in use of the laparoscope, and increased hospital costs due to the costs for the endoscopic equipment. Complications include hemorrhage, and trauma to the gastrointestinal and genitourinary systems. Unduly large fibroid tumors may require conversion to the abdominal approach to complete the surgery.

[c] Complications

Complications of hysterectomies include the following:

- postoperative bleeding;
- transfusion reaction;
- pulmonary complications—atelectasis, embolism, pneumonia;
- urinary tract injury—immediate injury to the bladder or ureter, delayed injury with fistula formation, or obstruction due to kinking or scarring of the ureter (s)
- gastrointestinal complications—paralytic ileus, intestinal obstruction, bowel injury;
- wound infection, hematoma or dehiscence (separation of incision); and
- infection with peritonitis or pelvic abscess.

Injury to the urinary tract is more likely where there is technical difficulty in performing the surgery, where there are dense adhesions from prior surgery, or where disease such as endometriosis or PID obscures the anatomy. The bladder may be injured as the abdomen is entered or as the bladder is freed from the cervix during either the abdominal or vaginal approach. The ureter may be ligated or kinked during hysterectomy by either route, but more commonly when the abdominal approach is used. Fistulas may develop, presenting as leakage of urine from the vagina. A fistula is a risk commonly associated with hysterectomy, and the physician should so counsel the patient preoperatively to obtain truly informed consent. Development of a fistula after hysterectomy has generated a number of lawsuits, but the decisions are not uniform because of different theories and the interpretations of these theories by the courts. The development of a fistula is not the kind of injury that, as a matter of common knowledge, can only be the result of negligence. The courts have generally required proof of negligence by expert testimony when the suit is based on principles of negligence rather than on lack of informed consent. The doctrine of res ipsa loquitur has also been applied inconsistently in these cases. The imposition of liability usually depends on whether the facts of the case show a marked deviation from the standard of practice, and how that standard is presented at trial and defined by expert medical testimony.

Injury to the bowel may occur during surgery because of its proximity to the uterus. Gastrointestinal complications after hysterectomy include nausea and vomiting, intestinal obstruction, and paralytic ileus. The risk of these complications is greater when the patient has had infection in the pelvic organs, or previous surgery with resulting adhesions of the bowel, to the uterus, to the anterior abdominal wall, or to the omentum (a fold of peritoneum). These adhesions must be separated during the hysterectomy.

Wound complications such as dehiscence (splitting open) often result after abdominal hysterectomy. Predisposing factors include age, obesity, anemia, chronic disease, carcinoma, hypoproteinemia and poor hemostasis. An improperly closed incision or postoperative coughing may trigger this complication. Dehiscence may indicate substandard care, but does not automatically constitute negligence, especially in a high-risk patient. Proper management is essential.

Nerve injury is another frequent complication occurring in abdominal or vaginal hysterectomy, often from improper positioning or exposure rather than the procedure itself. The femoral nerve may be injured by the self-retaining retractor used during abdominal hysterectomy. During a vaginal hysterectomy, lumbar injury may result from pressure on the ligaments of the lower back due to elevation and abduction of the lower extremities. Also, the peroneal nerve may be injured from pressure against the bar that supports the leg holder.

Deaths perioperatively may be due to cardiac arrest, coronary occlusion, or respiratory paralysis. Deaths postoperatively are usually from hemorrhage, infection, pulmonary embolus, or intercurrent disease. In a recent study of factors contributing to the risk of death, abdominal hysterectomies for cancer or pregnancy complications (about 8% of all hysterectomies) accounted for over 60% of deaths associated with hysterectomy. For both vaginal and abdominal hysterectomies, the mortality rates increase with age and medical complications.

[d] Legal Issues

To state a cause of action for lack of informed consent under a theory of battery, the patient must allege and prove that:

- the hysterectomy was performed by the physician without consent;
- a substantially different procedure from that consented to was performed;

- the physician failed to disclose a risk that was substantially certain to occur; or
- the scope of the consent granted was exceeded.

To state a cause of action for lack of informed consent under a theory of negligence, the patient must allege and prove that:

- there was a breach of duty to disclose all known information material to the patient's decision to undergo a particular operation or medical procedure;
- the plaintiff-patient was injured as a result of the undisclosed information; or
- that plaintiff-patient would not have submitted to the operation or treatment if she had known of the undisclosed information.

The majority of claims for lack of informed consent are brought under the negligence theory rather than the battery theory. A cause of action for lack of informed consent is generally unsuccessful under a battery theory if the physician adequately informs the patient about the procedure. If the cause of action for lack of informed consent is based on a negligence theory, liability may be found for failure to disclose the remote risks of the surgery or the alternative methods of treatment prior to obtaining consent of the patient. In recommending that the hysterectomy be performed, the physician must determine the requisite disclosure of the risks, and of the nonsurgical alternative treatments. The physician has a duty to disclose the potential of death or serious harm, and to explain in lay terms the complications that might occur. The duty to disclose other risks inherent in the surgery depends on whether the risks are material. The scope of the disclosure has been set traditionally by what is sound medical practice under the circumstances. Some jurisdictions have developed the material risk standard whereby the scope of disclosure is determined by what a reasonable person would consider material in deciding to undergo surgery. Material alternative treatments and their inherent risks must also be disclosed preoperatively for the patient to make an informed decision concerning treatment. A physician may be liable for an unnecessary hysterectomy. The patient who alleges that her hysterectomy was unnecessary and the result of the physician's failure to perform proper diagnostic tests, must establish:

- those tests a reasonable surgeon would have employed under similar circumstances;
- the failure of the surgeon to perform the tests; and

- that a reasonable surgeon would not have operated on the patient based on what the tests would have shown.

Preoperative evaluation of the pelvis for pelvic disease that may cause anatomic distortions in the genitourinary and gastrointestinal systems from PID (pelvic inflammatory disease), endometriosis, pelvic adhesive disease, chronic pelvic pain, or suspected malignancy include:

- pelvic ultrasound to detect masses in the patient who is difficult to examine (obese/tense) or to confirm a palpable mass on pelvic examination;
- intravenous pyelography (IVP) to delineate the ureters, especially helpful in pelvic inflammatory disease conditions, as well as in ruling out congenital abnormalities of the genitourinary tract;
- evaluation of the colon by proctosigmoidoscopy, colonoscopy, or barium enema, as indicated; and
- consultation with a colorectal or general surgeon preoperatively if bowel disease is suspected.

A physician may be liable for negligence if he/she cuts beyond the point where a reasonable surgeon would stop when performing a hysterectomy. Removal of healthy organs may be found to be not medically justifiable and the surgeon may be found negligent for having performed unnecessary surgery.

A physician may be held liable for negligence in the postoperative care of a hysterectomy patient. Failure to recognize that postoperative backache complaints could be evidence of fistula development or blockage in the urinary system could result in a physician being liable for negligent care. If the hysterectomy was a complicated procedure, intravenous pyelography (IVP) with or without cystoscopy, should be performed when complaints of backache arise, to rule out the possibility of trauma to the ureter(s).

[6] Laparoscopy

[a] Diagnostic Laparoscopy

Laparoscopy is an abdominal exploration with a type of endoscope (laparoscope), which is passed through the abdominal wall. It is the optimum diagnostic procedure for suspected ectopic unruptured pregnancy. Ultrasonography, however, is frequently of value in differentiating an intrauterine pregnancy from an unruptured tubal pregnancy. Although the diagnosis of endometriosis may be suggested by the history and physical examination, it can only be made definitively by laparoscopy or laparotomy (surgical opening of the abdomen). In patients with mild to moderate endometriosis, laparoscopy reveals the classic "powderburn" lesions, small purple spots visible on the pelvic peritoneum. Evaluation of ovarian masses by laparoscopy is difficulty, and the diagnosis of ovarian endometrioma (mass of endometrial tissue) should not be made solely by laparoscopic evaluation. Rather, a biopsy of small endometriotic lesions should be made via the laparoscope. Some endometriotic implants may only contain stroma with hemorrhage, making the diagnosis difficult for the pathologist.

Laparoscopy has almost completely eliminated the use of culdoscopy (vaginal endoscopy) at most institutions, and is far superior in lysing adhesions, fulgurating endometriosis, or for performing ovarian biopsies. When done as part of an infertility work-up, tubal lavage is performed, using a water-soluble dye introduced through an intrauterine cannula. While hysterosalpingography (X-ray examination of the uterus and tubes) has a specific role in the infertility work-up, namely, allowing the diagnosis of intrauterine malformations, adhesions, and fibroids (submucosal), and confirming tubal patency, laparoscopy may find pathologic lesions such as pelvic adhesions, tubal disease, and endometriosis in patients with unexplained infertility. The clinical diagnosis of pelvic inflammatory disease (PID) is inexact. There are potential multiple symptoms and signs ascribable to PID, but no symptoms or signs pathognomonic (characteristic) of PID. Criteria for diagnosis of PID by laparoscopy in the acute phase include erythema and edema of the fallopian tubes, and exudate from the fimbria or on the serosa of the tubes. Associated signs and symptoms are lower abdominal pain and tenderness; rebound tenderness of the lower abdomen; tenderness on motion of the cervix; adnexal tenderness with fever of over 100.4° F; or a white blood count (WBC) of over 10,500. Other signs and symptoms may include a mass documented by ultrasound or pelvic examination, or gram-negative intracellular diplococci on gram-stain from the cervix.

Diagnostic laparoscopy should be performed when the differential diagnosis of pelvic pain is between PID and a surgical condition, and in cases of nonresponse to therapy or recurrent clinical disease not associated with an obvious cause. Risk factors have been delineated for the occurrence of PID and should be considered when presented with a history of a patient with pelvic pain. These include sexual activity, age, and contraceptive practices. The number of sexual partners and frequency of activity are factors to be considered as increasing the risk of PID development. Prior to or concurrent documented STDs (sexually transmitted diseases-Herpes, Human Papilloma Virus, Chlamydia, Gonorrhea, Syphilis, HIV)), increase the risk of PID. The peak incidence of PID in the United States is in the 15 to 24-year age group. The incidence of PID declines markedly after age thirty. It is not clear if this decline is associated with sexual habits, development of protective antibodies with age, or other factors. Contraceptive practices influence the risk of PID. Both oral contraceptives and barrier methods decrease the risk of PID. The presence of an IUD increases the risk of PID over that of women using no contraception. This risk is most likely greatest immediately after insertion of an IUD, but continues regardless of the duration of IUD use, socioeconomic status, and parity. The diagnosis of PID and prompt treatment are clinically important because of the potential long-term sequellae of PID, including chronic pelvic pain, ectopic pregnancy, and involuntary infertility related to the tubal factor. Technological advances, particularly fiberoptic illumination, have made laparoscopy relatively free from mechanical problems and easier to use. Although complications are uncommon, the frequency of the procedure makes them important.

[b] Complications

The overall incidence of complications is difficult to ascertain because of differences in definitions and methods of collecting data. Mortality rates are probably less than one per 10,000 laparoscopies. Deaths have been due to hemorrhage, gas emboli, injury to intraperitoneal organs, cardiovascular collapse, hypoventilation, and sepsis. Most of these deaths are preventable. One study by the American Association of Gynecologic Laparoscopists found complications in 3.5% of laparoscopies for sterilization and 4.5% of diagnostic laparoscopies.

Conditions that may place patients at high risk for complications relate to the general health of the patient, including cardiac or respiratory diseases; the presence of a large hiatal hernia, which may contraindicate use of general anesthesia; pneumoperitoneum; and the Trendelenburg position, which is usually required. Conditions that preclude adequate intra-abdominal visualization, thus increasing the risk of complications, include obesity (which makes insertion of the verres needle and trocar more difficult), prior operations with known or suspected adhesions, acute peritonitis, and hemoperitoneum. None of these conditions absolutely contraindicates laparoscopy; if the information needed is vital and cannot be obtained any other way, the procedure should be performed after thorough evaluation of the patient's status and the risks and benefits involved.

Complications occasionally occur with anesthesia, either general or local. Complications of general anesthesia are often related to the anesthesia itself, as well as to the electrical system, the pneumoperitoneum, and the head-down position required for the procedure. In order of frequency, these complications are cardiac arrhythmias, circulatory insufficiency, hypercarbia (excess of carbon dioxide in the blood), gas emboli, regurgitation or aspiration, and pneumothorax (air or gas in the pleural space around the lung). While local anesthesia has few risks, patient discomfort may be present, and the decreased pneumoperitoneum compatible with local anesthesia may lead to poor visualization. Complications due to inadequate function of the equipment can usually be avoided by appropriate pre-use checking of equipment. This is a duty of the nursing personnel. he operator should understand the principles of use, however, and backup equipment should always be available. Sterilization precautions should be scrupulously observed, since contamination of the instruments may occur from many sources, and because the same equipment may be used repeatedly the same day.

Complications from technical errors decrease as experience grows with the procedure. They may occur, however, even among experienced operators. The most common ones are:

- bleeding at the site of puncture of the needle or trocar;
- failure to enter the peritoneal cavity;
- inability to produce pneumoperitoneum; and
- perforation of the intestine, mesentery, or an intra-abdominal vessel (with either instrument).

Abdominal wall bleeding on insertion of the insufflating needle or trocar seldom occurs when the puncture is made at the inferior margins of the umbilicus, because this is an avascular area. If lateral punctures are made because of midline scars from previous surgery, it is important to avoid the epigastric artery at the lateral margin of the rectus muscle. Incisional bleeding can usually be controlled by pressure. An enlarging hematoma, however, may need to be managed by open exploration. Failure to enter the peritoneal cavity may be due to incorrect insertion of the verres needle or trocar, or to intraperitoneal adhesions. If the free peritoneal cavity is not entered, insufflated gas may flow into the subcutaneous or preperitoneal space, or within the abdomen into intestine or small intraperitoneal pockets sealed off by adhesions. Subcutaneous insufflation usually results in recognizable emphysema and crepitation, which can be cured by expressing the air.

The trocar should not be inserted until pneumoperitoneum has been obtained. Intestinal perforation with the verres needle can be recognized by aspiration of intestinal contents and by high pressure on insufflation. However, because of the small size of the needle, intestinal puncture usually has no serious consequences. If perforation is suspected, a different site should be used for puncture, and the trocar should not be inserted until satisfactory pneumoperitoneum has been obtained. Intestinal injury with the trocar, however, is an indication for immediate laparotomy and repair of the perforation. The same is true if a serious trocar injury to the mesentery is suspected.

Intraperitoneal bleeding may be a complication of inserting the verres needle or the trocar. Vessels in the mesentery or major arteries and veins are more likely to be injured by the trocar. Prompt laparotomy is indicated for actual or suspected puncture with considerable blood loss. Consultation with a vascular surgeon is advisable if a major blood vessel is injured. By emptying the bladder prior to the procedure, and by visualizing the point of insertion by transillumination with the previously inserted laparoscope, injury to the bladder from the use of a second probe can be avoided.

Unsuccessful or failed laparoscopy may occur even with an experienced laparoscopist, due to failure to enter the peritoneum with the needle or trocar. The open method of laparoscopy has been suggested for such cases and can be performed in two ways that avoid the difficulties caused by the blind insertion of the needle and the trocar. In the first technique, a special blunt laparoscope is inserted under direct vision after all layers of the abdominal wall are incised in the region of the umbilicus. In the second method, a similar incision is made, the peritoneal cavity is entered with a finger, and a conventional laparoscope is used.

Intestinal injury, bleeding, and infection are complications that may be recognized in the early postoperative period. Intestinal injury may not have been appreciated at the time of the laparoscopy. After a varying time interval, the patient first complains of abdominal pain with tenderness, rebound tenderness, and diminished peristalsis over a 24-hour period accompanied by fever and leucocytosis (elevated white blood count). Continued postoperative monitoring of vital signs, with repeated blood counts and X-rays indicating free air in the abdomen, mandate immediate laparotomy and repair. Bleeding may occur at the site of the abdominal wall puncture or intra- or retroperitoneally. Bleeding at the incision may require resuturing under local or general anesthesia. Deeper bleeding with decreased hematocrit or paracentesis positive for blood are indications for exploratory laparotomy and identification and control of the bleeding vessel. Infection may occur intraperitoneally de novo or as an exacerbation of a prior peritonitis, salpingitis, or other infection. Treatment with a broad-spectrum antibiotic may improve the patient's condition within a few hours. Bladder infection may follow catheterization and is managed by antibiotics after obtaining a urine culture. Since most laparoscopies are performed with only a brief stay in a hospital or surgicenter, careful postoperative observation is essential. Persistent pain, elevation of pulse or temperature, hypotension, or hypertension all indicate the need for continued monitoring and may herald one of the complications listed above.

[c] Therapeutic Laparoscopy

Tubal occlusion may be performed by electrocoagulation, silastic bands, or clips. Complications arise from the type of occlusion employed. Electrothermal injury of the intestine is most common with bipolar fulguration, rare with unipolar fulguration, and absent with the use of bands or clips unless bleeding points have been coagulated. Other dangers of coagulation include electrical injury to a large area of the tube or mesosalpinx, and major malfunctions such as explosions.

Laparotomy is indicated if the serosa of the intestine is separated and the underlying mucosa, muscularis, or lumen of the bowel is seen. If the injury to the bowel is not recognized at the time of the laparoscopy, the burned area may undergo necrosis, and several days later perforation may occur with peritonitis. Immediate laparotomy and repair are indicated. There is danger of application to the wrong structure when silastic bands or clips are used. These structures include the round ligament, the infundibulopelvic ligament, and the intestine. Bands can usually be removed laparoscopically by forceps. Bands may be lost from the end of the applicator, but can usually be retrieved through the laparoscope. Postoperative pain may be somewhat greater after the use of bands. Bleeding from the mesosalpinx may occur, which is usually visible and often related to traction on the tube. Bleeding points should be visualized and coagulated. Laparotomy is indicated for continued bleeding.

Late postoperative complications of laparoscopic tubal occlusion include subsequent, unwanted pregnancies, whether the procedure initially was electrocoagulation or tubal rings placed laparoscopically. This may be due to either method failure or technical failure. Technical failure occurs with all methods and can result from spontaneous reanastomosis or operator inexperience. Some failures are due to "luteal phase pregnancies," which can be avoided by performing the operation only in the early proliferative phase of the menstrual cycle and by careful preoperative examination, including a pregnancy test. A high incidence of ectopic pregnancies among tubal occlusion failures has been reported by some authors. Thermal injury to the proximal part of the tube may be more likely to lead to fistula formation and the possibility of ectopic pregnancy, rather than the fibrosis that occurs when the distal part of the tube is coagulated. Long-term effects of sterilization on reproductive function have been found to be few.

Most women report no changes in menstrual pattern. When changes occur, they may be in equal proportion in opposite directions. Many can be attributed to discontinuation of oral contraceptives or IUDs prior to sterilization. While no increase in abnormal menstrual function seems to occur regardless of the method of tubal sterilization, some doubts remain about the circulatory and possible hormonal effects of tubal occlusion.

Psychological sequelae of tubal sterilization vary. Most women express satisfaction with the operation. Those who were persuaded to accept sterilization for medical reasons are more likely to regret the procedure. Also, with increasing divorce and remarriage, sterilized women may desire to become pregnant by their new partners. The possibility of reversing tubal ligation to restore fertility has generated interest in tubal reconstruction procedures. It is important to identify the procedure used when planning reversal of tubal sterilization. Removal of the fimbria by fimbriectomy, unipolar electrocoagulation, or loss of a large part of the tube with less than four centimeters remaining makes success less likely. Preoperative evaluation of the tubes by hysterosalpingography and diagnostic laparoscopy is essential, since these studies may reveal unsuspected adhesions or inoperable kinking of the tubes.

In a study of deaths attributable to tubal laparoscopy for sterilization, the Centers for Disease Control found that of the 17 deaths associated with the procedure, six followed general anesthesia complications; sepsis accounted for five (including sepsis from bowel burn injury); three from hemorrhage; and one each from myocardial infarction, pulmonary embolism, and heart block. The most common pre-existing condition in those patients who died was obesity.

[d] Laparoscopic Biopsy

Biopsy specimens may be taken from the ovary, especially as part of an infertility workup, and from other peritoneal sites as part of an evaluation for primary or recurrent pelvic cancer. Biopsy may be difficult because of problems in obtaining adequate exposure. Bleeding may complicate ovarian biopsy, but can usually be controlled by coagulation. There appear to be no long-term complications of one or more small ovarian biopsy procedures. Laparoscopic biopsy is used in patients with gynecologic cancer to evaluate the effects of treatment, usually chemotherapy, prior to, or sometimes instead of, laparotomy. At times biopsy is used in the initial evaluation of the patient.

Complications of biopsy include failure to enter the peritoneal cavity because of prior adhesions from tumor, perforation of the intestine at entry, and hemorrhage from bleeding biopsy sites. These complications can be prevented by appropriate selection of puncture site, proper visualization of the biopsy area, and, possibly, by the use of small instruments developed for the purpose.

[e] Other Procedures

In addition to laparoscopy for tubal sterilization and lysis of adhesions, this form of endoscopy has been used for cauterizing endometriosis implants, aspiration of ovarian cysts, removal of an extrauterine IUD, division of the uterosacral ligaments for pain, treatment of an ectopic pregnancy, myomectomy, biopsy of a tumor, and to assist in a vaginal hysterectomy by dividing adhesions, as well as the supporting ligaments of the uterus (so-called LAVH). With the use of these extended procedures has come the increased possibility of complications due to the performance without direct visualization of the involved structures.

[f] Legal Issues

In a number of cases, plaintiffs have alleged failure of the gynecologist to obtain informed consent to a sterilization procedure with respect to the various available sterilization techniques, the failure rates of each such technique, and the possibility of failure in a particular case. Physicians should never promise that the procedure will be absolutely successful. This has resulted in allegations of breach of an express warranty.

Since sterilization is a relatively simple and safe procedure, few cases have involved the allegation that the physician caused some physical injury to the patient during the course of the procedure, such as bowel perforation. In those cases where injury does occur, standard negligence principles would apply.

The American College of Obstetrics and Gynecology has set forth standards of care governing sterilization of women. Patients desiring elective surgical sterilization should be fully counseled about the implications of the surgery. Informed consent requires that the patient understand that:

- the procedure is intended to be permanent;
- there can be no guarantee of the effectiveness of the procedure; and
- restoration of fertility by a subsequent operation is uncertain.

While consultation is not necessary if sterilization is requested by the patient, if the decision for sterilization is based on medical or psychiatric indications, it is prudent for the gynecologist to have the opinion of a knowledgeable consultant.

A patient's consent is "informed" only if it is obtained after fair and reasonable explanation has been given of the contemplated treatment or procedure, including risks, benefits, and alternative courses of action.

§ 14.04 Gynecologic Diseases

[1] Pelvic Infections

Pelvic inflammatory disease (PID) is a disease of the upper genital tract. It is a polymicrobial infection resulting from organisms that are sexually transmitted and organisms that are considered to be part of the normal endogenous flora of the lower genital tract. Disease may be confined to the tubes (salpingitis) and/or may involve the ovaries (salpingo-oophoritis). Marked inflammation involving contiguous intraperitoneal structures and massive suppuration with tubo-ovarian abscess formation can result in destruction of the normal anatomy, as well as in functional impairment. PID is a disease of sexually active, menstruating women. It is rare in premenarchal, postmenopausal, or celibate women. Most cases are thought to be ascending infections caused by microorganisms that ascend from the lower genital tract through the cervix and uterus to the tubes. Infection may also spread to the tubes and ovaries via the parametrium from cervical vessels and lymphatics. Sexually transmitted organisms, such as Neisseria gonorrhea, Chlamydia trachomitis, and Mycoplasma hominis may be found as the sole pathogens or with other organisms. Liability may be imposed on a physician for the negligent failure to diagnose, appropriately treat, and monitor an infection of the pelvis, as well as for the negligent treatment resulting in sterility or some other permanent injury.

The diagnosis of PID is inexact. There are multiple potential signs and symptoms ascribable to PID, depending on the areas involved in the inflammatory process. No symptoms and signs are pathognomonic (characteristic) of PID. Differential diagnoses frequently include appendicitis, ectopic pregnancy, endometriosis, adhesions, and adnexal tumors, including ruptured hemorrhagic functional ovarian cysts. The signs and symptoms most often seen are adnexal tenderness, palpable mass or swelling, abnormal discharge, elevated sedimentation rate, elevated temperature, and chills and fever. Women who have had PID have an increased risk of infertility due to tubal obstruction. This risk is related to the number of episodes and severity of infections, and may also be associated with the infecting organism and adequacy of treatment. Pregnancy after an episode of PID is associated with an increased incidence of ectopic pregnancies. PID is thought to be the major factor in the increasing incidence of ectopic pregnancy in the United States.

Clinical awareness by the physician is one of the most important factors in diagnosis of pelvic infections in women. Patients at high risk usually present with fever as the first sign (postpartum, post abortion, or postoperative pelvic surgery).

[a] Human Papillomavirus (HPV)

HPV infection is increasing. It is estimated to have affected 30 to 60% of people at some point in their lives. By use of DNA probes over 20 types of HPV virus have been identified that can affect the genital tract. The virus is seen as a wart-like structure, condyloma acuminata, in the vagina, cervix, and perianal areas. HPV is responsible for dysplasia and cancer. Transmission is by sexual contact. Both partners can be affected. Small lesions in pregnancy do not require treatment. Therapy with trichloracetic acid (TCA) may be needed for large growths in the last month of pregnancy to avoid cesarean section, as the virus may infect the baby in a vaginal delivery.

In 2006 Gardasil vaccine was released by Merck Co. It is a vaccine that is designed to protect against HPV disease caused by HPV types 6,11,16, and 18. HPV 16 and 18 cause about 70% of cervical cancers. The vaccine is given as a series of three injections over a six month period in women up to the age of 26.

[b] Gonorrhea

Gonorrhea is one of the most prevalent sexually transmitted diseases (STD) in the United States today. More than one million cases are reportedly annually. The peak age of occurrence is under twenty-five years and is more common in urban populations and among lower socioeconomic groups. Gonorrhea may present as a localized infection of the lower genital tract, as an invasive infection of the upper genital tract, as a disseminated disease with systemic manifestations, or it may be completely asymptomatic. The majority of cases are transmitted by sexual activity. The incubation period is from three to five days in those cases in which symptoms are recognizable. The bacteria are harbored chiefly in the endocervix.

The manifestations of gonorrhea in women may be subtle. Endocervical gonorrhea is associated with a purulent vaginal discharge, which may or may not be noticed as being abnormal. Urethral involvement of Skene's glands may be associated with symptoms of lower urinary tract infection, such as dysuria and urinary frequency. Lower genital tract gonorrhea can lead to infection of the Bartholin glands with the formation of an abscess, which is most often unilateral, acutely suppurative, and painful. The organism involved, N. gonorrheae, can invade and infect the upper genital tract as a solitary pathogen or as part of a polymicrobial infection. Up to 40% of women also have chlamydia infection coexisting with N. gonorrheae.

The diagnosis of gonorrhea can be established only by bacterial culture. Material to be cultured may be obtained from several sources, including endocervical, anorectal, pharyngeal, blood, and synovial fluid, depending on symptomatology. The low yield of positive cultures in practice has led to the belief that discretion is allowed in determining the indication for culture in asymptomatic women. Given the high probability of crossover infection with syphilis, current recommendations are that gonococcal cultures should be done in all women with syphilis, and that screening for syphilis should be done prior to treating culture-proven gonorrhea. Recommendations for specific antibiotic therapy of gonorrhea may change, depending on the sensitivities of individual strains. Guidelines for treatment are available from the Venereal Disease Control Division of the Centers for Disease Control, Atlanta, Georgia. Gonorrhea is a reportable disease. Finding the carrier and treating her, as well as her sexual partner, is the cornerstone of controlling the disease.

[c] Syphilis

Syphilis occurs when the causative organism, the spirochete Treponema Pallidum, is inoculated into mucous membranes. This occurs most frequently during sexual activity and is predominantly in the fifteen- to forty-year age group. Syphilis exists in well-defined stages by clinical presentation and time course. The incubation period from contact to onset of lesions of primary syphilis ranges from nine to ninety days, with an average time of twenty-one days. The lesion is the chancre, a solitary, painless ulceration that forms at the site of inoculation, then breaks down to form a well-demarcated ulcer associated with bilateral, firm, nontender regional adenopathy. Spirochetes are found at the base of the ulcer and chancres are infectious. Generalized skin eruption typically develops in secondary syphilis on an average of from six to twelve weeks after exposure due to dissemination of spirochetes in the blood. Facial sparing and involvement of the palms of the hands and soles of the feet are classic manifestations. Other manifestations include alopecia, mucous membrane patches, and the condyloma lata, a confluence of raised, flat lesions occurring primarily in the intertriginous areas. Along with the skin lesions of secondary syphilis, there are often tender generalized lymphadenopathy, fever, malaise, headache, sore throat, and arthralgias. Following resolution of signs of secondary syphilis, the infection enters a latent phase, which is asymptomatic, not infectious, and may last from five to twenty years after the initial disease.

Syphilis can be transmitted to the fetus at any stage of pregnancy and can result in deformities, acute neonatal illness, or late manifestations. Congenital syphilis can be prevented or ameliorated by maternal treatment during pregnancy. For this reason, premarital and prenatal screening are the rule for syphilis detection. The diagnosis of syphilis is usually made by serologic testing. There is no satisfactory method for culturing T. Pallidum. The spirochete can occasionally be found by dark-field examination of secretions from a chancre or secondary lesion. Since there is a very brief recovery period of the treponema, the diagnosis usually depends on the serology tests plus the history. False-negative results can occur, especially when topical or systemic antimicrobial therapy suppresses the number of spirochetes. The nonspecific or reagin tests (VDRL, RPR) are most frequently used for screening. These tests detect the presence of a nonspecific antigen produced during syphilitic infection. These tests were qualitative and serial titers may be used to judge therapeutic response. The treponemal tests (FTA-ABS, MHA-TP), which are technically more difficult to perform, are most often used to confirm the diagnosis in patients with positive reagin tests. These test for the presence of specific antitreponemal antibodies. Biologic false-positives may occur with either type of serologic testing. Serologic tests may be falsely negative very early in the disease, but by six weeks to three months after exposure, practically all serologic tests will be positive. A chancre may be present prior to seropositivity, but secondary syphilis is almost always accompanied by a positive serology.

If a serologic test for syphilis remains negative three months after suspected exposure, the diagnosis of syphilis can be excluded. Special attention is given to assuring that pregnant women do not have or acquire syphilis during pregnancy. A reagin test should be performed at the first prenatal visit and again during the third trimester. A positive test mandates a repeat quantitative reagin test and a specific treponemal test. Treatment is required if the treponemal test is positive, or if the titer rises in the reagin test. As in the case of gonorrhea, the best source for current guidelines of treatment is the Venereal Disease Control Division of the Centers for Disease Control.

[d] Chlamydia

Chlamydia Trachomatis is a sexually transmitted organism more prevalent in those younger than nineteen years, in nulliparas (women never pregnant), and in oral contraceptive users. It is frequently associated with gonorrhea and may be cultured from the genital tract after successful therapy for gonorrhea. It is a major pathogen in postgonococcal and nongonococcal urethritis in the male. Female partners of males with these syndromes are at high risk for chlamydial colonization and disease. Chlamydia is a causative agent of PID, urethritis, and cervicitis. Chlamydial cervicitis has a distinct hypertrophic friable eversion covered with purulent cervical mucus. Antibiotic therapy will result in reversion of the cervical changes to simple eversion without purulence. The presence of C. Trachomatis is diagnosed most accurately by tissue culture demonstrating the intracellular organism. More specific and sensitive tests are becoming more widely available. Endocervical mucus will discolor the tip of a cotton-tipped applicator (positive "Q-Tip Test"), and microscopic examination will reveal the presence of white blood cells (WBCs) as a quick office-screening procedure. Antibodies are measurable by serologic testing methods. However, the usefulness of serologic analysis as a diagnostic tool is limited by the presence of preexisting antibodies, cross-reactivity of various serotypes of chlamydia serologic testing methods, and the lack of antibody response to some chlamydial infections. Treatment should be based on culture documentation. When such culture facilities are not available, or culture is impractical, presumptive therapy may be instituted for suspected disease in a high-risk population.

[e] Herpes

Herpes is a sexually transmitted disease (STD) of increasing concern for sexually active women of all age groups, races, and economic status. Symptomatic genital herpes is the most frequent cause of painful lesions of the lower genital tract in women in the United States. Herpes infection of the lower genital tract has been associated with cervical cancer, although a causative role remains undefined. Additionally, contact with genital herpes during passage through the birth canal has been associated with systemic neonatal infection with major risks of serious morbidity and a high rate of mortality. Recent studies for 1999-2004 compared with 1988-1994 show declines in HSV-2 prevalence in the United States. The incidence of HSV-1 caused genital herpes may be increasing..

Genital herpes may be one of the most frequently found STDs in the United States today. It is caused by the herpes simplex virus (HSV). There are two major types of HSV (HSV-1 and HSV-2), which are closely related and share some common antigens. The majority of genital lesions are caused by HSV-2 infections. HSV-1 infections primarily cause oral-labial lesions. There is, however, significant overlap. Genital herpes is a recurrent infection with periods of active infection separated by latent periods during which the virus resides in the dorsal root sacral ganglia. The virus is activated by various endogenous and exogenous stimuli. It travels down the sensory root to the lower genital tract where it replicates and where the outward manifestations of the disease become apparent. It is identified by cultures. The lesion typically is painful, begins as a fluid-filled vesicle or papule, progresses to a well-defined shallow ulcer, with healing of mucous membrane or crusting over of epidermal surfaces. The clinical presentation and duration of active infection vary widely and are dependent on the type of virus, as well as whether it is initial or recurrent disease. The initial presentation of genital herpes infection occurs one to forty-five days after exposure to the virus. Initial manifestations of infection are more severe and last longer than those of recurrent disease. Multiple painful, usually bilateral, lesions occur on the external genitalia. Symptoms tend to peak within eight to ten days and gradually decrease over the next week. Ulcers tend to last up to fifteen days, and the mean time from onset to total healing of the lesion is about a month. There may be bilateral tender inguinal, femoral, and/or iliac lymphadenopathy, with accompanying severe lower pelvic pain. The cervix is involved with initial genital herpes infection in most cases, with friability of the cervix, ulcerative and/or necrotic lesions, and increased discharge.

Recurrent herpes infection is typically less severe, of shorter duration, and less frequently involves systemic manifestations than the initial disease. Prodromal symptoms may occur several days prior to the onset of recurrent disease. This is described as a tingling sensation or hyperesthesia of the genital area where lesions will occur. There may also be a sacral neuralgia with pain radiating down to the buttocks and hips. Recurrent genital lesions are fewer, smaller, and more, often unilateral. They may not have the typical ulcerative appearance and may be similar in appearance to a fissure or excoriation. They tend to occur in the same location and have the same appearance at each episode. Symptoms last four to eight days, and the mean time for disappearance of recurrent lesions is nine to ten days.

Urethritis and cervicitis are seen less frequently with recurrent genital infection than with initial infections. Tender local adenopathy may be present, but is usually of short duration and not severe. The average number of recurrences in women who have symptomatic recurrent genital herpes is five to eight per year. Recurrences may be stimulated by an endogenous factor, such as cyclic hormonal variation or stress. Recurrences may also be precipitated by exposure to HSV through contact with an infected partner with exogenous virus, or by reinfection with a different viral strain. The clinical appearance of genital herpes does not always follow classic patterns. Evidence suggests that the frequency of recurrent disease is independent of time and does not necessarily decrease as time increases from the initial infection. About 25% of initial genital herpes infections show up in women who have preexisting antibodies to HSV. These initial episodes tend to be less severe, with fewer systemic manifestations, and are more typical of recurrent infection. Some of these mild initial episodes may actually be a recurrent infection in a person with previous asymptomatic infection. The presence of an antibody to HSV-1 of oral-labial origin may serve to ameliorate the clinical expression of infection in other cases. Initial HSV-1 infection cannot be clinically distinguished from that caused by HSV-2, but HSV-1 is less likely to cause recurrent infection and, when it does, recurrence is much less frequent and severe. It is unclear why this type of specific difference in recurrence rates occurs.

The diagnosis of genital herpes infection is made by recovery of herpes virus in culture, although the diagnosis may be suspected if the characteristic lesions are present. It is possible to distinguish antibodies to HSV-2 from antibodies to HSV-1. There is an approximately 20% crossover that may make such identification inaccurate. In these cases, the existence of antibody to HSV at the onset of an initial genital herpes infection may preclude identification at this episode as either a primary infection in a previously antibody-negative host or a recurrent infection in a previously asymptomatic host. The presence of antibody to HSV at the onset of a herpes genital lesion may identify past exposure to this virus, but not necessarily identify the etiology of an active lesion. Antibody testing can be of some value if there is no antibody to HSV present at the onset of a suspected primary genital herpes infection, and an antibody is documented to develop during the course of the illness.

There is no completely effective treatment available. (The high mortality rate in infected newborns has led to the recommendation for elective cesarean section for mothers with active infection prior to, or within four hours of, rupture of the membranes.) Infected newborns have a mortality rate approaching 60%. In a significant percent of the survivors, there may be both neurologic and/or ocular sequelae. Antivirals are available for topical application, as well as for oral or intravenous administration. Topical use decreases the duration of symptoms and the length of viral shedding for the initial disease. It must be applied at the onset of symptoms and frequently. It does not have as much effectiveness in recurrent genital herpes infection in altering the course of the disease. Intravenous antiviral therapy is effective in ameliorating the presentation of initial genital herpes infections and preventing recurrences in immunosuppressed individuals. Resistance to intravenous therapy has been documented. Oral use significantly reduces recurrences of genital herpes in healthy adults when administered on a long-term basis; however, recurrences of infection return to previous rates when treatment is discontinued. Drug-resistant viruses have been documented in patients receiving continuous oral therapy.

The potential for drug-resistance and long-term side effects of antiviral therapy exist. The exact role of oral antiviral treatment of genital herpes remains to be defined. It appears to prevent or reduce the frequency, as well as the severity of recurrences in most patients. Care of local lesions and supportive care through the systemic illness remain the mainstays of treatment of genital herpes. Hospitalization for observation and supportive care during episodes of acute systemic illness also may be necessary. Appropriate counseling must be provided to handle the emotional and informational needs of patients diagnosed with genital herpes infection.

[f] AIDS

AIDS, the acquired immune deficiency syndrome, is caused by the human immune deficiency virus (HIV). The exact extent of infection is unknown. HIV-infected women will be the source of many cases of pediatric HIV infection in the near future. Obstetricians and gynecologists will be involved in these cases, particularly in efforts to prevent infection in women and children. Women at risk for HIV infection should be tested by their gynecologists. HIV renders the individual susceptible to opportunistic (denoting a microorganism that does not usually cause disease, but becomes pathogenic under certain circumstances, such as impaired immune responses as a result of other disease or drug therapy) infections such as Pneumocystis Carinii pneumonia and CNS toxoplasmosis, and to neoplasms (Kaposi's sarcoma, rectal carcinoma) by progressive debilitation of the immune system. An HIV-infected patient with a specific opportunistic infection, neoplasm, dementia, or wasting syndrome is considered to have AIDS. The diagnosis can be made in the absence of laboratory evidence of infection if the patient has no other known cause of immune deficiency and has the definitive diagnosis of one of a number of indicator diseases, such as P. Carinii pneumonia.

There is a period of weeks or months, the so-called "window phase," when no detectable antibody is found in the infected individual's blood. Antibodies can be detected in most individuals six to twelve weeks after exposure, although in some cases the latent period has been found to be as long as eighteen months after sexual exposure. After seroconversion has occurred, an asymptomatic period of variable length follows. Laboratory evidence of immune dysfunction may be followed by clinical conditions of fever, weight loss, malaise, lymphadenopathy, and central nervous system (CNS) dysfunction, as well as HSV and Candida. These nonspecific conditions are usually progressive and may be a prelude to an opportunistic infection that is diagnostic of AIDS. While studies of infected homosexual men, IV drug users, and hemophiliacs have noted progression to AIDS five years after the infections were confirmed, no such studies of infected women have been reported. Patients without AIDS make up a small minority of the HIV-infected population. For each patient with AIDS, there are, at any given time, twenty to thirty asymptomatic infected individuals who presumably remain infected for life and who will, it is currently believed, eventually show symptoms of AIDS. Once the diagnosis of AIDS is made, the prognosis is poor. The probability of survival has been estimated at 49% at one year, and 15% at five years. In one recent study, approximately 11% of AIDS in the United States occurred in women. These were clustered in large metropolitan areas of Miami, New Jersey, and New York City. The high-risk groups of women include intravenous drug users, women with heterosexual contacts with men in high risk groups, those who received unscreened blood transfusions, and prostitutes. There is an over-representation of minorities in reported cases of AIDS, such as blacks more than Hispanics and Hispanics more than whites, in cases reported to the Centers for Disease Control.

The primary modes of transmission of HIV are through parenteral infection of blood, sexual activity (heterosexual and primarily male homosexual), and perinatal events. There is no evidence of transmission through casual contact, water, food, or environmental surfaces. Since 1985, all units for production of RhoGam (Rho (D)) immunoglobulin have been screened for HIV antibodies, and the fractionation process used to produce RhoGam has been shown to be effective in removing the virus. Because of the potential risk of transmission to women undergoing donor artificial insemination, donors should be screened at the time of donation, and again several months later prior to the use of frozen semen. Homosexual and bisexual males are the largest group of infected individuals in the United States at this time. Recent data, however, suggest that heterosexual activity is becoming an increasingly important mode of transmission. Women constitute an increasingly larger percentage of the infected population resulting from heterosexual transmission of HIV through an infected partner, partners with hemophilia, or from partners who are IV drug users. Most women contract HIV through the use of IV drugs or sexual relations with IV drug users. Eighty percent of women with children with AIDS are black or Hispanic. Most cases of AIDS have occurred in New York, New Jersey, Florida, and California, but cases have been reported in almost all areas of the country. Recent data demonstrate that HIV can spread heterosexually to men, as well as to women. A substantial proportion of infected women do not admit to having engaged in recognized risk behavior. The increasing rate of infection among women presages an important role for providers of health care to women. Obstetricians and gynecologists today face the need to provide health care to HIV infected women during pregnancy, and become involved in efforts to control the disease.

Management of HIV-related infections should be coordinated with an expert in infectious diseases. HIV-positive patients must be identified as early as possible. The most important factors that doctors and others may influence are duration of treatment and viral load. The life-threatening nature of opportunistic infections outweighs the risks from therapeutic agents. A small number of health care workers have contracted HIV infection from an accidental needle stick or cutaneous exposure to infected blood products. Seroconversion rates have been minimal or absent in health care workers after percutaneous and mucous membrane exposure to HIV. Occasional reports of seroconversion, however, have been documented with blood contamination of the mouth and hands. In the labor and operating rooms, care providers are exposed to infected patients' secretions and blood. Specific control measures are designed to prevent skin contact with all blood and secretions, and should not be limited to those patients known to be HIV-antibody-positive. A vigorously applied infection control program will also reduce the risk of other more common nosocomial infections, such as hepatitis A and B virus infections. Specific control measures include the use of water-resistant gowns and gloves, and frequent hand washing. Goggles should be used to protect the eyes in situations with potential for conjunctival contact.

Public health efforts must focus on education, since there is no known cure for AIDS and no vaccine for HIV. Gynecologists must play a role in these efforts since the health issues that bring patients to them (sexual and reproductive concerns) are also those that expose women to risks of contracting and transmitting HIV. Messages about safer sexual practices need to be reinforced as part of gynecologic care. Birth control and STD control have been closely linked historically. The use of condoms and abstinence help prevent the spread of STDs, but changing attitudes toward sex and alternative contraceptive technology have reduced that safety factor. Users of IUDs, oral contraceptives, and sterilization, though protected from pregnancy, are still at risk of STDs. The risk of sexual transmission is reduced by the use of a viricidal agent such as nonoxynol-9. (Nonoxynol-9 provides some protection in the event the condom ruptures.) The spermicide inactivates the HIV in vitro.

Testing for the HIV antibody is an important addition to counseling in certain circumstances. Testing without counseling serves no individual or public health good and should be discouraged. When combined with counseling, testing enables women to make informed decisions about their reproductive health and behavior. Testing and counseling are recommended for clinics offering services for gynecological care, prenatal care, family planning, and diagnosis and treatment of STDs. Testing should be offered to women in risk groups who are either pregnant or contemplating pregnancy.

Risk groups include current or former users of IV drugs and women whose sexual partners have used IV drugs, engaged in bisexual behavior, or had evidence of HIV infection. Individuals who may have STDs, engaged in prostitution, or received blood transfusions before screening began but after HIV infection occurred in the United States (between 1978-1985), should be offered testing. Preexisting acute and chronic STDs may predispose a woman to heterosexual infection with HIV. A woman who is uncertain or concerned about the drug use or sexual history of any sexual partner should also be offered counseling. Any woman from an area of known or suspected high prevalence should be offered testing. Since antibodies to HIV may not be detectable for several months after infection, women who have been recently exposed may need to be tested on a periodic basis to determine whether infection has occurred. An individual who has antibody to HIV must be considered infectious. No test should be considered positive unless a confirmatory test has been performed.

Standard testing procedures include an initial immunoassay (enzyme-linked immunosorbent assay, or ELISA) followed by a confirmatory western blot assay. Patients should be informed of the disadvantages, as well as the advantages of testing. Disadvantages include mental anguish and discriminatory sequelae, such as loss of employment or health care benefits, which can arise regardless of test results.

Counseling for HIV-positive individuals should include the following specific points:

- a description of the early clinical manifestations of HIV infection, with the advice to seek immediate medical attention if they occur;
- current understanding of the prognosis of HIV infection;
- emphasis on the need for responsible sexual behavior, and on avoiding the sharing of intravenous needles;
- a prohibition from donating blood products and body organs;
- advice not to share toothbrushes, razors, and other implements that could be contaminated with blood;
- suggestion that sexual and needle-sharing partners be notified and advised of counseling and testing;
- importance of notifying the health care worker of the patient's HIV antibody results; and
- discouragement of pregnancy and the need for effective contraception.

If HIV antibody-positive results are obtained during pregnancy, the patient should be informed immediately of the risks of perinatal transmission and the possible effects of pregnancy on the prognosis of the disease. Reproductive options, including pregnancy termination, should be discussed as a valid choice for HIV-infected women. Patients who test negative for HIV antibody should be provided with the information that false-negative results can occur (virus-positive, antibody-negative). The false-negative rate is due to the prolonged latent phase during which an exposed individual may test negative for HIV antibody while actually remaining infective. Physicians should be familiar with local statutory issues involving confidentiality, charting, and contact-tracing. Although confidentiality has long been considered a cornerstone of medical care, it is often difficult to achieve. Confidentiality issues surrounding HIV-antibody-positive patients are among the most problematic to confront. Medical records are frequently reviewed by insurance carriers, and many individuals are insured through their employers. Access to patients' serostatus should be limited to those with a medical need to know. Charting of serostatus, while limiting access to charts, would best serve the interests of optimal medical care.

Another issue is the patient's right to confidentiality and the physician's duty to warn. With appropriate counseling, most patients will inform their sexual partners of their infection. If they do not, a physician must then balance the patient's autonomy against the physician's obligation "to do no harm." Infected patients are entitled to compassionate, competent, and humane care. The physician has an obligation to prevent stigmatization of these patients in the hospital setting. The AMA Council on Ethical and Judicial Affairs has stated that "a physician may not ethically refuse to treat a patient whose condition is within the physician's realm of competence solely because the patient is seropositive."

[2] Endometriosis

[a] Diagnosis

Endometriosis may be defined as the presence of functioning endometrial tissue outside of its normal situation, which is usually confined to the pelvis in the region of the ovaries, uterosacral ligaments, cul-de-sac, and uterovesical peritoneum. The development and extension of endometrial tissue into the myometrium is termed adenomyosis, which is characterized by an entirely different clinical situation than endometriosis. The pelvic examination presents none of the characteristics of endometriosis. The term endometriosis implies proliferating growth and function (i.e., bleeding) in an extrauterine site. A key concept is that hormonal factors are of central importance in the pathogenesis of endometriosis.

Endometriosis is uncommon prior to the menarche (first onset of menses) or after the menopause; ovarian ablation usually results in complete and prompt regression of the endometriotic tissue, although scar tissue may remain. Endometriosis is rarely observed in amenorrheic (absence of periods) women but is commonly found in women with uninterrupted cyclic menstruation for over five years. Endometriosis improves or stabilizes during episodes of physiologically induced pregnancy or hormonally induced amenorrhea. Frequent pregnancies, if initiated early in reproductive life, appear to prevent the development of endometriosis. Malignancy in endometriosis is rare. The most common site of endometriosis is the ovary, with both ovaries being involved in about 50% of patients with endometriosis. The pathologic process, although microscopically benign, produces extensive havoc in the pelvis as important structures are gradually involved. The process spreads in a cancer like manner, but is frequently terminated by fibrosis and scarring. The ultimate result may be ovarian destruction, deformity of the fallopian tubes, bladder dysfunction, large bowel obstruction, ureteral constriction, and infertility.

Endometriosis is quite common, presenting in 5-15% of women ages 25-35 who undergo laparotomy. Approximately 30% of patients undergoing laparoscopy for infertility have endometriosis. The median patient's age at time of diagnosis is 36 years. Delayed and infrequent pregnancies may account for the increased incidence in upper middle-class professional women. Endometriosis can be recognized by various characteristics, depending on the severity of the disease. The lesions of early endometriosis are small, rounded bluish-red spots surrounded by a zone of puckered scar tissue and scattered over the pelvic surfaces. The implants may have the appearance of powder burns. As the disease progresses, the involved structures are restricted by dense vascular fibrous tissue. The cul-de-sac may be obliterated. The uterus may be immobilized. Cysts in the ovary (endometriomas) may measure up to 16 cm in diameter and contain thick dark residue of old blood giving rise to the term "chocolate cysts." Endometriosis may be asymptomatic, or it may present with significant pelvic pain. The pain is in the pelvis and lower abdomen and is described as dull, aching or cramping. Also, lower abdominal or back pain may occur with menstruation and increase in severity until the menstrual flow has ceased. The endometrium responds to cyclic hormonal change and will bleed during menses. The blood flows into the surrounding tissue space and causes reactions from irritation. Pain with defecation is often described by the patient. Abnormal uterine bleeding may also occur, with pain described as excessive, prolonged, and frequent. Acquired (secondary) dysmenorrhea is another common symptom, beginning a few days before, and continuing throughout, the period. The pain is often constant and severe, in contrast to the cramp-like pain of primary dysmenorrheal (painful periods). There may be no correlation between the amount of pain and the extent of disease.

Endometriosis must be distinguished from salpingitis and cancer of the rectum, colon, and ovary. X-rays may facilitate differentiation from inflammatory or malignant disease. Laparoscopy is generally preferred over hysterosalpingography as a diagnostic technique. A biopsy may be required to confirm the diagnosis. The differential diagnosis of endometriosis from other conditions includes: (1) pelvic infection; (2) ovarian carcinoma; and (3) urinary tract lesions.

Endometriosis may be confused with pelvic inflammatory disease. The two conditions exhibit similar symptoms, with the tubes and ovaries adhering to the posterior surface of the broad ligament and the rectosigmoid. In contrast to the implants of endometriosis, the lesions caused by infection are relatively smooth. Ovarian carcinoma may be distinguished by a lack of pain and tenderness until far advanced, but laparoscopy or laparotomy may be necessary to rule it out. Women with cyclic or intermittent hematuria may be suffering from urinary tract endometriosis. Pyelography may be used to demonstrate ureteral involvement. Kidney function may cease as a result of hydronephrosis caused by ureteral compression.

[b] Treatment

Treatment of endometriosis depends upon the stage of the disease, the age of the patient, and her desire for pregnancy, since infertility is often the reason why the patient consults the physician. Treatment may require surgical intervention to restore the reproductive capacity. Endocrine therapy is also used to treat endometriosis by suppressing the endometrium. Hormonal therapy is indicated for women who are not contemplating pregnancy in the near future and whose endometriosis is minimal or recurs after conservative surgery. Patients typically voice complaints of pelvic pain and/or infertility. Therapeutic interventions should be designed to adequately address both issues.

Prophylactic therapy may decrease the chance of developing endometriosis by producing amenorrhea or endometrial atrophy. While early or frequent pregnancies appear to decrease the frequency of endometriosis, this therapeutic strategy is incompatible with the life plans of most patients. Women taking oral contraceptives for prolonged periods, especially those with a potent progestin and a minimal amount of estrogen, may have a diminished chance of developing endometriosis. This is based on the observation that these agents produce endometrial atrophy and lessen menstrual flow, thus preventing retrograde menstruation of endometrium into the peritoneal cavity.

Many patients either "outgrow" their endometriosis or become pregnant and remain asymptomatic. Thus, merely watching and waiting may be worthwhile for the patient with minimal symptoms and minimal pelvic findings. Antiprostaglandins may be the analgesics of first choice to treat the pain of endometriosis, since excessive prostaglandin production may account for much of the pain. Reassurance is often effective along with analgesics in the mild cases.

Hormonal therapy may be used as a temporary treatment. Pseudopregnancy regimens of chronic, noncyclic stimulation with estrogens and progesterone render the endometrium inactive. This routine should only be used in a patient with endometriosis proven by laparoscopy. The side effects are dose-related, and are those commonly associated with oral contraceptives. Use of pseudopregnancy treatment prior to conservative laparotomy will often cause areas of endometriosis to enlarge and appear hemorrhagic, making identification, excision, and fulguration simpler and more complete.

Danazol, a synthetic androgenic steroid, has significantly advanced the medical management of endometriosis. Its therapeutic effect may be: the suppression of the pituitary hormones that stimulate endometrium production; inhibition of ovarian hormone production; an increase in the metabolism of ovarian hormones, thus producing an endocrine environment that inhibits the growth of endometrial tissue and/or produces atrophy of this tissue. By producing amenorrhea, Danazol prevents the introduction of endometrial tissue into the peritoneal cavity during menses. Danazol therapy results in a significant degree of symptomatic and objective improvement in patients with endometriosis. Guidelines concerning the use of Danazol continue to evolve.

GnRH agonists are used continuously to suppress hormonal secretions from the pituitary gland which would stimulate the production of hormones from the ovaries. The goal is to suppress the endometrial implants. Use of GnRH agents is limited to 6 months because of side effects, including the bone loss due to a hypoestrogenic state.

Surgical treatment is indicated where the following conditions exist:

- significant enlargement of one or both ovaries;
- tubes and ovaries that are bound down in women who cannot conceive;
- extensive involvement of the pelvic structures, with resultant severe pain and infertility; or
- suspected bowel obstruction accompanied by severe pain.

Laparoscopy may be useful in treating endometriosis in the management of infertility as well as in obtaining symptomatic relief from pain. Hysterectomy is often indicated when conservative surgery or hormonal therapy do not control symptoms. Endometriosis may be discovered during surgery for the treatment of pelvic or abdominal problems such as bowel obstruction. At this point, the operating physician must exercise his or her judgment in determining whether to treat the endometriosis surgically. In contemplating surgical treatment of endometriosis, one should always bear in mind that functioning ovarian tissue is necessary for the continued activity of the disease. Therefore, the successful treatment depends on a knowledge of when to destroy it. The majority of cases will fall between the extremes of very early and perhaps symptomless lesions when ovarian function should be conserved, and severe pelvic organ damage when ovarian function should be destroyed. one should err on the side of conservatism in the treatment of early and borderline cases, because endometriosis usually progresses slowly over a period of years; is not, and rarely becomes malignant; and regresses at the menopause.

The treatment of choice for extensive endometriosis in women who no longer desire pregnancy is total abdominal hysterectomy (TAH) with bilateral salpingoophorectomy (BSO). When there is extensive bladder, bowel, or ureteral involvement, TAH with BSO will effect a cure. Failure to castrate in the presence of marked endometriosis of the bowel is undoubtedly the most hazardous of all attempts at conservative surgery, because of the danger of subsequent intestinal obstruction. There is no contraindication to the continuous administration of estrogen in low doses following TAH with BSO to control the symptoms following surgical castration. Administration of estrogens may be gradually diminished, both in quantity and frequency, over a period of years. Vaginal cytology may be used to gauge the adequacy of endogenous estrogen, presumably of adrenal origin, to assist in the reduction of exogenous estrogen therapy as indicated. The use of estrogen-progestin combination in cyclic or sequential fashion has been shown to reactivate endometriosis. These preparations should never be used in a patient who has had a TAH with BSO for endometriosis. They should not be given to postmenopausal women for relief of menstrual symptoms if the past history suggests that endometriosis might be present.

Castration for endometriosis through radiation has by and large been abandoned. Besides the possibility of subsequent cancer of the cervix, uterus, or ovary, serious large and small bowel damage may occur as late sequelae. While some gynecologists may employ X-ray castration to relieve intolerable pelvic pain in the immediately premenopausal woman who has already undergone one or more operations for endometriosis, ovarian function may markedly diminish simply by giving 200 mg of Depo-Provera every two weeks for four to eight weeks, then 400 mg every month for one year. Subsequent ovulation will not occur for at least one year after the conclusion of treatment.

[3] Cancer

The frequency of cancer screening examinations depends on the risk status of the patient. Included in screening are examination of the thyroid, breasts, abdomen, pelvic, and rectum. Cervical cytology should be instituted at age eighteen, or at the onset of sexual activity. Uterine cytology and screening for colorectal cancer should be performed for women over the age of forty. A baseline mammogram is recommended for women between the ages of thirty-five and fifty. Abnormal findings during such screening tests require further evaluation.

[a] Breast Cancer

Breast cancer is a devastating disease affecting approximately 180,000 women per year in the United States, with about a 33% mortality rate. The median age of women with breast cancer is 60-61. The probability for developing breast cancer increases throughout the woman's life. It is estimated that one in nine American women will develop breast cancer during her life time. In the United States, breast cancer is more common in whites than non-whites. Failure to inform a gynecologist of a lump in the breast or a change in the breast skin or tissue often leads to a delay in diagnosis and treatment. Breast cancer most often presents as a lump. Other conditions that present as a dominant lump include fibrocystic disease, fibroadenomas, and other uncommon breast lesions such as lipomas or neurofibromas. Careful evaluation of breast lumps, with appropriate and rapid use of ancillary procedures, is necessary for maximum diagnostic success. Carcinoma will present as a painless, firm, and deep-seated mass. Local infiltration may cause fixation of the tumor to the chest wall. Cytologic findings of needle aspiration are suspicious or positive for malignancy in 95% of cases. Needle, incisional, or excisional biopsy is necessary to confirm the diagnosis. Mirror-image biopsy of the opposite breast, or upper outer quadrant site, is recommended at the time of definitive surgery. Screening for evidence of metastatic disease by radioactive bone scanning and by measurements of liver and bone enzymes should precede any therapy. The status of tumor markers from blood sampling may be valuable in general prognosis and in assessing further therapy.

Proper treatment for breast cancer is constantly undergoing reevaluation for several reasons. First is the multifocal nature of the process. Multiple foci of cancer origin may be found in up to 50% of cases. Random biopsy of the opposite breast may show bilateral disease in as many as 20% of cases. A second problem in the treatment of breast cancer is that, by the time of diagnosis, up to 70% of patients have disseminated disease. Treatment by total mastectomy with axillary lymph node sampling, or removal of the tumor followed by radiation therapy and axillary node sampling seem interchangeably adequate for local control. Metastatic disease treatment is diverse and depends on the estrogen and progesterone receptor assays of the tumors as well as the overall clinical picture. The only real hope for improved survival from breast cancer rests in effective preventive measures and improvements in early detection.

The first step in the diagnosis of breast cancer is the physical examination of the patient. Over 90% of all breast cancers are found by the patients themselves. The physician should take a thorough history, perform a physical examination and, when indicated, have a mammogram and/or biopsy performed. The history should include: a description of any mass; presence or absence of pain in, or discharge from, the nipple; any change in the contour of the breast or nipple; and general information about the patient and her genetic history. Most malignancies do not change shape with the menstrual cycle. Thus, it is extremely important to elicit information as to the length of time a mass has been present, its location, and any change in it during the menstrual cycle. Postdiagnostic studies, previous surgeries, family history, and prior births should also be recorded. Biopsy is indicated when the mass is persistent, dominant, and palpable. The only reliable means of diagnosing breast cancer before a mass can be felt is by mammography with or without sonography..Some cancers of the breast can be found by mammogram as much as 2 years before being palpable.

Mammography is used to:

- screen asymptomatic women;
- screen high-risk patients (over age forty, family history of breast cancer, or previous history of breast cancer);
- complete the physical examination in symptomatic women;
- screen for occult disease prior to biopsy;
- help reassure cancerphobics; and
- search for a primary lesion in patients having metastases.

Mammograms do not replace the need for a physical examination. A normal mammogram does not guarantee that no cancer is present.

Approximately 10% of breast cancers are detected by physical examination alone and are not visualized by mammogram.[6] The biopsy provides the definitive diagnosis, and may be by needle aspiration, needle biopsy, or open biopsy under local or general anesthesia.

Some of the risk factors for breast cancer include:

- obese Caucasian women over 40 who have a history of breast cancer in a mother or sister;
- previous history of cancer of the uterus, ovary, or colon;
- nulliparity or first full-term pregnancy after age thirty; or
- early menarche (under age twelve), or late menopause (over age fifty).

The patient with so-called fibrocystic disease is at two to three times greater risk for breast cancer than other women. A positive family history for breast cancer is a more important risk factor, however. Breast cancer associated with pregnancy is difficult to diagnose because of hormone-influenced tissue engorgement and the tendency to limit attention to the pregnancy. Better breast examination by both patient and physician, responsible screening techniques, early diagnosis, and prompt therapy are the bases for managing breast cancer during pregnancy. It seems that some breast cancers can be detected by mammography as much as two years before attaining a size that can be detected on physical examination. An experienced radiologist can more than likely interpret a mammogram correctly in roughly 90% of cases; yet there are occasional false-positive as well as false-negative results obtained with mammography.

Failure to diagnose breast cancer or an incorrect diagnosis of breast cancer may lead to allegations of negligence against the gynecologist. The patient typically alleges failure to timely diagnose cancer and seeks to prove that the gynecologist did not actively pursue the proper diagnostic procedures for an abnormality of the breast and that this failure subjected her to either more extensive surgery or to metastatic cancer. A physician who notes a new breast mass would be prudent to refer the patient for

---

[6] Ultrasonography is also used in examining breasts for cancer. Mammography shows cysts well, but ultrasonography shows them better. In a dense breast, a cyst could be obscured on mammography, yet stand out on ultrasonography. In a fatty breast, mammography shows rounded densities better, but one does not know whether a cyst is solid until ultrasonography is performed. A solid mass is easily seen with mammography, but it can be lost on ultrasonography. Although in the very dense breast, ultrasonography may distinguish a solid mass from a cystic mass and a glandular mass. Mammography is sensitive to the visualization of microcalcifications, which are seen earlier and can indicate cancer. Microcalcifications are not seen on ultrasonography.

mammography. A biopsy or referral to a general surgeon should be seriously considered even in the presence of a negative mammogram.

There are general standards for routine breast screening. Every patient should be taught breast self-examination and the medical record should record that teaching. A baseline mammogram should be obtained by any woman with a first-degree relative (mother, sister, or daughter) who had breast cancer, 5 years prior to the age that relative was diagnosed with the cancer. While the American Cancer Society has recommended that mammograms be done every one to two years in women between ages forty to fifty, and yearly after fifty, many gynecologists think these guidelines are somewhat overzealous. Failure to adhere to these widely publicized recommendations, however, may be difficult to defend.

Courts have held that gynecologists are not liable for failure of the radiologist to read a mammogram correctly. The physician, however, may be responsible for failing to refer the patient for an indicated biopsy. In general, the courts have upheld a finding of negligence when the physician has unreasonably failed to detect a breast abnormality upon examination, and when there has been a failure of the physician to go beyond a simple clinical evaluation of a suspicious abnormality of the breast. The courts have also recognized that not every incorrect diagnosis is the result of negligence. Clinical examination, in itself, is inconclusive in diagnosing a breast abnormality. The courts have recognized that a physician must take active steps to arrive at a conclusive and accurate diagnosis when faced with a patient with a breast abnormality. The physician can neither assume the condition is benign nor prescribe a wait-and-see attitude. The physician may be found negligent in failing to take action to determine the cause of a patient's complaint (i.e., a change in size or firmness of a breast), in failing to detect a breast mass, and in failing to adequately follow the patient after instituting a period of observation.

When the physician discovers a breast lump, he/she must see that further tests, such as biopsy, are performed to determine an exact diagnosis. A common procedure for breast lesion histopathologic diagnosis is for a frozen section to be made of a needle or excisional biopsy, then examined by a pathologist, often while the patient remains under anesthesia in the operating room. Frozen section is generally recognized as an accurate diagnostic method with a risk of error of less than one percent. In a number of cases, the courts have recognized the sufficiency of frozen section analysis as a diagnostic measure by finding no liability against the physician when a mistake was made. This is in sharp contrast to those cases in which negligence was found because of a misdiagnosis based only on the physician's clinical examination. Because the risk of misdiagnosis is so remote when frozen section analysis is used, the courts have not held disclosure of the risk to be part of the surgeon's duty of informed consent.

[b] Uterine Cancer

Carcinoma of the uterus is the most common malignancy seen today in the female pelvis. Occurrence is greater than two times more than ovarian cancer, and about two and one-half times more common than cancer of the cervix. Prognosis in this malignancy is generally good, since 75% of all cases are at stage I at the time of diagnosis. Multiple diagnostic factors must be taken into consideration in the treatment of patients with this cancer even within stage I:

- histopathologic differentiation is one of the most sensitive indicators of prognosis; survival rates decrease with lack of differentiation;
- uterine size is usually associated with the grade of tumor and degree of myometrial invasion; there is a progressive increase in lymph node metastasis with an increase in size of the uterus, although some investigators have found that size does not always reflect tumor volume;
- stage of disease has long been recognized as a prognostic factor and relates to the volume of the tumor; when disease is present in the endocervical canal or on the portio, stage II disease is present;
- myometrial invasion is an indicator of tumor virulence, and is associated with other poor prognostic factors, such as poor differentiation and lymph node involvement;
- peritoneal cytology, when positive, renders the individual at high risk for developing intraperitoneal recurrences;
- lymph node metastases is appreciable even in stage I cases and is directly correlated with other poor prognostic factors, such as grade of tumor and depth of myometrial invasion; and
- occult metastases to the adnexae occur in about 10% of patients with stage I disease, detectable only on microscopic examination.

The earliest stage of endometrial carcinoma that is not invasive has been termed carcinoma-in-situ in many clinics throughout the country. In other clinics, the same histologic picture has been designated as atypical hyperplasia, carcinoma stage 0. There is no single characteristic symptom associated with carcinoma-in-situ of the endometrium other than irregular bleeding in the premenopausal woman, or postmenopausal staining in the older patient. The highest incidence of carcinoma-in-situ was noted in the three to four years before invasive cancer of the uterus. An effort should be made to secure ovulation and cyclic secretory shedding of the endometrium.

If ovulation cannot be regularly established, substitutional therapy with cyclic or constant progestins may be administered. The situation is not acute, and hysterectomy is neither necessary nor indicated. Therefore, a thorough curettage must be performed in all patients to exclude the presence of endometrial carcinoma.

The presence of other pathology of the internal genitalia, or the inability to follow the patient adequately, may be valid reasons for hysterectomy. Although the patient most likely to benefit from a conservative approach is the young woman with irregular or absent ovulation, the endometrial hyperplastic process may occur in women approaching the menopause as a result of constant estrogen stimulation. The physician should keep this in mind when planning therapy.

Adenocarcinoma of the body of the uterus is a common disease. In the past two decades, there has been a marked increase in the incidence of cancer of the corpus and a marked decrease in the incidence of cervical cancer. The cause for the increased incidence of corpus cancer is unknown, but may be due to improved diagnostic methods, more precise histologic criteria, or simply an aging population. Increased use of estrogenic hormones has been suggested as a possible etiologic factor. Cancer of the corpus is the predominant genital malignancy in white women over age fifty and second to cancer of the breast in blacks.

The most common symptom of endometrial cancer is intermenstrual or postmenopausal bleeding. At the outset, symptoms may be those of excessive flow at the time of the normally expected period, and some bloody discharge between periods. After the menopause, irregular bleeding or just spotting may be the primary symptom. As the tumor enlarges, there may be a constant bloody discharge.

High risk factors for endometrial cancer include:

- postmenopausal bleeding, endometrial hyperplasia, and/or polyp;
- heavy or irregular bleeding after age forty;
- obesity;
- prior breast or ovarian cancer; and
- prolonged unopposed estrogen exposure - endogenous or exogenous.

Management of patients at high risk involves two basic principles — frequent office visits and adequate endometrial sampling by uterine curettage or office endometrial biopsy. Unopposed estrogen therapy should be avoided in patients with a uterus. Cyclic estrogen-progestin therapy is acceptable for patients with severe vasomotor symptoms. Fractional curettage of the uterus and microscopic examination of the curettings is the only acceptable method of diagnostic survey in endometrial cancer. If the disease has been diagnosed by endometrial biopsy, a thorough curettage is mandatory for proper management, including the polyp forceps, since the sharp curette may miss a polyp harboring carcinoma. The size of the uterus is not an absolute criterion as to the presence or absence of carcinoma. While the uterus is generally larger when tumor is present, a well-developed cancer may be found in a small or even atrophic uterus.

Among the most common errors in diagnosis of endometrial cancer are failure to investigate irregular bleeding in a premenopausal woman; correction of only the obvious causes of postmenopausal bleeding; reliance on cytology alone to detect endometrial cancer; complete reliance on endometrial biopsy to detect cancer; and inadequate curettage. The differential diagnosis includes dysfunctional (endocrine) uterine bleeding, submucous fibroids of the uterus, cancer of the cervix, polyps of the cervix and endometrium, and ovarian tumors.

In a recent study, HER-2, (human epidermal growth factor receptor-2), was associated with high-grade and high stage endometrial cancers but not with the more frequent low-stage and low grade cancers. The study suggested that cancer of the endometrium may have a distinct genetic or genomic mechanism that is responsible for progression to a more aggressive and extensive state. The ability to delineate these genetic mechanisms, may lead to more effective diagnosis and treatment for endometrial cancer.

Cancer of the endometrium is very rare before age forty, although significant numbers do occur before age fifty, and the disease has been reported in women as young as 20. It is imperative that curettage be done in all patients between thirty-five and fifty who are suspected of having ovarian dysfunction as the cause of abnormal bleeding. Hormonal therapy given prior to precise diagnosis may seriously delay early detection of cancer. Liability may be imposed on the gynecologist for negligent diagnosis of uterine cancer, including failure to make a timely diagnosis and misdiagnosis; endometrial biopsies should be obtained at regular intervals to rule out endometrial hyperplasia; pelvic ultrasonograms should be obtained at regular intervals to evaluate the thickness of the endometrial stripe; failure to obtain informed consent of the patient; and negligent treatment of the condition.

[c] Cervical Cancer

Cervical neoplasia is a major health problem. While the mortality rate from cervical cancer has declined dramatically over the past few decades, it still ranks sixth in cancer mortality, with an estimated 4,400 deaths in the United States each year. There are approximately 13,000 cases of invasive cervical cancer discovered each year in the United States. The peak age incidence of invasive cancer is between forty-five and fifty-five. There is an association between cervical cancer and certain social factors, including socioeconomic class (higher incidence in nonwhites); marital status (higher incidence in married and widowed women, and lower in never-married women); child bearing (multiparity, first pregnancy before age twenty); sexual exposure (first coitus before age twenty-six, prostitution, sexually transmitted disease); smoking; and circumcision status of the male partner. The common denominator seems to be related to coitus, with a greater risk on onset of regular sexual activity at an early age and with multiple sexual partners. Among ethnic groups practicing circumcision, there is thought to be a lower general incidence of genital cancer.

Carcinoma in situ (CIS) is an intraepithelial lesion with cytologic atypia similar to that found in invasive cancer, but without evidence of invasion into the stroma. Lesions composed of similar atypical cells but retaining some degree of surface maturation have been referred to as dysplasias. Dysplasias range in severity from mild with few mitoses to severe, resembling CIS but with some degree of epithelial polarity. Differentiation of severe dysplasia from CIS may be very difficult clinically, and is a diagnosis to be made by the pathologist. It would seem that the major significance of CIS lies in its being a precursor to invasive cancer. It is open to question, however, whether cervical dysplasias should be considered premalignant, since many dysplastic lesions regress spontaneously in the mild to moderate forms. The more severe the dysplasia, the higher the rate and speed of progression toward CIS and, correspondingly, the lower the rate of regression. The average age of patients without dysplasias is five to ten years lower than that of patients with CIS. Patients with CIS run ten to fifteen years behind the average age of patients with invasive cancer of the cervix. Cervical intraepithelial neoplasia (CIN) is thought to represent a continuum of disease and is classified as CIN I (mild dysplasia), CIN II (moderate dysplasia), and CIN III (severe dysplasia and CIS). There is an associated steady increase in the mitotic activity of these lesions. The transformation zone of the cervix has been established as the site of origin of virtually all CIN. Clinicians have depended on the Pap smear as a screening method for detection of cervical neoplasia. Serial sampling over time provides a longitudinal look at the cervix and decreases the impact of isolated false-negative smears.

Biopsy and histologic diagnosis remain the cornerstones in the management of cervical neoplasia. Every abnormal visible cervical lesion should be biopsied even though Pap smears are negative or exhibit only inflammatory changes. It is widely known that CIN occurs most frequently at the 6 o'clock and 12 o'clock positions in the transformation zone and less frequently toward the lateral angles on each side. To avoid a random biopsy that misses invasive lesions, the Schiller Test may be used to highlight cervical abnormalities, making them clearly visible for biopsy. Nonstaining of Schiller-positive areas stand out from the dark background painted with iodine and represent surfaces lacking glycogen, including neoplastic lesions. In conjunction with endocervical curettage (ECC), which is mandatory for evaluating a cytologically abnormal cervix, multiple Schiller-directed biopsies have been shown to be positive in 95% of patients with CIS, and in virtually all patients with early invasive cancer. Colposcopy has superseded Schiller's technique in most centers as the initial step in evaluating abnormal Pap smears, although the Schiller test may be highly efficacious when properly used.

Adequate colposcopic evaluation requires complete visualization of the transformation zone and the lesion in question, as well as correlation between the cytologic and histologic diagnoses and the clinical impression of the colposcopist. An ECC should be performed as part of every colposcopic examination. Cervical biopsy is perhaps the most frequent minor surgical procedure performed by the gynecologist. It is simple, relatively painless, and may be performed as part of the routine office examination. Contraindications to cervical biopsy are acute pelvic inflammatory disease and acute cervicitis. Patients with coagulation disorders should be managed in a hospital setting. Pregnancy is not a contraindication to biopsy. Cervical conization, properly performed, removes the entire transformation zone, virtually the entire endocervical canal, and provides the pathologist with the maximum amount of tissue to absolutely rule out invasive cancer. Drawbacks of conization include the need for anesthesia and hospital stay, a 10% incidence of complications (primarily postoperative hemorrhage), and a possible adverse effect on future fertility.

LEEP (loop electrosurgical excision) is one of the standard treatment procedures for cervical abnormality as detectd by pap smear or visualization (i.e., colposcopy). Its use is determined by physician preference and experience as well as the pathology involved. Its advantage over cervical conization is being an office procedure under local anesthesia. Complications are less frequent than with conization

Before outpatient therapy can be considered in evaluating a patient for CIN, a lesion must be limited to the portio vaginalis without extension into the endocervical canal; the entire transformation zone must be visualized; the ECC must be negative for neoplasia; biopsy and cytologic examination must reveal only intraepithelial disease; and cytologic and histologic diagnoses must correlate. If these conditions are not met, conization is required to rule out invasion. Conization for any degree of CIN, whether performed as part of the diagnostic evaluation or as primary therapy subsequent to outpatient evaluation, has a 98% cure rate when surgical margins are negative, and thus requires no further therapy. Close follow-up is suggested, however, with Pap smears, colposcopy, and ECC as necessary. Cure rates of 70-80% are reported after conization with positive margins. Conservative management with serial ECC, colposcopy, and cytology is acceptable if patient compliance can be expected. Otherwise, reconization or hysterectomy is indicated. Simple hysterectomy should be relied upon as primary treatment when pregnancy is no longer desired, or when there is coexisting pelvic disease. Cryotherapy and laser therapy are other simple and safe methods used to treat CIN. Failure rates may be correlated with the stage of CIN and/or with the size of the lesion. Cryocautery is useful as an office procedure; however, more experience and documentation with laser therapy is necessary before it can be considered as a replacement for cryocautery.

The most common symptom of cervical cancer is either a discharge or an abdominal vaginal bleeding in the form of excessively heavy or prolonged menses. Postcoital bleeding is a less frequent symptom. The discharge may be abnormal or foul smelling. The malignancy may develop entirely within the cervical canal, with the portio vaginalis appearing normal. Palpation may demonstrate a hard, indurated, barrel-shaped cervix. The malignancy may also appear as a small, shallow ulceration on the cervix. Conization or colposcopically directed biopsy may be used to detect the malignancy, leading to more accurate diagnosis and a decreased incidence of inappropriate therapy. The clinical staging of cervical cancer is determined primarily by inspection and palpation of the cervix, vagina, and pelvis, and by examination of the abdomen and supraclavicular lymph nodes.

Bimanual rectovaginal examination is the best method to diagnose extension of tumor into the parametrial tissues or from the cervix to the pelvic sidewall. The extent of the disease should be further evaluated by chest X-rays, intravenous urograph, and cystoscopy or proctoscopy, as indicated, to rule out metastatic disease. Other methods that may be helpful in determining the extent of disease, and thus the proper patient management, include barium enemas, liver and bone scans, computed tomography (CT scan), ultrasonography, and pretherapy surgical staging by para-aortic lymph-node biopsy. Management may range from conservative surgery for lesions with minimal invasion, to radical hysterectomy and pelvic lymphadenectomy or irradiation therapy, or systemic chemotherapy for metastatic disease.

Recent cases dealing with alleged negligence in the diagnosis of cervical cancer have frequently focused on the use of the Pap smear. The physician and the patient both have specific responsibilities in the use of the Pap smear as a diagnostic aid. The courts have emphasized the duty of the physician to disclose and discuss alternatives in the management of cervical cancer. The courts have also recognized that the Pap smear is a simple and effective way of diagnosing premalignant and malignant conditions of the cervix. Therefore, the physician undertaking the gynecologic care of a patient should inform that patient of the nature of the test, including the risks of not having it performed. All relevant information must be disclosed to the patient to enable her to make a decision regarding the submission to, or refusal of, a diagnostic test. When the Pap smear results indicate an abnormal condition of the cervix, the physician must take reasonable steps to inform the patient of the result. The patient is, therefore, responsible for providing the physician with enough information to enable communication to take place. The courts have recognized that the choices available in the treatment of cancer of the cervix impose on the physician a duty to disclose and discuss alternatives. Failure to do so may constitute lack of informed consent giving rise to liability. The issue of informed consent can also arise when a first physician refers the patient to a second physician for additional treatment. The courts have recognized that the second physician must obtain the patient's informed consent to the additional treatment. Since HPV infection is considered a cause of cervical cancer, studies are ongoing comparing the relative efficacy of Pap cytology versus HPV DNA testing in screening for cervical dysplasia and cancer. The best screening method will be guided in the future by availability of the HPV vaccine.

The standard of care is that which is reasonable under the circumstances, and nationally certified gynecologists are required to exercise the same degree of skill, care, and learning ordinarily possessed and used by a nationally certified specialist in gynecology acting in the same or similar circumstances. A reasonably competent gynecologist presented with a patient's symptoms indicating that a Pap test should be performed may be held liable for deviation from the standard of care for failing to perform that test, and for failing to disclose to the patient the risks of not doing so. The scope of the physician's duty to disclose is usually measured by the amount of knowledge a patient needs in order to make an informed choice. To establish negligence of the physician in failing to obtain informed consent, the patient must prove that the doctor failed to inform her of alternative treatments, the reasonably foreseeable material risks of each alternative, and the consequences of no treatment at all; that she would have chosen no treatment or a different course of treatment had the alternatives and the material risks of each been made known; and that she has been injured as a result of submitting to the recommended treatment. Material information must be disclosed to the patient, and is information that the physician knows or should know would be regarded as significant by reasonable persons in the patient's position when deciding to accept or reject a recommended medical procedure. The patient must be told of the risks inherent in the procedure, the risks of not undergoing treatment, and the probability of success. The final decision to either undergo or forego a proposed medical procedure, however, is for the patient to make.

[d] Ovarian Cancer

Ovarian cancer is the fifth leading cause of cancer deaths among American women. .Approximately 23,000 new cases are diagnosed each year, from which 14,000 deaths occur annually. One out of seventy women will develop ovarian cancer during her lifetime. Patients of low parity, decreased fertility, and delayed childbearing are at greater risk if they have not been using oral contraceptives (OC). Most, but not all, ovarian cancers occur in women over fifty. The use of OCs has been found to decrease the risk of epithelial ovarian cancer in patients ages forty to fifty-nine. The reduction in risk associated with OCs has been observed in older, parous patients and appears to persist for as long as ten years after discontinuing use of OCs. Women with previously treated cancers of the breast or endometrium are more likely to develop a second primary cancer in the ovary than at other sites. An increased prevalence of ovarian cancer noted in nuns, other single women, and nulliparous married women suggests that incessant ovulation uninterrupted by pregnancy may be a predisposing factor. Investigations into diet as a possible causation factor in ovarian cancer have not established a definite relationship between diet and cancer of the ovary. However, increased consumption of fat, as well as use of talcum powder on the external genitalia, have been proposed as possible risk factors. Talc granulomas found in the ovaries of women without prior pelvic surgery suggest entrance through the cervix into the uterine cavity and the fallopian tubes into the peritoneal cavity as instigating mechanisms.

Since no fully effective method of mass ovarian cancer screening has been developed, most patients present clinically with advanced stage disease. Only 30% of these cases are confined to the ovaries at the time of diagnosis. Careful pelvic examination remains the most effective screening method. Cervical cytology examination only occasionally shows malignant cells when ovarian cancer is present, and is not indicative of early-stage disease. While ultrasound is useful in the evaluation of a suspected ovarian mass, its value as a screening tool in patients without a distinct pelvic mass is still controversial. Ultrasound has an approximate 90% accuracy rate in detecting and localizing pelvic masses, but it cannot distinguish between benign and malignant disease with an acceptable accuracy. Vaginal ultrasound holds more promise for the future, with its more distinct image, than transabdominal ultrasound or CT scans. Tumor markers such as CA 125 are being evaluated clinically for use in detection of early-stage disease, although they are not sensitive or specific enough to be helpful in mass screening for ovarian cancer. About 10% of ovarian cancers occur in women with a genetic predisposition. Women with 2 first-degree relatives with cancer of the ovary have a 50% chance of developing ovarian cancer until the age of 70. There are two forms of hereditary ovarian cancer. First is BOC (breast and ovarian cancer syndrome); Lynch II syndrome is less common (HNPCC syndrome-hereditary nonpolyposis colorectal cancer syndrome). BOC is associated with the mutations in the BRCA1 gene. BRCA1 mutation carriers in the United States are found in about 1 in 800 women. Mutations have been found more frequently in Ashkenazi Jews and Icelandic women. The mutations are inherited as an autosomal dominant. Women from high-risk families, who have the BRCA1 mutation are at a 28-44% risk for ovarian cancer, and require a careful analysis of their family background. A normal CA 125 does not exclude the diagnosis of ovarian cancer, and is not a reason to delay surgical treatment.

To prevent ovarian cancer, many surgeons have advocated the prophylactic removal of normal ovaries at the time of hysterectomy. A significant number of patients with ovarian cancer have previously undergone ablative pelvic operations with conservation of one or both ovaries. Proponents of ovarian salvage, however, argue that the risk of developing cancer in a residual ovary is negligible, and is outweighed by the evils of early castration. The risk of ovarian cancer in women with residual ovaries does not differ from that of the general population, nor is the risk reduced by removing only one ovary. Failure of early diagnosis contributes to the meager overall survival rate for all cases of ovarian cancer. This failure reflects the asymptomatic character of early ovarian cancer and the lack of a means whereby asymptomatic women can be screened for this disease. The development of radioimmunoassay for ovarian tumor-associated antigens may facilitate the early diagnosis of ovarian malignancy as well as monitoring the response to treatment.

There is no evidence that the patient's age, itself, influences the biologic activity of ovarian carcinomas. A better prognosis noted among women under age forty, in whom the disease is less frequent, apparently results from a greater proportion of borderline tumors and those of low histologic grade. Although the incidence of ovarian cancer increases dramatically after age forty, neither the incidence nor the virulence of the disease is affected by the menopause. A relatively poor prognosis after age sixty most likely results from later diagnosis and the prevalence of intercurrent disease. The clinical stage, or anatomic extent of tumor growth, is considered the best indicator of prognosis. Staging and prognosis are closely related to survival time. Variation in survival rates within the major stages is partially determined by the histologic grade or degree of cellular differentiation and biologic differences in tumor growth. The majority of ovarian enlargements are physiologic cysts that will disappear without treatment. Some enlargements are true neoplasms and require surgical removal, whether benign or malignant.

Physiologic cysts are usually less than 5 cm in diameter. Neoplasms are usually greater than 5 cm in diameter. An abnormal ovarian mass will normally be detected by pelvic examination. The specific type of growth, however, cannot be determined without histologic examination. It is then the duty of the physician to communicate accurate information to the patient regarding the condition in order for the patient to make an informed decision concerning the need for additional therapy.

Ovarian cancer is treated with surgery by unilateral or bilateral oophorectomy and hysterectomy. The choice depends on several factors, including the type of tumor and whether the patient desires to maintain fertility. Radiotherapy and chemotherapy are also used in the management of ovarian tumors. Ovarian tumors generally present very few symptoms in their early stages, therefore, removal may be justified based on the need to know if it is benign or malignant by laboratory study. The signs and symptoms of ovarian cancer include an increase in abdominal girth, weight gain or loss, abdominal discomfort, and GI abnormalities. The malignancy may, however, grow quietly and painlessly, and produce few, if any, symptoms. This lack of symptoms in the early stages of the disease has led to the designation of ovarian cancer as the "silent killer."

Since early diagnosis of ovarian cancer is difficult and, at times, virtually impossible, pelvic examination at regular intervals is the most reliable means of discovering the presence of the cancer. The final diagnosis depends on surgical exploration, in conjunction with laboratory tests, X-rays, ultrasound, and CT scans. Surgery is not only the first step in the treatment of ovarian cancer, but is critical to the diagnosis of the disease, as well as to the determination of type and stage of the tumor. Surgery performed early enough in the disease progression may halt the spread as well as cure the patient. While some ovarian malignancies are more radiosensitive than others, the effectiveness of radiation therapy as a primary adjunctive treatment is questionable. Chemotherapy, however, is an established method of treating ovarian malignancies.

There is no effective test for screening for ovarian cancer currently. The use of serum CA 125 marker with transvaginal ultrasound of the ovaries shows promise for early detection with survival benefit. Early detection increases survival due generally to the detection of ovarian cancers at stage I or II *which have improved survivals.* The gynecologist may face liability for negligent misdiagnosis or treatment of ovarian cancer. The legal principles involved are the same as those in any other area of obstetric and gynecologic malpractice. Few malpractice actions have been reported involving ovarian cancer, perhaps because of the degree of difficulty in making the diagnosis.

§ 14.05 Related Topics

[1] Medical Records

As a form of documented data, modern medical records generally serve at least three important purposes:

1. memorialize data obtained with regard to patient's symptoms, condition, and history;
2. memorialize examination and test results with regard to diagnosis, proposed treatment, and patient's subsequent progress; and
3. provide information for use by other health care providers during the period of treatment or at some later date.

The medical records thus generated are also often used for purposes not directly related to the patient's treatment, e.g., internal peer review and medical research.

The *Accreditation Manual for Hospitals,* published by the Joint Commission on Accreditation of Healthcare Organizations, a private agency that establishes standards for hospitals and reviews their implementation, has outlined purposes of medical records as follows:

- to serve as a basis for the care and continuity in evaluation of treatment;
- to furnish documentary evidence of the course of the patient's medical care;
- to document communication between the practitioner responsible for the patient and any other health professional who contributes to the patient's care;
- to assist in protecting the legal interests of the patient, the hospital, and the practitioner responsible for the patient; and
- to provide data for use in continuing education and research.

Because of the nature of contemporary medical services and related record-keeping practices, a physician's records often contain a vivid sketch of some of the most intimate aspects of a patient's life. A complete medical record may contain more intimate details about an individual than can be found in any single document. Such a record can be potentially damaging to a patient, e.g., through the release of information that the patient tested positive for the AIDS antibody.

[a] Offices and Outpatient Clinics

An accurate medical record should be maintained for each patient. The record should be legible, concise, cogent, and complete, so that it should be easy to assess the care provided to determine whether the patient's health care needs have been managed effectively. Because medical practice frequently involves several physicians and other professionals, and because medical records serve as a vehicle for communication among all members of the health care team, the records should be readily accessible.

At the initial visit, a comprehensive data base and plan of therapy should be established, and it should be updated at each subsequent visit. Correspondence, operative notes, and laboratory data should be filed chronologically in the patient's medical record. Pertinent data regarding changes in the patient's health care status or inpatient care should be recorded. This may be in the form of a diagnostic summary.

All medical information should be retained for a period of time prescribed by law and good medical practice.

[b] Obstetric Records

Obstetric records cover two periods: the ambulatory-care period (during prenatal period and after release from the hospital) and the hospital-care period (during labor, delivery, and postdelivery).

[i] Ambulatory care

A standard database is desirable here, and there should be a common medical record used within the community. During pregnancy (the antepartum period), the medical record should contain documentation of the patient's history, physical examination, laboratory tests', and risk identification. During each regular visit, weight, blood pressure, fetal heart rate, fundal height, and urinary levels of glucose and albumin should be documented. Data pertaining to the course of the pregnancy, identification of the patient's needs and plans for management also should be included. By thirty-six weeks, an up-to-date copy of the prenatal record should be sent to the hospital labor and delivery department.

On discharge from the hospital (postpartum period), the ambulatory-care record should be updated to include pertinent information on the patient's in-hospital care, and the discharge summary, if appropriate, should be included.

The ambulatory care record is an important vehicle for communication among all members of the health care team; thus, it should be legible, concise, cogent, and complete. It should permit easy assessment of the care provided to determine that the patient's health care needs were identified, diagnosed, and treated effectively.

[ii] Hospital care

The patient's hospital record should contain her identification data; prenatal record; interval history and physical findings; provisional diagnosis, including preoperative diagnosis, if applicable; physicians' and nurses' labor and progress daily notes; summary of intrapartum events (maternal and neonatal); diagnostic and therapeutic orders; laboratory data; signed consent form; operative report; anesthesia record; medications record; and a discharge summary with instructions. The record should also indicate any transfer to and return from another facility because of the risk factors that necessitated additional services at another level of care.

If labor, delivery, and neonatal adaption were uneventful, the standardized check-off type of form is sufficient. The labor, delivery, and neonatal periods should be documented in the summary, so that they become part of the record. All significant complications—operative delivery, Cesarean section, neonatal morbidity, or stillbirth—should be documented in the discharge summary, which should become part of the patient's ambulatory care record.

Monitor tracings are part of the medical record and need not be stored with the patient's record, but they should be retained for the time period prescribed for the medical record. The patient's name, hospital number, date, and times of admission and delivery should be written on the tracings.

[c] Gynecology Records

A primary requisite for good patient care, the gynecology medical record should contain the following information: patient identification data, history and physical findings, provisional diagnoses, diagnostic and therapeutic orders, physicians' and nurses' progress notes, laboratory data, a signed informed consent form, and an operative report. The operative report should include a narrative description of the operation and any complication;

instrument, needle, and sponge counts; and blood-product administration record.

The discharge summary should briefly include the reason for admission, any significant physical and laboratory findings, the treatment rendered, any procedure performed, complications that may have been encountered, the patient's condition at discharge, medications to be continued, recommended follow-up care, and final diagnoses, including any histopathologic diagnoses. A copy of the discharge summary should be filed in the patient's ambulatory care record and sent to the physician providing the patient's follow-up care.

[d] Freestanding, Hospital-based Ambulatory Surgical Facilities

These facilities should maintain an accurate and efficient record system in which medical information is secure, confidential, and readily accessible. The patient's medical record should conform to a standard record used in the community or the backup hospital, and should be legible, concise, cogent, and complete. It should include details concerning any anesthetic used, procedure performed, any difficulties encountered, and the patient's subsequent condition. As all patient records, it should serve as a vehicle for communication among all members of the health care team and facilitate an assessment of the care provided to determine whether the patient's health care needs have been identified, diagnosed, and managed effectively. It should contain sufficient information not only to justify the preoperative diagnosis and operative procedure, but also to document the postoperative course. More specifically, it should contain: patient identification data; history and physical findings; provisional diagnosis; diagnostic and therapeutic orders; surgeons' and nurses' notes; results of laboratory tests; signed operative consent form; operative and anesthetic report; tissue report; medications record; and a discharge note with instructions.

The record should be completed promptly and signed by the attending physician. The ambulatory center should keep registries of admissions and discharges, operations, and controlled-substances dispensed. The records should be kept confidential and protected against fire, theft, and other possible damage for the duration of time prescribed by law and good medical practice.

[2] Current Malpractice Issues

Many alleged malpractice cases are won or lost because someone failed to do something. One of the major problems in gynecology involves failure to perform a biopsy on a breast lesion even in the presence of a "normal" mammogram. Failure to do a biopsy in the presence of a lump without delay, thus permitting further growth of the lump, is at the root of many cases of malpractice involving breast cancer. The physician should do a biopsy or a fine-needle aspiration of any suspicious lump at the first presentation for treatment. Statutes, hospital by-laws, regulations, and medical protocols by specialty are sources for standards of care for the physician, with expert testimony as one of the means of establishing the requisite standard. The physician's conduct or judgment is judged on a national, rather than a local standard.

Failure to order a mammogram in the presence of appropriate indications based on age, history, and physical examination also may lead to a suit for malpractice. While current recommendations of the American College of Radiology and the American Cancer Society are the ideal, they should be tempered with practicality in order not to overwhelm the facilities and in order to use resources wisely. Even in the case of a normal breast examination, the physician may be found negligent for failing to diagnose breast cancer in a timely manner. Any microcalcifications noted by the radiologist warrant further evaluation whether by breast examination, mammography, sonography, or any combination of the three.

Fistula formation and other complications of hysterectomy constitute another fertile field for the plaintiff's attorney and should be foremost in the mind of all gynecologists when performing this major surgery. Particular attention must be paid to the ureterovesical junction (UVJ) during the course of all hysterectomies. Any deviation from the routine or uncomplicated hysterectomy should set off warning bells. Does the patient need a urologic consultation prior to closing the abdomen or terminating a vaginal approach? Should the bladder be tested for integrity by an injection of methylene blue or the use of sterile milk? Have the ureters been palpated on both sides above the pelvic brim as well as down to the UVJ? Have I seen exactly where I was suturing the cardinal ligaments as well as the uterine arteries? These are a few of the questions that all prudent gynecologists should be asking themselves prior to closure of the peritoneum in an abdominal hysterectomy, complicated or not. Only by doing so will untoward events be discovered and addressed in a proper manner. Someone said that suturing and tying off a ureter was a mortal sin, but not recognizing it was a venal sin. How true!

Another area for negligence suits is failure to diagnose a pregnancy. Negligence on the part of a physician in failing to diagnose a pregnancy might make the physician liable for the foreseeable consequences, including injuries caused to the fetus because of the lack of proper prenatal care from the point of misdiagnosis. Liability may also be imposed for damage for loss of consortium and mental pain and suffering. Also, liability may be found for failure to diagnose pregnancy in time for the woman to obtain a legal abortion.

Failure to diagnose ectopic pregnancy is another area that engenders lawsuits. Vaginal bleeding and abdominal pain in a woman of childbearing age who presents with a history of a missed period (or sometimes without such a history) requires ectopic pregnancy to be included in the differential diagnosis. Pelvic inflammatory disease (PID) should also be considered. If on the right side of the abdomen, an ectopic pregnancy may be confused with acute appendicitis. This misdiagnosis can be avoided by the proper use of pelvic sonography and a test for beta-HCG levels. If the sonogram shows a mass in -the left tube and ovary complex with or without a possible gestational sac in the uterus, ectopic pregnancy (with or without intrauterine pregnancy) must be considered. If a dilation and curettage (D & C) reveals no pregnancy tissue in the presence of an adnexal mass, and the differential includes an ectopic pregnancy, then serious consideration must be given to an exploratory operation by laparoscopy or laparotomy.

Failure to perform a successful sterilization operation (tubal ligation or cauterization) may lead to a suit for malpractice. The cause of action may include an allegation of breach of warranty of sterility after the procedure. This should never happen! All sterilization procedures should be accompanied by a disclaimer by the physician that, while it is intended to produce permanent sterilization, such cannot be guaranteed. The plaintiff may not recover damages for future expenses incurred in raising a healthy child resulting from a failed sterilization procedure, because the plaintiff is not considered damaged by the birth of a health child.

"Bad Baby" cases with associated birth injury such as neurologic injury to the infant (Erb's Palsy associated with shoulder dystocia) are common medical-legal issues in obstetrics today. Wrongful birth cases involving infants with serious disabilities are brought alleging failure by the physician to recognize the genetic or hereditary basis and offer proper counseling. These cases differ from Wrongful Life cases which claim that the prenatal testing was negligent.

[3] New Technology

New surgical techniques are regularly being developed in gynecology. Practice with hands-on training is a must in order to acquire expertise in the utilization of these modalities. Advancements in therapy of the lower reproductive tract include surgery of the cervix and vulvovaginal areas for intraepithelial neoplasias. Seminars and tutorials are being offered on a regular basis throughout the country and include elective laboratories, hands-on experience, and patient models.

Potential problem areas must be identified so that risk-reduction methods can be instituted. Credentialing for new procedures requires a higher standard to avoid hospital and physician liability for negligence. Worker's safety in the use of these new modalities, especially lasers, demand a standard of care that is appropriate. This standard is at present in a state of flux. The most commonly performed operations in obstetrics/gynecology are biopsies, diagnostic D & Cs, excisions of skin lesions, hysterectomies (abdominal and vaginal), tubal ligations, Cesarean sections, oophorectomies, and cyst removals.

Negligent credentialing has given rise to corporate liability of hospitals. The hospital has a duty to select, supervise, and discipline the physician, through monitoring, if necessary, at reasonable intervals. With laser surgery, especially, it is important for the hospital to develop adequate credentialing criteria and apply these to all physicians. Worker's safety is an important issue, especially for operating room personnel because of increased respiratory and eye problems from the use of lasers. In-service training is vital, as is the use of proper safety equipment. Universal precautions are now required by law under the Occupational Safety and Health Act.

Operative endoscopy is another area where credentialing standards are being continually updated for gynecologists requesting privileges to perform new procedures. The mechanism for credentialing should be rigorous and requirements uniformly enforced. Procedures should be in compliance with relevant medical staff by-laws. To minimize liability, there should be regular review of compliance with recommended safety and treatment standards.

[a] Urogynecology

Urogynecology has developed as a specialized field in obstetrics and gynecology in response to the need for dealing with quality of life issues in the population of women living up to one-third of their life after the menopause and having to deal with problems of urinary incontinence and dysfunctional voiding issues. Dealing with lower urinary tract disorders and pelvic floor dysfunction issues are the goals of this new field of urogynecology with focus on evaluating and treating urinary incontinence in women. Urinary stress tests, urodynamics studies, cystourethroscopy, and imaging radiologic tests are the tools used for diagnosis. Treatment measures include nonsurgical (pharmacologic therapy, dietary changes, pessaries, exercises, and biofeedback) and surgical management (anterior vaginal wall repair, urethropexy, suburethral slings and tension-free vaginal tape.)

[4] Consent

Consent to treatment must be an informed one. While the physician has the knowledge of medicine as well as the patient's condition, the patient is the master. The physician is the servant in matters of consent to treatment. The physician has the obligation not to go beyond the patient's consent. The physician has the duty to reveal all facts necessary for the patient to give an informed (i.e., intelligent) consent to the proposed treatment. The disclosure must be complete, and given along with alternative treatments available to the patient, as well as the risks involved. Finally, the physician has an obligation to protect the best interests of the patient; the patient may therefore rely on such trust. The attending physician, not the nurse or resident, should obtain the written consent from the patient, thereby giving the patient the opportunity to raise questions (and receive answers).

§ 14.06 Selected References

- CANCER OF THE OVARY (ACOG Technical Bulletin No. 141, May 1990).
- Cohn, Legal Issues in Gynecology, CURR. PROB. OBSTET., GYNECOL. & FERTILITY, Vol. XII, No. 3, May/June 1989.
- HUMAN IMMUNE DEFICIENCY VIRUS INFECTIONS (ACOG Technical Bulletin No. 123, December 1988).
- THE INTRAUTERINE DEVICE (ACOG Technical Bulletin No. 104, May 1987).
- Kistner, GYNECOLOGY: PRINCIPLES AND PRACTICES, 4th ed. (Year Book Medical Publishers 1986).
- Meyers & Ellis, Genetic Screening for Mendelian Disorders, CONTEMP. OB/GYN., August 1990.
- Newton & Newton, COMPLICATIONS OF GYNECOLOGIC AND OBSTETRIC MANAGEMENT (W. B. Saunders 1988).
- Nichols, ed., CLINICAL PROBLEMS, INJURIES AND COMPLICATIONS OF GYNECOLOGIC SURGERY (Williams & Wilkins 1983).
- DeCherney & Nathan, CURRENT OBSTETRIC & GYNECOLOGIC Diagnosis and Treatment .
- (Lange Medical Books/McGraw-Hill 2003 9th ed. and 10th edition)
- Lee P. Shulman , YEARBOOK OF OBSTETRICS, GYNECOLOGY, AND WOMEN'S HEALTH 2007

CHAPTER 15

OBSTETRICS
Jeffrey P. Phelan, MD, JD

SYNOPSIS

§ 15.01 Introduction

[1] Development of Modern Obstetrics

Viewed historically, today's contemporary obstetrics may be said to stem from philosophies and principles unrelated to medicine in general. In ancient times, the care of the parturient (woman in childbirth) was thought to be unrelated to that of the sick, and, for reasons rooted in contemporary beliefs, the practice was perceived as a domain that men of dignity should not enter. Thus, in the early years of obstetrical care, physicians were generally prohibited from offering help to women experiencing childbirth; their care was left to wise women, forerunners of the modern "midwife," who, unlike the healers of civilized societies, pursued their trade without formal training or satisfying any state or federal licensing requirements.

As late as the 17th century, the participation of males, and thus physicians, in the management of childbirth was prohibited by law in many countries. Accordingly, it was only thereafter that midwifery became recognized as a branch of the science of medicine. Subsequently, the understanding of the childbearing process evolved with impressive speed. However, since the same process channeled parturients into hospitals where infections were rampant, the new interest that contributed to the development of modern obstetrics also led to a catastrophic increase of maternal mortality rates due to the spread through the maternity wards of puerperal fever. At this stage of the art, the end point of successful obstetric management was maternal survival.

The understanding of the nature of puerperal fever, comprehension of the labor process, the development of the technique of cesarean delivery, the feasibility of blood transfusion, the availability of potent antibiotics, and the development of advanced technology permitting entry into the environment of the fetus and providing life support for the premature neonate, opened avenues from the field of classical obstetrics to modern perinatal medicine. In this process, maternal survival became commonplace and a reflection of the improvements of perinatal care and obstetrical specialization. While there were tremendous advances in maternal healthcare, improvements in fetal healthcare were not advanced until the development of noninvasive techniques that provided a "window to the womb." With the ready availability of these new technologies outside the academic community and the availability of a new breed of obstetrician—the perinatologist—obstetrical care has experienced somewhat of a renaissance. Coupled by the incorporation of perinatal safety initiatives, maternal and perinatal morbidity and mortality have continued to decline.

In light of these changes over the past two decades, the difficulty for the attorney has become the establishment of the prevailing standards of care at the time and place of a particular event. The relevant dispute, the scope of which is set by experts, who often vary widely in their experience, expertise and motivations, serves as the background for the dramatic scenario that unfolds in the courtroom.

Conceding, in advance, the considerable difficulties of the task thus involved for the medical malpractice attorney, the following chapter attempts to provide simple guidelines with regard to locating the borderline between practice and malpractice in those clinical situations that frequently give rise to malpractice litigations.

§ 15.02 Provision of Maternal Health Care

[1] Medical Health Care Providers

[a] Obstetricians

By general definition, the obstetrician is a specially trained physician who provides health care for pregnant women. In the United States, duly trained and qualified obstetricians can become Diplomates of the American Board of Obstetrics and Gynecology following fulfillment of the applicable requirements as set forth by the American Board of Obstetrics and Gynecology (ABOG). The process of board certification is a long and arduous one. Not counting the years in college, the length of time from the start of medical school to the satisfactory completion of the basic certification in obstetrics and gynecology is 10 or more years. The first step towards becoming a diplomate of the ABOG is to satisfactorily complete one's residency training in obstetrics and gynecology and to fulfill the requirements for the written examination. A doctor who has completed his or her residency training and who has passed the written examination is considered an "Active Candidate" for basic certification in obstetrics and gynecology. The term "Board Eligible" is no longer used or recognized by the ABOG. Once Active Candidate status is achieved, the active candidate must fulfil all the requirements for admission to the oral examination *and* must not have exceeded the limitations to admissibility for the oral examination. Once the physician has satisfactorily completed the written and oral examinations and the board has awarded a certifying diploma, the physician has become a Diplomate of the ABOG. Beginning in 1986, diplomate certificates have a limited duration of validity. Recertification has given way to maintenance of certification (MOC) effective 1 January 2008. For details of this process and the duration of certificates under MOC requirements, the reader is advised to go to the ABOG website at www.abog.org.

[b] Maternal-fetal Medicine Subspecialists

Since the early 1970s, the ABOG has established requirements for subspecialty certification in maternal-fetal medicine. Here, the board certification process begins after the satisfactory completion of an OB/GYN residency. Each physician must then complete a three year fellowship in an approved program and documentation of satisfactory completion of the two required postgraduate courses. In addition, each physician must also pass the written and oral examinations in maternal-fetal medicine. For the oral examination, each applicant must submit a case list for year immediately preceding the examination along with a written thesis. The thesis need not be published prior to the oral examination. Recertification requirements have followed a similar course as the maintenance of board certification for OB/GYNs and can also be found at the ABOG website.

As the number of maternal-fetal medicine subspecialist have grown in numbers, a large percentage of these subspecialists have left academic medicine in pursuit of improving perinatal care in the "trenches" or community hospitals. As such, these subspecialists have brought not only a higher level of obstetrical care to these communities but also continued improvements in perinatal outcomes. What impact, if any, the departure of these subspecialists from the academic community will have on the training of future subspecialists is less clear. But, clearly, this group of physicians have had a positive impact on the health and well-being of the pregnant women and their babies throughout the United States and the world.

For additional information on Maternal-Fetal Medicine subspecialists, the reader is referred to their society website at www.smfm.org.

[c] Family Physicians and General Practitioners

Traditionally, physicians provided care in all areas of medicine, including obstetrics. The general practitioner, who made house calls, set bones, amputated gangrenous limbs and attended women at delivery lives today mainly through movies that depict life during the past century. Physicians working in rural areas still fulfill this role to some extent when more specialized care is not available. However, Family Medicine is now a recognized medical specialty which provides continuing, comprehensive health care for the individual and family. It is a specialty in breadth that integrates the biological, clinical and behavioral sciences. The scope of Family

Medicine encompasses all ages, both sexes, each organ system and every disease entity. To become a specialist in Family Medicine, three year training in family medicine will encompass general medicine, general surgery, and obstetrics and gynecology. The training in obstetrics is variable and depends on the desires of the trainee and their long term goals. In most cases, the exposure to obstetrical care is limited and is generally deemed to be adequate to provide an understanding of maternal and fetal care. Most Family Medicine physicians do not provide prenatal care and delivery as part of their practice focus. The amount of obstetrical care in any one practice will depend to a large extent on the practice location and the training, skill, and experience of the Family Medicine physician. (1) his or her activities are restricted to the care of normal gravidas and parturients; and (2) he or she is capable of recognizing significant high-risk factors, and in the presence of complications is prepared to refer the patient to a qualified specialist.

The American Board of Family Medicine (ABFM) also offers Certificates of Added Qualifications in Adolescent Medicine, Geriatric Medicine, Hospice and Palliative Medicine, Sleep Medicine and Sports Medicine, but does not offer one in obstetrics. As with the ABOG, the ABFM does not recognize the status of a physician being "board eligible." ABFM certification requires that all candidates for the ABFM certification examination must have satisfactorily completed three years of training in an accredited family medicine residency program. Upon certification by the ABFM, the physician becomes a diplomate of the ABFM. Diplomates are required to recertify every seven years. Similar to the ABOG, the ABFM has initiated a program entitled "maintenance of certification." For more details on the certification of Family Medicine specialists, the reader is referred to the ABFM website at www.theabfm.org.

Most Family Medicine physicians do not provide prenatal care and delivery as part of their practice focus. The amount of obstetrical care in any one Family Medicine physician's practice will depend to a large extent on the practice location and their training, skill, and experience. This may include prenatal care and delivery as well as cesarean delivery and operative vaginal delivery. But, in general and in most instances, the Family Medicine physician does not practice obstetrics. In those physicians that do practice obstetrics, the obstetrical care is usually limited to normal prenatal care and delivery. If a "high risk" condition is encountered, the Family Medicine physician will typically refer those patients to an obstetrician for continued prenatal care and delivery.

The medical-legal issues pertaining to Family Medicine physicians providing prenatal care and delivery are often related to one or more of the following:

1. In the absence of an emergency, the failure to recognize foreseeable complications and intervene in a timely manner.
2. The lack of awareness of one's clinical limitations.

[d] Osteopathic Physicians

Despite the somewhat differing goals and training requirements of osteopathic medicine, the quality of training and requirements for licensure and board certifications for osteopathic and medical school educated physicians are similar. With that as a backdrop, osteopathic physicians qualify for privileges in hospitals practicing traditional medicine, and osteopathic specialists are held to the same standard as their M.D. brethren. Accordingly, MDs and DOs who practice obstetrics and gynecology are expected to are held to similar standards of care. For more information on osteopathic physicians who practice OB/GYN, the reader is directed to the American College of Osteopathic Obstetricians and Gynecologists website at www.acoog.org.

[e] Physicians in Training

Medical and osteopathic students in the course of their undergraduate training are permitted to participate in medical and surgical activities under surveillance of residents in training and attending faculty. Since they cannot assume independent patient responsibilities, the responsibility for their action typically falls upon the supervising physicians. Since the medical or osteopathic student does not yet have a license to practice medicine, a student cannot portray himself as having one. At the same time, it is generally understood that the clinical activities of students in teaching hospitals rarely serve as a source of malpractice claims.

When physicians complete medical or osteopathic school and state licensing requirements, these physicians can obtain a license to practice medicine. This license permits them to fulfil certain medical functions within the limitations of their training, skill, and experience. To provide specialized care, such as obstetrics and gynecology, requires additional training as previously set forth earlier in §§ 15.02 [1][a] and 15.02 [1][b]. A residency training program in obstetrics and gynecology, for example, is designed to permit professional growth, starting with the acquisition of basic skills under supervision, and ending with the ability to make independent decisions and to perform major surgical procedures without direct supervision by an attending physician. Intrinsic to the concept of providing a broadening scope of responsibilities for physicians in training, is the understanding that independent functions by residents must be undertaken within the scope of their level of training and abilities.

Thus, the medical-legal issues that arise within a residency training program usually relate to the following:

1. The resident in training fails to practice within the scope of their training, skill, and experience.
2. The failure to keep the attending updated on the changing circumstances of a laboring patient.
3. In circumstances of ongoing maternal or fetal jeopardy, the nursing staffs' ineffective use of the chain of command. In a residency training program, the chain of command does not stop with the resident, but goes to the attending physician.

[f]   Patterns of Practice

After the fulfillment of training requirements in obstetrics and gynecology, physicians can seek career opportunities in the following major areas:

1. By entering a "Fellowship" program to gain additional training, skill, and experience in one of the subspecialties of the discipline such as maternal-fetal medicine.
2. By choosing an academic career and serving as a faculty member with not only clinical and teaching responsibilities, but also, clinical and/ or basic science research duties.
3. By entering a salaried hospital-based practice with duties predominantly involving patient care and administration.
4. By entering private practice as: (1) a solo practitioner; (2) a member of a group consisting of similarly trained specialists, or (3) an obstetrician and gynecologist member of a multispecialty group.

In any of the above environments, the obstetrician establishes a doctor-patient relationship with the patient under his or her care. Depending upon the nature of the obstetrical practice, this relationship may be a purely individual one, or may be shared by other physicians within the group. In a solo practice, the doctor-patient relationship assumes that the primary OB/GYN will have complete responsibility, unless indicated to the contrary, for a given patient's prenatal care and delivery. Alternatively, the physicians providing obstetrical care in a group setting also have similar doctor-patient relationships, but with all the group's patients. This means that patients followed by obstetricians working in a group practice have the expectation that all members of the group may provide necessary prenatal examinations and interpret appropriate diagnostic tests. At times, however, a member of a group may view his task in prenatal care through the narrow view of that prenatal care visit, rather than through the more global perspective of the group practice. Under these circumstances, the physician should always review the background of the patient and prior examinations, laboratory tests and diagnostic studies. While this can be tedious at times, the benefit is to reduce patient errors and improve perinatal outcome.

In the case of a hospitalized patient, or when her care is provided by a service rather than an individual physician, direct patient care can reasonably be assigned to residents working in a training program. In such situations, the clinical management will be usually governed by the instructions of the primary care OB/GYN or the attending faculty member.

It is not always understood by nonmedical providers that a qualified practitioner working within the scope of his or her privileges is not subject to interference or overruling by a physician in a senior administrative position with regard to the management of any individual patient under his or her care. Intervention generally requires the initiation of the chain of command by the nursing staff as a result of ongoing maternal and/or fetal jeopardy, or physician impairment due to a mental or physical health problem, the presence of substance abuse or some other form of physician impairment. If, for example, the physician is impaired due to alcohol, the Chairman of the Department, when notified, has the power to immediately suspend that physician. By so doing, the Chairman will need to identify a similarly trained physician to provide ongoing care to that patient or any other patients under the care of that physician. Subsequently, the suspended physician will be entitled to a hearing regarding the alleged substance abuse and will have a determination of whether the physician qualifies for a diversion program or will have their privileges terminated.

In American hospitals, peer review is conducted, depending on the size of the department, by the members of the Department of OB/GYN. These physician members of the department evaluate clinical care through retrospective chart review. In these meetings, numerous indicators of obstetrical care as well as near misses and misses are brought to the attention of the quality assurance committee. Relying on the collective wisdom of the members of the Department of Obstetrics and Gynecology, these cases are then reviewed. Unless circumstances dictate to the contrary, these reviews do not serve as a punitive review for the physician but as an opportunity to improve patient care and reduce patient errors.

The principle that solo practitioners can assume full care and responsibility for a gravida throughout the entire gestation and puerperium is, often, a difficult order to fill. Unpredictable events frequently place the physician in a predicament where one or more obligations are encountered simultaneously and not uncommonly in two separate hospitals. These competing interests only serve to increase the risk to these patients. As a result, the solo practitioner, unlike the group practitioner, is a potential source for a medical malpractice claim when providing care at more than one hospital. For example, the intrinsic weaknesses of solo practice are as follows:

1. The difficulty in meeting competing patient care obligations simultaneously;
2. Exhaustion from attending to multiple engagements for extended periods of time may impair the physician's physical and mental state;
3. The anticipation of other emergencies impacts upon the physician's management by turning the balance of considerations in favor of short cuts rather than paying attention to detail.
4. Being unable to provide continuous care, the physician is reluctant to leave the patient in the hands of a similarly qualified physician.

Physicians, especially solo practitioners, frequently work out coverage arrangements with other solo or group practitioners. This coverage relationship is sometimes hindered by an inability to access a patient's medical or prenatal care record. This circumstance may weaken the safety net provided by the system of mutual coverage, and impose undesirable professional risks upon the physician who provides coverage for his colleague.

In today's contemporary practice of medicine and specifically obstetrics, each physician should have a back-up physician. A back-up physician is a physician who is similarly trained and who has agreed in writing to be that physician's back-up. The information as to who is the back-up physician, and there may be more than one back-up for each physician, is available on labor and delivery. It is important to note that the back-up system is not necessarily a reflection of the coverage relationship between physicians. This system works to make available a physician when the primary physician is unavailable for whatever reason. This means, for example, that OB-1 is on call that evening. For whatever reason, OB-1 is called but fails to respond to a potential unattended birth and, there is no OB immediately available on labor and delivery. Under those circumstances, the back-up system would kick into place and the back-up OB would be contacted to come and deliver the patient. In the future, the back-up system will be replaced in larger facilities with in-house hospitalists. These hospitalists will serve in a number of capacities such as the handling of OB emergencies.

The principle that a properly trained obstetrician is capable of providing complete obstetrical care to a pregnant woman is no longer the norm for today's obstetrician. Since the availability of maternal-fetal medicine subspecialists in community based hospitals, a greater percentage of pregnant patients with "high risk" conditions are routinely referred for consultation and evaluation. A complete transfer of care is less common today because most perinatologists do not routinely conduct deliveries and limit their practices to consultation. Maternal-fetal transports to tertiary care centers are less common because most, if not all, clinical complications can be readily handled in Level II facilities. The most frequent reason transports are done to tertiary care hospitals are for fetuses that may require surgical correction due to a diaphragmatic hernia or congenital heart abnormality or heart transplant.

An obstetrician's failure to seek advice and help with a complicated gravida is an uncommon occurrence. However, there are several misconceptions regarding the clinical relationship between the primary care OB and the maternal-fetal medicine consultant:

1. The primary care OB is obligated to follow the recommendations of the consultant;
2. The consultant is not within his or her right to write direct instructions and orders; and
3. By seeking consultation the attending physician displays a lack of knowledge, ability to make decisions or self-confidence.

Despite these misconceptions, consultations are infrequently omitted in clinical situations when the potential benefits of input from an expert in a different discipline or with a higher level of expertise in the specialty itself, would have been beneficial. The difficulty in today's contemporary obstetrical care is not the failure to seek consultation on the part of the primary OB, but the hoops the primary care OB must jump through to get the carrier to agree that maternal-fetal medicine subspecialist consultation would be beneficial for the pregnant woman. Nevertheless, it is clear, at times, that a given physicians' persistence in handling difficult cases independently and without outside assistance can be fertile ground for not only an adverse maternal and/or fetal outcome but also for a potential medical malpractice claim.

Some physicians are unaware of their obligation to refer their patients to another physician when the required medical skill or experience is beyond the scope of their abilities. This duty to refer to a specialist is also embodied in the Civil Jury Instructions. Intrinsic to the understanding governing such referrals is the commitment on the part of the receiving physician that the patient is to be returned to the care of the referring doctor when her care no longer requires a specialist. Unlike the circumstance of subspecialist consultation, the obligations of the referring physician end once the specialist in question has accepted responsibility for the care of the patient. Sometimes the borderline between the respective responsibilities of each physician is obscured when the consultant and the primary care physician agree to "co-manage" a patient. When the areas of expertise of the respective physicians are clearly different and easily identifiable, subject to close cooperation and communication, both physicians may effectively remain in charge. However, when the disease or complication in question is clearly no longer within the training, skill, and experience of the primary provider and the expertise of the subspecialist are clearly superior to that of the other, a de facto co-management is not technically feasible. In this clinical situation, the activities of the co-managing physician, the primary provider in this case, is usually restricted to carrying out the instructions of the subspecialist.

It may be advantageous for the patient to have the maternal-fetal medicine consultant undertake her management in an area with which the obstetrician is not thoroughly familiar. For example, the maternal-fetal medicine consultant would manage the diabetes of an insulin dependent diabetic and the primary OB would be responsible for the overall care of the pregnant woman. Under these clinical circumstances, it needs to be understood, however, that the management of diabetes or other problems cannot be separated from that of the pregnancy. Thus, the functions of the two physicians must be closely and harmoniously coordinated. Therefore, each of the doctors carries responsibilities in such a situation. At the same time, there are relatively few clinical situations when the obstetrician does not share the responsibility of his or her colleague when he or she agrees to co-manage a patient with a specialist in a different discipline.

Contemporary obstetric practice is so highly complex these days because of the numerous skilled professionals who participate in maternal and fetal care. In addition to the Primary OB and the Maternal-fetal Medicine subspecialist, neonatologists, newborn specialists, and anesthesiologists are frequently involved. In most instances, the anesthesiologist's involvement is during labor to provide analgesia, pain relief, and to provide anesthesia during delivery or a cesarean. The neonatologist may consult on a preterm pregnancy with respect to the risks to the newborn after delivery. Often times, neonatal consultation may occur again as the clinical circumstances change with advancing gestation.

Two websites that the readers may find helpful to gather scientific evidence for their cases are as follows: www.OBfocus.com and www. perinatology.com. Each site carries helpful information on obstetrical care.

[g] Professional Standards

With the achievement of the "highest" level of expertise, the medical profession has paid relatively little attention to what constitutes the "standard of practice". Practicing within the standard of care means the level of care that is achievable by a similarly trained physician practicing under the same or similar circumstances. As a result, any reference to "standard of care" has inevitable legal connotations. In that context, whether a certain course of action in a particular clinical situation would be considered within accepted standards of care is subject to a number of potential confounding factors, rapid emergence and disappearance of new techniques, changing philosophies and multiplicity of viewpoints. As a result, practicing within the "standard of care" becomes a moving target that in some clinical situations may be difficult to identify.

Misconceptions among physicians with regard to the "standard of care" are numerous. However, the most common ones are as follows:

1. The standard of care varies in different geographic areas of the country.
2. Physicians with varying training and experience are bound by different standards.
3. Standards are created from occasion to occasion by members of a lay jury.

Recognizing its fallibility, the law perceives standards as a viewpoint held by the consensus of medical opinion at any particular time in the United States. With the exception of the state of Tennessee and some others, standards of obstetrical care are perceived as national, based on the consideration that identical examinations are held by the National Board of Medical Examiners, the American Board of Obstetricians and Gynecologists and other similar agencies throughout the United States. It is also assumed that whenever a certain standard of care, such as that adopted by specialists in a particular field, are available in the geographic area, a patient cannot reasonably be subjected to a lower level of care (such as that offered by a general practitioner), just because a doctor is unwilling to relinquish responsibility for the patient. Through this logic, standards adopted by specialists in a particular field became binding for less qualified physicians as long as the given standard could have been achieved through referring the patient to another, better qualified physician.

Far too often obscured by advocates' arguments and conflicting opinions presented by expert witnesses, in the courtroom the compliance with standards often boils down to the defendant him or herself and to relatively simple components that appear readily understandable to a lay jury:

1. Did the physician earnestly try to help his or her patient?
2. Was the doctor unselfish, or did he or she try to put his professional or economic interest before the welfare of the patient?
3. Is the doctor earnest and sincere in the courtroom, or did he or she try to obscure his or her professional shortcomings and cover up for his or her negligence?

While disputed and often even ridiculed from one side or the other, clear-cut statements presented in contemporary textbooks stand up in the minds of members of the jury as reliable yardsticks for establishing medical standards. Although sometimes confused by artful advocates, in a surprisingly high proportion of cases, jurors identify the validity of the claim and the truthfulness of the defense with a considerable degree of accuracy.

While advocating the achievement of excellence, the implication is that board examiners and scientific medical societies stand guard to maintain what the law perceives as reasonable standards. Whether or not these authorities are more successful in accomplishing their goals than our courts is open to question. The definition of the scope of knowledge that a specialist obstetrician must possess is a complex and difficult task which is not made easier by the fact that the appointed boards tolerate little dispute with regard to the validity of their perception of what should be the core material for the examinations. Since examination questions vastly differ in importance and applicability to everyday practice, there can be genuine doubt about the validity of 75% or even 90% passing scores obtained while answering 60–70 questions per hour; a pattern of problem solving that never emerges in actual medical practice and which, by its very design, precludes the process of reasoning. Nonetheless, it is conceded that the preparation for the examination has to be arduous, the amount of knowledge that needs to be displayed on the days of the examination is substantial, and the effort needed for successful passing of the examinations is not likely to be displayed by one who is poorly motivated or disinterested.

Other organizations, such as the American College of Obstetricians and Gynecologists (ACOG), attempt to maintain and promote professional standards by providing postgraduate learning opportunities, such as medical conventions and seminars, and by disseminating circulars and journals: functions designed to broaden and deepen the understanding of physicians of the art of medicine in general and the specialty of obstetrics (and gynecology) in particular. For more information, the reader is directed to ACOG's website at www.acog.org.

[2] Nonmedical Personnel

[a] Nurses

Working mainly in a hospital setting, but also in offices of physicians, nurses provide a broad range of perinatal care. Nurses pride themselves with being independent professionals who work with, rather than under the authority of, physicians. They claim, and appropriately discharge, independent responsibilities. The latter includes the right and obligation of not participating in professionally improper patient care. The scope of their abilities varies with the facility and the training skill and experience of the nurse. Clearly, a nurse's obligation is to the pregnant woman and her unborn child. These are usually identified in the policies and procedures of each hospital and are usually specific for the area of practice such as labor and delivery. In the labor and delivery setting, the nurse's obligation, in general, is to identify an abnormality and notify the OB. Additional medical-legal issues include the initiation of the chain of command in circumstances of ongoing maternal and/or fetal jeopardy in the absence of the primary OB and to guarantee the process of informed consent.

For more information on labor and delivery nurses, the reader is referred to the Association of Women's Health, Obstetric and Neonatal Nurses (AWOHNN).Their website may be located at www.awhonn.org and also the Nurse Practice Act in their respective state.

[b] Nurse-practitioners

Nurse practitioners are trained professionals. In maternal-child health settings, nurse practitioners may function depending on their training, skill, and experience in obstetrics, obstetrics and gynecology, perinatology or neonatology. These nurse specialists are usually under the supervision of a physician. They often work in physician offices but, can also be found in the hospital in a variety of clinical settings. For more information, the reader is referred to the American Academy of Nurse Practitioners website at www.aanp.org and also the Nurse Practice Act in their respective state.

[c] Certified Nurse-midwives

Certified nurse-midwives (CNM) are individuals who have been educated in nursing and midwifery and became certified by the American College of Nurse-Midwives.

Nurse-midwives are capable of independently taking care of uncomplicated pregnancies, labors and deliveries. The extent of their privileges varies from state to state and range from uncomplicated spontaneous vaginal deliveries to operative vaginal delivery. The scope of CNM care is usually found in a hospital policy and procedure. Additionally, each state defines the scope of CNM care in their respective Nurse Practice Act. In many instances, CNMs function similar to nurse practitioners serving as family planning counsellors, and of performing routine gynecological and obstetric examinations, including the acquisition of cultures, cytological smears, etc. In most, but not all circumstances, certified nurse-midwives work under the supervision of, and in collaboration with, a duly qualified obstetrician. For more information on CNMs, the reader is referred to the CNM website at www.midwife.org.

Medical-legally, the most common areas for error are that the CNM either operates outside the scope of their responsibilities or is unaware of their clinical limitations and does not readily consult their back-up OB.

[d] Technicians

With a variety of backgrounds and qualifications, paramedical personnel play significant roles in the perinatal health care system. With increasing frequency, technicians perform routine sonographic examinations and present findings for approval and signature to medical personnel. It is generally assumed that in this situation, the technician is responsible for the technical part of the evaluation, and the practitioner for the interpretation of the findings. In actual fact, the responsibilities are overlapping; without appropriate choice of focus by the technician, a proper interpretation by the physician is not possible.

In other areas technicians or specially trained nurses perform similar duties, such as fetal well-being testing, surgery, OB triage assistance, and outpatient care. As with other nonphysician professionals, technicians are under physician supervision and rarely are involved in medical malpractice claims.

§ 15.03 Management of Pregnancy

[1] Prenatal Care[1]

[a] Diagnosis of Pregnancy

The failure to diagnose pregnancy is an uncommon medical malpractice claim. Nevertheless, it is important to emphasize that any woman in the reproductive age group is at risk for pregnancy. This means that a woman

---

[1] Antepartum Care.: In, Guidelines of Perinatal Care 6[Th] Edition American Academy of Pediatrics and The American College of Obstetricians and Gynecologists 2007 pp 111-117.

may conceive before the occurrence of her first menstrual period (menarche) or many months after the last one (menopause). Pregnancies are usually not detectable during the estimated seven day interval between conception and implantation of the fertilized ovum. Apart from this seven day window, pregnancy can easily be detected through high sensitivity radio-immunoassays designed to detect the beta subunit of the human chorionic gonadotropin (HCG) molecule. Serum assays and sensitive urine assays can now detect pregnancy approximately 1 week after conception. In the first 4 to 8 weeks of pregnancy, HCG levels usually double every 2 days. If the HCG doesn't double in 48 to 72 hours, an ectopic pregnancy or abnormal intrauterine pregnancy is suggested. Levels of HCG return to normal approximately 2 weeks after delivery. After an abortion, levels return to normal in approximately 3 to 8 weeks.

Numerous signs and symptoms of pregnancy are listed in standard textbooks. Today, with the exception of missing the menstrual period, none of these are of practical significance. The diagnosis of suspected pregnancy in contemporary practice is the pregnancy test which relies on the identification of the HCG hormone in the maternal blood or urine. To confirm the pregnancy when indicated by the clinical circumstances, an ultrasound is usually performed to confirm the presence, the condition, and the location of the pregnancy. It is not uncommon for a hospital or department to have a negative pregnancy test prior to the performance of surgery, the receipt of an agent potentially harmful to the fetus, or any radiographic procedure.

Lawsuits in this section commonly arise from situations where the provider is unaware of the presence of the pregnancy. As a result, the pregnant woman and her fetus are exposed to any number of things that could be potentially harmful to the fetus.

[b] Routine Examinations and Tests[2]

In contemporary obstetric practice the impact of prenatal care upon the outcome of the pregnancy, in terms of maternal and the neonatal well-being, far exceeds that of intrapartum management. Regretfully, the general public is largely unaware of this fact and would rather focus on the three hours of labor and delivery and disregard the remaining seven thousand hours of the pregnancy. Even agencies involved in financing health care have failed to grasp the significance of antenatal care. The public image of the obstetrician is still the man who arrives in the delivery room at the moment of near

---

² *Id.*; Screening for Fetal Chromosomal Abnormalities. ACOG Practice Bulletin No.77 [January 2007]. American College of Obstetricians and Gynecologists. Obstet Gynecol 2007; 109: 217-27.

catastrophe and, through a heroic operation, saves the lives of both mother and child. No glory is attached in the mind of the public to the achievement of a physician who provides meticulous care for the mother during gestation, thus preventing the occurrence of complications and the need for spectacular intervention.

In the past decades little monetary value was assigned to the prenatal care provided by the physician. The fee for antenatal care was conveniently incorporated into that due for delivery which, in its turn, increased exponentially when it involved surgical procedures, such as a cesarean delivery. Even these days, an obstetrician's eligibility for a fee often hinges upon his presence at delivery: the time when (in the opinion of the author) the presence of the obstetrician is usually the least necessary. In actual fact, it has been increasingly recognized in recent times that the most important professional during the pregnancy is the maternal-fetal medicine subspecialist. What the MFM brings to the table is heightened prenatal care for mothers determined to be at risk for an adverse maternal or fetal outcome and the determination of the timing of delivery prior to and during labor.

As a result of this new breed of obstetricians is that antenatal care has evolved into a complex and intense process. The following schedule may be considered as the generally recognized timetable of prenatal care in low-risk pregnancies:

- Under 20 weeks: Visits 4 weeks apart
- 20–28 weeks: Visits 3 weeks apart
- 28–36 weeks: Visits 2 weeks apart
- 36–41 weeks: Visits weekly

Requirements concerning the scope of antenatal investigations are in a state of rapid evolution. The required prenatal routines change virtually from year to year.

Everyday clinical experiences, as well as review of malpractice claims, indicate that failure of carrying out required prenatal examinations and laboratory investigations is the most frequently observed deviation from standard obstetric practice. Besides, it is the deviation most easily identifiable in the course of retrospective reviews. The limitations of one's ability for remembering tedious details make it impractical and precarious for practitioners to rely on memory alone while providing antenatal care. The ever-increasing expansion of knowledge that impacts pregnancy imposes a greater requirement the use of appropriate prenatal forms that incorporate all necessary data and preclude the possibility of omission by oversight.

Less frequent, and less understandable, is the situation when printed prenatal forms remain unfilled by the physicians providing prenatal care. Clinical evaluation of the pelvic dimensions of the patient is no longer clinically relevant to the current practice of obstetrics. Labor has become the true test of pelvic adequacy. But, pregnant women with a prior history of pelvic fractures, certain orthopedic conditions, or genetic abnormalities may require a clinical and/or radiographic evaluation of the pelvis. What can be more troubling is the failure to take action when an abnormal lab test or diagnostic study is received in the office. Examples are persistent blood pressure elevations (140/90 mmHg) in a second or third trimester pregnant patient without preexisting hypertension, or a misplaced laboratory report containing an abnormal result such as a positive test for syphilis, one hour glucose screen.

In January 2007, ACOG recommended that "all women should be offered (chromosomal) screening before 20 weeks gestation."[3] While the recommendations were that "some" pregnant women would benefit from a referral to a specialist such as an MFM or a geneticist, most OB practitioners are not adequately equipped to handle all the potential genetic abnormalities associated with this recommendation. Prior to this recommendation, genetic evaluations were limited by maternal age ($\geq$ 35 years) or a positive maternal serum alpha-fetoprotein (MSAFP) test. The current recommendations are as follows:

1. For women who seek prenatal care in the first trimester, all women should be offered first and second trimester screening.

2. Those women who seek prenatal care in the second trimester should be offered quadruple screening and an ultrasound evaluation. The quadruple screen is the maternal serum measurement of the following blood tests:

    a. Maternal serum alpha-fetoprotein (MSAFP) is a second trimester test designed to detect a neural tube defect such as an open spinal defect known as a meningomyelocoele or anencephaly.

    b. Human chorionic gonadotropin (HCG) is a test designed to confirm pregnancy and other conditions such as hydatidiform mole or choriocarcinoma, but is also useful in enhancing the detection of Down's syndrome, Trisomy 21, when used in combination with the MSAFP and unconjugated estriol.

---

[3] Screening for Fetal Chromosomal Abnormalities. ACOG Practice Bulletin No.77 [January 2007]. American College of Obstetricians and Gynecologists. Obstet Gynecol 2007; 109: 217-27..

    c. Unconjugated estriol (E3) is measured in conjunction with the other tests to improve the detection of Down's Syndrome.

    d. Inhibin A is also helpful in the detection of Down's syndrome when used with the other tests.

Pregnant women who seek prenatal care in the first trimester should be offered first and second trimester screening. First trimester screening should include biochemical markers such as pregnancy-associated plasma protein A (PAPP-A) and free beta-HCG and the sonographic measurement of nuchal translucency. Those women found to be at risk for a chromosomal abnormality should be offered genetic counseling, if not already done, and chorionic villous sampling or second trimester amniocentesis. Regardless of the woman's choice, second trimester screening for neural tube defects should also be done.

Cancellation of antenatal visits is an infrequent occurrence that occasionally affects the outcome. For this reason, a carefully constructed prenatal record should include an explanation for any forfeited visit.

With the development of technology that permits the physician as well as the patient to literally see within the womb, the focus of prenatal care has shifted dramatically from that of the mother alone to one that focuses on the fetus as well as the pregnant woman. Along with technological improvements in obstetrical care, technology has aided neonatal care for babies born too soon. As we are in the new millennium, one could easily say that this millennium's focus will be even more so on the fetus. The focus on the fetus is underscored by the following:

1. The improvements in neonatal care have lowered the period in which the fetus is now "capable of a meaningful life outside the mother's womb" to around 24–25 weeks gestation. While more neonates are surviving at these lower gestational ages, the number of surviving children with permanent disabilities is staggering. The chances of survival increase rapidly between 24 and 28 weeks and further improve slowly between 32 and 36 weeks and finally at term. .

2. Fetal growth is known and is reasonably predictable.

3. Since normal fetal growth is predictable, ultrasound evaluation in the first or early second trimester permits the OB to more accurately confirm a patient's due date or EDC. In addition, ultrasound also permits the clinician to more readily monitor fetal growth and to determine intrauterine growth impairment. In circumstances of attempting to determine fetal macrosomia, clinical and ultrasound estimates are less reliable.

The risks of maternal death and major injury have also been dramatically reduced throughout the world. As such, the art of contemporary obstetrics essentially rests more upon the obstetrician's ability to quantitate fetal risks derived from the continuation of the pregnancy in the face of a specific complication, such as hypertension versus delivery at a given stage of the pregnancy. It has been through the application of this principle that the perinatal mortality rate has been substantially reduced throughout the world.

As alluded to earlier in this chapter, the technological advances in recent years have permitted the OB to actually see inside the womb and to be able to make a noninvasive determination of fetal health. While there is a split of opinion about the value of intrapartum fetal monitoring and its ability to prevent cerebral palsy, it continues to be a major factor in defining fetal health during labor. At the same time, fetal monitoring continues to play a major role in determining fetal health prior to labor. When fetal monitoring is combined with ultrasonography prior to labor, or antepartum, perinatal mortality is additionally reduced.

Modern obstetric practice relies extensively upon a variety of traditional and modern techniques that permit the determination of the fetal condition in utero with a considerable degree of accuracy:

1. Fetal weight that can be estimated clinically by palpation and also by sonographic measurements of various anatomic landmarks of the fetus. These techniques are particularly useful for the diagnosis of intrauterine growth impairment but less so for fetal macrosomia.

2. Measurement of the maternal pelvis is no longer considered clinically beneficial. Therefore, a trial of labor is generally considered appropriate for most patients. Of note, there is no role for X-ray pelvimetry in the contemporary practice of obstetrics.

3. By palpation, fetal presentation, position, and rotation can be assessed both before and during the labor process. To resolve questions of presentation, ultrasonography offers a noninvasive approach to provide confirmation of fetal lie.

4. Maternal weight changes provide limited clinical benefit in the contemporary practice of obstetrics. But, at times, identifiable changes in maternal weight may be associated with fetal growth impairment, fetal macrosomia, preeclampsia, and maternal malnutrition. However, maternal weight alone is insufficient to establish the diagnosis of any one of those clinical conditions.

5. Routine tests, such as a complete blood count, blood type, Rh and antibody screen, HIV and hepatitis screens, VDRL, urinalysis and culture, PAP smear, and cervical cultures for sexually transmitted

diseases such as gonorrhea and chlamydia, as well as specific tests performed on the basis of historical data and findings of clinical examination, permit the identification of additional risk factors. In addition, additional testing will be done in the third trimester such as screening for diabetes mellitus and Group B Streptococcal infection.

[c] High-risk Factors

At risk pregnancies can be identified with considerable accuracy through the identification of "high-risk factors." Some of these are derived from historical data pertaining to the family background and personal history of the patient. Others emerge in the course of routine examinations and investigations. It has been said that the so-called high-risk pregnancies constitute about 10–15% of all pregnancies in this country. With advanced planning, many of the complications associated with these high risk factors can be prevented, or at least countered. As the pregnancy advances, new or additional high risk factors may be identified. The referral of these "high risk" gravidas to MFMs is now one of the important aspects of prenatal care today. Due to MFMs practicing in community hospitals, usually Level II facilities, regionalization has not necessarily materialized around the United States. Thus, efforts are directed to keeping these "high Risk" pregnancies within the community so the patients can be near family and friends. However, where there are Level I facilities, the MFMs frequently reach out to evaluate patients with high-risk factors prenatally in an effort to reduce the likelihood of an adverse outcome. At the same time, MFMs offer continuing education to promote improvements in pregnancy outcomes. As such, Level I deliveries are usually limited to low risk pregnancies at the onset of labor. Others are frequently referred to higher level facilities for their deliveries. Depending on the distance between the Level I and Level II or III facilities, many OBs will have privileges at a Level I and Level II facility so they can continue to provide care to their patients.

High-risk factors fall into two major categories: (1) those identifiable through the patient's history or on the basis of the initial prenatal examination, and (2) those that develop, or become apparent, during the course of the pregnancy.

The interpretation of the magnitude of risk factors requires medical judgment. In many instances, the final gauge of appropriate interpretation of the magnitude of risk factors in malpractice litigation will be the action expected from a "prudent physician," a pattern of professional attitude that juries appear to have less difficulty in identifying than the medical profession itself. A list incorporating the most frequent high-risk factors is set out in

Table 1. In analyzing these risk factors, the reader should be mindful of the fact that these risk factors identify one or two specific issues. If these risks do not materialize or are resolved, the maternal and fetal status does not continue to be high risk. Rather, they become low risk. For example, a woman with advanced maternal age of 36 years alone and without a coexistent medical or surgical problem is at an increased risk of a genetic abnormality. Once the risk of a genetic abnormality is removed, she, in essence becomes low risk.

Table 1

ANTENATAL HIGH RISK FACTORS

Risk Factors Identifiable at Time of First Visit

1. Maternal age: < 15 years or > 35 years
2. Maternal weight: 20% below or above the ideal
3. Multiparity: > 5 births
4. Induced abortion under the age of 17 or repeated induced abortions at any age
5. Habitual abortions (3 or more)
6. Previous premature birth(s)
7. Previous birth of SGA (small for gestational age) newborn
8. Previous stillbirth or neonatal death
9. Previous macrosomic baby (*See* § 15.05 [2][c] for the definition.)
10. Personal or family history of childbirth with congenital abnormality
11. Short stature < 150cm
12. Past history of prolonged or arrested labor or midforceps delivery
13. Previous cesarean delivery
14. Previous birth of a child with neurologic deficit
15. History of major disease (e.g., anemia, hypertension, diabetes, thyroid dysfunction, heart disease)
16. History of uterine anomaly or uterine surgery
17. History of drug or alcohol abuse
18. History of a prior shoulder dystocia

Risk Factors That Develop during Pregnancy

1. Development of medical conditions such as gestationally induced hypertension, diabetes or anemia
2. Development of previously unrecognized circulatory incompetence
3. Finding of urinary tract infection
4. Weight loss in pregnancy > 5 pounds

5. Rh, ABO or other subgroup sensitization
6. Exposure for teratogenic drugs during embryogenesis
7. Exposure to fever during embryogenesis
8. Exposure to viral infections (TORCH agents and others)
9. Exposure to ionizing radiation (> 25R)
10. Evidence of in utero fetal growth restriction
11. Evidence of hydramnios
12. Abnormal glucose tolerance
13. Multiple gestation
14. Significant fetal size versus date discrepancy
15. Threatening abortion
16. Antepartum hemorrhage
17. Maternal psychosis
18. Evidence of fetal compromise
19. "Postdatism" (gestation $\geq$ 42 0/7 weeks)
20. Development of malignancies
21. Discovery of pelvic tumors

[d] Special Tests for Determining Fetal Well-being[4]

In many ways, the development of sonography has revolutionized obstetric practice. Through the use of ultrasound, one can determine with a high degree of accuracy the age of the fetus and the presence of twins. Later in gestation, it is possible to identify major congenital anatomic abnormalities and the site of placental implantation. In advanced pregnancy, sonography will detect inappropriate fetal growth patterns, the quantity of amniotic fluid with the use of the amniotic fluid index (AFI), and the vitality of the fetus through the use of the biophysical profile (BPP). Thus, the role of ultrasound has been an important adjunct in establishing fetal health, fetal growth, and abnormalities of the amniotic fluid volume, such as oligohydramnios and polyhydramnios.

The electronic fetal heart rate monitor serves as a highly effective instrument for the determination of the fetal condition prior to and during labor. Prior to labor the nonstress test (NST), either alone or in combination with the AFI, is used to determine fetal health. The contraction stress test, formerly the oxytocin challenge test, no longer has a role in the contemporary practice of obstetrics. When using the NST or the modified biophysical

---

[4] Phelan JP: Labor admission test. In: *Clinics in Perinatology.* Devoe L (ed.), W. B. Saunders Co., Philadelphia, Pennsylvania, 1994; 21:879-85; Tests of fetal well-being: In, Guidelines of Perinatal Care 6Th Edition American Academy of Pediatrics and The American College of Obstetricians and Gynecologists 2007 pp 111-117.

profile, NST and AFI, the goal is to try and estimate the risk of fetal death within the next 7 days. The antenatal testing results are used to determine whether the pregnancy should continue or whether should be admitted for inpatient care. Thus, if the fetal risk of death is low, the pregnancy can continue as an outpatient. If, however, the risk of fetal death is high based on the testing results, the patient will usually be admitted for inpatient care. There, continuous electronic FHR monitoring will be used to determine whether intervention in the form of induction of labor or cesarean will be done. The application of these tests have permitted the prevention of fetal death or critical compromise in utero in many cases, and have contributed to the worldwide reduction of perinatal mortality rates.

In general, maternal and fetal high risk conditions lead to antepartum fetal testing. The maternal conditions include, but are not limited to hypertensive complications of pregnancy, maternal diabetes, anemia, cardiovascular disease, thyroid dysfunction, renal disease, and advanced respiratory compromise. Fetal conditions include, but are not limited to Rh sensitization, non-immune hydrops, fetal anemia secondary to feto-maternal or feto-fetal transfusion, in utero fetal infections, congenital anatomic and chromosome anomalies, intrauterine growth impairment and post dates ($\geq$ 42 weeks gestation). However, the most common indication for testing has been the maternal perception of decreased fetal movement. What is clear is that through antenatal testing, high risk pregnancies become low risk and that by not testing low risk pregnancies, these patients become high risk.

The key to antenatal testing is that it offers the clinician the opportunity to identify the patient at risk for fetal death in-utero. Once identified, the patient is typically moved to inpatient care. Depending on the gestational age of the pregnancy and the maternal condition, the patient may or may not be delivered. To a large extent, the fetal basis for delivery will be primarily based on the findings of the intrapartum FHR pattern. Once the decision has been made to deliver the fetus, the focus will then shift to the best route of delivery, cesarean or vaginal, under the current clinical circumstances. If the fetus is term, the decisions are easier with respect to deciding in favor of delivery. However, the preterm fetus is significantly more complicated and there is no easy answer as to the timing of delivery.

Above all, it is important to remember that no test guarantees a perfect fetal outcome. Fetal death or brain damage may occur at any time following a normal test result.

[2] Common Complications of Early Gestation

[a] Hyperemesis Gravidarum

One of the unresolved enigmas in obstetrics is the cause of vomiting in early pregnancy that, on rare occasions, may become life-endangering. Evidence suggests a relationship between the rate of production of human chorionic gonadtropin (HCG) hormone and hyperemesis in early gestation. However, other clinical disease processes may predispose to this syndrome. For example, psychogenic factors, pancreatitis, thyroid dysfunction, viral gastroenteritis, and central nervous system disorders may also be responsible for the hyperemesis. Thus, a limited evaluation is usually undertaken in patients with persistent hyperemesis.

Complications of severe hyperemesis gravidarum rarely serve as a backdrop for a malpractice claim. The reason for this is that the course of hyperemesis usually is benign, and its signs and symptoms tend to disappear at the end of the first trimester. On rare occasions, hyperemesis and weight loss are progressive and can result in the deterioration of maternal health with disturbed liver function, electrolyte imbalance and dehydration. To offset this dietary disturbance, hyperalimentation has been used to re-establish a positive a dietary balance. Hyperalimentation can be through enteral via feeding tube or parenteral via the bloodstream.

With regard to the management of hyperemesis, it has been customary to hospitalize patients who have persistent hyperemesis unresponsive to home therapy. It is also important to note that despite the metabolic derangements associated with this condition, the fetal condition appears to be unaffected. Nonetheless, hospitalization of the patient for the treatment of fluid loss and electrolyte imbalance by intravenous fluids (and if necessary, for hyperalimentation) is usually done for those cases with persistent hyperemesis.

[b] Spontaneous Abortion

Evidence suggests that between 10% and 20% of pregnancies are expelled from the uterus during the first twenty weeks of gestation. This is known as a spontaneous abortion or a miscarriage. A considerable proportion of spontaneous abortions are due to defective products of conception. Some of them do not contain an embryo and are known as a blighted ovum whereas others involve embryos or fetuses with anatomic and/or chromosomal abnormalities. This phenomenon is known as a process of selection permitting the survival of healthy fetuses and leading to the early demise of defective and nonviable ones.

Abortions are classified according to the clinical circumstances in which they arise. A *threatened abortion* is one in which there is evidence of vaginal bleeding. When the bleeding is associated with cervical dilatation, the abortion is classified as *imminent*. When the bleeding becomes excessive as to preclude the possibility of continued gestation, the abortion is termed *inevitable*. When some of the products of conception have already been expelled from the uterus, the abortion is considered *incomplete*. Lastly, an incomplete abortion that has become infected is termed a *septic abortion*.

Evacuation of the uterus can be achieved medically or surgically. In the circumstances of an incomplete abortion, the usual approach is to evacuate the uterus by a dilatation and curettage (D&C). However, medical approaches in such instances have involved the use of ergot alkaloids or prostaglandins. Retention of some products of conception following instrumental evacuation occurs infrequently and is not a sign of improper obstetrical care. However, the failure to medically or surgically evacuate the uterus in the face of continued hemorrhage or infection would be considered unacceptable.

Occurrences that serve as a background for potential medical malpractice claims in this area are as follows:

1. Perforation of the uterus during the D&C is not by itself considered negligence per se. But, the medical-legal focus is usually on the management of the uterine perforation.
2. Failure to protect Rh negative women from becoming immunized by the administration of Rh immune globulin.
3. Failure to timely and appropriately manage an incomplete abortion.

[c] Ectopic Pregnancy[5]

An ectopic pregnancy is the clinical circumstance in which the fertilized egg implants in the fallopian tube rather than the uterus. Over the years, the incidence of ectopic pregnancies has increased dramatically to now where the current rate of occurrence is estimated to be around 2% of all pregnancies. One explanation for the increased incidence has been related to a prior genital tract infection. At the same time, the highest rates of ectopic pregnancy have occurred in patients with a history of a prior ectopic,

---

[5] Mukul LV, Teal SB: Current Management of Ectopic Pregnancy. Obstet Gynecol Clin of N Am; 2007; 34: 403-419; Medical Management of Ectopic Pregnancy. ACOG Practice Bulletin No. 94 [June 2008]. American College of Obstetricians and Gynecologists. Obstet Gynecol 2008; 111: 1479–85.

previous tubal surgery, prior in-utero DES exposure, and the current use of an intrauterine contraceptive device (IUD).

The most common location for an ectopic pregnancy is in the fallopian tube. This occurs in more than 95% of all ectopic pregnancies. Other less common sites include the abdomen, ovary, and the cervix. Ultrasound is the best method to determine the location of the pregnancy. Location is important because it may have an impact on the whether medical and/or surgical therapy will be used to treat the ectopic.

Ectopic pregnancy is usually manifested by the classic triad of abdominal pain, amenorrhea, and vaginal bleeding. The most common physical findings are usually abdominal and adnexal tenderness. Although these are the most common clinical manifestation for an ectopic pregnancy, the actual clinical presentation can vary. Thus, one should have a high index of suspicion when a patient who is at high risk for an ectopic pregnancy, such as someone with a history of a prior ectopic pregnancy, has clinical signs and symptoms of an ectopic, and has a positive pregnancy test.

The early diagnosis of an ectopic pregnancy can reduce the associated maternal morbidity and mortality with these cases. After a history and physical examination, the diagnosis of an ectopic pregnancy can be established with a combination of ultrasound, usually transvaginal, in combination with a serum HCG level. Confirmation of an intrauterine pregnancy tends to exclude an ectopic pregnancy. However, patients can, in rare circumstances, have a concomitant intrauterine and ectopic pregnancies. If the patient has previously undergone assisted reproduction, her risk for a combined intrauterine and an ectopic pregnancy is quite high and approaches 1%.

After the diagnosis of an ectopic is established, medical and/ or surgical therapy are available to treat the patient. The approach chosen will, in many instances, depend on the clinical circumstances at that time. For example, if the patient is clinically unstable, a surgical approach is generally recommended. In the past, the surgical approach was exploratory laparotomy with partial or complete removal of the tube (salpingectomy). However, laparoscopy has now become the surgical technique of choice because it is associated with a faster recovery, shorter hospitalization, less adhesion formation, and lower hospital costs. In the clinically stable patient, surgery is often preferred over medical therapy in the following circumstances:

1.   A ruptured ectopic pregnancy;
2.   An ectopic pregnancy at imminent risk of rupture;
3.   A patient unable to comply with medical treatment;
4.   Medical therapy with methotrexate is contraindicated.

In general, contraindications to medical therapy include a tubal pregnancy larger than 5 cm or evidence of fetal cardiac activity during ultrasound. If surgery is chosen, the surgeon must decide between salpingectomy, partial or complete, and salpingostomy. Salpingostomy is a surgical technique that involves opening the tube and removing the products of conception. This technique is preferred today because it permits the retention and preservation of tubal function. Additionally, salpingostomy is associated with higher intrauterine pregnancy rates subsequently. However, the newer techniques with "in-vitro fertilization" seem to offer a greater likelihood of future childbearing.

As an alternative to surgical therapy, medical management with methotrexate in eligible patients appears to be clinically effective. Methotrexate has been the most successful method of medical management for ectopic pregnancy and is currently the medical treatment of choice. The indications for methotrexate therapy include the following:

1. A hemodynamically stable patient;
2. A patient able to return for follow-up care;
3. The patients desire for future fertility;
4. A nonlaparoscopic diagnosis;
5. Methotrexate is not contraindicated;
6. General anesthesia poses a risk to the patient.

Additionally, methotrexate may be used when the unruptured mass is 3.5 cm or less, there is no cardiac activity, and serum HCG level does not exceed 6,000 to 15,000. Along with the contraindications to medical management, the use of methotrexate is also contraindicated in women who are breast feeding, have immunodeficiency, underlying liver disease, alcoholism, abnormal renal or pulmonary function, or ulcer disease, or a known sensitivity to the drug. Methotrexate may be used as a single or multiple dose protocol. Both have similar success rates and side effects. However, single dose appears to be a more cost effective approach. Regardless of whether a single or multiple dose approach is chosen, the patient should be advised of the potential side effects of the drug and the need for close follow-up. With single dose therapy, each patient should return for a serum HCG level and evaluation on days 4 and 7 following the start of therapy. The subsequent management will depend on her clinical findings and serum HCG levels.

The most frequent claims in connection with an ectopic pregnancy relate to the failure to establish an early diagnosis. This is especially true in cases in which the patient is at high risk for an ectopic pregnancy and also has signs and symptoms consistent with an ectopic pregnancy. However, the timing of the diagnosis, early or late, does not necessarily impact the clinical management. As such, there is not much, other than pain and suffering, which can be attributed to the delayed diagnosis. Thus, delayed diagnosis cases appear to be limited to a certain extent to those claims which involve maternal death or permanent disability, such as a permanent neurologic injury or the sequelae from a blood transfusion (HIV or Hepatitis B or C).

[d] Fetal Developmental Defects

Wrongful birth and life claims have increased over the past decade. These claims can be divided into pre– and post– conception liability. The current litigation trend has been to focus on post-conception rather than pre-conception claims. Post-conception liability claims typically arise in one or more of the following clinical settings:

1. Failing to offer chromosomal screening to any pregnant woman in the first or second trimester. In the first trimester, this includes biochemical markers and ultrasonography. If an abnormality is suspected based on the screening test results, an amniocentesis or CVS should be done. In the second trimester, abnormal screening will lead to a genetic amniocentesis.
2. Failure to offer a genetic evaluation to a woman in the reproductive age group prior to and/or during pregnancy with history of a prior child with a congenital abnormality or a family history of an inherited disorder.
3. The failure to refer or evaluate a pregnant patient with prior exposure to a potentially teratogenic agent.
4. Exposing a patient to radiation, or failing to explain the potential risks of the same.
5. Failing to detect the presence of a structurally or chromosomally defective fetus, or to properly interpret evidence suggestive of an abnormal fetus, such as a suspicious ultrasound.
6. Failing to offer the patient a reproductive choice in the circumstances of a fetus with the diagnosis of a structural or chromosomal abnormality.

The scope of potential pre-conception litigation may broaden further in the future through the emergence of legal theories that may recognize medical responsibility towards the as yet unborn, and even unconceived, individual. For example, the knowledge that uncontrolled or poorly controlled diabetes is conducive to the occurrence of congenital abnormality in the offspring may be a case in point.

Intrinsic to many of the relevant malpractice claims filed, and to some of the relevant court decisions, are misconceptions about the magnitude of teratogenic impact of a drug or agent. Since 2–3% of the population or more is born with a congenital abnormality, and since few pharmacologic agents in current medical use have a teratogenic potential exceeding one out of one thousand or more exposures, it is readily apparent that it is only rarely that any particular drug can reasonably be tied to a particular outcome with a probability exceeding 50%, (thus supporting proof of damage supported by the "preponderance of evidence"). To reach, or even approach, the degree of probability that would amount to a "proximate cause," the result needs to be specific to the particular drug in question, and the exposure must coincide in time with that stage of embryogenesis during which the affected organ or system is in the process of active development. To assist in the analysis of a potential claim, the reader is referred to the Reprotox website at www.reprotox.org. This website is an information resource on the environmental hazards to human reproduction and development.

Whereas the number of drugs that can reasonably be tied to a predictable occurrence of some type of developmental abnormality is relatively low, decisions concerning termination of pregnancy on account of preceding exposure to pharmacologic agents or irradiation are made with relative frequency. Surprisingly, such decisions are rarely made on account of exposure to industrial chemicals (a theoretically higher teratogenic risk). Instead, most relevant decisions rest upon exposure to drugs or to small doses of radioactive agents with minimal or nonexistent teratogenic potential. In this circumstance, many physicians will refer the patient to for genetic counselling and/or offer them a reproductive choice. Many times, the patient will seek a termination because of her concerns about delivering a child with a "drug induced" abnormality and regardless of whether the defect is related to the drug or teratogen exposure in question. Such recommendations, and the performance of abortions on the basis of that indication, are in keeping with today's medical-legal climate and many patients' attitudes toward pregnancy termination.

[e] Decisions Pertaining to Termination of Pregnancy

[i] Elective terminations

Matters relating to women's rights for terminating unwanted pregnancies are interwoven with philosophical, economic, religious, social and political overtones. After more than three decades, the country remains divided on the issue of abortion on demand. While the mantra from the left is that it is "women's right to decide," the question of the value of potential life and when life begins is spouted from the right. No matter which side one is on in this matter, the issue appears to remain a hotly debated one with no end in sight. From a medical-legal perspective, a woman's motivation for an elective pregnancy termination is primarily irrelevant. The reason is that the medical malpractice claims that arise from a termination of a pregnancy are related to the performance of the pregnancy termination procedure itself and to adequate follow-up.

Complications pertaining to a pregnancy termination are related primarily to the gestational age of the pregnancy. For example, abortions performed by dilatation and vacuum extraction during the first trimester carry few and relatively moderate short-range risks. Whereas, more advanced gestations at the time of the abortion carry greater risks. The risks attendant to a D&C are similar to the ones discussed earlier in this chapter under spontaneous abortions.

Thus, medical malpractice claims related to a pregnancy termination include the following:

1. The failure to terminate the pregnancy. In general, there is no pathological specimen because of the cost inefficiency of undertaking a pathological evaluation in all terminations. What is done is that the specimen is evaluated by the operating surgeon and the chart is documented accordingly. The issue is not so much the failure to evacuate the uterus as it is appropriate follow-up of the patient after the procedure. If she returns and the continued pregnancy is confirmed, the procedure can be repeated and the pregnancy terminated.

2. Uterine perforation during the procedure. In connection with abortions performed in more advanced gestations (14–24 weeks), uterine perforations with injuries to organs in the abdominal cavity and even those in the retroperitoneal space (ureter) have occurred in connection with the dilatation and evacuation technique. Here, the issues pertain to compliance with standard surgical technique and attention to signs suggesting intraoperative injury. In addition, appropriate short and long range follow-up, and timely response to her complaints that may indicate the emergence of one or another complication. In essence, the medical-legal focus is on the management of the uterine perforation.

3. The failure to administer Rh immune globulin to an Rh negative woman with resultant Rh sensitization in future pregnancies.

[ii] Medically indicated termination of pregnancy

With the availability of elective abortion, the importance of determining medical indications has decreased. Nonetheless, a distinction may be significant for at least two reasons: (1) to permit a patient who is opposed to abortion to take advantage of the option of termination of pregnancy for reasons of personal health or that of possible or probable occurrence of fetal abnormality; (2) to allow medical and paramedical personnel who are philosophically opposed to participating in abortions performed on demand to provide care for patients who require pregnancy termination for medical reasons. Once again and regardless of the patient's motivations, the reason for the medically indicated pregnancy termination should be documented in the medical record.

§ 15.04 Frequent Complications of Pregnancy

[1] Hypertensive Complications of Pregnancy[6]

Approximately 5% of all pregnancies are complicated by some form of hypertension. However, this incidence may vary depending on the population studied or the criteria used to establish the diagnosis. If the diagnosis is established, hypertensive disorders are associated with an increased risk of maternal and perinatal morbidity and mortality. Accompanying this increased risk of an adverse maternal and fetal outcome is a greater potential for a medical malpractice claim.

The first step in gaining an understanding of hypertensive disease complicating pregnancy is to master the definitions for chronic hypertension, preeclampsia, superimposed preeclampsia, and eclampsia. *Chronic hypertension* is defined as hypertension prior to pregnancy or before the 20th

---

[6] Chronic Hypertension in Pregnancy. ACOG Practice Bulletin No. 29 [July 2001, Reaffirmed 2008]. American College of Obstetricians and Gynecologists. Obstet. Gynecol 2001; 98: 177-185 [hereinafter *Chronic Hypertension in Pregnancy*]; Phelan JP: Obstetric critical care issues in prematurity. In: *Prevention of Prematurity*. Phelan JP (ed.), *Clinics in Perinatology*. W.B. Saunders Co., Philadelphia, Pennsylvania, 1992; 19(2):449-59 [hereinafter Phelan, *Obstetric critical care*]; Phelan JP: Medico-Legal Implications of the Diagnosis of Pre-eclampsia, In, *Pre-eclampsia Etiology and Clinical Practice* 2007. Lyall and Belfort,Editors Cambridge University Press, Cambridge, New York, pp. 522-534 [hereinafter Phelan, *Medico-Legal Implications*]; Chronic Hypertension: In, Guidelines of Perinatal Care 6[Th] Edition American Academy of Pediatrics and The American College of Obstetricians and Gynecologists 2007 pp 192-195 [hereinafter *Chronic Hypertension*]; Diagnosis and Management of Preeclampsia and Eclampsia. ACOG Practice Committee No. 33 [January 2002, Reaffirmed 2008]. American College of Obstetricians and Gynecologists. Obstet Gynecol 2008; 2002; 99: 159–167 [hereinafter *Diagnosis and Management*].

week of gestation. The blood pressure criteria are a systolic pressure of 140 mmHg or higher, a diastolic pressure of 90 mmHg or higher or both. In general chronic hypertension is present prior to the pregnancy and persists longer than 12 weeks postpartum. The pathological basis for chronic hypertension is usually related to underlying renal vascular disease or cardiovascular pathology (essential hypertension). In contrast, gestational hypertension or preeclampsia may be gestationally induced by a mechanism that is still poorly understood. *Preeclampsia* or toxemia of pregnancy can be distinguished from chronic hypertension because it appears after 20 weeks gestation in a patient who had normal blood pressures prior to the pregnancy and usually disappears during the postpartum period. Preeclamptics must satisfy the previously stated blood pressure criteria (systolic $\geq$ 140 mmHg and/or diastolic $\geq$ 90 mmHg) and usually have proteinuria. They may also have additional signs and symptoms of preeclampsia such as headache, scotomata (usually described as flashing lights, lightening bolts, sparklers), or epigastric pain. *Superimposed preeclampsia* is the development of preeclampsia in a woman with chronic hypertension. The diagnosis of superimposed preeclampsia is suggested in a chronic hypertensive when worsening hypertension is associated with significant proteinuria. *Eclampsia* is the clinical manifestation of seizures not attributable to other causes in a patient with preeclampsia. Preeclampsia may also be clinically manifested as *HELLP Syndrome.* The eponym, HELLP, means hemolysis, elevated liver enzymes, and low platelets (thrombocytopenia).

Hypertension complicating pregnancy is associated with an increased risk of adverse fetal and neonatal outcomes such as intrauterine growth restriction (IUGR), intrauterine fetal death (IUFD), placental abruption, and premature birth. The likelihood of these adverse consequences arising is more often linked to the severity and duration of the hypertension and to the association of other organ damage such as that encountered in cases of HELLP Syndrome. Since IUGR is increased in these cases, it is essential to monitor fetal growth during the pregnancy. This is usually done with clinical assessments using fundal height measurements and the selected use of ultrasonography.

Notwithstanding, the timing of delivery may also vary depending on the severity of the hypertension and any related hypertensive sequelae. As such, the obstetrician may be compelled, in selected circumstances, to deliver the baby prior to the patient's due date. The proper timing of delivery is complicated because there are multiple variables that go to determining the timing of delivery. These include but are not limited to the gestational age of the pregnancy, the severity of the maternal hypertension, steroid administration, fetal lung maturation, fetal growth characteristics, the impact of bed rest and in-hospital therapy, and evidence of fetal health. In a preterm pregnancy, the obstetrician must carefully balance the aforementioned risks of the mother and the baby. When these complications arise in a term pregnancy, the decision to deliver is less complicated.

[a] Preexisting Hypertensive Conditions[7]

Chronic hypertension, as previously defined, usually but not always requires some form of antihypertensive medication prior to and during the pregnancy to control blood pressure. When chronic hypertension precedes conception, the patient is usually being seen by her primary care physician and is already taking antihypertensive medications. Depending on the medication, the obstetrician will usually continue the current medication. At the initial prenatal visit or soon thereafter, the obstetrician will begin a baseline evaluation of her hypertension to determine the extent of the disease. Ideally, the primary care provider should have evaluated her prior to conception to ascertain potentially reversible causes and end organ involvement of the hypertension such as the heart and kidneys. The baseline evaluation will vary depending on the duration and extent of the disease. Often times, the obstetrician will refer the patient to the perinatologists for evaluation and future shared management of the pregnancy. In essence, the obstetrician will handle the prenatal care and conduct the delivery and the perinatologist will manage the pregnancy with respect to the chronic hypertension and its effects on the mother and the fetus. Obviously, variations on that management approach can also be done so long as the patient receives appropriate care.

Chronic hypertensive patients usually but not always require antihypertensive medications during pregnancy. Scientific data has shown that women with mild hypertension (systolic pressure of 140 – 179 mmHg or diastolic pressure of 90 – 109 mmHg) do well during pregnancy and do not, as a standard of care require antihypertensive therapy. Moreover, there is no scientific evidence to date that antihypertensives in this clinical situation will improve perinatal outcome. However, therapy should be instituted or reinstated in women whose blood pressures exceed 150–160 mmHg systolic or 100 – 110 mmHg diastolic.

Medications commonly prescribed to treat chronic hypertension during pregnancy include but are not limited to the following:

---

[7] See Chronic Hypertension in Pregnancy, *supra* note 6; See Chronic Hypertension, *supra* note 6.

1. Methyldopa;
2. Labetalol–a combined alpha and beta blocker;
3. Nifedipine–a calcium channel blocker;
4. Diuretics

With few exceptions, these agents are not associated with an increase in adverse outcomes. For example, diuretics are effective and safe but should not be used in the circumstances of preeclampsia or IUGR. However, diuretics are used on a short term basis to treat maternal pulmonary edema. Beta-blockers such as atenolol are contraindicated because of their known association with IUGR. Lastly, angiotensin-converting enzyme (ACE) inhibitors are also contraindicated in the second and third trimester due to an increased risk of an adverse perinatal outcome among users.

In general, most of the increased maternal and perinatal morbidity associated with chronic hypertension is associated with the development of superimposed preeclampsia or IUGR. Thus, the clinical management of chronic hypertensives is to monitor maternal health with frequent prenatal visits, blood pressure checks and kidney function studies throughout the pregnancy. With respect to the fetus, the issue is whether the fetus is growing adequately. This can be monitored through serial fundal height measurements during the pregnancy. If there is evidence of inadequate growth, ultrasonography is useful for the purpose of documenting fetal growth and the adequacy of the amniotic fluid volume. In patients with chronic hypertension, many investigators have recommended a baseline ultrasound at 18–20 weeks gestation, a repeat ultrasound between 28 and 32 weeks gestation and monthly ultrasounds thereafter. If IUGR is suspected or documented, fetal surveillance testing is warranted to assure fetal well-being.

[b] Preeclampsia and Gestationally Induced Hypertension[8]

The most frequently encountered type of hypertension in gestation is preeclampsia. Eclampsia means seizures. As such, preeclampsia means prior to seizures and is clinically manifested by a significant rise in maternal blood pressures in association with a high level of proteinuria. Preeclampsia is considered mild when the following are present:

---

[8] *See* Chronic Hypertension in Pregnancy, *supra* note 6; *See* Phelan, Obstetric critical care, *supra* note 6; *See* Phelan, Medico-Legal Implications *supra* note 6. *See* Chronic Hypertension, *supra* note 6; *See* Diagnosis and Management, *supra* note 6.

1. An elevation of the blood pressure ≥ 140 mm Hg systolic or ≥ 90 mm Hg after 20 weeks gestation in a woman with previously normal blood pressures.
2. Proteinuria is defined as the urinary excretion of 0.3 grams or more of protein in a 24 hour urine specimen

Preeclampsia is considered severe if one or more of the following are present:

1. Blood pressure levels of ≥ 160 mm Hg systolic or ≥ 110 mm Hg diastolic on 2 occasions at least 6 hours apart while the pregnant patient is at bed rest.
2. Proteinuria of 5.0 grams or more in a 24 hour urine collection or 3+ or greater on 2 random urine samples collected at least 4 hours apart.
3. Oliguria (Little Urine) of less than 500 ml in a 24 hour period.
4. Cerebral or visual disturbances.
5. Pulmonary edema or cyanosis
6. Epigastric pain
7. Impaired liver function
8. Thrombocytopenia or evidence of hemolysis
9. Fetal growth restriction in the setting of preeclampsia.

In general, the management of preeclampsia depends on the severity of the disease and the gestational age of the pregnancy. In the term pregnancy, the treatment is delivery with magnesium sulfate for seizure prophylaxis during labor and following delivery. During labor, intermittent antihypertensive therapy may be necessary to control markedly elevated maternal blood pressures. It is also important to remember that magnesium sulfate is not an antihypertensive. Its impact on maternal blood pressure is of short duration as patients return to pre-treatment blood pressures within minutes of its administration. The route of delivery should not be affected by the presence of preeclampsia. Attempted vaginal delivery or cesarean, depending on the clinical circumstances, are acceptable approaches. Most clinicians reserve cesarean for the usual obstetrical indications.

In the preterm pregnancy, the clinical management will vary and depend primarily on whether maternal and/or the fetal condition is worsening. Since prematurity carries significant risks, in and of itself, expectant management with steroids to enhance fetal lung maturity and reduce the likelihood of intraventricular hemorrhage is often attempted to prolong the pregnancy for enhanced fetal survival and a more favorable perinatal outcome. Suggested criteria for delayed delivery or expectant management in the hospital are as follows:

1. Normal fetal surveillance testing such as a reactive fetal heart rate pattern or a normal BPP;
2. The fetus should be appropriately grown for its gestational age;
3. Estimated gestational age < 33 weeks gestation;
4. Absent cerebral signs and symptoms;
5. Absence of labor

In addition, a plan should be established to indicate the maternal and/or fetal circumstances that would warrant delivery. While the patient is in the hospital, neonatal services should be consulted to keep the patient properly informed of the fetal chances of survival and disability for her gestational age. If the pregnancy is less than 32 weeks gestation, weekly neonatal consultation is sometimes clinically necessary because of the changes in neonatal outcome with advancing gestation.

If the patient improves with inpatient therapy, home healthcare with appropriate follow-up is an acceptable option for the patient with ready access to the hospital and an appropriate home environment. The use of antihypertensive agents to control maternal blood pressure is also acceptable. But, as previously discussed, their use will not prevent the development of preeclampsia. The long term goal of preterm preeclampsia management is to attain fetal lung maturity. Once fetal lung maturity is attained, delivery is usually indicated. The suggested criteria for the outpatient management of mild preeclampsia are as follows:

1. Highly reliable patient.
2. An absence of labor.
3. Normal fetal surveillance testing.
4. Normal liver enzymes and platelet count.
5. Ultrasound evidence of an appropriate for gestational age fetus.
6. Absent epigastric or right upper quadrant pain.
7. Absent cerebral signs and symptoms.
8. Proteinuria $\leq$ 1.0 grams total protein for 24 hours or $\leq$ 2+ on a dipstick urine.
9. Systolic blood pressure $\leq$ 150 mm Hg, or diastolic pressure $\leq$ 100 mm Hg.

Fetal lung maturity can be established by inference from an accurate gestational age (39 weeks gestation with accurate dates) or by amniocentesis to assess the lecithin to sphingomyelin (L/S) ratio and the presence of phosphatidylglycerol (PG).

Since the preterm management of preeclampsia and severe preeclampsia are complex pregnancy disorders appropriate consultation with an OB/GYN or maternal-fetal medicine subspecialist would be recommended. In many circumstances, these cases can be co-managed with a family practitioner in the same facility.

When the degree of hypertension at the time of the hospitalization is considered severe, the initial goal is to stabilize the patient and to determine the extent of the disease process. This means that the patient will require laboratory studies to exclude acute fatty liver of pregnancy, HELLP Syndrome, and thrombotic thrombocytopenic purpura (TTP) and a period of time to monitor maternal blood pressures and fetal health. During this time, the patient should receive magnesium sulfate for seizure prophylaxis and antihypertensives to lower maternal blood pressure in the case of the following blood pressure elevations: diastolic pressures $\geq$ 110 mmHg and/ or systolic pressures $\geq$ 180 mmHg. The clinical basis for reducing these blood pressures is to reduce the likelihood of a cerebrovascular accident or heart failure. After stabilization, the next decision is whether and how to deliver the patient. If delivery is decided, the route of delivery should be covered with the patient. It is important to note that cesarean is not mandated in cases of severe preeclampsia or eclampsia and will depend on a number of clinical factors that include but are not limited to the gestational age of the pregnancy, the estimated fetal weight, the inducibility of the cervix, the ability to control maternal blood pressure, maternal ability to clot, fetal condition, the presence of labor and many other clinical considerations.

[c]   Common Areas of Litigation in the Hypertensive Patient[9]

In view of the risks of hypertensive complications of gestation, their diagnosis rests upon long established principles that carry a broad support of medical opinion. The most common allegations arising from the management of cases with preeclampsia are often related to the severity of the maternal or fetal injury. When considering litigation in these types of cases, prematurity with all its neonatal sequelae is a significant confounding variable not only for the clinician but also for the litigator. The reason is that so many of these children will have to be delivered prematurely regardless of their ability to live independent of the mother because maternal health takes precedence over fetal health. Thus, neonatal sequelae are the direct result of delivery due to maternal health considerations. Bearing that in mind, the most common areas of litigation in the preeclampsia arena are as follows:

---

[9] *See* Phelan, Medico-Legal Implications, *supra* note 6.

1. The failure to investigate significant blood pressure elevations during prenatal care for evidence of preeclampsia.
2. In a patient with the diagnosis of mild preeclampsia or mild hypertension, the failure to institute fetal surveillance testing and/or to provide close maternal follow-up.
3. The failure to intervene in a term pregnancy with probable preeclampsia when there is no potential fetal benefit to continued pregnancy.
4. Failure to refer hypertensive patients to an obstetrician/gynecologist or maternal-fetal subspecialist for consultation and/or continued care.
5. Hospital or office telephone liability from the following:
    a. Failure to diagnose.
    b. Delay in treatment.
    c. Improper treatment from an inadequate evaluation.
    d. Failure to follow-up.
    e. Ineffective office or hospital telephone procedure.

[2] Dysmaturity or Fetal Growth Matters

The term "maturity" refers to the stage of development optimally suited for the change from in utero to an extrauterine existence. This transition occurs at the moment of birth: the end of an aquatic existence and the beginning of one dependent upon respiratory function.

The term "dysmaturity" defines the lack of the earlier outlined quality, namely, the capability of maintaining an adequate metabolic equilibrium either in utero (where nutrients and oxygen are provided through the placenta) or with the change of the environment in the outside world where oxygen and nutrients are absorbed through the lungs and intestinal tract respectively.

The prototypes of dysmaturity are "prematurity" and "postmaturity." The first defines a state where the fetus is eminently capable of thriving in the intrauterine environment but is ill equipped to do so outside the uterus. The second defines a fetus well suited for thriving in the extrauterine environment but no longer capable of doing so in utero.

The process that leads to fetal maturity is growth. The rate of growth under optimum circumstances is predictable for any species of animal. Subject to modifying factors, the growth, particularly in the advanced stages of gestation, can be unduly fast or slow. In case of the first alternative, the fetus is large for the calculated gestational age (LGA) whereas in the second, the opposite is true (SGA).

Accelerated growth (i.e., excessive weight gain and linear growth) usually occurs during the third trimester. In most instances, the same is true for retarded growth (asymmetrical growth retardation). In a considerable proportion of the instances, however, the deceleration of the growth process begins in early gestation (symmetrical growth retardation). The recognition of inappropriate growth rate is a major goal of the antenatal care.

The fetus may be small for its gestational age through a variety of pathological factors, including maternal hypertensive complications, multiple pregnancy, congenitally determined (hereditary) anomalies, intrauterine infection, nutritional deficiencies, maternal smoking and high altitude. Excessive fetal growth most frequently is brought about by maternal diabetes and by hereditary factors (including predisposition for diabetes in the family). The recognition of inadequate fetal growth is hindered by the ever-existent possibility of miscalculation resulting from human error, conception following a period of amenorrhea, or a postconception bleeding episode. However, the availability of ultrasonography has reduced the likelihood of erroneous due dates and enhanced the ability to determine the adequacy of fetal growth.

[a] Preterm Births[10]

Prematurity which is defined as a birth prior to 37 weeks gestation is the leading cause of neonatal morbidity and mortality and is estimated to occur in 10–15% of all pregnancies. Of all preterm births, it is estimated that approximately half are the result of premature labor with the rest equally divided between those with premature rupture of the membranes (PROM) or an indicated delivery due to maternal or obstetrical complications of pregnancy. In recent times, premature births have also been subdivided based on the gestational age and classified as follows: Near term or late preterm– 34 0/7-36 6/7 weeks gestation; preterm– 24 0/7-33 6/7 weeks gestation. When contrasted with term neonates, the earlier the gestational age is the pregnancy at the time of delivery, the greater is the likelihood of an

---

[10] Late-preterm infants. ACOG Committee Opinion No. 404 [April 2008]. American College of Obstetricians and Gynecologists. Obstet Gynecol 2008; 111:1029-32; Antenatal Corticosteroid Therapy for Fetal Maturation. ACOG Committee Opinion No. 402 [March 2008]. American College of Obstetricians and Gynecologists. Obstet Gynecol 2008; 111:805-7; Management of preterm birth: In, Guidelines of Perinatal Care 6Th Edition American Academy of Pediatrics and The American College of Obstetricians and Gynecologists 2007 pp 175-185; Management of preterm labor. ACOG Practice Bulletin No. 43 [May 2003]. American College of Obstetricians and Gynecologists. Obstet Gynecol 2003;101:1039-47; Assessment of risk factors for preterm birth. ACOG Practice Bulletin No. 31[October 2001, Reaffirmed 2008]. American College of Obstetricians and Gynecologists. Obstet Gynecol 2001; 98: 709-716.

adverse neonatal outcome. It is also evident that very low birth weight neonates, birth weight < 1,500 grams, should be delivered in a facility equipped to handle these newborns when technically feasible.

Of all the conditions in Obstetrics, prematurity is the most frequent cause of neonatal death and developmental delay. The risks are extremely high in neonates with low birth weight (<1000 grams). The major area of concern is the neonates at the threshold of viability. These are the neonates with a birth weight less than 750 grams or an estimated gestational age less than 26 weeks gestation. This group of neonates represent 1% of all births and 50% of all the neonatal mortality. As one can readily see, neonatal outcome, death and neurodevelopmental impairment is linked to birth weight, gestational age and gender.

With the introduction of tocolytic therapy into clinical practice during the late 70s and early 80s, the hope was that these agents could effectively reduce the likelihood of preterm births through the inhibition of premature labor. Although the use of such medications became a standard practice throughout the world, these drugs had virtually no impact on the prematurity rate. Thus, claims against an obstetrician for failure to suppress premature labor or to prevent a preterm birth with tocolytic agents are seldom justifiable.

It continues to be true that there is no effective method of preventing most preterm births. Thus, tocolytic agents, such as ritodrine, nifedipine or magnesium sulfate serve solely to prolong the pregnancy an estimated 2–7 days. This amount of time does permit the administration of steroids to enhance fetal lung maturity and to permit transfer, if medically necessary and/or technically feasible, to a higher level facility. The probable basis for the ineffectiveness of tocolytics is often related to underlying placental abruptions or latent intrauterine infections.

In the past, as it is today, the route of delivery in neonates less than 1,500 grams remains a split opinion among actively practicing clinicians. While cesarean delivery is associated with improved neonatal outcome, especially among neonates whose mothers had previously received prenatal steroids, the vertex presenting fetus can clearly deliver vaginally. But, it is important to note that fewer fetuses with birth weights less than 1,500 grams are being delivered vaginally. In contrast with the cephalic presenting fetus, it is generally believed that in the case of breech or other noncephalic presentations, cesarean delivery is preferred.

However, delivery by cesarean in a preterm pregnancy can be associated with significant maternal surgical complications. This is due primarily to the difficulty encountered at the time of the cesarean because of an undeveloped lower uterine segment in the preterm uterus. In the circumstance of an undeveloped lower uterine segment, a low vertical or classical cesarean may be obstetrically necessary to deliver the fetus and to avoid lateral extensions into the vascular supply of the uterus. The importance of the type of uterine incision rests with the future risks of uterine rupture in a subsequent pregnancy. For example, if the uterine incision is not confined to the lower uterine segment, there is a greater risk of a uterine rupture in a subsequent pregnancy. When the uterine incision is not confined to the lower uterine segment, a note in the chart about the downstream consequences of such an incision should be documented. These would include the following:

1. The type of uterine incision;
2. The patient has been advised of the following:
   a. The type of uterine incision.
   b. The risks of uterine rupture in a future pregnancy.
   c. The patient is not a candidate for a vaginal birth after a cesarean (VBAC) in a future pregnancy.

The use of forceps to deliver the preterm fetus with an estimated fetal weight less than 1500 grams in a vertex presentation, though less common today than in prior years, remains an acceptable approach to deliver these fetuses. Regardless of where one travels in the United States, a respectable number of clinicians continue to use forceps for the delivery of these infants. The theoretical basis for the use of the forceps is to "protect" the preterm fetal head from injury during its descent through the maternal pelvis. Since the pelvic dimensions are likely to be adequate in cases of premature delivery, careful use of the obstetric forceps probably entails minimal risk. In those patients who have chosen to attempt vaginal delivery, cesarean delivery is reserved for the usual obstetrical indications. One important reminder, the use of vacuum to deliver the preterm fetus (< 34 weeks gestation) is contraindicated.[11]

[b] Premature Rupture of the Membranes (PROM)[12]

Premature rupture of the membranes means the rupture of membranes prior to the onset of labor. These cases of PROM are subdivided based on gestational age into preterm (PPROM– < 34 weeks gestation) and PROM

---

[11] Operative Vaginal Delivery. ACOG Practice Bulletin No.17 [June 2000, Reaffirm 2008]. American College of Obstetricians and Gynecologists. [hereinafter Operative Vaginal Delivery].

[12] Premature rupture of membranes. ACOG Practice Bulletin No. 80 April 2007]. American College of Obstetricians and Gynecologists. Obstet Gynecol 2007; 109:1007-19; Preterm premature rupture of the membranes: In, Guidelines of Perinatal Care 6Th Edition American Academy of Pediatrics and The American College of Obstetricians and Gynecologists 2007 pp 178-185.

patients with a gestational age of 34 weeks or greater. PROM patients are usually managed with induction/augmentation of labor or expectant management (await the onset of labor) depending on the duration of ruptured membranes. The risk of intrauterine infection (chorioamnionitis) is related to the duration of the ruptured membranes. Thus, the standard of care is split with respect to the induction or augmentation of labor versus whether to wait for labor to start on its own. If the pregnant woman presents with signs and symptoms consistent with an intrauterine infection, cesarean is not indicated per se. In the circumstance of chorioamnionitis, cesarean is reserved for the usual obstetrical indications because of the increased maternal risks associated with operative delivery in the presence of underlying chorioamnionitis. The most common reason for a cesarean in this scenario is due to changes in fetal status due to the infection.

In the patient with PPROM, expectant management is generally the rule. The consequences form PPROM include but are not limited to preterm delivery, perinatal infection, pulmonary hypoplasia (underdevelopment of the fetal lungs), and deformation syndrome (facial and limb abnormalities). The latter two conditions are more commonly associated with PPROM in very early pregnancy. It is also important to remember that about 25% to 35% of all preterm births are related to PPROM.

At this time, the clinical management of the PPROM patient undergoing expectant management is usually reserved for those pregnancies with a gestational age from 24 0/7 weeks gestation to 33 6/7 weeks gestation. When PPROM occurs in the previable pregnancy expectant management is unlikely to result in the delivery of a healthy child. Therefore, those patients with a previable pregnancy should be counselled about the downstream consequences to her and her previable fetus.

The expectant management of a PROM patient varies throughout the United States. Nevertheless, the clinical management will include but is not limited to the following:

1. Electronic FHR monitoring. The use of fetal monitoring varies from continuous to intermittent with the focus on variable FHR decelerations that reflect umbilical cord compression. The mere presence of variable decelerations does not mandate delivery. Unless fetal status changes dramatically, fetal BPP are not indicated on a daily or weekly basis.

2. Repeated pelvic examinations are discouraged because of their potential impact on the latency of labor (shortening the period from PPROM to the start of labor) and the potential introduction of

infection. Digital examinations are generally avoided until there is active labor or the decision has been made to induce labor.

3. Prophylactic antibiotics are usually given to potentially prolong gestation and to prevent the vertical transmission of Group B Streptococcus.

4. All women with PPROM should be cultured for Group B Streptococcus.

5. A single course of antenatal steroids should be administered to potentially prevent neonatal RDS and IVH.

6. Tocolytics are acceptable and are typically used in the short term management of PPROM patients to permit the administration of antenatal steroids and antibiotics and to facilitate maternal-fetal transport.

7. Bed rest in the hospital is indicated. However, complete bed rest is not obstetrically necessary in all patients. Its use will depend on the clinical circumstances. The safety of expectant management at home has not been established.

In general, delivery in PPROM patients is indicated when there is evidence of infection, fetal jeopardy, or active labor. To date, the cause, prevention and optimum treatment of premature rupture of the membranes remain among the unresolved problems of contemporary obstetric practice.

[c] The Postterm Pregnancy[13]

The principle that unexplained prolongation of pregnancy beyond the 41st week carries serious fetal risks was first developed in Great Britain in the early 1970s. The underlying pathophysiology that predisposes a pregnancy to extend beyond the 41st week of gestation is poorly understood. But, what is clear is that some fetuses develop intrafetal shunting and begin to redirect blood flow in the fetal compartment away from the kidneys and other organ systems preferentially to the fetal brain. The triggering mechanism responsible for this physiologic adjustment is unknown but has been linked to meconium stained amniotic fluid and infection. Nevertheless, the intrafetal shunting causes impaired renal perfusion and decreased fetal urinary output. Ultimately, this leads to the development of oligohydramnios and a greater risk of cord compression.

The definition of a postterm pregnancy is one which has extended to or beyond 42 weeks gestation (294 days) or 14 days past the patients EDC. With

---

[13] Management of Postterm Pregnancy. ACOG Practice Bulletin No.55 [September 2004]. American College of Obstetricians and Gynecologists. Obstet Gynecol 2004; 104:639-46.

accurate dating, it is estimated that 7% of all pregnancies are considered postterm. The term post dates is no longer appropriate and is inaccurate reflection of the actual clinical circumstances.

Because of the increased risk of intrauterine fetal death (IUFD), opinions vary with regard to the appropriate course of action in the postterm pregnancy. At that point in the pregnancy, the patient has clearly three options available to her. These options are induction of labor with or without cervical ripening, primary or repeat cesarean or expectant management with some form of fetal surveillance testing. Thus, informed consent plays a role with respect to the clinical management beyond this point.

Assuming a patient did not choose delivery, expectant management requires some form of fetal surveillance testing. As of the writing of this chapter, there is no single test that ensures a favorable fetal outcome. However, most, but not all, obstetricians will do a modified BPP (AFI and NST) or a complete BPP twice a week. The timing of delivery depends on the results of the fetal surveillance testing, the inducibilty of the cervix, and the onset of spontaneous labor or PROM. In many instances, the finding of oligohydramnios or FHR decelerations on the NST will trigger intervention.

The conduct of the labor is similar to any other pregnancy and will include intrapartum fetal monitoring. However, the advanced gestational age of the pregnancy is associated with a greater likelihood of large for gestational age fetuses. As a consequence, labor abnormalities such as protraction and arrest disorders, prolongation of the second stage of labor, and dysfunctional uterine activity pattern are more common (§ 15.05[1]).

[3]   Third Trimester Bleeding[14]

It is customary to divide antepartum hemorrhage related to pregnancy into three major categories: (1) abruption of the placenta; (2) placenta previa; or (3) vasa previa or bleeding from an aberrant vessel. In a relatively small minority of cases, the bleeding that occurs antepartum is not of obstetric origin and may be due to urinary or gastrointestinal bleeding. In many cases, the cause of the bleeding may result from cervical trauma during coitus, decidualization changes on the cervix, cervical erosion or malignancy or blood dyscrasias.

The clinical management of these clinical conditions does vary to a certain extent. But, the initial clinical evaluation is similar and depends on the clinical circumstances. The clinical approach includes but is not limited to

---

[14] Francois, K. E., Foley, M.R.: Antepartum and Postpartum Hemorrhage In, *Gabbe SG: Obstetrics:Normal and Problem Pregnancies, 5th ed*. Churchill Livingstone Elsevier, Philadelphia, Pennsylvania, 2007 pp 456-485.

the following:

1. No digital exams until placenta previa has been excluded;
2. Continuous electronic fetal monitoring to assess fetal status;
3. Speculum examination to look for evidence of cervical or vaginal trauma and to estimate the extent of the vaginal bleeding;
4. Uterine examination;
5. Ultrasound evaluation;
6. Pertinent laboratory studies.

[a] Abruption of the Placenta[15]

Abruption of the placenta is the premature separation of the normally implanted placenta prior to the delivery of the fetus. Placental abruptions occur in approximately one in 140 pregnancies and are also subclassified as to the degree of placental separation, *partial* or *complete*. In the absence of vaginal bleeding, the placental abruption is termed *concealed*. The clinical manifestation of a typical placental abruption is the presence of abdominal pain, dark red vaginal bleeding, and uterine contractions. Although separation of the placenta from the uterine wall is largely unpredictable, abruption occurs at a greater frequency in pregnancies complicated by the following:

1. Patient with a prior placental abruption;
2. Maternal hypertensive disease such as preeclampsia or chronic hypertension;
3. Maternal smoking;
4. Substance abuse such as cocaine, amphetamines;
5. Multifetal gestations;
6. Maternal trauma such as motor vehicle accidents;
7. Premature rupture of the membranes;
8. Increasing parity;
9. Rapid uterine decompression in association with Multifetal gestations or polyhydramnios.

The clinical management of a placental abruption depends on a host of factors but primarily relate to the gestational age of the pregnancy, the severity of the abruption, and maternal and fetal status. These factors relate primarily to the timing and route of delivery. For example, a 30% placental abruption is usually associated with FHR abnormalities. A placental abruption of 50% or more usually results in fetal or neonatal death and

---

[15] *Id.*

permanent disability among surviving neonates. Thus, it is easy to understand that a complete placental abruption is almost always associated with fetal or neonatal death. Of the few survivors with a complete abruption, permanent neurologic impairment is generally the rule.

The ability to diagnose a placental abruption, to a large extent, rests with the presence of the classic history of painful dark red vaginal bleeding. Depending on the duration of the abruption, one may see port wine amniotic fluid with rupture of the membranes. Uterine examination will normally demonstrate uterine activity and uterine tenderness. The uterine tenderness is usually localized to one aspect of the uterus or an area of localized hypertonus. However, a concealed abruption can also occur and is more difficult to diagnose. While patients with a concealed abruption may present with pain, patients with a posterior concealed abruption usually go undiagnosed due to the lack of identifiable abdominal pain associated with this type of abruption. Sonographic examination may confirm an abruption, but, ultrasound evaluation is more reliable for confirming an anterior or lateral placental abruption as opposed to one that is implanted posteriorly. Again, the extent of the abruption will dictate whether the fetus will manifest FHR abnormalities on the fetal monitor strip. The severity of the abruption also dictates maternal condition. The more severe is the abruption, the greater is the likelihood of a maternal clotting abnormality. Thus, pertinent laboratory studies to exclude a clotting problem are usually obtained.

In the circumstance of a placental abruption, the timing and route of delivery depends on the gestational age of the pregnancy and maternal and fetal status on admission to the hospital. If maternal and fetal conditions are stable, vaginal birth can be attempted. In most cases, the patient will already be in spontaneous labor and will just require ongoing assessment of maternal and fetal status. Infrequently, induction or augmentation of labor with oxytocin may be obstetrically necessary, and its use is within the standard of care in the appropriate clinical setting. In many cases, cesarean will be performed not only because of an unstable fetus as indicated by the fetal monitor strip, but also because of the mere presence of an abruption. With an abruption, there is the potential risk of a maternal clotting abnormality. In the face of a maternal clotting abnormality, cesarean is delayed, even in the face of "fetal distress," until the pregnant woman has received sufficient replacement clotting factors to permit operative intervention.

Potential claims are usually linked to the following:

1. Failure to recognize changes in fetal status during labor as a sign of a placental abruption;

2. Failure to assess clotting status of the mother prior to operative intervention;
3. Failure to have adequate blood products available at the time of delivery;
4. Failure to recognize the association between maternal trauma such as a motor vehicle accident and a placental abruption.

[b] Placenta Previa[16]

Placenta previa is defined as the implantation of the placenta over or adjacent to the cervical opening. At term, the incidence of placenta previa is around 4 in 1000 pregnancies. The typical clinical manifestation of a placenta previa is painless vaginal bleeding in the latter half of pregnancy. Placenta previas are classified according to the amount the placenta covers the cervical os (opening): *Complete* –The placenta completely covers the opening; *Partial*– The placenta partially covers the opening of the cervix; *Marginal*–The placenta is within a short distance of the os. Patients more likely to have a placenta previa are as follows:

1. Increasing parity;
2. Prior uterine surgery such as a D&C or a Cesarean;
3. Maternal smoking;
4. Prior placenta previa.

The diagnosis of placenta previa is made with ultrasound. Most often, the diagnosis is made on a routine ultrasound evaluation before the onset of any bleeding. In a patient with vaginal bleeding without a prior ultrasound evaluation, ultrasound evaluation should be done prior to a digital examination to exclude a placenta previa. Ultrasound provides the best way to diagnose a placenta previa and has around a 95% or more diagnostic accuracy. As an aside, patients early in pregnancy may carry a diagnosis of placenta previa. But, as the pregnancy advances, the placenta seems to move away from the cervical os, and there is no longer a placenta previa. Some clinicians have used vaginal ultrasound to resolve whether the patient does or does not have a previa in these pregnancies. The reason is that vaginal ultrasound in some hands carries a 100% diagnostic accuracy.

The clinical management of placenta previa can be as an outpatient in asymptomatic patients or those with small bleeding episodes that have resolved for a period of time. Outpatient care is considered in the

---

[16] *Id.*

appropriately selected patient who is not only compliant but also has ready access to the hospital in the event of a reoccurrence of vaginal bleeding.

Most patients with a placenta previa are managed primarily in the hospital. There, the patient will undergo an evaluation to determine the extent of the bleeding and its impact, if any, on maternal or fetal status. In the preterm patient, expectant management is the generally the rule with the exception of patients with persistent, heavy, vaginal bleeding. In the latter circumstance, a cesarean will be performed as soon as the clinical and laboratory evaluation has been completed and ample blood is available for transfusion. In most instances, preterm placenta previa patients with a first episode of bleeding usually stop within a short period of time after hospitalization. Since these patients are at risk for a preterm birth, steroids are usually given on the first admission to enhance FLM and to reduce the likelihood of intraventricular hemorrhage, In the Rh negative pregnant woman, Rh immune globulin should also be given. After the patient has been stabilized and observed for a period of time in the hospital, she may be sent home, if she has the proper home environment, for outpatient management. In the patient with a second bleeding episode that requires hospitalization, outpatient management may again be considered. As before with the first vaginal bleeding episode, she and her fetus must be stable for a period of time in the hospital. Once a patient has experienced 3 or more vaginal bleeding episodes and is still preterm, hospitalization until delivery is usually the case.

In the term patient with a placenta previa, cesarean delivery is indicated. When cesarean is considered in the placenta previa patient, the following factors should be taken into account:

1. Blood for transfusion should be available at the time of delivery. Depending on the clinical circumstances and the risk of placenta accreta (An accreta is the circumstance in which the placenta grows into the wall of the uterus.), 2–6 units of packed red blood cells should be available.

2. Prior to incising the lower uterine segment, the vascularity of the region should be noted. If there is considerable vascularity in the lower uterine segment, the placenta is usually implanted in that region. If so, the surgeon should consider making the uterine incision in a different location to avoid the placenta because of the risks of fetal bleeding and/or a placenta accreta.

3. The uterine incision can be low transverse and one can go through the placenta, but the maternal and fetal risks may be higher depending on the presence or absence of a placenta accreta and the speed in

which the fetus is delivered. Many clinicians try to perform a low vertical incision in the circumstance of an anterior placenta previa.

4. After the fetus is delivered, the surgeon should try to allow the placenta to deliver spontaneously. If the placenta does not separate or deliver easily, the diagnosis of placenta accreta should be suspected.

The relatively frequent association of placenta previa with placenta accreta should be noted. The risk of placenta accreta is linked to the number of prior cesareans a patient has had. Placenta accretas are classified as follows:

1. *Placenta Accreta* — An abnormal attachment of the placenta to the wall of the uterus without penetration of the muscle of the uterus. This is the most common form of placenta accreta. Depending on the clinical circumstances, a hysterectomy may or may not be required.

2. *Placenta Increta* — Placenta attachment is into but not through the muscular layer of the uterus. In this case, a hysterectomy is required.

3. *Placenta Percreta* — Here, the placenta grows through the uterine wall into the covering of the uterus (serosa) and frequently involves adjacent structures such as the bowel or urinary bladder. Ultrasound may help in identifying the patient with a placenta accreta to permit operative intervention when sufficient surgical personnel are available. The surgical personnel that may be necessary include but are not limited to a general surgeon, a gyn oncologist, and/or a surgical subspecialist, such as a urologist.

Since the hemorrhage in a placenta previa/accreta case frequently necessitates the removal of the uterus, it is advisable to obtain consent for this procedure before the need for the cesarean arises.

The most common areas of litigation involving patients with a placenta previa are as follows:

1. Performance of vaginal examination in case of antepartum hemorrhage without first ruling out the possibility of placenta previa;

2. Expectant management of the preterm placenta previa patient in a level I facility;

3. Performance of a cesarean in a placenta previa patient without adequate blood products available;

4. The failure to administer Rh immune globulin in an Rh negative gravida. This failure can lead to Rh sensitization in future pregnancies.

5.   Improper surgical technique during the cesarean such as lower segment transverse incision in case of transverse lie or going through the placenta with a resultant delay in the delivery and/or bleeding of the fetus or maternal hemorrhage with a resultant hysterectomy;
6.   Delay in surgical intervention and/or transfusion in the face of severe hemorrhage from the placental implantation site following the delivery of the placenta;
7.   Persistent attempts at removal of the placenta in case of placenta previa/ accreta;
8.   In the case of suspected placenta increta, the failure to have adequate surgical personnel available at the time of surgery.

[c] Vasa Previa

Vasa previa is a rare obstetrical condition and is due to a velamentous insertion of the umbilical cord. (The umbilical cord normally inserts into the placenta. In a velamentous insertion of the cord, the umbilical cord implants in the membranes or amniotic sac and the vessels eventually insert into the placenta). A vasa previa is the circumstance in which the umbilical cord blood vessel(s) are in the membranes in front of the cervical opening. When the membranes are ruptured, spontaneously or by the clinician, the blood vessel(s) also rupture(s). As such, bleeding from vasa previa is potentially catastrophic for the fetus. Since the available time for rescuing the fetus is usually very short, almost invariably the deteriorating condition of the fetus serves as the first warning of the need for immediate abdominal delivery.

[4]   Diabetes and Pregnancy[17]

Diabetes mellitus is observed in 3–5% of all pregnancies. Diabetes that complicates pregnancy is divided into two subclassifications—Type 1 and Type 2. Type 1 diabetes mellitus occurs early in life, due to an autoimmune process that destroys the insulin-producing cells of the pancreas. As a result, Type 1 patients require replacement insulin to maintain their blood sugars in a normal range. Type 2 diabetes mellitus, on the other hand, is the most common form of diabetes mellitus in this country and in pregnancy. Type 2 diabetes mellitus is characterized by its onset later in life, peripheral insulin resistance, relative insulin deficiency, obesity, and the development of vascular, renal, and neuropathic complications. The incidence of Type 2 diabetes mellitus is rising rapidly, related in part to increasing obesity in the

---

[17] Gabbe SG, Graves CR: Management of Diabetes Mellitus Complicating Pregnancy. Obstet Gynecol 2003; Oct; 102(4):857-68.

US population. More than half of the women who develop gestational diabetes mellitus (GDM), which represents approximately 90% of all cases of diabetes complicating pregnancy, will develop Type 2 diabetes mellitus later in life.

Gestational diabetes mellitus has been defined as the onset or first recognition of diabetes mellitus during pregnancy. The definition applies regardless of whether insulin is used for treatment or the condition persists after pregnancy. It does not exclude the possibility that the diabetes mellitus may have antedated the pregnancy. The diagnosis is made by glucose screening during pregnancy between 24 and 28 weeks gestation. Earlier screening may be done in patients with a history of GDM in a prior pregnancy, a family history of diabetes mellitus, or significant obesity. To conduct a glucose screening test, a 50 gram glucose load is given to the patient without regard to the time of day or the time of the last meal. This test is usually done when the pregnant patient presents for her prenatal care visit. While she is in the OBs office, the patient is given the 50 gram load. One hour later, a blood glucose level is obtained. If the blood glucose level is 140 mg/dl or higher, a full three hour glucose tolerance test (GTT) is required to confirm the presence of GDM. A 3 hour GTT with the patient fasting. Once a fasting blood glucose is obtained, the patient is asked to drink a 100 gram glucose load. Blood glucoses are obtained as a fasting (FBS) and then 1, 2, and 3 hours after drinking the glucose load. If 2 or more values meet or exceed the maximum allowable for that time of the test, the patient is considered to have GDM.

Once the patient is diagnosed with GDM, she is started on dietary therapy to control her blood sugars. Infrequently, a GDM patient will require insulin therapy. These patients usually respond to diet and exercise. Maternal glucose monitoring is less stringent with GDM than it is with Type 1 diabetics. If after testing for several days the patient demonstrates adequate glucose control, less frequent testing can be recommended. The primary purpose of glucose monitoring is to determine whether the patient is responding to dietary therapy and whether insulin therapy will be medically necessary for the remainder of the pregnancy. A good gauge of whether insulin therapy will be necessary is the FBS on the 3 hour GTT. If the FBS is normal, it is less likely that the patient will require insulin therapy. Prenatal visits in GDM patients are usually every 1–2 weeks until 36 weeks gestation. Thereafter, prenatal visits are usually scheduled weekly.

The clinical management of the GDM patient is to treat with diet. GDM patients can be followed until 40 to 41 weeks' gestation. In the absence of a prior stillbirth or hypertensive disease, fetal surveillance testing with the NST is begun at 40 weeks gestation with delivery planned for 41 weeks gestation.

If the GDM patient has had a prior stillbirth or has hypertension, fetal surveillance testing is generally begun at, or around 32 weeks gestation and is done twice a week. In addition, clinical estimation of fetal size and or ultrasonography is done to detect fetal macrosomia. If the estimated fetal weight is 4,500 grams or more in a diabetic pregnancy, cesarean delivery should be offered to the patient. If the GDM patient requires insulin therapy, she should be managed similar to other insulin dependent diabetics. If they are well-controlled, these patients may be allowed to progress to their due date. In poorly controlled patients, an elective delivery may be considered at 38 to 39 weeks' gestation. If delivery is scheduled prior to 39 weeks' gestation, an amniocentesis to assess FLM is required. GDM patients who have been treated with insulin or glyburide during the pregnancy should have their capillary glucose levels checked at the bedside every 1 to 2 hours during labor. If the glucose level exceeds 110 mg/dL insulin therapy should be instituted.

It is essential that the GDM patient be evaluated postpartum to determine whether she continues to have diabetes mellitus. GDM patients that required some form of insulin therapy during the pregnancy will most likely demonstrate persistent diabetes mellitus after delivery. It is estimated that approximately 15% of GDM patients will continue to have diabetes mellitus. Those patients with persistent diabetes mellitus will require ongoing diabetic care with their primary care provider or endocrinologist. Most of these patients will respond to diet and exercise. However, some former GDM patients will require oral hypoglycemic agents, and even fewer will require insulin therapy.

The clinical management of Type 1 Diabetics and GDM patients that require insulin is similar. Management includes a combination of diet, exercise, and insulin therapy. Dietary therapy consists of a caloric intake of around 2,000–2,200 calories per day. The caloric composition consists of 40–50% from complex, high-fiber carbohydrates, 20% from protein, and 30–40% from primarily unsaturated fats. The calories may be distributed 10–20% at breakfast, 20–30% at lunch, 30–40% at dinner, and 30% with snacks, especially a bedtime snack to reduce nocturnal hypoglycemia.

Insulin therapy is designed to provide adequate insulin to maintain "euglycemia" without significant hypoglycemia during the pregnancy. This is usually accomplished with a combination of short and long acting insulins. The goal is to have the following their blood glucose on a daily basis and throughout each day: FBS– 95 mg/dL, premeal $\leq$ 110 mg/dL, 1 hour postprandial $\leq$ 140 mg/dL, 2 hour postprandial $\leq$ 120 mg/dL. The ability to achieve glucose control is difficult and requires the patient to be motivated and to understand the relationship between her diet, insulin, and exercise, as well as her ability to recognize a low blood sugar and to work with her diabetic team of professionals. It is important to note that even with meticulous diabetic care, it is estimated that 70% of patients will have hypoglycemic episodes requiring intervention and approximately a third will have severe hypoglycemia with loss of consciousness. Hypoglycemia is best handled with a glass of milk for moderate hypoglycemia. In the case of severe hypoglycemia, glucagon is administered.

The antepartum management of the insulin dependent diabetic is a complex issue that involves the following considerations:

1. More frequent prenatal visits depending on the adequacy of maternal diabetic control;
2. Frequent assessment of maternal diabetic control;
3. Fetal surveillance testing beginning at, or around 32 weeks gestation or sooner depending on the clinical findings; Testing is usually done twice a week until delivery; As with any pregnancy, no single fetal surveillance test ensures a favorable fetal outcome.
4. Referral to a specialist, such as a maternal-fetal medicine subspecialist, to co-manage or manage the pregnancy;
5. Attempt to maintain the pregnancy until there is evidence of fetal lung maturity; This requires a careful balancing of the risk of fetal death and prematurity. The problem is the delayed lung maturation among infants of diabetic mothers.
6. Since diabetes mellitus is also a vascular disease, patients with underlying involvement of their heart, kidneys and eyes are at the greatest risk of an adverse outcome.
7. Preconception counseling

Preconception counseling is an important component of maternal diabetic care. This is because major congenital anomalies are linked to the adequacy of maternal diabetic control preconception. Additionally, major fetal anomalies are the leading cause of perinatal mortality in pregnancies complicated by diabetes mellitus. The types of fetal anomalies are mostly identified with the following organ systems: cardiovascular, central nervous system, sacral agenesis, polycystic kidneys, or absence of kidneys.

To reduce the likelihood of these major anomalies, the diabetic patient should be under "good glucose" control prior to conception. Since these patients are usually not seen by their obstetricians until after the pregnancy is confirmed, the obligation to provide adequate diabetic control prepregnancy usually falls on the primary care physician and/or the endocrinologist. Since most of these major anomalies can be detected with a targeted ultrasound,

ultrasound evaluation should be undertaken prior to 20 weeks gestation. This is in addition to the genetic screening that is done earlier in the pregnancy and was previously discussed in § 15.03 [1][b].

In the contemporary obstetric practice, the management of the pregnancy and the labor and delivery of a diabetic mother belongs to duly trained experts, and should take place in properly equipped and staffed facilities capable of handling infants of a diabetic mother. The clinical management of the insulin dependent diabetic in today's environment usually falls in the hands of the maternal-fetal subspecialist to help manage the diabetes and to determine the timing of delivery. In some states, diabetic programs have been shown to be effective in reducing neonatal diabetic sequelae. These programs are in collaboration with the OB and MFM subspecialist. In the absence of MFM subspecialist, internists in collaboration with the obstetrician will typically manage the pregnancy together.

The most common areas of litigation with the diabetic patient are as follows:

1. Failure to perform a glucose screening test during the pregnancy;
2. Failure to refer insulin dependent diabetic patients to an MFM subspecialist;
3. Failure to refer patients for delivery in properly staffed and equipped facility capable of handling infants of a diabetic pregnancy;
4. Failure to hospitalize diabetic patients with documented inadequate diabetic control at home;
5. Dividing obstetric and diabetic care between two physicians without coordinating efforts, and often without communicating the details of the management;
6. Failure to institute fetal surveillance testing in the insulin dependent diabetic pregnancy at, or around 32 weeks gestation. Or, the failure to perform fetal surveillance testing in the GDM patient beginning at, or around 40 weeks gestation;
7. Failure to assess fetal lung maturity in a planned delivery prior to 39 weeks gestation;
8. Failure to control maternal diabetes preconception with a resultant major fetal anomaly.

It is also interesting to note that severe diabetics with an adverse outcome are less likely to pursue litigation.

[5] Multiple Gestations[18]

Over the past 2–3 decades, there has been a tremendous increase in the frequency of multifetal gestations in the United States. Most of this increase in twins and higher order multiples are a result of the increased use of ovulation inducing agents and assisted reproductive technologies. Multifetal gestations account for approximately 3% of all live births but, are responsible for a greater proportion of the perinatal morbidity and mortality. In general, as the number of fetuses increases in utero, the number of potential complications increases exponentially. It has been reported that whereas only about 1% of all pregnancies involve twins, approximately 10% of all obstetrical malpractice claims relate to problems related to the management of multifetal gestations. It is also important to note that with the introduction of ultrasonography into the contemporary practice of obstetrics, undiagnosed twins is rarely, if at all, an issue today.

The patient carrying twins or higher order multiples are considered high risk because of the increased incidence of:

1. Congenital fetal defects
2. IUGR
    a. Twin pregnancies do not grow at the same rate as singleton pregnancies. The greater concern is the development of discordant growth among twin gestations. Discordant growth is defined as a 25% reduction in the estimated fetal weight of the smallest twin from the largest twin. Twin weight discordance is associated with structural malformations, higher perinatal morbidity and mortality, and preterm birth. Discordant growth can be caused by multiple factors which include but are not limited to infection, structural or genetic abnormalities, a partial abruption, or twin to twin transfusion syndrome.
3. Premature Delivery
    a. Approximately one-half of all multiple gestations deliver prematurely and at the time of birth, weigh less than 2,500 grams. The higher the number of fetuses in-utero, the greater is the likelihood of premature delivery prior to 32 weeks gestation. Despite the increased frequency of premature delivery, effective

---

[18] Multiple Gestation: Complicated Twin Triplet, and High-Order Multifetal Pregnancy. ACOG Practice Bulletin No. 56 [October 2004]. American College of Obstetricians and Gynecologists. Obstet Gynecol 2004; 104:869-83; Multifetal Gestations: In, Guidelines of Perinatal Care 6Th Edition American Academy of Pediatrics and The American College of Obstetricians and Gynecologists 2007 pp 185-189.

protocols or therapies to prevent prematurity have not been developed.

4. Hypertension and Preeclampsia

    a. Among twin gestations, preeclampsia is significantly higher than in singleton pregnancies. Its incidence among triplets is higher than twin gestations. In multiple gestations, preeclampsia tends to occur earlier in pregnancy and is often more severe. Also, hypertensive complications appear to be more common among multiple gestations resulting from assisted reproduction than among those which occur spontaneously. Of note, placental abruption is also significantly more frequent among twin gestations.

5. Twin to twin transfusion syndrome

    a. Twin to twin transfusion syndrome occurs as a result of the anastomosis of an artery in one twin and vein of the other twin in a monochorionic or one placenta. This results in disproportionate blood flow to one twin at the expense of the other twin. This syndrome usually becomes manifested in the second trimester. The treatment usually takes two forms: serial therapeutic amniocentesis or endoscopic laser coagulation. Serial therapeutic amniocentesis of the recipient twin's sac is done to change amniotic fluid pressures. This permits redistribution of placental blood flow and normal amniotic fluid pressures. The other approach is to do endoscopic laser coagulation to abolish the placental anastomosis. Laser therapy is usually done in the more severe forms of this syndrome. On occasion, a third approach known as selective feticide is obstetrically necessary to preserve the pregnancy. In this latter circumstance the selective feticide is accomplished by umbilical cord occlusion.

6. Diabetes mellitus

    a. The incidence of type 2 diabetes mellitus is higher among twin gestations and even higher among triplets and other higher order multiples. Unlike singleton pregnancies, the optimum timing for diabetic screening, the best test for assessing fetal health, the optimal calories, and the ideal time for delivery is currently unknown.

7. Malpresentations (This means a presentation other than head first).

8. Difficulties associated with the delivery of the second twin.

9. Postpartum hemorrhage (Hemorrhage after the delivery of the fetuses).

10. Death of one fetus

    a. A unique complication of multifetal gestations is the death of one fetus. The ability to predict the demise of one fetus in this scenario is technically not feasible today. Once a fetal demise occurs, there is a split of opinion on the subsequent management of the surviving twin. Some advocate immediate delivery, while others favor expectant management. If the death is the result of an abnormality of the fetus itself rather than maternal or placental pathology, and the pregnancy is remote from term, expectant management may be appropriate. In the situation of monochorionic twins with shared vascular anastomoses, the surviving fetus is at risk of sustaining permanent neurologic injury or death. However, by the time the fetal demise is discovered, permanent neurologic injury has probably already occurred. Thus, immediate delivery would be of limited, if any, benefit and especially in the preterm pregnancy. In many of these preterm cases, continued expectant management may be the best approach.

As a result of the higher incidence of complications related to twins and higher order multiples, most of these pregnancies are referred to MFMs for co-management or ongoing prenatal care and delivery. The clinical management of these pregnancies includes but is not limited to the following:

1. Early genetic evaluation and ultrasonography to exclude the potential for a congenital fetal defect;
2. Performance of serial sonographic examinations throughout the pregnancy to monitor fetal growth;
3. Performance of fetal surveillance testing beginning at, or around 32 to 34 weeks gestation; In some cases, testing may begin earlier depending on the clinical findings such as discordant fetal growth.
4. The timing of delivery is complicated and depends on a host of factors. In general, the development of maternal or fetal complications, such as preeclampsia will typically result in an earlier delivery. In contrast, an uncomplicated twin gestation will continue until 37 weeks gestation. Thereafter, perinatal mortality among twin and triplet gestations begins to increase at 38 and 35 weeks gestation, respectively.

In the past, the delivery management of twins focused on the best candidates for vaginal birth. In today's contemporary environment, most, if not all, twin gestations or higher order multiples are routinely delivered by cesarean. The exceptions to cesarean delivery are twins in which both fetal heads are presenting or the patient delivers soon after she is admitted to the hospital. The primary reason for a higher cesarean delivery rate among twins is the risks associated with the delivery of the second twin. These complications include fetal deterioration, trauma and placental abruption. This does not preclude attempted vaginal birth in twins or higher order multiples. Vaginal delivery can be attempted in the properly informed patient and at the appropriate level facility with adequately trained medical and nursing staff. If the OB or MFM is currently competent to conduct such deliveries, multiple gestations can be safely delivered vaginally.

The most common claims related to multiple gestations arise in the following circumstances:

1. Failure to monitor fetal growth by serial sonographic examinations;
2. Failure to institute fetal surveillance testing in pregnancies complicated by IUGR or discordant fetal growth;
3. If vaginal delivery is attempted, the failure to have appropriately trained personnel and equipment in the delivery room in the event of complications related to the delivery of the second twin;
4. Failure to refer patients to level 2 or 3 facilities for labor and delivery;
5. Inadequate intrapartum fetal surveillance for both twins during an attempted vaginal birth.

§ 15.05 Labor and Delivery

[1] Labor: Normal and Abnormal[19]

Labor is defined as progressive dilatation and effacement of the cervix in response to effective uterine activity. Traditionally, labor is divided into stages — I, II, and III, and phases — latent, active and deceleratory.

1. The first stage begins with the onset of contractions and ends with the achievement of full cervical dilatation. The first stage of labor is typically divided into 3 phases-latent, active, and deceleratory phases. While some will divide the first stage of labor into 4 phases, 3 phases appears to be a more simplistic and functional approach. The latent phase begins with the onset of uterine activity and ends with the beginning of the active phase of labor. Entrance into the active phase is usually based on the number of centimeters the patient is dilated rather than a determination of whether she is or is not in the active phase of labor. The beginning of the active phase has been defined as a cervical dilatation of 3/4 cm, 4 cm and 5 cm. While many patients

---

[19] Management of labor: In, Guidelines of Perinatal Care 6Th Edition American Academy of Pediatrics and The American College of Obstetricians and Gynecologists 2007 pp 145-146.

will have entered the active phase by 3/4 cm, many other patients will still be in the latent phase. This is especially true in patients with incomplete effacement of the cervix. Once the patient is in the active phase of labor the greatest amount of cervical dilatation occurs. Once the patient attains a cervical dilatation of, or around 8 cm, the deceleration phase begins. From 8 cm until complete dilatation (10 centimeters), the dilatation rate slows down.

2. The occurrence of full cervical dilatation heralds the beginning of the second stage of labor. It is during this stage that the fetus descends deeper into the maternal pelvis and ultimately to the delivery of the fetus. This stage ends with the expulsion of the fetus from the uterus.

3. The third stage of labor begins with the birth of the fetus and ends with the expulsion of the placenta.

[a] Physiology of Labor: Uterine Function[20]

Contractions can be demonstrated from early gestation throughout the entire pregnancy; however, it is only with the occurrence of "active" labor that the uterine contractions become coordinated in such a manner that each stimulus activates all myometrial fibers in the entire organ. This contractility pattern leads to progressive cervical dilatation through the gradual shortening of the uterine muscles. In the process the fetus is forced out of its intrauterine home.

In the past, active labor was associated with the development of painful uterine contractions. However, active labor that is associated with progressive cervical dilatation generally does not begin until several hours following the first perception of painful uterine activity. It appears likely that the transition from ineffective "Braxton-Hicks" uterine activity to effective contractions, leading to cervical dilatation coincides with the onset of true rather than false labor. This circumstance makes the distinction between inactive "latent phase" labor and "active" labor a matter of considerable practical importance.

In response to uterine contractions during the active phase of labor, the cervix gradually dilates. In the same process, the length of the cervical canal becomes reduced, a phenomenon referred to as "effacement." The effacement is considered complete when the edge of the cervix becomes paper thin. In the process of cervical dilatation and effacement, the overall shape of the uterus changes from that of a "pear" to the appearance of a "globe." As a result of retraction of the lower "passive" segment of the uterus, the latter

---

[20] *Id.*

retracts and becomes virtually continuous with the upper "active" segment of the organ. Through the opening thus formed, the fetus is expelled by the continued uterine contractions supported at this stage of the labor by the semi-voluntary actions of the patient's abdominal and pelvic muscles.

[b] Physiology of Labor: the Passenger[21]

The position occupied by the fetus in utero is a determining factor with regard to the labor process. Optimal circumstances prevail when the fetus is head first or in a vertex presentation. The process of labor is more complicated when the presenting part is not the head but is the buttocks or feet of the fetus, as in a breech presentation or when the fetus is in a transverse lie. When the presentation is transverse, vaginal delivery is impossible except in some rare instances of gross immaturity of the fetus. Since breech and transverse presentations are uncommon, and occur only in about 4% of the cases, the following discussion will center upon the mechanism of delivery in the vertex presentation.

Prior to the onset of labor, the fetus begins to accommodate to the available space in the uterine cavity and, in advanced gestation, in the pelvis. The fetus who was once a noncephalic presentation earlier in the pregnancy spontaneous converts to a head first presentation with advancing gestational age. Once the fetus is in a vertex presentation, the fetus usually remains head first. Thereafter, the fetus further accommodates to the eventual labor process by the following mechanisms:

1. By flexion of the head, a position that presents the lowest diameter of the fetal head for passage through the pelvis;
2. Application of the head into the pelvic inlet that permits optimum utilization of the available space;
3. By rotation which ensures that the greatest diameter of the fetal head adjusts to the greatest diameter of the available pelvic space.

The maternal pelvis is designed to accommodate the fetus and permits its passage through the birth canal during labor. From a functional point of view, the distinction is made among the following pelvic planes: (1) the inlet; (2) the midpelvis; and (3) the outlet. The narrowest part of the pelvic canal is the midpelvis. Accordingly, successful vaginal delivery is highly likely once the greatest diameter of the fetal head has passed the plane of the midpelvis.

When the greatest diameter of the fetal head has passed the plane of the pelvic inlet, the head is considered "engaged." Engagement is defined as

---

[21] *Id.*

when the biparietal diameter is at the level of the pelvic inlet and corresponds with a station of 0 to +1. Engagement prior to the onset of labor is uncommon in multiparous women (those who have given birth before). On the other hand, in a substantial proportion of first time mothers or those women who have not given birth before, the head becomes engaged prior to the onset of labor. The prospects of vaginal birth in a first time mother (primagravida) relate to the presence of engagement prior to the onset of labor or at the time of presentation for delivery. This means that primagravidas who present for delivery and the fetal head is not engaged; there is a greater likelihood of an abnormal labor and the need for a cesarean. These women are referred to as "unengaged primagravidas."

Through vaginal examination, the position and station of the head, as well as the dilatation and effacement of the cervix, is determined. With a vertex presentation, the reference point for the position of the fetal head is the occiput or the back of the head and its relationship to the maternal pelvis or the time on a clock with 12 being anterior towards the maternal abdomen and 6 towards the maternal rectum. Thus, a fetus with its head in an occiput anterior position or OA would have the back of its head directed towards the maternal abdomen or at 12 on a clock. If the occiput is directed straight down towards the maternal rectum or at 6 on a clock, the position of the head is described as occiput posterior (OP). A fetus in a left occiput transverse (LOT) position, the occiput is directed towards the maternal left side at 3 on the clock. In contrast, a right occiput transverse (ROT) would be directed towards the maternal right side at 9 on the clock. If the fetal head is at 4 or 5 on the clock, the fetal head is described as left occiput posterior or LOP. On the opposite side at 7 or 8 on the clock, the position would be ROP. If the occiput is above the horizontal but has not reached OA, the presentation is LOA or ROA depending on the side of the maternal pelvis the occiput is directed.

Station is defined based on the relationship of the presenting part to the midpelvis or the level of the ischial spines. The ischial spines are prominent bony projections on the lateral pelvic side walls. If the presenting part is at the level of the ischial spines or the midpelvis, the presenting part is considered at 0 station. Fetal presentations above zero station are given a negative representation and those below zero station are given a positive notation. Presently, there are two approaches used to record station. One approach divides the upper and lower halves of the pelvis into thirds and the other uses fifths. This means that an OB who divides the upper and lower halves of the maternal pelvis into thirds will describe the presenting part above zero station as –1, –2, or –3 depending on the distance above zero station. In contrast, the OB who divides each half into 5 sections, one centimeter blocks would describe the presenting part above zero as -1 through -5. If the presenting part was below zero station, a plus would be used to describe the station of the presenting part. A key question in many OB negligence cases is which system the OB uses in their practice.

During labor, the occiput rotates anteriorly to accommodate to the shape of the midpelvis which, unlike the inlet, is shortest in the antero-posterior diameter. Thus, application of the shortest (biparietal) diameter of the fetal head into the shortest available space (intersciatic diameter) facilitates the passage of the presenting part through the pelvis.

The shoulders of the fetus, the diameter of which is in rectangle with the greatest diameter of the fetal head, follow the movements of the head during its passage through the birth canal. By entering the inlet in its biparietal diameter, and rotating into the antero-posterior diameter at the plane of the midpelvis, the rotation of the head facilitates and precedes the ensuing movements of the shoulders.

When the obstetrician elects to override the normal labor process by use of instrumental delivery with the forceps or vacuum, the rotations of the shoulder may not follow that of the head. Accordingly, the above procedures are associated with on rare occasions with a shoulder dystocia.

[c] The Labor Curve: Normal and Abnormal[22]

Through a retrospective review of a large number of labors without electronic fetal monitoring in Boston, Emanuel Friedman developed the "labor curve," a widely accepted diagrammatic representation of the labor process. The "Friedman curve" divides the first stage of labor into four phases: (a) latent phase, (b) acceleration phase, (c) maximum slope and (d) deceleration phase. As pointed out earlier in § 15.05 [1], many clinicians use a 3-phase approach and combine Friedman's acceleration and maximum slope phases into one phase known as the "active phase" of labor. Recent research concludes that the Friedman curve likely represents an ideal, rather than an average, curve.

According to Friedman, the acceleration phase occurs when the cervical dilatation exceeds 0.5cm./hour, or when cervix is dilated 3/4 cm. or more. Eventually, during the maximum slope of the labor curve, the labor progresses at or in excess of 1.5cm./hour in a multipara, and at or in excess of 1.2cm./hour in a woman giving birth for the first time. In the active phase of labor, an active phase arrest is defined as absence of cervical change for 2 or more hours in the face of adequate uterine activity. In other words, a

---

[22] Id.

pregnant patient is in the active phase of labor at 6 cm, when she no longer dilates and remains at 6 cm for 2-3 hours. This would be an example of an arrest in the active phase of labor. An arrest of the active phase of labor also assumes that the uterine activity is adequate. A protracted active phase is defined as the failure to dilate at or above the rate defined by the parity of the patient in the active phase of labor. Thus, a pregnant patient in the active phase of labor who dilates at a rate of 0.8 cm / hour would be considered to have a protracted active phase.

During the second stage of labor, the key feature is descent of the presenting part. The minimum criterion of acceptable progress depends on the parity of the patient. In a multipara, descent is normally at a rate of 2cm. /hour. In the primagravida, normal descent is defined as 1 cm. / hour. Descent disorders are classified as either an arrest of descent or protracted descent. An arrest of descent would be the absence of descent over one hour. A protracted descent would be considered if the fetal presenting part descends at a rate slower than 1 or 2 cm / hour. Obviously, protracted descent depends on the parity of the patient. It is also important to remember that descent disorders do not arise prior to the second stage of labor.

Protraction and arrest disorders usually relate to a discrepancy between the size of the maternal pelvis and the size of the fetus and sometimes on ineffective uterine contractions. Although an association of the two components is probably involved in most cases of a protraction or an arrest disorder, contemporary obstetric practice attempts to identify the primary cause of labor disorder and implement treatment accordingly. In keeping with this thinking, diagnosis of one of the above mentioned complications may warrant one of the following actions in the active phase of labor:

1. Delivery by cesarean if the failure of progress or an active phase arrest is attributable to cephalopelvic (CPD) or fetopelvic disproportion or the baby appears to be too big for the mother's pelvis. Some clinicians lump the lack of progress into the term "failure to progress" (FTP) or CPD.

2. Administration of oxytocin if hypotonic uterine activity is considered to be the cause of the lack of progress, protraction disorder, or the arrest of labor.

The distinction among the above etiologic alternatives is not always easy. Nonetheless, in most instances an experienced obstetrician can make a reasonable decision with regard to the cause of inadequate or absent progress. Of particular importance is the distinction (in the case of lack of progress) between the latent and active phases of labor. No intervention is required in the presence of an abnormal latent phase with respect to the use of oxytocin or cesarean delivery. However, the subsequent management of a laboring patient who develops an abnormality of the "active phase" of labor will depend primarily on the status of the fetus. As a general rule, if the FHR pattern is normal, the labor can continue and the performance of a cesarean is not necessarily mandated. As such, oxytocin is often administered to augment the labor in an effort to achieve a vaginal birth.

Some inpatient perinatal records incorporate a labor curve, and thus invite the development of relevant notations during the labor process. However, the construction of a labor curve is frequently omitted by obstetricians and paramedical personnel in those instances where the record does not contain a printed diagram. Whereas the drawing of a curve is not a requirement in itself, it is helpful, in some circumstances, to clarify the clinical situation.

[d] Abnormalities of Lie, Presentation and Position of the Fetus

When the axis of the body of the fetus is identical with that of the body of the mother, the lie of the former is "longitudinal." When the axis is between 30 and 90 degrees the lie is "oblique" or "transverse." The fetus in a transverse lie presentation can be characterized as a "back up" or "back down" transverse lie. Cases with a persistent back up transverse lie carry a greater risk of umbilical cord prolapse than does a back down transverse lie. When the buttocks or the feet of the fetus present over the pelvic inlet, the presentation is termed a "breech" presentation. Breech presentations are further subclassified as follows:

1. *Frank*—The fetus is in a position similar to a diver in the pike position.
2. *Complete*—In this presentation the fetus is sitting with its legs crossed or Indian style.
3. *Single footling*—One foot is presenting or the fetus is standing on one leg.
4. *Double footling*—The fetus is standing up in-utero or both feet are presenting first.

Those fetuses in a nonfrank breech presentation have a greater risk of cord prolapse than do fetuses in a frank breech presentation. The incidence of a cord prolapse in a frank breech is similar to that of a vertex presentation. Whether a vaginal delivery is technically feasible depends on not only the type of breech, but also attitude of the fetal head. The attitude of the fetal head refers to whether the fetal head is flexed or deflexed. If the fetal head is deflexed, the fetal head can be in a "military position" or "hyperextended." In either case, the risks of attempted vaginal delivery are greater than if the fetal head is flexed.

When the fetal head presents first, the presentation is termed a "vertex" presentation. Vertex presentations may be characterized by which part of the fetal head is presenting. As discussed earlier in § 15.05 [1][b], the occiput is usually used to orient the location of the fetal head to the maternal pelvis. In the breech presentation, the sacrum is used as a reference point. When a different part of the fetal head presents such as the face or the brow, the reference points for these presentations are the brow and the chin, respectively. If a face presents, the chin (mentum) is used to describe the pelvic orientation. As an example, a face presentation with the chin towards the maternal rectum would be called a mentum posterior or MP. If the chin is directed anterior, the face is presentation is termed a mentum anterior or MA. As with the occiput, if the chin is transverse and directed towards the maternal left or right, the position of the face is characterized as a left or right mentum transverse or LMT or RMT, respectively. In the case of a brow or forehead presentation, the "frontum" is used to describe the position of the brow with respect to the maternal pelvis. In general, a persistent brow or persistent mentum posterior presentation mandates a cesarean.

At times, a vertex presentation may become misaligned. This occurs when the sagittal suture of the head of the fetus is off the center. Normally, the sagittal suture roughly coincides with the greatest diameter of the pelvic inlet and the position of the vertex is termed "synclitic." When the sagittal suture is displaced anteriorly or posteriorly, the terms "posterior asynclitism" and "anterior asynclitism" are applicable. These two types of asynclitism also are associated with the names of Litzman and Naegele respectively. A posterior asynclitism is a severe complication that seldom corrects itself during the labor process. The opposite is true for the anterior (Naegele's) asynclitism.

Normally, during the process of passage through the birth canal, the small fontanelle of the vertex rotates anteriorly to an occiput anterior or OA position. Eventually the head of the fetus is born with the occiput of the fetus occupying the space under the symphysis and the head rolling out through the birth canal in this position. In a minority of the instances (about 5–6%), the rotation is in an occiput posterior or OP position and the fetus is eventually delivered with the chin occupying the space under the symphysis. In this situation, the head does not fit snugly into the available space in the pelvic outlet and delivery often is accomplished with extensions into the maternal rectum.

[e] Cephalopelvic Disproportion or Failure to Progress (CPD or FTP)

The ability of the fetal head to pass through the bony structures of the pelvic canal is facilitated by a variety of mechanisms:

1. Some relaxation of the pelvic joints usually attributed to the effect of the hormone Relaxin;
2. The earlier mentioned flexion, application and rotation of the presenting part;
3. The ability of the fetal cranium to mold, and thus adapt to the available space during the process of labor.

When all of the above mechanisms fail, cephalopelvic disproportion (CPD) or failure to progress (FTP) is present, and vaginal delivery is impossible. The term fetopelvic disproportion incorporates these terms as well.

[f] Obstetric Anesthesia and Analgesia[23]

Pain relief has long been promoted as a modality of obstetric management beneficial to both mother and fetus, but in recent years its role during labor and delivery has received a more realistic implementation. Currently, analgesia with a variety of narcotics continues to be the mainstay of labor pain relief. With the increased availability obstetrical anesthesiologists, the use of continuous epidural anesthesia through an infusion pump has increased and become the "Lexus" of intrapartum pain relief. As such, epidural anesthesia enjoys considerable popularity in contemporary obstetric practice. When administered by an experienced anesthesiologist, the technique interferes little with uterine activity and the progression of the labor. On rare occasions, epidural anesthesia may slow down uterine activity and reduce the pelvic musculature contribution to the rotation of the head during its passage through the pelvis. As a result, epidural patients may require oxytocin augmentation of their labors or instrumental deliveries.

In addition, epidural anesthesia may be associated with FHR abnormalities and ineffective maternal pushing during the second stage. Once an epidural is administered, it is not uncommon for the pregnant woman to experience hypotension. This is usually managed by position change to the left lateral recumbent position, an increase in IV fluids and treatment with ephedrine to help elevate the maternal blood pressure. When

---

[23] Analgesia and anesthesia: In, Guidelines of Perinatal Care 6Th Edition American Academy of Pediatrics and The American College of Obstetricians and Gynecologists 2007 pp 151-155.

the maternal blood pressure drops, this may interfere with uteroplacental perfusion and be associated with a transient episode of FHR decelerations. In most circumstances, the FHR decelerations disappear once the maternal blood pressure is back to normal. In rare cases, the FHR decelerations may continue or the FHR may remain down. In that latter scenario, if remedial measures fail to correct the fetal condition, delivery may be clinically necessary.

If the pregnant woman is unable to push effectively due to the epidural anesthesia, the typical clinical response is to discontinue the epidural or let it wear off. After a period of time, she will once again be able to push effectively and delivery will follow after a reasonable period of time.

In contemporary practice, epidural and spinal anesthesia are the most common anesthetic techniques used for vaginal and cesarean delivery. Since epidural anesthesia can be used for intrapartum analgesia, its use for instrumental and cesarean delivery makes it the preferred technique. In the case of "fetal distress," general endotracheal anesthesia is commonly used.

Litigation related to the use of anesthesia relates to the following:

1. The failure to detect that a spinal anesthetic has moved up to high on the patient's spinal column and has affected her ability to breath;
2. Delayed implementation of a successful anesthetic in the face of "fetal distress."
3. The failure to recognize a post anesthesia spinal cord infection;
4. The loss of a catheter tip in or around the injection site after epidural anesthesia;
5. The failure to recognize an esophageal intubation;
6. Failure to effectively monitor fetal status following the implementation of an epidural anesthetic.

[2] The Birth Process: Normal and Abnormal

[a] The Mechanism of Delivery

In the North American continent, great importance is attached to the delivery process. Accordingly, the delivery itself is conducted by the obstetrician who, by long established protocol, participates only intermittently in the conduct of the labor. Some medical insurers stipulate that payment of the fee of the obstetrician hinges upon his or her participation in the delivery process irrespective of the numerous hours spent at the bedside of the patient during the long and tedious process of labor. In contrast, in many parts of Europe, the obstetrician focuses on the provision of antenatal care and the conduct of the labor process, while the delivery itself is left to the midwife.

Only when the childbearing process is abnormal is intervention justifiable and, by design, productive. Since this situation only prevails in about 10–15% of the cases, it readily follows that interference in the overwhelming majority of cases not only is not desirable but is counterproductive. Thus, not surprisingly, in those instances when the outcome is unfavorable, meddlesome management on the part of the obstetrician, or the paramedical personnel, is recognizable with disturbing frequency.

The head of the fetus passes through the midpelvis after anterior rotation of the occiput that had previously passed the pelvic inlet in, or near to, the occipito-transverse position. The 90 degree rotation that follows brings the occiput under the symphysis where it snuggly fits under the pubic bones. In the same process, the shoulders rotate into a transverse position and pass through the pelvic inlet at the same time as the head negotiates the midpelvis, i.e., the space between the sciatic spines. As the biparietal diameter of the head passes through the midcavity, the head moves to the outlet while the shoulders descend towards the midplane of the pelvis. At this time, the head begins to "crown"; in other words, a goodly part of the cranium becomes visible in the vagina even between contractions. The determination of the whether the head will deliver with the next contraction is not easy. At the same time, an episiotomy may or may not be obstetrically necessary to facilitate the delivery and / or to reduce the likelihood of a perineal laceration.

It is seldom mentioned in contemporary obstetric textbooks that in the course of a normal delivery process, particularly in patients giving birth for the first time, the emergence of the head may not be followed by the delivery of the shoulders until the occurrence of the next uterine contraction. The time between the two events permits rotation of the shoulders to occur, accompanied by external rotation of the head of the fetus, in association with a uterine contraction and supportive action of the abdominal and pelvic muscles. This mechanism provides for the accomplishment of rotation of the shoulders by a purposeful, well designed and extremely powerful force, the uterine contraction in conjunction with maternal valsalva. In the same process, the contraction of the uterus gradually constricts the chest in such a manner that the force of the compression moves from the area of the lower lobes of the lung towards the trachea. In this process, a large amount of mucus and, when applicable, meconium is squeezed out of the respiratory tree and pours out of the mouth of the fetus. At the peak of this contraction, the extraction of the shoulders is almost always easy. In contrast, an attempt at extraction between contractions may entail considerable difficulties.

When the fetal head delivers, it is important for the clinician to check for a nuchal cord. In about 25% of all pregnancies, a tight or loose nuchal cord will be encountered at the time of delivery. In many cases, a single nuchal cord is found, but, in rare circumstances, 2 or more nuchal cords may be identified. When the OB encounters a loose nuchal cord, the nuchal cord is simply lifted over the head and the baby is delivered. If the cord is tight such that delivery is not technically feasible, the cord is doubly clamped, is cut between the clamps, and is unravelled. Once unravelled, the baby can be delivered.

Prior to cord clamping, the fetus may lose or gain blood depending on the height of the fetus in relation to the location of the placenta. For example, it has been shown immediately following delivery the fetus looses blood to the placenta when lifted higher than the placenta. When the fetus is held below the level of the placenta, the fetus gains blood from the placenta. Such a phenomenon is conducive to overloading the circulation of the neonate, and increases the risk of hyperbilirubinemia due to the breakdown of an excessive amount of red blood cells. Thus, in most instances, it appears beneficial to clamp and cut the cord several seconds after the birth of the child, prior to significant gain or loss of the circulating blood volume.

After delivery of the baby and the cutting of the cord, the third stage of labor begins. Here, the focus is on the delivery of the placenta. This is usually accomplished within 10–15 minutes following the birth of the child. Waiting patiently and noninterference with the process are usually conducive to full separation of the placenta from the uterine wall, and its uneventful expulsion. It is during and after this time that complications relating to postpartum hemorrhage (§ 15.07[1]) can arise.

[b] Operative Vaginal Deliveries—Forceps/Vacuum[24]

Operative vaginal delivery or the use of forceps or vacuum to facilitate delivery of the fetus is no longer the mainstay of obstetrical care and is becoming a dying art. Cesarean delivery and spontaneous vaginal deliveries are the rule. That does not mean that forceps and vacuums are no longer used, but their use has declined considerably during the past two decades. During this time, many institutions have made vacuum deliveries the preferred approach for operative vaginal delivery, and in the process, have put forceps on the path towards extinction. Nonetheless, operative vaginal delivery constitutes about 5–10% of all deliveries today. Even though the use of operative vaginal delivery has declined, forceps or vacuum will continued to be a viable option in selected circumstances to safely deliver the fetus.

---

[24] *See* Operative Vaginal Delivery, *supra* note 11;Belfort MA: Operative vaginal delivery 10 components of success. OBG Management February 2007; Vol.19 (2) 54-70 [hereinafter 10 components].

Regardless of the instrument used to facilitate delivery, the indications for use are the same and are as follows:

1. Maternal exhaustion;
2. Potential fetal jeopardy;
3. To shorten the second stage of labor in selected patients.

When an indication is present, the criteria for the types of forceps or vacuum are also similar. The criteria for the types of forceps or vacuum illustrated herein use the 5 cm system to describe station below zero station and are as follows:

1. Outlet Forceps/Vacuum
    a. The fetal scalp is visible at the opening of the vagina without separating the labia.
    b. The fetal skull has reached the pelvic floor.
    c. The sagittal suture is in the anteroposterior diameter or right or left occiput anterior or posterior position.
    d. The fetal head is at or on the perineum.
    e. Rotation of the fetal head does not exceed 45°.
2. Low Forceps/Vacuum
    a. The leading point of the fetal skull is at +2 cm or lower but the fetal head is not on the pelvic floor.
    b. The rotation of the fetal head is 45° or less (LOA or ROA to OA, or LOP or ROP to OP).
    c. The rotation of the fetal head is 45° or more.
3. Midforceps/vacuum
    a. The station is higher than +2 cm and the head is engaged.
4. High Forceps/Vacuum is contraindicated.

During the use of the vacuum, rocking movements or torque should not be done because of the increased risk to the fetus. If the vacuum is used, the provider should apply steady traction in the line of the birth canal.

When the use of forceps and vacuum are compared, the general finding is that maternal trauma and the need for anesthesia was significantly greater with forceps deliveries. In contrast, vacuum deliveries were more likely to be associated with neonatal trauma than were forceps deliveries. Vacuum related neonatal injuries include but are not limited to the following: subgaleal hematomas (The fetal scalp is lifted off its attachment to the skull. This results in bleeding under the scalp.), cephalohematomas (a collection of blood under the periosteum of the skull.), and intracranial bleeding. Forceps have also been associated with corneal abrasions and ocular injury from misapplication as well as cephalohematomas and intracranial hemorrhages. Along those lines, vacuum deliveries are contraindicated prior to 34 weeks gestation. The use of forceps and/or vacuum are contraindicated in the following circumstances:

1. The fetus has a bone demineralization condition such as osteogenesis imperfecta.
2. The fetus has a bleeding disorder such as Von Willebrand's disease, alloimmune
    thrombocytopenia, or hemophilia.
3. The fetal head is unengaged.
4. The position of the fetal head is unknown.

Critical to the use of forceps or the vacuum is that the provider has sufficient training, skill, and experience in their use and evidence of current competency. In addition, operative vaginal delivery should only be performed by persons with privileges for such procedures, and in clinical settings in which personnel are readily available to perform a cesarean in the event the forceps/vacuum fails. According to Belfort,[25] there are 10 components to a successful operative vaginal delivery and are as follows:

1. Consider the prior obstetrical history.
2. Ensure adequate informed consent.
    a. The issue of informed consent in the case of operative vaginal delivery is complicated by the fact that their use does not arise until the patient is in the second stage of labor. At that point of the labor, the patient is usually tired, is in pain and may be under the influence of narcotic analgesics. Informed consent under those circumstances would be difficult at best. As such, the author and others[26] have advocated informed consent with respect to operative vaginal delivery during prenatal care and especially during the third trimester. The timing of informed consent during the third trimester removes the potential issues of duress, coercion, or prior narcotic administration.
    b. Nonetheless, informed consent for operative vaginal delivery routinely occurs during the second stage of labor and continues to be the standard of care. As part of that process, she should be

---

[25] See 10 components, *supra* note 24.
[26] *Id.*

sufficiently aware that cesarean is an appropriate alternative to the attempted forceps or vacuum.

c. Once the patient has been informed and agrees to the operative vaginal delivery, she must remain cooperative and willing to undergo the procedure.

3. Abdominal examination prior to forceps/vacuum use.
    a. Estimate the fetal weight.
    b. Is the fetal head engaged?
    c. To ensure the fetal head is in an OA position.

4. Is the fetal head molded?
    a. If the fetal head is molded, the risk of intracranial injury is related to the severity of the molding.

5. Be aware of the fetal head position during labor.
    a. It is generally easier to determine the position of the fetal head in the first stage of labor than it is in the second stage of labor.

6. Be sure to have an indication to apply the forceps/vacuum.

7. Forceps and vacuum should not be used sequentially and is considered unacceptable.
    a. Vacuum manufacturers recommend that the use of the vacuum should be limited to 3 traction episodes. It is important to note that most fetuses will deliver within 3–4 traction episodes. Additionally, the greater are the number of traction episodes, the greater are the risks of fetal injury.

8. Was there a clear endpoint and exit strategy for the use of the forceps/vacuum?
    a. Did the provider document and explain the exit strategy to the patient?
        1. This means was there a discussion with the patient and her family that when certain conditions were met that the procedure would stop and a cesarean would be performed?
    b. Was the goal of the provider to achieve a vaginal birth rather than the health and safety of the pregnant woman and her fetus? For example:
        1. Was there a continued pursuit of vaginal birth with the use of the vacuum for an excessive number of traction episodes?
        2. Did the patient resume pushing after a failed attempt at an operative vaginal delivery?

9. Was the operative vaginal delivery documented adequately?
    a. Was there a preoperative note and did it include but was not limited to the following information:
        1. Estimated fetal weight

   2. Maternal pelvis adequate
   3. Degree of molding
   4. Cervical exam at the time
   5. Indication for the procedure
   6. Patient agreement to the procedure.
 b. Was there a postoperative note and did it include but was not
     limited to the following information:
   1. The type of instrument used
   2. The duration of use and the number of traction episodes
       a. A device, known as the Vaculink, has been developed and
           is currently in use to document and records on the fetal
           monitor strip the number and duration of the traction
           episodes, the amount of pressure used in the application,
           and the number of pop-offs.
   3. Maternal/fetal complications of the procedure
   4. Inform the parents of the outcome
   5. Post vaginal delivery pelvic exam findings
10. Were the parents informed of the outcome — good or bad?

The use of Belfort's 10 step analysis to successful operative vaginal delivery can also be used as a road map in a forceps or vacuum case.[27]

Litigation with respect to the use forceps/vacuum tends to arise in the following areas:

1. The performance of a high forceps or vacuum procedure;
2. Misapplication of the forceps blades resulting in injuries to nerves or the eye;
3. Use of excessive force with the forceps leading to direct injury of the skull (fractures, extensive lacerations);
4. Failure to discontinue forceps/vacuum attempt after an initial failure;
5. Prolonged efforts to deliver the fetus vaginally in the presence of potential fetal jeopardy;
6. Failure to alert newborn personnel that the fetus was delivered with forceps or vacuum.

---

[27] Id.

[c] Shoulder Dystocia[28]

Shoulder dystocia represents one of the true obstetrical emergencies. Once the shoulder is entrapped under the symphysis pubis, limited time is available to deliver the fetus prior to fetal death or permanent brain damage. Presently, there are two definitions for a shoulder dystocia. One definition is entrapment of the shoulders that requires ancillary maneuvers to deliver the fetus. The other definition is probably more objective and incorporates the time from emergence of the fetal head until the delivery of the shoulders. This latter definition uses a head-body interval of one minute and the requirement of ancillary maneuvers to relieve the entrapped shoulders. This means that if the head-body interval is less than a minute, there was no shoulder dystocia.

To relieve an entrapped shoulder, several techniques are currently available such as the following:

1. McRobert's maneuver (Hyperflexion of the hips);
2. Wood's or Rubin's Corkscrew maneuvers (Rotation of the shoulders);
3. Delivery of the posterior arm;
4. Suprapubic pressure.

When these maneuvers fail and the fetus remains undelivered, two techniques are available in addition to repeating the prior maneuvers. Those two maneuvers are the Zavanelli maneuver and a symphysiotomy. The Zavanelli maneuver involves recreating the cardinal movements of labor in reverse and literally pushing the fetus back into the uterus. Once the fetus has been pushed back into the uterus, a cesarean is performed to deliver the fetus. In contrast, the performance of a symphysiotomy requires simply cutting the symphysis pubis, a cartilaginous structure. Once the pubic bone is separated, the fetus will usually deliver.

---

[28] Shoulder dystocia. ACOG Practice Bulletin No. 40 [November 2002; Reaffirmed 2008]. American College of Obstetricians and Gynecologists. Obstet Gynecol 2002; 100:1045-50;Benedetti, T.J., Gabbe, S.G.: Shoulder Dystocia. A complication of fetal macrosomia and prolonged second stage of labor with midpelvic delivery. Am. J. Obstet. Gynecol. 1978; 52:526-529; Bofill, J.A., Rust, O.A., Devidas, M., Roberts, W.E., Morrison, J.C., Martin, J.N. Jr.: Shoulder dystocia and operative vaginal delivery. J. Matern. Fetal. Med. 1997; 6: 220-224; Gherman RB, Ouzounian JG, Goodwin TM. Brachial plexus palsy: an in utero injury? Am J Obstet Gynecol 1999; 180: 1303-7; Ouzounian JG, Korst LM, Ahn MO, Phelan JP: Shoulder dystocia and neonatal brain injury: Significance of the head-shoulder interval. Am J Obstet Gynecol 1998; 178(2):S244; Fetal Macrosomia: ACOG Practice Bulletin No. 22 [November 2000]. American College of Obstetricians and Gynecologists. Washington, D.C.

An issue commonly encountered but is not unique to a shoulder dystocia is that the child may sustain a brachial plexus injury (Erb's Palsy) or a partially paralyzed arm. In the past, the medical belief was that this injury was alleged to be related to "excess traction" at the time of delivery. However, recent scientific evidence has clearly established that brachial plexus injuries are unrelated to traction and are due to circumstances outside the control of the obstetrical provider.[29] One exception to that rule is the use of fundal pressure at the time of delivery. This technique should never be used to assist in the delivery of the shoulders. The use of fundal pressure not only exacerbates and prolongs the shoulder dystocia but also increases the probability of causing or worsening a brachial plexus injury.

An additional concern with a shoulder dystocia is the potential for fetal or neonatal death or permanent brain damage. The likelihood of death or permanent brain damage hinges on the head-body interval. According to Ouzounian and associates,[30] fetuses with a previously normal fetal monitor strip who were delivered within 5 minutes from the time the head emerged did not die or become brain damaged. A head-body interval between 5 and 7 minutes was a gray zone. In this time interval, some neonates were normal and others died or were brain damaged. After a 7 minute head-body interval, the risk of death or permanent brain injury rose significantly. Whether those time intervals apply to a fetus whose FHR pattern is abnormal prior to the onset of the shoulder dystocia is unknown at this time.

With respect to shoulder dystocia, the medical-legal issue typically comes down to whether the shoulder dystocia was reasonably foreseeable or should the obstetrical provider have been on notice of the potential for a shoulder dystocia. There are three clinical circumstances that give rise to a potentially foreseeable shoulder dystocia. Those are as follows:

1. A history of a prior shoulder dystocia.
2. Satisfying _all 3_ of the Bennedetti-Gabbe Triad.[31] If one or more are rebutted, the risk of shoulder dystocia is no greater than the general laboring population.
    a. Fetal Macrosomia as set forth by ACOG:[32]
        (1) In a diabetic pregnancy, an EFW of 4,500 grams or greater.
        (2) In a nondiabetic pregnancy, an EFW of 5,000 grams or greater.

---

[29] _See_ Gherman et al., _supra_ note 28.

[30] Ouzounian JG, Korst LM, Ahn MO, Phelan JP: Shoulder dystocia and neonatal brain injury: Significance of the head-shoulder interval. Am J Obstet Gynecol 1998; 178(2):S244.

[31] _See_ Benedetti & Gabbe, _supra_ note 28.

[32] Fetal Macrosomia: ACOG Practice Bulletin No. 22 [November 2000]. American College of Obstetricians and Gynecologists. Washington, D.C.

  b. A midpelvic forceps or vacuum procedure
  c. A prolonged second stage of 2 hours or longer.
3. A vacuum to delivery interval in excess of 6 minutes.[33]

In the absence of these three clinical situations, a shoulder dystocia is not reasonably foreseeable and should not have been anticipated by the obstetrician. This means that an alternative route of delivery, such as a cesarean was not warranted. However, the finding of an EFW of 4,500 grams or more in a diabetic pregnancy or 5,000 grams or more in a nondiabetic pregnancy or of a history of a prior shoulder dystocia does require maternal informed consent regarding the option of a cesarean delivery.

Fetal macrosomia is often alleged as something that should have been detected prior to delivery, and if fetal macrosomia had been detected, a cesarean could have been done and the shoulder dystocia. The problem is that estimating fetal weight is difficult and notoriously unreliable regardless of whether the EFW is done clinically or sonographically. The reason for the difficulty is that there is no way to weigh the baby inside the uterus. Errors in EFW go both ways – some overestimate and others underestimate the fetal weight. Until there is a more reliable technique to estimate fetal weight, errors in fetal weight estimates will always plague the obstetrical community.

To better handle shoulder dystocias and enhance communication, all hospitals are required to conduct critical events drills on the management of shoulder dystocias. This means that the nursing staff must practice these drills on a regular basis. This does not include the OB staff. For the OB staff to be required to participate in these drills, the OB staff which is independent of the hospital must incorporate the shoulder dystocia drills as a condition of reappointment to the medical staff. If the drills are not made a requirement, there is no obligation for any member of the OB staff to regularly participate in these drills.

Cases of shoulder dystocia and subsequent brachial plexus injuries, neonatal death or permanent brain damage usually fall into the following categories:

1. In a patient with a history of a prior shoulder dystocia, the failure to sufficiently document the shoulder dystocia and to inform the patient of the risk of shoulder dystocia in any future pregnancy;
2. In a patient with a prior shoulder dystocia, the failure to provide adequate informed consent and to offer her a cesarean in all future pregnancies;

---

[33] *See* Bofill et al. *supra* note 28.

3. The use of fundal pressure as part of the management of the shoulder dystocia;
4. The failure to recognize that Bennedetti-Gabbe Triad has been satisfied and the continued pursuit of a forceps delivery;
5. The failure to recognize that vacuum to delivery interval has exceeded 6 minutes;
6. The failure to practice shoulder dystocia drills.

[d] Management of Intrauterine Fetal Death

Intrauterine fetal death is an infrequent obstetrical finding. In most instances, the cause of the fetal death is unknown and usually nonpreventable. However, the presence of a fetal demise is conducive to the development of diffuse intravascular coagulation (the inability to clot) about four weeks following fetal death. As a result, and also for psychological reasons, it is consistent with prevailing standards of practice to terminate the pregnancy once fetal death has been demonstrated. When the presentation is longitudinal, labor can usually be induced by vaginal application of prostaglandin depending on the gestational age of the pregnancy followed by oxytocin stimulation. When the presentation is transverse and an external cephalic version is unsuccessful, the evacuation of the uterus may require cesarean.

Unlike the fact of fetal death itself, complications arising from the management of fetal death in utero seldom serve as a background for malpractice litigation.

[3] Intrapartum "Fetal Distress"[34]

The term "fetal distress" has been applied more broadly as new technical tools have permitted the assessment of fetal wellbeing in everyday clinical practice. As a result, the often loose application of the term has frequently led to its unduly liberal use in clinical practice and to misinterpretation of its implications in malpractice claims. Therefore, it has been recommended that

---

[34] Inappropriate Use of the Terms Fetal Distress and Birth Asphyxia. ACOG Committee Opinion No. 326 [December 2005]. American College of Obstetricians and Gynecologists. Washington, D.C. [hereinafter Inappropriate Use];Phelan JP: What Constitutes Fetal Distress? OBG Management 1999; 11:5(May): 78-91;Electronic fetal heart rate monitoring: research guidelines for interpretation. National Institutes of Child Health and Human Development Research Planning Workshop. Am J Obstet. Gynecol. 1997; 177: 1385-8 [hereinafter Electronic fetal heart rate]; Phelan JP: Perinatal Risk Management: Obstetric Methods to Prevent Birth Asphyxia. Clin Perinatol 2005; 32: 1-17.

the term be removed entirely from medical terminology.[35] This is due, in part, because many physicians have varying definitions for "fetal distress."[36] These numerous definitions could be considered representative examples of how current fetal monitoring approaches (NICHD) fail to define intrapartum fetal distress specifically.[37] As a result, considerable confusion abounds as to what should constitute "fetal distress." Though these differences in opinions exist, there is considerable agreement among obstetricians that "acute fetal distress" is present when there is a sudden, rapid, and sustained deterioration of the FHR that is also unresponsive to remedial measures and terbutaline."[38] Defining "fetal distress" accordingly eliminates any clinical confusion. In support of this definition is the shorter decision to incision times among patients with that type of FHR pattern.

It is also important to emphasize what does not constitute "fetal distress." First and foremost is the presence of meconium stained amniotic fluid. In the past, clinicians had used meconium stained fluid to indicate fetal distress. The "duration of the hypoxia" was somehow equated with quantity and the degree of meconium staining. Meconium stained amniotic fluid means simply that the fetus has a patent anus and very little more. Recent scientific evidence has suggested that the presence of meconium is a probable sign of intrafetal shunting and/or oligohydramnios.

Other factors that have previously been considered as signs of "fetal distress" and a causal nexus to fetal brain injury have included the following alone at, or around the time of birth:

1.   Apgar scores;
2.   The presence of a slow heart rate;
3.   Neonatal organ dysfunction;
4.   Seizures in the nursery;
5.   Metabolic acidemia in an umbilical artery cord gas.

It is clear from all available scientific evidence that no single factor will adequately identify the fetus at risk for permanent brain damage. In general, a mutlifactorial analysis is clinically required.

---

[35] *See* Inappropriate Use *supra* note 34.
[36] *See* Phelan, What Constitutes Fetal Distress? *supra* note 34.
[37] *See* Electronic fetal heart rate *supra* note 34.
[38] *See* Phelan, Perinatal Risk Management, *supra* note 34.

[a] Cerebral Palsy and Birth Asphyxia[39]

While the global cerebral palsy (CP) rate which is the rate for all types of CP is estimated to be approximately 1 to 2 cases per 1000 live births . CP that is due to hypoxic ischemic encephalopathy (HIE) which is the primary focus in a brain damaged baby case is even rarer. It is estimated that the reported prevalence is 1 in 12,500 live births and is a reflection that the rate has steadily declined over the last several decades. At the same time, there has been a societal presumption that most, if not all, cases of HIE-induced CP occur during the 3 hours that are related to the events of labor and delivery. Unfortunately for obstetrical providers, society has tended to overlook the remaining 7000 hours of the pregnancy. As a result of this societal perspective, often times the obstetrician has been targeted unfairly as the person who is responsible for a given child's neurologic injuries. Nevertheless, recent scientific evidence has come closer to unraveling the HIE-induced CP mystery.

One aspect of the HIE-induced CP mystery is that its rarity has precluded in-depth studies into its pathogenesis. Until recently, little information has been available to study these infants much beyond the moment of birth. As a result, many of the approaches to time or date fetal brain injury have focused primarily on birth-related end points, such as the newborn's umbilical artery pH that is measured at the time of birth. Rather, the entire pregnancy, labor, delivery, and well beyond birth require examination to understand fully the pathophysiologic mechanisms that are responsible for a given child's brain injuries, and their long-term impact on the child.

Before one can litigate a case, you have to understand the pathophysiologic mechanisms that give rise to fetal brain injury due to asphyxia or HIE. Certain FHR patterns, give rise to brain injury in specific areas of the fetal brain. For example, a fetus who has a sudden, rapid, and sustained deterioration of the FHR that is unresponsive to remedial measures and/or terbutaline and lasts for a prolonged period of time typically sustains an injury to the basal ganglia or in the deep gray matter. This type of fetal brain injury gives rise to athetoid or dyskinetic cerebral palsy and is the result of a sudden reduction of fetal cardiac output and/ or blood pressure or

---

[39] See Inappropriate Use, *supra* note 34; See Phelan JP: What constitutes Fetal Distress? *supra* note 34; See Electronic fetal heart rate, *supra* note 34; See Phelan, Perinatal Risk Management, *supra* note 34; Phelan JP, Martin GI, Korst LM: Birth Asphyxia and Cerebral Palsy. Clin Perinatol. 2005; 32: 61-76; Phelan JP, Korst L, Martin GI: Causation-Fetal Brain Injury and Uterine Rupture. Clin Perinatol 2007; 34:409-438; Neonatal Encephalopathy Committee Opinion-2003: American College of Obstetricians and Gynecologists and The American Academy of Pediatrics. Washington, DC.

"cerebral hypotension due to an ineffective or nonfunctional cardiac pump." It is important to understand that fetal cardiac output, the volume of blood pumped each minute, is dependent on the fetal heart rate. This means that a fetus whose normal heart rate is 120 bpm, as an example, suddenly drops and remains at, or around 60 bpm, will have a 50% drop in cardiac output and also blood pressure. This means that because the heart is not pumping normally, as reflected by a persistent slow rate, there is less blood flow going to the fetal brain. When this happens, the area of the brain typically affected is the deep gray matter (Basal Ganglia, thalamus, putamen et al).

To better understand this concept, I want you to imagine that we are sitting in a room and the room we are in represents a nerve cell. The door to the room is wide open. Outside the door is a blood vessel carrying oxygen and nutrients to the nerve cell, the room where we are sitting. In other words, the blood vessels supplying blood to the fetal brain are wide open and blood or oxygen can go freely through the door. But, this time, the heart stops functioning normally and its rate has slowed down considerably and remains persistently down and does not return to normal. As a result of the decreased volume of blood being pumped per minute, oxygen and nutrients cannot go through the open door. As time passes, the likelihood of injury to this area of the brain increases. That is not to say that the fetus cannot have injury to other areas of the brain such as the cerebral hemispheres in this clinical situation. Whether both areas of the fetal brain are affected often depends on the five factors a number of factors such as the following:

1. Fetal growth;
2. The percent reduction of fetal cardiac output;
3. The degree of intrafetal shunting;
4. The duration of the prolonged FHR deceleration;
5. The percent abruption.

In contrast to "cerebral hypotension due to an ineffective heart pump," damage to both cerebral hemispheres gives rise to spastic quadriplegia. In this scenario, the mechanism for fetal brain injury is not an ineffective pump, because these fetuses usually demonstrate normal or elevated baseline heart rates. The brain damage in this situation relates to cerebral ischemia or diminished blood flow to the cerebral hemispheres. Once again, let's go back into the room. As we discussed previously, the room represents the nerve cell and the door represents the portal of entry for nutrients and oxygen to the nerve cell or our room. In this case, however, the door is no longer open all the way. Rather, the door to the nerve cell is partially or completely closed (ischemia). The net effect is that oxygen and nutrients have a difficult time getting into the room, or they cannot get in at all. When this happens, the fetal response is to increase its heart rate. Over a protracted period of time, injury to the cerebral hemispheres occurs and spastic quadriplegia results. Often times, this will result in persistent seizures, cortical blindness, and mental retardation.

[b]   Timing of Fetal Brain Injury[40]

Determining the timing of fetal brain injury is a highly complex issue. Before an obstetric expert can consider whether the fetal brain injury was potentially preventable, one must be able to determine whether the fetus was already injured on admission to the hospital or to the obstetrician's office. After that initial assessment, one can then determine whether the fetus is at risk for asphyxia or is becoming asphyxiated. Then, the analysis necessarily switches to determine whether the fetal brain injury was or is potentially preventable.

The first step in any causation analysis is to determine whether the fetus is or is not, in all medical probability or certainty, neurologically normal on admission to the hospital or the physician's office. The initial FHR pattern on admission to the doctor's office or to the hospital offers tremendous insights into this question. If, for example, the patient's FHR pattern on admission to the hospital is considered to be reactive or the presence of FHR accelerations, labor and delivery personnel know that the fetus is, in all medical probability, neurologically normal. A common argument is that fetuses with a reactive FHR pattern can also have neurologic impairment such as anencephaly, hydrocephaly, or preexisting basal ganglia injury. While that may be true statement, the standard of proof for such an argument would be substantially higher or to level of beyond a reasonable doubt. Labor and delivery personnel also recognize that the presence of a reactive fetal admission test is a sign of a healthy fetus and symbolizes fetal well-being, normal fetal acid–base status, normoxia and absence of asphyxia, and a low probability of intrapartum fetal distress.

In contrast, a nonreactive fetal admission test or the absence of FHR accelerations is associated with a greater probability of an adverse outcome. If, for example, the fetus on admission to the hospital has persistent fetal nonreactivity, or is unable to generate a spontaneous or evoked FHR acceleration for more than 120 minutes from the time of admission to the hospital, increased rates of perinatal mortality and permanent neurologic

---

[40] *See* Phelan, Perinatal Risk Management, *supra* note 34; *See* Phelan JP, et al., *supra* note 39; *See* Phelan et al., Causation-Fetal Brain Injury and Uterine Rupture, *supra* note 39. *See* Neonatal Encephalopathy Committee Opinion-2003, *supra* note 39.

impairment are observed. In essence, and unlike the fetus that has a reactive FHR pattern on admission, the fetus who has a persistent nonreactive FHR pattern or an inability to accelerate is, in all medical probability or certainty, neurologically impaired prior to admission to the hospital. As such, the obstetric provider could not, in most if not all instances, have prevented the brain injury after admission to the hospital. The primary reason is that one cannot prevent that which has already been damaged.

Two approaches[41] have emerged to assist us with the timing of fetal brain injury. One approach was developed by the Neonatal Encephalopathy Committee (NEC) of the American College of Obstetricians and Gynecologists (ACOG) and the American Academy of Pediatrics and the other by the Childbirth Injury Prevention Foundation (Childbirth). Neither approach is perfect, but both approaches represent valiant attempts to address the highly complex issue of timing fetal brain damage. The Neonatal Encephalopathy Committee Opinion of 2003 focuses on metabolic acidemia, moderate or severe neonatal encephalopathy, and the diagnosis of spastic quadriplegia or dyskinetic CP. Additionally, the NEC injected a fifth clause that excluded many fetal brain injuries unrelated to HIE from the analysis. This includes but is not limited to autism, chromosomal abnormalities, and structural malformations. As with the early approaches, the emphasis was on the events that surrounded birth, including metabolic acidemia on an umbilical artery cord gas and the presence of neonatal encephalopathy or the presence of seizures. The ongoing dilemma with this approach is the requirement of metabolic acidemia to determine whether an insult occurred intrapartum. The reason is that the probability of child with metabolic acidemia at birth sustaining long term neurologic impairment is low. In fact many of these fetuses with metabolic acidemia at birth are neurologically normal on follow up.

The Childbirth approach is a flexible method to time fetal brain injury. This overall approach captures the key elements of fetal life and incorporates the essential ingredients of the neonatal period. The mainstay of the Childbirth method is the use of the intrapartum FHR pattern. The underlying rationale for using the intrapartum FHR pattern is that fetuses that become or have been brain damaged manifest their injuries in consistent ways on the fetal monitor strip. These distinct intrapartum FHR patterns are linked to findings in the neonatal period and the location of the fetal brain injury or the type of CP-spastic quadriplegia or dyskinetic or athetoid. The Childbirth

---

[41] Phelan JP, Korst L, Martin GI: Causation-Fetal Brain Injury and Uterine Rupture. Clin Perinatol 2007; 34:409-438; Neonatal Encephalopathy Committee Opinion-2003: American College of Obstetricians and Gynecologists and The American Academy of Pediatrics. Washington, DC.

approach uses both fetal and neonatal findings to time fetal brain injury. The fetal findings include the admission FHR pattern, the characteristics of fetal movement on admission, and the subsequent changes in the intrapartum FHR pattern, if any, during labor and delivery. The neonatal findings include but are not limited to hematologic markers, such as nucleated red blood cells (NRBC), the NRBC clearance times, platelet counts, liver enzymes, changes in the serum sodium,[42] the onset of neonatal seizures, neuroimaging for the location of the brain damage, and the long-term follow-up of the child. All of these neonatal findings have been linked scientifically to the intrapartum FHR pattern.

The Childbirth approach is analogous to viewing an impressionist painting. You must look at the entire painting to understand its overall significance and not limit your visual perspective to a postage stamp area of the painting. For example, you cannot use NRBC values alone to time fetal brain injury. In timing fetal brain injury, the Childbirth approach is also not limited to the findings that surround the moment of birth, such as umbilical artery cord gases and Apgar scores, but focuses on the continuum of life and the transition from fetal to neonatal life and beyond. Simply stated, the Childbirth approach requires visualization of the entire painting to understand the timing of a given child's fetal brain injury.

When the two approaches to time fetal brain injury are compared, the methods have many similarities. For example, each approach focuses on hypoxic ischemic encephalopathy as the basis for the CP, such as the type of cerebral palsy (spastic quadriplegia or athetoid or dyskinetic cerebral palsy (NEC) or the location of the brain injury (Childbirth). This distinction is important because certain FHR patterns, give rise to brain injury in specific areas of the fetal brain. As we discussed previously, a fetus who has a sudden, rapid, and sustained deterioration of the FHR that is unresponsive to remedial measures or terbutaline and lasts for a prolonged period of time typically sustains in an injury to the basal ganglia or the deep gray matter and that gives rise to athetoid or dyskinetic cerebral palsy. In contrast, the persistent nonreactive FHR pattern characteristically is associated with damage in both cerebral hemispheres and gives rise to spastic quadriplegia. Here the mechanism for injury is not an ineffective pump, because these fetuses usually demonstrate normal baseline heart rates but an absence of FHR accelerations. The brain damage in this situation relates more to cerebral ischemia or the door to the nerve cell is no longer operational.

---

[42] Benedetti, T.J., Gabbe, S.G.: Shoulder Dystocia. A complication of fetal macrosomia and prolonged second stage of labor with midpelvic delivery. Am. J. Obstet. Gynecol. 1978; 52:526-529;Bofill, J.A., Rust, O.A., Devidas, M., Roberts, W.E., Morrison, J.C., Martin, J.N. Jr.: Shoulder dystocia and operative vaginal delivery. J. Matern. Fetal. Med. 1997; 6: 220-224.

One of the key differences between these two approaches is that the Childbirth approach is broader and attempts to focus on the timing of fetal brain injury before and after hospital admission based on the characteristics of the admission and subsequent intrapartum FHR patterns. The NEC approach clearly focuses on the intrapartum period, and would be comparable to the Childbirth study population with a reactive FHR pattern at the time of hospital admission followed by a sudden, rapid, and sustained deterioration of the fetal heart rate usually attributable to a sentinel hypoxic event. In keeping with that approach, the NEC emphasizes and the Childbirth approach de-emphasizes the events surrounding birth as a means to time fetal brain injury, such as umbilical arterial cord blood gases, Apgar scores, and Sarnat criteria for neonatal encephalopathy. Both, however, arrive at the same conclusion as to the timing of the fetal brain injury during the intrapartum period. The Childbirth approach, when applied to the fetus with a reactive FHR pattern at the time of hospital admission followed by a sudden, rapid, and sustained deterioration of the FHR unresponsive to remedial measures usually attributable to a sentinel hypoxic event, also presumes metabolic acidemia (umbilical artery cord blood gas pH < 7.00 and a base deficit $\geq$ 12 mmol/L), moderate or severe neonatal encephalopathy, and spastic quadriplegia or dyskinetic cerebral palsy. The Childbirth approach arrives at the same conclusion as to the timing of the brain injury by using other neonatal factors, such as the NRBC counts and clearance times, the initial platelet count, the onset of neonatal seizures, the degree of organ dysfunction, and the location of the brain damage. Once again, the key distinction is that the Childbirth approach is an effort to incorporate all the different ways a fetus can become brain damaged into one overall approach to time fetal brain injury.

Another important aspect of the timing of fetal brain damage is that the reviewer of the case should not overlook or ignore the fifth factor in the NEC approach. These are lumped under the heading of identifiable exclusion factors. These include but are not limited to congenital fetal anomalies, which probably represent the greatest single group, autism, chromosome defects, or metabolic disorders. Causation can be determined in the course of a thorough investigation of the child. Regretfully, in a certain number of the cases, the developmental delay may derive from a hereditary or acquired congenital abnormality which is difficult to identify in retrospect. Into this group, belong pharmaceutical products, potentially teratogenic industrial chemicals, radioactive substances, etc. One key component of the case analysis is to have the child evaluated for dysmorphologic features because the child may fit into a known syndrome or a specific inheritance pattern.

Even if the effects of chronic hypoxia deriving from a congenitally determined cause may be irreversible, superimposition of additional hypoxic insult resulting from the effect of excessive intrapartum stress upon an already compromised fetus may increase the magnitude of the damage. On the other hand, in the face of evidence of preexisting and otherwise unpreventable chronic fetal compromise, it is generally inappropriate to assume that an unfavorable long-range outcome could have been avoided by quick abdominal delivery at the first documented sign of "fetal distress."

Although the investigations of the last two decades have resulted in the identification of a variety of potentially significant heart rate patterns, it is probably fair to say that the fetal condition can be determined with reasonable accuracy in the overwhelming majority of the instances on the basis of classical heart rate patterns described in the 1960s. According to the classification proposed at that time, the fetal heart rate decelerations can be early, and thus coincidental with the uterine contraction (a generally innocent pattern). Late decelerations that follow uterine contraction, if recurrent, are indicative of fetal hypoxia. The loss of beat-to-beat variability may simply represent fetal sleep or relaxation as an effect of drugs administered to the mother; however, it may be the harbinger of profound hypoxia of the control of the central nervous system upon cardiac function. Sudden and irregularly shaped decelerations of the fetal heart rate with abrupt return to the baseline usually indicate cord compression that may be non-recurrent, and thus entirely benign, or if sustained for several minutes, can be immediately life-endangering for the fetus.

Frequent errors in the interpretation of fetal heart rate monitoring tracings include:

1. The failure to recognize that the external monitor is recording the maternal heart rate and not the FHR. The maternal heart rate is usually manifested by accelerations with contractions in a pregnant woman with a heart rate in excess of 100 bpm.
2. The failure to recognize the progressive change in fetal status from a previously reactive admission FHR to one that demonstrates a progressive rise in rate to a level of tachycardia in association with fetal nonreactivity, repetitive FHR decelerations and usually a loss of variability.
3. The failure to have a physician capable of performing a cesarean available for a patient at substantial risk for asphyxia such as a VBAC patient whose fetus is suddenly exhibiting moderate to severe variable decelerations with or without a FHR tachycardia at an unexpected time in labor.
4. The continued administration of oxytocin in the face of patent FHR abnormalities.

One with experience in the atmosphere of labor and delivery rooms cannot be but impressed by the fact that the presence of a functioning monitor tends to reassure the medical and paramedical personnel. This means that so long as the FHR tracing is normal, the labor may continue in the face of a prolonged second stage, a protracted active phase or other labor abnormalities.

[4] The Use of Uterotonic Agents

The knowledge that the activity of the uterus can be enhanced by the use of certain pharmacologic agents has captured the minds of physicians at least since the turn of the century. Initially, crude extracts of ergot were used as uterine stimulants, often with catastrophic results. Eventually, the development of new and more easily controllable drugs changed the picture. During the last several years, the following agents have played a significant role in everyday obstetric practice.

[a] Oxytocin

A hormone produced by the pituitary gland under natural circumstances, oxytocin has been synthesized chemically and sold in a pure form for about 25 years. Ever since its introduction into obstetric practice, the drug has been used for three major purposes: (1) Induction of labor; (2) Stimulation of uterine activity in cases of ineffective contraction pattern during labor (Augmentation of labor); and (3) Contraction of the uterus after delivery for the purpose of preventing or treating postpartum hemorrhage.

When used in intramuscular or subcutaneous injections for the stimulation of the pregnant uterus, oxytocin relatively frequently causes tetanic contractions and fetal distress, or even uterine rupture. In the last approximately two decades, it has become axiomatic that oxytocin must be used greatly diluted and in slow intravenous infusion via a pump. Even when administered in this manner, the use of the drug is usually subject to strict indications and contraindications. Elective induction of labor with oxytocin is acceptable so long as the patient has achieved 39 0/7 weeks gestation.

With the administration of oxytocin, the level of uterine activity is often alleged to be a factor in fetal outcome. The following definitions are currently in place to describe uterine activity. The terms hyperstimulation and hypercontractility are no longer considered valid clinical terms and should be abandoned. Thus, the definitions for "uterine activity events" are as follows:[43]

---

[43] Macones, GA, Hankins, GDV, Spong, CY, Hauth, J. Moore, T: The 2008 National Institute of Child Health and Human Development Workshop Report on Electronic Fetal Monitoring: Update on Definitions, Interpretation, and Research Guidelines. JOGNN 2008; 37: 510-515.

1. *Tachysystole* refers to the presence of 5 or more contractions within a 10 minute time period, averaged over 30 minutes. The term tachysystole applies to spontaneous as well as stimulated labor and should always be qualified based on the presence or absence of associated FHR decelerations. Additionally, other factors such as the duration, intensity, and relaxation time between contractions are equally important in clinical practice. A review of each institutions policies and procedures will usually provide guidance as to the definition in effect at the time in question.

2. *Tetany* refers to the duration of a contraction. To be considered a titanic contraction, the contraction should last a minimum of 2 minutes or 120 seconds. As with the definition for tachysystole, their clinical significance should be interpreted in light of associated FHR decelerations.

3. *Hypertonus* refers to the resting tone of the uterus. The normal resting tone is 20-25 mm Hg. To determine the uterine resting tone an intrauterine pressure catheter must be in place. Once the IUPC is in place, the IUPC should be zeroed to ensure the accuracy of the recordings. One point to remember is that one cannot determine the baseline uterine tone with an external fetal monitor. There are many reasons why one may see hypertonus such as the use of amnioinfusion (This technique is the use of normal saline to re-establish the amniotic fluid volume or to dilute meconium.), or catheter related complications. To document that there is not hypertonus, the nurse or the physician can simply palpate the uterus between contractions. If the uterus is soft, the readings from the IUPC are probably erroneous.

If a "uterine activity event" is confirmed clinically in a patient who is receiving oxytocin, the oxytocin can be decreased or stopped. Then, the patient can be observed for a period of time. Once the uterine activity pattern goes away and the FHR pattern returns to normal, the oxytocin may be resumed. It is also interesting to note that "uterine activity events" are similar whether oxytocin is used or not. This means that "uterine activity events" occur with a similar frequency in spontaneous or oxytocin induced labors. Additionally, uterine activity is indistinguishable regardless of whether the labor is spontaneous or induced with oxytocin or prostaglandins.

To monitor oxytocin administration, pre- and in- use oxytocin check lists have been developed in an effort to reduce oxytocin related complications.[44]

---

[44] Clark, S.L., Belfort, M.A., Byrum, S.L., Meyers, J.A., Perlin, J.B.: Improved outcomes, fewer cesarean deliveries, and reduced litigation: results of a new paradigm in patient safety. Am J Obstet Gynecol. 2008; 199: 105-107.

Examples of the pre- and in- use oxytocin protocols illustrated in Tables 1 and 2, respectively, and are from the Department of Obstetrics and Gynecology of Citrus Valley Medical Center in West Covina, California.

Despite the numerous rules and regulations that govern the use of oxytocin in contemporary obstetrics, malpractice claims frequently arise in association with fetal or less frequently maternal, damage attributed to the use of the drug. In the course of retrospective reviews, oxytocin use is commonly encountered in malpractice litigation in the following circumstances:

1. Administration in the presence of persistent "tachysystole" and a patently abnormal FHR pattern;
2. Administration in the absence of appropriate fetal and maternal surveillance;
3. Elective induction of labor prior to 39 0/7 weeks gestation without prior documentation of fetal lung maturity.

[b] Ergot Alkaloids

Ergot alkaloids, such as methergine, are still used extensively in many parts of the world, including the United States, for the treatment and prevention of postpartum hemorrhage (The management of postpartum hemorrhage is covered in more detail in (§ 15.07[1])). In the case of postpartum hemorrhage, oxytocin is usually the primary agent. If oxytocin does not stop the bleeding, ergot alkaloids are used to firm up the uterus. Since the use of ergot alkaloids can be associated with hypertensive crisis, the drug cannot be given intravenously and is contraindicated in women with hypertensive disease of pregnancy. The side effects attributed to ergot alkaloids include the most severe complications of acute hypertension, such as circulatory failure and cerebral hemorrhage.

[c] Cervical Ripening[45]

In the pregnant patient at term or in need of induction of labor, the unfavorable cervix has plagued the contemporary obstetrician. Over the past several decades, numerous approaches have been employed in an effort to soften the cervix and make it more favorable for induction and ultimately a

---

[45] See Cervical Ripening: In, Guidelines of Perinatal Care 6Th Edition American Academy of Pediatrics and The American College of Obstetricians and Gynecologists 2007 pp 148-150; New U.S. Food and Drug Administration labeling on Cytotec (Misoprostol) use and pregnancy: ACOG Committee Opinion No. 283 [May 2003]. American College of Obstetricians and Gynecologists. Washington, D.C; Battista, L.R., Wing, D.A.: Abnormal Labor and Induction of Labor In, *Gabbe SG: Obstetrics: Normal and Problem Pregnancies, 5th ed.* Churchill Livingstone Elsevier, Philadelphia, Pennsylvania, 2007 pp 322-343.

vaginal birth. Some of the accepted techniques to ripen the cervix include but are not limited to the following: mechanical dilatation with laminaria (Hygroscopic seaweed placed in the cervical canal to permit dilatation gradually over time.) or a 30 ml foley catheter placed in the cervical canal, the use of misoprostol and intra-vaginal or intra-cervical administration of prostaglandin E2.

Misoprostol (a prostaglandin E1 analog) is probably the most common agent used to ripen the cervix. Because of its known association with tachysystole, misoprostil should be used under a policy and procedure that details its use and associated complications. Some of the suggested requirements include but are not limited to the following:

1. A physician capable of performing a cesarean should be readily available.
2. The fetus should have a normal FHR pattern and a normal AFI prior to the start of the cervical ripening.
3. 25 micrograms (one-quarter of a 100 microgram tablet) should be given. Complications, such as uterine tachysystole, are less common with this dose.
4. Doses should not be more frequent than every 3–6 hours.
5. Oxytocin should not be administered less than 4 hours after the last dose of misoprostol.
6. Patients with a history of prior uterine surgery, such as a prior low transverse cesarean, should not be given misoprostol.
7. During the use of misoprostol therapy, continuous monitoring of the FHR pattern and uterine activity should be done in a hospital setting.

Since the most common reason to use cervical ripening agents is when delivery is indicated, cesarean delivery rather than attempted vaginal delivery is also an available option. Thus, as part of the consenting process, cesarean delivery should be covered.

In the situation of fetal death at or less than 28 weeks gestation, high dose prostaglandin E2 can be used to deliver the fetus. Because of the risk of uterine rupture, patients with a prior cesarean should be discouraged from receiving high dose prostaglandin E2.

[5]   Breech Presentation

With few exceptions, vaginal breech delivery is no longer done in the United States. Almost all breeches, regardless of the type of breech are delivered by cesarean. The reasons for this change are the risks attendant to a vaginal breech delivery such as a prolapsed umbilical cord, intrapartum "fetal distress," and trauma to the aftercoming head. In general, external cephalic version is offered. If the patient refuses or fails the ECV, a cesarean will usually be scheduled. On the other hand vaginal breech delivery is not beneath the standard of care so long as the following criteria are satisfied prior to the attempted vaginal delivery:

1. Adequate maternal pelvis;
2. Flexed fetal head;
3. Estimated fetal weight between 2,500 grams and 4000 grams;
4. A frank breech presentation. (Nonfrank breech deliveries can also be done in the appropriate clinical setting. However, the risk of umbilical cord prolapse is higher with nonfrank breeches.);
5. Patient with a prior term delivery or a proven pelvis;
6. A term pregnancy;
7. The labor is spontaneous and not induced.

§ 15.06   Cesarean Delivery[46]

Although cesarean delivery has been known about for centuries, it was not until the development by Senger of a useful technique for abdominal delivery little more than 100 years ago that the procedure became a practical means for delivery. While at the turn of the century this was still a precarious surgical procedure that carried maternal mortality rate of approximately 10%, the odds changed dramatically as a result of the following milestones in obstetric care:

1. The introduction of aseptic techniques into practice as originally proposed by Semmelweis in the 1840s;
2. The feasibility of blood transfusion following the identification of the main blood groups by Landsteiner in the 1930s;
3. The discovery of antibiotics based on the fundamental observations of Fleming in the same decade.

The availability of cesarean delivery and its development into a safe procedure revolutionized what was earlier called "midwifery." Once believed insurmountable, difficulties resulting from feto-pelvic disproportion, various forms of antepartum hemorrhage and ascending infection could now

---

[46] Phelan JP, Clark SL (eds.): *Cesarean Delivery*. Elsevier Science Publishing Co., Inc., New York, New York, 1988.

be resolved through by passing the natural birth canal and removing the products of conception abdominally. Contemporary obstetrics is simply a product of this fundamental change. Today, cesarean delivery can be done electively in the properly consented patient. In light of the increased demand for elective cesareans, the prior requirement of an indication for the procedure may become extinct in the foreseeable future.

[1] Indications

Traditionally, indications for a cesarean were divided into two groups, maternal and fetal. In the contemporary practice of obstetrics, maternal indications, other than elective, no longer exist. The reality is that most, if not all, cesareans are done for fetal indications. Is it any wonder that the cesarean delivery rate is approaching 50%? There is considerable discussion regarding the reasons for the rise in cesareans. When all the dust settles on this subject, the reasons for the rise are clear. The introduction of fetal monitoring and ultrasonography has created a window to the womb. With this technological transformation, the societal and obstetrical "focus on the fetus" continues to be the underlying basis for the rise.

Another common driving force for increased cesareans is related to malpractice litigation. Even today, it is rare that an obstetrical claim does not include the allegation that a cesarean should have been performed. It is estimated that at, or around 80% of all obstetrical malpractice claims involve a claim that a cesarean was not performed or should have been performed in a timely manner. From a legal point of view, malpractice claims seldom arise in connection with the ever-increasing rate of cesareans. At the same time, when attempted vaginal delivery involves an unfavorable outcome, malpractice claims often hinge upon the contention that an intervention by cesarean would have resulted in a better outcome. This being the case, there is little doubt that American obstetricians are under tremendous pressure to avoid the difficulties that occur with vaginal delivery, and readily resort to a cesarean.

[2] Cesarean Delivery—Uterine Incisions

Essentially, three major techniques are available for abdominal delivery: (1) operation through a lower segment transverse incision; (2) surgery through a lower segment longitudinal or vertical incision; and (3) delivery through a classical (corporeal) or an upper segment uterine incision. The uterine incision in almost all cesareans is made as a low transverse uterine incision. A low vertical uterine incision is usually reserved for preterm pregnancies when the lower uterine segment is inadequately developed. This means that a low vertical uterine incision is made to avoid injury to the uterine vessels. For example, if a low transverse uterine incision is made in a patient with an undeveloped lower uterine segment, there is a greater risk that the incision could extend laterally into the uterine vessels and result in intraabdominal bleeding. A classical uterine incision is usually reserved for a back down transverse lie, multifetal gestations of 3 or more, or, in selected cases, to avoid the lower uterine segment in the face of a prior low transverse cesarean and a co-existent anterior placenta previa. In this latter circumstance, there is a greater risk of placenta accreta. Under the circumstances of a placenta accreta, going through the placenta would exacerbate any hemorrhage.

Occasionally obstetrical malpractice claims arise from the technical performance of a cesarean. These include but are not limited to the following:

1. Use of a lower uterine segment incision (such as a low transverse incision in the presence of a back down transverse lie) resulting in fetal compromise or death;
2. The performance of a classical uterine or upper uterine segment incision without an obstetrical indication; A classical uterine incision is associated with a greater risk of uterine rupture in a subsequent pregnancy.
3. Injury to neighboring structures (such as the ureter, bowel, or bladder);
4. Difficulty in mobilizing the deeply engaged head of the fetus through vaginal manipulation, resulting in delayed delivery or traumatic damage to the fetus during a cesarean.

Maternal complications in contemporary obstetric practice predominantly consist of postoperative infection, hemorrhage, and thromboembolic events. To reduce the likelihood of perioperative infection, prophylactic antibiotics are given within one hour of the start of the cesarean. The risks of hemorrhage are reduced through the availability of blood products for transfusion. Postoperatively, pressure stockings are applied to reduce the probability of deep venous thrombosis and/ or a pulmonary embolus. Apart from infection, the leading cause of maternal deaths in connection with a cesarean is general anesthesia.

[3] Vaginal Birth after a Cesarean (VBAC)[47]

The dictum "Once cesarean, always cesarean" was introduced in the early decades of the 20th century. At that time a substantial proportion of abdominal deliveries were performed through a vertical uterine incision. Despite the eventual shift in favor of low transverse uterine incisions, the earlier thinking survived, and until recent years almost all women with a previous cesarean were delivered by the abdominal route electively. In recent years, the principle came under scrutiny, and almost overnight the prevailing philosophies changed by almost 180 degrees. Since the eye opening scientific article of the author, "VBAC: A Time to Reconsider" appeared in OBG Management in 1996,[48] the VBAC trend has reversed itself once again 180 degrees. Presently, the dictum of "once a cesarean always a cesarean" has returned once more and, VBAC has once again become a stranger to labor and delivery units across America.

However, the prevailing standards of obstetrical practice continue to accept the validity of attempting vaginal delivery following one or two prior cesareans even if the preceding surgery had been performed for CPD. Unlike prior times, VBAC is considered reasonable so long as certain preconditions are met. This typically includes adequate informed consent with an emphasis on the potential risk of uterine rupture and its impact on the pregnant woman and her baby. Thus, most programs that continue to do VBACs require the availability of anesthesia and a physician capable of performing a cesarean. The primary reason for the shift relates to "catastrophic uterine ruptures." Catastrophic uterine ruptures are defined as a uterine rupture with a partial or complete expulsion of the placenta and/or fetus into the maternal abdomen. While the risk of uterine rupture is estimated to be around 1%, the risk of a catastrophic uterine rupture is estimated to be around 1/800 to 1/1,200 VBACs. In the event of a catastrophic uterine rupture, the risk of fetal brain injury or death is the highest.

It is important to note that the risks involved with vaginal delivery following a previous cesarean were overestimated in preceding decades. On the other hand, it appears that the benefits of VBAC have been largely overshadowed by the risks to the fetus from a catastrophic uterine rupture. With respect to maternal complications, the risk of postoperative infection and/or other morbidity is significantly more likely in a laboring VBAC patient than one who has had an elective repeat cesarean. A simple way to

---

[47] Phelan JP, Korst L, Martin GI: Causation-Fetal Brain Injury and Uterine Rupture. Clin Perinatol 2007; 34:409-438; Phelan JP: VBAC: Time to reconsider? OBG Management. 1996; 8 (November):62-8

[48] Phelan JP: VBAC: Time to reconsider? OBG Management. 1996; 8 (November):62-8.

compare the risks between vaginal and cesarean birth is to remember that vaginal birth carries a greater risk to the fetus and a lower risk to the mother. In contrast, cesarean delivery reverses those risks as a cesarean is riskier for the mother than it is for the fetus.

Labor may be augmented with oxytocin. However, recent scientific evidence suggests that induction of labor with oxytocin or cervical ripening agents is associated with a greater risk of uterine rupture. As a result, many institutions have gone away from inducing prior cesarean patients or limiting inductions to cases of an IUFD. A final note on oxytocin use during a VBAC is that uterine rupture is not increased from the use of oxytocin or is it related to uterine "tachysystole" or the number of contractions per hour. The probable mechanism for a uterine rupture in a VBAC patient appears to be an abnormally implanted placenta.

§ 15.07 Postpartum Complications

[1] Postpartum Hemorrhage[49]

Obstetric hemorrhage has probably killed more women than any other obstetrical complication. Traditionally, postpartum hemorrhage (PPH) has been defined as blood loss in excess of 500 ml after a vaginal delivery and 1000 ml after a cesarean delivery. Such traditional definitions tend to reflect the average blood loss at, or around the time of delivery and are not an accurate estimate of true PPH. Some clinicians have suggested that a more useful definition of PPH would include blood loss sufficient to cause symptoms of hypovolemia, a 10% drop in the hematocrit after delivery or the requirements of a blood transfusion. If this definition is used, the incidence of PPH would be approximately 4% of vaginal deliveries and 6% of cesarean deliveries.

The majority of PPH occurs within the first 24 hours after delivery and is called "primary PPH." Secondary PPH occurs between 24 hours and 6 weeks after delivery and occurs in about 1% of pregnancies. Primary PPH usually relates to the events surrounding the delivery and is primarily caused by uterine atony (inability of the uterus to contract) in around 80% of the cases. The other causes include but are not limited to genital tract lacerations from

---

[49] Francois, K. E., Foley, M.R.: Antepartum and Postpartum Hemorrhage In, *Gabbe SG: Obstetrics: Normal and Problem Pregnancies, 5th ed*. Churchill Livingstone Elsevier, Philadelphia, Pennsylvania, 2007 pp 456-485; Postpartum Hemorrhage. ACOG Practice Bulletin No. 76 [October 2006]. American College of Obstetricians and Gynecologists. Obstet Gynecol 2006; 108: 1039-47; Oyelese Y, Scorza WE, Mastrolia R, Smulian JC: Postpartum Hemorrhage. Obstet. Gynecol Clin N Am 2007; 34: 421-441.

the delivery, such as vaginal, cervical and perineal lacerations, retained products of conception, uterine inversion, abnormal placentation and uterine rupture. Secondary PPH which occurs between 24 hours and 6 weeks postpartum is usually caused by retained products of conception, subinvolution of the uterus or infection.

Treatment of Primary PPH is directed at the most common causes for the bleeding. Thus, the clinical approach is as follows:

1.   Visual inspection of the genital tract for lacerations;
2.   Manual exploration of the uterine cavity for retained products of conception, and a uterine rupture;
3.   If a genital tract laceration is the cause of the PPH, the laceration is sutured.
4.   If uterine atony is the source of the bleeding, uterine massage and uterotonic agents, such as oxytocin, prostaglandins, and methergine are used to arrest the bleeding. As stated in (§ 15.05[4][b]), methergine should not be used in patients with a history of hypertension or preeclampsia;
5.   If these medical measures fail to stop the hemorrhage, a surgical approach is probably indicated and may include a hysterectomy;
6.   Depending on the extent of the hemorrhage, blood transfusions may be necessary to correct any maternal hypovolemia.

Uterine inversion is a rare and special clinical circumstance that involves the uterus turning inside out at the time of delivery. Uterine inversions may be partial or complete. Once the uterus inverts, the normal ability of the uterus to contract is impeded. As such, the bleeding will continue until the uterus is re-inverted. The suggested causes for a uterine inversion are an adherent placenta, the combination of magnesium sulfate, chorioamnionitis, and prolonged labor, and a VBAC. Clinical management involves manual replacement of the uterus or, if this fails, replacement through laparotomy is surgically necessary. In addition to a skilled obstetrical provider, blood products for transfusion will usually be obstetrically necessary.

Uterine rupture is 15–16 times more common in a prior cesarean patient than one with an unscarred uterus. Most often, the clinical diagnosis is made prior to the delivery of the fetus. The single most reliable indicator or notice of a uterine rupture is sudden change in fetal status at a time in labor when it is least expected. In the case of a uterine rupture, the fetus manifests the sudden appearance of moderate to severe variable FHR decelerations with or without a change in the baseline fetal heart rate to a level of FHR tachycardia or in the absence of warning, a sudden, rapid, and sustained deterioration of the FHR that is unresponsive to remedial measures and/or terbutaline. An intrapartum uterine rupture does not appear to be clinically manifested by any of the following: Uterine "tachysystole," a loss of uterine tone, vaginal bleeding, or abdominal pain. In the case of vaginal bleeding and abdominal pain, these may be encountered subsequent to the changes in the fetal heart rate. In rare circumstances, a uterine rupture is clinically manifested postpartum. In this situation, the hemorrhage may be internal, and thus only detectable through close observation of the vital signs of the mother.

An infrequent but potentially serious form of postpartum blood loss is the so-called "late postpartum hemorrhage" or Secondary PPH. This generally refers to severe bleeding days, or even weeks, following childbirth. In many instances, the blood loss may be severe. Treatment may include uterotonic agents, antibiotics, or curettage. Prior to and during the D&C, ultrasound may be useful to identify any retained products of conception and to avoid a uterine perforation. Prior to the D&C, the patient should be counselled for the potential of a hysterectomy. Traditionally, curettage of the uterus is the typical management for late postpartum hemorrhage. This procedure frequently reveals the presence of retained products of conception. Alternatively, the absence of retained products of conception permits the diagnosis of "subinvolution of the implantation site" of the placenta. This condition is related to the sloughing of the "scab" over the implantation site and can be source of significant hemorrhage prior to and at the time of the D&C. As such, sufficient blood products for transfusion should be immediately available.

The most common reasons for litigation in cases of postpartum hemorrhage are as follows:

1. Delayed blood transfusion due to the failure to recognize ongoing hemorrhage;
2. Failure to resort to surgical therapy in the face of continued hemorrhage that is unresponsive to medical therapy;
3. The failure to recognize the clinical relationship between a history of a prior cesarean and a placenta previa and the increased likelihood of a placenta accreta.

TABLE 1-PRE-OXYTOCIN CHECKLIST FOR WOMEN WITH SINGLETON TERM BABIES

"This Pre-Oxytocin checklist represents a guideline for care: however, individualized medical care is directed by the physician."

If the following components are not met, Oxytocin should not be initiated.

Date and time completed: _____

1. ☐ Physician Order on chart.
2. ☐ An admission note including estimated fetal weight within the past week (clinical or ultrasound) at less than 5000 grams in a non-diabetic woman or less than 4500 grams in a diabetic woman*
3. ☐ Prenatal Record on chart*
4. ☐ Indication for induction is documented.
5. ☐ Pelvis is documented by physician to be clinically adequate in primagravidas (should be on prenatal record) or based on prior vaginal births*
6. ☐ Gestational age of 39 0/7 weeks or greater for all <u>elective inductions</u>
7. ☐ Procedural Consent and Informed Consent signed (Induction or Augmentation)
8. ☐ Physician with c-section privileges is aware of the induction and is readily available.
9. ☐ Status of cervix is assessed and documented.
10. ☐ Presentation is assessed and documented (physician required to evaluate if nurse is unable to determine presentation).
11. ☐ Fetal assessment completed and indicates: (Complete all below)
    ☐ A minimum of 30 minutes of fetal monitoring is required prior to starting the Oxytocin
    ☐ A reactive FHR pattern is evident, or a biophysical profile of 8 of 10 is present within the past 4 hours**
    ☐ No repetitive or prolonged decelerations in the last 30 minutes.

* May be delayed for non-elective admissions.
** There will be some situations in which alterations in management from that described in the protocol are clinically appropriate. If, after reviewing the fetal heart rate strip and course of labor the responsible physician feels that in his or her judgment, continued use of Oxytocin is in the best interest of the mother and baby, the physician should write or dictate a note to that effect and order the Oxytocin to continue. The RN will continue to provide safe, high quality nursing care.

TABLE 2- OXYTOCIN IN USE CHECKLIST FOR WOMEN WITH SINGLETON TERM BABIES

"This Oxytocin 'In Use' Checklist represents a guideline for care; however, individualized medical care is directed by the physician."

Checklist will be completed every 30 minutes. Oxytocin should be stopped or decreased if the following components are not met.

Date and Time Completed: _____

☐ Fetal Assessment Indicates:

   ☐ At least 1 acceleration of 15 bpm x 15 seconds in 30 minutes and a normal baseline FHR; consideration should be given to patients who have received medications that may have decreased variability and lack of accelerations in response to medication.

   ☐ No repetitive or prolonged decelerations

☐ Uterine Contractions

   ☐ No more than 5 uterine contractions in 10 minutes averaged for 30 minutes

   ☐ No two contractions greater than 120 second duration

   ☐ Uterus palpates soft between contractions

*If Oxytocin is stopped the Pre-Oxytocin Checklist will be reviewed before Oxytocin is reinitiated.

§ 15.08 Selected General References

1. Antepartum Care.: In, Guidelines of Perinatal Care 6ᵀʰ Edition American Academy of Pediatrics and The American College of Obstetricians and Gynecologists 2007 pp 111-117.

2. Screening for Fetal Chromosomal Abnormalities. ACOG Practice Bulletin No.77 [January 2007]. American College of Obstetricians and Gynecologists. Obstet Gynecol 2007; 109: 217-27.

3. Phelan JP: Labor admission test. In: Clinics in Perinatology. Devoe L (ed.), W. B. Saunders Co., Philadelphia, Pennsylvania, 1994; 21:879-85.

4. Tests of fetal well-being: In, Guidelines of Perinatal Care 6ᵀʰ Edition American Academy of Pediatrics and The American College of Obstetricians and Gynecologists 2007 pp 111-117.

5. Mukul LV, Teal SB: Current Management of Ectopic Pregnancy. Obstet Gynecol Clin of N Am; 2007; 34: 403-419.

6. Medical Management of Ectopic Pregnancy. ACOG Practice Bulletin No. 94 [June 2008]. American College of Obstetricians and Gynecologists. Obstet Gynecol 2008; 111: 1479–85.

7. Chronic Hypertension in Pregnancy. ACOG Practice Bulletin No. 29 [July 2001, Reaffirmed 2008]. American College of Obstetricians and Gynecologists. Obstet. Gynecol 2001; 98: 177-185.

8. Phelan JP: Obstetric critical care issues in prematurity. In: Prevention of Prematurity. Phelan JP (ed.), Clinics in Perinatology. W.B. Saunders Co., Philadelphia, Pennsylvania, 1992;19(2):449-59.

9. Phelan JP: Medico-Legal Implications of the Diagnosis of Pre-eclampsia, In,Pre-eclampsia Etiology and Clinical Practice 2007. Lyall and Belfort, Editors Cambridge University Press, Cambridge, New York, pp. 522- 534.

10. Chronic Hypertension: In, Guidelines of Perinatal Care 6ᵀʰ Edition American Academy of Pediatrics and The American College of Obstetricians and Gynecologists 2007 pp 192-195.

11. Diagnosis and Management of Preeclampsia and Eclampsia. ACOG Practice Committee No. 33 [January 2002, Reaffirmed 2008]. American College of Obstetricians and Gynecologists. Obstet Gynecol 2008; 2002; 99: 159–167.

12. Late-preterm infants. ACOG Committee Opinion No. 404 [April 2008]. American College of Obstetricians and Gynecologists. Obstet Gynecol 2008; 111:1029-32.

13. Antenatal Corticosteroid Therapy for Fetal Maturation. ACOG Committee Opinion No. 402 [March 2008]. American College of Obstetricians and Gynecologists. Obstet Gynecol 2008; 111:805-7.

14. Management of preterm birth: In, Guidelines of Perinatal Care 6Th Edition American Academy of Pediatrics and The American College of Obstetricians and Gynecologists 2007 pp 175-185.

15. Management of preterm labor. ACOG Practice Bulletin No. 43 [May 2003]. American College of Obstetricians and Gynecologists. Obstet Gynecol 2003;101:1039-47.

16. Assessment of risk factors for preterm birth. ACOG Practice Bulletin No. 31[October 2001, Reaffirmed 2008]. American College of Obstetricians and Gynecologists. Obstet Gynecol 2001; 98: 709-716.

17. Operative Vaginal Delivery. ACOG Practice Bulletin No.17 [June 2000, Reaffirm 2008]. American College of Obstetricians and Gynecologists.

18. Premature rupture of membranes. ACOG Practice Bulletin No. 80 April 2007]. American College of Obstetricians and Gynecologists. Obstet Gynecol 2007; 109:1007-19.

19. Preterm premature rupture of the membranes: In, Guidelines of Perinatal Care 6Th Edition American Academy of Pediatrics and The American College of Obstetricians and Gynecologists 2007 pp 178-185.

20. Management of Postterm Pregnancy. ACOG Practice Bulletin No.55 [September 2004]. American College of Obstetricians and Gynecologists. Obstet Gynecol 2004; 104:639-46.

21. Francois, K. E., Foley, M.R.: Antepartum and Postpartum Hemorrhage In, Gabbe SG: Obstetrics: Normal and Problem Pregnancies, 5th ed. Churchill Livingstone Elsevier, Philadelphia, Pennsylvania, 2007 pp 456-485.

22. Gabbe SG, Graves CR: Management of Diabetes Mellitus Complicating Pregnancy. Obstet Gynecol 2003; Oct; 102(4):857-68.

23. Multiple Gestation: Complicated Twin Triplet, and High-Order Multifetal Pregnancy. ACOG Practice Bulletin No. 56 [October 2004]. American College of Obstetricians and Gynecologists. Obstet Gynecol 2004; 104:869-83.

24. Multifetal Gestations: In, Guidelines of Perinatal Care 6Th Edition American Academy of Pediatrics and The American College of Obstetricians and Gynecologists 2007 pp 185-189.

25. Management of labor: In, Guidelines of Perinatal Care 6Th Edition American Academy of Pediatrics and The American College of Obstetricians and Gynecologists 2007 pp 145-146.

26. Analgesia and anesthesia: In, Guidelines of Perinatal Care 6Th Edition American Academy of Pediatrics and The American College of Obstetricians and Gynecologists 2007 pp 151-155.

27. Belfort MA: Operative vaginal delivery 10 components of success. OBG Management February 2007; Vol.19 (2) 54-70.

28. Shoulder dystocia. ACOG Practice Bulletin No. 40 [November 2002; Reaffirmed 2008]. American College of Obstetricians and Gynecologists. Obstet Gynecol 2002; 100:1045–50.

29. Benedetti, T.J., Gabbe, S.G.: Shoulder Dystocia. A complication of fetal macrosomia and prolonged second stage of labor with midpelvic delivery. Am. J. Obstet. Gynecol. 1978; 52:526-529.

30. Bofill, J.A., Rust, O.A., Devidas, M., Roberts, W.E., Morrison, J.C., Martin, J.N. Jr.: Shoulder dystocia and operative vaginal delivery. J. Matern. Fetal. Med. 1997; 6: 220-224.

31. Gherman RB, Ouzounian JG, Goodwin TM. Brachial plexus palsy: an in utero injury? Am J Obstet Gynecol 1999; 180: 1303–7.

32. Ouzounian JG, Korst LM, Ahn MO, Phelan JP: Shoulder dystocia and neonatal brain injury: Significance of the head-shoulder interval. Am J Obstet Gynecol 1998; 178(2):S244.

33. Fetal Macrosomia: ACOG Practice Bulletin No. 22 [November 2000]. American College of Obstetricians and Gynecologists. Washington, D.C.

34. Inappropriate Use of the Terms Fetal Distress and Birth Asphyxia. ACOG Committee Opinion No. 326 [December 2005]. American College of Obstetricians and Gynecologists. Washington, D.C.

35. Phelan JP: What constitutes Fetal Distress? OBG Management 1999; 11:5(May): 78-91.

36. Electronic fetal heart rate monitoring: research guidelines for interpretation. National Institutes of Child Health and Human Development Research Planning Workshop. Am J Obstet. Gynecol. 1997; 177: 1385–8.

37. Phelan JP: Perinatal Risk Management: Obstetric Methods to Prevent Birth Asphyxia. Clin Perinatol 2005; 32: 1-17.

38. Phelan JP, Martin GI, Korst LM: Birth Asphyxia and Cerebral Palsy. Clin Perinatol. 2005; 32: 61-76.

39. Phelan JP, Korst L, Martin GI: Causation-Fetal Brain Injury and Uterine Rupture. Clin Perinatol 2007; 34:409-438.

40. Neonatal Encephalopathy Committee Opinion-2003: American College of Obstetricians and Gynecologists and The American Academy of Pediatrics. Washington, DC.

41. Macones, GA, Hankins, GDV, Spong, CY, Hauth, J. Moore, T: The 2008 National Institute of Child Health and Human Development Workshop Report on Electronic Fetal Monitoring: Update on Definitions, Interpretation, and Research Guidelines. JOGNN 2008; 37: 510-515.

42. Clark, S.L., Belfort, M.A., Byrum, S.L., Meyers, J.A., Perlin, J.B.: Improved outcomes, fewer cesarean deliveries, and reduced litigation: results of a new paradigm in patient safety. Am J Obstet Gynecol. 2008; 199: 105-107.

43. Cervical Ripening: In, Guidelines of Perinatal Care 6Th Edition American Academy of Pediatrics and The American College of Obstetricians and Gynecologists 2007 pp 148-150.

44. New U.S. Food and Drug Administration labeling on Cytotec (Misoprostol) use and pregnancy: ACOG Committee Opinion No. 283 [May 2003]. American College of Obstetricians and Gynecologists. Washington, D.C.

45. Battista, L.R., Wing, D.A.: Abnormal Labor and Induction of Labor In, Gabbe SG: Obstetrics: Normal and Problem Pregnancies, 5th ed. Churchill Livingstone Elsevier, Philadelphia, Pennsylvania, 2007 pp 322-343.

46. Phelan JP, Clark SL (eds.): Cesarean Delivery. Elsevier Science Publishing Co., Inc., New York, New York, 1988.

47. Phelan JP: VBAC: Time to reconsider? OBG Management. 1996; 8 (November):62-8.

48. Postpartum Hemorrhage. ACOG Practice Bulletin No. 76 [October 2006]. American College of Obstetricians and Gynecologists. Obstet Gynecol 2006; 108: 1039-47.

49. Oyelese Y, Scorza WE, Mastrolia R, Smulian JC: Postpartum Hemorrhage. Obstet. Gynecol Clin N Am 2007; 34: 421-441.

CHAPTER 16

PEDIATRICS

Julius Landwirth, MD, JD and Mary M. Carrasco, MD, MPH

SYNOPSIS

§ 16.01 The Practice of Pediatrics

[1] Introduction

This chapter reviews the field of general pediatrics, emphasizing those aspects of the activities of the pediatric practitioner that may have important medico-legal implications. While not encyclopedic in its coverage of diseases of childhood, the chapter will focus on problems and disorders that are either unique to children or require a significantly different approach to management than would be the case in adults. Together, those special considerations in the care of children comprise the standards of pediatric care to which clinicians will be held. The common clinical pitfalls in pediatric practice, stemming most often from failure to appreciate age-related physiologic and developmental distinctions, often provide the grounds for medical malpractice actions.

This chapter will focus on pediatric practice from the perspective of the primary care, office-based practitioner, rather than the pediatric sub-specialist, e.g., pediatric cardiologist, pediatric neurologist. Reflecting that orientation, issues of general health care supervision organized by age group are discussed first, followed by a survey of diseases of childhood by organ system.

[2] The Scope of Pediatrics

Pediatrics may be broadly defined as the area of medical practice concerned with disturbances in the growth and development of the child. This concern covers the life span between birth and the attainment of biologic maturity at young adulthood. The American Academy of Pediatrics has set the upper age for the purview of pediatrics at twenty-one years, however many pediatricians limit their practices to younger age groups.

Medical care for children is provided by practitioners with a variety of educational backgrounds, organized into a number of different practice models. Pediatricians provide between 30 and 80% of office visits for children, with younger children being more likely to see pediatricians than family practitioners. Family practitioners, internists, surgeons, medical and surgical specialists, and obstetricians and gynecologists who may treat pediatric and adolescent patients are generally guided by the standards of their particular professional groups. The various models under which pediatric care may be delivered include solo, single and multispecialty group practices, alternate delivery systems such as health maintenance organizations, community-based "walk-in" facilities, hospital-based ambulatory care services, school health clinics, and neighborhood health centers. Large institutionally owned group practices, with less personalized care are becoming more common. Changes in health insurance incentives have made it more likely that children are seen in a primary care office for most illnesses.

[3] Requirements for Board Certification

The American Board of Pediatrics accepts applications for examination for certification in that specialty. Qualified applicants must be graduates of an approved medical school, have an unrestricted license to practice medicine, and have completed three years of a prescribed mix of general and subspecialty pediatric training in an accredited program. The application process includes verification by the program director of the candidate's satisfactory completion of training, as well as an evaluation of the applicant's acceptability as a practitioner of pediatrics. The evaluation includes an assessment of clinical and interpersonal skills. Documented weaknesses in either area may require the candidate to pass a screening examination or complete an additional period training, or other remedial intervention before being admitted for the certifying examination.

The Board has a specific policy regarding chemical use by candidates. Candidates who have a current problem of chemical dependency or who are in active treatment will not be admitted for examination. Candidates with a past history of chemical or drug dependency must submit documentation that their disease is known to be under control for five years from the time of the most recent occurrence of their disease.

Applicants must achieve certification within ten years of their initial acceptance into the certification process; otherwise they must reapply and pass a screening examination.

Recertification is required after seven years for certificates issued after May 1, 1988. Voluntary recertification is available to all diplomates of the Board.

Grounds for revocation of certificates include: subsequent determination that the physician was not eligible in fact; misstatements of fact by the physician; conviction of a felony or any misdemeanor involving the practice of medicine; revocation of a license to practice medicine; repeated statements by the physician contrary to sound medical science and practice, which raise fundamental questions about competency.

Accredited training programs exist in a number of pediatric subspecialties, including pediatric cardiology, pediatric endocrinology, pediatric hematology-oncology, pediatric nephrology, pediatric neurology, pediatric pulmonology, and pediatric critical care and neonatal-perinatal medicine. Subspecialty certification is available in many of these areas to qualified candidates after demonstration of appropriate additional training.

Just as the aforementioned subspecialties became recognized, some emerging subspecialties do not yet have board certification but are recognized by committee sections within the American Academy of Pediatrics structure. Child abuse and Neglect is an example of this. Where available, subspecialty certification provisions regarding duration, renewal, and revocation are similar to those for general pediatrics

[4] Office Personnel and Procedures

An efficiently operating pediatric practice is heavily dependent upon established routines for effective and reliable communications among patients, office staff, and physicians, clinical laboratories, X-ray facilities, maintenance of well organized medical records, and judicious delegation of responsibility. Important medicolegal considerations attend each aspect of the pediatric office environment.

[a] Office Personnel

Increasingly, office-based physicians rely on delegation of responsibilities to various office personnel in order to distribute the tasks of patient care efficiently. This may range from performance of screening interviews by receptionists, routine measurement of body parameters or vision and hearing acuity by assistants, to virtual complete patient care by nurse practitioners or physician assistants. The physician will be held vicariously liable for the acts of his office personnel. Offices should, therefore, maintain written descriptions of the scope of responsibility for each individual involved with patient care to any extent, as well as the qualifications required, training requirements, and procedural policies. Scopes of practice for certain allied health professionals, such as nurse practitioners, are generally prescribed by state statutes.

Physicians working in a legally organized group practice will share liability for the acts of their associates. Physicians are generally not vicariously liable for the independent acts of physicians covering their practices during their absence. However, failure to exercise reasonable care in the selection of the covering physician or in "signing out" serious pending clinical problems, may form the basis of a medical malpractice claim.

[b] Medical Records

A standardized and organized approach to maintenance of off-ice medical records is especially important in a primary care practice, where relatively large numbers of patients are seen for reasons that range from health care supervision to serious acute illness. Many medical record systems are available, most of which share common features that facilitate documentation of key parameters measured during office visits, e.g., essential data concerning immunizations, drug allergies, growth and development, personal and family health history, acute complaints, relevant positive and negative findings on physical examination, diagnostic tests performed in the office or at remote facilities, treatment (including medications), use of consultants, and follow-up plans.

In addition to its value in promoting efficiency in office practice management, standardization of medical records serves to establish a routine system for documentation that may avoid the pitfalls of speculation about significant details of an office encounter and their possible relationship to a subsequent adverse outcome. A standardized record of continuing ambulatory care also facilitates transfer of relevant information to succeeding physicians.

[c] Care by Telephone

Office-based pediatric practice involves an enormous volume of patient telephone contact. The majority of telephone calls to pediatricians' offices are for an immediate problem requiring care by phone or a same day office visit. Physicians are heavily dependent upon their office staff to obtain accurate information over the phone and make reliably safe initial assessments about the general nature and level of urgency of the problems. Care by telephone is an important source of patient confusion, dissatisfaction, and malpractice actions. It is the physician's responsibility to provide office personnel with explicit guidelines, preferably written, for dealing with inquiries and clinical complaints transmitted by telephone. Significant problems managed by phone should always be documented in the patient's medical record. A number of manuals and other publications are available as resources to physicians in the organization of this important aspect of pediatric practice. There has been a recent increase in the number of services that offer initial phone call screening and consultation, usually by a nurse following a prescribed protocol. The physician or group should demonstrate the use adequate caution in selecting such coverage, and should demonstrate continued interest in the quality of the service.

While thresholds for potential liability may vary among jurisdictions, it is generally accepted that telephone interaction between a patient and the physician's office may be sufficient to establish the legal basis for a physician-patient relationship.

[d] Office Procedures

Many pediatricians perform minor surgical or orthopedic procedures in their offices as well as a variety of specialized diagnostic studies such as chest or skeletal X-rays, especially in geographic areas where availability of qualified specialists may be limited. Questions may arise about whether the scope of the primary care pediatrician's practice includes performance of such procedures. An individual physician's training and experience as well as customary community practice patterns will influence whether the physician will be held to the standard of care of a reasonable practitioner with his qualifications or that of a specialist in that field. Adequate equipment and trained personnel must be available to deal with potential complications that may arise from these procedures.

[5] Standards for Routine Newborn Care

Newborn care is the "bread and butter" of primary care pediatric practice. It is the most common reason for families to develop a professional relationship with a pediatrician, and represents the main context for pediatrician and hospital interaction. The scope of newborn care, for which standards have evolved, ranges from prenatal visits with expectant parents to the first newborn office visit.

[a] Prenatal Visit

Many pediatricians recommend prenatal interviews with expectant parents, especially primiparous mothers (those who are giving birth for the first time). In addition to offering counseling in the care of the new baby, the visit offers an opportunity to obtain clinical data important for appropriate management of the neonate. This should include review of the pregnancy history with emphasis on pregnancy complications, illnesses, medications, history of any prior neonatal problems, and significant genetic and metabolic disorders or congenital malformations. This is also an opportunity for the physician to obtain significant psychosocial data that may guide the need for further intervention. As a result of data obtained during prenatal visits, the pediatrician may be able to anticipate a number of high-risk situations in the immediate neonatal period, such as multiple births, prematurity, diabetes, and malformations such as intestinal obstructions. The growing trend of having newborns seen in the hospital by hospitalists rather than their primary care physician makes the prenatal visit especially useful as parents may have questions for the pediatrician even before the babies first pediatric office visit.

[b] Initial Assessment of the Newborn

Under normal circumstances, the initial assessment of the newborn conducted in the delivery room is the responsibility of the obstetrician. When a pediatrician is present, usually because of anticipated problems, he or she assumes that responsibility. The purpose of the assessment immediately after birth is to detect abnormalities in the infant's physiologic adaptation to the extrauterine environment that might require specific treatment, such as oxygen, airway management or fluid therapy. This initial evaluation follows a routine procedure and is accompanied by assignment of an Apgar Score at one and five minutes after birth, which provides a standardized measure of cardiopulmonary and neurologic status and serves to identify infants requiring immediate intervention, as well as those at risk for sequelae of perinatal injury. The Apgar score was not intended to predict neurologic outcome. The five minute Apgar is a good predictor of neonatal death. Hospitals are required to maintain updated policies concerning delivery room procedures, delineation of responsibilities, provisions for presence of at least one person skilled in neonatal resuscitation, availability of resuscitation equipment, and procedures for documentation of critical events and treatments provided.

Hospital policies should also specify situations of high risk at which identified categories of skilled personnel are expected to attend. These may include instances of recognized fetal distress, emergency cesarean sections, third trimester vaginal bleeding, very low birth weight, multiple gestations, prolonged or unusual labor, infants of diabetic mothers, prenatal detection of major anomalies, and known blood group incompatibilities.

Contrary to the long-held view, childhood neurologic disorders, such as cerebral palsy, epilepsy or mental retardation, correlate poorly with perinatal events, especially as reflected in the Apgar Score. Gestational age less than thirty-two weeks, lowest fetal heart rate less than or equal to sixty beats per minute, breech presentation, chorioamnionitis, low placental weight, placental complications, and birth weight less than or equal to 2000 grams, are risk factors for later neurologic problems. However, factors related to events at the time of labor and delivery, especially intrapartum asphyxia manifested as neonatal depression, account for only a small portion of children with cerebral palsy. For a causal relationship to be seriously suspected, asphyxia must be severe and prolonged, immediately apparent in the delivery room, and accompanied by other evidence of hypoxic/ischemic encephalopathy, such as hypotonia, poor feeding, problems with respiratory control, and seizures.

Hospital policies for routine newborn care should also include the following elements: criteria for transfer of babies from the delivery room to the transitional nursery for early observation, and then transfer to the routine care nursery; time within which the baby must be assessed by nursing staff, examined by a physician; procedures for routine immediate care, such as ophthalmic prophylaxis and administration of Vitamin K; cord care; identity labeling; and routine initial feeding orders. Documentation of vital signs and events that require nursing personnel to contact the physician on call immediately must also be clearly stated.

Many hospitals permit physicians to issue "standing orders" to be invoked automatically when a newborn baby is admitted to their service. Written policies should define the limits of such orders.

Routine screening programs for a number of metabolic diseases are statutorily mandated in all states. Depending on the state, this may include several of the following diseases: phenylketonuria, hypothyroidism, galactosemia, homocystinuria, histidinemia, maple syrup urine disease, and cystic fibrosis, with the list of cost effective screens for inborn errors of metabolism growing rapidly. Screening newborns for evidence of maternal substance abuse during pregnancy and for transmission of human immunodeficiency virus (HIV) has become increasingly prevalent, especially in high-risk areas. Because such practices raise serious confidentiality issues, they should be governed by explicit hospital policies that are in compliance with state law and regulations of state health departments.

Nursery policies should also provide explicit procedures for prompt notification of the responsible physician about the birth of a baby assigned to the physician's service, and about any problems that may arise.

[6] Common Problems in the Neonatal Period

In the course of routine delineation of hospital privileges, as part of the standard credentialing process, most board-certified or eligible pediatricians will indicate their qualifications to manage the more common, and usually self-limiting, problems that arise during the neonatal period, without consultation with a neonatologist. In practice, these qualifications may be limited by the level of staffing and equipment available at the particular facility. Transient respiratory distress, jaundice, hypoglycemia, work-up for suspected neonatal sepsis, moderate, otherwise uncomplicated prematurity, and the appropriate use of oxygen are examples of common problems that can usually be managed without the aid of a neonatologist or transfer to a tertiary care unit. More physicians are opting for hospital care to be provided by hospitalists. As this occurs standards of care will change in different areas.

[a] Transient Respiratory Distress

Full-term or premature neonates may experience transient episodes of tachypnea (rapid breathing) and mild respiratory distress immediately following birth and lasting one to three days. Routine evaluation for more serious underlying problems, such as infection or cardiac abnormalities, missed hyaline membrane disease, include chest X-ray, blood count, and blood gas determination.

[b] Neonatal Jaundice

Neonatal jaundice is among the most common problems encountered by the pediatrician. In general, the primary objective in its management is to differentiate benign, transient, so called "physiologic" forms of jaundice from cases in which jaundice is an indication of more serious underlying pathology, and to identify circumstances in which abnormally high levels of bilirubin may result in neurologic damage (kernicteris). By careful review of the pregnancy history, physical examination of the infant, blood tests, and serial determination of the type and level of serum bilirubin, the pediatrician should be able to identify, and transfer to the care of a neonatologist cases in which jaundice accompanies underlying perinatal cornplications such as infection, hepatic disease, or hemolytic disease, which may need alternative treatment such as an exchange transfusion.

Physicians should be knowledgeable about the relationship between breast feeding and neonatal jaundice. Breast-fed infants generally have a greater degree of "physiologic" jaundice during the first week of life, which requires no treatment or feeding changes. Rarely, breast fed infants develop more pronounced jaundice after the first week, for which a temporary interruption of breast feeding may be all that is required.

While most cases of physiologic jaundice do not require treatment, pediatricians should be familiar with the appropriate indications for the use of phototherapy and exchange transfusion. More recently most phototherapy is done at home so appropriate follow-up is more vulnerable to breakdowns in communication.

[c] Hypoglycemia

Transient hypoglycemia (low blood sugar) is most common in infants of diabetic mothers, but can also occur in prematurity, intrauterine growth retardation, cold stress, or perinatal asphyxia. Pediatricians should be able to anticipate situations at high risk for hypoglycemia, recognize its clinical manifestations, such as jitteriness, apnea, or seizures, and should be familiar with the range of normal plasma glucose levels in neonates and the appropriate immediate treatment with intravenous infusions of glucose, when needed. Babies with prolonged or recurrent episodes of hypoglycemia should be referred to the care of a neonatologist. Nursery protocols should indicate that the physician be notified of any of the aforementioned symptoms as they may occur at any time during the hospital stay in the absence of risk factors.

[d] Neonatal Sepsis

Pediatricians must be able to recognize infants at risk for neonatal sepsis (presence of pus-forming and other pathogenic organisms) and the clinical features of this relatively common problem. Risk factors for neonatal sepsis include premature labor, low birth weight, prolonged rupture of fetal membranes and maternal fever. Clinical features that should cause suspicion of sepsis include unexplained respiratory distress, feeding difficulties, temperature instability, apnea, irritability, lethargy, thrombocytopenia, and neutropenia. A complete evaluation for suspected neonatal sepsis should include a lumbar puncture and chest X-ray, as well as a routine blood count and blood and urine cultures, followed by initiation of parenteral antibiotic therapy while awaiting laboratory results. A high level of suspicion, early detection, and initiation of therapy are important standards for this common condition that is associated with high morbidity and mortality. A high level of suspicion is essential because the symptoms are non-specific in the neonate.

[e] Use of Oxygen

Perhaps the most common treatment modality employed in the neonate, and the area of the greatest legal hazard, is the appropriate use of oxygen. The early recognition that prolonged use of oxygen may be associated, under certain circumstances, with retrolental fibroplasia (RLF) (or retinopathy of prematurity (ROP)) and blindness has led to a better understanding of this serious ophthalmologic complication as well as more sophisticated monitoring techniques.

It is now apparent that ROP is not limited to premature infants exposed to prolonged periods of hyperoxia, but may occur in infants without hypoxia, and in mature neonates as well. Because the etiology, pathogenesis and prevention of ROP are still incompletely understood, the physician's emphasis must be on the appropriate indications for the use of oxygen and methods of monitoring. As a rule, supplemental oxygen should be used only for specific indication, such as cyanosis or respiratory distress with documented hypoxia. If oxygen is needed beyond the emergency period, monitoring of arterial oxygen tension (PaO2) is mandatory, along with measurements of carbon dioxide tension (PCO2) and blood pH. Transcutaneous oxygen monitors and pulse oxymeters are unreliable for detecting hyperoxia, and must be accompanied with PaO2 measurements of arterial blood.

[f] Other Problems

Routine physical examination of the newborn is also intended to detect asymptomatic, hidden defects. Examples are congenital dislocation of the hip, a potentially handicapping disorder which can be detected by standard manipulations of the hip joint, and coarctation of the aorta, a potentially life-threatening cardiovascular defect easily detected by palpation of peripheral pulses, a standard part of routine physical examination.

Feeding intolerances are common problems of the neonatal period. While usually self-limiting or relieved by varying feeding routines, symptoms such as "spitting-up" must be distinguished from significant vomiting that may indicate the presence of intestinal obstruction. Persistent vomiting or the presence of bile-stained fluid in the vomitus should alert the pediatrician to the possibility of an underlying metabolic or anatomic problem. The failure to defecate may indicate an intestinal obstruction and rarely an intestinal torsion which may result in loss of intestinal tissue if not recognized early.

[7] Common Clinical Problems in Early Infancy

The nonverbal infant has a limited repertoire of subjective complaints and symptoms by which to offer clues to underlying disease. Thus, a relatively narrow range of clinical manifestations may be indicators of disorders ranging from the mild and self-limiting to the severe and rapidly progressive. The standard of care expected of pediatricians here includes the ability to interpret common complaints correctly and to distinguish serious from self-limiting problems in a timely and effective manner.

[a] Gastrointestinal Complaints

Regurgitation of feedings is probably the most common gastrointestinal problem encountered in young infants. Usually self-limiting, simple "spitting-up" must be differentiated from significant regurgitation or vomiting that may indicate gastroesophageal reflux, intestinal obstruction, or underlying neurologic or metabolic disturbances. Regurgitation that is persistent, projectile, associated with failure to gain weight, tinged with bile or blood, or accompanied by alteration in stool pattern, fever, or a change in sensorium, should raise the suspicion of a serious underlying disorder, and warrant careful evaluation.

Equally common are complaints involving changes in stool pattern, specifically diarrhea or constipation. Normal young infants typically exhibit considerable variability in the consistency and frequency of their bowel movements. An abrupt change to stools of watery consistency, especially when accompanied by vomiting, fever, refusal of feeds, or blood in the stools, suggest significant gastroenteritis or underlying systemic infection requiring an immediate examination for the presence of infection and the state of hydration. Young infants are particularly prone to develop dehydration, especially when fluid intake is impaired because of vomiting. Because specific therapy is generally unavailable for most cases of gastroenteritis, close follow-up and monitoring of body weight are essential.

[b] Complaints about Urination

Complaints related to the voiding of urine by young infants should always be taken seriously. Crying with urination, bloody urine, change in voiding frequency, or a weak urinary stream in males, may be indicators of underlying anatomic, infectious or traumatic lesions. Immediate physical examination, urinalysis, and further studies such as bacterial culture or radiographic imaging may be indicated.

[c] Sleep Disturbances

Parents frequently complain about their infant's sleep patterns, usually about nighttime wakefulness or erratic sleep. Normal infants exhibit a variety of sleep patterns that are generally self-adjusting. However, abrupt changes in pattern, such as sudden onset of wakefulness and irritability or somnolence, are clues to the possibility of significant underlying disease such as infection, injury, or adverse medication effect. These may require immediate assessment. Sleep problems in normal infants should also be given attention as they often cause much stress for the parents and are a common reason for calls to physicians.

[d] Crying

Excessive crying especially when atypical for a particular infant and accompanied by inconsolability, may be a non-specific indicator that the infant is in pain. Unusual crying behavior, whether in duration, intensity, consolability, or the quality of the sound, especially when high-pitched or weak, or when associated with other clinical symptoms, suggest the need for careful physical examination. Typical, self-limiting "colic" is distinguishable by its predictable pattern, general state of good health, and lack of associated manifestations as described. Occasionally colic may be difficult to differentiate from significant pathology until a pattern of behavior is established. Many infants go through an unexplained period of crying, peaking at six to eight weeks and then subsiding. This can be quite stressful to caretakers. Only a very small percentage of these infants have any physical cause for the crying, such as gastrointestinal reflux. This "normal" infant crying needs to be differentiated from other conditions that may cause crying.

[e] Difficulty in Breathing — Coughing

A child with sudden onset of abnormal respiratory pattern will often prompt an immediate call to the physician. Because this is one of the most common complaints in infancy, the physician must be able to distinguish minor causes of distress, such as upper respiratory infections, from more serious upper airway, pulmonary, or cardiac disorders. Young infants with sudden onset of significant respiratory difficulty should be examined promptly, unless the parental report includes data pointing to an obvious and minor cause, such as a simple "cold." Reports of wheezing require evaluation in early infancy to rule out respiratory syncytial virus (RSV) infantile asthma, bronchiolitis, and congestive heart failure, and foreign body in the respiratory tract. Predominantly inspiratory distress, accompanied by cough, may indicate laryngotracheobronchitis ("croup"), a common condition that may lead to respiratory failure. Distinguishing between croup and epiglotitis is important as the treatments differ and epiglotitis more commonly has poor outcomes and requires hospitalization. There may be the need for emergency airway access.

Respiratory distress due to any cause, accompanied by changes in sensorium, such as somnolence or irritability, suggests impending respiratory failure and should be regarded as an emergency.

[f] Fever

The causes of fever in pediatrics can fill a textbook; nevertheless, it is virtually axiomatic that the presence of significant fever in a young infant, with or without associated symptoms, mandates immediate assessment, including a detailed history and physical examination to identify any underlying infectious disease in its early stages. In the absence of focal infection discovered at physical examination, specific laboratory tests, such as blood culture and spinal tap, may be indicated. Infants with recurrent episodes of unexplained fever should be evaluated for urinary tract infections, often associated in such circumstances with malformations of the urinary system.

In evaluating the presence or absence of fever, it is important to remember that small infants can have serious infections with normal, or even subnormal, body temperatures. Any marked change in the behavior of an infant should be assessed.

[g] Growth and Development

The main purpose of continuing health care supervision in the pediatric primary care setting is to monitor progress in physical growth, including height, weight, head circumference, and psychomotor development. Aberrations in these processes may reflect primary disorders of growth or neurologic systems, or represent secondary manifestations of pathology in a wide variety of environmental or systemic diseases. Standardized growth charts, using data compiled by the National Center for Health Statistics, are generally used to plot consecutive data in office practice. Standards for assessing and documenting psychosocial development include the use of widely disseminated screening instruments and charts. A variety of interventions for common disorders of growth and development are available depending on the cause and extent of the problem. Disorders of development are frequent and often missed early, despite recommended screening for developmental delays.

[h] Failure to Thrive

This term generally refers to infants whose weight consistently falls below the third percentile for age on standard growth charts, or an abrupt loss of weight or significant decrease in the previous rate of weight gain as demonstrated by changes in growth percentiles, or a significant mismatch between weight and height. Virtually any disorder in infancy can affect weight gain, including environmental stresses such as parental-infant disturbances that may deprive infants of the nurturance necessary for continued weight gain. The standard of pediatric practice requires that detailed data concerning weight, height, and head circumference be obtained regularly to identify infants in this disease category who require further investigation for underlying etiologies.

[i] Short Stature

Short stature generally refers to infants whose linear growth is delayed with respect to normal increments in weight for height. That is, their general state of nutrition is normal, but they are abnormally short. This condition is discussed later in the chapter, under endocrine disorders of childhood.

[j] Developmental Delay

Pediatricians must be able to assess progress in psychomotor development. Parents frequently express concern about an infant's apparent failure to achieve an expected developmental milestone, such as sitting or walking. Pediatric standards of care require that a screening assessment of progress in this area be performed at each routine health care visit, and those patients requiring further diagnostic evaluation by specialists be identified promptly in order that therapeutic intervention, where possible, be introduced. These assessments should include hearing and language development if a delay in diagnosis might be especially injurious. The pediatric standard of care in this area includes the identification of significant deviations from the ranges of normal development, and a preliminary diagnosis of variations that may be related to underlying organic, psychological, environmental, or genetic factors.

Routine screening of young children for evidence of environmental exposure to lead has become a standard part of pediatric primary care. Recent evidence suggests that children may suffer lasting effects on neuropsychological development at lower levels of exposure than had previously been believed, although there is much controversy about the levels at which intervention is indicated. Standards of pediatric practice now include screening at appropriate intervals in high risk areas, with appropriate testing methodology, and the capacity to correctly interpret test results and initiate treatment and exposure abatement programs as indicated.

There has been a recent and substantial increase in the diagnosis of autism spectrum disorder. There is no evidence relating the use of vaccines to the development of this disorder. Neither is there evidence that low levels of 'heavy metals' cause this disorder. This is of special concern as practitioners using chelation therapy for treatment of heavy metal poisoning may cause harm or death by its inappropriate use.

[k] Anemia

A significant number of infants develop anemia, usually caused by a mild degree of iron deficiency related to rapid physical growth during the first year, coupled with inadequate bioavailability of dietary iron. The condition is usually discovered in the course of routine testing, generally toward the end of the first year. Because the overwhelming number of cases of anemia in this age group respond to appropriate doses of exogenous iron, some physicians will initiate a therapeutic trial as part of the diagnostic evaluation, while others prefer to perform more detailed laboratory testing to search for other causes of anemia, such as hereditary disorders of hemoglobin or the presence of occult blood loss, usually via the intestinal tract. The standard of care in the management of anemia in infancy includes routine screening as part of regular health surveillance, a careful dietary and family history, and, where indicated, treatment with exogenous iron for an appropriate time period, with follow-up to ensure compliance and to detect failure to respond or recurrence of the anemia. A recurrence should prompt an investigation for more complex underlying causes. Children at risk for various hereditary forms of anemia such as sickle cell anemia should be tested early.

[l] Seizures

Convulsive disorders in early infancy may be a manifestation of a long list of possible organic, metabolic, neurodevelopmental, infectious, or traumatic disorders (see § 16.09, *infra*). The most common type of convulsive disorder encountered in early infancy is the benign febrile seizure, occurring in a previously normal infant, with no apparent indications of any underlying disorder that might predispose to seizures. Most seizures occurring in this setting are associated with an acute febrile illness, are considered "benign" in terms of risk of future development of epilepsy, and leave no abnormal residua.

The standard of pediatric care includes prompt, assessment, identification of patients in whom the associated fever is due to serious infection (especially meningitis), and close follow-up to detect patients in whom the seizure heralds more complex neurological problems. The primary care physician should regard a convulsive seizure associated with high fever in an infant as an emergency until any underlying serious infection is ruled out.

Anticonvulsant medication is generally not indicated for simple febrile seizures but may be indicated in prolonged or complex or atypical seizures

[m] Injuries and Poisonings

Childhood injuries and toxic ingestions are among the leading causes of pediatric morbidity and mortality in any age group, including early infancy. A major function of primary pediatric care is preventive counseling in this area.

A significant number of telephone calls to the pediatric office come from parents concerned about an injury or potentially toxic ingestion. The initial task of the physician is to differentiate injuries that can be observed at home from those that require immediate assessment. This decision is particularly important in the case of head injuries, typically caused in early infancy by a fall from a bed or changing surface. Generally, infants experiencing such injuries should be examined, especially if there is report of transiently altered consciousness, or behavior change. As a rule, clinical examination and careful observation by the parents, after detailed instructions by the physician, are more reliable indicators of neurologic status than skull radiographs.

Poisonings are among the most common injuries in childhood, occurring with peak frequency between one and five years of age. Repeated accidental ingestions are suspicious of parental neglect. General principles of management are discussed later in the chapter (see § 16.03 [2]).

Health professionals are expected to recognize the clinical manifestations that should raise suspicions of inflicted injury to a child, and, in all states, they are required by law to report such cases to the local child protection agency In some states reporting to law enforcement is also required although many physicians are unaware of these regulations.

[n] Immunizations

Childhood immunizations against a number of communicable diseases are an important preventive and public health measure for which primary care physicians are responsible. With some variation among jurisdictions, states mandate completion of prescribed immunization schedules as condition of entry into school. In most states parents may elect not to immunize their children for religious reasons. Potential complications of immunizations, directly to the child, or indirectly to third parties, as in the case of transmissible live, attenuated, oral polio virus, represent areas of potential liability. There have been concerns raised about the association of the pertussis and measles vaccine and various neuro developmental disorders. A causal relationship has not been established and it is important to note that the age at which these disorders are diagnosed often coincide with the administration of these vaccines.

National standards for immunization schedules and for contraindications related to increased risk of serious complications are published and periodically updated by the Center for Disease Control of the National Institutes of Health, and by the Academy of Pediatrics.

The National Childhood Vaccine Compensation Act of 1986 provides a system for compensation for complications for childhood injuries which must be utilized before litigation in civil court becomes available. The act provides definitions of compensable vaccine-related injuries, requirements for documentation of administered vaccines, and a standard form for obtaining informed consent.

[o] Sudden Infant Death Syndrome — Infant Apnea

Sudden infant death syndrome (SIDS) is the most common cause of death in the first year of life after the first month. It is here discussed with infant apnea because that condition, while not the cause of SIDS, is frequently associated with the syndrome.

Physician involvement in cases of SIDS typically occurs when notified that a young infant, usually under the age of one year, who has been previously well, or who may have had a minor upper respiratory infection, has been found lifeless in its crib in the early morning hours. Attempts at resuscitation are usually unsuccessful, but occasionally some vital functions can be transiently restored. Post-mortem examination should always be performed in these cases, to rule out underlying causes such as overwhelming infection, congenital malformations, or child abuse.

Apnea of infancy refers to episodes of cessation of breathing, sometimes associated with cyanosis, limpness, and bradycardia, which require vigorous stimulation to restore respiration. Some such episodes are also referred to as "acute life threatening events" (ALTE). While infants with recurrent, severe episodes of ALTE may be at risk for SIDS, there is generally a weak correlation between the two syndromes. Not all apneic episodes are life threatening.

Causes of apnea in infancy include prematurity, infections, seizures, cardiac arrhythmias, gastroesophageal reflux, or any type of upper-airway obstruction.

Where possible, treatment should be directed at the specific cause; however, frequently no cause can be discovered. Many infants are placed on home cardiorespiratory monitors for prolonged periods. A decision to implement a home-monitoring program involves coordination of a home-management program, including technical support, training parents in cardiopulmonary resuscitation, and close family support. It is generally advisable for the pediatrician to embark on such a program in consultation with experts in respiratory disorders in infancy.

[8] Common Problems of Late Infancy and Childhood

[a] Enuresis and Encopresis

Complaints about bladder and bowel function are common in this age group. Bed-wetting (enuresis), constipation, and fecal soiling (encopresis) are typical symptoms brought to the physician's attention. In most cases, these problems are minor and self-limiting; however, pitfalls in management are encountered where clues in the history suggest that the symptom might be secondary to a serious underlying disorder.

While bed-wetting is a relatively common and benign developmental problem in most cases, further evaluation is indicated when there is a history of urinary tract infection, or when the problem arises following a period of complete continence, or is associated with dysuria. Fecal soiling may be a manifestation of delayed bowel training; however, when associated with constipation that can be dated to the neonatal period, further evaluation for the presence of congenital megacolon (Hirshprung's Disease) is indicated. Constipation and fecal soiling also may follow stool withholding during toilet training. This needs early recognition and treatment.

[b] Developmental Delay

Mental retardation affects approximately 3% of the population. Although usually diagnosed after age five, when standardized psychometric tests are reliable, psychomotor developmental delay can be recognized in infants and toddlers at a time where early intervention may be particularly important.

The role of the primary care physician is to identify these patients through the use of developmental-screening protocols during routine health care visits, and to be alert to parental concerns about deviations from expected developmental patterns. Possible underlying disorders that must be considered in the evaluation of developmental delay include genetic diseases, metabolic disorders, central nervous system malformations, perinatal infections, neuromuscular disease, and serious dysfunctional family problems, including extreme neglect.

Many regions of the country offer specialized diagnostic and treatment programs for pre-school children with developmental disorders, including government-mandated services. Physicians should be knowledgeable about services available in their community and initiate timely referral when indicated.

[c] Hearing, Speech and Vision Problems

Normal development of hearing is critical for normal language development in this age group. Even mild hearing loss can have a significant adverse effect on language development. Depending on the criteria used for testing, the incidence of hearing impairment in childhood is about 1%, ranging to 5% in high risk groups, such as children with a history of serious illness during the neonatal period. Early diagnosis, with particular attention to testing high-risk groups, is, therefore, essential. Physicians should be particularly attentive to parental concerns about delayed or unusual vocalization patterns and should perform appropriate hearing tests on neonates whose illnesses were treated with potentially ototoxic drugs. There is increasing advocacy for routine hearing screening in infancy as early recognition and intervention can have dramatic benefit.

Vision screening is an important part of routine health care supervision. In infancy and early childhood, the emphasis is on early detection of progressive disorders of vision that may benefit from early intervention. Most prominent among these is strabismus, in which the eyes are improperly aligned when focusing on objects. Delay in recognition of this condition, which can generally be diagnosed by simple physical examination, is one cause of amblyopia, a serious loss of vision to the point of blindness in one eye. Amblyopia should be recognized early and treated appropriately when possible. It is also important to recognize amblyopia as early as possible as contact sports without protective eye gear poses additional danger. Routine screening examinations and early referral to an ophthalmologist are mandatory.

[d] Failure to Thrive

This term refers to a condition in which the child fails to maintain incremental growth in height and weight along an anticipated growth curve. The energy requirements necessary to support the rapid growth normal for this age period makes growth a sensitive indicator of disturbances that might be present in various organ systems. These include gastrointestinal, renal, cardiac, central nervous system, pulmonary, and metabolic disorders. Serious environmental disturbances in parenting should be considered as a possible cause of failure to thrive during the initial assessment of failure to thrive and must be considered when an underlying cause is not apparent.

Because infants and children tend to grow incrementally with relatively persistent percentiles of statistical normalcy, sequential measurements, using standard reference charts, are an important part of primary health care.

Children who fall below the third percentile or whose growth pattern changes significantly should be more fully evaluated.

[e] Cryptorchidism

Although cryptorchidism, or undescended testes, occurs in less than 1% by six months of age (higher in prematures), it is mentioned here because of the potentially serious consequences of failure to diagnose, for which the primary care physician may be held accountable.

Unilateral or bilateral undescended testes, i.e., testes that cannot be palpated in the scrotum, persisting beyond six months of age, require further evaluation. It is unlikely that testes that are truly undescended, as opposed to simply retractile, will descend spontaneously after that time.

The consequences of a delay in medical or surgical intervention to place testes in proper anatomical position include infertility, risk of trauma, and development of testicular cancer during the third or fourth decade. Optimal time for treatment appears to be between age nine and fifteen months.

[f] Abdominal Pain

Abdominal pain is one of the most common symptoms brought to the attention of the primary care physician, whose task it is to differentiate the majority of minor, self-limiting conditions from those representing emergency situations or non emergent serious conditions requiring more thorough evaluation.

Causes of acute abdominal pain are myriad, ranging from transient, non-specific intestinal upset to appendicitis, urinary tract infection, or intestinal obstruction. Indicators of potentially serious acute problems include associated vomiting, diarrhea, fever, dysuria, bloody stools, changes in sensorium, respiratory distress, or history of abdominal trauma. In infants, alternating paroxysms of crying with lethargy accompanied by passage of stools that resemble "currant jelly" should suggest the presence of intestinal intussusception, a surgical emergency.

Chronic, recurrent abdominal pain is said to occur in up to 15% of school-age children. These episodes may recur over many months, without any other evidence of systemic illness. An organic cause of the pain is rarely found. Although frequently thought to have a large emotional component, these children may have distinguishable physiological characteristics. Their prolonged course tends to subject some of them to lengthy and complex diagnostic evaluations in a quest for an organic cause, sometimes resulting in unwarranted invasive diagnostic procedures. It is generally recommended that, after a careful history, accompanied by simple screening tests such as hemogram, urinalysis, and screening tests for underlying inflammatory disorders, close follow-up and counseling is appropriate as long as general good health continues.

[g] Child Abuse and Neglect

Professionals are expected to recognize and are required to report to state child protection agencies cases of suspected child abuse or neglect. The risk of recurrent injury is high, and the overall mortality rate in these cases is approximately 3%.

Any physical injury without a plausible explanation consistent with the physical findings or the child's stage of development, or an unexplained delay in seeking medical attention, should raise the suspicion of abuse. The vast majority of serious head injuries in children under one year of age will fall under this category.

Physicians should be familiar with local child abuse and neglect statutes, which require reporting and permit limited unconsented hospitalization for evaluation and child protection when indicated. Children who are placed at risk of injury because of lack of supervision or lack of basic necessities, such as shelter, clothing, or adequate nutrition, fall within the category of child neglect and should be reported depending on the state regulation.

An increasing number of reports of child abuse are for suspected sexual abuse. Physicians should be aware of the clinical findings that should raise suspicions of sexual abuse and, if such findings are present, they should promptly refer the matter to specialists in the field. Sexual abuse should be suspected in any prepubertal child presenting with a sexually transmitted disease or with genital trauma. In contrast to physical abuse the majority of cases of sexual abuse have no physical findings suspicious for abuse. This makes documentation of the history of abuse, if given to the physician by the child very important. It is important not to ask leading questions of a child if possible in interviewing for possible sexual abuse. In areas where forensic evaluation services are available it may be best to have the child interviewed by someone with special training in this area.

[9] Common Problems in Adolescence

[a] Short Stature

Adolescence begins with the onset of puberty and extends to adulthood. There is wide variation among normal children with respect to the timing and rate of development during this period. However, the sequence of developmental events, including development of secondary sex characteristics, growth spurts, and onset of menarche (first menstrual period), is relatively consistent. Familiarity with this normal sequence is essential as a guide to the appropriate evaluation of problems in adolescent development.

The wide variation in onset of puberty leads to considerable variation in physical stature among early adolescents, giving rise to situations where normal from abnormal shortness of stature must be distinguished. Using serial growth measurements, careful history of growth patterns, radiographic determination of bone age, and laboratory testing, several categories of short stature can usually be distinguished. The most common is *constitutional growth delay,* which usually occurs in children who have grown normally, who will experience a later onset of puberty and growth spurt, and who will ultimately attain normal sexual development and stature as genetically determined. *Familial short stature* refers to those children whose sexual development occurs near the average time, but who are, and will remain, shorter than average, based on their genetic determinants.

Less commonly, specific endocrine disorders may be discovered, such as hypothyroidism or growth hormone deficiency, which require specific treatment. Inflammatory bowel disease, especially regional enteritis, is an example of a relatively common underlying disorder, which can present as failure to develop normally during adolescence in the absence of overt gastrointestinal symptoms.

Careful history taking and physical examination, followed by routine, standard laboratory tests and X-rays as indicated, will often yield clues about the existence of a variety of rare, underlying genetic and metabolic causes of short stature.

With the more widespread availability of synthetic growth hormone a wider array of children, including those with constitutional growth delay may be eligible for treatment with growth hormone, although risks and benefits must be explained. There are published guidelines for the use of growth hormone in children with relative growth hormone deficiency.

[b] Menstrual Disorders

Common menstrual disorders in adolescents include amenorrhea, dysfunctional bleeding, and dysmenorrhea.

In evaluating complaints of primary amenorrhea, or delayed onset of the first menstrual period (menarche), it is important to be aware of the wide range of normalcy and the patient's family pattern. Physical examination may reveal findings such as short stature, webbing of the neck, and widely spaced nipples, which may suggest the presence of gonadal dysgenesis, a condition in which delay in diagnosis and timely removal of the abnormal gonad may increase the risk of cancer. Secondary amenorrhea may result from use of oral contraceptive agents or pregnancy.

Dysfunctional bleeding refers to acquired heavy bleeding or irregularity of menstrual cycles. Menstrual irregularity is common and self-limiting during the first two years after menarche. Underlying causes of dysfunctional bleeding may include infections, foreign bodies, polycystic ovaries, and neoplasms. Where necessary, dysfunctional bleeding in adolescence can usually be controlled by imposing regularity with oral contraceptive agents, an approach that requires experience with the use of these agents in the adolescent age group.

Dysmenorrhea, or painful menstruation, is often accompanied by systemic symptoms such as headache and nausea, and can usually be managed symptomatically. Important underlying causes, such as infection, congenital malformations, and endometriosis, should be considered.

Management of these menstrual problems requires skill and experience in performing vaginal and rectovaginal examinations in adolescent patients, and an understanding of physical and psychological developmental issues pertaining to that age group.

[c] Gynecomastia

As many as 60% of adolescent males will experience breast enlargement (gynecomastia) usually unilateral. The condition is generally transient, lasting from a few months to two years, and is of no clinical significance except for the psychological stress which may occur in more pronounced cases. Rarely, the cause may be traced to underlying liver disease, primary testicular disorders, or certain medications, but in the vast majority of cases no etiology is found, and the mainstay of treatment is reassurance. Cosmetic Surgery to improve appearance is rarely indicated, however the adolescent's emotional status should be a guide as to the need for this.

[d] Eating Disorders

Anorexia nervosa (extreme aversion to food) and bulimia (binge eating and purging) are serious disorders which typically manifest initially during adolescence. When voluntary nutritional restriction has resulted in loss of 25% of body weight, intense intervention by an experienced group may be necessary. A 5-10% mortality rate is associated with anorexia nervosa. Because the disorder occurs predominantly in young women, other underlying causes, such as disseminated malignancy or pituitary tumors should be considered in males presenting with what appears to be anorexia nervosa.

Bulimia is thought to be related to disturbance in body image. As in anorexia nervosa, initial symptoms frequently appear during adolescence, although the two conditions may be pathophysiologically distinct. Both disorders are increasingly common in adolescents with manifestation earlier than had been recognized in the past.

Complications of severe eating disorders include cardiac arrhythmias, pancreatitis, metabolic alkalosis, hypovolemia, and dental problems and death.

[e] Common Skeletal Problems

Physicians who care for adolescents must be familiar with several common skeletal disorders that require early recognition to prevent potentially serious and permanent disability.

Scoliosis occurs most commonly in girls, frequently in families with a positive family history. Routine screening by use of simple physical maneuvers during regular health care visits is recommended to detect spine curvature. This should be done during and before the adolescent growth spurt, during which the condition may progress rapidly. Early referral to experienced orthopedists is indicated as soon as scoliosis is suspected.

Joint pain, especially involving the knees and hips and often associated with limp and painful gait, is a common symptom in adolescence. Evidence of inflammation based on physical examination and laboratory tests suggest infection or a chronic rheumatoid disorder. Osgood-Schlatter's disease is a common and usually benign cause of pre-tibial pain and often swelling. Primary skeletal disorders that have the potential for chronic disability if diagnosis and treatment is delayed include slipped capital femoral epiphysis, Legg-Perthes disease, osteochondritis dissicans, and chrondromalacia. Orthopedic referral is indicated for any non-inflammatory, persistent limp, or complaint of painful joint. A common diagnostic pitfall is failure to recognize the presence of serious hip disease in children who complain of pain referred to the knee.

§ 16.02 Selected Topics by Specialty Area

[1] Neonatology

Neonatology is a specialty that involves the care of sick newborns. While neonatologists are not available at every facility at which babies are delivered, every such facility must be able to meet the standard of care for certain neonatal problems that may arise unexpectedly. Sick newborns are generally cared for in special or intensive care units described under a classification system ranging from Level I to Level III, according to the severity and complexity of problems the unit is capable of managing. Appropriate emergency care for unexpected situations, stabilization, and timely referral and transport to a facility of the required level of expertise are essential elements of the standard of care of newborns in every hospital offering obstetrical services.

[a] Delivery Room Emergencies

Emergencies occurring in the delivery room usually require neonatal resuscitation capabilities. Key to the successful management of these problems is anticipation of high-risk deliveries and preparation with appropriate personnel and equipment. Examples of situations in which neonatal emergencies should be anticipated include emergency cesarean section for any reason, pre-term delivery, multiple gestations, maternal diabetes, fetal bradycardia, prenatally identified congenital anomalies, and meconium-stained amniotic fluid.

It is the hospital's responsibility to ensure the availability in the delivery room of necessary equipment and personnel skilled in neonatal resuscitation, with the emphasis on capability for prompt airway intubation, effective administration of oxygen and parenteral fluids, and the ability to monitor vital functions and to maintain patient stability until transport can be achieved if necessary. Typically, the hospital's department of pediatrics has the responsibility to develop and recommend appropriate policies for the management of neonatal emergencies.

[b] Respiratory Emergencies

Respiratory distress in the immediate neonatal period may be a manifestation of pathology at any level of the respiratory tract or a reflection of serious cardiovascular disturbances. Although relatively uncommon, congenital obstruction of the nares (nasal openings) is an easily recognizable and manageable problem, but it can be life-threatening in the neonate, who is an obligate nose-breather. Esophageal atresia and diaphragmatic hernia are two conditions that can present with neonatal respiratory distress, which ultimately require surgical correction; however, early diagnosis and intervention with appropriate life-supports can significantly influence the outcome. Meconium (fecal discharge of the fetus) in the amniotic fluid is an indicator of fetal distress. When aspirated into the lungs, the resulting pneumonitis can be life-threatening. Prompt recognition of the significance of meconium in the amniotic fluid and emergency tracheal suctioning and respiratory support where indicated can be critical.

Respiratory distress due to severe anemia or hypovolemia (deficiency in blood volume) must be recognized and appropriate fluids administered through peripheral or central vascular routes.

Although neonatal respiratory distress may be caused by congenital cardiac malformations, a definitive cardiac diagnosis will usually require availability of pediatric cardiology consultation services. Essential aspects of neonatal resuscitation and stabilization include attention to airway patency, oxygen supply, circulatory volume, maintenance of normal body temperature, provision of appropriate amounts of fluids and glucose, and use of blood gas monitoring techniques.

[c] Gastrointestinal Emergencies

Emergencies stemming from disorders of the neonatal gastrointestinal tract generally reflect serious underlying congenital malformations. In some cases, such as neonates with omphalocele or gastroschisis, the diagnosis is obvious and the acute management in preparation for emergency surgery at an appropriate facility involves attention to the elements of neonatal resuscitation and stabilization described above, in addition to appropriate care for the exposed intestinal tract to help secure its viability.

Intestinal obstruction in the newborn, due to malformations at one or more sites, should be suspected whenever an infant vomits or spits up bile-stained fluid. Immediate investigation for an obstructive malformation is indicated. Intestinal volvulus is a rare cause of obstruction that needs immediate attention to prevent loss of viable intestinal tract and development of short gut syndrome.

[d] Cardiac Emergencies

Life-threatening emergencies in the neonatal period due to cardiac malformations may be suspected by careful physical examination and supportive laboratory and radiographic data. Respiratory distress or rapid respirations without obvious distress accompanied by cyanosis should suggest cardiac disease. The likelihood is increased when the concentration of circulating oxygen, as measured by blood gas analysis, does not significantly increase despite administration of 100% oxygen through the airway. The presence of cardiac murmurs, abnormal peripheral pulses, and abnormalities on chest X-ray and electrocardiogram can quickly diagnose the presence of cardiac malformations and the need to further investigate in that area. Immediate referral to a medical center staffed and equipped to manage neonates with cardiovascular disease is indicated. It is increasingly common for life threatening cardiac malformations to be diagnosed prenatally.

[e]   Neonatal Jaundice

While most normal neonates experience some degree of mild jaundice of no clinical consequence, the severity, type, and etiology of neonatal jaundice relate to underlying conditions that might result in serious consequences if recognition is delayed.

Jaundice produced by elevations of serum bilirubin of the unconjugated, or "indirect," type may be caused by transient or prolonged immaturity of the hepatic enzyme systems, or by an abnormally excessive breakdown of red blood cells, typically due to maternal-fetal blood group incompatibility. These causes must be distinguished by use of simple laboratory tests such as blood types and Coombs testing. The degree and rate of rise of the level of bilirubin must be monitored to anticipate the risk of brain damage from very high levels. Infants born prematurely or acutely ill are especially vulnerable to the central nervous system toxicity of unconjugated bilirubin.

Elevations of conjugated or "direct" bilirubin are generally an indication of underlying hepatic disorder, such as hepatitis or obstruction of the biliary tree. Elevations of either or both types of bilirubin may indicate the presence of neonatal sepsis.

The treatment of neonatal jaundice includes focus on the underlying cause and prevention of central nervous system damage from toxic indirect hyperbilirubinemia. Phototherapy is a commonly used and effective modality for reducing circulating levels of unconjugated bilirubin. Visual estimates of the serum bilirubin level are unreliable while under phototherapy. Monitoring of phototherapy by laboratory testing is important to ascertain that a safe level of circulating bilirubin has been achieved and maintained. The use of exchange transfusion may be considered depending on the bilirubin level. Complications should be watched for especially as most phototherapy is conducted at home now.

[f]   Neonatal Sepsis

Physicians involved in the care of neonates must maintain a high index of awareness of the possibility of a generalized infection as the cause of a wide range of nonspecific symptoms. Delay in diagnosis and intervention with appropriate antibiotics significantly increases the mortality and risk of serious sequelae of neonatal sepsis.

Newborns delivered after premature rupture of amniotic membranes, especially if accompanied by maternal fever, should be suspected of being infected. Newborns who develop unexplained jaundice, apnea, hypothermia, seizures, respiratory distress, lethargy, irritability, vomiting, or feeding disturbances should be suspected of having sepsis. Because the signs and symptoms of sepsis in the newborn period are so variable and may be subtle, parents with newborns should be encouraged to contact their physicians with any marked change in the infant's status.

In the neonatal period, suspicion of sepsis presumes the existence of sepsis and should lead to obtaining a battery of confirmatory laboratory tests, including cultures of blood, urine, and cerebrospinal fluid, and to initiating treatment with antibiotics while awaiting the results.

[g] Hyaline Membrane Disease

Also known as Respiratory Distress Syndrome (RDS) this condition occurs primarily in the premature infant. Signs and symptoms of RDS are generally apparent shortly after birth. The X-ray appearance is classic, although the severity and progression vary. There can be a need for nasal continuous positive airway pressure, mechanical ventilation or nasal intermittent mandatory ventilation, which may reduce the incidence of bronchopulmonary dysplasia.

[h] Birth Defects

Birth defects occur in approximately 3-5% of newborns. Although many are not apparent during the neonatal period, the physician's responsibility for recognizing birth defects and hereditary disorders will be discussed here because these issues frequently arise shortly after birth.

In many instances, the birth defects will be anticipated because of the increased use of prenatal testing, such as alpha-fetoprotein screening and ultrasound imaging. When assessing the significance and recurrence risks, special attention should be given those cases associated with a history of fetal loss, similar defects in family members, amniotic fluid abnormalities, the presence of multiple major or minor malformations, and evidence of general intrauterine somatic growth failure.

Laboratory tests such as chromosome analysis are available in most communities to aid in specific diagnosis. Where available, a qualified genetic counseling service should be consulted to evaluate the significance of apparent birth defects and to provide reliable recurrence-risk counseling for family members. The body of knowledge concerning recurrence-risk patterns of a large number of defects is expanding rapidly; physicians should avoid the pitfall of offering parents reassuring estimates based on limited familiarity with relevant data.

[2] Infectious Diseases of Childhood

[a] Fever

Fever is usually defined as temperature above 100.4F and is the most common manifestation of infection in childhood. However, in very young infants, serious infection may lead to temperature instability and hypothermia, it is therefore important to assess the infants overall status even in the absence of a fever.

[b] Occult Bacteremia

Children between the ages of six months and two years who develop fever of 102 F or more, without an identifiable focus of infection, and with a peripheral white blood cell count greater than 15,000, have a 5-10% likelihood of having an occult form of bacteremia (presence of viable bacteria in the circulating blood). Children who fit this clinical description should have a blood culture and be given appropriate antibiotics while awaiting the results. While some of these infections appear to resolved spontaneously, the evolving standard of care requires consideration of the possibility of occult bacteremia in febrile infants.

[c] Meningitis

This relatively common but potentially life-threatening infection occurs most frequently in infants and young children. Early diagnosis and prompt initiation of antibiotic treatment is critical to preventing death or serious neurologic sequelae. The more benign viral forms of meningitis are usually clinically indistinguishable from the bacterial variety without analysis and culture of cerebrospinal fluid.

Fever, vomiting, headache, lethargy, irritability, and seizures should raise suspicion of meningitis. In young infants, fullness of the fontanel (membranous interval at the junction of the cranial bones) suggests increased intracranial pressure and a presumptive diagnosis of meningitis. Meningeal irritation may cause pain on flexion of the neck or lower extremities. When suspected, the diagnosis should be confirmed by a lumbar puncture and analysis of the cerebrospinal fluid. The patient should be hospitalized for immediate administration of intra-venous antibiotic therapy pending results of the laboratory tests.

Physicians must be aware that diagnostic lumbar punctures are not without hazard and should be deferred in patients in whom an intracranial mass is suspected or who are in significant respiratory or cardiovascular distress.

Where the identified bacterium is *H. influenzae*, or meningococcus, prophylactic treatment of persons in close contact with the patient and the index case is indicated.

[d] Otitis Media

Acute and chronic infections of the middle ear are the most common infections receiving treatment in the pediatric age group. Repeated episodes of middle ear infection are common, sometimes resulting in chronic functional disturbances and hearing impairment. The essential aspects of management include prompt attention to symptoms of ear pain (with or without fever), careful examination with appropriate equipment suitable for visualizing the structure and mobility of tympanic membranes in small infants, appropriate use of antibiotics, close follow-up, consideration of the use of prophylactic antibiotics to prevent recurrences in certain groups of children, and timely consultation with otolaryngologists, and where indicated allergists for children with persistent recurrent or chronic problems. Complications of otitis media such as acute mastoiditis and cholesteatoma should be monitored.

[e] Tonsillo-pharyngitis

The management of common sore throat in children involves a preliminary determination as to the likelihood of a bacterial (specifically streptococcal) etiology. When accompanied by fever, purulent tonsillar exudate, and tender enlargement of lymph nodes in the cervical area, the likelihood of "strep throat" calls for testing before initiating antibiotic therapy. The availability of office based 'rapid strep' testing makes this easier now.

The recognition of a peritonsillar cellulits/abscess is essential as this usually warrants intravenous antibiotics and may need surgical intervention.

In evaluating the significance of enlarged cervical lymph nodes, other causes must be considered. These include infectious mononucleosis (discussed below), tuberculosis, and neoplastic diseases.

[f] Croup and Epiglottitis

"Croup" is the description commonly given to symptoms caused by a viral infection of the larynx and upper trachea. Cute symptoms include inspiratory stridor, some respiratory distress, cough, hoarseness, and low-grade fever. Most cases with this constellation of symptoms can be treated expectantly and are self-limiting. Occasionally, upper-airway narrowing caused by the infection will progress to the point of impending respiratory failure, requiring emergency hospitalization and airway management. This degree of serious progression of an otherwise minor infection should be suspected when cyanosis, severe distress and use of accessory respiratory muscles, and changes in sensorium are observed. In these instances respiratory support will be needed.

Epiglottitis is an acute, life-threatening bacterial infection of the supraglottic area that must be clinically differentiated from simple "croup" so that emergency measures can be promptly instituted. Children with sudden onset of high fever, severe inspiratory stridor accompanied by severe sore throat, drooling, a "toxic" appearance, and reluctance to be placed in a supine position should be suspected of having epiglottitis. Immediate admission to an emergency center for controlled direct visualization of the epiglottitis and, if necessary, immediate tracheal intubation and tracheotomy, is essential. Fatal laryngospasm and cardiopulmonary arrest are known to occur during the course of examination. Emergency departments in many hospitals have established protocols involving pediatricians, anesthesiologists, and otolaryngologists for immediate inter-disciplinary response to this life-threatening emergency. The overriding goal of emergency care is securing a reliable airway.

Once the airway is stabilized, usually by nasotracheal intubation, the emergency is essentially over and a favorable response to antibiotic therapy can be expected.

As with other systemic infections caused by the *H. influenzae* bacterium, prophylactic treatment of close contacts and the index case to eliminate the carrier state is indicated.

[g] Respiratory Syncytial Virus

Respiratory Syncytial Virus or RSV is a relatively common respiratory infection and passive immunoprophylaxis is indicated in high risk infants. RSV can cause bronchiolitis and serious respiratory distress and even death. It can have some residual effects such as recurrent wheezing

[h] Infectious Mononucleosis

Infectious mononucleosis refers to a clinical syndrome of fatigue, fever, sore throat and lymphadenopathy and is most often caused by the Epstein Barr virus although a number of other pathogens may produce the same relatively non specific clinical picture. It rarely occurs in very young children or in older adults. Symptoms usually last 2-4 weeks although persistent fatigue lasting for several months may be a complication.

Infants and children may develop pulmonary infections from a wide variety of viral and bacterial agents. In most situations, the physician will not need (or readily be able) to identify the specific etiologic agent. Effective management focuses on recognition of signs and symptoms suggesting the presence of pneumonia, signs of progression of disease and impending respiratory failure, and situations in which specific etiologic diagnosis is required.

While a diagnosis of pneumonia in older children is strongly suggested by the presence of fever and cough, younger infants and children may development nonspecific manifestations such as fever, irritability, gastrointestinal symptoms, and minimal or no cough. In some children, abdominal pain is the major clinical manifestation, without obvious symptoms referable to the respiratory system.

Children with recurrent episodes of pneumonia should be evaluated for an underlying explanation. This may lead to the discovery of a congenital airway malformation, foreign body, immune deficiency, or infection caused by an unusual organism not affected by the prescribed antibiotic. Aspiration of foreign bodies into the respiratory tree should be suspected where radiographs suggest obstruction of a segment or lobe of the lung, or when choking or coughing during eating.

Complications that may require consultation and further evaluation include extension of disease despite treatment, development of pulmonary cavitation, abscess or pleural effusion, or persistent collapse of a lung segment.

[i] Bone and Joint Infections

These serious, but relatively uncommon, infections are mentioned here because of the potentially serious consequences of delay in diagnosis when young infants are affected. While in older children, skeletal and joint infections are more readily diagnosed based on symptoms of fever and localized pain, corroborated by appropriate radiographic and laboratory data, symptoms in young infants may be general and nonspecific. Fever and irritability may be the only symptoms, with bone or joint infection, suspected only after careful physical examination. Joint infection in infancy may lead to rapid destruction of the joint and a potential for permanent disability. Where suspected, prompt referral for orthopedic consultation should lead to diagnostic aspiration of the joint space and, if indicated, aggressive medical and surgical management to ensure prompt eradication. This is especially important in cases of hip joint infection, where serious damage to the joint my result from delay in treatment.

§ 16.03 Gastrointestinal Disorders in Childhood

[1] Gastroesophageal Reflux

Reflux of gastric contents into the lower espophagus is a common occurrence in young infants, and usually results spontaneously without ill effects. However, in some children, gastroesophageal reflux can be the cause of a variety of acute and chronic clinical problems.

Significant regurgitation may result in failure to thrive, secondary to inadequate caloric intake. Reflux of acidic fluid may result in esophagitis, chronic occult blood loss leading to anemia, and eventually stricture due to fibrosis. In some infants, reflux may cause recurrent episodes of aspiration and pneumonia. In others, episodes of apnea, related to esophageal reflux, may occur.

Although esophageal reflux, when associated with any of the above manifestations, is usually suspected because of obvious symptoms of regurgitation or episodes of coughing when supine, frequently overt symptoms of reflux are absent and the diagnosis is established by special techniques, such as barium swallow and continuous monitoring of esophageal pH levels.

Precise diagnosis may require consultation with an experienced radiologist and gastroenterologist. Treatment is usually medical, consisting of postprandial positioning, thickened feedings, and use of pharmacologic agents to reduce gastric acidity and promote gastric emptying. Surgical intervention aimed at mechanically preventing reflux is generally reserved for intractable cases.

[2] Ingestion of Caustic Agents

Accidental ingestion of toxic substances is a common occurrence among children in the toddler age group. Caustic agents such as drain cleaners and some polishes are substances with which physicians must be familiar because of their potential for immediate and long-term complications.

In contrast to the management of most other potentially toxic ingestions, induced emesis is contraindicated with caustic agents. Immediate chest X-ray for evidence of aspiration or mediastinitis, direct visualization of the esophagus by endoscopy within 24 hours, followed by barium swallow several weeks later is recommended to detect evidence of mucosal injury and late stricture. The presence or absence of oral burn lesions is an unreliable indicator of the extent of esophageal injury. Use of corticosteroids to reduce inflammation is sometimes considered.

Pitfalls in management result from underestimation of the seriousness of the problem. This usually results from an under-assessment of the amount ingested and the lack of injury evident within the oral cavity.

[3] Gastrointestinal Bleeding

Hemorrhage from the gastrointestinal tract can be a manifestation of underlying disease at any anatomic level within that system. An orderly approach to management is indicated to arrive at an accurate diagnosis and to ensure the safety of the patient. Common causes of gastrointestinal hemorrhage in children include infectious or allergic enterocolitis, peptic ulcers, inflammatory bowel disease, Meckel's diverticulum, intussusseption and rectal fissure.

Hemodynamic stability must be assured before embarking on a diagnostic plan that might include radiographic and endoscopic procedures. Compromised hemodynamic status in young children is suggested in the presence of tachycardia or orthostatic hypotension, despite otherwise normal blood pressure. Volume replacement and a secured route for emergency vascular access should be the first priority.

[4] Peptic Ulcer Disease

The diagnosis of this disorder is frequently delayed in children, because of lack of awareness about the range of symptoms common to children. Peptic ulcers can occur as early as the newborn period, where acute hemorrhage and perforation may be the presenting manifestations. During infancy, vomiting, failure to thrive, or documented weight loss may be the only symptoms leading to a diagnosis of peptic ulcer disease. Vomiting associated with poorly localized, often vague, abdominal pain are typical symptoms in pre-school age children. As many as 5-15% of school-age children have complaints of chronic, recurrent abdominal pain, usually in the midabdomen. While most will have no underlying organic etiology for these complaints, peptic ulcer disease will occasionally be discovered as the cause. Peptic ulcer should be suspected in a child with a positive family history, even if the symptoms are vague.

Secondary peptic ulcers occur in patients with head injury, burns, sepsis, and shock. Upper gastrointestinal hemorrhage during the course of a critical illness is the typical mode of presentation.

A common pitfall in diagnosis is excessive reliance on radiographic studies, which will miss up to 25% of peptic ulcers in children. Direct visualization by endoscopy is the preferred procedure.

Recent research has identified a specific bacterium that may cause infection of the stomach lining and peptic ulcers. Such cases, which require special diagnostic procedures, may response to antimicrobial treatment.

[5] Pyloric Stenosis

This entity causes a partial obstruction of the pylorus, leading to progressive vomiting. It affects young infants, most commonly between one and three months of age. The diagnosis should be suspected in an infant who develops progressive and characteristically projectile vomiting, especially if accompanied by failure to gain weight, or weight loss. The diagnosis is generally confirmed by radiographic studies, although the obstructing mass of pyloric muscle may occasionally be palpated on physical examination. Treatment is surgical and highly successful. Delay in diagnosis can lead to dehydration and serious metabolic disturbances secondary to prolonged vomiting. Pre-operative assessment includes evaluation of fluid and metabolic status prior to surgery.

[6] Diarrhea in Infants and Children

Diarrhea is one of the most common complaints encountered in pediatric practice. Both acute and chronic forms occur. The practitioner must be able to identify those patients in each category in whom diarrhea, a relatively nonspecific symptom, is a manifestation of underlying disease requiring more extensive evaluation and treatment. In young children the underlying disease may or may not relate to the gastrointestinal tract.

In early infancy, intolerance of cow's milk or soy protein may cause diarrhea. In some cases this may be associated with vomiting or bloody diarrhea, suggesting a more severe form of protein-induced enterocolitis. The dietary etiology of most mild cases of infantile diarrhea is usually established by a trial elimination of the offending substance. Careful follow-up and observation is indicated to ensure adequate nutritional intake during the several weeks of dietary manipulation that may be necessary. Iatrogenically induced failure to thrive may occur when dietary manipulations are not carefully monitored.

Carbohydrate intolerance (usually lactose) leading to diarrhea is a common, usually transient condition, typically following a course of infectious diarrhea. In infants, a trial of carbohydrate-free formula will frequently be confirmatory. Where indicated, laboratory tests demonstrating acidic stools containing sugars, or a breath hydrogen test, will provide additional evidence.

[a] Celiac Disease

This is an uncommon cause of chronic diarrhea in early childhood, but is mentioned here because of the pitfalls associated with diagnostic and follow-up practices. Sensitivity to the gliadin portion of the gluten in certain foods causes diarrhea, abdominal distention, vomiting, and poor growth in infants up to approximately two years of age. Because management requires strict adherence to a difficult dietary regimen for a prolonged period, diagnostic criteria are strict.

Intestinal mucosal biopsy demonstrating characteristic lesions establishes the diagnosis. In some medical centers, repeat biopsies demonstrating regeneration of normal mucosa after dietary management and recurrence of pathologic lesions following test challenge with gluten, are also required for a definitive diagnosis. Diagnosis on clinical grounds alone may subject infants to unwarranted, severe dietary manipulation with adverse effect on growth and development.

Follow-up requires documentation of continued adequate physical growth. Recurrence may cause growth failure, accompanied by little or no diarrhea.

[b] Chronic, Nonspecific Diarrhea

This is the most common type of chronic diarrhea. It may occur in otherwise robust children, typically one to three years of age, who are growing and developing normally. Loose stools are often precipitated by a variety of dietary factors and may contain undigested food particles. This benign condition probably represents a disorder of gastrointestinal motility. The presence of blood in the stools, or poor growth should prompt a search for a more specific etiology.

[c] Infectious Diarrhea

Infections with a variety of viruses, bacteria, and other agents can cause acute diarrhea in childhood. The objective of management is to treat the secondary effects of the diarrhea, such as fluid and metabolic imbalances, and to distinguish those causes of diarrhea that require treatment with specific antimicrobials from those that are self-limiting. Diarrhea associated with signs of systematic illness or with bloody stools is more likely to be caused by a specific pathogen that may be identifiable by stool culture. Organisms that may cause more serious complications of sepsis in association with diarrhea include salmonella, Shigella, Yersinia, and Campylobacter. Shigella infection should be suspected where bloody diarrhea is associated with high fever and seizure. Antibiotic treatment of Salmonella infections is generally contraindicated because of the risk of prolonging the carrier state and the infectiousness of the patient to others. A possible exception is in the case of young infants with Salmonella and evidence of sepsis, where treatment with appropriate antibiotics may be considered. It is important to obtain a travel history as ceratin infectious causes of diarrhea are more common after travel to high risk locations.

[7] Inflammatory Bowel Disease

This category includes two major clinical entities, ulcerative colitis and regional enteritis (Crohn's disease). While these complex conditions are generally managed in consultation with specialists in gastroenterology, primary care physicians should be aware of the range of presenting symptoms to effect prompt diagnosis, as well as the extraintestinal complications that may arise during follow-up of these chronic conditions.

Abdominal pain associated with grossly bloody stools are typical presenting symptoms that should prompt an evaluation for inflammatory bowel disease. In some cases, overt gastrointestinal symptoms may be preceded by prolonged periods of unexplained fever, poor growth, or, in the case of young adolescents, delayed puberty.

Significant extraintestinal complications that may occur include hepatitis, arthritis, thrombophlebitis, cutaneous manifestations such as erythema nodosum, inflammation of the eye, and delayed sexual maturation. These extraintestinal symptoms are more common in Crohn's disease. When extraintestinal symptoms predominate, a specific diagnosis may be significantly delayed. Toxic megacolon is a severe complication of ulcerative colitis which may be life-threatening. The goal of treatment is control of symptoms and maintenance of nutritional balance and adequate growth. Patients with ulcerative colitis must be followed closely. They have up to a 2% per-year cumulative risk of developing colonic carcinoma after ten years of disease.

[8] Hepatitis

Hepatitis is usually a mild, self-limiting disease in childhood, caused by one of a group of related viruses. The condition is suspected when nausea, vomiting, fever, and hepatomegaly or jaundice occur and are confirmed by laboratory tests for hepatic inflammation. Treatment is supportive for the patient and protective for close contacts. Physicians should refer to the American Academy of Pediatrics and United States Public Health Service current recommendations for active and passive immunization.

Some types of acute hepatitis caused by other members of the hepatitis virus group may evolve into a chronic phase, which in some cases progress to destructive hepatic disease and hepatic failure.

Neonatal hepatitis is one of the causes of jaundice in the newborn and must be considered whenever elevations of conjugated serum bilirubin are found. Infants are infected by intrauterine or intrapartum exposure to mothers in whom circulating hepatitis virus antigens can be detected. Current American Academy of Pediatrics and United States Public Health Service recommendations concerning maternal and infant screening and immunization practices should be consulted although routine immunization for hepatitis B is recommended starting in the newborn period and Hepatitis A immunization may be recommended for travel to certain high risk areas.

[9] Foreign Bodies

Children's mouthing habits commonly result in ingestion of foreign bodies. Most objects pass harmlessly through the intestinal tract. The esophagus is the most common site for the object to become lodged. Radiographs showing the full length of the esophagus, followed by removal of the object, are indicated to avoid possible complications of ulceration and perforation. Certain high risk ingestions — such as batteries require different levels of observation and potential intervention as there is the risk of corrosion. Young children may not uncommonly, in the course of exploration, insert foreign bodies in their ears and noses too. Management depends on object inserted.

§ 16.04   Cardiovascular Diseases in Childhood

Pediatric cardiology deals predominantly with the diagnosis and management of congenital malformations of the heart and great vessels. Newer diagnostic techniques and surgical innovations emphasize the need for early diagnosis and consultation with qualified specialists. The primary care physician should be skilled in identifying the presence of cardiac disease on the basis of history and physical examination.

Cardiac disease as a cause of respiratory distress or cyanosis in the neonatal period was discussed in § 16.02[1][d], *supra*. Routine physical examination of an apparently normal newborn may also detect the presence of congenital malformations through heart murmurs, unusual location of heart sounds, or diminished or absent peripheral pulses.

[1] Routine Examinations

Recommendations for routine health care visits call for an initial visit at approximately two weeks of age. Malformations such as ventricular septal defects, which may not be evident in the immediate newborn period because of the transition from intrauterine to extrauterine blood flow circuits, are often detected at this visit. Typical heart murmurs may be heard in an otherwise asymptomatic baby. Symptoms of early cardiac decompensation caused by the defect include rapid respirations, sometimes associated with wheezing, poor feeding, and irritability.

[2] Murmurs

Cardiac murmurs are frequently heard in normal children during the course of physical examination. In most cases, primary care physicians should be able to distinguish these "innocent" murmurs from those requiring further diagnostic evaluation, based on detailed history and careful physical examination. Cardiac conditions that may not require surgical intervention in childhood, but that put the child at risk for subacute bacterial endocarditis following routine procedures such as dental cleaning should be recognized so that the child may be put on prophylactic antibiotics prior to such procedures.

[3] Dysrhythmias

Infants and children may develop disorders of cardiac rhythm, including heart block and tachyarrhythmias. Most common among these is supraventricular tachycardia, which occurs typically in young infants. Presenting symptoms are usually nonspecific, such as poor feeding, irritability, and rapid breathing. On examination, the heart rate exceeds 220 beats per minute. Heart failure may develop within hours. Immediate referral is indicated for treatment with pharmacological agents or electroconversion to normal rhythm. The older child may present with the sense of irregular heartbeats and may have Wolf Parkinson White syndrome or other dysrythmia. Diagnostic measures may include the use of twenty four hour monitoring such as a Holter monitor. Detection of potentially serious arrhythmias is important as it may affect participation in competitive sports.

§ 16.05   Respiratory Diseases in Childhood

[1] Asthma

Asthma is an increasing cause of mortality even in the pediatric age group. The clinical hallmark of asthma is expiratory wheezing. However, wheezing can be caused by many other conditions that have an effect on narrowing the terminal bronchiolar tree. Infections, pulmonary vascular congestion in children with congestive heart failure, foreign body aspiration, and cystic fibrosis are examples of diverse pathological processes that may cause wheezing and must be considered in the initial evaluation of a child who seems to be developing asthma.

Most cases of childhood asthma are caused by responses to exogenous allergens or toxins which result in the release of endogenous substances that cause airway hyper-reactivity and constriction. The mainstay of treatment is avoidance of exposure to known toxins and appropriate use of pharmacologic agents (selected from a large group of, beta-2-adrenergic agonists and corticosteroids). While highly efficacious, many of these drugs have narrow toxic-therapeutic ratios, especially in infants and young children. Physicians must be familiar with the appropriate use of these drugs, which are available in parenteral, oral and inhalant forms, as well as in the recognition of early symptoms of drug toxicity. There is increasing evidence that the early use of inhaled steroids for a period of time can do much to decrease the severity of future asthma episodes or prevent them altogether. Although steroid use has been recommended for quite some time it is not used frequently enough.

When an acute attack of asthma does not respond to initial treatment, the condition of *status asthmaticus* exists. Further treatment generally requires hospitalization and careful monitoring of blood gases and drug levels, with the goal of preventing respiratory failure. A major cause of morbidity and mortality in the management of status asthmaticus is failure to recognize early clinical and laboratory indicators of impending respiratory failure.

The national Asthma Education Program's Expert Panel of the National Heart, Lung and Blood Institute of the National Institutes of Health, recently issued a report titled "Guidelines for the Management of Asthma." This report covers diagnostic, therapeutic, and monitoring guidelines, and is a standard of practice reference.

The use of inhaled steroids has been shown to be effective in prevention of progression of and reversal of symptoms of asthma, however this proven therapy is not used frequently enough, even when indicated.

§ 16.06 Diseases of the Urinary Tract in Childhood

Urinary tract infections, hematuria, proteinuria and hypertension are common problems of the urinary tract which will come to the attention of the primary care practitioner caring for children.

[1] Urinary Tract Infection

These are usually categorized as "upper" urinary tract (kidney) and "lower" urinary tract (bladder) infections. In infancy and early childhood, infections may be clinically indistinguishable. Infants with urinary tract infections may develop only nonspecific symptoms, such as vomiting, diarrhea, and fever.

Underlying congenital malformations of the urinary tract predispose to infection. Infections occurring in the absence of underlying predisposing causes are much more common in school-age females. Therefore, infants, males, and any child with recurrent episodes of infection should be investigated for the presence of malformations.

Diagnosis and appropriate treatment depends on identification of specific organisms by urine culture. Efficacy of treatment also should be demonstrated by negative follow-up urine cultures. Routine examination of the urine for presence or absence of white blood cells is a notoriously *inaccurate* way to search for infection or assess adequacy of treatment: Urine culture (obtained by clean-catch, catheter, or suprapubic aspiration techniques depending on age) are the diagnostic procedures of choice for these purposes.

Patients with urinary infection must be followed closely for possible asymptomatic recurrence after completion of a course of a therapy. Urine cultures or other reliable tests for infection should be performed routinely to document the absence of infection. Children with recurrent urinary tract infections should be evaluated for the presence of vesicoureteral reflux and if it is present should be followed to assess its degree and the need for prophylactic antibiotics and possible surgical reimplantation of the ureters.

[2] Hematuria

Gross or microscopic hematuria may be caused by disorders at any point in the urinary tract. Trauma, infection and glomerular diseases are the most common causes. The goal in the initial evaluation of hematuria is to differentiate those patients who may be followed expectantly from those who need more extensive evaluation.

Gross hematuria may present as red- or tea-colored urine. Further evaluation by ultrasound or intravenous urography is usually indicated to detect the presence of renal stones, tumors, traumatic lesions, or other causes of bleeding. When associated with proteinuria, renal function studies to rule out glomerular involvement are indicated.

Microscopic hematuria may be detected by a positive "dip-stick" during routine testing. This is a highly sensitive test which can detect a very small amount of red blood cells in the urine. In an otherwise healthy child, further evaluation is indicated if the finding persists in subsequent urine tests over the next one to two weeks. Many cases will resolve spontaneously. If proteinuria is also detected, further studies, including possible renal biopsy, to rule out significant glomerular disease are indicated.

[3] Proteinuria

The presence of proteinuria (greater than normal amount of protein in the urine) may be discovered during routine testing in an asymptomatic patient or during an evaluation of a clinical problem. Physicians must be able to differentiate benign forms of proteinuria from those indicative of underlying glomerular disease. A small amount of protein may be found in the urine of normal children and young adults, and may represent benign orthostatic proteinuria. This can be differentiated by comparing urine obtained while the patient is recumbent with the first morning voiding when upright. Larger, persistent amounts of protein, especially when accompanied by microscopic hematuria, are suggestive of underlying glomerular disease.

[4] Nephrotic Syndrome

Young children may develop edema characterized by periobital swelling, pedal edema, and ascites. When laboratory investigation reveals the presence of heavy proteinuria, hypoalbuminemia, and hyperlipidemia, the patient may be diagnosed as having nephrotic syndrome. The vast majority of such children will respond favorably to a course of corticosteroids and have so-called "minimal change" disease. Children who fail to respond to treatment as expected, or become refractory to treatment during future recurrences of edema and proteinuria, require further investigation for more serious underlying glomerular pathology. This may require performance of renal biopsy for appropriate histologic classification and subsequent treatment.

The development of fever during treatment of edematous patients may indicate the presence of serious systemic infection, especially bacterial sepsis or peritonitis.

[5] Glomerulonephritis

The most common form of glomerulonephritis in the pediatric age group follows infection with certain types of streptoccocal bacteria. Tea-colored urine, indicating hematuria, and proteinuria are present. Glomerular function may be reduced, leading to decreased urine output, fluid retention and hypertension. In contrast to the case in adults with glomerulonephritis, the disease in children carries a favorable prognosis for complete recovery of renal function. Treatment is generally supportive, with special attention to control of hypertension. Rarely, severe, life-threatening hypertensive crisis may occur, which would require emergency hospitalization.

[6] Hypertension

Measurement of blood pressure should be performed as part of routine health care supervision in all children over the age of two years. Appropriate blood pressure cuffs, available for neonates, infants, and children must be used to obtain accurate readings. Normal data for children from infancy to late adolescence should be used as reference.

A finding of mild to moderately elevated blood pressure should be checked again on at least three separate occasions before embarking on an extensive diagnostic evaluation or prescribing an antihypertensive drug regimen. As in adults, primary or essential hypertension is the most common form. Secondary hypertension is usually due to underlying glomerulonephritis and occasionally leads to a diagnosis of cardiovascular malformations, such as coarctation of the aorta.

Initial therapy focuses on weight reduction, salt avoidance, and exercise, once specific underlying causes have been excluded. Pharmacological management with antihypertensive agents may be used in children with persistent hypertension. Sudden elevations of blood pressure or recordings in excess of 180/110 mm mercury, associated with headache and confusion, should be treated on an emergency basis. Children with a family history of Type 1 Hyperlipidemia should be followed especially closely and should be counseled regarding diet, medication and exercise.

[7] Hemolytic Uremic Syndrome

This syndrome, which occurs most commonly in children under four years of age, is the most frequent cause of acute renal failure in young children. The entity should be considered in a child who develops sudden onset of pallor, oliguria, lethargy, and weakness following an episode of gastroenteritis. Cutaneous petechiae, hepatosplenomegaly, and marked irritability may occur. Laboratory tests will reveal severe anemia with abnormal red blood morphology, thrombocytopenia, and evidence of renal failure. Prognosis for complete recovery is favorable, following aggressive management of renal failure. Early consultation with nephrologists experienced with this syndrome is indicated.

§ 16.07 Hematologic and Oncological Disorders of Childhood

Anemia, neutropenia, and thrombocytopenia are three relatively common abnormalities of the hematologic system occurring in the pediatric age group. In each case, familiarity with the range of possible underlying etiologies is essential for the selection of appropriate treatment and referral to specialists.

[1] Anemia

The most common form of anemia in childhood occurs between the ages of ten months and two years, and is the result of iron deficiency. The combination of marginal transplacentally delivered iron stores, rapid somatic growth, and inadequate intake or bio-availability of exogenous iron, contribute to the development of anemia. Infants born prematurely tend to develop more severe anemia earlier in infancy. The diagnosis is suspected from the birth and nutritional history, and is corroborated by laboratory studies reporting red blood cell indices consistent with a microcytic, hypochromic anemia typical of iron deficiency. Although other possible causes of anemia is sufficiently more common to permit a trial of therapy with appropriate doses of iron. Follow-up is important, with further investigation should be initiated if anemia does not resolve or recurs.

Blood transfusions are extremely rarely indicated and should be reserved for infants with severe anemia who show clinical signs of hemodynamic instability related to the anemia. When administered, caution must be exercised to avoid the development of heart failure due to fluid overload.

Hemolytic anemias occur infrequently in childhood and are usually associated with infection or immune disorders. Hereditary spherocytosis is a relatively common from of hemolytic anemia which may present in the newborn period as jaundice associated with splenomegaly. Splenectomy is generally curative in this disease, although the procedure is usually deferred until approximately age six to reduce the risk of overwhelming sepsis. During that interval, acute episodes of severe anemia may occur.

[2] Sickle Cell Disease

This is most common cause of hemolytic anemia in the African American population. Approximately 10% of African Americans are asymptomatic carriers of the gene for sickle cell disease. Homozygous sickle cell disease is readily recognized by the presence of characteristic red blood cell morphology and confirmed by identification of the abnormal hemoglobin by electrophoretic analysis.

Early diagnosis is important because of the risk of serious complications, such as overwhelming sepsis in infancy, vaso-occlusive crisis causing severe pain syndrome, pulmonary infarctions, strokes, and potentially life-threatening acute splenic engorgement (splenic sequestration syndrome) in infancy. Because of these serious complications, which may occur before the anemia is recognized, some communities have instituted routine newborn screening programs for early identification of infants with the disease.

Complications from impaired perfusion of organs (caused by the effects of abnormally shaped red blood cells) tend to be precipitated by infections that may cause transient episodes of dehydration and metabolic acidosis. The management of otherwise mild infections in children with sickle cell disease includes special attention to adequacy of hydration and tissue perfusion.

Individuals who are asymptomatic carriers of the gene for sickle cell disease have "sickle cell trait." Although anemia and other significant clinical complications do not occur in carriers, microscopic hematuria is occasionally seen. In addition children with sickle cell trait may develop an infarction or sequestration of the spleen if exposed to extremely high altitudes in an unpressurized environment. The recognition of sickle trait is also important for purposes of counseling regarding reproductive risks especially with another person who has sickle trait.

[3] Thrombocytopenia

In otherwise healthy children, the sudden development of petechiae or bleeding from mucous membranes may lead to the finding of acquired platelet deficiency. In childhood, this condition, termed idiopathic 'thrombocytopenic purpura (ITP), typically follows an uneventful viral infection and is an expression of an auto-immune response to the infection. In contrast to ITP in adults, the disease in children is usually self limiting and only very rarely becomes chronic. Bone marrow aspiration is recommended to confirm the diagnosis and to exclude other potential causes. Treatment is generally with corticosteroids. Intravenous transfusions of gamma globulin has been employed in some medical centers. The major complication is intracranial hemorrhage, with the greatest danger being during the early stages of the disease. Splenectomy is rarely necessary in children, and is generally reserved for cases in which thrombocytopenia has persisted beyond six months. Thrombocytopenia may also occur from other causes and its onset in a very ill child may be ominous as the outcomes following the development of disseminated intravascular coagulation is still poor.

[4] Neutropenia

For the primary care practitioner, the finding of neutropenia, either during routine blood testing or in the course of a diagnostic evaluation, suggests the presence of a potentially serious underlying bone marrow disorder and the potential susceptibility to infection. Familiarity with age-related normal blood cell values is important for an accurate interpretation of laboratory results. Up to age five years, there is a normal predominance of lymphocytes in the circulation that may give the erroneous impression of abnormal deficiency of neutrophils. The risk of infection generally is not significant if the absolute neutrophil count exceeds 1000 per cubic millimeter. Complete evaluation includes examination of other circulating blood elements, physical examination for stigmata of clinical complex syndromes associated with neutropenia, a history of frequency and severity of past infections, examination of family members where familial forms of neutropenia are considered, and timely consultation with qualified hematologists. Cyclic neutropenia is a condition in which there is a cyclic variation in the neutrophil count, generally resulting in mild infections during neutropenic phases. On rare occasions infections may result in death.

[5] Leukemia

Acute and chronic lymphocytic and non-lymphocytic forms of leukemia account for the majority of cases of cancer in the pediatric population. The role of the primary care physician is to effect early diagnosis and referral to an appropriate center. This entails an awareness of the range of clinical features that should suggest leukemia.

Anemia is the most common presenting complaint. When accompanied by neutropenia or thrombocytopenia, leukemia should be suspected The clinical manifestations of neutropenia are recurrent bacterial infections; the clinical manifestations of thrombocytopenia are profuse nosebleeds, bleeding in the skin (petechiae), bruising, or sudden, severe hemorrhage. Usually, leukemic cells in large numbers will be identified on the peripheral smear. However, the diagnosis must be considered even in the face of a normal-appearing peripheral smear, and occasionally can only be confirmed by bone marrow examination. Enlargement of lymph nodes or spleen is another relatively common mode of presentation.

[6] Wilm's Tumor and Neuroblastoma

The incidental discovery of an abdominal mass is the typical presentation of these two relatively common solid tumors occurring in early childhood. With early diagnosis and initiation of appropriate surgical, chemotherapeutic, and radiation therapy under the supervision of experienced oncologists, the prognosis for survival is optimistic for many children.

Physicians should be aware of non-specific symptoms that may raise suspicion of underlying neoplastic disease. Fever and weight loss may be the first manifestation of metastatic disease in children. Infants with neuroblastoma may develop periorbital ecchymosis, proptosis, persistent watery diarrhea, skin nodules, or rarely, a form of myoclonic encephalopathy. They may also present with an absence of the 'red reflex' which is routinely looked for in early infancy routine examinations.

§ 16.08   Endocrine Disorders of Childhood

[1]   Diabetes Mellitus and Impaired Glucose Tolerance

This condition is generally thought of as occurring in two forms, insulin-dependent diabetes (type 1) and noninsulin-dependent diabetes (type 11). Type I is by far the most common type occurring in childhood, although with increasing obesity type II is becoming more frequent. As the name implies, treatment requires lifelong insulin replacement with Type I.

Management of diabetes mellitus in childhood involves special considerations with which the practitioner must be familiar. The disease typically presents with frequent day and nighttime urination and increased thirst, sometimes with weight loss. The onset may occur at any age, although the disease often appears in early adolescence. The diagnosis is established by documentation of hyperglycemia with a blood sugar above 200 milligrams per decaliter on a random blood sample. The diagnosis in the very young child is more difficult to make by history and may be discovered in the course of testing or when the child presents in keto acidosis.

The goals of management in childhood include controlled glucose metabolism accompanied by normal physical growth and psychosocial development. The approach, therefore, must be comprehensive and include attention to insulin dosage as well as counseling on diet, exercise, self-administration of insulin and general developmental issues, with particular attention given to helping the child function in as normal a fashion as possible.

Early in the course of juvenile diabetes, patients often experience a period of weeks or months during which insulin requirements may greatly diminish — the so-called "honeymoon period." Careful follow-up to prevent overdosage of insulin and subsequent hypoglycemia and for renewed increases in insulin requirement is necessary during this time. This phase also unfortunately encourages the not infrequent denial of the diagnosis that is common with serious health conditions.

Long-term follow-up of children with juvenile diabetes includes attention to progress in growth and development, psychosocial adjustment, careful physical examinations to identify elevations of blood pressure and early onset of retinal complications (in older children), examination of urine for evidence of renal complications, periodic assessment of thyroid function, and determinations of blood glycosylated hemoglobin levels, which provide an index of glucose control over the preceding two months.

Two common acute complications are diabetic ketoacidosis and hypoglycemia.

Insulin deficiency eventually leads to progressive hyperglycemia and metabolic acidosis. While some patients develop this acute syndrome at the onset of the disease, most often this complication occurs during the course of the diabetes, usually precipitated by intercurrent illness or omission of insulin dose. Typical clinical features include a sudden increase in frequent urination and thirst, lethargy, and often abdominal pain and vomiting. Metabolic acidosis may progress rapidly to a state of severe metabolic derangement and central nervous system manifestation. It must be recognized in its early stages and is most appropriately managed in an intensive care setting where careful, continuous monitoring can be performed.

Episodes of hypoglycemia commonly occur during periods of adjustment of insulin dosage or insufficient glucose supply. Important early symptoms include behavior change, jitteriness, sweating, and hunger. Caretakers of young children with diabetes quickly learn to recognize these symptoms and should be encouraged to offer sugar-containing fluids. Administration of intravenous fluids is safer if the child is not awake and alert, and there is the possibility of aspiration of fluids taken orally.

[2] Hypoglycemia

Hypoglycemia is a relatively uncommon condition after the neonatal period. In the pediatric age group it may be caused by increased production of insulin associated with a tumor within the pancreas or abnormal carbohydrate metabolism associated with adrenal insufficiency. More commonly, hypoglycenmia in childhood occurs in otherwise well children who experience recurrent episodes of pallor, sweating, seizures, and a positive test for ketones in the urine. This condition, termed "ketotic hypoglycemia" is thought to be due to abnormal response to fasting, and is usually diagnosed by measuring blood glucose levels during a prolonged period of fasting. Treatment focuses on dietary manipulation until late childhood, by which time the symptoms tend to disappear in most children.

[3] Hypothyroidism

Thyroid deficiency occurs in two forms in children: congenital and acquired. Congenital hypothyroidism is caused by failure of normal development of the thyroid gland. Most cases are now discovered through neonatal routine screening programs (state-mandated in most areas). The goal is early identification and replacement with exogenous thyroid hormone. Delay in implementation of treatment beyond three months will result in permanent neuro-developmental impairment. Early clinical symptoms in infancy may be subtle, and include feeding problems, diminished muscle tone) cool skin, constipation, hoarse cry, and a large, open anterior fontanel of the skull.

Most cases of acquired hypothyroidism are caused by auto-immune destruction of the thyroid gland, secondary to Chronic lymphocytic thyroiditis (Hashimoto's disease). It is usually discovered during evaluation of short stature or delayed onset of puberty in young adolescents. Diagnosis is by determination of circulating thyroid hormone, assessment of thyroid gland uptake activity, measurement of pituitary thyroid-stimulating hormone activity, and identification of circulating thyroid anti-bodies. Radioactive- thyroid-scanning I procedures are usually not performed in children. Treatment is with exogenous thyroid hormone. Patients should be followed for the possible development of antibodies to other endocrine organs leading to symptoms of diabetes mellitus or adrenal insufficiency.

[4] Hyperthyroidism

Abnormally excessive production of functioning thyroid hormone leads to hyperthyroidism, a condition appearing most commonly during adolescence. It is thought to be the result of an auto-immune reaction resulting in disturbance of the autoregulatory function of the pituitary-thyroid axis, causing diffuse enlargement and overactivity of the thyroid gland. Presenting manifestations may be subtle, and include emotional liability, deterioration in school performance, behavior problems, weight loss, and sleeplessness. On examination, there may be resting tachycardia, tremor, and a palpably enlarged thyroid gland. The diagnosis is confirmed by laboratory tests demonstrating abnormally high serum levels of active thyroid hormone, increased glandular iodine-uptake activity, and inadequate pituitary suppressor response indicating disturbance of the regulatory system. Treatment is usually initially medical, using thyroid-blocking. Partial surgical removal of thyroid tissue and radioactive ablation of the thyroid gland are the preferred approaches in some cases.

[5] Thyroiditis

The most common thyroid disease occurring during childhood and adolescence is chronic lymphocytic thyroiditis (Hashimoto's disease). The disease usually presents as a diffuse enlargement of the thyroid gland in an asymptomatic child. Demonstration of high levels of thyroid antibodies in the serum is confirmatory. Patients usually have normal thyroid function, although, occasionally, symptoms of hypothyroidism may occur. In most cases, the disease resolves spontaneously, although patients should be followed for the possible late development of hypothyroidism.

[6] Adrenal Insufficiency

Adrenal insufficiency occurs in congenital or acquired forms. While rare in infancy and childhood, delay in diagnosis may have life-threatening consequences. Congenital adrenal hyperplasia and adrenogenital syndrome are the terms used to describe adrenal insufficiency as it occurs in infancy. It is caused by an inherited defect in one of several enzyme systems that control cortisol synthesis. Symptoms typically develop during the first month of life. Vomiting and dehydration may progress rapidly to shock. The disease is suspected when emergency laboratory tests show hyponatremia, hyperkalemia, acidosis and, often, hypoglycemia.

The disease may be suspected in female infants who, on physical examination, are shown to have ambiguous genitalia or clitoral enlargement.

Immediate treatment should be provided in an intensive care setting and should include administration of saline-containing fluids and corticosteroids. Attempts to identify the specific enzyme defect, which may be important for long-term management, should be deferred until the emergency situation is past and the patient is stabilized. Follow-up management, usually in collaboration with an experienced endocrinologist, involves continuous replacement therapy with corticosteroids, careful monitoring of linear growth as an indicator of the adequacy of treatment, and particular attention to stress producing intervening events such as febrile illness or surgery during which relative adrenal insufficiency may suddenly occur.

Acquired adrenal insufficiency is rare in the pediatric age group and is usually a manifestation of an autoimmune disorder that may be associated with thyroid disease or diabetes mellitus. In the acute stage of adrenal insufficiency, or during periods of exacerbation that may be triggered by stress, the condition is life-threatening. It is important that emergency treatment focus on support of adrenal function with intravenous saline and replacement corticosteroids, and that this not be delayed while other attempts are under way to define the underlying precipitating event.

[7] Ambiguous Genitalia

During routine newborn examination, abnormal development of the genitalia may be discovered, suggesting an abnormality of embryologic sexual differentiation. It is the primary care physician's responsibility to recognize the abnormality and its significance, and to resolve questions of sexual gender ambiguity as rapidly and accurately as possible to avoid serious psychosocial complications. Evaluation requires collaboration among pediatrician, geneticist, and often the surgeon, to determine the genetic sex and the appropriate phenotypic gender for childrearing and functional purposes. Some types of abnormal gonads have the potential for malignant transformation later in life. Appropriate plans for follow-up and possible removal are necessary.

§ 16.09 Neurologic Diseases of Childhood

Central nervous system manifestations can accompany many categories of diseases in childhood. The discussion in this section highlights conditions and considerations of particular importance in the pediatric age group.

[1] Seizures

The causes and types of convulsive seizures vary according to age at presentation. In the neonatal period, birth injury, asphyxia, and hypoglycemia are the most common causes of seizures. Clinical recognition of neonatal seizures may be difficult. Normal newborn tremulousness must be distinguished from convulsive activity; episodes of apnea, blinking, or mouthing behaviors, however, may be manifestations of seizures.

Seizures with onset between six months and five years are most often associated with fever. This may represent a benign febrile seizure, an underlying seizure disorder, or the presence of infection involving the central nervous system, e.g., meningitis. After ruling out acute infection, attempts should be made to distinguish benign febrile seizures from those that herald the onset of chronic epilepsy later in childhood. In general, brief, generalized seizures that accompany the sudden onset of high fever in a child without a family history of epilepsy suggest the presence of the benign form. Although benign febrile seizures are likely to recur in early childhood, especially if the initial episode occurs within the first six months of life, they can be expected to cease by age five. The use of anticonvulsants to avert recurrences of febrile seizures is generally ineffective and not indicated. In the rare instances when what appear to be febrile seizures are prolonged, asymmetric, or focal anticonvulsant medication may be indicated.

Seizures with onset after age five, with or without fever, should not be presumed benign, and should prompt thorough evaluation for underlying causes and initiation of continuous anticonvulsant therapy. Evaluation includes a detailed history beginning with the perinatal period, review of developmental progress, behavioral changes, past trauma, and family history of seizures or developmental disorders. Physical examination, in addition to the standard general and neurologic examination, should include a search for major and minor congenital malformations, as well as cutaneous lesions that may suggest the presence of associated malformations of the brain. Subtle manifestations of seizure activity in childhood include brief lapses of consciousness, staring spells, and abrupt changes in behavior or affect. While often mistaken as primary psychological disturbances, these activities may indicate the presence of absences" (petit mal) or "complex partial" (psychomotor) seizures requiring specific anticonvulsant medications.

Evaluation of seizure disorders involves the use of electro-encephalographic (EEG) studies. Performance and. interpretation of these studies in infants and children require a consultant who is familiar with age-related norms and clinical correlations.

With respect to treatment, a large number of anticonvulsant drugs are available which, when tailored to the specific type of seizure disorder, can control seizures in a large number of cases. Physicians managing children with seizure disorders must be familiar with the relative effectiveness of anticonvulsants for specific seizure types, the range of potential adverse side effects, and the appropriate use of serum drug levels to monitor efficacy of treatment.

When a succession of generalized or partial seizures occurs without interruption, the condition is referred to as *status epilepticus*. This condition must be regarded as a serious emergency. Management requires skill and knowledge in the administration of parenteral anticonvulsants in appropriate age related doses and the ability to provide assisted ventilation, including endotracheal intubation in the event respiratory depression occurs during the course of emergency treatment.

[2] Head Injury

Diagnosis and assessment of severity of head injury in children is usually straightforward, but some special pediatric considerations are noteworthy.

Concussions, i.e., head injuries associated with transient loss of consciousness with temporary amnesia for the event, may be followed by variable periods of headache, dizziness, irritability and behavior change. Child abuse should be suspected in any case of serious head injury occurring in a non-ambulatory child.

Epidural hematoma, a potentially life-threatening complication of head injury, may be delayed for several days in children. Following a period of apparent normalcy, there may be a sudden deterioration of neurologic status requiring emergency surgical intervention to remove the blood accumulated in the epidural space.

Infants under one year of age may develop slowly accumulating hematoma in the subdural space. This expanding intracranial lesion may, in the infant, produce no symptoms other than progressive enlargement of the head circumference. In children under the age of three years, so-called "expanding skull fractures" may occur, in which healing is delayed due to the interposition of a fluid-filled arachnoid cyst in the fracture

Children who experience a seizure at the time of injury are not more prone to develop later epilepsy; however, recurrent seizures are a common complication of depressed skull fractures and penetrating brain injuries. Prolonged treatment with anticonvulsant medication is often considered in these cases.

[3] Brain Tumors

Brain tumors account for approximately 20% of childhood cancers. Most brain tumors in children arise in the posterior fossa and cause early symptoms of headache, especially when arising in the morning, vomiting, and ataxia. Careful examination of the optic fundi for signs of increased intracranial pressure is required for any child presenting with such symptoms.

Supratentorial tumors, i.e., those above the posterior fossa, may cause focal seizures or focal neurologic deficits in addition to symptoms of increased pressure. The majority of childhood brain tumors are of the astrocytoma variety and have a favorable prognosis for surgical removal. The most common malignant brain tumor is medulloblastoma, arising in the posterior fossa with a propensity for spread through the cerebrospinal fluid. Prognosis is generally poor, but may be favorably affected by radiation and chemotherapy if instituted before spread has occurred. Early suspicion should be based on the symptoms of vomiting, headache and ataxia.

Craniopharyngioma is a brain tumor of childhood occurring in the region of the pituitary sella. It is selected for mention here because delay in diagnosis is not unusual. The tumor may appear at any time during childhood or adolescence and include slowing of linear growth, visual loss and headache. Calcifications noted on skull X-rays may offer a diagnostic clue.

[4] Headaches

Most headaches in children are benign, but must be distinguished from those symptomatic of more serious problems, such as brain tumor or migraine.

This is usually accomplished on the basis of careful examination and history, particularly of the pattern of headache episodes and family history.

The following are distinguishing features that should alert the physician to consider evaluation for specific underlying causes: severe, acute onset of headache in a child not subject to recurrent headaches; headache associated with nausea and vomiting; headache occurring in the early morning upon arising; family history of migraine; highly localized headaches lasting a prolonged period of time or associated with physical findings such as hypertension, localizing hemispheric signs, disturbances of gaze or gait, cranial nerve palsies, or cutaneous lesions.

§ 16.10 Kawasaki's Disease

Kawasaki's disease (mucocutaneous lymph node syndrome) is a multi-system disorder that may mimic many other conditions. It requires early recognition in order to provide proper treatment and monitoring aimed at preventing potentially life-threatening complications. Physicians should suspect the disease in children who acutely develop unexplained prolonged high fever, conjunctivitis, cracking and fissuring of the lips, rash, reddened and swollen palms and soles, swelling of the extremities, and enlarged cervical lymph nodes. Not all of these symptoms, however, need be present to suspect the diagnosis. While appropriate laboratory tests may be helpful, there are no tests available that establish the diagnosis definitively.

The most serious complications of Kawasaki's disease are cardiovascular, including serious damage to the coronary vessels of the heart, which has a significant potential mortality tumor rate. Patients with Kawasaki's disease require careful cardiac evaluation and follow-up for at least two to three months before they can be considered safe from the risk of cardiovascular complications.

Current treatment consists of aspirin and intravenous infusions of gammaglobulin in appropriate doses until the threat of cardiovascular complications is past.

§ 16.11 Methicillin-resistant Staphylococcus Aureus

This is recognized increasingly as a cause of skin and soft tissue infections and less frequently of invasive infections that can result in death. Early diagnosis is essential.

§ 16.12   Selected General References

Green, et al, AMBULATORY PEDIATRICS 5th ed.(Saunders1999)

Nelson, et al, eds., NELSON TEXTBOOK OF PEDIATRICS, 18th ed. (W. B. Saunders 2007).

Berg, et al, Current Pediatric Therapy, 18th edition, 2006

CHAPTER 17

ORTHOPEDIC SURGERY*

Ernest H. Neighbor, MD, JD,
Matthias I. Okoye, MD, JD, and David L. Samani, MD

SYNOPSIS

---

* An earlier version of this chapter was written by Richard S. Goodman, MD, JD, and Keith London, MD.

           [iii]   *The shoulder*
           [iv]   *The clavicle*
           [v]   *The foot and ankle*
           [vi]   *The knee*
           [vii] *The hip*

     [b]   Tendon and Ligament Repairs
     [c]   Reconstructive Surgery
           [i]   *The hand and wrist*
           [ii]   *The elbow*
           [iii]   *The shoulder area*
           [iv]   *The foot and toes*
           [v]   *The knee*
           [vi]   *The hip*
           [vii] *The spine*

  [13] Failure to Provide Adequate Postoperative Care
  [14] Inadequate Documentation of Treatment

§ 17.05 Conclusion

---

§ 17.01 Training and Certification

[1] Introduction

Orthopedic surgery is the medical specialty that includes the preservation, investigation and restoration of the form and function of the extremities, spine and associated structures by medical, surgical and physical methods.[1]

The American Board of Orthopedic Surgery is the certifying organization for competency in orthopedics in the United States of America. To be certified by the board, an applicant must meet the minimum educational requirements in the specialty and pass a two part certifying examination.[2]

[2] Premedical Education

The requirements for certification by the American Board of Orthopedic Surgery include graduation from a recognized undergraduate educational institution in the United States. This program must include the necessary courses for acceptance into an approved medical school program that, on graduation, will confer a Doctorate in Medicine.[3]

---

[1] DIRECTORY OF MEDICAL SPECIALISTS 2053- 2066 (Marquis 1992-92).

[2] ABMS DIRECTORY OF CERTIFIED ORTHOPEDIC SURGEONS 7 (American Board of Medical Specialists 1986).

[3] *Id.*

This is no different from any other medical specialty.[4] There is a different, but basically similar pathway for Doctors of Osteopathy.

[3] Medical School

After undergraduate studies, orthopedists must graduate from an approved medical school program. Medical schools differ in the amount of time spent in lectures and rotation through orthopedics as well as in the availability of elective options in orthopedics.

[4] Internship and Residency

After medical school, graduate education for those electing a career in orthopedics consists of five years of accredited postdoctoral education. The first year was formerly called an internship. This is an introduction to the practice of medicine with decreasing supervision and increasing responsibility. The subjects covered through the first year are broadly based study of medicine and surgery with no more than three months in orthopedic surgery. This is followed by one year of accredited residency in surgery or medicine, or one year of clinical or laboratory research with submission of documentation of a research problem. Following this, the formal orthopedic residency starts. This is a mandatory thirty-six months as an orthopedic surgery resident in an accredited orthopedic surgery residency educational program. This includes training and study in the fields of adult orthopedics, surgery of the spine (including removal of protruded intervertebral discs), children's orthopedics, fractures and trauma, surgery of the hand and foot, rehabilitation and orthopedic basic science. This must include a minimum of twelve months of adult orthopedics, six months of children's orthopedics, and nine months of trauma/fracture rotation.

This training must also include education in the care of the foot, the hand, the spine, the neck, the major joint areas, and the contents of the spine and extremities. The effects of trauma and athletic injuries, emergency, acute and chronic care, and rehabilitation of orthopedic conditions also must be covered. All phases of diagnosis and treatment of orthopedic pathology, including musculoskeletal radiology and evaluation of appropriate laboratory tests, must be reviewed. Education is also required in related areas of neurology, rheumatology, basic science, orthotics, prosthetics and physical medicine.

This is now commonly followed by six months to two years in a fellowship with advanced sub-specialty experience and training.

---

[4] DIRECTORY OF MEDICAL SPECIALISTS, *supra* note 1, at 5, 6.

[5] American Board of Orthopedic Surgery

Upon completion of the above training and educational requirements, the acquiring of a license to practice medicine in at least one of the States, and completion of a minimum of twenty-four months of continuing and active practice restricted to orthopedics, one is then eligible to submit examination for certification. This is the only certifying orthopedic board in the United States at present. The application remains in force for three consecutive examinations. Three months before the examination the Committee on Eligibility reviews the application and declares which candidates are eligible to take the examination. The candidate is now considered a Board-eligible Orthopedist. A passing grade on the examination then certifies one as a Diplomate of the American Board of Orthopedic Surgeons. Formerly, certification was for the lifetime of the applicant; however, those certified recently have an expiration date, with the exact plans for recertification to maintain their credentials still not definite, although an examination process is in effect.[5]

[6] American Academy of Orthopedic Surgeons

Fellowship in the American Academy of Orthopedic Surgery requires certification by the American Board of Orthopedic Surgeons plus proof of a practice limited to orthopedic surgery of at least three years after completion of the period of training. This is the only general national orthopedic organization (as opposed to regional and subspecialty organizations in orthopedics) in the United States.

The American Academy of Orthopedic Surgeons nominates members to the Board of the American Board of Orthopedic Surgeons and also conducts the only nationally attended general orthopedics convention. The Academy also sponsors the *Journal of Bone & Joint Surgery*, as well as various instructional course lectures and symposiums.[6]

[7] Fellowships

As an alternative to entering the practice of orthopedics immediately upon completion of residency training, a significant number of orthopedists take additional training in a fellowship program known as PG years six and seven. These are available in areas including: Pediatric Orthopedics, Knee Reconstructive Surgery, Sports Medicine, Adult Foot and Ankle Surgery, Adult Hip Reconstructive Surgery, Joint Replacement Surgery, Research,

---

[5] By-Laws of the American Academy of Orthopedic Surgeons (Feb. 1985).

[6] *Id.*; DIRECTORY OF MEDICAL SPECIALISTS, *supra* note 1, at 20.

Orthopedic Pathology, Hand and Microsurgery, Arthritis, Spine Surgery and Research, and Trauma. The length of these programs varies from six to twenty four months each. Such a fellowship legitimizes an orthopedist to limit his practice to a subspecialty (even though a fellow is not usually required to call oneself a subspecialist or to join one of the subspecialty organizations). In addition, certification exists for hand surgeons and is being planned for many of the other orthopedic subspecialties.

[8] Subspecialty Societies

Although the only national general orthopedic convention is the American Academy of Orthopedic Surgeons, its meeting coincides in time and place with many subspecialty organizations and societies. Among the related orthopedic organizations that hold meetings concurrently with the Academy are American Orthopedic Foot and Ankle Society, American Society of Biomechanics Engineers in Orthopedics, The Hip Society, Mid-American Orthopedic Association, American Shoulder and Elbow Surgeons, the Knee Society, Orthopedic Foot Club, Orthopedic Research Society, Pediatric Orthopedic Society, Scoliosis Research Society, Society of Orthopedic Surgeons of India in North America, Irish-American Orthopedic Society, American Orthopedic Society for Sports Medicine, and American Society for Surgery of the Hand.

[9] Types of Practice

The overwhelming predominance of orthopedists is in the clinical practice. Those in private practice will perform routine orthopedics with referrals to tertiary care centers or subspecialists for technically difficult and unusual tumor surgery, spinal surgery with instrumentation, reconstructive hand surgery and revision joint replacement surgery. In addition, there are orthopedists in private practice who limit their practice to such subspecialties as hand surgery, foot surgery, spine surgery, hip surgery replacements, hip surgery including but not limited to replacements including fractures of the hip, sports medicine, knee surgery, scoliosis surgery or children's orthopedics.

Besides private practice, there are orthopedists in academia. These can be subdivided into those in patient care and those in orthopedic research. Those in pure research generally are not into patient care and do basic research in such areas as metabolism of bone, cartilage, synovial fluid and synovia, tendons and ligaments. Those in clinical orthopedics teach orthopedics to medical students, interns and residents, and generally carry on a practice in their field of special interest.

§ 17.02 The Orthopedic Examination

[1] Initial Tests

Orthopedic examination includes x-rays of the extremities, joints or the cervical and thoracic lumbar spine as well as the pelvis. This may be accompanied by adjunctive examinations such as MRI scans and CT scans to further evaluate these areas in much greater detail. After a diagnosis is made and especially if surgery is indicated an informed consent explaining the potential risks, complications and benefits of surgery and alternative treatments are discussed with the patient. Before consideration of total joint replacement or other more invasive orthopedic surgery, conservative care is given. Orthopedic surgeons will often be involved in the conservative care including the administration of non steroidal anti-inflammatory drugs, medications, intra-articular cortisone injections to joints as well as intra-articular injections of Hyalgen or hyaluronic acid into specifically the knee joint. Other conservative treatments that the orthopedic surgeon orders includes physical therapy. If the patient is to undergo surgery we will work conjointly with internists as well as the anesthesiologist. If the patient is a multisystem trauma patient we will work conjointly with general surgeons, vascular surgeons, neurosurgeons, plastic surgeons, urologists and also possibly even obstetricians and gynecologists.

The implants that we use for orthopedic surgery vary greatly. The most common type of implant material is 316L stainless steel which is usually applied in trauma situations as well as plates and rods for bones. This also includes stainless steel screws. Other orthopedic materials used include pure titanium for total joints; cobalt chrome as well as tantalum are also metals that are used. The articulating surface that is use to articulate with metals is highly crossed linked polyethylene. Methyl methacrylate is sometimes used as well in total joints or bone ingrowth with roughened surfaces approximately with 300 micron spaces to allow bony growth.

Surgery can be completed with minimally invasive techniques, percutaneous techniques, arthroscropic techniques as well as arthrotomies and larger incisions for total joint replacements.

[2] Source of Referrals

Orthopedists are in the group of physicians known as secondary or tertiary physicians, as opposed to family practitioners, pediatricians, general practitioners, and general internists, which are known as primary physicians. Orthopedists traditionally had their practices based upon referrals from primary physicians. Today the other sources of referral are emergency room physicians and emergency room staffs, walk-in doctor offices, and other healthcare providers such as chiropractors, therapists, etc. These patients are referred for definitive care of orthopedic problems, including fractures and suspected orthopedic injuries, arthritis, back and neck disorders, and joint disorders. In addition, many patients are referred to orthopedists for evaluation of real or alleged orthopedic injuries, impairments, disabilities and/or handicaps arising out of workers' compensation injuries, motor vehicle accidents, and other traumatic events, as well as claims of disabilities. These referrals can be from insurance carriers, plaintiff attorneys, defense attorneys, state and federal agencies, and the courts.

[3] Preliminary Information

Prior to the establishment of the physician-patient relationship, the orthopedist usually will acquire basic information about the patient, which is recorded by the clerical staff of the emergency room, the clinic or the office or is supplied by the referral source. This will frequently include, but is not limited to name, address, date of birth, social security number, date of injury, place of injury, type of injury, site of injury, previous care for the injury job description, name of employer, date of onset of any disability, history of previous injuries and claims, and the name, address, policy number, and claim number of relevant insurance carriers.

[4] Types of Contacts

Whereas in the past physician-patient relationships were simply described as an office visit, hospital visit or consultation, these types of contact have now been subclassified for billing purposes. To determine the category of the relationship or the type of contact made, information is necessary, including the place of the contact (office, home, hospital room or emergency room), the time of the visit, whether it is a new patient, an established patient with subsequent a visit, or an established patient with a new complaint.

In addition, the scope of the examination must be defined as either brief, limited, intermediate, or comprehensive, depending upon the depth, breadth, and time expended in the visit, and is judged based upon the documentation supplied by the physician's reports. The contact is also classified according to whether the history and the physical examination are "problem-focused," "expanded problem-focused," "detailed," or "comprehensive," and the number of possible diagnoses or treatment options, the complexity of the records reviewed, the risk of treatment options, and the time involved. There exists both standard coding numbers to identify the specific type of patient contact,[7] as well as specific codes limited to state compensation systems and other carriers.

[5] Physician-acquired Data

[a] History

After a physician-patient relationship is established in the doctor's office, clinic, emergency room, hospital bedside, or other site by a referral or one of the types of contact specified above, the orthopedist will take a "history." This is the story of the events that gave rise to the *present illness* for which the patient will be receiving care. This story is obtained from the patient if possible but, if necessary, is obtained through a translator or from friends or relatives who may accompany the patient, or from pertinent documents that accompany the patient.

The present illness is a chronological order of the events that directly necessitated the need for the patient-physician relationship. Since a significant number of orthopedic patients complain of conditions related directly or indirectly to trauma (and possibly litigation), the relationship of their complaints to possible defendants or third-party insurance carriers is included in the history. This includes the date of the injury, the mechanism of the injury, the geography of the site of injury, and the care received from EMS personnel, police, bystanders, and other health providers prior to the orthopedist's care.

[b] Past History

The past histories of orthopedic patients will not be significantly different from those obtained from patients by other physicians. A past history records previous injuries, allergies, medication intake, previous significant illnesses, previous and present medical conditions, any previous major or minor surgery, and any previous trauma or traumatic events.

In addition, the precise care the patient received for any previous injury or disease in the area of the present complaint must be thoroughly delved

---

[7] Understanding the Medicare Fee Schedule and Related Practitioner Payments (New York State Department of Social Services 1992); The Empire Plan, Schedule of Allowed Charges (Metropolitan Life Insurance Company, Oct. 1, 1990); St. Anthony's Updatable ICD.9.CM Code book for Physician payment, 10/95, St. Anthony's Publishing; Travelers Physician Manual (Travelers Health Network of New York 1991); Official New York Workers' Compensation Medical Fee Schedule, 1996.

into. This information should be obtained, if possible, by a review of previous medical records, hospital records, health insurance bills and reports, and bills and reports of other health care professionals if available.

This past history is important in orthopedics not only for the usual medical reasons, but, in addition, the past history can be of significance in apportioning handicap, impairment, and disability claims between the present event and the previous event, as well as causality, and also aids in determining financial responsibility for medical and other benefits[7] among recent and previous insurers.

[c] Physical Examination

The physical examination of a patient by an orthopedist should include most of the same general physical examinations done by all other physicians. This includes the measurement of the vital signs, pulse, blood pressure, temperature and respiratory rate and, in addition, examination of the heart and lung sounds, general body demeanor and palpation of the abdomen should be included.

The specific orthopedic examination should be directed to the presence or absence of pertinent findings related to the area of orthopedic pathology as determined by the history. The patient's record should show whether the examination revealed signs of tenderness to palpation as well as the presence or absence of any spasms.

It should include any neurological finding such as asymmetry or absence of sensory perception to pinprick or touch, the status of the usual reflexes, as well as any absence, decrease or asymmetry of motor power or strength of individual muscles or functional groups. In addition, as estimate of vascular supply to the involved area should be noted with a record of the presence or absence of pertinent arterial pulsations, venous return and capillary filling. Finding of muscle atrophy should be noted, as well as the passive and active range of motion of joints, and the stability of the joints to stress, the presence of swelling, the general condition of the skin (with a record of lacerations, abrasions, contusions, discoloration or drainage), and finally, the general ability of the part to function in a normal manner.[8]

---

[8] Huppenfeld, Physical Examination of the Spine and Extremities (Appleton-Century-Crofts 1976); Polley & Hunder, Rheumatologic Interviewing and Physical Examination of the Joints (W.B. Saunders 1978); Joint Motion: Method of Measuring and Recording (American Academy of Orthopedic Surgeons 1965).

[6] Laboratory and Other Objective Tests

This part of the orthopedic record consists of the reports of studies that do not rely upon the patient's response or cooperation. This part of the chart will record the results of the tests and the results of the analysis of the examination of samples of body fluid or tissues. It will also include reports on microscopic analysis of samples of body fluid or tissues, examination of radiological studies, including CAT scans, Doppler studies, ultrasound, MRIs, and bone scans. In addition, studies electrodiagnostic studies which document sensory and/or motor nerve function are included, such as EMG, NCV, H-Reflex, Baer and SSEP.

The studies requested by most orthopedist on the admission of a patient to a hospital are those required by the Joint Commission on Accreditation of Healthcare Organizations, hospital regulations, and state codes. These tests usually include an electrocardiogram, a chest x-ray, a complete blood count, a urinalysis, and a multiple-test blood profile which include the measurements of the blood sugar and other blood components.

In addition, most orthopedic complaints necessitate an x-ray of the affected area to demonstrate the presence or absence of bone pathology in the area in question. This may consist of routine views or special views to visualize the particular area in question. Tomograms, computerized axial tomography studies (CT scans), single photon emission computed tomography studies (SPECTs), magnetic resonance imaging studies (MRIs), or scintigraphic scans may be indicated, depending upon the history, physical examination, diagnosis and x-ray findings.

Besides the noninvasive radiographic studies mentioned above, orthopedic patients frequently will also have invasive x-ray studies. These studies are done after the introduction of appropriate radiopaque material to delineate structures not otherwise visualized. Some of the common tests are arteriograms, myelograms, venograms, arthrograms, and discograms, and post myelogram CAT scans. These studies may be needed to define various soft tissue lesions and pathological conditions.

Although other medical specialties may rely upon the radiologists' interpretation of the images produced through the uses of X-rays, magnetic resonance, or nuclear medicine, most orthopedists prefer to interpret the images themselves in cooperation with the radiologist.

As noted, to arrive at a diagnosis, orthopedic patients may need to have electrodiagnostic studies performed by neurologists and physiatrists. This includes the "electromyogram" (EMG), which records electrical impulses produced by nerves and muscles upon appropriate stimulation, as well as

NCV, H-Reflex and SSEP tests. The electrodiagnostic study can record the site of nerve or muscle damage and the type of pathology present.

When there is a question of the vascular status on an extremity, "Doppler tests" are ordered. These are done by technicians and interpreted by vascular surgeons or vascular radiologists. This test records the sound impulses produced by vascular structures and analysis can be determined as well as the type of pathology and presence or absence of vascular damage or disease, usually without the necessity of invasive radiological techniques.

Specific blood tests may also be indicated. The LE Prep, FANA, latex fixation, Lyme Titer, serium uric acid tests, and other tests can be used to determine the presence or absence of systemic arthritis. Synovial fluid aspiration and analysis are also done to determine etiology of a swollen joint. The analysis of the fluid includes cultures for infection, microscopic examination for crystals, and chemical analysis. In addition, other laboratory studies may be indicated in specific patients.

[7] Computer Interactive Assessment

Computers and other "high tech" apparatus are alleged to have increased the accuracy of some orthopedic diagnoses and are advertised to measure a quantitive dynamic evaluation of patient dysfunction.

Computer integrated imaging systems utilize stationary lasers and light activity-related tasks. Similar systems utilize sensors located on the patient or video cameras to gather like data. Information gathered from an observation is analyzed by the unit to allegedly identify malfunction in the patient's musculoskeletal systems and to determine the degree of disability. This technology is also allegedly used to rehabilitate patients, and assess muscle strength, range of motion, and levels of pain caused by dysfunction.

Among devices available on the market include those manufactured by Spinex Medical Technologies, Motion Analysis Corp., Ariel Life Systems, Inc., Peak Performance Technologies, Inc., Chattanooga Group, Inc., and MEDmetric Corp. Each company's product is promoted upon its ability to accurately reflect and quantify "real life" functions of the musculoskeletal systems.

Spinex's Spinoscope, a "non-invasive spinal imaging system," is employed in the analysis of lumbar, thoracic, and cervical spine functionality. Its literature emphasizes its ability to "evaluate intersegmental mobility" and enable gait analysis and knee evaluation.[9] Similar imaging technology is employed in Motion Analysis' products.

---

[9] Spinex Medical Technologies, Montreal, Quebec, 1992.

Reflectors are placed at strategic points upon the patient, who then performs several assessment-related tasks. Diagnosis is facilitated by the computer units' interpretation of the data colleted by the video monitor. Motion Analysis produces equipment for foot, gait, spine, and strength assessment.[10] Although their databases reflect differences, Ariel's performance Analysis System[11] and Peak's Video and Analog Motion Measurement Systems[12] employ similar technologies to evaluate a wide range of patient movement. Both manufacturers' products utilize video modules to record three-dimensional motion and computer software to quantify recorded actions. Actions may be further represented through stick-figure animation of the patient's performance.

The Chattanooga Group's Chattecx Lumbar Motion Monitor provides on-site evaluation by utilizing a sensory module placed upon a patient's back by a harness. Information is relayed to a databank that evaluates range of motion, velocity, and acceleration movements, and which may be programmed to analyze job tasks or isolate ergonomic factors.[13] MEDmetric's Electrogoniometer employs patient-mounted sensors to measure and evaluate joint rotation.

Other types of computer interactive systems, some produced by Isotechnologies, Inc., MedX Corp., and Biodex Medical Systems, Inc., resemble exercise machinery and isolate musculoskeletal functions. By grading the degrees of resistance an apparatus provides, these systems evaluate patient disability according to the strength of patient response and are also employed in patient rehabilitation.

Isotechnologies' B-200 is used in back testing and rehabilitation, and its LiftStation is used for "functional lifting assessment." Each systems' database may be programmed to reflect specific job parameters.[14] MedX Corporation, founded by Nautilus Exercise Equipment's Arthur Jones, produces the Lumbar Extension Machine, which rehabilitates lumbar spine and cervical spine function.[15] Biodex Medical Systems' modular and multifunction assessment equipment is flexible enough to test and rehabilitate most joint and limb segments.[16]

---

[10] Motion Analysis Corp., Santa Rosa, Cal., 1989.

[11] Ariel Life Systems, Inc. La Holla, Cal., 1992.

[12] Peak Performance Technologies, Inc. Englewood, Col., 1991.

[13] Chattanooga Group, Inc., Hixson, Tenn., 1990.

[14] Isotechnologies, Inc., Hillsborough, N.C., 1992.

[15] MedX Corp. Ocala, Fla., 1992.

[16] Biodex Medical Systems, Inc., Brookhaven, N.Y., 1992.

[8]   Consultations

Orthopedists generally request consultations from other physicians especially in four different situations: (1) evaluation of general medical conditions; (2) evaluation of the chief complaint by another specialist (which involves the gathering of data from a different viewpoint and therapeutic approach); (3) consultation for a nonrelated condition; and (4) second opinions from other orthopedists, usually a subspecialist, to confirm a diagnosis and plan of care and provide tertiary care if indicated.[17]

General Medical or pediatric consults are usually requested by an orthopedist when an orthopedic patient is admitted to a hospital for surgery, especially in a higher than normal risk situation when the patient is believed to have a condition that increases the overall likelihood of morbidity or mortality. This is also done when the procedure itself is a high risk procedure. The consultant in this situation is asked to evaluate the general medical status of the patient and to provide an estimate of the risk of the surgical procedures, as well as the risk of the anesthesia, and any measures or medications which will reduce the risk to the patient. An evaluation of the patient's pulmonary, cardiac, hepatic, renal and hemopoietic status is usually done.

A second group of consultations is called for where non-orthopedic expertise is needed for the care of an orthopedic problem. In cases of infection an internist specializing in infectious diseases" is frequently consulted.   Examples are major skin loss requiring a plastic surgeon's assistance, bladder and urinary tract damage complicating pelvic fractures needing urologic consults, or spinal cord trauma in a patient with a vertebral fracture requiring neurological and neurosurgery consults. In addition, Physical Medicine and Rehabilitation Specialists called "Physiatrists' (PM&R)" consultants or vascular consultants to treat concurrent vascular pathology are also used to aid in postoperative rehabilitation.[18]

A third type of consultation is for evaluation of unrelated medical conditions. An example would be a patient with a fractured leg and a lacerated eye. The ophthalmology consultant will be treating the eye problem while the orthopedist treats the leg injury. The therapeutic regimes are essentially nonrelated, but in the same patient coordination is necessary because of possible conflicts in medications, timing and positioning for surgery, and interference in performing diagnostic tests.

The fourth type of consultation is a second opinion from another orthopedist. The consultant in this case may or may not have a greater level

---

[17] Goodman, *Second Opinion*, 6 ORTHOPEDICS 1501-19 (1983).

[18] Gossling & Pillsbury, Complications of Fracture Management (J.B. Lippincott 1984).

of expertise. These are done to satisfy doubts on the part of the patient as to the necessity of the planned surgery, requirements of the insurance carrier to determine the necessity and the relationship to their policy, the hospital, or to reinforce the physician's recommendations should questions arise later. For certain selected procedures, hospital bylaws or insurance plans may require such an opinion or consultation prior to a list of specified elective surgical procedures.

The specific type of consultation made will be identified by name as well as the billing code used with a plethora of different designations with separate code numbers and fee schedules.

[9] Informed Consent

After a diagnosis is made, a plan of therapy based upon the diagnosis must be made and agreed upon by mutual oral consent, acquiesced on the part of the patient or a signed consent form as is present in hospital records between the patient and the physician. All plans of therapy have inherent risks of failure, a success rate, a complication rate, and a goal if successful, is achieved. The entire event, including the patient's signature, is called the "informed consent", the process of informing the patient of the benefits, alternatives and risks and a consent of the patient to proceed with the proposed plan. After the patient's consent (or the consent of a responsible party) is obtained, therapy is instituted.[19]

[10] Diagnosis

A diagnosis is the summary of the relevant information obtained through the history, physical examination and data, and images, as of the time it is made. This is also called a provisional or working diagnosis. This provisional diagnosis should use the standard nomenclature as found in or one of the accepted coding formulas. The code used will determine the need for second opinions, the length of reimbursable hospital stay, the length of inpatient or outpatient care, the amount of physical therapy allowed, the hospital fee, the physician's fee, and the general reimbursable level of other care for the patient as well as the reimbursable testing. The diagnosis code is based upon the site of the condition, the type of condition, and the severity of the condition.[20]

---

[19] Goodman, Informed Request, 7 Orthopedics 1764-66 (Nov. 1984); *see also* F. Rozovsky, Consent to Treatment: A Practice Guide (2nd ed., Little, Brown & Co. 1987).

[20] Understanding the Medicare Fee Schedule and Related Practitioner Payments (New York State Department of Social Services 1992); The Empire Plan, Schedule of Allowed Charges (Metropolitan Life Insurance Company, Oct 1,1990); The 3-in-1 Code Book for Orthopaedics

[11] Conservative Care

Based upon the diagnosis, various therapeutic modalities will be entertained. These treatments may consist of conservative (nonoperative) care or surgery (immediate, secondary, or deferred). Among the modalities available for most orthopedic conditions are medications, appliances, physical therapy, and surgery. The care of fractures is usually considered surgery and is so defined by the nomenclature and coding in most code books. The surgery is the immobilization of the fracture after reduction or setting with a splint, a sling, or other soft wear such as a brace, a plaster cast, a synthetic cast, or hospitalization for the application of traction or the performance of a surgical procedure, including the use of implants, closed reduction with anesthesia, an external fixation device, internal fixation, or the insertion of an implant or reconstruction. The care of soft tissue injuries and diseases is usually not considered surgery unless a definitive procedure is done such as a reconstruction or an arthroscopy or biopsy.

[12] Electrical Stimulation

Trauma often reduces the body's indigenous electrical impulses, which contribute to the bones' recuperative ability. This decrease in electrical activity has been found in certain instances to retard tissue repair. More and more frequently, orthopedic patients suffering from recalcitrant nonunion of fractures are being treated with electrical bone-growth stimulation devices that supplement reduced indigenous electrical impulses.[21]

These systems may be implantable or externally applied and generally consist of a charge or battery pack and stainless-steel capacitor plates, or "electrodes," which are to be located on surfaces above opposite sides of the fracture. While the device is on, the field of increased electrical activity in the traumatized region stimulates bone tissue-growth activity.[22]

These systems are most successful with long bone fractures.

Electrical bone-growth stimulation is indicated in the treatment of nonunions in which nine months have elapsed since injury, and the fracture

---

(St. Anthony Publishing 1992); Travelers Physician Manual (Travelers Health Network of New York 1991); Schedule of Medical Fees (New York State Workers' Compensation Board, September 1986); 1993 CP Code Book (American Medical Association); 1992 ICD Code Book (American Medical Association).

[21] N. Kahanovitz & S. Arnoczky, *The Efficacy of Direct Current Electrical Stimulation to Enhance Spinal Fusions*, in BACK SERVICE (The National Spine Center, Arlington, Va. 1988).

[22] C. Brighton & S. Pollack, *Treatment of Recalcitrant Nonunion with a Capacitively Coupled Electrical Field*, 67A J. BONE JOINT SURG. 577-85 (1985).

site shows no progressive signs of healing for at least three months. Three major brand manufacturers: EBI Medical Systems of Parsippany, New Jersey, Biolectron, Inc. of Hackensack, New Jersey, and AME of Richardson, Texas, have identified no adverse side effects from application of this technology, but caution that these devices may interfere with pacemakers and are not recommended to be used for pathological fractures due to malignant tumors or in the presence of active osteomyelitis.

§ 17.03 The Surgical Process

[1] Pre-Surgical Planning

If surgery is elected by the patient as the option to restore function, relieve pain or correct a deformity, the preoperative process can range from short and simple to prolonged and complicated. After a history and physical exam are completed, a diagnosis is made. The diagnosis is then confirmed by appropriate objective studies. If conservative management fails or is not an option and if a surgical procedure is a viable option to correct the malady, it is offered to the patient with adequate and reasonable information to create an informed patient. Having been informed as to the benefits, alternatives and risk of this procedure, the patient then has the right to consent or refuse consent for the proposed operation. If the patient consents then an "informed consent" is obtained.

Except for unusual circumstances consent "authorization" must then be obtained from the appropriate insurance carrier, usually by letter or phone call, to describe the "medical necessity" for the procedure.

Arrangements are then made with the surgical facility. These include the time and date, expected length for the procedure, type of anesthesia, completion of preoperative testing, history and physical exam and "medical clearance" if appropriate, and a second opinion if necessary.

When all is completed, at the appropriate time the patient is admitted to the surgical facility, hospital or medical center, the medical record is evaluated, the patient is identified and then brought to the operating room. In the OR the patient is positioned for the procedure and anesthesia is admitted. Vital sign monitoring is carried out by a member of the nursing staff or the anesthesia staff.

[2] Positioning of the Patient

Many orthopedic patients undergo surgery to correct an abnormal spine or extremity. Preoperative laxity or stiffness can complicate the transportation of these patients. In some cases, moving the patient from his bed to the operating room can be critical even to survival. In addition, many orthopedic procedures require the patient to be in unusual positions, or require the use of attachments to the operating table that are unfamiliar to the operating room personnel. In a general hospital, all of this may be outside the expertise of the operating room staff, and is a risk to the patient.

[3] Anesthesia

Concurrent with the positioning of the patient, appropriate anesthesia or analgesia must be administered. This is given by either an anesthesiologist, an anesthetist, or the surgeon himself. General or spinal anesthesia is usually in the province of the anesthesia staff. Local anesthesia is usually done by the surgeon himself. Regional anesthesia done by nerve blocks or intravenous techniques can be given by the surgeon or a member of the anesthesia staff. This subject is covered in Chapter 21 of this book.

[4] Instruments

Orthopedic operative procedure requires use of appropriate surgical instruments some of which are general, and others specific for a particular procedure. These are sterilized and usually maintained generally by the operating suite staff. Many surgeons, however, maintain their own instruments, which are either stored at the hospital or transported by the surgeon. In this situation, the responsibility for maintenance, sterilization and breakage is not always clear. Special surgical instruments designed for a specific operation by a particular manufacturer to be used during the insertion of a specific implant of that manufacturer may be essential and are important in orthopedics and must be available. Many orthopedic procedures require certain specific instrumentation designed for a particular operation. Unavailability of specific instruments or lack of the complete set should foreclose any possibility of attempting the operation. More and more of the newer implants, fixation devices, and arthroscopes now come with a complete set of matched and specifically machined tools designed for that procedure. In addition, removal or review of an implant or fixator device may require procedure-specific equipment, examples being screws to be removed with straight, phillips, X, hexagonal or other unusual head requiring a matches driver for removal.

[5] Sutures

Besides instruments, the surgeon is also dependent upon the operating room staff and the hospital administration for the availability of appropriate suture material. This material is purchased from various manufacturers, and may be supplied sterile or unsterile (to be sterilized by the hospital staff).

Suture material usually is classified under the "A0" systems with #5 being the thickest. The material becomes thinner as the number decreases to 0, with the finest made today being eleven "0". Wire sutures are measured either under this system or by the diameter in fractions of a millimeter. Sutures are also subdivided into absorbable or nonabsorbable and natural or synthetic, monofilament, tinted, braided or coated.

The choice among suture material is dependent upon the surgeon's training and experience, and the specific requirements at each particular stage of the operation.

[6] Implants for Joint Reconstruction

Implants for joint reconstruction are also supplied by the hospital. These are also known as prostheses and are preformed from metals, ceramics, silicon, plastics, and combinations of metals, ceramics, and plastics. The metals usually used are stainless steel, vitallium or titanium. Carbon implants also are now being used in a limited capacity. The type of the implants vary from complete freedom of option by the surgeon as to the manufacturer, material and style to those institutions who have a contract with a single manufacturer from a single line with a single material, except for unusual cases with documentation as to need.

Implants are held in place by muscle or capsule tension, methyl macrylic cement, screws, or the contour of the implant's surface. Implant either replace one surface of a joint (hemiarthroplasty) or the total joint (arthroplasty). The total joint replacements are either two implants that articulate together (with or without a mechanical locking device) or are made in one piece with built-in flexibility.

The joints for which implant arthroplasty is commonly done (with acceptable level of functional results) are the hips, knees, shoulders, finger joints and toe joint. Artificial replacements for the ankle, elbow and wrist are less common, but are no longer considered experimental. Joint implant are commonly used to replace stiff, deformed and painful arthritic joints, although their place in fracture care, where the articular surface of a bone has been destroyed, also exists.[23]

---

[23] Your Orthopaedic Resource. 1992 Annual Product Catalog (Howmedica, Rutherford, N.J.); Biomet 1992 Catalog (Biomet, Warsaw, Ind.); DePuy 1991-92 (DePuy, Warsaw, Ind.); Prosthetic Implants Manual & Specialty Orthopaedics Products (Zimmer, Warsaw, Ind.); Original Instruments and Implants of the Swiss Association for the Study of Internal Fixation

Total hip joint arthroplasty consists of a replacement of the hip joint which is a ball and socket joint. The acetabulum is the cup and the femoral head is the ball. The acetabulum replacement is a cup with or without metal backing. It can be one piece or assembled by the surgeon from interlocking components. It is held in place with screws, protruding pins, cement or press-fit-bony ingrowth. The femoral component can be one piece or multiple components which are assembled by the surgeon. The components have various head sizes, neck lengths, stem diameters, offsets and stem lengths, and may be designed to be cemented or designed to be press fitted or porous coated to be used with or without cement.[24]

[7]   Fracture Fixation Devices

Fracture care requires the immobilization of the bone fragments in acceptable alignment until adequate healing occurs. The alignment is established by the reduction of the fracture by either the closed or open method. "Closed" is by definition reduction with the skin intact, and "open" reduction is through any opening of the skin.

[a]   Internal Fixation

Immobilization of a fracture can be by internal devices, percutaneous devices or external devices. The standard internal devices are either intramedullary rods or cortical plates and screws. For a few specialized areas, other devices exist, including combinations of intramedullary rods with a cortical plate and screws, bands, pins, etc.

Intramedullary rods are either rigid or flexible. Rigid rods maintain alignment by their inherent strength and size. These include the Kunchner, Lotte, and Hansen-Street devices. Flexible rods rely on three-point fixation, and common examples are the Rush or Ender nails. Rods also may have a locking device or holes for the insertion of transfixing screws to prevent rotation or telescoping and shortening of the fractured bone (Gross Kempfe nail or Brooker device).

Cortical plates are either malleable or rigid. The rigid plates have been popularized by Swiss orthopedists. Besides the plates, the Swiss have developed an entire armentarium of drills, screws, screw drivers, clamps, soft tissue protectors and other instruments to be used with their plates. The entire system, technique and philosophy is known as the "A-O" school of

---

(Synthes, Paoli, Pa. 1991); Intermedics Orthopedics, Inc. 1991 Catalog (Intermedics Orthopedics, Inc., Austin, Tex.).

[24] Campbell's Operative Orthopaedics (8th Ed. C.V. Mosby 1992).

fracture treatment. Failures and poor results are believed by true A-O devotees to be related to failure to follow precisely their philosophical and technical approach to fractures. The A-O group also is responsible for the term "cast disease," a definition given for the muscle atrophy and joint stiffness that follow the use of casts. Malleable cortical plates have the advantage of easily being bent to the contours of the fracture and bone; however, this is also their drawback, because force can bend the plate after it has been placed. For this reason malleable plates have lost much popularity.

For fractures where open reduction and internal fixation has been selected, the choice usually is either intramedullary or extramedullary fixation. There are, however, a few fractures where special combined devices are used. The primary indication for a combined device is the hip fracture where a short intramedullary screw fixes the femoral head and neck; this short rod is then attached, according to the particular design of the appliance used, to a rigid plate, which is affixed to the femoral shaft with appropriate screws. A newer device uses an intramedly screw for the femoral head and neck with an intramedullary rod for the femoral shaft.

Besides intramedullary rods and cortical plates, other metallic implants are used either independently or in combination with the primary devices. The most common are the screws. These are used to attach plates to the bone, and also by themselves. They are made of various metals and come in different diameters, lengths, and head conformations. They may be self-tapping or not self-tapping, and lag or regular thread. Also, they will vary in thread-to-shaft diameter ratios. The various metals, besides having their own inherent advantages and disadvantages, should be of the same alloy as other metallic plates or rods placed in the same bone (to prevent electrolytic or "battery" effects).

The various lengths and diameters of screws are available to compensate for the diameters of the different bones, as well as to satisfy the specific requirements of the procedure, the patient, and the surgeon. The head conformations (cross, straight, Phillips or octagonal) are at the option of the designer and manufacturer. Self-tapping and not self-tapping are also optional. The advantages and disadvantages of these two types of screws are the subject of current literature. The lag screws, or those with threads absent from a significant length of the screw near the head, provide a compression force not available with a continuous thread. This type of screw has precise and limited indications. Increased thread-to-shaft diameters exist with various numbers of threads per inch to provide deeper and wider screw fixation in medullary or soft bone. The opposite, with a closer thread-to-shaft ratio and more threads per inch, provide a more intense grip in hard or cortical bone.

A newer type of system is the "locking plate." In this situation the holes in the plate have threads on them which correspond to threads at the heads of the screws. With this system there is more stability of the construct since the screws have purchase not only on the bone, but also on the plates. The screws are rigidly attached to the plate and will not change their position.

[b]   Percutaneous Fixation

Another significant fracture fixation technique is the percutaneous type of fixation. Although no significant incisions are used, and the fracture itself is reduced or positioned without direct vision as in open reductions, skin incisions are used to insert "pins" into the patient. These incisions may be only 1/8" or less, but the risk of infections and other complications from incisions, although less, is still present. Percutaneous pins are used either to fix the fracture directly or to apply traction to a bone distal to a fracture. The traction can be either functional or rigid. The rigid traction devices commonly in use with percutaneous pins are known as "external fixators." They include the Hoffman device for long bones, as well as other brands, including the now popular "Halo" device and its modifications for cervical fractures. These devices have various moveable joints which allow for correction of alignment, rotation and angulation and length, during and after the procedure. The advantages of these devices are absolute fixation through the device, exposure of the skin for observation of infection or for treating skin conditions, less risk of infection because of minimal skin incisions, and freedom of the patient to be ambulatory. Functional traction was common for fractures of the pelvis, femur and humerus. This traction is accomplished by inserting the pin into an appropriate site in a bone. The pin is then attached to ropes, pulleys and weights so that the force is constant as the patient shifts in bed.

[c]   External Fixation

True external fixation devices, without any skin penetration, include casts that may be made from plaster of paris, plastic, fiberglass or other synthetics, as well as "soft goods." The casts are applied over some type of padding and are molded to the patient. Their length and specific contour is adjusted to the particular requirements of the immobilization.

Instead of molded custom-made casts, some fractures are supported by prefabricated devices (slings, collars, splits, corsets, cam boots, wrist splints, air casts and orthoses. These devices can be combined in various groups according to the specific injury, and can be used in conjunction with percutaneous pin and internal fixation devices.

[d] Prostheses

Fractures can also be treated by replacement of the damaged bone with use of replacement prosthesis similar to those used for arthritis.[25]

[8] Arthroscopy

Arthroscopy is by definition the visual inspection of the inside of a joint. (Arthro meaning joint, and scope meaning to look.) The procedure is performed without a major incision into the joint, but with small incisions and the use of instruments known as arthro scopes. After appropriate anesthesia and positioning of the patient, incisions of less than 2" in length are made, and the arthro scopes are inserted into the joint. This is presently being done most often on the knee, although instruments are available for investigation of the shoulder, ankle, hip, carpal tunnel and other body areas. In addition, there is experimental work on use of arthroscopes into the spine.

With the arthroscope, the inside of a joint can be examined visually or on a television monitor. If pathology is found, surgery can then be performed by the use of other instruments which are also inserted into the joint through small incisions. Arthroscopy therefore involves both diagnostic and therapeutic surgery.

In diagnostic arthroscopy, any pathology is noted and recorded. The surgeon may obtain specimens of tissue or fluid for examination by a pathologist. In addition, photographs of the television screen showing the pathology can be obtained. This has the advantage of visual confirmation of a pathological condition without major surgery on the joint.

Following diagnostic arthroscopy, a certain number of pathological conditions can be corrected with the use of the arthroscope. After the pathology is identified visually, surgical instruments are placed into the joint through the same or other incisions, and surgery is carried out. These instruments can be used for extensive removal of the lining of the knee (snyovectomy). They also can be used to remove loose bodies, menisci, scar tissue, adhesions, plicas and ligaments. Furthermore, by the use of these instruments, rough, softened, or otherwise pathological conditions of cartilage can be removed or smoothed out. Arthritic spurs can similarly be removed, and "relaxing" incisions into offending ligaments and tendons can be done to lengthen these structures.

---

[25] *Id.*

[9] Arthrotomies

As opposed to arthroscopy, which requires small incisions into joints, arthrotomy is a major incision into a joint. Arthrotomies are performed for major reconstruction of joint ligaments and other joint conditions where the area to be visualized or the surgery to be performed is greater than that which can be achieved with arthroscopy.

[10] Fusions

Fusions are simply the elimination of a joint. Joints that produce pain on motion, or those that are functionally unstable, can be corrected by the removal of the joint. Since fusions no longer depend upon muscle or ligamentous stability for motion, a fused joint has the advantage of inherent stability and lack of pain. However, they do, of course, have the disadvantage of total lack of motion.

[11] Tendon and Ligament Repairs

Injuries to tendons and ligaments can cause lacerations or stretching of the tissues. The stretching can be microscopic or complete tearing. If the stretching is in a ligament it is referred to as a sprain. If in a muscle it is a strain.

Primary repair of a tendon is either immediate or delayed, but either type involves the suturing of the two ends of the original tendon or ligament to each other so that the original function is restored. This can be done either immediately or at a reasonably short time after the injury, or it can be done much later (delayed primary suture).

A second means of restoring the function of a tendon or ligament is the secondary repair. Here, because the original trauma caused a loss of segment structure or because of some intervening pathological condition, the two ends of the tendon can no longer be sutured to each other. In this situation, tendon tissue is obtained from a different source (either from another part of the patient or from a synthetic source), and the new material is used to bridge the gap. The end result should be a restoration of original function.

[12] Spinal Surgery

The function of the spine is to provide a stable support for the shoulder girdle and head, as well as semi-rigid protection of the enclosed spinal cord and nerves. The function of the spinal cord, as a component of the central nervous system, is to relay messages from the brain to the peripheral organs and, in return, to relay sensory impulses from the peripheral organs to the brain. In addition, reflex reactions can be generated in the spinal cord. If there is pressure upon the spinal cord or enclosed nerves from an organic lesion (e.g., herniated disc, tumor, bone spurs, thickened ligaments or fracture bone chips), a laminectomy is performed to remove the offending cause. (A laminectomy or laminotomy is the removal of the lamina to visualize and correct the underlying abnormality).

The diagnosis depends upon the history, physical examination, and X-rays. In addition, computerized studies such as CAT and MRI studies, discograms, myelograms, and electrical studies of spinal cord function, including EMG, NCV, and similar studies, may be needed to confirm the diagnosis and delineate the surgery needed.

Spine operations are of two basic types or combined; the laminectomy removes tissue, bone spurs, osteophytes, disc material, thickened ligaments or a tumor which is pressing on tissue. The fusion immobilizes the vertebrae to prevent further irritation.

A spinal fusion is an operation which, like fusions of other joints, is used to provide stability of an unstable joint, and also to prevent pain which may occur upon motion of the joint. Spinal joints commonly become unstable after laminectomies, trauma, and diseases such as spondylolysis, spondylolithesis and scoliosis. Also, spinal joints can become painful due to arthritic conditions. These operations can be done from several approaches: front (anterior), rear (posterior), or lateral. Successful spinal fusions should prevent painful motion, prevent instability, and protect the spinal cord.

Scoliosis is a circumstance of the spine. It usually occurs in children and the cause is usually not known. Treatment depends on the age of the patient and the degree of curvature and can consist of either observation, bracing or fusion.

§ 17.04 Malpractice

[1] Origins of Malpractice

Malpractice is determined by a legal process. Failure of the healthcare provider to practice acceptable medicine or surgery is a deviation from the standard of care and is a component of the legal finding of malpractice.

Malpractice actions are won by legal proof of negligence, but are products of patient dissatisfaction with a medical outcome. Patients come to healthcare providers with a predetermined concept of their diagnosis. Those diagnoses that agree with their predetermined idea, or are reasonably similar to those they expect, are readily accepted, and a planned treatment that is close to their envisional treatment plan is generally acceptable as well. In addition, patients and families maintain perceptions of what the end results should be. Diagnosis, treatment and results that are unexpected and unfavorable fall under the term "poor results," and unless such "poor results" can be rationalized or explained to the patient's satisfaction, this can result in legal action.[26]

Malpractice can occur in orthopedic surgery. The most common cause of malpractice specifically in total joint replacements is leg length discrepancy. Malpositioning of the components can lead to dislocations specifically of total hip replacements. There can be loss of range of motion and loosening of the components in total knees and total hips. This can be accelerated by improper cement technique and improper implant positioning such as increased varus or valgus positioning within total joints.

Other things that can lead to malpractice in orthopedics include operating on the wrong side which can be a catastrophic failure of the physician patient relationship. Failure to perform the proper physical exam, specifically pre-op can also lead to orthopedic malpractice as well as failure to obtain laboratory test including CBC, Sed Rate, CRP as well as metabolic profiles pre-operatively. Failure to obtain appropriate x-rays can lead to malpractice including for example a patient sustaining a fracture and missing fractures both x-raying the joint above and below the fracture and missing fractures both proximal and distal to the item of interest. A good rule of thumb when x-raying a bone is to make sure that the joint proximal and distal to the fracture is obtained.

Other potential problems in malpractice when dealing with fractures is inadequate placement of hardware, inadequate number of screws placed above and below the fracture. Missing a compartment syndrome in a patient.

In dealing with pediatric fractures the orthopedic surgeon must be cognoscente of future bone growth. Abnormal alignment of the growth plate, violation of the growth plate either by screw fixation or bridging a growth plat with plate can lead to growth plate arrest causing growth plate abnormalities. This can lead to non symmetrical limb lengths in children as well as abnormal varus or valgus of joints.

Tibial shaft fractures can be significant fractures occurring in the human body mainly because 1/3 of the boarder of the tibia is subcutaneous. These fractures can be open with the least amount of trauma. The bone is also exposed to significant forces especially in motor vehicle accidents specifically motorcycle vs. car and/or even in car wrecks.

There is a significant incidence in infection with these types of fractures. Fracture of the proximal tibia specifically tibial plateau fractures can also be a source of concern in that if the joint is inappropriately aligned at the time of fixation this can lead to severe arthritis or malalignment of the knee. The

---

[26] W.N. Harsha, Medical Malpractice: Handling Orthopedic Cases 8 (McGraw-Hill 1990).

femur fractures are usually addressed with intramedullary nails. Should the fixation of the femur be such that we have limb length discrepancies this can lead to a potential source of litigation as well as inappropriate placement of the rod entry point in the proximal femur which can lead to increased tube stresses and fracture iatrogenically of the proximal femur.

Fractures of the pelvis and acetabulum are an extremely demanding surgery. This is one of the few types of orthopedic surgery that can actually lead to the death of the patient due to bleeding, damage to the sciatic nerve. Acetabular surgery is also extremely demanding in that the joint must be reconstructed to within 1 millimeter to prevent or delay the onset of osteoarthritis.

Radius and ulna fractures need to be fixed anatomically to prevent abnormal pronation supination. Distal radial fractures need to be aligned anatomically to preserve flexion extension of the wrist as well as potential scarring of the extensor and flexor tendons. Fractures of the humerus can lead to litigation in that the radial nerve can commonly be injured if one is not careful to protect the nerve at all time especially with a posterior exposure.

Dislocations of the joints, specifically of the shoulder are initially treated closed. Multiple dislocations due require surgical reconstruction of the capsule and ligamentous structures about the shoulder. This can lead to a potential source of litigation with loss of range of motion or recurrent dislocation or failure to recognize multidirectional instability to the shoulder. Dislocations of the elbow once reduced should begin early motion to prevent post operative stiffness. Early motion should occur within the first week or so after surgery. Dislocations of the wrist are rare and most likely are accompanied by a Colles' fracture. Dislocations of the hip can lead to avascular changes due to loss of blood supply within the femoral head and should be reduced within the first 6 hours after the incident occurred to prevent avascular necrosis. Dislocation of the knees can be catastrophic injuries in that we can have popliteal artery laceration or intimal year. This can lead to loss of the lower extremity and needs to be addressed within the first 6 hours of occurrence either with a clinical evaluation angiography and consultation of vascular surgeons once the knee dislocation is reduced. Again the knee dislocation should be reduced prior to 6 hours after the initial injury occurred. Dislocations of the ankle can occur and again need to be reduced due to neurovascular compromise to the foot.

Again to review total joint replacements, alignment of the components is of paramount importance. Should the components specifically in total knee or total hip replacement be placed in varus, valgus this can lead to abnormal wear within the total joint prosthesis, early loosening of the total joint prosthesis of limb length discrepancy. Specifically in total hip replacement.

This can be a potential source of litigation. Total ankle replacement is quite rare as is total elbow replacement

[2] Failure to Note Significant Complaints

In taking a history from an orthopedic patient (as opposed to a general medical history), the chief complaint or basic reason for seeing the doctor is usually quite circumspect and limited. However, malpractice has occurred commonly in multiple trauma patients where the medical staff's focus is on one or more major injuries and others are ignored.

[3] Failure to Obtain a Significant Past History

Orthopedic patients who also are diabetics may have decreased sensation and nerve function as well as an increased incidence of infection. Also, diabetics require a longer time for skin and fractures to heal. Other systemic conditions that can have local repercussions on orthopedic problems are anemias, leukemias, and metabolic conditions in general. An orthopedist's failure to obtain a history of these conditions can result in malpractice, as can his failure to appreciate the effect of these systemic conditions on the local pathology being treated.[27]

There are also general medical illnesses that affect the patient's tolerance of certain treatments, prolonged bed rest and medications frequently prescribed by the orthopedist for the local condition under his care. For example, it would likely be held malpractice to fail to note a significant history of a serious pulmonary, cardiac, allergic or alcoholic condition.[28]

In addition, family histories may reveal factors critical to a patient's treatment, and conditions arising from negligence in recognizing genetic dispositions may provide grounds for legal action.[29]

The failure to obtain a true past surgical history can have local and general repercussions for an orthopedist. Locally, the site of the previous scars, external and internal, mobilized structures, types of implants and their position as well as previous infections all can be significant.

Additionally, the course of the patient's previous surgery and anesthesia may effect the outcome of any planned surgery or anesthesia. Also significant is a history of any abnormal reactions to common operating room procedures, such as allergies to skin preparation solutions or tape, anesthetics or suture materials.

---

[27] Daniels v. Weiss, 385 So. 2d 661 (Fla. App. 1980).

[28] *See, e.g.,* Landeros v. Flood, 551 P.2d 389 (Cal. 1976); Holderfield v. Helton, 549 So. 2d 79 (Ala. 1989).

[29] Kaplan v. Berger, 184 Ill. App. 3d 224, 539 N.E.2d 1267 (1989).

[4] Failure to Perform a Proper Physical Examination

The orthopedist is a medical school graduate and is expected to do a reasonably complete general physical examination of the entire patient. Failure to record obvious clinical findings, such as distinctly abnormal blood pressure or pulse, or cardiac arrhythmias, to modify the care or to obtain tests or to institute care for the abnormality, is evidence of a deviation from the standard of care.[30]

The failure to perform and record a reasonable orthopedic examination also can be grounds for a successful malpractice suit.[31] An examination of a component of the locomotor or musculoskeletal system is highly different from routine medical examination. This examination is necessary to record the physical stability and mobility of the patient's component part. This examination is closer to that of a structural or mechanical engineer than that of a physician. The orthopedist's report should note the absence of presence of any deformity, static or flexible, and whether such deformity is present as an abnormal angulation, rotation or displacement of a bone fragment or an entire bone. The presence of absence of joint instability, swelling, tenderness or shortening, if significant, should also be noted.

[5] Failure to Perform Pertinent Specific Examinations

In addition to the general physical examination and the orthopedic examination, pertinent specific examinations by other specialists may be indicated. Among the common tests are those of the neurologist in examination of the spine and extremities. These tests, by checking reflexes, presence of various types of sensory ability, and motor power, can determine the presence or absence of concurrent neurological damage that can commonly occur with orthopedic injuries. The failure to order these tests when pertinent can be considered evidence of failure to perform an adequate and complete orthopedic examination.[32]

Similarly, a pertinent vascular examination for the presence or absence of adequate arterial supply, capillary filling and venous drainage to an extremity or damaged component of an extremity can be very significant.[33]

---

[30] *See, e.g.,* Rostron v. Klein, 178 N.W. 2d 675 (Mich. App. 1970); Chisher v. Spak, 471 N.Y.S.2d 741 (A.D.2d 1983).

[31] Addison v. Whittenberg, 512 N.E.2d76 (Ill. App. 1987).

[32] WIESEL, FETTER & ROTHMAN, INDUSTRIAL LOW BACK PAIN (Michie Co. 1985).

[33] GOSSLING & PILLSBURY, COMPLICATIONS OF FRACTURE MANAGEMENT (J. B. Lippincott 1984).

[6] Failure to Obtain Laboratory Tests

Certain laboratory tests are required by hospital regulations and hospital by-laws for admission, (or admission of patients above a certain age), for patients undergoing surgery under specific kinds of anesthesia, and for certain other procedures. These tests include CBC, urinalysis, EKG, and chest X-ray. The patient's blood type, for example, must be noted on the chart where hospital regulations or the Joint Commission on Accreditation of Healthcare Organizations so require for a particular diagnosis, admission or clinical category.

In addition, certain suspected diagnoses will necessitate specific tests to confirm or deny their presence; e.g., cultures and sensitivity tests where infection might be suggested by drainage, or an elevated CEA (carcinoembryonic antigen) if cancer is a possibility.[34]

Even if a study was ordered, malpractice can exist if the study was not done, and the orthopedist makes no record of extenuating circumstances, such as patient refusal or equipment failure. And even if the appropriate test is done, obtaining a proper report is the obligation of the treating orthopedist.[35]

[7] Failure to Obtain X-rays

Almost all orthopedic patients require X-rays to document the status of the bone components. These may include routine films of the entire bone, and, when indicated, special views, CT scans, MRIs, Doppler and Ultrasound studies, etc. Failure to have adequate X-rays and appropriate radiological reports or consultations before treatment instituted is evidence of malpractice.[36]

[8] Failure to Consult

Many orthopedic patients require additional consults before or during their care. In the very young and very old or debilitated patients, pediatric or medical consults may be indicated to manage the patient's general care, and failure to have such a consult can be grounds for malpractice. Also, a consult is often needed in cases with significant wound infections. Similarly, vascular, neurological and oncological consults may be indicated.[37]

---

[34] Jines v. Young, 732 S.W.2d 938 (Mo. App. 1987).

[35] *See, e.g.,* Haney v. Mizell Mem. Hosp., 744 F.2d 1467 (11th Cir. 1984).

[36] Slosser v. Logorin, 44 Ohio App. 253, 185 N.E. 210 (1933).

[37] *See, e.g.,* Lipsius v. White, 458 N.Y.S.2d 928 (A.D.2d 1983).

[9] Failure to Arrive at a Reasonable Diagnosis

Assuming that an appropriate history was obtained, that an appropriate physical examination was performed, and that relevant laboratory studies, X-rays and consultations were ordered and appropriately reported, the question then is whether or not the orthopedist arrived at a reasonable diagnosis. Granted that the orthopedist's evaluation of the information acquired can be interpreted as a "medical judgment," nevertheless there are boundaries of medical competence, and outside these boundaries lies the area of medical malpractice.

Malpractice exists where a missed diagnosis or a mistake in diagnosis is based upon a *gross* error in judgment (as opposed to a *relative* error in judgment). Such an error would be equivalent to incompetence or a prima facia case of gross negligence.[38]

Malpractice also can occur on failure to diagnose nonorthopedic conditions. An orthopedist is not held to the level of expertise of a physician who practices in another subspecialty, but he is held to a reasonable level equal to that of other orthopedists or medical school graduates in diagnosing pathological conditions *in general.* To avoid this problem, the orthopedist should order appropriate screening tests, consultation, or document the patient's refusal to have such tests or consultation. A failure to pursue a diagnostic work-up after a negative screening test, or after an appropriate consultation by a qualified consultant, however, is not evidence of malpractice, even if further events would have justified such a course of action.[39]

[10] Failure to Obtain the Patient's Informed Consent

Proper care of a patient includes obtaining his "informed consent" to whatever treatment is selected. Malpractice claims occur frequently in this area in orthopedics, because often the goal in orthopedics is improvement of the quality of life rather than to preserve life itself. Since what a person considers "quality of life" is dependent upon personal psychological, emotional, financial and social values, an orthopedist is, perhaps, more vulnerable to these lawsuits than other specialists.

Consent, express or implied, seems to be viewed by the judiciary as the foundation of "modern" applied medicine; all practices descend within the limits of assent provided by the subject party. Implied consent relies upon a cognizance of the treated party and can be indicated by voluntary conduct on the part of the patient. This deliberate action would evince an understanding

---

[38] *See, e.g., id.*; Nolen v. United States, 571 F. Supp. 295 (W.D. Pa. 1983).

[39] *See, e.g., id.*

or knowledge of the planned procedure, such as the occasion of a patient maintaining an appointment for a perfunctory examination. These conditions are highly subjective, and as a result, have limited practicality. Implied consent should be depended upon exclusively for simple, routine practices.[40]

Express consent, the legal rudiment of more complex procedures, dictates a thorough record of a substantive interchange between doctor and patient. This exchange is intended to lead to the latter's "informed request" for treatment.[41]

Although requirements vary according to a patient's capacity to consent and the circumstances under which treatment is given, forensic decisions have connoted a "checklist" of informed consent dialogues that are inclined to satisfy the court. Disclosure considerations for properly documented "informed request" reflect the necessity for a patient to be briefed, by the physician, of all considerations that could reflect upon the decisions surrounding treatment.[42]

These subjects include suspicions resulting from inconclusive diagnostic test abnormalities; alternate diagnoses and treatments; options of greater potential risk, no matter how remote;[43] and the right to refuse care. The courts appear to believe that, as the probability or severity of risk increases, so does the responsibility to inform. If these instruments contain the necessary information in terms that are easily understood, and if they are suitably executed and made a part of the medical record, they place the physician in a positive position for defending a medical malpractice action based on lack of informed consent.[44]

If a patient is unable either physically or mentally unable to understand or give consent for emergency surgery, the surgeon should document the patient's inability and detail the emergent nature of the procedure to preserve life or limb.

[11] Malpractice in the Treatment of Fractures

Orthopedic surgery can be divided into three major categories: treatment of fractures, treatment of other traumatic musculoskeletal injuries, and reconstructive surgery.

---

[40] C. Wecht & H. Hirsch, Medicolegal Primer 288 (American College of Legal Medicine Foundation 1991).

[41] R. Goodman, *Informed Request*, 7 Orthopedics 1764 (Nov. 1984).

[42] Hondroulis v. Schumacher, 531 So. 2d 450 (La. 1988), *modified*, 533 So. 2d 1221 (La. 1988), *rev'd*, 553 So. 2d 398 (La. 1989).

[43] Douget v. Touro Infirmary, 537 So. 2d 251 (La. App. 1988).

[44] Wecht & Hirsch, *supra* note 40, at 288; Goodman, *supra* note 41, at 1764; *Rights of the Risk-Bearer*, 8 Orthopedics 559 (May 1985); *Doctor-Patient Communication*, 8 Orthopedics 1476 (Dec. 1985); F. Rozovsky, Consent to Treatment: A Practical Guide (2d., Little, Brown & Co. 1987).

[a] Types of Fractures

Fractures can be classified into a number of different categories. These categories have value in helping to predict prognosis and method of treatment.

[i] Open versus closed

An open fracture is any fracture in which there is the slightest defect in the skin envelope that surrounds the fractured bone that communicated with the fracture. It can be as small as a puncture wound where a spike of the fractured bone has penetrated the skin or a large gash in the skin so that the entire bone is exposed. A closed fracture is one in which the soft tissue envelope is intact and there is no communication between the fractured bone and the outside.

All open fractures have the potential to become infected and lead to osteomyelitis (infection of the bone itself). Even the smallest defect in the skin requires special attention including antibiotics and almost always irrigation and debridement. It is generally believed that six hours is the maximum time that should be allowed between injury and debridement to have the best chance of preventing infection. This is not always possible because of the need to fully evaluate and treat life threatening injuries in the poly-trauma patient.

[ii] Comminuted versus noncomminuted

A noncomminuted (sometimes referred to as a simple) fracture is one in which there are only two parts. They are relatively easy to line up and get secure fixation. A comminuted fracture has more than two parts. For instance, humeral head fractures are referred to as two, three, or four part fractures. Sometimes the fracture parts are so small and so many that internal fixation with screws cannot be used and in these cases external fixation may be the best choice of treatment.

[iii] Articular versus nonarticular

Articular fractures are those in which the fracture line or lines violate the joint surface of the fractured bone. They can be further divided into displaced and non-displaced. The displaced articular fractures have the potential to create the largest disability even with the best possible treatment. The joint architecture has been disrupted and this will most likely lead to traumatic arthritis. Displaced articular fractures must be restored and fixed as close to their original position as possible. This is sometimes an impossible task. Nondisplaced articular fractures must be fixed to avoid displacement.

Traumatic damage to the cartilage itself with or without fracture of the supporting bone may be such that traumatic arthritis will result.

Nonarticular fractures do not involve the joint and in most cases reduction does not have to be as precise. The main goals here are to avoid excessive shortening, angulation and rotation.

[b] Treatment of Fractures

The treatment of all fractures starts with arriving at a reasonable diagnosis of the pathological condition. Once the fracture is recognized, it is then the duty of the orthopedist to align the bone fragments into an acceptable position. After alignment is obtained by appropriate means and appropriate anesthesia (perfect or anatomical reduction may be contraindicated because of risks to the patient), the orthopedist should inform the patient of the various means of maintaining fixation of the fracture fragments to prevent loss of the reduction. Depending upon the specific fracture and the condition of the patient, the fixation device may range from a sling and splint, or cast and traction, to an external fixation device, or even to internal fixation requiring general anesthesia and open surgery.

Malpractice during this stage of care can arise from failure to diagnose the presence of the fracture or its severity, failure to align the bones, or failure to adequately fixate the bones in proper alignment until healing has occurred.

A second major malpractice problem in fracture care is the failure to use properly the equipment inherent in treatment. Fractures are fixated after alignment by three techniques: casts, fixation devices and traction.

Cast technique consists of applying a layer of a rigid material (traditionally plaster of Paris, but more recently fiberglass or plastics) over a layer of padding against the skin. Proper technique requires sufficient pressure properly distributed over the surface of the involved limb or trunk to immobilize the fracture without causing local necrosis (skin slough) or impaired vascular or neurological supply (which can result in gangrene, paralysis, or contractures). In almost all of these conditions a conscious patient will complain about the cast. These complications may represent malpractice in cast technique or more likely failure to properly evaluate the patient's complaints.[45]

Besides skin slough, contracture of the forearm muscles (Volkman's contracture) may be an indication of malpractice. It can be caused by the original injury to vascular striations, casting or positioning. Significant pain

---

[45] *See, e.g.,* Lewis v. Johnson, 148 P.2d 99 (Cal. 1939); Duvardo v. Moore, 98 N.E.2d 855 (Ill. App. 1951); Allen v. Giuliano, 136 A.2d 904 (Conn. 1957).

is associated with this condition so failure to investigate abnormal pain may be the source of the malpractice.[46]

Another common area of malpractice in the treatment of fractures is in the use of multiple fixation devices. These may consist of both internal fixation and percutaneous devices (e.g., intramedullary rods, screw and plate combinations for extramedullary compression, combinations of plates and rods for hip fixation, and external compression devices). Although many of these devices appear simple, they can be fraught with danger if the exact details of the recommended technique are not followed scrupulously.

Possibly because the field of orthopedics seems to attract surgeons with a mechanical or engineering bent, new devices are constantly being produced for the maintenance of fractures. Some of these products appear fairly easy to apply, but in reality they can be quite complicated, and can lead gullible orthopedists into attempting to use them without proper training. Unless the manufacturers' specific directions are followed, complications will occur at a high incidence.

Another area of frequent malpractice is traction technique. Proper traction depends upon the basic theory that when flexible material is pulled taut, it will pull in a straight line. Thus, traction depends on applying forces to either end of an extremity or limb in such a manner that the fracture fragments are aligned in a line that approximates the original or anatomical position. Maintenance of this traction in the proper position will result, if done properly, in the healing of the fracture in the appropriate position.

Malpractice in the use of traction usually involves either the application of the pull on the extremity (in which vital structures are damaged), or the placement of the pin from which the traction is applied (which can damage vascular or nerve structures).

No matter what method of reduction is used—closed, traction, or internal/external fixation—frequent x-rays are necessary to make sure that satisfactory alignment is maintained.[47]

Another serious problem in fracture treatment is the failure to diagnose concurrent trauma. Forces applied to a limb that are significant enough to cause a disruption of the continuity of a bone also, by their nature, can cause concurrent injuries to arteries, veins, nerves, growth plates, ligaments and tendons. It is not unheard of for physicians, while treating fractures, to fail to

[46] See, e.g., Hanson v. Thelan, 173 N.W. 457 (N.D. 1919); Phifer v. Baker, 244 P.2d 637 (Wyo. 1926); Brown v. Dark, 119 S.W.2d 529 (Ark. 1938); Bartholomew v. Butts, 5 N.W.2d 7 (Iowa 1942); Winters v. Rance, 251 N.W. 167 (Neb. 1933); Bowles v. Bourdon, 219 S.W.2d 779 (Tex. 1949); Atkins v. Humes, 110 So. 2d 663 (Fla. 1959).

[47] Pierce, Complications of Traction, in COMPLICATIONS IN ORTHOPAEDIC SURGERY (Epps, ed., J.B. Lippincott 1978).

diagnose other significant injuries in the same limb. For instance a patient with a knee dislocation even if it reduces on its own may have a serious vascular injury. This is grounds for malpractice. This does not mean, however, that other injuries must be vigorously treated with surgical exploration or repair, but only that a diagnosis should be made (or at least suspected), and appropriate consultation should be obtained.

[c] The Upper Extremities

[i] Bones of the hand

Treatment of fractures of the fingers rarely is a cause of a malpractice action. If and when malpractice occurs in the care of fractured fingers, it is usually related to the failure to appreciate rotation of one of the fragments, or a tilt of an articular surface. Such a failure to identify rotation or tilt of a fragment results in the involved finger crossing one of the other digits when the patient makes a fist. The presence of one of these fractures, which usually is an oblique fracture of the proximal or middle phalanges, usually involves offering the patient the option of an open reduction and internal fixation to prevent such a deformity. The failure to identify such a rotary disturbance and the failure to offer the patient such an option may be evidence of malpractice.[48]

Metacarpal fractures are infrequently aligned in improper angulation or displacement; however, the failure to appreciate the rotation of a metacarpal fracture, which is determined by the rotation of the fingernails and not by review of the X-rays themselves, is also evidence of malpractice. Carpal fractures in general, without dislocations, are of minor consequence and seldom lead to malpractice actions.

The navicular bone of the wrist is unique, however, and failure to suspect a fracture, and thus failure to provide immobilization until the diagnosis is confirmed or ruled out, can lead to necrosis of the navicular bone and/or nonunion. While failure to diagnose and treat such a fracture in its early stages may result in such a problem, the medical literature is replete with a high incidence of these complications in properly treated navicular fractures.

[ii] The forearm and elbow

Treatment of fractures of the distal forearm or the wrist had a very low incidence of malpractice. Most of these injuries occur in young children or the elderly. Almost all fractured wrists in the young will realign themselves

---

[48] *See, e.g.,* Scott v. Mendoza, 428 So. 2d 8 (Ala. 1983); Barnette v. Potenza, 359 N.Y.S.2d 432 (N.Y. Sup. Ct. 1974); Gomez v. Long Island College Hosp., 517 N.Y.S.2d 85 (A.D.2d 1987).

into reasonably normal wrists. In the very elderly, limited use of the extremity usually precludes any significant decrease in function, even when only minimal care is provided. However, many chronologically aged patients with fractures are emotionally and physically middle-aged and expect a return to their previous lifestyle.

Fractures of the mid-forearm are injuries with a high incidence of poor results from cast and improper fixation technique, and can result in significant deformities with marked loss of function.[49] Fractures in the mid forearm in children are generally treated closed with casting and will remodel. Good results are almost always obtained. However, in adults these fractures almost universally re-occur open reduction and internal fixation. Failure to align these fractures properly can result in a significant delay in healing, obvious angulation, and sometimes "cross-union", which results in an inability to supinate and pronate the forearm. Nonunion is also a complication, which requires further surgical intervention.[50]

The proximal radius is fractured by forces generated on the hand and wrist, which are then transmitted down the forearm, forcing the proximal end of the radius against the distal end of the humerus in the manner of a "battering ram." On receiving this force, if the proximal radius bends or displaces to one side, it results in a fracture of the neck of the radius. If the head of the radius becomes discontinuous, it results in a fracture of the head of the radius. Either of these fractures will cause some failure of alignment of the proximal end of the radius with the distal humerus in elbow motion. Except in extreme cases, whether this malalignment is significant enough to affect the patient's use of the elbow, and whether it is of a significant nature to require surgical excision of the displaced or deformed proximal radius (or simply require a short period of immobilization followed by physical therapy with later reconstructive excision of the radial head), is a matter of judgment on the part of the treating orthopedist. Malpractice here occurs when the severity of the fracture, and the need for early surgery, is not identified.[51]

Another bone that can be fractured is the proximal ulna or olecranon. Simple fractures of the olecranon seldom involve claims for malpractice. These fractures can be treated by open or closed reduction, or excision of the fragments with reattachment of the muscles. Nonunion can occur no matter what type of treatment is provided. Malpractice in these cases arises when

---

[49] Gomez v. Long Island College Hosp., 517 N.Y.S.2d 85 (A.D.2d 1987); Moore v. St. Paul Fire & Marine Ins. Co., 395 So. 2d 838 (La. App. 1981).

[50] See, e.g., Mack v. Garcia, 433 So. 2d 17 (Fla. App. 1983); In re Compensation of Holub, 646 P2d 105 (Or. App. 1982); Cunningham v. Yankton Clinic, 262 N.W.2d 508 (S.D. 1978).

[51] Gunter v. Whitener, 75 S.W.2d 588 (Mo. App. 1934).

the injury is accompanied by other fractures of the radius, or dislocations of either end of the radius or ulna, and these are not identified.[52]

A third bone in the elbow is the distal humerus. Treatment of this fracture is fraught with malpractice in all age groups. In young children the negligence can be either failure to identify the fracture or the failure to identify major displacement of fragments which appear to be nondisplaced on X-ray (because the displacement is in the non-radiopaque cartilaginous piece of the fracture fragment). A second major ground for malpractice in the treatment of these fractures is the failure to identify massive swelling with compression of vascular structures, and secondary necrosis of muscles and nerves of the distal extremity. Still another area for malpractice is the failure to identify angulation of the fracture reduction. Since many of these fractures are treated by closed reduction or surgery with the arm held in flexion (and with an apparently proper position on X-ray taken with the elbow in flexion), the poor reduction is not apparent until the elbow is extended after the fracture has healed. It is at this time, when the elbow is first extended, that rotary or angulation deformities will be apparent. For this reason, many orthopedic surgeons prefer internal or percutaneous fixation of the fracture fragments, so that the elbow can be extended and rotary and angulation deformities can be checked before healing has occurred.

A final cause of malpractice in elbow fractures is the late development of scar tissue with secondary loss of vascular or neurological functions. Failure to appreciate, at the time of the fracture, possible damage to arteries, veins or nerves (or that reduction will result in damage to these structures) can be considered grounds for malpractice.[53]

[iii] The upper arm

Fractures of the mid-humerus, also known as fractures of the shaft of the humeral bone, have a great propensity for healing. Furthermore, the shoulder and the elbow, at opposite ends of the humerus, can also compensate for a tremendous angulation or rotary deformity at the fracture site. The only area where poor medical care occurs with any frequency in fractures of the mid-humerus is where the physician fails to recognize damage to the radial nerve which is located very close to the humeral shaft. The malpractice here usually is failure to diagnose the original nerve damage, but there also can be a secondary failure to observe the recovery of the nerve. This nerve has a great tendency for spontaneous recovery. If the

---

[52] Fourquet v. Cardonia Hosp., 439 N.Y.S.2d 435 (A.D.2d 1981).

[53] Thone v. Palmer, 489 N.E.2d 1163 (Ill. App. 1986).

nerve damage is not recognized, or if the damaged muscles and tendons are not protected, when nerve recovery recurs, a permanent deformity may ensue. Therefore, the malpractice also can be failure to appreciate the extent of the nerve damage, and failure to institute proper rehabilitation so that when the nerve recovers, the muscles, tendons and joints are not permanently deformed.

[iv] The shoulder area

Fractures of the proximal humerous (The arm portion of the shoulder joint) can range all the way from non-displaced and impacted which can be treated with a sling and subsequent physical therapy to multi-fragmented fractures which will be quite disabling unless addressed. The orthopedist must consider the age and activity level of the patient along with the quality of the bone. In most cases, the best treatment will be reduction with either open or percutaneous fixation or replacement of the humeral head with a metal prosthesis.

Fractures of the clavicle and scapula are rarely involved in malpractice cases.

[d] The Lower Extremities

[i] The foot

Few malpractice cases arise out of treatment of fractured toes. The only toe involved in ambulation (and therefore needs to be treated, except for cosmetic purposes) is the large toe. Fractures of the other toes usually need to be treated only if they become irritated by the shoe or other toes. The first toe, however, is a major force in ambulation, and inadequate reduction of a fracture (or maintenance of the reduction) can result in loss of foot dynamics.

Metatarsal fractures generally heal without consequence. Two exceptions are where there are multiple metatarsal fractures and the so called "Jones fracture" at the base of the fifth metatarsal. This fracture has a high incidence of non-union and is frequently treated with internal fixation.

Fractures of the tarsal bones are frequently missed and can result in significant problems if not properly treated. Displaced fractures of the talus usually require internal fixation. The so called Lis Frass Mid foot fracture can result in altered alignment of the foot with resultant chronic pain.

[ii] The ankle

The distal tibia (with the tibial-fibular ligament) and the distal fibula (with the tibial talar and fibula talar ligaments) together form the ankle joint.

This combined structure essentially approximates a letter "C" (or a C clamp) holding the talus in place and allowing the talus with the foot to pivot.

Forcing the ankle into either inversion or eversion will fracture the bone against which the talus is buttressed, and will either tear the opposite ligament or avulse the bone to which the opposite ligament attaches. Therefore, all fractures of the ankle will cause damage medially and laterally to some degree and, in addition, the ankle will, at the time of the injury, suffer some dislocation. Reduction of the fracture, therefore, requires reduction of the dislocation, so that the talus and the tibia are in appropriate position to each other. Furthermore, the medial and lateral structures must be aligned in proper position to the talus to allow healing of any stretched or torn ligaments on the sides. Failure to obtain and maintain a proper reduction of the ankle can be malpractice.[54]

[iii] The tibial shaft

Tibial shaft fractures are probably the most severe fractures that occur in the human body, and the least understood. Closed fractures of the tibia have a significant incidence, even in the best of hands, of developing compartment syndromes. These can cause loss of nerve and blood supply to the distal extremity, and possibly paralysis, anesthesia, and loss of the limb. Malpractice in the case of compartment syndrome almost always revolves around the failure to diagnose timely and treat appropriately with surgical compartment releases.

Frequently tibial fractures are open and lead even in the best of hands to infection. If there is malpractice it is once again in the failure to diagnose and treat appropriately.

Despite apparently good reduction as seen on X-rays, these fractures can result in nonunion and malunion, with secondary complications and eventual amputation, especially in major compound wounds. There is also a significant incidence of shortening and cosmetic deformities. Notwithstanding this high complication rate, it is not uncommon for orthopedic surgeons to underestimate the seriousness of these fractures.[55]

[iv] The knee

Fractures of the proximal tibia are commonly known as fractures of the tibial plateau. The knee consists of essentially three bones: the proximal tibia, the patella and the distal femur. Fractures of the proximal tibia are caused by

---

[54] *See, e.g.,* Stockman v. Hall, 65 P.2d 348 (Kan. 1937); Welch v. Frisbie Mem. Hosp., 9 A.2d 761 (N.H. 1939).

[55] *See, e.g.,* DeWitt v. Brown, 669 F.2d 516 (8th Cir. 1982).

compression of the tibia up against the distal femur. The reduction of the fracture requires restoration of the surface of the tibia with sufficient support for healing. Malpractice, if any, usually occurs in failure to identify these fractures, with resulting instability of the knee.[56]

If the proximal fibula is also fractured in this injury, it is important to determine if there has been damage to the peroneal nerve.

There are seldom any grounds for malpractice in treatment of a fractured patella except possibly in over-enthusiasm for treatment of a "congenital bipartite" patella which, on X-ray, can sometimes be confused with a fracture. Usually, however there is no harm in conservative care (casting) of a bipartite patella for a few weeks, so little recoverable damage occurs with these mistakes.

Distal femur fractures are generally recognizable, and standard open or closed reduction can be applied with minor difficulty.

[v] The femur

Fractures of the femoral shaft also are usually easily identified, and reduction is well standardized by either closed or open methods. Despite this, however, malpractice frequently occurs. This is likely due to the seriousness of the overall injury, and the fact that major surgery is required.[57]

[e] The Hip

The proximal femur (the hip) is divided into specific areas: subtrochanteric, intertrochanteric, femoral neck extracapular, and femoral neck intracapular.

A subtrochanteric fracture of the femur has the propensity to delude the surgeon into believing it is actually either a femoral shaft fracture or an intertrochanteric fracture. The subtrochanteric fracture, although many times requiring surgical intervention, also requires the use of mechanical fixation devices distinct and separate from those used on either femoral shaft or intertrochanteric fractures. It is not uncommon for orthopedic surgeons to fail to recognize that the fracture is subtrochanteric, and use one of the standard fixation devices designed for the other fractures.

Another problem is that patients with subtrochanteric fractures often fail to recognize the prolonged healing process required, and do not

---

[56] *See, e.g.,* Weise v. United States, 724 F.2d 587 (7th Cir. 1984).

[57] *See, e.g.,* Lemon v. Kessel, 209 N.W. 393 (Iowa 1926); Kinsley v. Carravetta, 7 N.E.2d 691 (N.Y. 1937); Kuhn v. Banker, 13 N.E.2d 242 (N.Y. 1938); Watterson v. Conwell, 61 So. 2d 696 (Ala. 1952).

meticulously follow the surgeon's postoperative instructions. This can result in disastrous healing patterns.[58]

Intertrochanteric, extracapular neck and intracapular neck fractures can all be treated with one of the numerous hip fixation devices. Careful documentation and review of the x-rays is necessary in these cases to determine the appropriateness of the device selected, and the adequacy of its insertion. The surgery if fairly standardized. Malpractice usually stems from a failure to obtain adequate x-rays in the operating room to ensure that any errors in technique are corrected prior to the completion of the operation. Improper positioning of guide pins, screws, bolts, nails or prosthesis *during the operation* is not grounds for malpractice, but in fact show that the surgeon is properly monitoring the procedure through adequate roentgenographic control. However, deciding post operatively without adequate intraoperative films showing appropriate positioning is a deviation from the standard of care and can lead to an assumption of inappropriate intraoperative position.

[f] The Pelvis and Spine

In injuries of the pelvis and spinal column, malpractice usually involves the failure to diagnose properly and prevent continued damage.[59] Many emergency rooms are routinely ordering CT-scans of spine and pelvis to check for fractures to those areas.

Patients with fractures of the hip socket must be considered for open reduction, internal fixation. This may or may not present traumatic arthritis, but it will restore the architecture so that a total hip replacement can be done at a later date if traumatic arthritis does occur.

It is the duty of the physician to order appropriate X-ray studies to determine the presence or absence of fractures, and to obtain adequate neurological examinations to demonstrate the presence or absence of nerve damage.[60]

Further care of these injuries mainly involves the prevention of damage to the spinal cord or peripheral nerves. This is generally achieved by internal fixation, traction, percutaneous fixation, or pelvic immobilization.[61]

---

[58] *See, e.g.,* Cyr v. Giesen, 108 A.2d 316 (Me. 1954); Russell v. Harwick, 182 So. 2d 241 (Fla. 1966); Mott v. Clay, 225 N.E.2d 185 (Ind. App. 1967).

[59] Brown v. North Broward Hosp. Dist., 521 So. 2d 143 (Fla. App. 1988).

[60] Jackson v. Brinegar, 165 Ga. App. 432, 301 S.E.2d 493 (1983).

[61] 2 AM. JUR. PROOF OF FACTS 3d *Pelvic Injuries* 657-719 (1988).

[12]   Malpractice in the Treatment of Other Musculoskeletal Injuries

[a]   Dislocations and Fracture-dislocations

Dislocations generally involve traumatic injuries that affect tendons and ligaments. Tendons by definition are structures that connect muscles to bones, and ligaments are structures that connect bone to bone. Ligaments and tendons are similar in that, although they are reasonably pliable, they re not fixed in shape (as are bones), and they do not have the elastic or contractual power of muscles.

Dislocations are the disassociation of the bones constituting a joint. A joint is composed of the surfaces of two opposing bones, the fluid between the two bones, the synovial membrane that maintain the fluid, and ligaments (either inside or outside the synovial membrane) that maintain the relative position between the two bones. When the two bones move into positions that are outside the normal range of motion, the restraining ligaments undergo tension. As this tension increases, the ligament starts to fatigue, and goes through three phases: microscopic tears, tears visible to the naked eye and complete ruptures.

Instead of failing, however, the ligament may remain intact and avulse a fragment of bone on either end. This is fracture dislocation, as opposed to a simple dislocation, where the ligament has either become pathologically stretched, or has been torn to allow the two bones to come out of their relative positions. As the ligaments fail or fragments of bone are avulsed, the two bones go from their normal position to subluxation and then complete dislocation.

Malpractice in the diagnosis and treatment of these injuries usually is related to the failure to identify that a subluxation or dislocation has occurred.[62]

Malpractice also can arise from the failure to adequately reduce the dislocation and provide an environment for property healing of the bone fragments or ligaments. One of the most serious problems occurs when a ligament folds back on itself after being torn. The ligament fragment is then inside the joint, and prevents complete reduction of the dislocation. Also, by being displaced, the ligament fragment cannot unite with the opposite fragment of joint capsule, and recurrent dislocations will occur. In these situations, open reduction of the dislocation usually is needed, as well as open repair of the torn ligament.

---

[62] Thone v. Palmer, 489 N.E.2d 1163 (Ill. App. 1986).

[i] The hand and wrist

Dislocations and fracture-dislocations of the fingers are known as interphalangeal dislocations, and are commonly recognized by the physician. Reduction is usually simple. However, small chip fractures of the volar plate, which is one of the ligamentous structures connecting the fingers, often are overlooked. Failure to identify this concurrent fracture and the displaced ligament fragments sometimes can result in an unreduced subluxation or an unstable reduction of the dislocation, and can be grounds for malpractice.

Dislocation of the metacarpophalangeal joint occurs at the base of the finger. Although rare, it may be irreducible if appreciation is not made of a possible "buttonhole" protrusion of one of the bones through the ligaments and membranes that form the joint capsule. Failure to recognize this possibility and the resulting need for an open reduction can lead to repeated unsuccessful attempts at closed reduction and permanent damage to the articular surfaces of the bones and surrounding structures.

The wrist joint consists of multiple anatomically different joints, and each one can suffer a dislocation. These joints consist of multiple articular surfaces, including those between the metacarpals and carpals, those between the numerous carpal bones, and those joints between the carpal bones and the two bones of the forearm. As a group, these dislocations are not common, but failure to diagnose any one of these multiple dislocations, subluxations or rotary dislocations, is evidence of malpractice. This is despite often subtle radiographic findings that may not be revealing to an unexperienced emergency room physician, orthopedist or radiologist. The damage that occurs from failure to diagnose any one of these dislocations, results almost uniformly in severe degenerative arthritic changes of the wrist, which may eventually require wrist fusion, excision of degenerative avascular bones or replacement with synthetic inserts.

The radius and ulna have two articulating surfaces: near the wrist joint (distal) and close to the elbow joint (proximal). At the distal radioulna joint, chronic subluxations are noted in patients who have residual complaints following wrist injuries that were originally diagnosed as sprains. The diagnosis of chronic subluxation can almost never be made on plain X-ray, and require a wrist CT-scan or MRI.

[ii] The elbow

Dislocations of the proximal radio-ulnar joint are usually accompanied by significant findings at the area of the elbow, including fracture. In addition, X-rays that appear to show dislocations of the proximal radio-ulnar joint may in reality be accompanied by fractures of the distal humerus (upper arm bone). Therefore, this area, as in fractures of the elbow, is fraught with misdiagnoses.

True dislocations of the elbow itself, which is the ulna-humeral joint, also occur. As in other dislocations, the failure to appreciate concurrent damage to vital ligaments, tendons, vascular structures and nerves, both at the time of reduction and thereafter, can be considered evidence of malpractice. A classic misdiagnosis here is overlooking an avulsion fracture from the humerus, which can result in an unstable reduction.

[iii] The shoulder

Dislocations of the shoulder are usually anterior and easily diagnosed and treated. There is, however, a second injury, posterior dislocation, that can be missed from failure to obtain a *lateral* X-ray film of the shoulder. (The standard AP X-ray of the shoulder can be misleading, and appear to be within normal limits.) It is not uncommon for X-ray technicians in emergency rooms and other radiographic facilities to fail to obtain a lateral view.

The lateral view of the shoulder may be one of three kinds: (1) across the chest, (2) the "swimmer's view," or (3) the axillary view. Failure to obtain a lateral view when the patient clinically has evidence of a posterior dislocation (even though the straight or classical anterior-posterior view is normal), can be grounds for malpractice. Liability here falls not only on the X-ray department, but also on the treating physician who fails to insist upon a lateral view. A posterior dislocation left unreduced can result in severe traumatic arthritic changes.

[iv] The clavicle

Dislocations can occur at either end of the clavicle (collar bone). The lateral end of the clavicle forms a psuedo-type joint with the acromion or acromial process of the scapula (shoulder blade). Since it is held in place by multiple ligaments, the dislocation here is called a *separation*, and is classified as to severity according to the number of ligaments injured. As the number of ligaments injured increases, the two bones become further separated. The range is from Grade I to Grade IV, or complete separation. Although one might think that failure to diagnose one of these injuries could be evidence of malpractice, an acceptable treatment for any of these separations is *nontreatment*.

On the other hand, dislocations at the other end of the clavicle, the medial aspect of the sternum or "breast bone" (sternoclavicular dislocations), are true dislocations. The dislocations here can be either anterior or posterior.

The dislocation itself can be commonly treated without surgical intervention or reduction, but the concurrent injuries may include rupture of vital structures in the patient's mediastinal area. Therefore, in sternoclavicular dislocations, the prime area for malpractice is not in the diagnosis or treatment of the dislocation itself, but in failure to diagnose concurrent (and here, serious and occasionally even fatal) injuries.

[v] The foot and ankle

Toes can become dislocated similar to fingers; however, because of the lack of dexterity of toes (and common abnormal positions of many toes), failure to reduce a dislocation of a toe results in no significant damage and therefore seldom creates a malpractice claim.

Dislocations in the midfoot area are often accompanied by major injuries to the blood vessels, nerves and tendons of the foot. Like the wrist, there can be injury to one or a combination of several of the joints between the tarsal and metatarsal bones. Malpractice in this area usually involves the failure to identify significant vascular compromise, especially venous compromise. Failure to allow for swelling of the foot, through appropriate fascial incisions, and failure to appreciate the significance of the injury, can result in amputations. The dislocations themselves here, even when properly reduced, frequently leave the patient with gait disturbances.

Dislocations of the ankle, i.e., between the talus and the tibia, seldom occur without fractures or ligamentous injuries. The failure here to appreciate residual subluxations or recognize unstable fracture reductions can be grounds for malpractice. This instability can be posterior, anterior, medial or lateral, and can be caused by failure of reduction of the medial malleolus, the lateral malleolus, posterior or anterior lip fractures, or widening of the ankle mortise.

[vi] The knee

The knee area consists of three major joints: between the fibula and tibia, between the tibia and femur, and between the patella and femur. Fibula-tibia dislocations are seldom seen, seldom need acute intervention, and seldom result in disability if not treated. Dislocations between the femur and the tibia, however, are fraught with significant acute, sub-acute, and chronic injuries to the major blood vessels, nerves and ligaments. The failure of the treating physician to appreciate an acute injury to these structures, and to perform appropriate tests for a significant period of time (to ensure that delayed onset of the above mentioned problems does not occur), can be evidence of malpractice. A tibial-femoral joint dislocation is so damaging to surrounding structures that some writers believe that a vascular consultation should be obtained immediately upon making the diagnosis.

Rotary dislocations and subluxations can occur with injuries to the menisci, and the collateral and cruciate ligaments, without total dislocations of the knee. The proper modality for evaluating these injuries is the MRI, but since these injuries are not time sensitive, the ordering of the MRI can be at the discretion of the treating physician. Malpractice in knee surgery often rests upon the appropriateness of the therapeutic modality carried out.

The third joint of the knee is the patella-femoral joint. Acute dislocations, when reduced, can still be unstable due to the ligamentous injury and the presence of unrecognized fractures, including small chip fractures that become free floating bodies in the knee joint. In addition, chronic subluxations of the patella are common with secondary degeneration of the articular surfaces of the patella and femur.

[vii] The hip

A hip dislocation is readily diagnosed, but reduction may require general anesthesia and stabilization by surgical means. Malpractice here usually arises out of the failure of the surgeon to appreciate the significance of the instability of the dislocation due to the disruption of the acetabular surface or the continued interposition of bone fragments. Many centers now require a CAT scan to ensure a stable reduction with no interposition of soft tissue or bone fragments, and to ensure that the acetabular surface maintains its stability.

One of the late complications of hip dislocation is aseptic necrosis of the femoral head which will require total hip arthroplasty. The blood circulates to the femoral head may be disrupted during the time the hip is dislocated. This can lead to death of the cells in the bone and collapse of the round shape of the head. Generally, it is felt that reducing the hip within the first 6 hours after the dislocation occurs gives the best chance of avoiding this complication.

[b] Tendon and Ligament Repairs

Tendon and ligament repairs can be divided into: (1) primary or end-to-end repairs, (2) repairs with insertion of tendon/ligament or synthetic grafts, (3) tendon/ligament transfers, (4) transfers of either the origin or insertion of the tendon/ligament, and (5) tendon/ligament releases.

When a tendon is torn or ruptured, and the diagnosis is made within a reasonable period of time, function can be restored by suturing the two ends together. Malpractice in this area usually stems from either the failure to recognize that the tendon rupture has occurred, or the failure to reconstruct concurrently injured ligaments. Another cause of malpractice can be failure to restore a ligament to a reasonable length. Excess laxity or tautness will result in instability, inaction of the joint, or a subsequent loss of motion.

The requirements applicable to primary or end-to-end repair of ligaments and tendons apply also to the repair of the structures with grafts. It is important that the surgeon identify the origin and insertion of the tendon or ligament, identify the proximal and distal fragments of the involved structure, and ensure that the final length, with or without a graft, be of a reasonable length.

In surgery involving transfers of tendons with secondary transfer of the function of that tendon, malpractice, if any, usually occurs upon the failure to use an *appropriate* tendon or ligament for the transfer, or upon the failure to see that the surgical position is appropriate for the proposed function.[63]

Surgical releases are necessary where a tendon or ligament has previously (for whatever reason) become scarred in place. The release is to restore motion. Such surgery is fraught with the possibility of devascularization of the tendon, which can result in rupture.

[c] Reconstructive Surgery

Conditions that require reconstructive surgery may have been caused originally by trauma or pathological conditions such as infections, arthritis, tumors or metabolic disorders. Reconstructive surgery is performed in orthopedics, except for occasional malignancies, to restore function. Malpractice in this area usually involves surgical misadventure or failure to obtain the patient's informed consent.

Loss of function here is defined not only as loss of motion of a particular joint or extremity, but also loss of desired power and loss of a specific range of motion. Further, it would include cosmetic deformity and pain or tenderness. Once the diagnosis is made, the question arises whether or not the patient desires correction of the abnormality after being informed of the benefits, alternatives and risks involved.

Joints can be reconstructed by muscle ligament and tendon transfers that provide stability and continued motion, but there may be eventual secondary loss of tendon function from the same pathology that caused the original loss of stability. Joints can also be reconstructed by corrective angulation osteotomies of the bones proximal or distal to the joint. This offers the benefit of realigning the joint and allowing proper function, but the procedure

---

[63] Rames v. Pyati, 534 N.E.2d 472 (Ill. App. 1989).

carries with it the risk of loss of bone healing at the osteotomy site. Still another means of joint reconstruction is to resurface the bone through techniques such as arthroscopy. Lastly, there can be total replacement of the joint, with the accompanying risks of infections and possible loss of the joint.

[i] The hand and wrist

Finger joints are usually treated by either fusion or replacement of the joint. The choice is based upon the presence or absence of suitable supporting structures, including tendons and ligaments that are needed to provide stability and motion for a synthetic joint. In the absence of those structures, a fusion would be necessary to provide stability. If both are present, the choice would be up to the patient, depending upon his vocation and avocation, and his need for interphalangeal joint motion. Any malpractice here would most likely occur in the selection of the wrong procedure for a particular patient, the failure to insert the prosthesis in proper alignment, or the failure of the fusion to be in alignment with the remainder of the finger.

The wrist joint also can be reconstructed by either fusion or replacement with a prosthesis. There is, however, a third alternative: excision of the offending bone fragments. Again, the greatest chance for negligence is the selection of the wrong procedure for the particular patient: fusions provide stability but loss of motion; prostheses provide motion, but only if supported by adequate ligamentous tendon and muscular structures.

Wrist surgery may involve the entire wrist or, as in the case of dislocations, simply a partial fusion of one of the many intercarpal and metacarpal carpal joints. Similarly, a prosthesis can replace the entire joint or just one of the carpal bones. Excision of bone fragments can mean merely bone chips, the entire proximal row of carpal bones, or the distal ulna. The choice depends upon an accurate anatomical diagnosis of the offending pathology.

[ii] The elbow

The same three choices exist in orthopedic reconstructive surgery of the elbow: fusion, replacement of the entire elbow or offending anatomical bony structures, or excision of parts of the elbow. Again, the patient's need for motion versus stability must be considered.

[iii] The shoulder area

The entire shoulder area includes the humeral-glenoid, clavicula-scapula, acromio-clavicular, coraco-clavicular, and sterno-clavicular joints. Prostheses for this area, however, only exist for the humeral head or humeral-glenoid joint. Malpractice claims here usually stem from either inappropriate selection of the joint to be operated upon, or inappropriate surgery for the patient's needs.

[iv] The foot and toes

Reconstructive surgery of the foot and toes involves a varied array of surgical procedures. All of these operations have the basic intent of reconstructing a foot so that it will conform to the interior of a shoe and accept weight bearing and ambulation. Unfortunately, a significant number of these operations are done without proper preoperative evaluation and consideration of the desires of the patient. Many operations with excellent functional results have disappointed patients who are more interested in cosmetic improvement, and vice versa. In addition, bone and tendon reconstruction without proper preoperative evaluation can result in muscular or tendon imbalance. Also, surgery on patients with vascular disease, neurological disease with sensory impairments, or diabetes (which frequently is unrecognized by the operating surgeon), can lead to failure in healing, gangrene and necrosis. Thus, in reconstructive surgery of the foot, malpractice usually arises out of the surgeon's failure to appreciate the goals expected by the patient, or the failure to recognize concurrent local or systemic disease that precludes a favorable result.

With regard to subtalar (midfoot) joints and the ankle joint, although tendon reconstruction exists, as do prostheses, the commonly accepted procedure is fusion. Malpractice, again, most likely will derive from failure to recognize a concurrent disease that affects healing.

[v] The knee

Reconstructive surgery of the knee is a major field of orthopedic surgery. The basic operations here are late reconstruction of previously undiagnosed knee subluxations (which involve tears of the collateral and cruciate ligaments), revision of torn menisci (cartilage), and major or minor reconstruction of the articular surfaces of the femur and tibia. The diagnosis, which determines the procedure of choice, is usually made by plain x-rays, CT scans, MRIs or arthroscopy. Negligence is most likely to occur from the failure to do a complete arthroscopy or to arrive at an accurate diagnostic interpretation of the findings.

Once a diagnosis is made of ligamentous knee injury, the question of informed consent can arise because of the choices available: (1) repair of the ligament with its inherent risks, or (2) application of an external brace.

Intra-articular lesions, either meniscal tears or erosion of the articular surfaces of the patella, tibia or femur, can be corrected at the present time by use of the arthroscope and excision of the pathological condition.

As in any other joint, stability is inherently due to ligament continuity. Failure to appropriately reconstruct these ligaments under adequate tension will allow for continued instability of the joint and invite secondary arthritic conditions.

Artificial knees can be used if ligamentous or bony reconstruction is impossible. The selection of the appropriate prosthesis, knowledge of the proper instrumentation and technique needed for its insertion, a close adherence to the recommended use of the instruments, and proper insertion of the implant are all essential. Failure to follow the implant manufacturer's recommended technique can be considered grounds for malpractice.

[vi] The hip

Reconstruction of the hip joint may involve replacement of both articular surfaces, (the femur and the pelvis), and is known as a "total hip" operation. If there is removal of the hip joint as a functioning joint the operation is considered a fusion. There can also be an excision of the hip joint with removal of the articular surface of the femur, which is commonly called a "girdlestone," or there can be a replacement of simply one surface of the hip (hemiarthroplasty).

Total hip replacements consist of two components: the cup or acetabular replacement and the femoral component. The common areas for malpractice in total hip reconstruction are the failure to align the components properly with each other, failure to align the femoral component with the femur, and failure to align the acetabular component with the pelvis.

Hip fusions rely on proper positioning of the femur to the pelvis so that when the fusion does become rigid, the position is appropriate. Failure to perform the procedure according to standard methods, or failure to obtain X-rays and align the femur and pelvis per the published guidelines (so that when the fusion becomes solid the alignment is unacceptable, and repeat surgery is necessary) is negligence.

The girdlestone operation, or removal of the hip joint itself, is only done in drastic circumstances, such as in severe infections or in debilitated patients where no other surgery can be carried out.

Hemiarthroplasty is a replacement of the femoral half of the hip joint, and the procedure is similar to a total hip operation.

In all of these operations, it is possible to damage the sciatic nerve which is very close in proximity to the hip joint, and which can be seen during the posterior approach. This can be malpractice. Although failure to place a component in proper alignment *during* the procedure is not malpractice (when correction can be obtained), failure to identify misalignment until *after* the patient has recovered from anesthesia, thereby necessitating a second operation, is evidence of malpractice.

[vii] The spine

In surgery of the spine (laminectomy or fusion), injury to nerves or proximal major structures (including the aorta and vena cava), can be grounds for malpractice. Furthermore, it is not uncommon for surgery on the spine to be performed at an *inappropriate level* due to failure to have adequate X-rays in the operating room. Also, failure to remove the pathology that is compressing the spinal cord or nerves can be negligence.

[13] Failure to Provide Adequate Postoperative Care

In orthopedic surgery, as in all areas of surgery, the operating surgeon has a duty to provide adequate postoperative care. Whether he provides this himself or through an associate, he is nevertheless responsible that such care be provided. This care must include instructions for postoperative rehabilitation and monitoring, to ensure that if complications do occur, whether systemic or local, appropriate measures are immediately undertaken.

[14] Inadequate Documentation of Treatment

Negligence here may involve failure to dictate an operative report, failure to record progress notes in the office or hospital records, and failure to document the patient's consent for surgery (or his refusal to undergo surgery). In addition, there may be failure of the documents in the patient's chart *to coincide.* An X-ray report might document a fracture while the physician's records show no evidence of a fracture. Similarly, the nurse's notes might show a complication of surgery, but the surgeon failed to record it. Other problems include lack of correlation between X-ray reports, or between X-ray films and the surgeon's clinical impression of the patient.

§ 17.05 Conclusion

Again the best defense, if one could put it this way, against potential litigation of the orthopedic surgeon is to be honest with the patient and his or her family, to thoroughly explain the potential risks and benefits of surgery prior to undergoing surgery and to adequately document pre-operatively and intra-operatively, the appropriate and correct extremity that is to be operated and is being operated on. In other words, a time out should be taken for marking the extremity and signing of the extremity by the orthopedic surgeon involved. There should also be administration of pre-operative antibiotics within 30 minutes prior to incision to prevent post operative infections, adequate administration of low molecular weight Heparin, factor 10 inhibitors such as Arixtra or Coumadin to prevent post operative DVT—especially in surgery of the hip and knee. This should be continued for a minimum of 3-4 weeks post operatively. However, some orthopedic surgeons do use aspirin and if the patient is allowed to bear weight early this is acceptable and is being used at this time by the Mayo Clinic.

Furthermore, there should be adequate pre-operative planning, measuring of leg lengths, recording of leg length discrepancies pre- and post operatively and correction of these intraoperatively, documenting both pre- and post operative abnormalities with x-ray. Should a mistake be made it is of paramount importance to discuss this with the patient and his or her family at the soonest possible time and to offer potential remedies for any abnormality within the joint or the axial appendicular skeleton as a whole.

INDEX

A

ABBREVIATIONS
Table of, cardiology, § 2.09[6]

ABDOMINOPLASTY
Plastic surgery, § 10.02[10]

ABORTION
Spontaneous, complications of early gestation, § 15.03[2][b]
Voluntary, legal aspects of, § 14.03[3]

ADENOIDECTOMY
Otolaryngology, § 13.06[3]

AIDS
Employee safety, risk management, § 1.04[1]
Gynecological diseases, § 14.04[1][f]

ALCOHOLIC BEVERAGES
Emergency medicine, intoxicated patients, § 4.03[10]

ALZHEIMER'S DISEASE
Neurology, § 11.09[17][b]

AMBULATORY SURGICAL CENTERS
Neurosurgery, § 12.04[4]

AMERICAN ACADEMY OF NEUROLOGY (AAN)
Neurology, professional organization, § 11.03[6]

AMERICAN ACADEMY OF ORTHOPEDIC SURGEONS
Orthopedic surgery, § 17.01[6]

AMERICAN ASSOCIATION OF NEUROLOGICAL SURGEONS (AANS)
Neurosurgery, § 12.02[7]

AMERICAN ASSOCIATION OF NEUROMUSCULAR AND ELECTRODIAGNOSTIC MEDICINE (AANEM)
Neurology, professional organization, § 11.03[6]

AMERICAN BOARD OF MEDICAL SPECIALTIES (ABMS)
Quality assessment of physicians, § 1.11[3][a]

AUTOPSIES
Malpractice. *See* PATHOLOGY
Postmortem examination. *See* PATHOLOGY

B

BILIARY TRACT
Specific problems in general surgery, § 7.04[11]

BIRTH ASPHYXIA
Labor and delivery, intrapartum fetal distress, § 15.05[3][a]

BIRTH DEFECTS
Neonatology, § 16.02[1][h]

BLEEDING
Gastrointestinal in children, § 16.03[3]
Specific problems in general surgery, § 7.04[2]

BLEPHAROPLASTY
Plastic surgery, § 10.02[1]

BLINDNESS
Anesthesiology, special problems, § 8.09[5]

BLOOD BANK
Clinical pathology. *See* PATHOLOGY
Risk management, § 1.07

BLOOD TESTS
Clinical pathology, hematology. *See* PATHOLOGY

BLOOD TRANSFUSIONS
Plastic surgery, § 10.03[2]

BORROWED SERVANT DOCTRINE
General surgery, § 7.02[9]

BOTULISM TOXIN INJECTIONS
Plastic surgery, § 10.02[21]

BRAIN
See NEUROLOGY

BREAST CANCER
Gynecological diseases, § 14.04[3][a]
Surgical options for, § 7.04[8][a]

BREAST SURGERY
Breast augmentation, § 10.02[9]
Breast reconstruction, plastic surgery, § 10.02[6]
Breast reduction, plastic surgery, § 10.02[7]
Mastopexy, plastic surgery, § 10.02[8]
Specific problems in general surgery, § 7.04[8]
    Breast carcinoma, surgical options for, § 7.04[8][a]

BREECH PRESENTATION
Labor and delivery, § 15.05[5]

BRONCHOESOPHAGOLOGY
See OTOLARYNGOLOGY

BULIMIA
Adolescents, problems in, § 16.01[9][d]

C

CANCER
Breast
    Gynecological diseases, § 14.04[3][a]
    Surgical options for, § 7.04[8][a]
Cervical
    Gynecological diseases, § 14.04[3][c]
    Risk of oral contraceptives, § 14.02[1][a][iii]
Children, oncological disorders of. *See* PEDIATRICS
Larynx, § 13.05[7]
Oral contraceptives, risks of, § 14.02[1][a][iii]
Ovarian
    Gynecological diseases, § 14.04[3][d]
    Risk of oral contraceptives, § 14.02[1][a][iii]
Pharynx, § 13.06[5]
Uterine
    Gynecological diseases, § 14.04[3][b]
    Risk of oral contraceptives, § 14.02[1][a][iii]

CAPTAIN OF THE SHIP DOCTRINE
General surgery, § 7.02[9]

CONGRESS OF NEUROLOGICAL SURGEONS (CNS)
Neurosurgery, § 12.02[7]

CONSENT
Anesthesiology, informed consent, § 8.02
General surgery, § 7.03
    Extending scope of operation, § 7.03[3]
    Informed consent, § 7.03[2]
    Operation other than by surgeon, § 7.03[4]
    "Reasonable or prudent patient" standard, § 7.03[5]
    "Reasonable physician" standard, § 7.03[6]
    Who may consent, § 7.03[1]
Genetic screening, informed consent, § 14.02[5][b][i]
Hysterectomy, informed consent, § 14.03[5][d]
Informed consent
    Anesthesiology, § 8.02
    General surgery, § 7.03[2]
    Gynecology, § 14.05[4]
        Genetic screening, § 14.02[5][b][i]
        Hysterectomy, § 14.03[5][d]
        Sterilization, § 14.02[4][d]
    Neurosurgery, medical-legal problem areas, § 12.07[9]
    Orthopedic surgery, malpractice for failure to obtain, § 17.04[[10]
    Otolaryngology, § 13.03[1]
    Radiology, screening procedures, § 9.07[7]
Orthopedic surgery, malpractice for failure to obtain, § 17.04[10]
Otolaryngology, informed consent, § 13.03[1]
Radiology, screening procedures, § 9.07[7]
Sterilization, informed consent, § 14.04[4][d]

CONTRACEPTION
See GYNECOLOGY

COSMETIC SURGERY
See PLASTIC SURGERY

CROUP
Infectious diseases of childhood, § 16.02[2][f]

CRYING
Excessive, early infancy, problems in, § 16.01[7][d]

CT SCANS AND SCREENING
Cardiology. *See* CARDIOLOGY
Neurology, § 11.08[4]

F

G

H

M

MAGNETIC RESONANCE IMAGING (MRI)
Cardiology, § 2.07[2]
Neurology, § 11.08[4]
Neurosurgery, § 12.06[6]

MALPRACTICE
Hospital psychiatry. *See* PSYCHIATRY
Orthopedic surgery. *See* ORTHOPEDIC SURGERY
Outpatient psychiatry. *See* PSYCHIATRY
Pathology. *See* PATHOLOGY
Radiology, § 9.01[4], § 9.01[5]
    Defined, § 9.02[9], § 9.02[10]
    Errors and, public perception, § 9.02[12]

MAMMOGRAPHY
Breast cancer and, § 9.04[1], § 9.04[12]
    Public education and, § 9.04[13]
Controversies surrounding efficiency of, § 9.04[6], § 9.04[12]
Defending malpractice lawsuits alleging delay of breast cancer diagnosis, § 9.04[7]
Delay in breast cancer diagnosis
    Defending malpractice lawsuits alleging, § 9.04[7]
    Dilemma of, § 9.04[9]
    Versus patient injury, § 9.04[10]
Diagnostic versus screening, § 9.04[14]
Overpromotion of, § 9.04[11]
Perceptions and misperceptions regarding, § 9.04[2]
    Controversies surrounding efficiency of mammography, § 9.04[6]
    Perception of high risk of developing and dying from breast cancer, § 9.04[3]
    Perception of perfection, § 9.04[4]
    Perception that early detection will cure breast cancer, § 9.04[5]
    Perception versus reality dilemma, § 9.04[8]
Public education, § 9.04[13]
Screening versus diagnostic, § 9.04[14]

MAMMOGRAPHY QUALITY STANDARDS ACT (MQSA)
Radiology, impact on malpractice litigation and referring physicians, § 9.03[10]

MASTOPEXY
Plastic surgery, § 10.02[8]

MATERNAL HEALTH CARE
See OBSTETRICS

P

R

RADIATION
Exposure, CT screening, § 9.07[5]
Pregnancy
    Minimizing radiation exposure from radiopharmaceuticals, § 9.06[5]
    Radioactive iodine and, § 9.06[4]
Risk management, § 1.03[2][a]
X-rays, harmful effects of exposure to, § 9.06
    Burns and other injuries, § 9.06[1]
    Interventional radiology, § 9.06[2]
    Minimizing radiation exposure, § 9.06[3]
    Radioactive iodine and pregnancy, § 9.06[4]
        Minimizing radiation exposure from radiopharmaceuticals, § 9.06[5]

RADIOLOGY
American College of Radiology, practice guidelines and standards, § 9.03[3],
    § 9.03[4], § 9.03[5], § 9.05
    Expert witness and professional practice guidelines, § 9.05[1]
Communication, § 9.03
    Alliterative error, § 9.03[1]
    American College of Radiology practice guidelines and standards, § 9.03[3],
        § 9.03[4], § 9.03[5]
    Comparing current radiological exams with previous ones, § 9.03[1]
    Direct communication of radiologic findings to referring physicians, § 9.03[2]
    Problems, prevalence and causes of, § 9.03[11]
    Results of radiologic studies
        Communication of results to patients, § 9.03[6], § 9.03[8], § 9.03[12]
            Stanley v. McCarver decision, § 9.03[9]
        Communication of results to referring physician, § 9.03[6], § 9.03[7]
Courts
    Decisions, standard of care, § 9.01[2]
    Radiographs as evidence, § 9.01[3]
    Stanley v. McCarver decision, communication of radiologic findings to patients,
        § 9.03[9]
CT screening, § 9.07
    Contract media and, § 9.07[9]
    Duty to disclose, § 9.07[7]
    Ethics of, § 9.07[8]
    False negatives, § 9.07[2]
        Case example, John Ritter lawsuit, § 9.07[3]
    Informed consent, § 9.07[7]
    Overdiagnosis, § 9.07[4]
    Potential malpractice pitfalls of, § 9.07[1]
    Present status and future directions, § 9.07[10]

S

T

V

VASA PREVIA
Pregnancy, complications of, § 15.04[3][c]

VENEREAL DISEASES
Clinical pathology, failure to report to health authorities, § 5.07[4][h], § 5.07[5][g]

VERTIGO
Otolaryngology, § 13.03[23]

W

WILM'S TUMOR
Oncological disorders of childhood, § 16.07[6]

WITNESSES, EXPERT
Neurology, § 11.10
    Securing medical records, § 11.10[1]
    Securing the expert witness, § 11.10[2]
Neurosurgery. *See* EXPERTS

WOUND HEALING AND INFECTION
Specific problems in general surgery, § 7.04[3]

X

X-RADIATION
See X-RAYS

X-RAYS
Harmful effects of exposure to, § 9.06
Burns and other injuries, § 9.06[1]
Interventional radiology, § 9.06[2]
Minimizing radiation exposure, § 9.06[3]
Neurosurgery, diagnostic studies, § 12.06[1]
Orthopedic surgery, failure to obtain, § 17.04[7]
Radioactive iodine and pregnancy, § 9.06[4]
    Minimizing radiation exposure from radiopharmaceuticals, § 9.06[5]